DATE DUE

~~(scribbled)~~		
JAN 0 4 1994		
AUG 0 1 2007		

SOIL NITROGEN

AGRONOMY

A Series of Monographs Published by the

AMERICAN SOCIETY OF AGRONOMY

General Editor, Monographs 1 to 6, A. G. NORMAN

1   C. EDMUND MARSHALL: The Colloid Chemistry of the Silicate Minerals, 1949

2   BYRON T. SHAW, *Editor:* Soil Physical Conditions and Plant Growth, 1952

3   K. D. JACOB, *Editor:* Fertilizer Technology and Resources in the United States, 1953

4   W. H. PIERRE and A. G. NORMAN, *Editors:* Soil and Fertilizer Phosphate in Crop Nutrition, 1953

5   GEORGE F. SPRAGUE, *Editor:* Corn and Corn Improvement, 1955

6   J. LEVITT: The Hardiness of Plants, 1956

7   JAMES N. LUTHIN, *Editor:* Drainage of Agricultural Lands, 1957
General Editor, D. E. GREGG

8   FRANKLIN A. COFFMAN, *Editor:* Oats and Oat Improvement, 1961
Managing Editor, H. L. HAMILTON

9   C. A. BLACK, *Editor-in-Chief,* and D. D. EVANS, J. L. WHITE, L. E. ENSMINGER, and F. E. CLARK, *Associate Editors:* Methods of Soil Analysis, 1965

> Part 1—Physical and Mineralogical Properties, Including Statistics of Measurement and Sampling
> Part 2—Chemical and Microbiological Properties
Managing Editor, R. C. DINAUER

10   W. V. BARTHOLOMEW and F. E. CLARK, *Editors:* Soil Nitrogen, 1965
Managing Editor, H. L. HAMILTON

Monographs 1 through 6, published by Academic Press, Inc., should be ordered from:

Academic Press, Inc.
111 Fifth Avenue
New York, New York 10003

Monographs 7 through 10, published by the American Society of Agronomy, should be ordered from:

American Society of Agronomy
677 South Segoe Road
Madison, Wisconsin, USA 53711

SOIL NITROGEN

Edited by

W. V. BARTHOLOMEW

North Carolina State University
Raleigh, North Carolina

and

FRANCIS E. CLARK

Agricultural Research Service, USDA
Fort Collins, Colorado

Published by the
AMERICAN SOCIETY OF AGRONOMY

Number 10 in the series
AGRONOMY

American Society of Agronomy, Inc., *Publisher*
Madison, Wisconsin, USA
1965

THE AMERICAN SOCIETY OF AGRONOMY, INC.
677 SOUTH SEGOE ROAD, MADISON, WISCONSIN, USA 53711

LIBRARY OF CONGRESS CATALOG CARD NUMBER: 65-24932

PRINTED IN THE UNITED STATES OF AMERICA

GENERAL FOREWORD

AGRONOMY—An ASA Monograph Series

The need for comprehensive treatments of specific subject matter areas in agronomy was realized by members of the American Society of Agronomy several years ago. As a result, the first monograph of a series entitled "Agronomy" was published in 1949. Dr. A. G. Norman, an eminent member of the Society, was appointed general editor. Since the Society, a nonprofit organization, was not initially able to finance the project, arrangements were made with Academic Press, Inc., of New York, to publish the monographs. These editorial and business arrangements were used for the first six monographs and this explains why the early volumes are available from Academic Press, Inc., and not available from the Society Headquarters Office in Madison, Wisconsin.

By 1957 the Society had developed considerably and had in operation a Headquarters Office with a competent editorial staff which made it possible to editorially manage its publications. Also, the improved financial stability of the Society enabled it to pursue independently the monograph project, including complete financing and publishing of the series.

The American Society of Agronomy now presents *Soil Nitrogen* as its tenth monograph. The timeliness of the topic is very much in evidence during this period when the manufacture and sales of nitrogen are increasing annually by enormous proportions. The importance of soil nitrogen in determining the needs for fertilizer nitrogen, its predominant direct effect as a nutrient on plant growth, and its direct and indirect influences on the utilization of other elements which markedly affect crop production make this contribution an invaluable one at this time.

This tenth number in this series was preceded only recently in 1965 by Monograph 9 on *Methods of Soil Analysis* which came in two parts, entitled: Part I—Physical and Mineralogical Properties, Including Statistics of Measurement and Sampling; and Part II—Chemical and Microbiological Properties. The subjects of "Oats and Oat Improvement" and "Drainage of Agricultural Lands" constituted Volumes 8 and 7, respectively. These publications were handled entirely by the American Society of Agronomy.

Monographs on other subjects are presently under preparation. Within a year, Number 11 on Irrigation will be available. Within two years, other numbers on Liming and Soil Acidity and on Wheat will be released. Still others are under consideration as assurance that the ASA Monograph program will remain active.

In view of the fact that some of the Monograph titles are largely in the area of soil science while others are mainly oriented to crop science, clarification of the relationship of the American Society of Agronomy to the Crop Science Society of America and the Soil Science Society of America may benefit our readers. The latter societies are actually outgrowths of the American Society of Agronomy. A close association is maintained among the three societies since members of CSSA and SSSA are automatically given membership in ASA. The three societies, incorporated in Wisconsin, work harmoniously together and share a Headquarters Office and staff in Madison,

Wisconsin. In view of the many mutual professional and scientific objectives of the three groups, the readiness of the American Society of Agronomy to publish subject matter in these areas is understandable.

August 1965

MATTHIAS STELLY,
Executive Secretary-Treasurer
American Society of Agronomy
Crop Science Society of America
Soil Science Society of America

FOREWORD

Soil nitrogen is prominent among the many nutrients essential for crop growth and has probably received more study and attention than any other. Nitrogen occupies a unique position among the major nutrients because it occurs only in trace amounts in soil parent materials but is required by plants in relatively large quantities. At a time when food production is an increasing concern in the world, a monograph on the general subject of soil nitrogen is pertinent and timely.

Cropping systems have been much influenced by the availability of synthetic nitrogenous fertilizers and it appears that this trend will continue with the steadily increasing efficiency of chemical technology.

A major objective of modern soil science and agronomy is to put together farm management systems that will maximize the efficiency of food production and reduce costs. This monograph summarizes known facts and principles for an important component of the system and therefore will find extensive application and use.

The wide range of subject matter specialization among the members of the American Society of Agronomy, along with the skills and facilities of the Society Headquarters, makes possible a comprehensive treatment like this monograph on soil nitrogen. We are much indebted to the authors and editors for their willingness and years of effort to produce this book.

16 April 1965

L. A. RICHARDS, *President*
American Society of Agronomy

PREFACE

Soil Nitrogen is published with the hope that it will mark the beginning of an era of better understanding of the many problems involved in the chemistry and utilization of nitrogen in the soil. Exposition and evaluation of past work often serve to bring a degree of order and perspective to extensive existing information and to point the way to further research. This monograph will serve its purpose well if a better understanding of what is currently known about soil nitrogen is disseminated among agriculturalists. The authors and editors have no illusions that the current volume will provide answers to all the innumerable questions about soil nitrogen.

This monograph is not intended to present an exhaustive survey of the literature nor to present uniform detail in review coverage within the sixteen chapters. *Soil Nitrogen* is to be viewed as a collection of chapters written by competent authors who treated their subject as they considered best. No attempt was made by the editors to influence the treatment of subject matter nor to reconcile differences of opinion among the authors. Although few workers are authorities on even one aspect of soil nitrogen, the editors, nevertheless, believe that the competent and qualified individuals selected provide the coverage needed to correlate current knowledge and to stimulate further research.

The monograph had its formal beginning in 1957 at the American Society of Agronomy meeting in Atlanta, Georgia. A committee under the chairmanship of W. P. Martin held the first of several discussions that led in 1959 to petitioning the Society for approval of this monograph. Following such authorization, W. V. Bartholomew was elected editor-in-chief and an enlarged steering committee was appointed to advise on subject matter organization and selection of contributors.

In planning and preparation of the monograph many individuals became involved and made noteworthy contributions. In addition to the authors of chapters, who contributed their enthusiasm in planning, monumental efforts in writing, and cooperation and patience during the editorial processes, others to whom acknowledgment is made include W. P. Martin, J. E. Dawson, A. G. Norman, and L. E. Orth as members of the original steering committee who did not write chapters; R. L. Balser, C. F. Eno, L. R. Frederick, J. M. MacGregor, J. L. Mortensen (deceased), R. W. Pearson, and E. L. Schmidt of the enlarged steering committee; and G. Chesters, A. P.

Edwards, C. B. Davey, C. A. I. Goring, A. E. Hiltbold, E. J. Kamprath, W. D. Kemper, R. J. Millington, L. K. Porter, C. A. Rich, S. B. Weed, and J. L. Young for editorial assistance.

W. V. BARTHOLOMEW
March 4, 1965   F. E. CLARK

THE AUTHORS

Martin Alexander

Associate Professor of Soil Science, Department of Agronomy, Cornell University, Ithaca, New York

Franklin E. Allison

Chief Soil Scientist, retired, Agricultural Research Service, U. S. Department of Agriculture, Beltsville, Maryland

W. V. Bartholomew

Professor of Soil Science, North Carolina State of the University of N. C., Raleigh, North Carolina

J. M. Bremner

Professor of Soils and Biochemistry, Department of Agronomy, Iowa State University, Ames, Iowa

F. E. Broadbent

Associate Soil Microbiologist, Department of Soils and Plant Nutrition, University of California, Davis, California

Francis E. Clark

Chief Microbiologist, Agricultural Research Service, U. S. Department of Agriculture, Fort Collins, Colorado

W. R. Gardner

Physicist, U. S. Salinity Laboratory, Agricultural Research Service, U. S. Department of Agriculture, Riverside, California

G. W. Harmsen

Head, Soil Biology Department, Institute for Soil Fertility, Groningen, The Netherlands

H. L. Jensen

Director, State Laboratory for Soil and Crop Research, Lyngby, Denmark

G. J. Kolenbrander

Soil Scientist, Soil Biology Department, Institute for Soil Fertility, Groningen, The Netherlands

A. D. McLaren

Professor of Soil Biochemistry, University of California, Berkeley, California

M. M. Mortland

Professor of Soil Science, Michigan State University, East Lansing, Michigan

Hans Nõmmik

Assistant Professor, Department of Soils, Royal College of Forestry, Stockholm, Sweden

P. S. Nutman

Head, Department of Soil Microbiology, Rothamsted Experimental Station, Harpenden, England

George H. Peterson

Assistant Professor of Biological Science, California State College at Hayward, Hayward, California

C. E. Scarsbrook

Professor of Soils, Department of Agronomy and Soils, Auburn University, Auburn, Alabama

F. J. Stevenson   Professor of Soil Chemistry, Department of Agronomy, University of Illinois, Urbana, Illinois

Frank G. Viets, Jr.   Chief Soil Scientist, Agricultural Research Service, U. S. Department of Agriculture, Fort Collins, Colorado

J. M. Vincent   Professor of Agricultural Microbiology, University of Sydney, Sydney, N.S.W., Australia

A. R. Wolcott   Associate Professor, Department of Soil Science, Michigan State University, East Lansing, Michigan

CONTENTS

15   Movement of Nitrogen in Soil

W. R. GARDNER

16   Evaluation of Incoming and Outgoing Processes That Affect Soil Nitrogen

FRANKLIN E. ALLISON

Chapter 1

Origin and Distribution of Nitrogen in Soil

F. J. STEVENSON

University of Illinois
Urbana, Illinois

I. INTRODUCTION

The nitrogen cycle in soil is an integral part of the overall cycle of nitrogen in nature. The primary source of soil nitrogen is the atmosphere, where the strongly bonded gaseous molecule N_2 is the predominant gas (79.08% by volume of the gases). The plow layer of a rich prairie soil may contain as much as 3 tons of combined nitrogen per acre; in the atmosphere over this same area there will be about 35,000 tons of elemental nitrogen. Only a very limited number of microorganisms have the ability to utilize elemental nitrogen; all other living organisms on the earth require combined nitrogen for carrying out their life activities.

The combined nitrogen in soil is largely bound to organic matter and mineral material; in general, only a few pounds per acre will exist in available mineral forms (as nitrates and exchangeable ammonium) at any one time. In some soils, such as the dark-colored brunizems of the Corn Belt section of the United States, sufficient quantities of nitrogen are present for a century of cropping, even without any external additions. However, when land is cultivated, the nitrogen content of the soil declines rapidly, and new equilibrium levels are established which are characteristic of the climate, cultural practices, and soil type. At equilibrium, the nitrogen removed by harvested crops must come from external sources.

Systems of agriculture which rely heavily on soil reserves to meet the nitrogen requirements of plants cannot long be effective in producing high yields of crops. In the past, biological nitrogen fixation was the chief means of supplying nitrogen for cultivated crops; in recent years, nitrogen fertilizers have become available, which, when used to augment the nitrogen supplied by natural processes, can increase yields and improve the quality of crops. A major concern of present-day farmers is the effective use of nitrogen fertilizers.

An outline of the nitrogen cycle in soil is depicted in Fig. 1. Under natural conditions, gains in nitrogen occur through fixation of elemental nitrogen by microorganisms, and from the accession of ammonia and nitrate in rain water; losses occur through crop removal, leaching, and volatilization. Within the soil, an internal cycle is operative, through

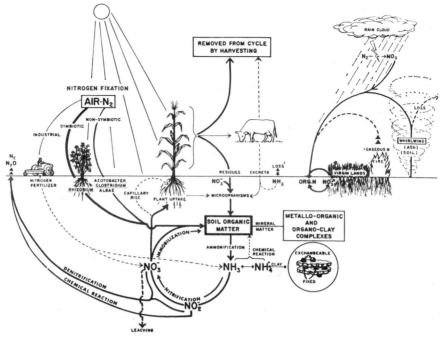

Fig. 1—The nitrogen cycle in soil. (From Stevenson, 1964. Used by permission, Reinhold Publishing Corp.)

which mineral nitrogen becomes immobilized during decay of carbonaceous residues. The formation of mineral complexes protects nitrogenous constituents against attack by microorganisms. The positively charged ammonium ion (NH_4^+) undergoes substitution reactions with metal cations on the exchange complex and can be fixed by clay minerals.

A solution to the problem of providing adequate nitrogen for crops is contingent upon a thorough knowledge of all aspects of the nitrogen cycle, including an understanding of the factors affecting nitrogen accumulation and distribution. The process of nitrogen accretion in relation to geochemistry and the soil-plant environment will be considered in this chapter. Subsequent chapters will be concerned with the other facets of the nitrogen cycle shown in Fig. 1.

II. GEOCHEMISTRY OF NITROGEN

The geochemistry of nitrogen deals with the distribution and transformations of nitrogen within the earth in space and time. Hutchinson (1944, 1954), who has done much work on problems of geochemistry, has been particularly active in this field. In this section, only those aspects of the geochemistry of nitrogen which relate to the nitrogen cycle in soil are discussed.

The events leading to the formation of combined nitrogen in soil are outlined in Fig. 2. The first event was the formation of an atmosphere enriched with elemental nitrogen. The second event, which was a pre-

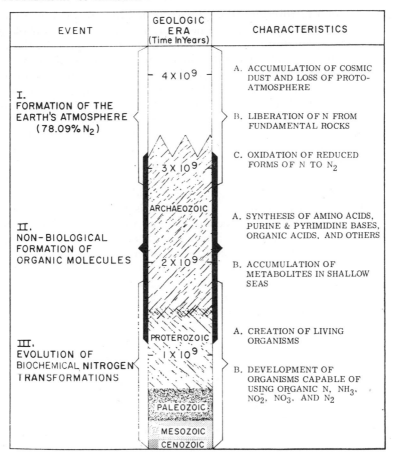

EVENT	GEOLOGIC ERA (Time InYears)	CHARACTERISTICS
I. FORMATION OF THE EARTH'S ATMOSPHERE (78.09% N_2)	— 4×10^9 —	A. ACCUMULATION OF COSMIC DUST AND LOSS OF PROTO-ATMOSPHERE
		B. LIBERATION OF N FROM FUNDAMENTAL ROCKS
	3×10^9	C. OXIDATION OF REDUCED FORMS OF N TO N_2
	ARCHAEOZOIC	
II. NON-BIOLOGICAL FORMATION OF ORGANIC MOLECULES	2×10^9	A. SYNTHESIS OF AMINO ACIDS, PURINE & PYRIMIDINE BASES, ORGANIC ACIDS, AND OTHERS
		B. ACCUMULATION OF METABOLITES IN SHALLOW SEAS
III. EVOLUTION OF BIOCHEMICAL NITROGEN TRANSFORMATIONS	PROTEROZOIC 1×10^9	A. CREATION OF LIVING ORGANISMS
	PALEOZOIC	B. DEVELOPMENT OF ORGANISMS CAPABLE OF USING ORGANIC N, NH_3, NO_2^-, NO_3^-, AND N_2
	MESOZOIC	
	CENOZOIC	

Fig. 2—Evolution of the nitrogen cycle. (Adapted from a drawing by Calvin, 1956).

liminary step in the evolution of the biosphere, was associated with the nonbiological formation of organic molecules. The third event was the development of organisms capable of bringing about nitrogen transformations.

The various aspects of the origin of nitrogen in soil, including a more detailed account of the events illustrated in Fig. 2, are discussed below. Additional information on the geochemistry of nitrogen in the terrestrial atmosphere can be obtained from the works of Hutchinson (1944, 1954), Rubey (1951), Sokolov (1959), and Urey (1952). For a discussion of the nonbiological synthesis of organic molecules, the publication of Calvin (1956) is of interest. Manshard (1958) and Schmalfuss (1958) have reviewed certain aspects of the geochemistry of soil nitrogen.

A. Origin of Nitrogen in the Earth's Atmosphere

Geologists, geochemists, and astronomers are agreed that the atmosphere of the earth (Fig. 2, Event I) arose through the gradual giving off of gases from the interior. The theory generally accepted is that the earth, and the solar system as a whole, originated by accretion of small solid particles (planetesimals). Following the accretion process, the earth warmed up from the heat generated by compression, by radioactive decay of U^{238}, U^{235}, Th^{232}, and K^{40}, and possibly by other exothermic processes. The primary atmosphere, if present, was gradually dissipated. Vapors and gases were driven off from the interior of the earth due to their evaporation with the rising temperature. As the earth cooled, the vapors condensed to form the oceans. The nitrogen, which is believed by many geochemists, Hutchinson (1944, 1954), Sokolov (1959), Urey (1952), to have consisted mostly of ammonia, was ejected largely during the early stages of the existence of the earth. Small quantities of nitrogen have been liberated during the course of geological times, and the process is continuing today. The free oxygen of the atmosphere is believed to have formed through photosynthesis by green plants, as well as by photochemical dissociation of water vapor in the atmosphere. As the atmosphere became enriched with oxygen, reduced nitrogen became oxidized to elemental nitrogen.

The evolution of the ancient crust of the earth (3×10^9 years ago) was characterized by intense tectonic and volcanic activity. Small additions of nitrogen have been made to the atmosphere by volatilization of nitrogen compounds from meteorites during entry into the earth's atmosphere (Hutchinson, 1944, 1954).

1. GEOCHEMICAL DISTRIBUTION OF NITROGEN

An indication that the nitrogen in the earth's atmosphere, and consequently in present-day soils, arose by outgassing of the earth's crust has come, in part, from considerations of the geochemical distribution of nitrogen. Rayleigh (1939) found a remarkably constant value of 0.04 cc/g (or 50 ppm by weight) for the nitrogen in igneous rocks, and this value has been used to calculate the total mass of nitrogen in the fundamental rocks ($1,930 \times 10^{20}$ g). The total mass of nitrogen in the atmosphere is 38.648×10^{20} g; that in ancient sedimentary rocks is considered to be about 4.0×10^{20} g.

Table 1 presents data on the geochemical distribution of nitrogen. The estimates for nitrogen in terrestrial humus and sea-bottom organic compounds were based on Goldschmidt's (1954) estimate that there are 1.5×10^{12} tons of carbon in the "pedosphere," 60% of which occurs in terrestrial humus, and that the C/N ratio of soil and marine humus is 10. The amount of nitrogen in living organisms (the biosphere) was

Table 1. Geochemical distribution of nitrogen.

	Total mass $\times 10^{20}$ g	% of N
In fundamental rocks	1,930.0	97.82
In the atmosphere	38.648	1.96
In ancient sedimentary rocks	4.0	0.2
In terrestrial humus	0.0082	negligible
In sea-bottom organic compounds	0.0054	"
In living organisms	0.00028	"

based on the assumption that the total amount of carbon in living organisms is 2.8×10^{17} g (from Borchert, 1951), and that the average C/N ratio of living tissue is 10.

According to Table 1, the bulk of the nitrogen in the earth (97.82%) is held by the fundamental rocks, the amount being 50 times that present in the atmosphere as elemental nitrogen. The mass of nitrogen in ancient sedimentary rocks is equivalent to about one-tenth of the elemental nitrogen in the atmosphere.

The estimate given above for the nitrogen in primary rocks may be high, as recent research (Mayne, 1957; Stevenson, 1962) indicates that the average nitrogen content may be as low as 10 to 12 ppm. Nevertheless, the data place in proper perspective the significance of the soil as a reservoir of earth nitrogen. In comparison to the nitrogen contained in primary rocks and the atmosphere, the amounts held in terrestrial humus, sea-bottom organic compounds, and biological tissues are negligible.

2. CHEMICAL STATE OF THE NITROGEN IN ROCKS

The nature of the nitrogen in fundamental rocks which served as a source of atmospheric nitrogen is not known with certainty. Earth scientists appear to support the theory that the nitrogen was present in combined form, the general view being that it existed as nitrides of iron, titanium, and other metals, or as ammonium salts. Nitrides have been found in effervescences from volcanoes, as well as in meteorites.

Rayleigh (1939) observed that ammonia was released from igneous rocks by fusion with alkali and concluded that the nitrogen was "ammoniacal nitrogen." Some of the nitrogen may exist as ammonium ions held within the lattice structures of primary silicate minerals (Mayne, 1957; Stevenson, 1959, 1960, 1962).

B. Prebiological Formation of Organic Molecules

The prebiological formation of organic molecules (Fig. 2, Event II) set the stage and established the pattern for the evolution of living organisms, including those which fix elemental nitrogen. This event, which was dominant throughout the whole of the Archaeozoic era, may occur to some extent under present-day conditions, although biogenesis is unlikely because predatory organisms destroy the biochemicals (Oparin, 1938).

Calvin (1956) pointed out that organic compounds could have arisen in the following ways:

(1) By an electric discharge in the upper atmosphere. In an atmosphere of ammonia, N_2, methane, and water (a reduced atmosphere), an electric discharge yields a variety of organic compounds, many of which are nitrogenous (Miller, 1955).

(2) Through the energy of ultraviolet light from the sun. Pavlovskaya and Pasynskii (1959) obtained a number of compounds, including amino acids, by illumination of a solution containing ammonia, carbon dioxide,

nitrate, and simple carbon compounds such as formic acid and formaldehyde.

(3) By the high-energy radiation liberated by decay of radioactive elements (Garrison et al., 1951).

(4) By the action of superheated aqueous vapor on metallic carbide. Oparin (1938) suggested that hydroxylamine, produced by this reaction, was converted to organic molecules of the types found in biological materials.

The biochemicals synthesized by one or more of the ways listed above are believed to have become concentrated in the shallow seas formed by the condensation of vapors during cooling of the earth. According to Haldane (1933), the oceans had "reached the consistency of hot dilute soup." It is in this type of environment that life is believed to have arisen.

C. Evolution of Biochemical Nitrogen Transformations

The biosphere, that part of the earth which sustains life, developed later than other earth spheres—life was not possible until conditions on the earth's surface were satisfactory. Once living cells became established, the formation of organisms with complex enzyme systems became possible.

Living organisms first emerged during the early history of the earth (Fig. 2). Well-preserved fossils have been identified in limestone formations dating to the Proterozoic era, and structures believed to be those of primitive algae have been observed in Pre-Cambrian limestone. As Mason (1958) pointed out, the formation of these organisms must have been preceded by a long evolutionary cycle. Hutchinson (1944, 1954) concluded that life, the oceans, and oxygen appeared concurrently, a hypothesis which implies that the biosphere developed rather early in the earth's history.

Numerous investigators (for example, Oda, 1959; Oparin, 1938; and Urey, 1952) have emphasized that the development of complex living organisms proceeded from heterotrophs to autotrophs, and from anaerobes to aerobes. This arrangement suggests that nitrogenous compounds synthesized by nonbiological means (Event II) were the mother substances of primitive nitrogen metabolism. With the liberation of ammonia from primary organic matter during fermentation by anaerobic organisms, other heterotrophs developed which were capable of utilizing ammonia (Hutchinson, 1944).

The appearance of oxygen on the earth led to the evolution of organisms capable of oxidizing ammonia to nitrate. Sorokin (1959) suggested that organisms with different types of metabolisms originated from a common root (a heterotrophic one), and that the biochemical functions of autotrophs were derived from systems developed earlier by heterotrophs. On this basis, the oxidizing enzymes of autotrophic nitrifying organisms were inherited from those developed earlier by heterotrophs. It is of interest that many heterotrophic organisms are able to oxidize ammonia to nitrite or nitrate (Alexander et al., 1960; Eylar and Schmidt,

1959). Oda (1959) concluded that nitrogen (N_2) reduction processes developed concurrently with carbon dioxide reduction processes and that both were maintained throughout the transition from the utilization of chemical energy to radiant energy. On the other hand, Hutchinson (1944) believed that biological nitrogen fixation developed later than other biological processes. Thus far, every organism capable of fixing elemental nitrogen has been found to have the ability to utilize nitrate.

Symbiotic nitrogen fixation did not develop until the Mesozoic period, presumably in Upper Cretaceous times when the angiosperms dominated the earth's flora. Bond et al. (1956) postulated that the possession of root nodules and the ability to use atmospheric nitrogen were very ancient characteristics which dated from a time when only woody flowering plants existed and when conditions were favorable for the initiation of symbiotic associations. Norris (1956) and Tutin (1958) emphasized that the angiosperms originated under conditions resembling the modern wet tropics and that their subsequent history was a progressive adaptation to temperate zones. According to Tutin (1958), the ancestral legume was probably a large tropical tree, and herbaceous annuals were formed according to the sequence: trees > shrubs and woody climbers > perennial herbs > annual herbs.

The development of the highly specialized root nodule probably proceeded through several less complex stages before reaching the present degree of organization. The major stages were envisaged by Parker (1957a) to be: (1) casual association between free-living nitrogen-fixing bacteria and the root surfaces of plants; (2) loose symbiosis on the surface of the root; (3) entry into, and symbiotic establishment within, the cortical tissues of the root; (4) specialization of root tissue, resulting finally in the organized nodule. Derx (1953) proposed that *Beijerinckia,* an organism confined almost exclusively to tropical soils, represented a transition form in the development of symbiotic nitrogen-fixing organisms from free-living nitrogen fixers.

The development of organisms capable of utilizing nitrate, either by reduction into organic compounds (nitrate assimilation) or by the formation of elemental nitrogen (denitrification), is believed by Hutchinson (1944) to have taken place soon after the appearance of organisms capable of oxidizing ammonia. Wilson (1951) suggested that, without these organisms, life would have been threatened by the conversion of ammonia into highly toxic compounds, while the premature development of denitrifying organisms could have led to the depletion of combined nitrogen. The enzyme systems of microorganisms which permit the oxygen of nitrate (or nitrite) to serve as an electron acceptor during respiration were probably adapted from those in which elemental oxygen was the acceptor; even in modern denitrifying organisms, nitrate and nitrite are used as electron acceptors only in the complete absence of elemental oxygen (see Chapter 9).

The basic processes in nature are generally considered to be photosynthesis and respiration. In the former, inorganic carbon (CO_2) is returned from the atmosphere to the biosphere; in the latter, CO_2 is released to the atmosphere. Wilson (1951) presented strong arguments for including biological nitrogen fixation as a basic process. To this list should be added denitrification. Like organic carbon, combined nitrogen is eventually returned to the atmosphere through the activities of micro-organisms.

III. MECHANISMS BY WHICH NITROGEN IS ADDED TO SOIL

Several mechanisms have been proposed for the exogenous addition of nitrogen to soils under natural conditions, but thus far only the fixation of elemental nitrogen by biological agents and the accession of ammonia and nitrate in rain water are considered important to the nitrogen cycle.

Hutchinson (1954) estimated that the total amount of nitrogen returned to the land surfaces of the earth each year was between 8 and 70 γ/cm^2, equivalent to about 0.7 to 6.2 pounds per acre per year. This corresponds to from 12 to 105 $\times$ 10^{12} g of atmospheric nitrogen. Assuming that about 100 g of carbohydrates are required for the fixation of 1 g of nitrogen, and that the rate of carbohydrate production is 30 mg/cm^2/year, about 23.3% of the carbohydrates produced annually by photosynthesis would be needed for fixation of nitrogen at the higher rate (70 γ/cm^2). As Hutchinson (1954) pointed out, this value is impossibly high, unless microorganisms carry out nitrogen fixation more efficiently under natural conditions than under laboratory conditions.

In this section, a brief résumé is given of the fixation of nitrogen by natural processes. The subject of biochemical fixation will be confined to a discussion of ecological relationships, as this topic is covered adequately in Chapters 10, 11, and 12. Henzell and Norris (1962) have discussed the process by which nitrogen is added to soil.

A. Biological Nitrogen Fixation

1. BLUE-GREEN ALGAE

Fogg (1947) pointed out that there is satisfactory evidence for nitrogen fixation by the following species of blue-green algae: *Nostoc punctiforme*, *N. muscorum*, *N. paludosum*, *Anabaena variabilis*, *A. gelatinosa*, *A. naviculoides*, *A. humicola*, *A. cylindrica*, *A. ambigua*, *A. fertilissima*, *Cylindrospermum licheniforme*, *C. maius*, *C. gorakhporense*, and *Aulosira fertilissima*, all of which belong to the Nostocaceae family. Their importance in soil and in soil-forming processes has been discussed by numerous investigators (Cameron and Fuller, 1960; Fogg, 1947; Fuller et al., 1960; Henzell and Norris, 1962; Shields et al., 1957; Wilson, 1951).

The blue-green algae represent an archaic group of organisms that has persisted during long epochs of the earth's history. They occur in almost every environmental situation where sufficient sunlight is available for photosynthesis, including barren rock surfaces and uninhabited wastelands. Their colonizing ability is due to the fact that they are completely autotrophic, being able to synthesize all of their biochemical requirements from CO_2, free nitrogen, water, and mineral salts. Of additional importance is that they form symbiotic relationships with a variety of other organisms, such as lichen fungi.

Geographically, the lichens are distributed widely over the land masses of the earth. They comprise a considerable part of the vegetation on the Antarctic continent (Brightman, 1959). Besides being the pioneering plants on virgin landscapes, they disintegrate rocks to which they are attached; thus, they form soil in which higher plants can get a start. In the southwestern desert areas of the United States, they form surface crusts of varying density and cling to surface stones (Cameron and Fuller, 1960; Fuller et al., 1960). Fuller et al. (1960) found that the algae crusts were 4 to 5 times higher in nitrogen than the soil below and concluded that the blue-green algae were contributing the nitrogen. Shields et al. (1957) identified crusts of blue-green algae on lava flows in New Mexico, an area with an annual rainfall of 8 to 10 inches. The initial vegetation on the pumice and volcanic ash of Krakatao after the volcanic explosion of 1883, which completely denuded the island of all visible forms of plant life and left a thick covering of volcanic ash, was a dark-green gelatinous layer containing blue-green algae (see account given by Fogg, 1947).

Tchan and Beadle (1955) found that blue-green algae were present in the semi-arid soils of Eastern Australia, where their favorite habitat was the under-surface of light-colored quartz stone pebbles. Williams (1943) described accumulations of peat-like material beneath translucent pebbles in the semi-arid regions of the Great Plains.

The importance of blue-green algae in supplying fixed nitrogen to the soil is probably limited to the initial stages of soil formation. Fixation of nitrogen by these organisms occurs only in the presence of sunlight, so their activity is confined largely to the most superficial layers of the earth's crust. There is good evidence that blue-green algae are the main agents responsible for the fixation of nitrogen in rice fields (Fogg, 1947; Henzell and Norris, 1962; Wilson, 1951).

2. FREE-LIVING BACTERIA

The classical examples of nitrogen fixation by free-living bacteria are by species of the photosynthetic *Rhodospirillum*, the anaerobic saprophyte *Clostridium*, and the aerobic saprophyte *Azotobacter*. To this list should be added *Beijerinckia*, an organism first classified with *Azotobacter*, but now believed to warrant generic rank (Tchan, 1953a).

According to Stanier and Cohen-Bazire (1957), nitrogen fixation by photosynthetic bacteria is of negligible ecologic significance, as the requirement of these organisms for both irradiation and anaerobiosis restricts their activity to shallow, muddy ponds or estuarine muds. They are generally found as a layer overlying the mud and covered by a layer of algae; fixation of nitrogen is possible because the pigments of the photosynthetic bacteria absorb light rays in the region of the spectrum not absorbed by the pigments of the overlying algae.

Tchan (1953b) proposed that the world could be divided into three zones, depending upon the distribution of non-symbiotic nitrogen-fixing microorganisms. The distribution is as follows:

Zone	*Beijerinckia*	*Azotobacter*	*Clostridium*	Blue-green algae
Tropical	x	x	x	x
Temperate		x	x	x
Arctic and Antarctic			x	x

The anaerobic nitrogen-fixer *Clostridium* is almost universally present in soils, including those too acid for *Azotobacter*. For any given soil it is more abundant than *Azotobacter,* and it occurs in tropical soils. The normal condition of *Clostridium* is the spore form, vegetative growth occurring only during brief anaerobic periods following rains.

Azotobacter also is widely distributed in soils, but is not normally found in acid soils. In lateritic soils of the tropics its place seems to have been taken by *Beijerinckia*. This organism has only been reported in such areas as India, Burma, Java, Tropical Africa, Northern Australia, and South America. Ruinen (1956) claims that the normal habitat of *Beijerinckia* is on the leaves of tropical plants and that this is the reason this organism has not been detected in soils of the temperate zone. Earlier, Derx (1953) suggested that the occurrence of *Beijerinckia* in soils of the humid tropics might be due to an association with specific tropical plants.

Under natural conditions, the nitrogen-fixing capabilities of free-living bacteria are greatly restricted. These organisms require a source of available energy, a factor which limits their activities to environments with relatively high organic matter contents. Jensen (1950) concluded that many of the estimates for nitrogen fixation by nonsymbiotic nitrogen-fixing bacteria—frequently as high as 20 to 50 kg per hectare per year (18 to 45 pounds per acre per year)—are unrealistically high, because the level of available organic matter in most soils is too low to support fixation of this magnitude. Lipman and Conybeare (1936) estimated that about 6 pounds of nitrogen per acre are added each year to the soils of the United States by the combined activities of nonsymbiotic nitrogen-fixing microorganisms. For the semi-arid soils of Eastern Australia, Tchan and Beadle (1955) estimated that the maximum contribution of *Azotobacter* and algae was 0.1 and 3 pounds per acre per year, respectively.

3. BACTERIA LIVING IN SYMBIOSIS
WITH LEGUMINOUS PLANTS

The symbiotic genus *Rhizobium,* commonly associated with the Leguminosae, has been recognized for many years for its contribution to the nitrogen fertility of soils under permanent agriculture (Chapters 11 and 12). The fact that the association plays an active role in the nitrogen economy of natural plant communities is not so well known. Norris (1956) and Richards (1952) commented on the abundance of leguminous trees in tropical rain forests, and MacConnell and Bond (1957) emphasized the importance of wild legumes in the fixation of nitrogen in natural ecosystems. Jenny et al. (1948) found that soils in the tropical area of Colombia had nitrogen contents considerably higher than were anticipated from nitrogen-temperature functions developed in the United States. According to Jenny (1950), the presence of leguminous trees accounted for the higher nitrogen contents. The single dominant tree species in rainforest associations is frequently leguminous (Richards, 1952).

Norris (1956) summarized the information available on the global distribution of the Leguminosae, from which he compiled the tribal and species distribution. A summary of his tabulation is reproduced in Table 2. As Norris (1956) pointed out, the data are obsolete, particularly with

Table 2. Distribution of Leguminosae.

Sub-family	Number of genera and species	Genera and species in tropics and subtropics	Genera and species in temperate regions	Genera occurring in both tropic and temperate zones
Mimosoideae	31-1,341	31-1,200	1-141	1
Caesalpinioideae	95-1,032	89-988	7-44	1
Papilionatae	305-6,514	176-2,430	141-3,084	12
Total	431-8,887	296-4,618	149-3,269	14

* Adapted from Norris (1956).   The tabulation is based on early records and does not account for all of the known genera and species of Leguminosae.

respect to the number of species; nevertheless, the material is adequate for arriving at some generalizations regarding the distribution of the Leguminosae.

The results presented in Table 2 show that smaller numbers of genera and species of Leguminosae are indigenous to the temperate regions of the earth than to the tropics and subtropics. With the exception of 1 genus (141 species), the subfamily Mimosoideae is entirely tropical and subtropical, while 89 of the 95 genera of plants in the subfamily Caesalpinioideae (over 95% of the species) are confined to the tropics and subtropics. In the subfamily Papilionatae there are 141 genera of plants (3,084 species) that are located in the temperate regions, while 176 genera (2,430 species) occur in the tropics and subtropics.

4. BACTERIA LIVING IN SYMBIOSIS
WITH NONLEGUMINOUS PLANTS

Nitrogen fixation similar to that of the symbiotic relationship between Rhizobia and legumes has been demonstrated for many angiosperms, including plants belonging to the families Betulaceae, Elaeagnaceae, Myricaceae, Coriariaceae, Rhamnaceae, and Casuarinaceae. As Bond (1958) pointed out, nodulated nonlegumes are not freak plants of limited distribution but are important sources of fixed nitrogen for plants in general.

The geographic distribution of the nonleguminous families for which nitrogen fixation has been established is outlined in Table 3. Docu-

Table 3. Distribution of nodulated nonlegumes.

Family	Genus	Species nodulated	Geographical distribution
Betulaceae	*Alnus*	15	Cool regions of the northern hemisphere
Elaeagnaceae	*Elaeagnus*	9	Asia, Europe, North America
	Hippophae	1	Asia and Europe, from Himalayas to Arctic Circle
	Shepherdia	2	Confined to North America
Myricaceae	*Myrica*	7	Temperate regions of both hemispheres
Coriariaceae	*Coriaria*	3	Widely separated regions, chiefly Japan, New Zealand, Central and South America, and the Mediterranean region
Rhamnaceae	*Ceanothus*	7	Confined to North America
Casuarinaceae	*Casuarina*	12	Tropics and subtropics, extending from East Africa to the Indian Archipelago, Pacific Islands, and Australia.

mentary evidence of nitrogen fixation by microorganisms living in association with these plants has been given by Allen and Allen (1958) and
reviews are available by Bond (1958) and Norris (1962). Very little information is available concerning the organisms responsible for nitrogen
fixation (see Chapter 5).

The family Betulaceae, consisting of the alders and birches, is confined
almost entirely to the cool temperate to arctic zones of the northern
hemisphere. Thus far, only the alder (*Alnus*) has been found to bear
nodules. Crocker and Major (1955) estimated an annual gain of 55 pounds
of nitrogen per acre by *A. crispa* during colonization of the recessional
moraines of Alaskan glaciers. Studies of fossil pollen and tree stumps in
peat show that the alder was formerly an abundant tree in the less-well-
drained parts of England (Bond, 1958). Ferguson and Bond (1953) concluded that a moderately sized alder tree (*A. glutinosa*) was capable of
fixing 0.25 to 0.5 kg (0.55 to 1.10 pounds) of nitrogen per year.

The family Elaeagnaceae, consisting of the genera *Elaeagnus, Hippophae,* and *Shepherdia,* is distributed widely in the temperate regions
of both hemispheres. The genus *Elaeagnus,* with 30 species (one-third of
which bear nodules), occurs in Asia, Europe, and North America. *Hippophae* consists of 2 species, 1 of which (*H. rhamnoides*) forms nodules.
Pollen records show that this plant was prominent in Europe following
the Ice Age. *Shepherdia,* a plant confined to North America, consists of
3 species, 2 of which (*S. canadensis* and *S. argentea*) nodulate. Crocker
and Major (1955) reported that *Shepherdia,* in company with *Alnus,*
colonized the moraines of receding glaciers in Alaska.

The family Myricaceae (the galeworts) is distributed widely in the
temperate regions of both hemispheres. The family consists of about 60
species of *Myrica,* of which 7 species have been found to nodulate. A
few species occur in the tropics. Bog myrtle (*M. gale*) may be involved in
the fixation of nitrogen in acid peats.

Three of the 15 species of the family Coriariaceae, namely, *Coriaria
arborea, C. japonica,* and *C. myrtifolia,* have been found to bear nodules.
Bond and Montserrat (1958) suggested that the discontinuous distribution of this family indicates that, in ancient times, it made a far greater

contribution to the supply of fixed nitrogen for plant life than at present.

The family Rhamnaceae contains 40 genera of trees and shrubs that are spread over most of the globe. However, the 7 species which have been reported to nodulate occur in *Ceanothus,* a genus of about 55 species confined to North America. More than half of the species are found in the southwestern part of the United States. Vlamis et al. (1958) have found that one species of *Ceanothus* (known locally as deer brush) occurred in practically every plant association in California. In their report on a study of nitrogen accumulations during soil development on the Mt. Shasta mudflows in California, Dickson and Crocker (1953) suggested that the build-up may have been due to the symbiosis of nitrogen-fixing microorganisms with species of *Ceanothus.*

Nitrogen fixation has been reported for 12 of the 35 species of Casuarinaceae, the main non-leguminous angiosperm family of nodulating plants occurring in tropical and subtropical areas. Plants of this family are of great ecological significance in the Australian environment (Norris, 1962).

In addition to the above-mentioned families, nodulation has been reported by species of the families Zygophyllaceae, Podocarpinaceae, and Cycadaceae. Allen and Allen (1958) and Norris (1962) have summarized the information available on nitrogen fixation by these plants. Daubenmire (1947) reported that about 370 species of nonleguminous plants contain colonies of nitrogen-fixing microorganisms in their leaves.

B. Nitrogen in Atmospheric Precipitation

It is well known that combined nitrogen, consisting of ammonia, nitrate, nitrite, and organically bound nitrogen, occurs in atmospheric precipitation. Nitrite normally occurs in trace amounts only ($< 3\%$ of the inorganic nitrogen), and this fraction is usually either ignored or included with the nitrate determination. The organically bound nitrogen (albuminoid nitrogen) is associated with cosmic dust, and, while this nitrogen does not represent a new addition to the soil, its occurrence in precipitation leads to a redistribution of terrestrial nitrogen (Hutchinson, 1944).

The amount of nitrogen brought into the soil in atmospheric precipitation is normally too small to be of significance in crop production. However, this nitrogen may be of considerable importance to the nitrogen economy of mature ecosystems, such as undisturbed natural forests and virgin grasslands. Natural plant communities, unlike cultivated crops, are not subject to continued large losses of nitrogen through cropping and grazing, and the nitrogen in precipitation serves to restore the small quantities that are lost from these so-called "closed" systems.

Eriksson (1952) summarized the earlier measurements for the nitrogen in atmospheric precipitation. For Europe and the United States, the values for ammonia and nitrate ranged from 0.74 to 21 kg per hectare per year

(0.7 to 18.7 pounds per acre per year) the majority of which was in the range of 4 to 7 pounds per acre. As Eriksson (1952) pointed out, many of the high results reported for the nitrogen in precipitation represent either sampling and analytical errors, or contamination. Eriksson (1952) and Virtanen (1952) concluded that the unusually high values occasionally obtained for the nitrogen in precipitation in Europe (often higher than 20 pounds per acre per year) could be due to the heavy industrial activity in that area.

An unusually high value for the nitrogen in precipitation was reported by Jones (1960). He found that 50.8 pounds of nitrogen per acre was added to the soils of Northern Nigeria in 1 year. Roelofsen (1941) recorded an average of 27.1 pounds of nitrogen per acre per year (ranging from 14.9 to 43.3 pounds) over a 15-year period in Sumatra. These results are in disagreement with most other published data from tropical areas (see review by Eriksson, 1952; Meyer and Pampfer, 1959).

Ångström and Högberg (1952a, b) concluded that the concentration of mineral nitrogen in precipitation decreased with increasing latitude and that tropical air contained from 10 to 30% more mineral nitrogen than polar air and nearly twice as much as arctic air. In temperate regions of the earth the mineral nitrogen in precipitation appears to be highest during the warmer period of the year (Ångström and Högberg, 1952b; Eriksson, 1952) and, for any given rainfall, the concentration decreases progressively with the duration of precipitation (Herman and Gorham, 1957). Rain water contains higher quantities of ammonia and nitrate than snow, a result which may be due to greater adsorption of ammonia and nitrate in the liquid phase, as compared to the solid phase (Herman and Gorham, 1957).

Very few data are available on the amounts of organically bound nitrogen in atmospheric precipitation. The survey conducted by Eriksson indicated that as much as 4 to 6 pounds of organic nitrogen per acre may be added to the soil each year in precipitation.

Hutchinson (1944) gives the following sources of combined nitrogen in atmospheric precipitation:

(1). From soil and the ocean
(2). From fixation of atmospheric nitrogen
    (a). Electrically
    (b). Photochemically
    (c). In the trail of meteorites
(3). From industrial contamination

The relative importance of the above sources to the nitrogen in atmospheric precipitation is unknown. According to Russell and Richards (1919) and Virtanen (1952) the most important source of ammonia is volatilization from land surfaces; on the other hand, Larson and Hettick (1956) concluded that the ammonia came largely from industrial contamination (combustion of fossil fuel), and possibly from fires. Eriksson (1952) and Hutchinson (1944) presented evidence which indicated that the ocean was not a major source of ammonia, as many earlier workers were inclined to believe (see review by Eriksson, 1952). The quantities of nitrogen fixed in the trails of meteorites can be considered negligible (Hutchinson, 1944).

The formation of nitrate by electrical discharge during thunderstorm activity has been a favored theory for a long time. However, nitrate distribution patterns have seldom correlated with thunderstorm activity (Ångström and Högberg, 1952a, b; Eriksson, 1952; Junge, 1958). According to Hutchinson (1944) only 10 to 20% of the nitrate in precipitation can be accounted for by electrical discharge. Junge (1958) postulated that the nitrate had an origin over land, either from soil or from industrial contamination.

The information obtained thus far on the nitrogen compounds in atmospheric precipitation shows a marked consistency in the ratio of ammonia to nitrate (of the order of 2 to 1). On this basis, Ångström and Högberg (1952b) concluded that two compounds were formed by a similar mechanism; namely, a photochemical one. The reaction was considered to be as follows:

$$12 \, N + 18 \, H_2O \rightarrow 4 \, NH_4NO_3 + 4 \, NH_4OH + O_2$$

The interdependence of ammonia and nitrate in atmospheric precipitation can also be explained by the oxidation of ammonia to nitrate, such as photochemical oxidation (Eriksson, 1952; Hutchinson, 1954; Virtanen, 1952).

The atmosphere also contains nitrous oxide. Adel (1951), Arnold (1954), and Goody and Walshaw (1953) concluded that the nitrous oxide was derived from the soil. Nitrous oxide is produced in soil by denitrifying bacteria, and it may be formed by combustion of nitrogen compounds during the burning of fossil fuel (Eriksson, 1952).

The lack of agreement among the various investigators about the nature, origin, and distribution of the nitrogen compounds in atmospheric precipitation emphasizes the paucity of information in this area. Regular and systematic determinations of nitrogen compounds in precipitation are now being made in several laboratories throughout the world, and data should be forthcoming which will clarify our understanding of the importance of precipitation as a source of nitrogen for plant growth.

C. Nonbiological Nitrogen Fixation

For many years, Dhar and his co-workers in India have claimed that nitrogen fixation in soil is due to photochemical activity. Many papers on this subject have been published over the past 25 years, mostly in Indian soil science journals. The views of this group have been summarized in review articles by Dhar (1960, 1961).

The following quotation from Dhar (1960) illustrates adequately his view on photochemical nitrogen fixation: ". . . all types of organic matter containing carbohydrates, celluloses, lignins, fats, etc. when mixed with soil undergo slow oxidation on the soil surface liberating energy. This energy of oxidation can fix atmospheric nitrogen and enrich the soil from the nitrogen point of view even in the dark. Moreover, our experimental results show that sunlight or artificial light is appreciably absorbed by a mixture of soil and organic matter and is readily utilized in increasing nitrogen fixation in the soil and improving its nitrogen status."

Another statement by Dhar (1961) reads: "Assuming that only 40% of the carbon introduced by photosynthesis in the world soils is oxidized per year and there is a fixation of only 20 milligrams of nitrogen in sunlight per gram of carbon oxidized, the amount of nitrogen fixed on the surface of the world soils would be approximately 110 million tons per year, half of which is caused by sunlight absorption. Hence, this nitrogen fixation seems to be the chief source of soil nitrogen and crop production in the world."

Dhar's photochemical theory has been conspicuously ignored by soil scientists, a consequence arising from almost complete rejection of the theory. Examination of papers published in the *Proceedings* of the *Soil Science Society of America* shows that the theory has received scant mention, and that no paper has been published which either supports or rejects the theory.

The reason for the increases in total nitrogen obtained by Dhar and his co-workers during incubation of soil in the presence of sunlight is difficult to determine. Russell (1950) suggested that blue-green algae may have been responsible for the fixed nitrogen.

D. Sorption of Combined Nitrogen from the Atmosphere

Soils have the ability to absorb small quantities of ammonia from the atmosphere, and the earlier investigators (notably Liebig) placed considerable emphasis on this process as a means of providing nitrogen to plants. The opinion of modern soil scientists is that the process is of little practical significance.

Ingham (1950a, b) has recently taken exception to the viewpoint expressed above. According to Ingham, sufficient nitrogen is absorbed from the air to maintain soil fertility. His concept is expressed in the following quotation (Ingham, 1950b): "—soil fertility is to be regarded, not as a static condition, but as a dynamic process taking place continuously at the surface of the soil and depending chiefly on the presence of cellulose or other organic colloids, which play the part of catalysts, alternately adsorbing ammonia and mineral matter from the air and transferring them in aqueous solution by the agency of rain to the roots of the growing crop," and elsewhere in his publication, "Although little has been said about the microorganisms of the soil, they nevertheless play an important part of any theory of fertility, not because they add anything to the soil, but because they break down the waste organic matter of crop residues and by resolving it into simpler compounds render it available as new building material for another generation of plants."

The experimental results presented by Ingham (1950a, b), like those of Dhar (discussed in the previous section), cannot easily be evaluated or disproved. In any event, neither theory can be reconciled with results obtained under field conditions. In order to evaluate the claims of these men, carefully controlled experiments must be conducted, using N^{15}.

After this paper was prepared, Malo and Purvis (1964) published data on ammonia absorption by soils under "field conditions" at New Brunswick, N.J. Absorption varied from 0.05 to 0.2 pound per acre per day, equivalent to 18 to 73 pounds per acre per year.

IV. THE NITROGEN CONTENT OF THE SOIL

A. Nitrogen Accumulation on Youthful Landscapes

The nitrogen in soil, particularly that in the surface layer, occurs largely in organic combination (see Chapters 2 and 3); thus, the process of nitrogen accumulation bears a close relationship to the accumulation of organic matter. A carbon-nitrogen ratio of from 10 to 12 is considered typical for organic matter in the surface layer of the agriculturally important soils of the temperate regions of the earth.

As noted previously, microorganisms living in symbiosis with higher plants, both legumes and nonlegumes, are primarily responsible for the increase in nitrogen during soil development. The causative agent has seldom been identified, because the botanical composition of immature ecosystems changes constantly during formation; thus, the plant types which prevailed during periods of rapid nitrogen accretion are not always known. It is possible that the high nitrogen contents of some of the legume-free grassland soils of the world are due to the previous occurrence of species of Leguminosae; however, fixation of nitrogen by nonsymbiotic nitrogen-fixing organisms living in the rhizosphere of plant roots cannot be excluded (Parker, 1957b).

Unfortunately, few natural ecosystems are available which provide a chronosequence of plants representative of all stages of soil development. The problem is complicated by the fact that very little is known of the various symbiotic relationships which exist between nitrogen-fixing microorganisms and higher plants (see section III).

1. PLANT CHRONOSEQUENCE AND NITROGEN ACCUMULATION

Information on the rate of nitrogen accumulation in soil during colonization by plants has come from studies of time sequences on the moraines of receding glaciers (Chandler, 1943; Crocker and Dickson, 1957; Crocker and Major, 1955), mud flows (Dickson and Crocker, 1953), spoil banks (Leisman, 1957), sand dunes (Olson, 1958; Salisbury, 1922, 1925), road cuts (Andrew and Rhoades, 1948), Indian mounds,* and an abandoned fortress (Akimtzev, 1932). In general the results show that the rate of nitrogen accumulation is rapid during the first few years, diminishes

---

* Li, L. Rate of soil development as indicated by profile studies of Indian mounds. Ph.D. dissertation, University of Illinois, 1943.

slowly, and reaches equilibrium in periods of time which vary from 110 to 1,500 years.

The research by Chandler (1943) and Crocker and Dickson (1957) on nitrogen accumulation on recessional moraines of the Herbert and Mendenhall glaciers in southeastern Alaska, and by Crocker and Major (1955) at Glacier Bay, illustrates clearly the relation between the chronosequence of plants and the rate at which nitrogen accumulates in the soil. A descriptive account of vegetative development in these ecosystems has been given by Lawrence (1958).

The pioneer plants on the morainic debris of Alaskan glaciers, consisting mainly of species of willow and cottonwood, exhibited symptoms characteristic of soil-nitrogen deficiency (Lawrence, 1958). Apparently, the amount of nitrogen left in the mineral material from receding glaciers, or added to it through fixation of nitrogen by the blue-green algae component of earlier-invading lichens, was insufficient to meet the nitrogen requirements of these plants. After about 10 years, the landscape was invaded by the alder (*Alnus crispa*), to some extent by *Dryas*, and occasionally by the willow (*Salix*). Both the alder and *Dryas* form symbiotic relationships with nitrogen-fixing microorganisms. Of these two plants, the alder appeared to be more effective in supplying fixed nitrogen on the morainic debris (Crocker and Major, 1955). The entry of combined nitrogen into the ecosystem produced dramatic changes in the nature and composition of the plant flora and, subsequently, in the rate at which nitrogen accumulated in the soil. The pioneering plants, which formerly grew prostrate and had sickly yellowish leaves, suddenly grew erect and showed a healthy appearance (Lawrence, 1958). After about 15 to 20 years, the pioneering plants were replaced almost completely by a dense thicket of shrubs, predominantly alders, and after 35 to 40 years the alder cover was nearly continuous (Crocker and Dickson, 1957). At this early date, the cottonwood (*Populus trichocarpa* T. -G.) had started to overtop the alder and, before long, the spruce (*Picea sitchensis* Carr.) predominated. After 60 to 70 years, the spruce had outgrown both the alder and the cottonwood and, after 100 to 120 years, the landscape was essentially a spruce forest.

Fig. 3 shows the relation between the chronosequence of plants and the accumulation of nitrogen in the upper 18 inches of soil developed on the moraines at Glacier Bay in Alaska. For the period of about 10 to 70 years after the initial vegetative growth, nitrogen accumulated at the rate of about 4.9 g per square meter per year (equivalent to about 44 pounds per acre per year), of which as much as 60% was in the forest floor. The fall in the rate of nitrogen accumulation at about 60 to 70 years paralleled closely the decline in alder dominance. The decrease continued through the period of alder senescence and no further addition occurred in the final spruce stage; however, during all stages a redistribution of nitrogen took place by transfer from the forest floor to the mineral soil, as illustrated in Fig. 4.

At Glacier Bay, there appeared to be slight loss of nitrogen from the upper 18 inches of soil beyond 120 years (Fig. 4). This result contrasts

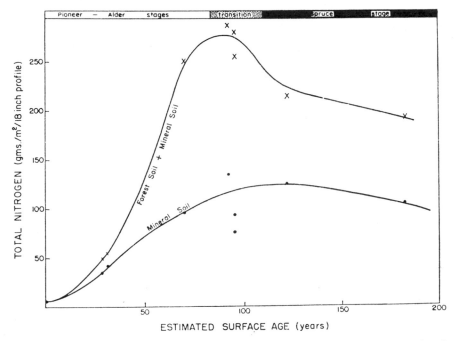

Fig. 3—Chronosequence of plants in relation to nitrogen accumulation on recessional moraines of Alaskan glaciers. (From Crocker and Major, 1955).

with depth functions obtained for the moraines of the Herbert and Mendenhall glaciers, where nitrogen continued to increase slightly beyond the period of alder senescence (Crocker and Dickson, 1957).

Time functions of nitrogen build-up during soil development on the Mt. Shasta mudflows in California (Dickson and Crocker, 1953) bear a striking resemblance to those obtained for the moraines of Alaskan glaciers. However, in the case of the Mt. Shasta mudflows nitrogen ac-

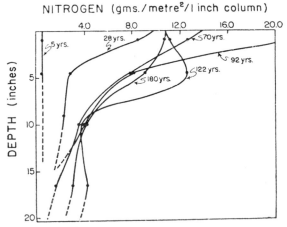

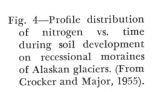

Fig. 4—Profile distribution of nitrogen vs. time during soil development on recessional moraines of Alaskan glaciers. (From Crocker and Major, 1955).

cumulated in the mineral soil at a much faster rate (3,360 pounds per acre in 60 years). The rapid increase in nitrogen during the early stages of soil development on the Mt. Shasta chronosequence may have been due to microorganisms living in symbiosis with species of *Ceanothus* (Dickson and Crocker, 1953).

2. THE TIME FACTOR

A consideration of published reports on nitrogen-time functions during soil development shows that the time required to reach equilibrium levels varies widely. As was noted in the previous section, about 110 years was required to reach apparent steady-state levels of nitrogen on the recessional moraines of Alaskan glaciers; for the 10- to 70-year period, rates of from 43 to 55 pounds of nitrogen per acre per year were recorded. Similar results were obtained by E. H. Tyner (personal communication) and Leisman (1957) for nitrogen accumulation on strip-mine spoil banks. The results obtained by Tyner showed that only 75 years were required to bring the nitrogen content of the surface 6 inches of the spoil area up to that of the surface 6 inches of adjacent virgin soil. Leisman (1957) concluded that a high incidence of species of Leguminosae accounted for the rapid increase in nitrogen during soil formation on Minnesota iron-ore spoil banks.

Periods of time considerably longer than 110 years appear to be required for nitrogen levels to reach equilibrium in other ecosystems. Time functions obtained by Dickson and Crocker (1953) for soils developing on the Mt. Shasta mudflows show that nitrogen in the mineral soil (36-inch depth) approached apparent steady-state conditions in about 566 years, although total nitrogen in the system (soil plus mineral floor) had reached a maximum in 205 years. The increase in soil nitrogen after 205 years was found to be due to a pronounced redistribution of nitrogen from the forest floor to the soil during the 205- to 566-year period. Dickson and Crocker (1953) pointed out that profile adjustments in nitrogen continued to take place on the Mt. Shasta mudflows for more than 1,200 years, and that if the profiles had been sampled below 36 inches total nitrogen in the system would have continued to increase until the most advanced state of the system was reached.

The rather rapid rate of nitrogen accumulation on the Mt. Shasta mudflows and on the moraines of the Alaskan glaciers can best be illustrated by considering the time required to reach halfway to equilibrium. Examination of the data reported for these ecosystems shows that in each case this time period was of the order of 40 to 50 years.

The results Salisbury (1925) obtained for accretion of nitrogen on the sand dunes at Blackney Point, England, show that nitrogen was still accumulating on the oldest dunes studied (280 years), and that the system was a long way from equilibrium. According to Olson (1958), more than 1,000 years may be required for nitrogen levels to reach equilibrium on the Lake Michigan sand dunes. Burges (1960) concluded that 4,000 years would be needed for a podzol to reach maturity in Eastern Australia.

The rather slow rate at which nitrogen accumulates on sands during soil development can be attributed to the retarded growth of plants resulting from frequent periods of severe moisture stress and to the fact that, in such ecosystems, a rather long lag phase is required before the initiation of plant growth. Another important factor may be the loss of nitrogen through leaching.

The factors which contribute to the leveling off in nitrogen content during soil development include the following:

(1) Decrease in the number of plants which form symbiotic relationships with nitrogen-fixing microorganisms. As was noted for the Alaskan moraines, an increase in available nitrogen (brought about primarily through fixation of nitrogen by microorganisms living in symbiosis with *Alnus*) enhanced the growth of plant species not involved in the fixation process; ultimately, these plants became the dominant flora.

(2) Reduction in the quantity of nitrogen fixed by microorganisms. It is well known that as the amount of available nitrogen in the soil increases the amount of nitrogen fixed by microorganisms, both the free-living and those living in symbiosis with higher plants, decreases.

(3) Saturation of the soil mineral complex with organic matter. As will be noted later, the texture of the soil is a major factor influencing the nitrogen content of aerated soils.

Under steady-state conditions, the rate at which nitrogen is added to the soil in atmospheric precipitation, and by biological nitrogen fixation, equals the rate at which nitrogen is lost by such processes as leaching and denitrification. Over long periods of time, of the order of geological time, the nitrogen level may undergo further changes due to variations in climate, or to alteration in the composition of the soil resulting from pedogenic processes.

B. Factors Affecting the Nitrogen Content of the Soil

In natural ecosystems, the nitrogen content of the soil approaches an equilibrium value. The magnitude of this value depends upon such factors as climate, type of vegetation, nature of the terrain, physical characteristics of the soil, and activities of the microflora and microfauna organisms. The soil-nitrogen system is a dynamic one, and any alteration in the environment, such as a change in climate, may lead to a new equilibrium level of nitrogen. The extreme variability in the nitrogen content of the soil (from less than 0.1% in desert and semi-desert soils to as much as 2.0% in highly organic soils) attests to the diverse combinations in which the factors operate. As will be shown later, disruption of the equilibrium through the activities of man produces marked changes in the nitrogen content of the soil.

Jenny (1928, 1930, 1941) attempted to evaluate the relative importance of the "soil-forming factors" (climate, vegetation, topography, parent material, and age) on the nitrogen content of the soil by treating each one as an independent variable. For this purpose, all factors except the one under consideration had to be kept constant, or adjustments made for their potency. In an examination of the influence of climate on the nitrogen content of soils from the central and eastern United States,

Jenny (1928, 1929, 1930, 1931) restricted his sampling to soils with similar texture, slope, and exposure, and having a common pool of plant species. Later, Jenny and Raychaudhuri (1960), working with Indian soils, were obliged to use samples having variable textures; this factor was controlled by adjusting the nitrogen values to uniform texture by using moisture retention data. In forest soils, horizontal gradients in nitrogen occur, and the nitrogen content varies with exposure. These variables were standardized by Harradine and Jenny (1958) to the extent that the samples were taken at a uniform distance from a tree trunk (6 feet) and at the same exposure.

According to Jenny (1930), the order of importance of the soil-forming factors in determining the nitrogen contents of loamy soils within the United States as a whole is as follows: climate > vegetation > topography = parent material > age.

The concept developed by Jenny, namely, that each factor can be treated as an independent variable, has been criticized on the grounds that an alteration of any one factor produces changes in remaining factors. Leeper (1938) pointed out that while the theory takes into account the influence of temperature on the rate of decomposition of organic matter by microorganisms and the influence of rainfall on the synthesis of plant material, no consideration is given to the effect of *both* temperature and moisture on *both* synthesis and destruction. Despite these shortcomings, Jenny's studies have contributed substantially to our understanding of the factors influencing the nitrogen content of the soil, and they have provided a better appreciation of the problems involved in maintaining nitrogen reserves on land placed under cultivation.

Tyurin (quoted by Kononova, 1961) expressed the limiting value of humus accumulation (S) by the equation

$$S = (1 - a)A/x \qquad [1]$$

where a is the decomposition coefficient of plant residues, x is the decomposition coefficient of humus, and A is the amount of plant residues added to the soil annually.

1. CLIMATE

Climate is the most important single factor which determines the array of plant species available at any given location, the quantity of plant material produced, and the intensity of microbial activity in the soil; consequently, this factor plays a prominent role in determining the nitrogen and organic matter levels in the soil. As was mentioned earlier, the level of nitrogen in soil parallels closely that of organic matter.

Considering climate in its entirety, a humid climate leads to forest associations and the development of podzolic-type soils (podzols, gray-brown podzolic, red-yellow podzolic); a semi-arid climate leads to grassland associations and the development of brunizem, chernozem, and chestnut soils. Chernozem and brunizem soils exceed all other well-aerated soils in nitrogen content; desert, semi-desert, and laterite soils have the lowest. Intermediate between these types are the chestnut, gray-brown podzolic, and red-yellow podzolic soils. Soils formed under restricted drainage (humic gley) do not follow a climatic pattern. In these soils, oxygen deficiency prevents complete destruction of organic residues by microorganisms over a wide temperature range.

The profile distributions of nitrogen in soils representative of the various great soil groups are given in Fig. 5.

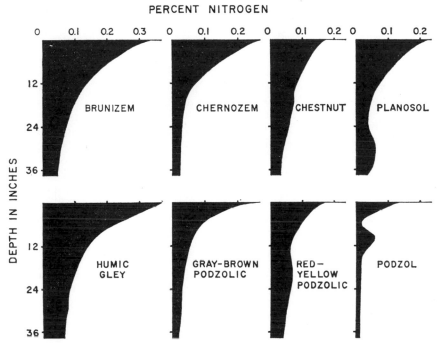

Fig. 5—Distribution of nitrogen in profiles representative of several great soil groups. The data for the chestnut was taken from Brown and Byers (1935), for the humic gley from Brown and Thorpe (1942), and for the podzol from Byers et al. (1935).

The effect of increasing rainfall on nitrogen levels in the soil is to cause greater plant growth, and, consequently, the production of larger quantities of raw material for synthesis of humic substances. For grassland soils, a definite correlation exists between the depth of the root system and the thickness of the grass cover with depth of penetration of nitrogen and organic matter, as illustrated in Fig. 6 for a west-to-east transect along the Great Plains region of the United States. The profile distribution of nitrogen in the chestnut and chernozem soils typical of the central and eastern parts of this area, respectively, and of the brunizem soils to the east of this region, is shown in Fig. 5.

Jenny and his co-workers (Jenny, 1928, 1929, 1930, 1931, 1950; Jenny et al., 1948; Jenny and Leonard, 1934; and Jenny and Raychaudhuri, 1960) made extensive studies of the importance of the components of climate (temperature and moisture) on nitrogen levels in soil. The influ-

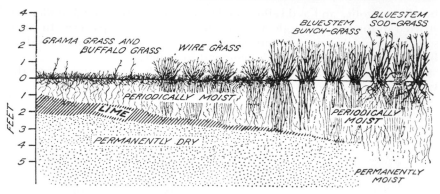

Fig. 6—Relationship between vegetative growth and moisture supply in the soils along a west to east transect of the Great Plains. (From Shantz, 1923).

ence of moisture was evaluated by use of the NS quotient of Meyers, which is the ratio of precipitation (in mm) to the absolute saturation deficit of the air (in mm of Hg).

A distinguishing feature of the nitrogen-temperature function reported by Jenny was that the relationship conformed to van't Hoff's temperature rule. Thus, the nitrogen content of the soil decreased 2 to 3 times for each fall of 10°C in mean annual temperature, and the reaction was defined adequately by the formula:

$$N = a/(1 + Ce^{-kt}) \qquad [2]$$

where N is the total nitrogen content of the soil, t is the temperature, e is the base of the natural logarithm, and a, C, and k are constants.

The relationship between mean annual temperature and the nitrogen content of the soils in the semi-humid region of central United States is illustrated in Fig. 7. Jenny (1928, 1930) found that the nitrogen contents

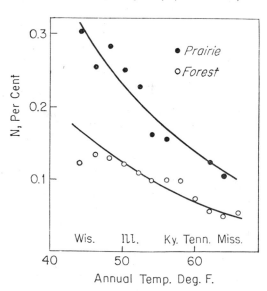

Fig. 7—Nitrogen content of soils in the semi-humid region of the United States, as influenced by temperature (From Jenny, 1941. Used by permission, Mc-Graw-Hill Book Co.)

of the soils along a north to south transect of this region conformed to the equation:

$$N = 1.55/(1 + e^{0.065(t-18.5)})\qquad[3]$$

The expression for the nitrogen content of the soils along a similar transect for the semi-arid region was:

$$N = 1.70/(1 + e^{0.045(t-1.5)})\qquad[4]$$

With the mean annual temperature held constant, Jenny (1928, 1930) found that the nitrogen content of the soils in central United States increased logarithmically with increasing moisture, as evaluated by the NS quotient. Fig. 8 gives the nitrogen contents of the soils along a west to

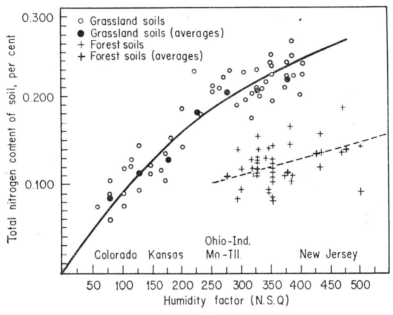

Fig. 8—Soil nitrogen-rainfall relation along the annual isotherm of 11°C in the United States. (From Jenny, 1941. Used by permission, McGraw-Hill Book Co.)

east transect of the United States from the Rocky Mountains to the Atlantic coast (isotherm of 11°C). The nitrogen content of Australian soils has been found to correlate well with the NS quotient (Leeper, 1938).

Using nitrogen-climate functions developed in the United States as the basis, Jenny et al. (1948) found that the soils of Colombia had unusually high nitrogen contents. Later, Jenny (1950) attributed this finding to the more favorable climatic conditions in the tropics for plant growth, and to the presence of species of Leguminosae in the equatorial forests of Colombia. Hawaiian (Dean, 1938) and Puerto Rican (Smith et al., 1951) soils also appear to have higher nitrogen contents than would be predicted from climatic functions developed for the soils of continental United States.

Enders (1943a, b) concluded that the best soil conditions for the synthesis and preservation of humic substances having high nitrogen contents were frequent and abrupt changes in such factors as humidity and temperature; consequently, soils formed in harsh continental climates should have higher nitrogen contents. Harmsen (1951) used this same theory to explain the greater synthesis of humic substances in grassland soils as compared to arable land, claiming that in the former the combination of organic substrates in the surface soil and frequent and sharp fluctuations in temperature, moisture, and irradiation led to a better synthesis of humic substances. According to Harmsen (1951) the extreme surface of the soil (upper few millimeters) is the site of the synthesis of humic substances and the fixation of nitrogen.

Senstius (1958) concluded that the increase in soil organic matter (consequently, nitrogen) with decreasing temperature in an aerobic environment occurs because, at lower temperatures, the activities of microorganisms decrease more than does the photosynthetic process of higher plants. He emphasized that the life activities of higher plants start out at lower temperatures than do those of microorganisms (0°C vs. 5°C), and that the optimum is lower (25°C vs. 30°C); therefore, temperatures below about 25°C should favor the production and preservation of humic substances. The influence of temperature on the accumulation of organic matter (as proposed by Senstius, 1958) is illustrated diagrammatically in Fig. 9. The diagram shows that, under aerobic conditions, organic matter fails to accumulate at high temperatures, whereas, under anaerobic conditions, accumulations are possible over the entire temperature range.

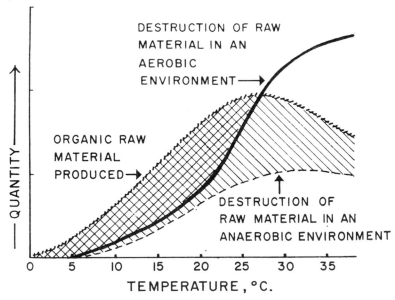

Fig. 9—Influence of temperature on organic raw material production through photosynthesis and organic matter destruction by microorganisms. The shaded areas depict humus accumulations. (Adapted from Senstius, 1958).

Waksman and Gerretsen (1931) found that, in the temperature range of from 5 to 30°C, the lower the temperature the lower the rate of decomposition of organic residues and the higher the nitrogen content. Some interesting results obtained by Jensen (1936, 1939) indicated that the rate of decomposition of organic matter increased with increasing temperature, while, on the other hand, the abundance of microorganisms decreased. According to Jensen (1939), the increase in soil humus with decreasing temperature cannot be explained entirely by the retarding influence of temperature on biological processes (according to van't Hoff's law), but also to the fact that, with decreasing temperature, larger proportions of the transformed organic matter are converted into microbial tissues.

Jenny and Raychaudhuri (1960) compared the nitrogen contents of some Indian soils with those of California, Texas, and the Atlantic Coast region of the United States. When the sites studied had comparable mean annual temperatures and precipitations, the Indian soils were decidedly superior in nitrogen. On the other hand, the Indian soils contained less nitrogen than the tropical soils of Central and South America.

2. TYPE OF VEGETATION

According to Jenny (1941), the vegetation factor of soil formation is concerned with the pool of plant species available to a given location, not the quantity of vegetative growth produced; the latter is considered to be controlled by the other soil-forming factors, especially climate.

Soils developed under plants with extensive root systems generally have higher nitrogen (and organic matter) contents, other factors being equal, than those developed under plants with restricted root systems. Under forest-type vegetation, where most of the plant debris is added to the soil in the form of fallen leaves, light-colored soils (for example, gray brown podzolic) are formed which contain relatively low amounts of nitrogen. Under grass vegetation, where considerable debris is added in root excretions and as sloughed off roots, dark-colored soils (for example, brunizem) are formed which contain relatively high amounts of nitrogen. In commenting on the unusually high nitrogen values obtained by Smith et al. (1951) for some tropical soils of Puerto Rico, Joffe (1955) suggested that the human factor was partly responsible, namely, through cultivation of plants having sod characteristics.

The reason for the high nitrogen content of grassland soils, as compared to forest soils, has been the subject of considerable conjecture. It is common knowledge that the nitrogen (and organic matter) level of most soils cannot be maintained, or increased, without putting them into grass sods; consequently, the conditions in grassland soils are considered favorable for the retention of all available nitrogen as humic substances. Harmsen (1951) concluded that the accumulation of nitrogen and organic matter in grassland soil cannot be explained entirely by the higher amounts of plant residues produced, because luxuriously growing crops, together with high applications of organic matter in the form of manures, composts, or green manures cannot avert completely the depletion of nitrogen and organic matter during cropping. The claim that lack of sufficient aeration in densely populated grassland soils contributes to the preservation of nitrogen and organic matter runs into the difficulty that well-drained grassland soils are generally better aerated than arable land (Harmsen, 1955).

Mattson and Koutler-Andersson (1943, 1944) offered still another explanation for the high nitrogen contents of grassland soils. These workers claimed that a high base status in the soil leads to the absorption of atmospheric oxygen and the fixation of ammonia by lignin, or lignin-nitrogenous constituents of the organic matter. According to this concept, grassland soils (high base status) should have higher nitrogen contents and lower C/N ratios than forest soils (low base status). Moodie (1951) used this theory to explain the variable results obtained by application of the hypoiodite method for studying the nature of soil organic matter.

The rhizosphere is a zone of intense microbial activity due to the presence of abundant energy from root excretions and sloughed off roots. The fixation of nitrogen in this zone through the activities of non-symbiotic nitrogen-fixing heterotrophs, such as *Azotobacter* and *Clostridium,* may facilitate the production of humic substances in grassland soils.

Theron (1951) and Theron and Haylett (1953) recently revived an earlier hypothesis that substances secreted from living roots suppress nitrification; consequently, nitrogen is preserved and can accumulate to high levels. This view has been challenged severely by Harmsen and van Schreven (1955) who presented a series of arguments in rejection of the theory. On the other hand, Soulides and Clark (1958) concluded that nitrification was retarded by living plant roots.

With regard to soils formed under forest vegetation, differences in the profile distribution of nitrogen occur by virtue of the manner in which the leaf litter becomes mixed with mineral matter. In soils formed under deciduous forests on well-drained sites adequately supplied with calcium (gray-brown podzolic), the litter becomes well mixed with the mineral layer through the activities of earthworms and other organisms of the microfauna. In this case, the nitrogen profile shows little if any accumulation in the *B* horizon (see Fig. 5). On the other hand, in soils formed under coniferous forests on soils low in available calcium (podzol), the leaf litter does not become mixed with the mineral matter, but forms a mat on the soil surface. The nitrogen profile of a podzol (see Fig. 5) generally shows a bulge in the *B* horizon as a result of the eluviation of soluble organic constituents (partly as metal complexes) into this horizon.

3. TOPOGRAPHY

Topography, or relief, affects the nitrogen content of the soil through its influence on climate, runoff, evaporation, and transpiration. Degree of slope, length and shape of slope, and position of the water table are all important (Aandahl, 1949).

In mountainous areas, where pronounced changes in elevation occur, differences in soil nitrogen result from vertical zonation in the composition of the plant flora, and from variations in climate. Harradine and Jenny (1958) found that the amounts of nitrogen in soils occurring on the western slopes of the Sierra Nevada Mountains in California were related to climate, namely, that the nitrogen content of the soil increased with decreasing temperature and with increasing precipitation. Exposure also was involved, as north-facing slopes were higher in nitrogen than south-facing slopes.

Local variations in topography, such as knolls, slopes, and depressions, modify the plant microclimate, defined by Aandahl (1949) as the climate in the immediate vicinity of the soil profile. Soils occurring in depressions, where the climate is "locally-humid," have higher nitrogen contents than those occurring on the knolls, where the climate is "locally-arid." Aandahl found large differences in total nitrogen, and in the percentage of nitrogen in any given horizon, for a series of virgin soils occurring on different slope positions in Iowa; in brief, soils taken from the knolls and slopes had lower nitrogen contents than those taken from depressions.

Naturally moist and poorly-drained soils are usually high in nitrogen, because the anaerobic conditions which prevail during wet periods of the year prevent destruction of organic matter. The distribution of nitrogen in the profile of a humic gley (Wiesenboden) soil is shown in Fig. 5.

4. CHEMICAL AND PHYSICAL CHARACTERISTICS OF THE SOIL

It is a well-known fact that, for any given climatic zone, and provided vegetation and topography are constant, the nitrogen content of the soil depends upon textural properties. The fixation of humic substances in the form of organo-mineral complexes serves to preserve nitrogen. Thus, heavy-textured soils have higher nitrogen contents than loamy soils, which in turn have higher contents than sandy soils. The organic matter in soil has several characteristics, such as resistance to oxidation by microorganisms and to removal by chemical extractants, which suggest that it occurs in intimate association with mineral matter.

Numerous studies have shown that the nitrogen content of the soil is related to clay content. Jenny and Raychaudhuri (1960) found that when the nitrogen contents of some Indian soils having variable textures were converted to a common texture, the values followed the usual climatic pattern. In the study conducted by Harradine and Jenny (1958), some soils derived from basalt were found to be higher in nitrogen than adjacent soils derived from granite. The soils formed from basalt were clay loams; those formed from granite were sandy loams. When the nitrogen contents of the two groups of soils were compensated for texture, their nitrogen contents were nearly identical.

The retention of nitrogen compounds in soil is also affected by the type of clay mineral present. Montmorillonitic clays, which have high absorption capacities for organic molecules, are particularly effective in protecting nitrogenous constituents against attack by microorganisms.

The fact that soils high in exchangeable calcium often have higher nitrogen and organic matter contents than soils low in exchangeable calcium has led to the conclusion that calcium (lime) helps to preserve humic substances. Supposedly, either calcium humates and organo-mineral compounds are formed which are less available to microorganisms, or calcium coagulates humic substances and prevents their dispersion and subsequent removal. According to Joffe (1955), the relatively high level of humic acid in the organic matter of the chernozem, as compared to that of the podzol, is due to stabilization of humic acid by bases.

5. SOIL ORGANISMS

To some extent, all of the factors influencing the soil's ability to retain nitrogen are interdependent; microbial activity is no exception. Soils vary in the types and numbers of microorganisms present, but, because microbial activity is influenced strongly by such factors as vegetation, temperature, humidity, pH, texture, and drainage, the significance of these variations cannot be evaluated very easily.

When it was feasible to do so, the influence of the soil microflora on the nitrogen content of the soil was discussed in the appropriate sections under climate, type of vegetation, topography, etc. By way of summary, it is sufficient to mention that nitrogen can be maintained at high levels in soil only when microbial activity is arrested during some period of the year.

The factors which tend to restrict the activities of soil microorganisms, and thus promote the accumulation of nitrogen, can be summarized as follows:

(1). *Low temperatures.* As the study of Jenny and his co-workers (Jenny, 1928, 1929, 1930, 1931, 1950; Jenny et al., 1948; Jenny and Leonard, 1934; Jenny and Raychaudhuri, 1960) indicated, the nitrogen content of the soil increases 2 to 3 times for each 10°C fall in mean annual temperature, provided other factors are equal. At high altitudes, a combination of low temperatures and high precipitation may result in the formation of highly organic soils, for example, alpine humus soils.

Harsh fluctuations in the physical environment of the soil, such as those caused by desiccation and freezing, curb the activities of microorganisms and facilitate the accumulation of nitrogen and organic matter. Under moderate climates, especially where there are no killing frosts, nitrogen and organic matter seldom accumulate in large amounts.

(2). *Restricted drainage.* Under anaerobic conditions, such as occur frequently in poorly drained soils, microbial activity is low and nitrogen accumulates to high levels. In stagnant ponds, particularly those low in pH and with inadequate nutrients, plant residues remain untouched and peat is formed.

(3). *Low pH.* The more acid the soil, the greater the restriction is in bacterial activity. In strongly acid soils, fungi often predominate over bacteria. The unique patterns of nitrogen and organic matter distribution in the profile of the podzol (low levels in the bleached A_2 horizon, high levels in the B horizon) have been attributed to the influence of pH on the activities of soil organisms (Russell, 1950).

(4). *Presence of inhibitors.* Toxic substances, produced in soil by both microorganisms and higher plants, are known to have the potential for altering the activities of nitrifying and nitrogen-fixing bacteria (Krasil'-nikov, 1958). Mention was made previously of the possible effect of toxins secreted from plant roots on the inhibition of nitrification in grassland soils, and, subsequently, on the accumulation of nitrogen.

(5). *Formation of metal-clay-organic complexes.* Nitrogen compounds, such as proteins, may be protected against microbial attack through interaction with mineral matter.

C. Effect of Cropping on Nitrogen Levels in Soil

Extensive studies have shown that the nitrogen content of most soils declines when land is cultivated. The loss is most rapid during the first few years, following which the rate diminishes slowly. Ultimately, equilibrium levels are reached which are characteristic of the climate, cultural practices, and soil type. At equilibrium, essentially all of the nitrogen required for plant growth must come from external sources, for example, through biological nitrogen fixation and fertilizer nitrogen applications.

Ensminger and Pearson (1950) reviewed the literature dealing with the effect of cropping practices on nitrogen levels in soil. For this reason, no attempt will be made in this section to present a comprehensive historical review of the subject.

According to Salter and Green (1933), the nitrogen content of the soil after "t" years of cropping can be described by the equation

$$N = N_0K^t \tag{5}$$

where N is the nitrogen content of the soil at time t, N_0 is the initial nitrogen content, and K is the fraction of the nitrogen remaining after a single year's cropping. This expression is based on the assumption that the amount of nitrogen lost is proportional to the total amount of nitrogen in the soil.

Equation [5] can be expressed as

$$N = N_0(1-r)^t \tag{6}$$

where r is the annual rate of nitrogen loss.

From equation [6] the following differential equation can be obtained:

$$dN/dt = -rN \tag{7}$$

which by integration becomes

$$N = N_0e^{-rt} \tag{8}$$

According to equations [6], [7], and [8], the soil nitrogen should decline until an absolute minimum is reached, e.g., until the nitrogen content of the soil reaches zero. In agronomic practice, this situation never exists, for when soils are placed under cultivation the nitrogen level assumes a new *equilibrium* value. Usually, but not always, the new level is lower than the original.

Jenny (1941) expanded equation [7] by including a factor for the annual addition of nitrogen from the atmosphere. Thus, the expression becomes

$$dN/dt = -rN + A \qquad [9]$$

where A is the annual rate at which nitrogen is added.

Bartholomew and Kirkham (1960) utilized equation [9] to follow nitrogen changes in soil. Integration of equation [9] gives

$$N = \frac{A - (A - rN_0)}{r} e^{-rt} \qquad [10]$$

from which the following can be obtained

$$A = (rNe^{rt} - rN_0)/(e^{rt} - 1) \qquad [11]$$

This equation can be written in the form

$$N = \frac{A}{r} + \left(\frac{A}{r} - N_0 \right) e^{-rt} \qquad [12]$$

Graphical methods were used by Bartholomew and Kirkham (1960) to obtain the constants A and r for the experimental plots of several long-time rotation experiments. From these values, past changes in nitrogen contents were determined and expected equilibrium levels were established.

The ratio A/r in equation [12] describes the expected nitrogen equilibrium, while the term $(N_0 - A/r) e^{-rt}$ describes the change process. Thus, the change in the magnitude of the latter with time provides a measure of the rate of establishment of equilibrium.

Woodruff (1950) envisioned that soil organic matter consisted of components which decomposed at different rates. Thus, equation [12] (slightly rearranged) becomes

$$N = N_1 e^{-r_1 t} + \frac{A_1}{r_1} (1 - e^{-r_1 t}) + N_2 e^{-r_2 t} + \frac{A_2}{r_2} (1 + e^{-r_2 t}) + \cdots \text{etc.} \qquad [13]$$

When $t = 0$, equation [13] reduces to $N = N_1 + N_2 + \cdots$ etc., which is the original amount of nitrogen in the soil. As t approaches infinity, the equation reduces to $N = A_1/r_1 + A_2/r_2 + \cdots$ etc. This expression (as well as equation [12]) can be simplified to give $N = A/r$, which is the expected equilibrium value.

From calculations based on equations of the type described above, Bartholomew and Kirkham (1960) concluded that steady-state conditions for nitrogen were generally attained within a 50- to 100-year period of cultivation. The data Haas et al. (1957) obtained for nitrogen loss from soils of the Great Plains showed that the nitrogen declined sharply during the first 10 to 20 years of cultivation, after which there was a strong tendency to level off. According to Jenny (1930, 1941), under average farming conditions in the Corn Belt region of the United States, about 25% of the nitrogen is lost the first 20 years, about 10% the second 20 years, and about 7% the third 20 years. The overall pattern of nitrogen loss is illustrated in Fig. 10.

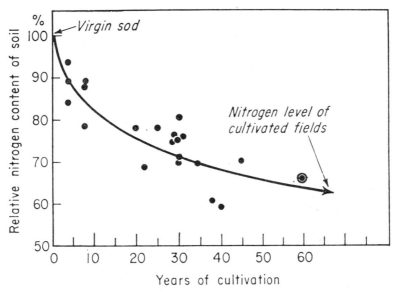

Fig. 10—Decline of soil nitrogen under average farming practices in the North Central region of the United States. (From Jenny, 1941. Used by permission, McGraw-Hill Book Co.)

In soils of the humid tropics, rapid mineralization of nitrogenous organic constituents occurs, and equilibrium levels of nitrogen may be reached in cropped soils in a few years, especially when the initial nitrogen content of the soil is low and the cultural practices have included burning. Nye and Greenland (1960) give an interesting account of the nitrogen and organic matter changes in soil under shifting cultivation in the humid tropics. According to Jenny and Raychaudhuri (1960), the low levels of nitrogen in the soils of India are due primarily to climate and only secondarily to cropping.

In the Southeast region of the United States, where the land has been under cultivation for long periods and the climate is favorable for microbial activity over a large portion of the year, equilibrium levels for nitrogen have been, or soon will be, reached.

The Morrow Plots, which were established in 1876 at the Agricultural Experiment Station at Urbana, Illinois, offer an excellent opportunity for determining long-time changes in nitrogen as influenced by rotations and soil treatments. The soil type is similar to Flanagan silt loam, a brunizem developed from moderately thick loess on calcareous glacial drift of Wisconsin age. The nitrogen changes in these plots, given in Table 4, show that only the treated corn-oats-clover rotation plot failed to show a large deficit in nitrogen. For many of the plots, equilibrium levels have yet to be reached.

Table 4. Nitrogen in the plow layer of soil on the Morrow Plots at different sampling dates.

Cropping system‡	Treat- ment‡	Nitrogen present in						1953 as % of 1904 value
		1904	1913	1923	1933	1943	1953	
C	none	4,165	3,510	3,090	2,890	2.640	2,390	57.4
C-O	none	4,050	3,900	3,500	3,320	3,190	2,970	73.3
C-O-Cl	none	4,595	4,340	4,130	3,810	3,700	3,510	76.4
C	MLP	3,960	3,910	3,670	3,450	3,180	3,115	78.7
C-O(SCl)	MLP	4,065	4,260	4,220	4,040	3,920	4,060	99.9
C-O-Cl	MLP	4,895	4,750	4,690	4,450	4,550	4,555	93.1

* Data to 1943 taken from Nine-Year Report, Illinois Agricultural Experiment Station, p. 11. 1938-1947.   † C - corn; O - oats; Cl - clover; SCl - sweet clover.
‡ MLP - manure, lime, phosphate.

Nitrogen losses of a magnitude similar to those reported from the Morrow Plots have been obtained for other long-time rotation experiments in the Corn Belt region of the United States (Jenny, 1928; Lee and Bray, 1949; Salter and Green, 1933; Woodruff, 1950). In most cases, the cropping system employed had a pronounced influence upon the amount of nitrogen lost. Loss of nitrogen was greatest with intertilled crops, intermediate with cereal crops, and smallest with legume and sod crops. In long-time cropping systems at Wooster, Ohio, described by Salter and Green (1933), continuous corn caused the greatest decline in nitrogen content (60% in 32 years), followed in order by continuous wheat, continuous oats, a 5-year rotation of corn-oats-wheat-clover-timothy, and a 3-year rotation of corn-wheat-clover. On the other hand, the study conducted at Manhattan, Kansas by Dodge and Jones (1948) showed that, at that station, fertilizer treatments and cropping systems had little influence upon nitrogen trends, although they did appear to influence the speed at which equilibrium was reached.

The survey Haas et al. (1957) made on the decline of nitrogen in soils of the Great Plains, encompassing portions of the states of Colorado, Kansas, Montana, Nebraska, New Mexico, North Dakota, South Dakota, Wyoming, and Texas, showed that, over a 30- to 43-year period, from 24 to 60% of the soil nitrogen was lost through cropping. Contrary to results obtained in other sections of the United States, green manuring was of little value in reducing nitrogen loss under the dryland conditions characteristic of the Great Plains area. Other published reports from this region (reviewed by Haas et al., 1957) have shown similar results.

Data obtained by White et al., (1945), for the nitrogen content of the Jordan Soil Fertility Plots in Pennsylvania showed that, after 72 years of cropping (4-year grain rotation of corn-oats-wheat-mixed hay), the adjacent grassland soil had a nitrogen level 68.2% above the untreated plot, 40.0% above the phosphorus-potassium treatment, 42.1% above the nitrogen-phosphorus-potassium treatment, 19.1% above the treatment with 6 tons of manure and lime, and 11% above a 10-ton manure treatment. Bracken and Greaves (1941) recorded large losses of nitrogen from semi-arid cultivated soils in Utah, and a similar result was obtained in Georgia by Giddens and Garman (1942). Smith et al. (1954) found that, during 70 years of cultivation, the blackland soils of Texas lost about 50% of their surface organic matter. Numerous other studies in the United States reviewed by Ensminger and Pearson (1950) have confirmed that large losses of nitrogen occur when soils are placed in cultivation.

For a given soil type, and provided climate and fertility are constant, cropping appears to lead to a more uniform distribution of nitrogen, for soils with higher nitrogen contents lose correspondingly larger amounts of their nitrogen. This effect has been observed in several studies (Haas et al., 1957; Jenny, 1930, 1941).

Whereas numerous investigations have shown losses of soil nitrogen through cropping, few have shown increases. In general, when increases have occurred, they have been attributed to the introduction of legumes on soils initially low in nitrogen. For example, Bracken and Larson (1947) and Greaves and Jones (1950) obtained increases in soil nitrogen by growing alfalfa on arid land in Utah, and similar results were obtained by Gosdin et al. (1950), Moser (1942), and Tidmore and Volk (1945) for some soils of the Southeast. Ensminger and Pearson (1950) concluded that many soils in the Southeast were increasing in nitrogen because cropping systems have been adopted which include winter or summer legumes, or both. Greaves and Bracken (1946) reported losses of nitrogen from some Utah soils through cropping, but increases in carbon. In contrast to other published reports (Giddens and Garman, 1942; Haas et al., 1957; Lee and Bray, 1949; Myers et al., 1943), their results showed that the C/N ratio of the soil increased as a result of cropping.

The decline in the nitrogen content of the soil when land is cultivated cannot be attributed entirely to a reduction in the quantity of plant residues available for humus synthesis. According to Russell (1950), improved aeration resulting from cultivation leads to increased microbial activity and loss of organic matter. A temporary increase in respiration rate occurs each time an air-dried soil is wetted (Birch, 1958, 1959), and since considerable amounts of fresh soil are subjected to repeated wetting and drying through cultivation, losses of organic nitrogen by this process could be appreciable. Rovira and Greacen (1957) suggested that a major effect of cultivation in stimulating microbial activity was the exposure of organic matter not previously accessible to microbial attack.

Not all of the nitrogen released from the soil organic matter when land is placed under cultivation can be recovered in the crop. Losses occur through leaching, erosion, denitrification, and chemical volatilization. Evidence for nitrogen losses through chemical and/or biological volatilization has come from lysimeter experiments, where estimates for the amounts of nitrogen taken up by crops, or removed by leaching and erosion, have failed to account for all of the nitrogen lost. Allison (1955) summarized the results obtained for nitrogen balance sheets in lysimeter experiments. Indirect evidence for gaseous loss of nitrogen from soil has been obtained by Bracken and Greaves (1941), Gainey et al. (1929), Haas et al. (1957), and Myers et al. (1943).

During the past few years, the concept has evolved that the periodic addition of large quantities of crop residues to the soil—supplied as a result of the increased production of plant material brought about through adequate fertilization with nitrogen—will permit nitrogen and organic matter to be maintained at high levels without using legumes or sod crops in the rotation. This theory, which has not been adequately tested under field conditions, is exemplified by Melsted's (1953) conclusion that corn can become a "soil building" crop. According to Melsted (1954), crop rotations previously considered to be undesirable may, when supplemented with nitrogen, prove to be better than present-day good legume rotations. In his short-term experiments, continuous corn growing on relatively flat land fertilized with adequate quantities of nitrogen did not cause a measurable decrease in soil organic matter. In one experiment cited, a slight increase in soil organic matter occurred during a 5-year period when continuous corn was provided with adequate nitrogen and extra residues were returned to the soil.

Considerable research will be required before the validity of the newer concepts of organic matter management can be established. Past experience indicates that the nitrogen content of most soils can be maintained only when crops with sod characteristics are a prominent part of the rotation. In warm climates, the practicability of increasing significantly the nitrogen content of the soil under any system of intensive cultivation would appear negligible. Many investigators have mentioned the difficulties involved in maintaining nitrogen and organic matter levels in southern soils (Ensminger and Pearson, 1950; Giddens and Garman, 1942; Gosdin et al., 1950; Jenny, 1930; Joffe, 1955; Tidmore and Volk, 1945).

LITERATURE CITED

Aandahl, A. R. 1949. The characterization of slope positions and their influence on the total nitrogen content of a few virgin soils of western Iowa. Soil Sci. Soc. Am. Proc. (1948) 13:449-454.

Adel, A. 1951. Atmospheric nitrous oxide and the nitrogen cycle. Science 113:624-625.

Akimtzev, V. V. 1932. Historical soils of the Kamenetz-Podolski fortress, Proc. 2nd Intern. Congr. Soil Sci., Leningrad-Moscow. Comm. 5:132-140.

Alexander, M., Marshall, K. C., and Hersch, P. 1960. Autotrophy and heterotrophy in nitrification. Trans. 7th. Intern. Congr. Soil Sci., Madison, Wisconsin 2:586-591.

Allen, Ethel K., and Allen, O. N. 1958. Biological aspects of symbiotic nitrogen fixation. In Handbuch der Pflanzenphysiologie. Edited by W. Ruhland. Springer-Verlag. Berlin. Vol. 8:48-118.

Allison, F. E. 1955. The enigma of soil nitrogen balance sheets. Adv. Agron. 7:213-250.

Andrew, L. E., and Rhoades, H. F. 1948. Soil development from calcareous glacial material in eastern Nebraska during seventy-five years. Soil Sci. Soc. Am. Proc. (1947) 12:407-408.

Ångström, A., and Högberg, L. 1952a. On the content of nitrogen (NH_4-N, and NO_3-N) in atmospheric precipitation. Tellus 4:31-42.

Ångstrom, A., and Högberg, L. 1952b. On the content of nitrogen in atmospheric precipitation in Sweden. II. Tellus 4:271-279.

Arnold, P. W. 1954. Losses of nitrous oxide from soil. J. Soil Sci. 5:116-128.

Bartholomew, W. V., and Kirkham, D. 1960. Mathematical descriptions and interpretations of culture induced soil nitrogen changes. Trans. 7th. Intern. Congr. Soil. Sci., Madison, Wisconsin 2:471-477.

Birch, H. F. 1958. The effect of soil drying on humus decomposition and nitrogen availability. Plant and Soil 10:9-31.

Birch, H. F. 1959. Further observations on humus decomposition and nitrification. Plant and Soil 11:262-286.

Bond, G. 1958. Symbiotic nitrogen fixation by non-legumes. In Nutrition of the Legumes. Edited by E. G. Hallsworth, Butterworths Publications Ltd., London 216-231.

Bond, G., MacConnell, J. T., and McCallum, A. H. 1956. The nitrogen-nutrition of Hippophaë rhamnoides L. Ann. Bot. (London) N.S. 20:501-512.

Bond, G., and Montserrat, P. 1958. Root nodules of Coriaria. Nature (London) 182:474-475.

Borchert, H. 1951. Zur Geochemie des Kohlenstoffs. Geochim. et Cosmochim. Acta 2:62-75.

Bracken, A. F., and Greaves, J. E. 1941. Losses of nitrogen and organic matter from dry-farm soils. Soil Sci. 51:1-15.

Bracken, A. F., and Larson, L. H. 1947. Increases in nitrogen from growing alfalfa on dry land. Soil Sci. 64:37-45.

Brightman, F. H. 1959. Neglected plants—Lichens. New Biol. 29:75-94.

Brown, I. C., and Byers, H. G. 1935. The chemical and physical properties of dry-land soils and of their colloids. USDA Tech. Bul. 502:1-56.

Brown, I. C., and Thorp, J. 1942. Morphology and composition of some soils of the Miami family and the Miami catena. USDA Tech. Bul. 834:1-55.

Burges, A. 1960. Time and size as factors in ecology. J. Ecol. 48:273-285.

Byers, H. G., Alexander, L. T., and Holmes, R. S. 1935. The composition and constitution of the colloids of certain of the great groups of soils. USDA Tech. Bul. 484:1-38.

Calvin, M. 1956. Chemical evolution and the origin of life. Am. Scientist 44:248-263.

Cameron, R. E., and Fuller, W. H. 1960. Nitrogen fixation by some algae in Arizona soils. Soil Sci. Soc. Am. Proc. 24:353-356.

Chandler, R. F. 1943. The time required for podzol profile formation as evidenced by the Mendenhall glacial deposits near Juneau, Alaska. Soil Sci. Soc. Am. Proc. (1942) 7:454-459.

Crocker, R. L., and Dickson, B. A. 1957. Soil development on the recessional moraines of the Herbert and Mendenhall glaciers, southeastern Alaska. J. Ecol. 45:169-185.

Crocker, R. L., and Major, J. 1955. Soil development in relation to vegetation and surface age at Glacier Bay, Alaska. J. Ecol. 43:427-448.

Daubenmire, R. F. 1947. Plants and Environment. John Wiley and Sons, Inc., New York, p. 324.

Dean, L. A. 1938. The effect of rainfall on the carbon and nitrogen contents, and carbon-nitrogen ratios of Hawaiian soils. Soil Sci. Soc. Am. Proc. (1937) 2:455-459.

Derx, H. G. 1953. Sur les causes de la distribution geographique limitée des Beijerinckia. Proc. 6th. Intern. Congr. Microbiol. Rome 3:116-117.

Dhar, N. R. 1960. Role of organic matter in soil fertility. Trans. 7th Intern. Congr. Soil Sci., Madison, Wisconsin 3:314-320.

Dhar, N. R. 1961. Nitrogen problem. Proc. 48th. Indian Science Congr. 1-32.

Dickson, B. A., and Crocker, R. L. 1953. A chronosequence of soils and vegetation near Mt. Shasta, California. II. The development of the forest floors and the carbon and nitrogen profiles of the soils. J. Soil. Sci. 4:142-154.

Dodge, D. A., and Jones, H. E. 1948. The effect of long-time fertility treatments on the nitrogen and carbon content of a prairie soil. Soil Sci. Soc. Am. Proc. (1947) 12:294.

Enders, C. 1934a. Über den Chemismus der Huminsäurebildung unter physiologischen Bedingungen. III. Biochem. Z. 313:352-371.

Enders, C. 1943b. Über den Chemismus der Huminsäurebildung unter physiologischen Bedingungen. IV. Biochem. Z. 315:259-292.

Ensminger, L. E., and Pearson, R. W. 1950. Soil nitrgen. Adv. Agron. 2:81-111.

Eriksson, E. 1952. Composition of atmospheric precipitation. I. Nitrogen compounds. Tellus 4:215-232.

Eylar, O. R., and Schmidt, E. L. 1959. A survey of heterotrophic micro-organisms from soil for ability to form nitrite and nitrate. J. Gen. Microbiol. 20:473-481.

Ferguson, T. P., and Bond, G. 1953. Observations on the formation and function of the root nodules of *Alnus glutinosa* (L.) Gaertn. Ann. Bot. (London) N. S. 17:175-188.

Fogg, G. E. 1947. Nitrogen fixation by blue-green algae. Endeavour 6:172-175.

Fuller, W. H., Cameron, R. E., and Raica, N. 1960. Fixation of nitrogen in desert soils by algae. Trans. 7th. Intern. Congr. Soil Sci., Madison, Wisconsin 2:617-624.

Gainey, P. L., Sewell, M. C., and Latshaw, W. L. 1929. The nitrogen balance in cultivated semi-arid western Kansas soils. J. Am. Soc. Agron. 21:1130-1153.

Garrison, W. M., Morrison, D. C., Hamilton, J. G., Benson, A. A., and Calvin, M. 1951. Reduction of carbon dioxide in aqueous solutions by ionizing radiation. Science 114:416-418.

Giddens, J. and Garman, W. H. 1942. Some effects of cultivation on the Piedmont soils of Georgia. Soil Sci. Soc. Am. Proc. (1941) 6:439-446.

Goldschmidt, V. M. Geochemistry. 1954. The Clarendon Press, Oxford, England.

Goody, R. M., and Walshaw, C. D. 1953. The origin of atmospheric nitrous oxide. Quart. J. Roy. Meteorol. Soc. 79:496-500.

Gosdin, G. W., Stelly, M., and Adams, W. E. 1950. The organic matter and nitrogen content and carbon-nitrogen ratio of Cecil soil as influenced by different cropping systems on classes II, III, and IV land. Soil Sci. Soc. Am. Proc. (1949) 14:203-208.

Greaves, J. E., and Bracken, A. F. 1946. Effect of cropping on the nitrogen, phosphorus, and organic carbon content of a dry-farm soil and on the yield of wheat. Soil Sci. 62:355-364.

Greaves, J. E., and Jones, L. W. 1950. Influence of legumes on soil nitrogen. Soil Sci. 69:71-76.

Haas, H. J., Evans, C. E., and Miles, E. F. 1957. Nitrogen and carbon changes in Great Plains soils as influenced by cropping and soil treatments. USDA Tech. Bul. 1164:1-111.

Haldane, J. B. S. 1933. Science and Human Life. Harper, New York.

Harmsen, G. W. 1951. Die Bedeutung der Bodenoberfläche für die Humusbildung. Plant and Soil 3:110-140.

Harmsen, G. W., and Van Schreven, D. A. 1955. Mineralization of organic nitrogen in soil. Adv. Agron. 7:299-398.

Harradine, F., and Jenny, H. 1958. Influence of parent material and climate on texture and nitrogen and carbon contents of virgin California soils. I. Texture and nitrogen contents of soils. Soil Sci. 85:235-243.

Henzell, E. F., and Norris, D. O. 1962. Processes by which nitrogen is added to the soil/plant system. *In* A Review of Nitrogen in the Tropics with Particular Reference to Pastures. Bul. 46. Commonwealth Agricultural Bureaux. Farnham Royal, Bucks, England. pp. 1-18.

Herman, F. A., and Gorham, E. 1957. Total mineral material, acidity, sulphur and nitrogen in rain and snow at Kentville, Nova Scotia. Tellus 9:180-183.

Hutchinson, G. E. 1944. Nitrogen in the biogeochemistry of the atmosphere. Am. Scientist 32:178-195.

Hutchinson, G. E. 1954. The biochemistry of the terrestrial atmosphere. *In* The Solar System. Vol. II. The Earth as a Planet. Edited by G. P. Kuiper, University of Chicago Press, Chicago. pp. 371-433.

Ingham, G. 1950a. The mineral content of air and rain and its importance to agriculture. J. Agr. Sci. 40:55-61.

Ingham, G. 1950b. Effect of materials absorbed from the atmosphere in maintaining soil fertility. Soil Sci. 70:205-212.

Jenny, H. 1928. Relation of climatic factors to the amount of nitrogen in soils. J. Am. Soc. Agron. 20:900-912.

Jenny, H. 1929. Relation of temperature to the amount of nitrogen in soils. Soil Sci. 27:169-188.

Jenny, H. 1930. A study on the influence of climate upon the nitrogen and organic matter content of the soil. Missouri Agr. Exp. Sta. Res. Bul. 152:1-66.

Jenny, H. 1931. Soil organic matter-temperature relationship in the eastern United States. Soil Sci. 31:247-252.

Jenny, H. 1933. Soil Fertility losses under Missouri conditions. Missouri Agr. Exp. Sta. Bul. 324:1-10.

Jenny, H. 1941. Factors of Soil Formation. McGraw-Hill Book Co., New York.

Jenny, H. 1950. Causes of the high nitrogen and organic matter content of certain tropical forest soils. Soil Sci. 69:63-69.

Jenny, H., Bingham, F., and Padilla-Saravia, B. 1948. Nitrogen and organic matter contents of equatorial soils of Colombia, South America. Soil Sci. 66:173-186.

Jenny, H., and Leonard, C. D. 1934. Functional relationships between soil properties and rainfall. Soil Sci. 38:363-381.

Jenny, H., and Raychaudhuri, S. P. 1960. Effect of climate and cultivation on nitrogen and organic matter reserves in Indian soils. Indian Council Agr. Res., New Delhi, India, pp. 1-126.

Jensen, H. L. 1936. Contributions to the microbiology of Australian soils. IV. The activity of microorganisms in the decomposition of organic matter. Proc. Linnean Soc. New South Wales 61:27-55.

Jensen, H. L. 1939. Contributions to the microbiology of Australian soils. V. Abundance of microorganisms and production of mineral nitrogen in relation to temperature. Proc. Linnean Soc. New South Wales. 64:601-608.

Jensen, H. L., 1950. A survey of biological nitrogen fixation in relation to the world supply of nitrogen. Trans. 4th. Intern. Congr. Soil Sci., Amsterdam 1:165-172.

Joffe, J. S. 1955: Green manuring viewed by a pedologist. Adv. Agron. 7:141-187.

Jones, E. 1960. Contribution of rainwater to the nutrient economy of soil in Northern Nigeria. Nature (London) 188:432.

Junge, C. E. 1958. The distribution of ammonia and nitrate in rain water over the United States. Trans. Am. Geophys. Union 39:241-248.

Kononova, M. M. 1961. Soil Organic Matter. Translated by T. Z. Nowakowski and G. A. Greenwood. Pergamon Press Ltd., London.

Krasil'nikov, N. A. 1958. Soil Microorganisms and Higher Plants. Translated by Y. Halperin. Office of Technical Services, U. S. Department of Commerce, Washington, D. C.

Larson, T. E., and Hettick, Irene. 1956. Mineral composition of rain water. Tellus 8:191-201.

Lawrence, D. B. 1958. Glaciers and vegetation in southeastern Alaska. Am. Scientist 46:89-122.

Lee, Ching-Kwei, and Bray, R. H. 1949. Organic matter and nitrogen contents of soils as influenced by management. Soil Sci. 68:203-212.

Leeper, G. W. 1938. Organic matter of soil as determined by climate. J. Austr. Inst. Agr. Sci. 4:145-147.

Leisman, G. A. 1957. A vegetation and soil chronosequence on the Mesabi iron range spoil banks, Minnesota. Ecol. Monographs 27:221-245.

Lipman, J. G., and Conybeare, A. B. 1936. Preliminary note on the inventory and balance sheet of plant nutrients in the United States. New Jersey Agr. Exp. Sta. Bul. 607:1-23.

MacConnell, J. T., and Bond, G. 1957. Nitrogen fixation in wild legumes. Ann. Bot. (London) N. S. 21:185-192.

Malo, B. A., and Purvis, E. R. 1964. Soil absorption of atmospheric ammonia. Soil Sci. 97:242-247.

Manshard, E. 1958. Herkunft und Vorkommen von gebundenem Stickstoff in Boden und Gewässern (Assimilierbarkeit). In Handbuch der Pflanzenphysiologie. Edited by W. Ruhland. Springer-Verlag, Berlin. Vol. 8:119-149.

Mason, B. 1958. Principles of Geochemistry. 2nd. edition. John Wiley and Sons, Inc., New York.

Mattson, S., and Koutler-Andersson, E. 1943. The acid-base condition in vegetation, litter, and humus: VI. Lantbruks-Högskol Ann. 11:107-134.

Mattson, S., and Koutler-Andersson, E. 1944. The acid-base condition in vegetation, litter, and humus: VIII. Lantbruks-Högskol Ann., 12:70-100.

Mayne, K. I. 1957. Natural variations in the nitrogen isotope abundance ratio in igneous rocks. Geochim. et Cosmochim. Acta 12:185-189.

Melsted, S. W. 1953. King corn—soil builder or destroyer? What's New in Crops and Soils. Vol. 5, No. 4, p. 7-9.

Melsted, S. W. 1954. New concepts of management of Corn Belt soils. Adv. Agron. 6:121-142.

Meyer, J., and Pampfer, E. 1959. Nitrogen content of rain water collected in the humid Central Congo basin. Nature (London) 184:717-718.

Miller, S. L. 1955. Production of some organic compounds under possible primitive earth conditions. J. Am. Chem. Soc. 77:2351-2361.

Moodie, C. D. 1951. The hypoiodite method for studying the nature of soil organic matter: II. Application to the organic matter and organic matter fractions of different soils. Soil Sci. 71:51-65.

Moser, F. 1942. Influence of leguminous plant additions on the organic matter content and available nutrient supply of southern soils. J. Am. Soc. Agron. 34:711-719.

Myers, H. E., Hallsted, A. L., Kuska, J. B., and Haas, H. J. 1943. Nitrogen and carbon changes in soils under low rainfall as influenced by cropping systems and soil treatment. Kansas Agr. Exp. Sta. Tech. Bul. 56:1-52.

Norris, D. O. 1956. Legumes and the *Rhizobium* symbiosis. Empire J. Exp. Agr. 24:247-270.

Norris, D. O. 1962. The biology of nitrogen fixation. *In* A Review of Nitrogen in the Tropics with Particular Reference to Pastures. Bul. 46, Commonwealth Agricultural Bureaux, Farnham Royal, Bucks., England. pp. 113-129.

Nye, P. H., and Greenland, D. J. 1960. The Soil under Shifting Cultivation. Commonwealth Agricultural Bureaux Tech. Comm. No. 15. Harpenden, England.

Oda, Y. 1959. Significance of molecular hydrogen metabolism on the transitionary stage from anaerobiosis to aerobiosis. *In* The Origin of Life on the Earth. Edited by A. I. Oparin, et. al. Pergamon Press. Ltd., London. pp. 593-605.

Olson, J. S. 1958. Rates of succession and soil changes on southern Lake Michigan sand dunes. Bot. Gaz. 119:125-170.

Oparin, A. I. 1938. The Origin of Life. Translated by S. Morgulis. The Macmillan Co., New York.

Parker, C. A. 1957a. Evolution of nitrogen-fixing symbiosis in higher plants. Nature (London) 179:593-594.

Parker, C. A. 1957b. Non-symbiotic nitrogen-fixing bacteria in soil. III. Total nitrogen changes in a field soil. J. Soil Sci. 8:48-59.

Pavlovskaya, T. E., and Pasynskii, A. G. 1959. The original formation of amino acids under the action of ultraviolet rays and electric discharges. *In* The Origin of Life on the Earth. Edited by A. I. Oparin, et al. Pergamon Press, Ltd., London. pp. 151-157.

Rayleigh, L. 1939. Nitrogen, argon and neon in the earth's crust with applications to cosmology. Proc. Roy. Soc. London, Ser. A. 170:451-464.

Richards, P. W. 1952. The Tropical Rain Forest. Cambridge University Press, London. p. 221.

Roelofsen, P. A. 1941. Stickstof in Regenwater. Natuurw. Tydschr. Nederland. Indie. 101:179-180.

Rovira, A. D., and Greacen, E. L. 1957. The effect of aggregate disruption on the activity of microorganisms in the soil. Austr. J. Agr. Res. 8:659-673.

Rubey, W. W. 1951. Geologic history of sea water. Bul. Geol. Soc. Am. 62:1111-1147.

Ruinen, J. 1956. Occurrence of *Beijerinckia* species in the "Phyllosphere." Nature (London) 177:220-221.

Russell, E. J. 1950. Soil Conditions and Plant Growth. 8th. Edition. Longmans, Green and Co., London.

Russell, E. J., and Richards, E. H. 1919. The amount and composition of rain falling at Rothamsted. J. Agr. Sci. 9:309-337.

Salisbury, E. J. 1922. The soils of Blackeney Point: A study of soil reaction and succession in relation to the plant covering. Ann. Bot. (London) 36:391-431.

Salisbury, E. J. 1925. Note on the edaphic succession in some dune soils with special reference to the time factor. J. Ecol. 13:322-328.

Salter, R. M., and Green, T. C. 1933. Factors affecting the accumulation and loss of nitrogen and organic carbon in cropped soils. J. Am. Soc. Agron. 25:622-630.

Schmalfuss, K. 1958. Die Geochemische Bedeutung des Stickstoffs unter besonderer Berücksichtingung der Landwirtschaftlichen Produktion und der Dünger. *In*

Handbuch der Pflanzenphysiologie. Edited by W. Ruhland. Springer-Verlag, Berlin. Vol. 8:1128-1146.

Senstius, M. W. 1958. Climax forms of rock-weathering. Am. Scientist 46:355-367.

Shantz, H. L. 1923. The natural vegetation of the Great Plains region. Ann. Assoc. Am. Geog. 13:81-107.

Shields, Lora M., Mitchell, C., and Drouet, F. 1957. Alga- and lichen-stabilized surface crusts as soil nitrogen sources. Am. J. Bot. 44: 489-498.

Smith, R. M., Samuels, G., and Cernuda, C. F. 1951. Organic matter and nitrogen build-ups in some Puerto Rican soil profiles. Soil Sci. 72:409-427.

Smith, R. M., Thompson, D. O., Collier, J. W., and Hervey, R. J. 1954. Soil organic matter, crop yields, and land use in the Texas blackland. Soil Sci. 77:377-388.

Sokolov, V. A. 1959. The evolution of the atmosphere of the earth. In The Origin of Life on the Earth. Edited by A. I. Oparin, et al. Pergamon Press, Ltd., London. pp. 54-66.

Sorokin, Y. I. 1959. The evolution of chemosynthesis. In The Origin of Life on the Earth. Edited by A. I. Oparin, et al. Pergamon Press Ltd., London, pp. 626-634.

Soulides, D. A., and Clark, F. E. 1958. Nitrification in grassland soils. Soil. Sci. Soc. Am. Proc. 22:308-311.

Stanier, R. Y., and Cohen-Bazire, Germaine. 1957. The role of light in the microbial world: some facts and speculations. In Microbial Ecology. 7th. Symp. Soc. for Gen. Microbiol. Cambridge University Press, London. pp. 56-89.

Stevenson, F. J. 1959. On the presence of fixed ammonium in rocks. Science 130:221-222.

Stevenson, F. J. 1960. Some aspects of the distribution of biochemicals in geologic environments. Geochim. et Cosmochim. Acta 19:261-271.

Stevenson, F. J. 1962. Chemical state of the nitrogen in rocks. Geochim. et Cosmochim. Acta 26:797-809.

Stevenson, F. J. 1964. Soil nitrogen. In Fertilizer Nitrogen: Its Chemistry and Technology. Ed. by V. Sauchelli. Reinhold Publishing Corp., New York. pp. 18-39.

Tchan, Y. T. 1953a. Studies of N-fixing bacteria. IV. Taxonomy of genus Azotobacter (Beijerinck, 1901). Proc. Linnean Soc. New South Wales 78:85-89.

Tchan, Y. T. 1953b. Studies of N-fixing bacteria. V. Presence of Beijerinckia in northern Australia and geographic distribution of non-symbiotic N-fixing microorganisms. Proc. Linnean Soc. New South Wales 78:171-178.

Tchan, Y. T., and Beadle, N. C. W. 1955. Nitrogen economy in semi-arid plant communities. Part II. The non-symbiotic nitrogen-fixing organisms. Proc. Linnean Soc. New South Wales 80:97-104.

Theron, J. J. 1951. The influence of plants on the mineralization of nitrogen and the maintenance of organic matter in soil. J. Agr. Sci. 41:289-296.

Theron, J. J., and Haylett, D. G. 1953. The regeneration of soil humus under a grass ley. Empire J. Erp. Agr. 21:86-98.

Tidmore, J. W., and Volk, N. J. 1945. The effect of plowing under and the time of plowing under legumes on the conservation of nitrogen. J. Am. Soc. Agron. 37:1005-1010.

Tutin, T. G. 1958. Classification of the legumes. In Nutrition of the Legumes. Edited by E. G. Hallsworth, Butterworths Publications Ltd., London. pp. 3-14.

Urey, H. C. 1952. The Planets: Their Origin and Development. Yale University Press, New Haven, Connecticut.

Virtanen, A. I. 1952. Molecular nitrogen fixation and nitrogen cycle in nature. Tellus 4:304-306.

Vlamis, J., Schultz, A. M., and Biswell, H. H. 1958. Nitrogen fixation by deerbrush. California Agr. 12:11 and 15.

Waksman, S. A., and Gerretsen, F. C. 1931. Influence of temperature and moisture upon the nature and extent of decomposition of plant residues by microorganisms. Ecol. 12:33-60.

White, J. W., Holben, F. J., and Richer, A. C. 1945. Maintenance level of nitrogen and organic matter in grassland and cultivated soils over periods of 54 and 72 years. J. Am. Soc. Agron. 37:21-31.

Williams, B. H. 1943. The formation of moss peat beneath translucent pebbles in semi-arid regions of the Great Plains. Science 97:441-442.

Wilson, P. W. 1951. Biological nitrogen fixation. *In* Bacterial Physiology. Edited by C. W. Werkman and P. W. Wilson. Academic Press Inc., New York. pp. 467-499.

Woodruff, C. M. 1950. Estimating the nitrogen delivery of soil from the organic matter determination as reflected by Sanborn Field. Soil Sci. Soc. Am. Proc. (1949) 14:208-212.

Chapter 2

Soil Inorganic Nitrogen

G. W. HARMSEN AND G. J. KOLENBRANDER

Institute for Soil Fertility
Groningen, The Netherlands

I. INTRODUCTION

Most of the nitrogen in normal soils is organically bound. Only a small fraction is in the inorganic form. However, it is this inorganic nitrogen which is available for the direct uptake by plants. The big stock of organic nitrogenous substances in soil must be considered as the potential reserve of nitrogen for nutrition of plants. The aim of this chapter, therefore, is to summarize our knowledge about the amounts, kinds, and fluctuation patterns of inorganic nitrogen compounds in soil. The transformation of organic into inorganic nitrogen or vice versa will be mentioned only as far as it might be necessary for an understanding of the fluctuations in the amount of inorganic nitrogen in soil. A more detailed discussion of mineralization and synthesis of organic nitrogen compounds is given in other chapters.

Since in practically all papers dealing with nitrogen the inorganic phase is mentioned in one way or another, it is impossible in this chapter to refer to all publications mentioning the soil inorganic nitrogen. Also, nearly all publications which are summarized in this chapter will be reviewed more elaborately in the more specialized chapters which follow. Therefore no attempt will be made to refer to as many papers as possible. Only communications presenting important fundamental aspects about soil inorganic nitrogen will be reviewed and discussed. Omitted also will be an historical introduction. Those fundamental pioneering investigations may be considered as sufficiently known and understood. For modern research the classic research has mainly a historical value.

The investigations and concepts of the great workers of the past, such as Pasteur, Boussingault, Müntz, Hoppe-Seyler, von Liebig, Deherain, Schlösing, Stoklasa, Beijerinck, Warington, and Winogradsky, have already emphasized the importance of the processes of mineralization and nitrification of soil nitrogen, of the dissimilation of nitrate and of the fixation of atmospheric nitrogen for the growth of plants. Even such secondary processes as the leaching of soluble nitrogen from the topsoil by rain was investigated and understood long ago as demonstrated by the paper of Boussingault (1856) dealing with the decrease in the amount of "salpetre" after a rainy period.

The stage of the development of our knowledge about nitrogen in soil, attained by the end of the 19th century was clearly summarized by Wiley (1896) in the Yearbook of Agriculture for 1895: "In the absence of heavy rainfall the stores of available nitrogen in such a soil will undoubtedly be increased during the summer, in as much as the processes of nitrification will be continued and the stores of nitrogen thus oxidized in the absence of absorbing bodies will remain in the soil. Even in the case of rainfall, which may carry the soluble plant food below the arable soil, there may not be any notable loss, especially if such a downpour be followed by dry weather. But in case of heavy rains, producing a thorough saturation and leaching of the soil, the losses in a field lying fallow during the summer will be very great and it is not well at any time to take the risk."

This statement demonstrates that the fundamental problems concerning the nitrogen transformations in soil were well understood in those days. Jansson (1958) in his elaborate treatise also summarized the old classical investigations and then arrived at the conclusion that ". . . What remained to be done after the fruitful pioneer period of soil microbiology was to extend and consolidate the findings for a wide variety of environmental conditions and to find out the connections and interactions between the basic processes . . .". It can be said that the research during the last 60 years has provided a much more detailed picture of the transformation processes of nitrogen in soil. However, the application of our knowledge to the needs of agriculture requires both a correct understanding of the processes and a quantitative evaluation of the transformations. We must admit that our knowledge is still far from complete.

II. AMOUNT AND FORMATION OF INORGANIC NITROGEN COMPOUNDS IN SOIL

The inorganic nitrogen in soil constitutes only a small part of the total nitrogen, and it undergoes rapid changes. Most of the inorganic nitrogen is soluble in water and therefore can be translocated easily by diffusion and even more so by the flow of the water through the soil. Moreover, the formation of microbial cell substance, the immobilization in humus and the absorption reactions in the crystal lattices of clay minerals are rather fast processes. Also the uptake by plants and losses by volatilization can rapidly alter the amount of inorganic nitrogen in a soil. Consequently, a determination of the amount of inorganic nitrogen is no more than a snapshot. Only periodically repeated measurements will provide information about the level and fluctuations of the amount of inorganic nitrogen. A review of all these gains and losses will be given in section III. In this section only the relation between organic and inorganic forms of nitrogen and the general levels of inorganic nitrogen in different soils and climates will be discussed.

A subject not treated in this chapter is the fixation of atmospheric nitrogen by living organisms. By this process organic, not inorganic, nitrogenous compounds are synthesized. The total amount of nitrogen in a soil may thereby be increased, but the level of inorganic nitrogen will be influenced only after mineralization of the synthesized organic compounds.

A. Relation between Inorganic and Organic Nitrogen in Soil

Under normal soil conditions inorganic nitrogen is continuously formed from the organic nitrogen by mineralization processes. In turn some inorganic nitrogen is transformed to organically bound nitrogen by soil microbes. Although originally only some specific microbes were considered responsible for this uptake of mineral nitrogen (Löhnis, 1910), in the study of soil microbiology it soon was understood that all microbes necessarily consume soluble nitrogen in growth (Stoklasa, 1908a; Doryland, 1916).

1. IMMOBILIZATION OF NITROGEN BY ORGANIC MATTER
WITH A HIGH C/N RATIO

Hirschler (1886) stated that carbohydrates can suppress the liberation of ammonia from proteins. However, Doryland (1916) appears to be the first to give a clear explanation of this relation between nitrogenous substances and carbohydrates during the mineralization of organic matter. Doryland also understood that not only carbohydrates, but all organic substances rich in energy but with a low content of mineral nutrients, were acting in the same way. He, and later Waksman (1917, 1927), studied this phenomenon more extensively, and stressed that the microbes decomposing the organic matter multiply rapidly with the consequent vigorous synthesis of microbial protoplasm. The protoplasm of microbes has a rather high nitrogen content (varying between 3 and 12%), and in most cases higher than the decomposing substrate. The mineralized nitrogen will therefore be used for the formation of that protoplasm, and if the C/N ratio of the substrate is high, all mineralized nitrogen will be reabsorbed by the microorganisms and no inorganic nitrogen will accumulate. Substances with a very high C/N ratio will result in the absorption of inorganic nitrogen already available in the soil and originating from other sources. The C/N ratio of the decomposing material must be below 20 to 25 (corresponding to about 1.5 to 2.0% N) for an appreciable net mineralization of nitrogen.

The reimmobilization of mineralized nitrogen during the decomposition of substances with a C/N ratio above the critical value of 20 to 25 might bring about a depletion of the available nitrogen and, thereby, induce the well known effect of nitrogen deficiency when such substances are added to the soil. Innumerable reports can be found in the literature dealing with this problem. The practical consequences of the effect for the farmer should not be underestimated. The first clear discussion of this problem was given by Rahn in 1919, who advised additional fertilization with nitrogen to overcome the nitrogen depletion by the straw.

Later many investigators tried to determine the amount of fertilizer nitrogen needed to overcome nitrogen deficiency when straw and similar substances are applied. A detailed review of this literature is given by Dubber (1955). A critical account of the mineralization and immobilization processes is given in Chapter 7.

2. INFLUENCE OF THE C/N RATIO ON THE MINERALIZATION OF NITROGEN

The above mentioned studies tend to indicate that the formation and persistence of inorganic nitrogen in soil depends mainly on the C/N ratio of the organic substances in soil. However, this conclusion is a simplification of a rather complicated problem. Even Doryland (1916) and Waksman (1917, 1927) recognized the complexity of the processes and that the nitrogen content per se was not the only factor which influenced immobilization and mineralization. The importance of the resistance of the organic substrate to microbial attack was studied by Waksman and Tenny (1927) and later by Smith (1940), Rubins and Bear (1942), and Peevy and Norman (1948). In many cases fresh organic residues have a rather high C/N ratio which gradually decreases during the decay. This decrease often is in part the consequence of the fact that the fractions with the highest ratio are the most readily disintegrated parts of the substrate.

Old stabilized humus is very resistant to decomposition and often yields little inorganic nitrogen in spite of its low C/N ratio. This effect of variation in resistance against microbial attack and of aging of the substrate has been studied by many investigators. An excellent discussion has been given by Jensen (1952). Another review of the problem has been given by Winsor (1958). The general rule that the mobilization of organic nitrogen depends primarily on the nitrogen content of the substrate must consequently be altered in so far as this holds only for the mineralizable part of the decaying material.

3. TURNOVER OF NITROGEN IN SOIL

Since the work of Doryland (1916) it has been understood that the enzymatic mineralization of organic matter by microbes is accompanied by immobilization of a part of the originally mineralized substances. Perhaps the most elaborate treatise of mineralization-immobilization relationships in soil is that of Jansson (1958). The same year Winsor (1958) published a short review on the subject.

In considering the nitrogen mineralization and immobilization processes it must be kept in mind that the turnover can follow different pathways. The shortest is that in which the original organic substrate is partly disintegrated and becomes soluble but remains in organic form. These products then may be absorbed by the microbes and incorporated in their synthesized tissue. This is not complete mineralization. In most cases the substrate is largely or entirely mineralized and the nitrogen is transformed to the ammonium form. Part of this ammonium is then assimilated by the microbes or incorporated in humus. When the conditions are favorable, the ammonium formed is oxidized to nitrite or nitrate before its absorption by microbes. All these pathways can be followed simultaneously in the complex process of mineralization and immobilization going on in the soil under the influence of thousands of different microbes.

Another characteristic of the turnover is that it is repeating itself again and again since the synthesized microbial tissue is in turn disintegrated and mineralized by the succeeding generations of microbes. Therefore Jansson (1958) used the term "continuous internal cycle." Of course, without introduction of fresh organic substrate, the total amount of energy will decrease during the consecutive stages of decay and synthesis. But, when starting with substances with a high C/N ratio, the carbon is rapidly liberated and lost as carbon dioxide while the nitrogen is mainly retained in organic form until the energy/nitrogen ratio has become sufficiently reduced to allow for an accumulation of inorganic nitrogen. Only from that moment onward we can speak of a "net mineralization" of nitrogen. During the foregoing stages the nitrogen of the original substrate may have been mineralized repeatedly but there was no accumulation of mineral nitrogen. Such temporary, reversible mineralization can be designated as "primary mineralization," whereas the accumulation of inorganic nitrogen is the "net mineralization."

Jansson (1958) differentiated between the part of the nitrogen in a soil that is included in the "continuous internal cycle" and another part that does not participate in the turnover. That latter part appears to be permanently locked up in forms not available for the turnover reactions. He considers the very pesistent, nearly inert, organic substances (the stabilized humus often constituting up to 90% of the total organic nitrogen in a soil), the ammonia firmly absorbed by clay-minerals, and the accumulating nitrate as such passive parts of the nitrogen content.

There is, however, a contradiction between this formulation of passive fractions of soil organic nitrogen and the statement of Jansson (1958) that added fertilizer nitrogen, immobilized in the soil, rather soon proved to be equilibrated with the nitrogen in the passive fractions. During the decay of an organic substrate the net nitrogen mineralization and accumulation of inorganic nitrogen generally will be the logical consequence of the decreasing C/N ratio and therefore an increasing part of the total nitrogen will be pushed out from the "internal cycle" and will accumulate in one form or another as a "pool." The reason why Jansson (1958) included nitrate in the passive pool and did not include free (not firmly absorbed) ammonium is the observation (Jansson et al., 1955) that microbes prefer ammonia to nitrate. Nitrified nitrogen would therefore not be readily absorbed by the microorganisms, whereas the free ammonium would be readily absorbed and reintroduced into the turnover cycle. Sometimes the conditions are unfavorable for nitrification and then ammonia can accumulate. Very acid soils or anaerobic conditions prevent nitrification. A striking example of very high concentrations of ammonium has been reported recently by van Schreven (1963), who found accumulations of free ammonium but no nitrate in the deeper anaerobic layers of soils under fresh or salt water. But in normal soils inorganic nitrogen accumulates mainly as nitrate. Most investigators agree about the preference of heterotrophic microorganisms for ammonia (Nightingale, 1948; Jansson, 1952, 1955; Jansson and Clark, 1952; Jansson et al., 1955; Winsor and Pollard, 1956). Only Rahn (1919) obtained an opposite result. However, there remain some questions yet to be answered.

Jansson (1958) applied the computations developed by Kirkham and Bartholomew (1954, 1955) and Kirkham (1956) for a determination of the nitrogen turnover in soil. However, the nitrogen escaping the "continuous internal cycle" and accumulating in one of the "passive pools" raised questions about the validity of the resulting computations.

4. FACTORS INFLUENCING MINERALIZATION AND IMMOBILIZATION

Mineralization may not be regarded as entirely independent of the supply of available mineral nitrogen. Very high concentrations of soluble mineral nitrogen in the soil reduce the apparent process of mineralization of nitrogen (Gerretsen, 1942; Harmsen and Lindenbergh, 1949). This reduction might be caused by a high concentration of electrolytes, but it also might be a stimulation of the immobilization of inorganic nitrogen, thereby giving the impression of a reduced mineralization (Jansson, 1958). However, this effect becomes apparent only at high concentrations of soluble nitrogen; 100 to 200 ppm in normal soils and in some peaty soils even much higher concentrations did not exert the suppressing action (Kaila et al., 1953; Kivekäs and Kivinen, 1959). At lower levels of soluble nitrogen, little if any depressing influence has been observed. In some soils which exhibit slow mineralization, an addition of fertilizer nitrogen sometimes even stimulates the disintegration of the organc matter and results in an increased accumulation of inorganic nitrogen.

High concentrations of inorganic nitrogen are likely to occur in soils only under rather special circumstances. Processes of removal such as crop absorption, leaching and volatilization generally keep the inorganic nitrogen at low levels. However, clean fallow or high rates of fertilization may result in abnormally high concentrations of inorganic nitrogen in soil for varying periods of time.

Mineralization of organic nitrogen is possible only when the biological environment is favorable. This environment includes mineral nutrients, aeration, temperature, moisture content, and pH as factors. Many papers have reported investigations of these factors.

When the influence of temperature on the mineralization of organic nitrogen is studied, a sharp differentiation should be made between ammonification and nitrification (Schloesing and Müntz, 1879; Warington, 1892; King and Whitson, 1901, 1902; Russell et al., 1925; Panganiban, 1925; Jenny, 1941; Gerretsen, 1942; Meiklejohn, 1953b; Pathak and Shrikhande, 1953; Sabey et al., 1956; McIntosh and Frederick, 1958; Janisch, 1962). Both ammonification and nitrification are limited by low temperatures. Nitrification is inhibited at temperatures in the upper part of the mesophilic range while ammonification proceeds vigorously in the thermophilic temperature range, 50 to 70°C. At 45°C practically no nitrification takes place. Below the optimum temperature, 25° to 35°C, nitrification decreases gradually, following an asymptotic curve and practically ceases near the freezing point.

From these investigations it is reasonable to conclude that retardation of nitrification by high temperatures may be expected to occur frequently only in tropical climates (Tandon and Dhar, 1934; Meiklejohn, 1953a; Geiger, 1961), and seldom in temperate regions. On the other hand, low temperatures during the winter season must be expected to reduce the nitrification in many temperate areas. Significant losses of nitrogen through denitrification consequently may not be expected in the winter season. However, rather contradictory results have been reported by different investigators. Comparatively vigorous nitrification at temperatures as low as 3°C has been reported by Tyler et al. (1959), while Gerretsen (1942), Anderson (1960), and others obtained considerable nitrification only above 6 to 7°C. Most investigators agree that at low temperatures the nitrification is more retarded than the ammonification, whereby ammonia can accumulate even in sufficiently aerated soils with an adequate pH (Tyler et al., 1959). Frederick (1956) has shown that the nitrification responds favorably to fluctuations in the temperature.

Mineralization under different levels of aeration and moisture content has been studied and reviewed by Reed and Sturgis (1937), Jewitt (1945), Willis and Green (1949), and Kaila et al. (1953). Nitrification, apart from ammonification, has been investigated by Gaincy and Metzler (1917), Greaves and Carter (1920), Lees (1948), Amer and Bartholomew (1951), Calder (1957), Robinson (1957), Frederick (1957), Greenland (1958), Jansson (1958), and Dommergues (1959). Most investigators agree that a reduced aeration, as in water-logged soils, curbs or even entirely suppresses the nitrification, but ammonification is less affected. Such soils therefore sometimes contain very high concentrations of inorganic nitrogen, up to more than 100 ppm, but mainly as ammonium and not as nitrate.

However, there is a lack of agreement about the optimum moisture content. The data published by the different investigators vary between 40% of the water holding capacity of the soil to more than field capacity. The variation of other factors and the broad flat top of the curve near the optimum are apparently responsible for this disagreement.

There is also no agreement about the limitation of nitrification and ammonification at very low moisture contents. Greaves and Carter (1920) found an appreciable nitrification at 10% of the water holding capacity, corresponding with 3-8% moisture content. Greenland (1958) claimed the same at 4% moisture, and Robinson (1957) observed nitrification at the wilting point (pF = 4.2). Ammonification has been reported to occur even at lower moisture contents, sometimes under air-dry conditions (Robinson, 1957; Greenland, 1958; Dommergues, 1959). Consequently ammonium might slowly accumulate in very dry soils. Calder (1957) demonstrated a stimulation of nitrification by fluctuation of the moisture content.

The optimum pH-level for the mineralization of organic substances in soil is slightly on the alkaline side. Remy (1902) recognized the dominant influence of the reaction of the soil on the mineralization of organic substances. Later reviews have been given by Waksman (1923b), Kappen et al. (1949), and Schachtschabel (1953). The latter obtained an increase in nitrogen mineralization varying between 100 and 1500 kg of nitrogen per ha per year when acid sandy soils with a high content of humus were limed.

Since the specific nitrifying organisms are much more sensitive to soil reaction than the complex population of ammonifying microbes, mineralization proceeds to the formation of nitrate only within the range of pH-values between ca 5.0 and 8.0, whereas at low and high pH-values the process stops at the formation of ammonium-compounds. However, complete agreement has not been reached about the optimum and the limiting pH values for nitrification (Norman, 1943; Harmsen and van Schreven, 1955). A critical discussion of the problems can be found in the papers of Thomas and Elliott (1932), Hwang and Frank (1938), Martin et al. (1943), Fraps and Sterges (1947), Kaila et al. (1953), Cornfield (1953), Sen and Asija (1953, 1954), and Morrill (1959). The generally accepted opinion that nitrification is not possible below about pH of 5, however seems to have some exceptions. Kaila and Soini (1957), Kivinen and Kaila (1958), and Kivekäs and Kivinen (1959) observed formation of nitrate in some very acid peat soils in Finland.

pH-values near the upper limit of the range for nitrification sometimes cause an accumulation of nitrite. Under average soil conditions nitrite seldom if ever accumulates. This is because the oxidation of nitrite to nitrate by *Nitrobacter* generally proceeds faster than the formation of nitrite from ammonium by *Nitrosomonas*. However, around pH 7.5 to 8.0 the nitrate formation from nitrite is markedly retarded while the oxidation of ammonium still proceeds vigorously. A temporary accumulation of nitrite is the result. Among the investigators who described this nitrite accumulation in calcareous soils or in normal soils after a heavy liming are: Fraps and Sterges (1947), Drouineau et al. (1948), Morrill (1959), and Tyler et al. (1959). Chapman and Liebig (1952), Broadbent et al. (1958), and Soulides and Clark (1958) found increased nitrite contents when applying urea to soils, whereby the pH was raised temporarily.

A "partial sterilization" of a soil by desiccating, heating, steaming, or disinfecting, results in an apparent stimulation of the microorganisms in soil. The activity reaches levels often far above the level before the sterilization. Buddin observed this effect of desiccation in 1914. The effect was confirmed by Lebedjantzev in 1924. Generally the "flush" was ascribed to chemical and physical changes of the organic substances in the soil by the sterilization, making it more suitable for disintegration. The many dead microbes, representing easily available organic matter, were also considered partly responsible for the peak in the production of CO_2 and inorganic nitrogen. Recently Birch (1958, 1959, 1960) proposed the theory that it is the predominance of the very young cells of the population, still in the logarithmic phase of growth, with their high metabolic activity, which causes the "flush" following desiccation. This concept has support in the observation of Jager (unpublished, 1961), who found that the CO_2 production in a dried and remoistened soil reached its maximum one or two days earlier than the number of microbes.

In humid climates desiccation of more than the few centimeters of the uppermost part of the soil is an exception. However, in arid and especially in tropical regions with pronounced dry and rainy seasons the effect of such "partial sterilization" may be significant. Such cases have been described by Hall (1924), Prescott and Piper (1930), Hardy (1946a), Jones (1956), and Wetselaar (1961). Birch (1958) subjected a soil sample to many consecutive desiccation-remoistening treatments and each time observed a "flush" in activity. However each succeeding activity period became less pronounced than the preceding one. Birch (1958) as well as Harpstead and Brage (1958) observed that the magnitude of the "flush" of activity after desiccation was related to the length of time the soil was kept in the dry state.

This "partial sterilization effect" on the balance of nitrogen or humus in the soil should not be overestimated. Birch (1959) found a mineralization of only 0.33% of the total nitrogen in the soil by each "flush" in Kenya soils. This corresponded to about 3 kg of nitrogen per ha in the top soil for each percent of humus.

A similar "partial sterilization effect" has also been claimed for freezing and thawing of the soil (Hall, 1924; Payne et al., 1956), but Harmsen (1962) and Jager (unpublished, 1961) observed only small increases in microbial activity.

An acceleration of the mineralization of the stable humus in soils by an addition of fresh organic substances has been reported (Löhnis, 1926a, b; Norman and Werkman, 1943; Thornton, 1947; Broadbent and Norman, 1947; Broadbent, 1948; Broadbent and Bartholomew, 1949; Hiltbold et al., 1951; Walker et al., 1956). In some of these investigations fresh organic substances containing labeled carbon were applied while in others nitrogenous fertilizers containing N^{15} were added to the soil. This "priming" effect (Bingeman et al., 1953) by the fresh organic matter was ascribed to the development of an active and violent microbial population attaching also part of the stable humus. Though these investigations were intended to elucidate the carbon balance in the soil, the same reasoning can be applied for the nitrogen balance. However, later investigations (Bingeman et al., 1953; Hallam and Bartholomew, 1953; Allison, 1955a; Stotzky and Mortensen, 1957; Bartholomew, 1957; McDonald, 1957; Barrow, 1960) resulted in divergent and, at times, contradictory results. Recently the computation followed in most of the above investigations has been criticized by Jansson (1958), who claimed that the "continuous internal turnover" of nitrogen makes the calculation inapplicable. The implications and importance of the "priming effect" of fresh organic matter await further clarification. A short but clear presentation of this problem is given by Winsor (1958).

5. RHIZOSPHERE EFFECT

Beside the artificial addition of fresh organic matter, the excretions of plant roots and the sloughing off of root hairs, root caps and sometimes even part of the root system can provide considerable amounts of fresh organic substances and exert an effect on the soil flora similar to that of green manure, stable manure, and other materials. Goring and Clark (1949) and Bartholomew and Clark (1950), have reported a rhizosphere effect similar to that of an addition of fresh organic matter, resulting in an acceleration of the turnover of nitrogen. However, there appears to be no reliable data on the amount of organic matter excreted by plant roots under normal growth conditions in soil and on the C/N ratio of the excretions. A short preliminary paper dealing with the problem has been published by Harmsen and Jager (1962). Only the effect of the root excretions on the inorganic nitrogen in soil is mentioned here. Reviews by Krassilnikov (1934) and by Starkey (1958) have treated the broad subject of the rhizosphere.

6. NITRIFICATION

Nitrification processes are reviewed in detail in Chapter 8. It is sufficient here to point out that by processes of nitrification nitrogen may be removed from the more active immobilization-mineralization turnover cycle (Jansson, 1958). However, nitrifiers are not good competitors with the heterotrophs for ammonified nitrogen. Nitrification processes, therefore, probably are nil except where the net mineralization has proceeded to the extent that ammonium accumulates.

7. COMPETITION BETWEEN PLANTS AND MICROBES FOR NITROGEN

Since the days of Liebig it has been accepted that plants need soluble inorganic nitrogen for growth. When the immobilization of a part of the primarily mineralized nitrogen by the microbes was understood, the logical consequence was to presume a competition between the microflora and the plants for the available nitrogen. A detailed discussion of this concept was first given by Wright (1915) and some years later by Lemmermann (1919), Rahn (1919), and Martin (1925). Since then innumerable publications have mentioned this competition. The heterotrophic microbes are so much more widely dispersed through the soil than plant roots that it appeared self-evident that the liberated organic nitrogen would be immediately reabsorbed by the microbes until the needs of the microbial flora were satisfied. This concept has recently been discussed by Jansson (1958), Ehrhardt (1961), and Zöttl (1960a, b, c). However, a recent investigation (Harmsen, 1963), with the use of an ion exchange technique, has suggested a much greater ability of plant roots to compete for mineralized nitrogen than was heretofore thought possible. The ion exchange technique was first used by Tepe (1956, 1958) and by Tepe and Leidenfrost (1958, 1960) but was criticized by Schachtschabel (1961). The ion exchangers absorbed more nitrate and ammonia from a limited amount of soil than accumulated in parallel samples treated in the same way without ion exchange resins.

B. Amount of Inorganic Nitrogen in Different Soils

Mineral nitrogen contents vary markedly among soils and between seasons of the year for the same soil. A number of methods and devices have been employed to evaluate not only the mineral nitrogen content of soil at a particular time but also the total quantity of mineral nitrogen that may be produced during a season. Some of the early work was done by King and Whitson (1901, 1902), Russell (1914), and Greaves et al. (1917). A few years later there appeared the publications of Waksman (1923a), Crowther and Mirchandani (1931), Rheinwald (1933), Russell (1937), and Richardson (1938). Most of these early investigators empirically determined the amount of inorganic nitrogen in the soil, and from the fluctuations of the values deduced conclusions about the mineralization of nitrogen and about the consequences in agriculture.

1. INCUBATION METHODS

Incubation methods have been extensively employed to evaluate the capacities of soils to supply nitrogen to growing crops. In general, these methods consist of incubating a sample of soil under near optimum conditions and evaluating the net quantity of mineral nitrogen produced during the incubation. The soil may or may not be treated or modified prior to incubation. Bogdanow (1900) was the first to use the incubation method. Other early papers include those of Brown (1916), Hesselman (1916, 1917), Fraps (1920), Waksman (1923b), and Süchting (1933). More recent studies have been made by Allison and Sterling (1949), White et al. (1949), Harmsen and Lindenbergh (1949), Drouineau and Lefèvre (1949), Cornfield (1952, 1953, 1959), Wittich (1952), and van Schreven (1956b, 1957, 1958). A review of the whole subject has been given by Harmsen and van Schreven (1955). The incubation method has a number of shortcomings. The homogenized samples are incubated under very favorable laboratory conditions with the consequence that only the potential mineralization ability is determined and not the real mineralization under field conditions. In use of the method laboratory results are correlated with field data. Recent discussions on incubation methods are found in publications by Harmsen and van Schreven (1955), van Schreven (1956b, 1957, 1958), Hardy (1946b), Fitts et al. (1955), Stanford and Hanway, (1955), Cornfield (1959), Lefèvre and Hirous (1958, 1960), and Synghal (1960).

In incubation studies the rate of net mineralization has been found to be rapid at first and then to decline with length of incubation period. Harmsen and Lindenbergh (1949) have proposed that this decline in rate of net mineralization actually resulted from an increase in immobilization as the concentration of available nitrogen increased. If this suggestion is correct then the maximal level of net mineralization would have a real significance. Some investigations have shown that the gradual retardation in net mineralization could be overcome by periodic leaching of the soil samples with water (Lyon et al., 1920; Jensen, 1940, 1952; Stanford and

Hanway, 1955; van Schreven, 1956b). On the other hand, Acharya and Jain (1954) found that an addition of nitrate had no depressing effect on the mineralization. It, therefore, must be presumed that other substances may be formed which adversely affect the mineralization. The supposition was expressed by Allison and Sterling (1949) that nitrate formation decreased the pH to a level which was detrimental to mineralizing organisms. However, this hypothesis does not explain the retardation of mineralization in soils with enough buffer capacity to prevent changes in pH during mineralization.

Eno (1960) proposed to perform the incubation method in polyethylene bags in the soil in the field thereby approaching natural conditions. The bags are permeable to O_2 and CO_2 but not to nitrate or ammonium ions. Daschewsky (1960) claimed a good correlation between the incubation method and the much faster extraction of the soil with 1% KCl solution. A similar treatment was proposed by Cornfield (1960), who also found a good correlation between the conventional incubation method and the release of ammonium from soil by 1 N NaOH solution. A good correlation with the incubation method has also been claimed for a modification of the method of Truog (unpublished, 1955), extracting the soil with alkaline permanganate (Subbiah and Asija, 1956). Micah (1960) and Purvis and Micah (1961) proposed an acid hydrolysis of the soil as a measure of the natural release of inorganic nitrogen. Pepsin digestion has been used for the determination of the readily mineralizable nitrogen in farm manure and composts. Livens (1959, 1960) extracted soil samples with boiling water and obtained a reasonable correlation between his data and those from the conventional incubation method.

2. LYSIMETER STUDIES

Lysimeter studies have provided important information on nitrogen movement in soil and on gain and loss processes. The oldest lysimeter study has been attributed to Dalton (1802). He determined only the amount of water drained through the soil. Kohnke et al. (1940) have made a detailed review of lysimeters and discuss the values and shortcomings of lysimeter techniques. Two main types of lysimeters are of interest here. They are the "monolith" type containing soil in its undisturbed state and the "filled in" type in which the soil is filled in after careful mixing. The first mentioned type has the advantage to resemble closely the natural conditions, whereas the "filled in" lysimeters guarantee a good homogeneity. As the construction of "monolith" lysimeters is very difficult, most studies have used the "filled in" type. However, this latter type is much more artificial and possesses several shortcomings. First of all, the strata in the profile are disturbed, and many profile properties are changed. Winnik (1935) observed a greater permeability of "filled in" lysimeters than of "monoliths." Another serious fault of "filled in" lysimeters is the stimulation of the disintegration of the organic matter as a result of the "flush," brought about by mixing and agitating the soil. Often it takes a couple of years to come back to the normal level of mineralization (Maschhaupt, 1941; Geering, 1943; Bizzell, 1944). The first years after construction must be considered of little value.

A shortcoming, characteristic for all types of lysimeters without a ground water level, is the retention of more moisture than corresponds with the field capacity. The moisture content is hereby maintained on a higher level than under field conditions, with the danger of anaerobiosis and denitrification (Colman, 1946; Maschhaupt, 1938, 1949).

There is a time lapse between the entry of rain water into the surface soil and its effect on the effluent at the bottom of the lysimeter. The time lapse is greater the deeper the profile in the lysimeter and the higher the water holding capacity of the soil (Russell and Richards, 1920; Mooers et al., 1927; Collison et al., 1933; van Doorn, 1951).

From a review of the literature (Maschhaupt, 1938, 1941, 1948; Russell and Richards, 1920; Mooers et al., 1927; Collison et al., 1933, Winnik, 1935; Geering, 1943; Bizzell, 1943, 1944; Smith, 1944; Chapman et al., 1949; Broadbent and Chapman, 1950; Bastisse, 1951; and Kolenbrander, 1961) a rough estimation can be made of the average percentage of the rainfall that is lost as drainage to the deeper subsoil. For the humid temperate climate with a yearly rainfall of about 700 mm this percentage is some 45% on bare fallow and about 30% on cropped land. A crop reduces the drainage by using much of the water as evapo-transpiration. Crops also reduce the drainage losses of nitrogen by uptake of the latter and also by its immobilization in the rhizosphere. On grassland this effect is most pronounced.

Most of the shortcomings of lysimeters can be avoided by the use of drainage field trials. The construction of such arrangements is very expensive and reliable results can be obtained only on land with a ground water level a little below the drainage level. Conditions in the Netherlands with its flat land and often high water table are favorable for this method (Hudig and Welt, 1911; Kolenbrander, 1961).

3. AVERAGE LEVELS OF INORGANIC NITROGEN IN DIFFERENT SOILS

Climatic patterns associated with land areas have a marked influence upon the quantity of mineral nitrogen in the soil at any time and upon the formation and loss processes. For convenience of discussion of the available information the climatic patterns have been divided into several categories. However, each climatic category is broad and includes a rather wide spectrum of conditions.

In temperate humid climatic zones nitrogen would generally move down in the soil profile with water movement during the winter when there is a surplus of precipitation over evaporation but may not move downward during the summer season except under conditions of heavy rainfall. Consequently, the content of inorganic nitrogen is low in winter, rises in spring and is again reduced by the autumn rains. Moreover, mineralization during the winter season is reduced (Russell, 1914; Crowther and Mirchandani, 1931; Barnes, 1950). With the onset of the warmer weather in spring the mineralization is stimulated and the concentration of inorganic nitrogen starts rising rapidly. But this rise slows down gradually during the summer.

It has been supposed by many investigators that the rapid increase in spring might be the result of the "partial sterilization effect" by frost during the winter. However, recent investigations of Jager (unpublished, 1961) showed that the freezing of soil—except peaty soils and the mull or mor-layer in forests (Ehrhardt, 1961)—has only a small influence on mineralization. The sharp increase in the content of inorganic nitrogen in spring presumably must be due to the higher temperature and to the retardation of the process of mineralization during the winter.

The decrease in the rate of the net mineralization during the summer is most pronounced in Western Europe, where the highest nitrate content in fallow soils generally is reached in June or July (Solberg and Braadlie, 1957; Harmsen, 1959). The reason may be due to the relatively low rainfall in the spring and much higher rainfall in July and August. It is possible that the mineralization remains active during the summer while the higher rate of leaching in the summer tends to remove the available nitrogen (Harmsen, 1962).

In other humid temperate regions, for example the eastern states of the U.S.A., the increase in the content of inorganic nitrogen often continues until the end of the summer. The accumulation patterns in the less humid areas, for example, southern Russia, European areas bordering the Mediterranean, and the central part of the U.S., generally reach the maximum content of inorganic nitrogen in August or September (Koudriawtsewa, 1925; Lefèvre and Drouineau, 1951).

Of course, such general rules often are disturbed by deviations from the normal type of weather, such as heavy rains or a drought (Smith, 1928; Eggleton, 1935c; Maasz, 1961). But some investigators observed heavy fluctuations of the content of inorganic nitrogen even during periods of normal weather (Diamond, 1937; Griffith, 1951; Hagenzieker, 1957; Maasz, 1961). No satisfactory explanation for such erratic fluctuations have been found. Griffith (1951) and Maasz (1961) consider a periodicity in the mineralization-immobilization pattern the most probable reason.

A voluminous literature reports data on the amount of inorganic nitrogen in soil. Such data vary from plot to plot and from day to day. Only the general orders of magnitude of accumulation and change will be mentioned here. Where no nitrogenous fertilizers nor organic manures have been applied the level of inorganic nitrogen in winter in bare fallow soils seldom exceeds 10 ppm and often remains below 5 ppm in the topsoil (Baumann and Maasz, 1957; Vanstallen, 1959; Ogata and Caldwell, 1960). During spring and summer the content may rise to around 40-60 ppm in fertile topsoils. With a high content of organic matter even higher levels may be reached (Russell, 1914; Rheinwald, 1933). In peaty soils values of 400-600 ppm have been reported (Rappe, 1950; Kaila and Soini, 1957; Kivekäs and Kivinen, 1959). However, these very high values may be due to soluble organic substances (fulvic acids) that are characteristic for these soils since some analytical procedures may not distinguish among nitrate, ammonia, and soluble organic nitrogen. Russian literature confirms that from Europe and the United States (Koudriawtsewa, 1925). An item of interest in this work was the claim that any kind of soil tillage brought about a stimulation of mineralization. Andreëwa (1958) has recently reported a similar effect of tillage or physical disturbance of the soil.

In most instances in the literature, data on inorganic nitrogen in soil has been reported as parts per million (ppm) or as weight units per weight unit of dry soil. In some instances, however, this way of expressing the data may be unrealistic. A good example is that of peat soils which have a high water holding capacity and a low volume weight. Since concentration of nitrogen in soil solution as well as total available nitrogen are important, other methods of reporting the data may be helpful in certain instances.

In tropical and subtropical climates as well as in arid temperate regions the fluctuations of the content of inorganic nitrogen follow the sequence of the dry and wet periods, not the warm and cold seasons. The high temperature in the tropical countries tends to increase the rate of all biological processes. Shortage of moisture during the dry season often retards all activities of microbes such that the rates of mineralization become very low. However, if the subsoil contains nitrate, this soluble nitrogen is moved upward with the moisture during the dry season. Thereby nitrogen may accumulate in the surface soil layers. The general aspects of nitrogen in tropical soils have been discussed by Leather (1909, 1911).

In humid tropical regions the content of inorganic nitrogen is negatively correlated with the rainfall. During the dry season nitrate may accumulate. Schofield (1945) reported formation of high concentrations of mineral nitrogen in Queensland during the long but not entirely rainless dry period, attaining levels as high as 100 ppm without any additives in the topsoil of fallow plots. Where green manure was ploughed in, as much as 400 ppm accumulated. With the onset of the rains there occurred a rapid and nearly complete leaching of the nitrogen from the topsoil. Similar, but less pronounced, fluctuations of the nitrogen content with season were reported by Hardy (1946a, b) from Trinidad.

An entirely different situation has been described by Griffith and Manning (1949), Griffith (1951), and Mills (1953, 1954) from Uganda. There the climate is tropical but moderately dry, with two dry and two wet seasons in a year. The soil was relatively heavy. The content of inorganic nitrogen dropped during the dry season to very low values, often less than 10 ppm, even in fallow soil, but increased as soon as the first rains wetted the topsoil. As the wet season progressed and heavy rains moved part of the inorganic nitrogen downward in the profile, the topsoil decreased in available nitrogen. The sharp rise in the beginning of the wet season apparently was the result of a vigorous ammonification and nitrification. The "partial sterilization effect" of the desiccation of the soil presumably enhanced this process (Hagenzieker, 1957; Robinson, 1957; Birch, 1958; Greenland, 1958). The data of Robinson (1957) and Greenland (1958) are not comparable with those of Hagenzieker (1957) and Birch (1958) as the former investigators determined only nitrate. They interpret the partial sterilization effect of the drought as an accumulation of easily "nitrifiable" substances during the dry season.

Robinson (1957) presumes ammonia to be that substance but this presumption was not confirmed by other investigators. Some authors have not found "flushes" of mineralization upon rewetting a dry soil (Drouineau and Lefèvre, 1951; Simpson, 1960). However, Simpson (1960) considers the possibility of the vigorous mineralization of organic nitrogen being offset by simultaneous denitrification and leaching, especially when the rainy season does not start gradually but comes on abruptly. The conditions then may be favorable for denitrification and leaching.

Most authors have reported gradual increases in inorganic nitrogen in soil during the dry season (Hall, 1924; Diamond, 1937; Schofield, 1945; Hardy, 1946b) or have observed a constant level (Drouineau and Lefèvre, 1951). However, in some instances a distinct decrease during the drought has been found (Griffith and Manning, 1949; Griffith, 1951; Mills, 1953, 1954). This decline is difficult to reconcile with current knowledge of loss processes. A similar observation was made by van Burg (1959) in the Netherlands during the exceptionally dry and hot summer of 1959. On a silt loam soil fertilized in spring with different amounts of nitro-chalk, the inorganic nitrogen decreased rapidly during the dry period in May and June. After a short rainy season in July, extractable nitrogen again reappeared in proportion to the amount of the fertilizer applied.

Reports about tropical countries with two dry and two rainy seasons each year have been given by Vine (1953) and Sen and Rewari (1958). More extreme arid tropical conditions have been studied by Jewitt (1945, 1950) in the Sudan Gezira, where the leaching of nitrate in the very heavy clay soil was insignificant. Still no higher concentration of nitrate N than 40 ppm was observed. Jenny et al. (1949), Jenny (1950), and Greenland (1958) also have reported information on inorganic nitrogen in tropical climates.

Dhar and some of his associates in India (Rao and Dhar, 1931; Dhar, 1935; Dhar and Plant, 1944) have reported high mineralization of nitrogen under dry conditions and have proposed that chemical, not enzymatic, processes were responsible. However, their work could not be confirmed by other workers (Joshi and Biswas, 1948; Meiklejohn, 1953a).

Early work on inorganic nitrogen in arid soils may be found in reports by Frankfurt and Doushechkin (1904) and Sazanow (1907) from the "black earth" (Tschernozem) soils off southern Russia. Later work by Schmuck (1924) confirms the earlier work. In the climatic conditions of the prairie region of Russia the leaching of soluble nitrogen from the topsoil is less pronounced than in the more humid regions. Only in the late autumn or in the period of the melting of the snow was the amount of inorganic nitrogen in the topsoil decreased. During the spring and summer under fallow conditions a gradual increase was observed. In spring the nitrogen content was about 5 ppm but rose to around 40 ppm by the end of summer. The high amount of organic matter and of total nitrogen in the "black earth" soils resulted in rather vigorous mineralization in spite of the shortage of moisture. The use of bare or summer fallow to conserve moisture has probably tended to enhance mineralization.

In other climatic areas in Russia with longer growing seasons and slightly more rainfall, higher rates of mineralization have been observed. Mokin (1926) observed from 80 to 100 ppm of mineral nitrogen in a fallow soil in the Stavropol region by September. From studies in the Kaukasus, Chyzevski and Charuiskaya (1958) also found more than 100 ppm of nitrogen in the soil. Doiarenko (1955, 1958) gives some information on nitrogen in "tschernozem" soils in review papers.

The general information shows that the mineralization of nitrogen in soils in arid climates is not necessarily high, as has been supposed by Hilgard (1906) and by Headden (1910, 1911). It is only the much slower leaching in the arid than in the humid climate that results in the topsoil of the former containing more inorganic nitrogen than the latter. Stewart suggested this explanation in 1913 and some years later it was confirmed by Stewart and Peterson (1915, 1916) and by Lipman et al. (1916).

In arid soils which are irrigated the nitrate content migrates with water movement. Some early observations were made on this movement by Prescott (1919) in Egypt. Jewitt (1945) has reported on studies in Sudan Gezira. The methods of irrigation along with the quantity of water applied determine the movement pattern. A more detailed discussion of nitrate movement with water is given in Chapter 15 of this monograph.

A pronounced stimulation of mineralization by irrigation was reported in work done in the arid Koubanj district in Russia (Bolotina, 1959; Sobornikowa, 1959; Prostakow, 1960). During the period of irrigation and cropping the nitrate content in the soil did not accumulate. When irrigation was discontinued and the crop harvested, the mineral nitrogen content accumulated to high levels, sometimes as much as 200 ppm. These investigators as well as Antipow-Karatajew and Filippowa (1955) have concluded that the high mineralization rates under or following irrigation may serve to deplete the organic matter and total nitrogen supplies in soil.

The flooding, as practiced on sawahs or paddy fields, results in anaerobic conditions through nearly all the soil (Gerretsen, 1921; Kapp, 1933; Sreenivasan and Subrahmanyan, 1934; Reed and Sturgis, 1937, 1939; Bhuiyan, 1949; Willis and Green, 1949). However, ammonification of organic nitrogen has been found to be rather active in spite of the anaerobic conditions. Nitrification is not possible and nitrates are rapidly denitrified and lost. In the beginning of the growing season the content of the ammonium nitrogen increases, often reaching values of 40 to 80 ppm. During the growth of the rice it is gradually depleted. After the end of the vegetation period, when the water is drained, normal conditions are restored and nitrification of the ammonium soon is resumed.

General experience has shown that paddy fields may maintain a moderate level of fertility more or less permanently even without any addition of nitrogen. Fixation of atmospheric nitrogen is thought to be responsible for the annual nitrogen additions. This subject is considered in more detail in Chapter 12. The fixation of atmospheric nitrogen in rice fields, however, is not high enough to produce maximum yields. Fertilization with nitrogen is generally necessary (Boerema and Mc-

Donald, 1963). Ammonia volatilization (Sreenivasan and Subrahmanyan, 1935) and denitrification (Kapp, 1933) are also thought to occur extensively in the alkaline paddy soil conditions.

Two types of saline soils are of interest. They are the "alkali soils" with insufficient drainage, as are often found in arid climates, and the soils recently reclaimed along the seashores, such as the new polders of the Zuider Sea in the Netherlands and the reclaimed mangrove swamps in Sierra Leone. Moderate salt concentrations have not seriously inhibited ammonification (Chaloust, 1948). Furthermore, nitrification, although more sensitive to salt concentrations than ammonification, has seldom been seriously reduced in soils where cultivation of crops is possible (Yankovitch and Yankovitch, 1953).

In the newly reclaimed sea bottom or tidal land the concentration of inorganic nitrogen sometimes is abnormally high during the first years after reclamation. In the reclaimed Zuider Sea soils up to 100 ppm of mineral nitrogen have been observed by Harmsen (1932, 1955, 1958). Originally this temporarily high level of mineral nitrogen was ascribed to organic substances in the sea bottom, which were rapidly mineralized after reclamation and aeration of the soil (Harmsen, 1955). However, the recent discovery of unexpectedly high concentrations of free ammonium in the deeper layers of the soil under salt or fresh water by van Schreven (1963) makes it very probable that the main reason for the high level of inorganic nitrogen in the topsoil of the new polders was the capillary upward movement of a part of the ammonium from the subsoil.

C. Influence of Plant Growth on Inorganic Nitrogen in Soil

Plant absorption is generally the chief channel of removal of inorganic nitrogen from normal soil. Each kind of crop and soil situation results in a unique removal pattern. The subject will be considered by examining several kinds of cropping systems. A comprehensive review of crop needs and use of nitrogen is found in Chapter 14.

In temperate climates on arable land the inorganic nitrogen generally disappears rapidly as soon as the crop starts growing. It depends on the crop and its growth habits as to when the plant starts absorbing so much nitrogen as to compete with the mineralization. Perennial crops have a developed root system and can begin absorbing nitrogen as soon as conditions are favorable for growth. During mild weather they may absorb some nitrogen even in the winter. The annual crops, on the other hand, absorb nitrogen slowly at first until their root systems have developed. Even legumes deplete the soil inorganic nitrogen supplies since their ability to utilize soil nitrogen is similar to that of other plants (Jewitt, 1956; Baumann and Maasz, 1957; Vanstallen, 1959; Harmsen, 1959; Dalbro and Nielsen, 1959; Gasser, 1961). At harvest time the amount of inorganic nitrogen is negligible in cropped land.

After the harvest of the annual crops in the autumn, mineralization generally brings about a rise of the amount of inorganic nitrogen because absorption by the crop has stopped. The decay of roots, stubble, and other parts of the crop may even stimulate mineralization. This accumulation of nitrogen, however, may disappear from the topsoil by leaching during the late autumn and winter (Vanstallen, 1959; Harmsen, 1959; van der Paauw, 1959). The autumn peak can be conserved by the use of a second or catch crop (Vanstallen, 1959). A number of papers have dealt with this phenomenon. Only a few of them are cited here (Koudriawtsewa, 1925; Rheinwald, 1933; Goring and Clark, 1949; Harmsen and van Schreven, 1955; Allison, 1956; Walker et al., 1956; Baumann and Maasz, 1957; Livens, 1960; Gasser, 1962; Mokin, 1926; Chyzevski and Charouiskaya, 1958).

The effect of plants on the inorganic nitrogen in soil, however, is not restricted to uptake of nitrogen by the plant in growth followed by release of the nitrogen after the death and decay of dead parts. Excretions of living roots in the rhizosphere are also very important. The rhizosphere and its influence on the nitrogen in soil have been discussed in detail by Clark (1949), Gerretsen (1948, 1949), and Lochhead (1958). Some early quantitative evaluations of the rhizosphere effects were made by Czapek (1896), Stoklasa and Ernest (1909), and Wilson (1921). But a careful determination of the amount of the organic substances excreted by plant roots and of the C/N ratios of these substances is still not available. Only a preliminary report has been published (Harmsen and Jager, 1962). The significance of the immobilization of mineral nitrogen in the rhizosphere can be derived from the well-known fact that the recovery of applied nitrogen in the crop always is much lower than the decrease of the amount of inorganic nitrogen in the soil during the growth of the crop (Black et al., 1947; Hiltbold et al., 1952; Goring and Clark, 1949; Viets, 1960; Dorph-Peterson, 1946; Gerretsen, 1950). The lowest crop recoveries are often associated with high rates of application (Viets, 1960; Rogers, 1948). Some immobilization of added fertilizer nitrogen occurs in uncropped land (Hiltbold et al., 1951), but it is generally accompanied by rapid mineralization such that the result is net mineralization. Investigators generally agree that immobilization is much higher under cropping than under fallow (Bartholomew and Clark, 1950). Goring and Clark (1949) found that immobilization in the rhizosphere was rather temporary. A part of the nitrogen was soon mineralized after removal of the crop. The rapid mineralization after crop maturity in the autumn might be due in part to nitrogen immobilized in the rhizosphere.

Grassland soils are generally characterized by low levels of inorganic nitrogen throughout the whole year (Prescott, 1935; Eggleton, 1934; Lyon and Bizzell, 1936; Richardson, 1938; Newton et al., 1939a, b; Bizzell, 1922, 1944; Cornish, 1949; Martin, 1949; Stöckli, 1949; Penman, 1949; Theron, 1951; Theron and Haylett, 1953; Stevenson and Chase, 1953; Martin and Cox, 1956; Soulides and Clark, 1958; Cunningham and Cook, 1958; Vanstallen, 1959; Dalbro and Nielsen, 1959). The concentration usually ranges between a trace and 5 ppm. Reports of high inorganic nitrogen in grassland soil are few (Thompson and Coup, 1940; Rappe, 1950; Hardy, 1946a, b). The observations of Rappe (1950) were made in the study of a peat soil. The work of Hardy (1946a, b) was made with a tropical soil of high fertility.

Grasses in general have a large capacity to absorb nitrogen and to respond in growth to nitrogen fertilization. Added fertilizer is rapidly taken up by the crop. This absorption is most rapid when the grasses are actively growing but absorption also has been noted under mild winter conditions (Bosch, 1946; Cunningham and Cook, 1958; van Burg, 1958, 1960; Gasser, 1959; Kolenbrander, 1961). Blackman (1936) observed uptake of nitrogen by grass at temperatures below 5°C. The high efficiency of absorption of soil nitrogen by grasses is probably due to the dense mat of roots in grass soil wherein the entire root zone functions as a rhizosphere. Not only crop absorption but microbial absorption as well is thereby enhanced. Several investigators (Goedewaagen and Schuurman, 1950a; Köhnlein and Vetter, 1953a, b; Chyzevski and Charouiskaya, 1958; Muzychkin, 1959) have shown that grass culture deposits more organic residue in the soil each year of growth than do arable crops. Harmsen (1951), following the theory of Enders (1943) and Enders and Segurdsson (1942, 1943), proposed that the synthesis of stable humus was more rapid under perennial vegetation than under annual crops. However, the general absence of appreciable amounts of inorganic nitrogen in grassland soils may be due also to low rates of mineralization and not only to high rates of immobilization. A literature too numerous to list has reported that net mineralization rates are lower under grass than under arable cropping.

In view of the large capacity of grasses to absorb and use nitrogen and because of the extensive root systems, increases in organic matter and nitrogen have been expected as a result of permanent grass culture. However, such increases have seldom occurred. Richardson (1938) and others found a decrease in the rate of humus formation with age of grass stands. Although there has been little loss of nitrogen from grass crops in lysimeters to which no nitrogen had been applied, rather large losses have occurred where nitrogenous fertilizers have been added (Allison, 1955b; van Burg, 1960, 1962; Kolenbrander, 1961). The quantity of nitrogen lost through leaching increased with the age of the grassland. Moreover, Woldendorp (1962), by the use of nitrogen tracer techniques, demonstrated that grasslands, even those sufficiently aerated, lose nitrogen through volatilization mechanisms, probably denitrification. The establishment of an equilibrium between gains and losses of organic matter and nitrogen in grassland consequently is understandable. The small amount of nitrogen found in grassland is generally in the ammonium form (Lawes, 1889; Miller, 1906; Lyon and Bizzell, 1918; Bizzell, 1922, 1944; Lyon et al., 1930; Eggleton, 1934, 1935a, b; Richardson, 1938; Parbery, 1945; Rappe, 1950; Theron, 1951; Theron and Haylett, 1953). A number of explanations have been proposed. The presence of ammonium is unlikely to be due to preferential absorption of nitrate by the grass since grasses readily absorb and utilize ammonium fertilizers. Insufficient aeration for the oxidation of ammonia seems likely to obtain only under wet or waterlogged conditions (Michniewicz, 1951; Cyplenkin and Zjilin, 1936). However, Woldendorp (1962, 1963) found denitrification to occur under grassland conditions and concludes that grass culture produced sufficient oxygen accepting substances to reduce the oxygen content in the soil and thereby permit considerable losses of nitrogen through denitrification. Similar observations were made by Walker et al. (1956). However, failure to recover added tracer nitrogen has been observed also under annual crops (Bartholomew, 1957). The failure to find nitrate accumulation under crops, therefore, may be due in part to enhanced denitrification of oxidized nitrogen in the root zone of growing crops. The theory had been proposed that living roots suppressed nitrification (Lyon and Bizzell, 1918; Starkey, 1929; Lyon, 1930; Theron, 1951; Theron and Haylett, 1953; Rosselet, 1953). This suppression might operate through the production of substances which tend to enhance the denitrification processes.

It is quite possible that the small quantity of ammonium nitrogen found in grassland soils is an artifact of the extraction and analytical procedures (Harmsen and van Schreven, 1955). Methods of distillation of ammonia frequently employ magnesia. Bruins (unpublished, 1963) recently found that the highest ammonia yields came from distillation with magnesia, much less from the use of the Conway (1950) method, and very little by distillation from a buffer solution at pH 8.5.

Wet conditions in grassland areas and the high water tables associated with many grass soils may have had important influences upon the accumulations and losses of nitrogen (Minderhoud, 1960). Not only is aeration frequently poorer under wet conditions but high water tables restrict the depth of the root zone.

The capacity of grasses to absorb nitrogen and the resulting low levels of inorganic nitrogen which prevail under grass have caused peculiar problems where grass is grown in orchards (Savage, 1944; Palmer and van Haarlem, 1944; Rogers et al., 1948; Hill, 1952; Rosselet, 1953; Bould and Jarrett, 1956; Ljones, 1958; Dalbro and Nielsen, 1959; van der Boon and Kolenbrander, 1960; Butijn, 1961; Delver, 1962; Rebour, 1962).

The uptake of a large part of the nitrogen by the grass tends to reduce nitrogen uptake by the trees. Attempts to solve the problem have included applying the fertilizer nitrogen in midwinter in temperate humid climates, permitting part of the nitrogen to move down in the soil profile beyond the reach of grass roots but still within reach of the tree roots.

The capacity to immobilize all mineralized or added nitrogen is not restricted to grassland. It is a general characteristic of all permanent vegetation covers which are untilled. Low quantities of inorganic nitrogen have been found not only in cultivated grassland but also in virgin prairies, savannas, and forests (Romell, 1924; Süchting et al., 1933; Süchting, 1950; Smirnow, 1958; Ivarson and Sowden, 1959; Zöttl, 1960a, b; Ehrhardt, 1961), and even in the tundra (Cyplenkin and Zjilin, 1935). However, Jenny and co-workers described an exceptional case in a humid tropical forest in Colombia, where a rather high level of inorganic nitrogen was observed (Jenny et al., 1949; Jenny, 1950). They ascribed this abnormal situation to the high percentage of leguminous species among the trees and shrubs.

III. MOVEMENT OF INORGANIC NITROGEN THROUGH THE SOIL

Movement of nitrogen in the soil has a marked influence on the quantity of inorganic nitrogen found in the soil at any time and upon the availability of the nitrogen to crop plants. The theories and fundamental descriptions of movement are treated in Chapter 15. Of concern here will be some quantitative aspects of movement and the influence of movement on the supply of inorganic nitrogen in soil.

The major mechanism of movement of nitrogen in soil is in solution or in suspension in water. Some movement occurs by soil tillage and by other forms of physical displacement of soil particles. These latter types may have important effects over long periods of time in determining the lateral and vertical distribution of nitrogen in soil. Such distribution mechanisms and patterns are discussed in Chapter 1. Only the implications of water movement will be evaluated here.

One of the early discussions of the subject of nitrogen leaching was given by Boussingault (1856). Since the beginning of the 20th century many papers have provided information on leaching (Russell, 1914; Hall, 1924; Koudriawtsewa, 1925; Smith, 1928; Hansen, 1928, 1929; Yankovitch, 1933; Greene, 1935; Hardy, 1946b; Drouineau and Lefèvre, 1951; Leutenegger, 1956; Solberg and Braadlie, 1957; Cunningham and Cooke, 1958; Gliemeroth, 1958, 1959; Harmsen, 1959, 1961; Gasser, 1959, 1961).

Nitrate nitrogen is the form which is moved most readily in water. Urea and some other amino compounds are also soluble in water and, because they are only mildly absorbed by soil particles, move readily with water. However, these latter substances generally have a transient existence in soil, being readily hydrolyzed to ammonium.

Ammonium nitrogen can be rather strongly absorbed on soil colloids provided the absorption capacity at the site is not saturated. A slow leaching of ammonium is possible but it depends upon the rate of exchange of NH_4^+ with other cations (Smith, 1952; Linser et al., 1959). In most cultivated soils the concentration of ammonium, apart from that which is fixed, is insignificant compared with the quantity of nitrate (Nelson, 1953; Ray et al., 1957).

The leaching of cations such as ammonium depends upon displacement reactions with other cations. Such processes have been studied by ion exchange techniques (Wilson, 1940; Martin and Synge, 1941; DeVault, 1943; Glueckauf, 1949). The relationship of this kind of reaction to leaching of soil cations has been considered by Ribble and Davis (1955).

The application of the principles of movement of ions in soils to desalinization of the newly reclaimed sea bottom land of the Zuider Sea has been discussed by van der Molen (1956, 1958). The downward migration of soluble substances with rainfall depends not only on the amount of rain, but also on the water-holding capacity of the soil. The higher this capacity the less nitrogen will be lost to deeper layers by the same rainfall, even if all soils were at field capacity. This explains why nitrogen moves downward more readily in sandy than in clay or peat soils (Cooke and Cunningham, 1947).

The course of the leaching process has been studied empirically by Soubiès et al. (1952) in a homogenous profile. They showed that nitrate, originally accumulated near the surface of the soil, was pushed down by rain as a smooth wave, following the theory of Martin and Synge (1941). According to this theory a soluble substance put on the top of a homogenous permeable substrate will be moved downward by percolating liquid as a wave with the shape of the normal error curve. During the movement the wave will gradually become wider and flatter, corresponding with the increasing "standard deviation."

In cases where soils are impermeable or where heavy rain occurs, oversaturation occurs at the soil surface. Water then accumulates in depressed areas resulting in irregular movement into the soil or in surface runoff.

Laboratory studies of the influence of soil structure on percolation and ion movement were made by Bates and Tisdale (1957). Wetselaar (1962) compared the permeability of different soil types under field conditions. In granulated clay soils rain water runs quickly through the intergranular or large pores carrying with it only a part of the soluble substances. The soluble ions within the granules equilibrates by slow diffusion processes with the concentration of ions in the larger pores. This serves to further decrease the rate of leaching of nitrate nitrogen from heavy soils. Studies of the leaching of soluble substances from clay soils with a granulated structure have been performed by Webster and Gasser (1958, 1959), Moore (1960), and Gasser (1961). Gardner and Brooks (1957) developed a mathematical description of the course of leaching in such soils. Their approach was different from that of van der Molen (1956).

The height of the water table in the soil may influence leaching. Two opposite effects may occur. Kolenbrander (1961) observed in marshland a pronounced slowing down of the leaching when the water table was high. In periods of dry weather, however, when the level of the water in the ditches and drain tubes was falling, much of the soluble substances in the soil was drained towards the ditches and lost entirely. Owens (1960), applying the N^{15}-technique, also found more losses of nitrogen by leaching at high than at low water table.

Upward movement of nitrogen may occur as water is evaporated from the soil surface and as water is transpired through plants. This upward movement may serve to supply the plant with nitrogen from subsoil waters or it may make nitrogen unavailable to the plant by carrying it to the dryer layers of surface soil. The height of rise of capillary water is inversely proportional to the minimum diameter of the communicating pores while the rate of rise is proportional to the size of the bigger pores. A study of the rise in soil of water from a water table has been made by Gardner and Fireman (1958).

In most cases the amount of mobile nitrogen in the subsoil is rather low and rising moisture brings little nitrogen to the topsoil. However, in some instances soil conditions have favored an accumulation of nitrate in subsoil layers (Koudriawtsewa, 1925; Smith, 1928; Greene, 1935; Jewitt,

1956; Leutenegger, 1956; Wetselaar, 1960), and then the upward displacement of the moisture has brought about an increase in nitrogen in the root zone of the soil (Greene, 1935; Drouineau and Lefèvre, 1951; Jewitt, 1956; Harmsen, 1961; van der Paauw, 1962a).

Where water tables are deep in the soil they have little or no influence on the upward movement of water. Under such conditions upward movement of moisture is not dependent upon moisture being supplied by a free water table; the moisture moves now in the unsaturated state. Consequently, water evaporated from a soil surface will be in part replaced by liquid movement from unsaturated layers below. This movement is slow but it carries soluble ions with it, as does liquid movement in the saturated state (Marshall, 1959).

Because of the continuous production and removal of nitrate in soil, difficulty is encountered in detecting small increments of change in nitrogen by movement processes. To overcome this difficulty Griffith (1951), Wetselaar (1960), and Simpson (1960) used chlorides injected into the subsoil to determine the rate of capillary transport of soluble substance. Since chloride and nitrate ions are transported in similar ways by the moisture (van der Molen, 1956; Gardner and Brooks, 1957) the method permits an evaluation of nitrate movement. In some cases the upward and downward movements are so rapid and important that mineralization in the topsoil may be considered negligible (Harmsen, 1959, 1962).

Horizontal translocation is seldom important except in instances where sloping soils have a parched impervious zone. After heavy rains lateral movement in such instances may be appreciable. Lateral movement associated with furrow irrigation may serve to concentrate the soluble nutrients in the ridges between the furrows. Lateral spreading of nitrate by diffusion from placed fertilizers has not been large (v. d. Boon, unpublished, 1960).

The quantitative aspect of nitrogen gains and losses from soil are reviewed in detail in Chapter 16. Leaching may constitute the most important mechanism of removal of inorganic nitrogen from the plant root zone other than crop absorption. Leaching losses have generally been measured in lysimeter experiments or in controlled field drainage plots by measuring the nitrogen in the effluent water. However, nitrogen may be unavailable to a crop well before it has been carried sufficiently far into the soil to enter the drainage water. Therefore, leaching can be followed better by repeatedly measuring the nitrogen content in the different layers of the soil profile. It is difficult to decide at what depth in the soil nutrients must be considered lost, because it depends on the extent to which they may be carried back into the root zone by upward movement of water and on the depth to which roots penetrate and are active. It was recently shown by de Roo and Wiersum (1963) that in sufficiently aerated soils the ability of the roots to take up nutrients did not decrease with the depth. Yet, it can generally be said that the deeper the nitrogen is moved down the smaller is its value for the nutrition of plants since most crops develop the greatest root density in the topsoil.

The vertical downward displacement of nitrogen in sandy soils, beginning with moisture content around field capacity, was about 45 cm per 100 mm rainfall entering the surface, about 30 cm in soils with 20-40% of the particles less than 20 microns in diameter, and only about 20 cm displacement per 100 mm of rainfall for heavy clay soils (Rousselle, 1913; Soubiès et al., 1952; Gliemeroth, 1958, 1959; Moore, 1960; van der Boon and Kolenbrander, 1960; Harmsen, 1961). Such data indicate the net quantity of downward water movement to carry the soluble nitrate down beyond the reach of roots in particular soils. They demonstrate the relatively slow rate of leaching even under humid conditions. It is thus understandable that in the heavier-textured soils even in temperate humid climates part of the soluble nitrogen can remain in the upper levels of the subsoil throughout the winter. Gliemeroth (1959) found some 25-40 kg/ha of soluble nitrogen in the layer between 20 and 60 cm at the end of the winter season in an unfertilized heavy loess soil. However, Dalbro and Nielsen (1959) observed only about 11 kg of nitrogen in a similar layer in a sandy soil. Complete loss of nitrogen from permeable sandy soils may occur in humid climates during normal winters but from heavy soils only during wet winters. During summer growing seasons nitrate nitrogen is seldom carried downward beyond the reach of plant roots except during unusually rainy periods (Harmsen, 1961).

Nitrate nitrogen seldom is carried down into the soil beyond the reach of roots in arid or semi-arid climates except when irrigation water has been applied. Interesting data about displacement of soluble nitrogen and its accumulation in deeper layers for tropical conditions have been published by Snow and Greene (1935). They found an accumulation of soluble nitrogen of about 150 kg per ha in a layer between 100 and 150 cm from the surface.

IV. OTHER FACTORS CAUSING LOSSES OF INORGANIC NITROGEN FROM SOIL

Ammonia volatilization losses can occur from soil surfaces when ammonia is applied as fertilizer or formed near the surface and when the absorption capacity of the soil is not sufficiently large to hold the ammonia. Concern about ammonia losses can be found among the writings of the agricultural research workers of the early nineteenth century (Sprengel, 1839; Boussingault, 1844). These writers were convinced that in soils containing $CaCO_3$ severe losses of ammonia might be expected. Later Liebig (1862) and Stoklasa (1892) denied the possibility of such loss processes while Berthelot and André (1887) reported ammonia loss from soils, especially those rich in carbonate. Losses were also reported by Frank (1888), Winter (1894), Warington (1900), and Schneidewind (1904). One of the main reasons for the contradictory opinions about the influence of lime on the value of sulphate of ammonia as nitrogen fertilizer and on the release of ammonia was the prevailing idea that only nitrate could be used by the plants and that ammonia first had to be nitrified. On very acid soils, liming often stimulates nitrification and the sulphate of ammonia soon become transformed to nitrate. It was supposed, therefore, that it was protected against further volatilization by nitrification. The incorrect interpretation of the benefits from lime and the polemic about the losses of some 10% of the nitrogen from ammonia during its nitrification, as claimed by Wagner in a series of publications (1892, 1898, 1901, 1903a, b, 1907) and by Wlodek (1911), are the reasons for all the misunderstandings around the ammonia volatilization in those days. The opinion of Wagner was criticized and finally rejected by subsequent investigators (Pfeiffer, 1906; Stoklasa, 1908b; Löhnis and Blobel, 1908; Blobel, 1908; Ehrenberg, 1907, 1911, 1912). A revival of interest in volatilization processes has occurred in an attempt to account for nitrogen fertilizer added to soil and to evaluate the value of ammonia and ammonium producing fertilizers (Crowther, 1941; Jewitt, 1942; Kappen et al., 1943; Steenbjerg, 1944; Tovborg-Jensen and Kjaer, 1948, 1950; van Schreven, 1950, 1955, 1956a; Gerretsen, 1950; Lehr, 1950; Martin and Chapman, 1951; Volk, 1959, 1961; Kresge and Satchell, 1960; Ernst and Massey, 1960; Vanstallen, 1960; Nõmmik and Varlin, 1960; Lehr and Wesemael, 1961; Brown and Bartholomew, 1962). These studies provide information about the loss processes and about the factors which influence volatilization.

Ammonia can be produced in soil provided the pH is sufficiently high to induce the formation of ammonia. $CaCO_3$ in the soil may result in a pH above 8 which is sufficiently high to induce the formation of ammonia from ammonium ions. Loss processes appear to be accentuated when the lime is finely divided and well dispersed in the soil.

The production of ammonia in excess of acidic anions such as is found in the decomposition of proteins (Liechti and Ritter, 1910; Heck, 1931; Jewitt and Barlow, 1949; Doak, 1952; Lindhard, 1954) and the hydrolysis of urea results in high pH values and may permit the loss of ammonia (Martin and Chapman, 1951; Volk, 1959, 1961; Ernst and Massey, 1960; Kresge and Satchell, 1960).

Ammonia loss from soil arises because ammonia which is formed does not become sorbed in some way on soil particles. The nature of the sorption process is reviewed in Chapter 4. Ammonia by acquisition of a hydrogen ion or proton becomes an ammonium ion and as such can be held on the soil exchange complexes. Ammonia can also be physically adsorbed on mineral soil particles and on organic matter. In these latter processes the sorbed ammonia is in equilibrium with gaseous ammonia in the soil air. Furthermore, ammonia can dissolve in soil water. Such ammonia also establishes equilibrium with ammonia in the soil air. Organic matter reacts with ammonia as well as with oxidized forms of nitrogen. These reactions are discussed in Chapter 4.

Loss of ammonia generally occurs when ammonia is formed at or diffuses to the soil surface in situations where concentration of ammonia exceeds the capacity of the soil to strongly sorb and hold the ammonia. Rates of loss may be strongly influenced by environmental factors. The ways to prevent nitrogen losses due to ammonia volatilization are also discussed in Chapter 4. Drying the soil has been reported to increase ammonia volatilization (Jewitt, 1942; Tovborg-Jensen and Kjaer, 1948, 1950; Martin and Chapman, 1951; Volk, 1949; Kresge and Satchell, 1960; Ernst and Massey, 1960). Lehr (1950) and van Schreven (1955) have claimed that desiccation is not a factor.

Most investigators expect that as long as there is a surplus of $CaCO_3$ in the soil a further increase in it will not influence the pH and the ammonia losses. However, Lemmermann and Fresenius (1913) claimed a relation between the amount of $CaCO_3$ and the volatilization of ammonia. This opinion was supported by Steenbjerg (1944), and by Lehr and Wesemael (1961). The experience that the ammonia losses in the newly reclaimed polders of the Zuider Sea are higher than on old arable land with less $CaCO_3$ but with the same pH values seems also to be a confirmation of the influences of lime. The particle size of the lime and the dispersion in the soil may also influence ammonia volatilization (Harmsen, 1935; Smeding, 1935; Bosma, 1946).

The reduction of oxidized forms of nitrogen with the production of nitrogen gas (N_2) or some of the volatile oxides of nitrogen, may be a mechanism of considerable importance in the loss of nitrogen from soil. This biological reductive mechanism and the attendant possible losses were known and discussed rather early in the development of soil microbiology (Gayon and Dupetit, 1886; Tacke, 1910; Beijerink and Minkman, 1910). Interest in the biological reductive processes have been revived in the past couple of decades (van Olden, 1940; Sacks and Barker, 1949, 1952; Allen and van Niel, 1952; Verhoeven, 1952, 1956; Kluijver and Verhoeven, 1954; Baalsrud and Baalsrud, 1954; Najjar and Allen, 1954; Wijler and Delwiche, 1954; Delwiche, 1956; Chung and Najjar, 1956; Nõmmik, 1956; Iwasaki and Mori, 1958). These studies and others have demonstrated that denitrification processes can take place but that specific environmental conditions appear necessary. A detailed discussion of the processes and the factors controlling denitrification is given in Chapter 9.

The extent to which this process operates in normal soils is still open to question. That some volatile losses occur under greenhouse conditions has been repeatedly shown by tracer studies (Bartholomew, 1957). Lysimeter studies have suggested denitrification but in many instances the magnitudes of loss have been of the orders of magnitude of the analytical errors (Allison, 1955b).

The denitrification processes have been shown to depend upon the microflora, the level of oxygen in the media, the moisture content, the temperature, and the available food energy sources for the microbes. Soil types, soil texture, and soil structure influence many of the controlling factors.

The presence of organisms capable of carrying on denitrifying reactions is not considered to be a limiting condition in that many kinds of organisms in all soils have this ability. Studies of limiting factors indicate low oxygen and high microbial respiration and the presence of nitrate or nitrite as necessary conditions for active denitrification. Since these conditions seldom occur in normal upland soils, questions have been raised concerning the importance of denitrification. The questions center about the oxygen supply situations within soil granules and at sites of intense microbial activity in soil (Nõmmik, 1956; Gilmour et al., 1957;

McGarity et al., 1958; Bremner and Shaw, 1958; Allison et al., 1960; Greenwood, 1962). Woldendorp (1962, 1963) has stressed the effect of root respiration as well as microbial respiration in the rhizosphere in the depletion of soil oxygen.

The rate of denitrification is dependent on temperature. Below about 10°C the denitrification does not appear important (Nõmmik, 1956; Gilmour et al., 1957; Bremner and Shaw, 1958). Since some thermophilic microbes are active denitrifiers, the maximum temperature may be rather high. During the winter, when the soil moisture content may be high, low temperatures tend to prevent nitrogen losses by this mechanism.

Since denitrification is in part at least an enzymatic process, it is sensitive to pH levels below 4 and above 10. The optimum pH is between 7.0-7.5. The influence of the pH has been studied by Jensen (1934), and recently by Nõmmik (1956), Loewenstein et al. (1957), Bremner and Shaw (1958), and Valera and Alexander (1961).

Apart from the strictly biological denitrification, other mechanisms for the production of nitrogen gas and volatile nitrogen oxides have been claimed. In slightly acid soils, rich in humus, the van Slyke reaction has been proposed as a loss mechanism (Wilson, 1943; Allison and Sterling, 1948; Gerretsen, 1948, 1949, 1950; Allison and Doetsch, 1951; Allison et al., 1952; Wijler and Delwiche, 1954; Gerretsen and de Hoop, 1957). In this reaction nitrite reacts with amino groups or ammonium forming elemental nitrogen $(RNH_2 + HNO_2 \rightarrow ROH + H_2O + N_2)$. There is disagreement about the pH range which favors this reaction and about the extent to which the reaction occurs in normal soil. Jones (1951), Allison et al. (1952), Wijler and Delwiche (1954), and Clark et al. (1960) discount the importance of the van Slyke reaction and propose a direct disintegration of nitrites as the main pathway of loss. Cady and Bartholomew (1961) claimed that disintegration of nitrites proceeded even in sterilized soil.

Ammonium may be removed from the plant available pool in soil through fixation by some clay minerals. This fixation process occurs mainly in the micaceous minerals, such as illite or vermiculite. The mechanisms and conditions of fixation are discussed in Chapter 5.

Although the bonds in ammonium fixation are rather strong, fixation is reversible. An equilibrium must be supposed between the fixed and the free or loosely absorbed ammonium. By decreasing the readily available ammonium ions, therefore, a gradual but slow release of the fixed ions can be attained. This release is accelerated by addition of cations, which cause the crystal lattices to expand (Barshad, 1954). Nõmmik (1957) observed a significant increase in the capacity of heterotrophic microorganisms to utilize fixed ammonium when easily disintegrated carbohydrates (glucose) were added to the soil. In unamended soil only a minor part of the fixed ammonium was released on incubation, while the application of glucose permitted the utilization of most of it. Nitrifying organisms proved to have a weak ability to use fixed ammonium; oxidizing only about 20% (Bower, 1950; Allison et al., 1953; Allison, 1955b). The ability of plants to utilize fixed ammonium is rather high but depends on the concentration of potassium. Potassium ions prevent the expansion of the crystal lattices and the release of fixed ammonium. This factor together with the acidity of the root exudates influences the degree of utilization of fixed ammonium by crops (Elgabaly and Wiklander, 1949; Drake et al., 1951; Nõmmik, 1957).

An excellent review of this problem has already been given by Allison (1955), and in Chapter 16 a detailed discussion again can be found. Although the magnitude of each of the several ingo and outgo processes vary widely with kind of soil, with environmental conditions and with season, a number of generalities may be formulated. On the average in field experiments about half the fertilizer nitrogen finds its way into crop plants. There is no conclusive evidence to indicate whether nitrogen mineralized from crop residues or animal and green manures is more or less efficiently used than that from fertilizer. The other half of the nitrogen which appears in the soil in mineral forms is lost from the soil through the different processes.

Losses by volatilization may range from 5 to 20% of the fertilizer nitrogen added. Both lysimeter studies and greenhouse experiments with tracer nitrogen have been consistent in indicating some loss by these channels. The precise mechanisms which result in such losses are still matters of some speculation.

Average losses from leaching range from 20 to 40% of the fertilizer nitrogen applied. It must be remembered that in some instances leaching losses are nil while in others they are very large. Yet in the major crop producing areas of the world leaching of nitrogen or the movement of this nitrogen with water down in the soil profile beyond the reach of plant roots is the largest single mechanism of loss.

Additions of nitrogen to the soil by rain water (Marggraf, 1761; Barral, 1852; Boussingault, 1853; Eriksson, 1952; Wetselaar and Hutton, 1963) and by nonsymbiotic fixation (Chapter 12) have not been large and have little effect on the estimation of magnitude of loss processes.

V. IMPLICATIONS TO AGRICULTURE

A measure of control over many of the ingo and outgo processes of soil inorganic nitrogen is among the objectives of research on soil nitrogen. The foregoing discussion has indicated the magnitude and rapidity with which many of these processes occur and the effect they can have on the supply of nitrogen to crop plants. The natural supplying processes, mineralization from soil organic matter, nitrogen fixation and addition with rainwater, seldom provide enough nitrogen for economic crop production in modern agriculture. Manures and fertilizers are found to be necessary to make up the deficiency. There is a growing realization among agriculturists that a mere concern with the quantity of nitrogen needed is not sufficient for maximum plant production. Attempts are under way to determine the season or stage of growth in which nitrogen is needed and to provide the nitrogen at the proper time either by application schedules or by controlled release after application. Practical experience has provided general guides concerning the patterns of need for nitrogen by plants. However, there are yet many questions to be answered relative to the nitrogen supply schedules which will result in the best yield and quality of crop plants. But all these problems of nitrogenous fertilization and the nutrition of plants are considered too comprehensive to be reviewed in this chapter. The problem is very old and has developed gradually throughout centuries from empirical agricultural trials to the modern concept. The literature is very extensive. Here only two special items of the whole subject will be mentioned: (1) The use of fertilizers with a gradual slow release of nitrogen, and (2) The determination and prediction of the nitrogen needs of the crops.

Interest has developed in the production of fertilizers which release nitrogen slowly. Among the materials proposed are reaction products of urea and aldehydes, resistant coating on conventional fertilizers, slowly soluble ammonium-magnesium-phosphates, and ammoniated organic products. The efficiency of these products as measured by plant recovery has not equaled that of conventional fertilizers. Except for some specialized uses they have not yet found a practical place in agriculture (Yee and Love, 1947; Armiger et al., 1948; Clark et al., 1956; Atanasiu, 1959; Kuntze, 1959; Prostakoff, 1960; Jung, 1961; Ansorge, 1962).

The idea for a slow-nitrogen-release fertilizer is old. It originated in part from the efforts to prevent losses of ammonia from farm manure and liquid manure by the addition of formaldehyde (Blanck and Giesecke, 1923).

Since it proved difficult following these lines to manufacture fertilizers fully answering the purpose, recently the use of the slowly dissolving ammonium-magnesium phosphates or a coating of soluble conventional fertilizers was proposed. These efforts however are still in the experimental stage (Scheffer et al., 1957; Jung, 1960).

The need for the addition of nitrogen fertilizer is determined by the total crop requirement and the quantity which will be naturally supplied by the soil. Fertilization with nitrogen is to supply the crop need deficit. Different methods have been employed to determine the supply from the soil. The oldest are vegetative tests, performed as field trials or as pot experiments. Since such trials are expensive and time consuming, more rapid methods have been devised. Both incubation and chemical extraction methods have been formulated. However, all such indirect methods must be compared with field trials, and their value depends on the degree of correlation with these vegetation tests.

Variations of the incubation method determine the nitrogen mineralization under artificial conditions. Chemical treatments extract all or some fraction of the soil organic nitrogen, and are less comparable with the mineralization under field conditions.

A rather good correlation has been observed by some investigators between the total nitrogen content of the soil and the formation of inorganic nitrogen during incubation (Fraps, 1912; Fraps and Sterges, 1939b, 1947; Allison and Sterling, 1949; Woodruff, 1950; Smith, 1952; Carpenter et al., 1952), but only for soils of the same type. Soils belonging to different types, even if they contained the same amount of total nitrogen, sometimes released quite different amounts of inorganic nitrogen. This has been shown by Gainey (1936) and by Gainey et al. (1937).

Nitrogen release per se during an incubation interval is not the only factor which has an influence on quantity of nitrogen a soil may supply to the crop. The length of season of accumulation preceding and during crop growth and the environmental factors during this period also influence the supply of nitrogen the crop gets from the soil. This problem was recognized by Russell (1914) for situations in England. Later, Fisher (1924) studied the problem. In the Netherlands Lehr and Veen (1952) and van der Paauw (1959, 1962a, b) investigated the problem in detail.

Available nitrogen contents in the layer below the surface soil, conditions favorable for mineralization during winter months and a minimum of leaching preceding and during crop growth may markedly influence the nitrogen available to a crop. Only frequent sampling of several soil horizons could provide this kind of information and relate it to climatic factors and to subsequent fertilizer response data (Harmsen, 1961).

The laboratory soil test methods, at best, provide an indirect measure of the capacity of the soil to supply nitrogen to the crop. Correlations with field results provide the mechanism for making fertilizer need predictions from the tests. Notwithstanding the difficulties besetting the test methods reasonable correlation has been claimed by many investigators (Kellerman and Allen, 1911; Fraps, 1912, 1921; Lipman et al., 1916; Gainey, 1917; Waksman, 1923a, 1923b; Várallyay, 1937; Black et al., 1947; Fraps and Sterges, 1947; White et al., 1949; Ishizuka and Tanaka, 1955; Fitts et al., 1955; Stanford and Hanway, 1955; Hanway and Dumenil, 1955; Munson and Stanford, 1955; van Schreven, 1956b; Cook et al., 1957; Hagin et al., 1959; Hagin and Shmueli, 1960; Pritchett et al., 1960; Malik, 1960; Chu Chao-liang, 1960; Gasser and Williams, 1962; Polhill, 1962, verbal communication). Most of these publications were dealing with one soil type or with one soil treated in various ways. This, no doubt, contributed to the success experienced with the tests.

A further difficulty in making soil test for nitrogen is the variable crop response to nitrogen from one season to the next on the same soil area. Owing to climatic variations more nitrogen is needed in some years than in others. Moderate correlations have been reported by Allison and Sterling (1949), Andharia et al. (1953), Fitts et al. (1953), Allison (1956), Kresge and Merkle (1957), and Ferguson (1957). Poor results or complete failures have been experienced by Pritchett et al. (1948), Harmsen and Lindenbergh (1949), Richardson (1952), Harmsen (1956), Eagle and Matthews (1958), and Peterson et al. (1960).

Other methods which have been less extensively used are the Mitscherlich-law technique (Gericke, 1947), the method of Neubauer (1946) or the response of microbes as test organisms (Shishelova, 1936; McCool, 1947). Analysis of the nitrogen content of specific plant organs during certain parts of the growing season is another general approach to ascertaining the nitrogen supplying capacity of soils and the nitrogen need of the crop. This method has been most extensively applied to tree crops and in tropical agriculture. Adaptations for annual field crops have been proposed (Yuen and Hance, 1939; Wark, 1938; van Burg, 1962).

Gassner and Goeze (1936) proposed the use of vegetation color analyses as a measure of the nitrogen nutrition status of plants. Recently Lehr et al. (1962) reexamined the technique and reviewed the information on the method.

REFERENCES

Acharya, C. N., and Jain, S. P. 1954. Nitrifiability of soil organic matter. J. Indian Soc. Soil Sci. 2:43 48.

Allen, M. B., and Niel, C. B. van. 1952. Experiments on bacterial denitrification. J. Bacteriol. 64:397-412.

Allison, F. E. 1955a. Does nitrogen applied to crop residues produce more humus? Soil Sci. Soc. Amer. Proc. 19:210-211.

Allison, F. E. 1955b. The enigma of soil nitrogen balance sheets. In A. G. Norman, ed. Advances in Agronomy, Academic Press Inc., N. Y. 7:213-250.

Allison, F. E. 1956. Estimating the ability of soils to supply nitrogen. Agr. Chemicals 11, no 4:46-48, 139.

Allison, F. E., Carter, J. N., and Sterling, L. D. T. 1960. The effect of partial pressure of oxygen on denitrification in soil. Soil Sci. Soc. Amer. Proc. 24:283-285.

Allison, F. E., and Doetsch, Janet, H. 1951. Nitrogen gas production by the reaction of nitrites with amino acids in slightly acid media. Soil Sci. Soc. Amer. Proc. (1950) 15:163-166.

Allison, F. E., Doetsch, Janet, H., and Sterling, L. D. T. 1952. Nitrogen gas formation by interaction of nitrites and amino acids. Soil Sci. 74:311-314.

Allison, F. E., Kefauver, M., and Roller, E. M. 1953. Ammonium fixation in soils. Soil Sci. Soc. Amer. Proc. 17:107-110.

Anderson, O. E. 1960. The effect of low temperatures on nitrification of ammonia in Cecil sandy loam. Soil Sci. Soc. Amer. Proc. 24:286-289.

Andharia, R. M., Stanford, G., and Schaller, F. W. 1953. Nitrogen status of Marshall silt loam as influenced by different crop rotations. Soil Sci. Soc. Amer. Proc. 17:247-251.

Andrëewa, E. A. 1958. The effect of various methods of deepening the plowed layer on the agrochemical properties of sod-podzolic soil. (In Russian). Pochvovedenie (Pedology) no 4:41-50. English Summary.

Ansorge, H. 1962. Stickstoffnachlieferung und Stickstoffausnutzung von langsam wirkenden N-Düngemitteln (Ureaformen). Z. Landw. Versuchs-Untersuch.-Wesen 8:357-368.

Antipow-Karatejew, I. N., and Filippowa, W. N. 1955. The influence of irrigation in the long run on the soil. (In Russian.) Transact. Dokoutschajev Soil Instit. In Compt. Rend. Acad. Sci. U. S. S. R. New Ser. M.

Armiger, W. H., Forbes, I., Wagner, R. E., and Lundstrom, F. O. 1948. Urea-form. A nitrogenous fertilizer of controlled availability: Experiments with turfgrasses. J. Amer. Soc. Agron. 40:342-356.

Atanasiu, N. 1959. Zur Wirkung schwer löslicher N-Verbindungen. Z. Pflanzenernähr., Düng., Bodenk. 84:103-110.

Baalsrud, K., and Baalsrud, K. S. 1954. Thiobacillus denitrificans. Arch. Microbiol. 20:34-62.

Barnes, T. W. 1950. The formation of nitrates in soil following various crop rotations. J. Agr. Sci. 40:166-168.

Barral, J. A. 1852. Premier memoire sur les eaux de pluie de l'observatoire de Paris. Compt. Rend. Acad. Sci. (Paris) 34:283-284.

Barrow, N. J. 1960. Stimulated decomposition of soil organic matter during the decomposition of added organic matter. Australian J. Agr. Res. 2:331-338.

Barshad, I. 1954. Cation exchange in micaceous minerals. Soil Sci. 77:463-472; 78:57-76.

Bartholomew, W. V. 1957. Use of isotopes in following nitrogen transformations in soil. A conference on radioactive isotopes in agriculture. U. S. Atomic Energy Comm. Rep. T. I. D. 7512:337-347.

Bartholomew, W. V., and Clark, F. E. 1950. Nitrogen transformations in soil in relation to the rhizorphere microflora. Trans. Intern. Cong. Soil Sci., 4th Cong. Amsterdam 2:112-113.

Bastisse, E. M. 1951. Dixhuit années d'études lysimetriques appliquées à l'agronomie. Ann. Agron. 6:727-781.

Bates, F. E., and Tisdale, S. L. 1957. The movement of nitrate nitrogen through columns of coarse-textured soil materials. Soil Sci. Soc. Amer. Proc. 21:525-528.

Baumann, H., and Maasz, G. 1957. Über den Verlauf des Nitratgehaltes unter verschiedenen Früchten im Ackerboden. Z. Pflanzenernähr. Düng., Bodenk. 79:155-167.

Beijerinck, M. W., and Minkman, D. C. J. 1910. Bildung und Verbrauch von Stickstofoxydul durch Bakterien. Centralbl. Bakteriol. Parasitenk., Infektionskrankh. Abt. II 25:30-63.

Berthelot and André. 1887. Sur les principes azotés de la terre vegetale. Ann. Chimie et Physique 6eme serie 11:368-382.

Bhuiyan, S. 1949. Transformation of nitrogen in rice soil. Soil Sci. 67:231-252.

Bingeman, C. W., Varner, J. E., and Martin, W. P. 1953. The effect of the addition of organic materials on the decomposition of an organic soil. Soil Sci. Soc. Amer. Proc. 17:34-38.

Birch, H. F. 1958. The effect of soil drying on humus decomposition and nitrogen availability. Plant and Soil 10:9-31.

Birch, H. F. 1959. Further observations on humus decomposition and nitrification. Plant and Soil 11:262-286.

Birch, H. F. 1960. Nitrification in soils after different periods of dryness. Plant and Soil 12:81-96.

Bizzell, J. A. 1922. Disappearance of nitrates from soil under timothy. J. Amer. Soc. Agron. 14:320-326.

Bizzell, J. A. 1943. Lysimeter experiments V. Comparative effects of ammonium sulfate and sodium nitrate on removal of nitrogen and calcium from the soil. Cornell Agr. Exp. Sta. Mem. 252.

Bizzell, J. A. 1944. Lysimeter experiments VI. The effect of cropping and fertilization on the losses of nitrogen from the soil. Cornell Agr. Exp. Sta. Mem. 256.

Black, C. A., Nelson, L. B., and Pritchett, W. L. 1947. Nitrogen utilization by wheat as affected by rate of fertilization. Soil Sci. Soc. Amer. Proc. (1946) 11:393-396.

Blackman, G. E. 1936. The influence of temperature and available nitrogen supply on the growth of pasture in the spring. J. Agr. Sci. 26:620-647.

Blanck, E., and Giesecke, F. 1923. Mono- und Dimethylolharnstoff in ihrer Wirkung auf die Pflanzenproduktion und ihr Stickstoffumsatz im Boden. Z. Pflanzenernähr., Düng., Bodenk. 2:393-420.

Blobcl, E. 1908. Untersuchungen über den Wirkungswert von schwefelsaurem Ammoniak und Chilisalpeter als Düngemittel. Ph.D. thesis. Leipzig. 100 pp.

Boerema, E. B., and McDonald, D. J. 1963. A review of the fertilizer requirements of rice on the Nurrumbidgee irrigation area. Australian J. Exp. Agr. Animal Husb. In press.

Bogdanov, S. 1900. Über die Bestimmung der Fruchtbarkeit des Bodens. (Fourth report). (In Russian.) Sel'sk. Khoz. i Ljesow. 198:241. German summary.

Bolotina, N. I. 1959. The effect of irrigation on the nutrient regime of Cis-Caucasian chernozems. (In Russian). Pochvovedenië (Pedology) no 1:40-50. English Summary.

Boon, J. van der, and Kolenbrander, G. J. 1960. Downward displacement of nitrogen in an orchard with grass-cover. (In Dutch.) Landbouwk. Tijdschrift 72:904-915.

Bosch, S. 1946. Nitrogen fertilization on grassland. (In Dutch.) Versl. Landbouwk. Onderz. 52:209-264. English Summary.

Bosma, W. A. 1946. Investigation on the nitrogen fertilization in the Northeastern Polder. (In Dutch.) Versl. Ontwikkelingsdag 4 dec: 13-33.

Bould, C., and Jarrett, R. M. 1956. Cover crops in relation to soil fertility and tree nutrition: II Experiments with dessert bush apple trees. Progress Report 1. Ann. Rep. Long Ashton Res. Sta.: 76-84.

Boussingault, J. B. 1844. Economie rurale. Béchet Jeune, Paris, 648 pp.

Boussingault, J. B. 1853. Sur la quantité d'ammoniaque contenue dans l'eau de pluie recueillie loin des villes. Compt. Rend. Acad. Sci. (Paris) 37:207-208.

Boussingault, J. B. (1856). In E. Heiden, ed. Lehrbuch der Düngerlehre. 2nd edition. Philipp Cohen, Hannover. p. 158. 1879.

Bower, C. A. 1950. Fixation of ammonium in difficultly exchangeable form under moist conditions by some soils of semi arid regions. Soil Sci. 70:375-383.

Bremner, J. M., and Shaw, K. 1958. Denitrification in soil. J. Agr. Sci. 51:22-39, 40-52.

Broadbent, F. E. 1948. Nitrogen release and carbon loss from soil organic matter during decomposition of added plant residues. Soil Sci. Soc. Amer. Proc. (1947) 12:246-249.

Broadbent, F. E., and Bartholomew, W. V. 1949. The effect of quantity of plant material added to soil on its rate of decomposition. Soil Sci. Soc. Amer. Proc. (1948) 13:271-274.

Broadbent, F. E., and Chapman, H. D. 1950. A lysimeter investigation of gains, losses and balance of salts and plant nutrients in an irrigated soil. Soil Sci. Soc. Amer. Proc. (1949) 14:261-269.

Broadbent, F. E., and Norman, A. G. 1947. Some factors affecting the availability of organic nitrogen in soil. A preliminary report. Soil Sci. Soc. Amer. Proc. (1946) 11:264-267.

Broadbent, F. E., Hill, G. W., and Tyler, K. B. 1958. Transformation and movement of urea in soils. Soil Sci. Soc. Amer. Proc. 22:303-307.

Brown, J. M., and Bartholomew, W. V. 1962. Sorption of anhydrous ammonia by dry clay systems. Soil Sci. Soc. Amer. Proc. 25:258-262.

Brown, P. E. 1916. Relation between certain bacterial activities in soils and their crop-producing power. J. Agr. Res. 5:855-869.

Burg, P. F. J. van. 1958. The influence of nitrogen applied in the autumn on grassland. (In Dutch). Agricult. Bureau Netherl. Nitrogen Fertilizers Industry, Mimeogr. Rep. B 27, 10 pp.

Burg, P. F. J. van. 1959. Top-dressing experiments with nitrogen on grain-crops and potatoes. (In Dutch). Agricult. Bureau Netherl. Nitrogen Fertilizers Industry, Mimeogr. Rep. B 63, 31 pp.

Burg, P. F. J. van. 1960. Influence of the amount and time of application of nitrogenous fertilizers on the growth-rate of grassland in the spring. (In Dutch). Strikstof no 29:187-194.

Burg, P. F. J. van. 1962. Internal nitrogen balance, production of dry matter and ageing of herbage and grass. (In Dutch.) Ph.D. thesis Wageningen, English Summary,

Butijn, J. 1961. Soil management in fruit culture. (In Dutch.) Ph.D. thesis, Wageningen. English Summary.

Cady, F. B., and Bartholomew, W. V. 1961. Influence of low pO_2 on denitrification processes and products. Soil Sci. Soc. Amer. Proc. 25:362-365.

Calder, E. A. 1957. Features of nitrate accumulation in Uganda soil. J. Soil Sci. 8:60-72.

Carpenter, R. W., Haas, H. J., and Miles, E. F. 1952. Nitrogen uptake by wheat in relation to nitrogen content of soil. Agron. J. 44:420-423.

Chaloust, R. 1948. Note sur le pouvoir ammonifiant des sables de la Camargue. Ann. Inst. Pasteur 74:62-66.

Chapman, H. D., and Liebig, G. F. 1952. Field and laboratory studies of nitrite accumulation in soils. Soil Sci. Soc. Amer. Proc. 16:276-292.

Chapman, H. D., Liebig, G. F., and Rayner, D. S. 1949. A lysimeter investigation of nitrogen gains and losses under various systems of cover cropping and fertilization and a discussion of error sources. Hilgardia 19:57-128.

Chu Chao-liang. 1960. Investigation of nitrogen supplying regime of soils. I Rate of liberation of ammonia in alkaline hydrolysis as an index for predicting nitrogen supplying status of rice fields. (In Chinese.) Acta Pedologica Sinica 10:55-72. English Summary.

Chung, C. W., and Najjar, V. A. 1956. A cofactor requirement for enzymatic denitrification. J. Biol. chem. 218:617-625.

Chyzevski, M. G., and Charuiskaya, L. P. 1958. On the results of investigation of the dynamics of some elements of soil fertility in crop rotations in the southern part of Kuban. (In Russian.) Pochvovedenië (Pedology) no 7:66-75. English Summary.

Clark, F. E., Beard, W. E., and Smith, D. H. 1960. Dissimilar nitrifying capacities of soils in relation to losses of applied nitrogen. Soil Sci. Soc. Amer. Proc. 24:50-54.

Clark, K. G., Yee, J. Y., Gaddy, V. L., and Lundstrom, F. O. 1956. Solubility relationships and nitrification characteristics of Urea-form. J. Agr. Food Chem. 4:135-140.

Collison, R. C., Beattie, H. G., and Harlan, J. D. 1933. Lysimeter investigations. III Mineral and water relations and final nitrogen balance in legume and non legume crop rotations for a period of 16 years. Geneva (N.Y.) Agr. Exp. Sta. Tech. Bul. 212. 81 pp.

Colman, E. A. 1946. A laboratory study of lysimeter drainage under controlled soil moisture tension. Soil Sci. 62:365-382.

Conway, E. J. 1950. Microdiffusion Analysis and Volumetric Error. Crosby Lockwood and Son, 3rd. ed. London.

Cook, F. D., Warder, F. G., and Daughty, J. L. 1957. Relationship of nitrate accumulation to yield response of wheat in some Saskatchewan soils. Canadian J. Soil Sci. 37:84-88.

Cooke, G. W., and Cunningham, R. K. 1957. Inorganic nitrogen in soils. Rothamsted Exp. Sta. Report 1956: 53-54.

Cornfield, A. H. 1952. The mineralization of the nitrogen of soils during incubation. Influence of pH, total nitrogen, and organic carbon contents. J. Sci. Food Agr. 3:343-349.

Cornfield, A. H. 1953. The mineralization of nitrogen in a soil acidified with sulphur, aluminum sulphate or ferrous sulphate. J. Sci. Food Agr. 4:298-301.

Cornfield, A. H. 1959. Mineralization during incubation of the organic nitrogen compounds in soils as related to soil pH. J. Sci. Food Agr. 10:27-28.

Cornfield, A. H. 1960. Ammonia released on treating soils with sodium hydroxide as a possible means of predicting the nitrogen-supplying power of soils. Nature 187:260-261.

Cornish, E. A. 1949. Yield trends in the wheat belt of South Australia during 1896-1941. Australian J. Sci. Res. ser. B 2:83-137.

Crowther, E. M., and Mirchandani, T. J. 1931. Winter leaching and manurial value of green manures and crop residues for winter wheat. J. Agr. Sci. 21:493-525.

Crowther, F. 1941. Form and data of nitrogenous manuring of cotton in the Sudan Gezira. Empire J. Exp. Agr. 9:125-136.

Cunningham, R. K. and Cooke, G. W. 1958. Soil nitrogen II. Changes in levels of inorganic nitrogen in a clay-loam soil caused by fertilizer additions, by leaching and uptake by grass. J. Sci. Food Agr. 9:317-324.

Cyplenkin, E. I., and Zjilin, D. G. 1936. On the nitrification in tundra soils. (In Russian.) Chemisation socialistic Agr. (U.S.S.R.) 5:59-63.

Czapek, F. 1896. Zur Lehre von den Wurzelausscheidungen. Jahrb. Wissenschaftl. Bot. 29:321-390.

Dalbro, S., and Nielsen, G. 1959. Soil nitrate investigations in orchards. (In Danish.) Tidsskr. Planteavl 62:1-25. English Summary.

Dalton, J. 1802. Experiments and observations to determine whether the quantity of rain and dew is equal to the quantity of water carried off by the rivers and raised by evaporation; with an inquiry into the origin of springs. Mem. Literary and Philosoph. Soc. Manchester 5, part II:346-372.

Dashevsky, L. I. 1960. Improvement of a method for determining exchangeable ammonia in soil (In Russian.) Pochvovedenië (Pedology) no 8:100-106. English Summary.

Delwiche, C. C. 1956. Denitrification. In W. D. McElroy and B. H. Glass, ed. Symposium on Inorganic Nitrogen Metabolism. Johns Hopkins Press, Baltimore. 233-259.

Dhar, N. R. 1935. Influence of light on some biochemical processes. Soc. Biol. Chem. (Indian Inst. Sci. Bangalore) 73 pp.

Dhar, N. R., and Plant, N. N. 1944. Nitrogen loss from soils and oxide surfaces. Nature 153:115-116.

Diamond, W. E. de B. 1937. Fluctuations in the nitrogen content of some Nigerian soils. I Fluctuations of nitric nitrogen. Empire J. Exp. Agr. 5:264-280.

Doak, B. W. 1952. Some chemical changes in the nitrogenous constituents of urine when voided on pasture. J. Agr. Sci. 42:162-171.

Doiarenko, A. G. 1955. Some urgent scientific research problems in the field of agronomy. (In Russian.) Pochvovedenië (Pedology) 1:12-15.

Doiarenko, A. G. 1958. The Life of the Field. (In Russian.) State Publish. Instit. Agric. Literature. Moscow.

Dommergues, Y. 1959. L'activité de la microflore tellurique au faibles humidités. Compt. Rend. Acad. Sci. (Paris) 248:487-490.

Doorn, Z. van. 1951. A hydrological observation on the lysimeters of the P.W.N. at Castricum. (In Dutch.) Water. 35:23-25. English Summary.

Dorph-Petersen, K. 1946. Experiments with farm manure and fertilizers at Lyngby 1910-1942. (In Danish.) Tidsskr. Planteavl. 50:555-616.

Doryland, C. J. T. 1916. The influence of energy material upon the relation of soil microorganisms to soluble plant food. North Dakota Agr. Exp. Sta. Bul. 116.

Drake, M., Vengris, G., and Colby, W. G. 1951. Cation-exchange capacity of plant roots. Soil Sci. 72:139-147.

Drouineau, G., Gouny, P. and Lefèvre, G. 1948. Sur la nitrification dans les sols calcaires. Compt. Rend. Acad. Sci. (Paris) 226:957-958.

Drouineau, G., and Lefèvre, G. 1949. Première contribution à l'étude de l'azote mineralisable dans les sols. Ann. Agron. 19:518-536.

Drouineau, G., and Lefèvre, G. 1951. Influence du climat mediterranéen sur la teneur en azote minéral dans les sols calcaires. Compt. Rend. Acad. Agr. (Paris) 37:200-204.

Dubber, H. J. 1955. Die Veränderung des Nitratgehaltes im Boden nach Zusatz von Stroh. Ph.D. thesis Hohenheim. 87 pp.

Eagle, D. J. and Matthews, B. C. 1958. Measurement of nitrate supplying power of soils by an incubation method and correlation with crop yield response. Canadian J. Soil Sci. 38:161-170.

Eggleton, W. G. E. 1934. Studies in the microbiology of grassland soil. J. Agr. Sci. 24:416-434.

Eggleton, W. G. E. 1935a. The nitrification of ammonia in the field and in laboratory incubation experiments. Ann. Appl. Biol. 22:419-430.

Eggleton, W. G. E. 1935b. The assimilation of inorganic nitrogenous salts, including sodium nitrite, by the grass plant. Biochem. J. 29:1389-1397.

Eggleton, W. G. E. 1935c. The nitrogen status of grassland soil. Trans. Intern. Cong. Soil Sci. 3rd Cong. London 1:216-217.

Ehrenberg, P. 1907. Die Bewegung des Ammoniakstickstoffs in der Natur. Paul Parey, Berlin. 254 pp.

Ehrenberg, P. 1911. Zur Frage der Ammoniakverdunstung bei gedüngtem Ackerboden. Fühlings Landw. Ztg. 60:441-452, 479-500.

Ehrenberg, P. 1912. Zur Ammoniakverdunstung aus Erdboden; gleichzeitig eine Ausführung über Stickstoffbilanz-Gefässversuche. Fühlings Landw. Ztg. 61:41-53.

Ehrhardt, F. 1961. Untersuchungen über den Einfluss des Klimas auf die Stickstoffnachlieferung von Waldhumus in verschiedenen Höhenlagen der Tiroler Alpen. Forstwissensch. Centralbl. 80:193-215.

Elgabaly, M. M., and Wiklander, L. 1949. Effect of exchange capacity of clay mineral and acidoid content of plant on uptake of sodium and calcium by excised barley and pea roots. Soil Sci. 67:419-424.

Enders, C. 1943. Über den Chemismus der Huminsäurebildung unter physiologischen Bedingungen. IV. Mitteilung: Die Rolle der Mikroorganismen bei den Humifizierungsvorgängen. Biochem. Z. 315:259-292.

Enders, C., and Segurdsson, S. 1942/1943. Über den Chemismus der Huminsäurebildung unter physiologischen Bedingungen. II. Mitteilung: Über das Vorkommen von Methylglyoxal in Erde. Biochem. Z. 313:174-181.

Eno, Ch. F. 1960. Nitrate production in the field by incubating the soil in polyethelene bags. Soil Sci. Soc. Amer. Proc. 24:277-279.

Eriksson, E. 1952. Composition of atmospheric precipitation. Tellus 4:215-232; 280-303.

Ernst, J. W., and Massey, H. F. 1960. The effect of several factors on volatilization of ammonia formed from urea in the soil. Soil Sci. Soc. Amer. Proc. 24:87-90.

Ferguson, W. G. 1957. Note on the effect of stubble and straw residues on the availability of nitrogen. Can. J. Soil Sci. 37:145-146.

Fisher, R. A. 1924. The influence of rainfall on the yield of wheat at Rothamsted. Phil. Trans. Roy. Soc. London, Ser. B 213:89-124.

Fitts, J. W., Bartholomew, W. V., and Heidel, H. 1953. Correlation between nitrifiable nitrogen and yield response of corn to nitrogen fertilization on Iowa soils. Soil Sci. Soc. Amer. Proc. 17:119-122.

Fitts, J. W., Bartholomew, W. V., and Heidel, H. 1955. Predicting nitrogen fertilizer needs of Iowa soils. I Evaluation and control of factors in nitrate production and analysis. Soil Sci. Soc. Amer. Proc. 19:69-73.

Frank, B. 1888. Untersuchungen über die Ernährung der Pflanze mit Stickstoff und über den Kreislauf desselben in der Landwirtschaft. Landwirtsch. Jahrb. 17:421-553.

Frankfurt, S. L., and Doushechkin, A. I. 1904. Investigation on the course of nitrification in the conditions of field-trials. (In Russian.) J. Sugar-Industry. (Russ.) 7, no. 50:870-874 and 7 continuations.

Fraps, G. S. 1912. Relation of soil nitrogen, nitrification and ammonification to pot experiments. Texas Agr. Exp. Sta. Bul. 151. 16 pp.

Fraps, G. S. 1920. Nitrification in Texas soils. Texas Agr. Exp. Sta. Bul. 259. 37 pp.

Fraps, G. S. 1921. Relation of soil nitrogen, nitrification and ammonification to pot experiments. Texas Agr. Exp. Sta. 283. 51 pp.

Fraps, G. S., and Sterges, A. J. 1939. Effect of phosphates on nitrifying capacity of soils. Soil Sci. 47:115-121.

Fraps, G. S., and Sterges, A. J. 1947. Nitrification capacities of Texas soil types and factors which affect nitrification. Texas Agr. Exp. Sta. Bul. 693. 60 pp.

Frederick, L. R. 1956. The formation of nitrate from ammonium nitrogen in soils. I Effects of temperature. Soil Sci. Soc. Amer. Proc. 20:496-500.

Frederick, L. R. 1957. The formation of nitrate from ammonium nitrogen in soils. II Effect of population of nitrifiers. Soil Sci. 83:481-485.

Gainey, P. L. 1917. The significance of nitrification as a factor in soil fertility. Soil Sci. 3:399-416.

Gainey, P. L. 1936. Total nitrogen as a factor influencing nitrate accumulation in soils. Soil Sci. 42:157-163.

Gainey, P. L. and Metzler L. F. 1917. Some factors affecting nitrate nitrogen accumulation in soil. J. Agr. Res. 11:43-64.

Gainey, P. L., Sewell, M. C., and Myers, H. E. 1937. Nitrogen—the major cause in the production of spotted wheat fields. Kansas Agr. Exp. Sta. Tech. Bul. 43. 58 pp.

Gardner, W. R., and Brooks, R. H. 1957. A descriptive theory of leaching. Soil Sci. 83:295-304.

Gardner, W. R., and Fireman, M. 1958. Laboratory studies of evaporation from soil columns in the presence of a water table. Soil Sci. 58:244-249.

Gasser, J. K. R. 1959. Soil nitrogen IV. Transformations and movement of fertilizer nitrogen in a light soil. J. Sci. Food Agr. 10:192-197.

Gasser, J. K. R. 1961. Transformation, leaching and uptake of fertilizer nitrogen applied in autumn and spring to winter wheat on a heavy soil. J. Sci. Food Agr. 12:375-380.

Gasser, J. K. R. 1962. Effect of long continued treatment on the mineral nitrogen content and mineralisable nitrogen of soil from selected plots of the Broadbalk experiment on continuous wheat, Rothamsted. Plant and Soil 17:209-220.

Gasser, J. K. R. and Williams, R. J. B. 1962. Soil nitrogen. VII. Correlation between measurements of nitrogen status of soils and nitrogen % and nitrogen content of crops. Symposium J.S.F.A., Bristol.

Gassner, G., and Goeze, G. 1936. Einige Versuche und ein Vorschlag zur Bestimmung des aufnehmbaren Bodenstickstoffs. Z. Pflanzenernähr., Düng., Bodenk. 42:263-276.

Gayon, E., and Dupetit, G. 1886. Recherches sur la reduction des nitrates par les infiniments petits. Soc. Sci. Phys. Nat. Bordeaux, ser. 3.2:201-307.

Geering, J. 1943. Lysimeter-Versuche. Landw. Jahrb. Schweiz 57:107-182.

Geiger, R. 1961. Das Klima der bodennahen Luftschicht. 4th ed. Friedr. Vieweg und Sohn, Braunschweig. 121 pp.

Gericke, S. 1947. Untersuchungen über das Ertragsgesetz. III. Z. Pflanzenernähr. Düng., Bodenk. 39 (84):245-258.

Gerretsen, F. C. 1921. Investigation of nitrification and denitrification in tropical soils. (In Dutch.) Archief Suikerind. Ned. Indië. 29:1397-1532.

Gerretsen, F. C. 1942. Some observations on the influence of the temperature on the nitrification and immobilization of nitrogen. (In Dutch.) Landbouwk. Tijdschr. 54:313-383.

Gerretsen, F. C. 1948/1949. The nitrogen balance and changes in pH in some soils as influenced by microbes and plant growth. (In Dutch.) Versl. Landbouwk. Onderz. 54:68 pp. English Summary.

Gerretsen, F. C. 1950. Microbiological transformation of nitrogen and its influence on nitrogen availability in the soil. Trans. Intern. Congr. Soil Sci. 4th Cong. Amsterdam 2:114-117.

Gerretsen, F. C., and Hoop, H. de. 1957. Nitrogen losses during nitrification in solutions and in acid sandy soils. Canad. J. Microbiol. 3:359-380.

Gilmour, C. M., Teresa, G., and Bollen, W. B. 1957. Determination of soil nitrogen losses in Palouse soils. Bact. Proc. 57:9(A3).

Gliemeroth, G. 1958. Stickstoffverlagerung über Winter in Abhängigkeit von der Wasserführung eines Lösslehmbodens. Z. Acker- und Pflanzenbau 107:129-146.

Gliemeroth, G. 1959. Stickstoffverlagerung über Winter auf einem Lösslehm in Abhängigkeit von Form, Menge, Termin und Verteilung der Herbstdüngung. Z. Pflanzenernähr. Düng., Bodenk. 85:20-31.

Gleuckauf, E. 1949. Theory of chromatography. VI Precision measurements of adsorption and exchange isotherms from column elution data. J. Chem. Soc. part IV no 687:3280-3285.

Goring, C. A. I., and Clark, F. E. 1949. Influence of crop growth on mineralization of nitrogen in the soil. Soil Sci. Soc. Amer. Proc. (1948) 13:261-266.

Greaves, J. E., and Carter, E. G. 1920. The influence of moisture on the bacterial activities of the soil. Soil Sci. 10:361-387.

Greaves, J. E., Stewart, R., and Hirst, C. T. 1917. Influence of crop, season, and water on the bacterial activities of the soil. J. Agr. Res. 9:293-341.

Greene, H. 1935. Soil nitrates in the Sudan. Trans. Intern. Cong. Soil Sci. 3rd. Cong. Oxford 1:217-219.

Greenland, D. J. 1958. Nitrate fluctuations in tropical soils. J. Agr. Sci. 50:82-92.

Greenwood, D. J. 1962. Nitrification and nitrate dissimilation in soil. Plant and Soil 17:365-391.

Griffith, G.ap. 1951. Factors influencing nitrate accumulation in Uganda soil. Empire J. Exp. Agr. 19:1-12.

Griffith, G.ap., and Manning, H. L. 1949. A note on nitrate accumulation in an Uganda soil. Tropical Agr. 26:108-110.

Hagenzieker, F. 1957. Soil nitrogen studies at Urambo, Tanganyika Territory, East Africa. Plant and Soil 9:97-113.

Hagin, J., and Shmueli, E. 1960. Determination of available nutrients and fertilizer requirements of winter tomatoes in the Jordan valley. KTAVIM Quart. J. Nation. and Univ. Inst. Agr. 10:43-52.

Hagin, J., Rovikovitch, S., and Halevy, J. 1959. Methods of estimating available plant nutrients in the soil and determination of requirements: I Irrigated hybrid corn. KTAVIM Records of Agr. Res. Sta. 9:209-218.

Hall, T. D. 1924. Nitrification in some South African soils II. Soil Sci. 18:219-235.

Hallam, M. J., and Bartholomew, W. V. 1953. Influence of rate of plant residue addition in accelerating the decomposition of soil organic matter. Soil Sci. Soc. Amer. Proc. 17:365-368.

Hansen, F. 1928. Nitrogen transformation in field soils. (In Danish.) Tidsskr. Planteavl 34:741-777. 1929; 35:713-753 English Summary.

Hanway, J., and Dumenil, L. 1955. Predicting nitrogen fertilizer needs of Iowa soils: III Use of nitrate productions together with other information as a basis for making nitrogen fertilizer recommendation for corn in Iowa. Soil Sci. Soc. Amer. Proc. 19:77-80.

Hardy, F. 1946a. Seasonal fluctuations of soil moisture and nitrate in a humid tropical climate. Tropical Agr. 23:40-49.

Hardy, F. 1946b. The significance of carbon-nitrogen ratio in soils growing cotton. III Nitrate fluctuations in relation to planting data and soil manurial requirements in the British West Indies. Tropical Agr. 23:201-211.

Harmsen, G. W. 1932. Microbiological analyses of the soil in the experimental polder at Andijk 1927-1931. (In Dutch.) Commissie Advies Landbouwtechn. Aangelegenh. Proefpolder Andijk, Meded. II:279-334.

Harmsen, G. W. 1935. The microbiology of the soils in the Zuiderzee polders. (In Dutch.) Landbouwk. Tijdschrift 47:852-875.

Harmsen, G. W. 1951. Die Bedeutung der Bodenoberfläche für die Humusbildung. Plant and Soil 3:110-140.

Harmsen, G. W. 1955. Microbes in the young soils. (In Dutch.) In: Directie Wieringermeer, ed. Origin and Development of the Wieringermeer Polder. H. Veenman en zonen, Wageningen: 116-128. English Summary.

Harmsen, G. W. 1956. Inquiry into the possibility of an analytical estimation of the nitrogen fertilization requirement of soil. Intern. Cong. Soil Sci. 6th Cong. Paris Rep. D.:457-463.

Harmsen, G. W. 1958. Some considerations on the instability of humus, having special regard to the recently reclaimed soils of the Wieringermeer and the North-Eastern Polder. (In Dutch.) Van Zee tot Land 26:14-25. English Summary.

Harmsen, G. W. 1959. Was kann uns die Bestimmung des Gehaltes löslichen Stickstoffs im Boden lehren? Z. Pflanzenernähr., Düng, Bodenk. 84:98-102.

Harmsen, G. W. 1961. Einfluss von Witterung, Düngung und Vegetation auf den Stickstoffgehalt des Bodens. Landw. Forschung SH 15:61-74.

Harmsen, G. W. 1962. Agricultural and pedological problems concerning the nitrogen in soil. (In Dutch.) Landbouwk. Tijdschr. 74:505-519. English Summary.

Harmsen, G. W., and Jager, G. 1962. Determination of the quantity of carbon and nitrogen in the rhizosphere of young plants. Nature 195:1119-1120.

Harmsen, G. W., and Lindenbergh, D. J. 1949. Investigations on the nitrogen nutrition of plants. Plant and Soil 2:1-29.

Harmsen, G. W., and Schreven, D. A. van. 1955. Mineralization of organic nitrogen in soil. *In:* A. G. Norman ed. Advances in Agronomy, Academic Press Inc., N. Y. 7:299-398.

Harpstead, M. I., and Brage, B. L. 1958. Storage of soil samples and its effect upon the subsequent accumulation of nitrate nitrogen during controlled incubation. Soil Sci. Soc. Amer. Proc. 22: 326-328.

Headden, W. P. 1910. The fixation of nitrogen in some Colorado soils. Colorado Agr. Exp. Sta. Bul. 155. 48 pp.; 1911; 178. 32 pp.

Hesselman, H. 1916-1917. Studies on the formation of nitrate in virgin soils and its effect on plant-ecology. (In Swedish.) Meddel. Statens Skogsförsöksanstalt 13/14:297-528. German Summary.

Hilgard, E. W. 1906. Soils, Their Formation, Properties, Composition and Relation to Climate and Plant growth in the Humid Regions. The MacMillan Co., New York. 593 pp.

Hill, R. G. jr. 1952. Sod as a soil management practice for peaches. Proc. Ohio. Hort. Soc.:104-110.

Hiltbold, A. E., Bartholomew, W. V., and Werkman, C. H. 1951. The use of tracer techniques in the simultaneous measurement of mineralization and immobilization of nitrogen in soil. Soil Sci. Soc. Amer. Proc. (1950) 15:166-173.

Hirschler, A. 1886. Über den Einfluss der Kohlehydrate und einiger anderer Körper der Fettsäurereihe auf die Eiweissfäulniss. Z. Phys. Chem. 10:306-317.

Hudig, J., and Welt, H. 1911. The drainage field trial at Uithuizermeeden during the years 1900-1910. (In Dutch.) Versl. Landbouwk. Onderz. 10:124 pp.

Hwang, Y., and Frank, M. 1938. Microbiological and biochemical investigations of the two maxima in the increase of ammonia in soils. Arch Mikrobiol. 9:469-476.

Ishizuke, I., and Tanaka, A. 1955. A proposed method to determine adequate amounts of fertilizers to be applied to crops. Soil Plant Food 1:5-6.

Ivarson, K. C., and Sowden, F. J. 1959. Decomposition of forest litters. I Production of ammonia and nitrate nitrogen, changes in microbial population, and rate of decomposition. Plant and Soil. 11:237-248.

Iwasaki, H., and Mori, T. 1958. Studies on denitrification III. J. Biochem. (Tokyo) 45:133-140.

Janisch, E. 1962. Biomathematische Gesetzmässigkeiten für die Tempera turabhängigkeit der Oxydationsleistung nitrifizierender Baktërien. Zentralblatt Bakteriol., Parasietenk., Infektionskrankh. 115:748-765.

Jansson, S. L. 1952. The small nitrogen cycle. (In Swedish.) Växt-näringsnytt 8-9:16-20.

Jansson, S. L. 1955. Orientierende Studien über den Stickstoffkreislauf im Boden mit Hilfe von N¹⁵ als Leitisotop. Z. Pflanzenernähr., Düng. Bodenk. 69:190-198.

Jansson, S. L. 1958. Tracer studies on nitrogen transformations in soil with special attention to mineralization-immobilization relationships. Kungl. Lantbrukshögskolans Ann. 24:101-361.

Jansson, S. L., and Clark, F. E. 1952. Losses of nitrogen during decomposition of plant material in the presence of inorganic nitrogen. Soil Sci. Soc. Amer. Proc. 16:330-334.

Jansson, S. L., Hallam, M. J., and Bartholomew, W. V. 1955. Preferential utilization of ammonium over nitrate by micro-organisms in the decomposition of oat straw. Plant and Soil 6:382-390.

Jenny, H. 1941. Factors of Soil Formation. McGraw-Hill, New York. 278 pp.

Jenny, H. 1950. Causes of the high nitrogen and organic matter content of certain tropical forest soils. Soil Sci. 69:63-69.

Jenny, H., Gessel, S. P., and Bingham, F. T. 1949. Comparative study of decomposition rates of organic matter in temperate and tropical regions. Soil Sci. 68:419-432.

Jensen, H. L. 1934. Contributions to the microbiology of Australian soils. Linnean Soc. New South Wales Proc. 59:101-117.

Jensen, H. L. 1940. Contribution to the nitrogen economy of Australian wheat soils, with particular reference to New South Wales. Linnean Soc. New South Wales Proc. 65:1-221.

Jensen, H. L. 1952. On the microbiological decomposition of farmyard manure. I Nitrification of the organic fraction in soil. (In Danish.) Tidsskr. Planteavl 55:237-264. English Summary.

Jewitt, T. N. 1942. Loss of ammonia from ammonium sulfate applied to alkaline soils. Soil Sci. 54:401-409.

Jewett, T. N. 1945. Nitrification in Sudan Gezira soil. J. Agr. Sci. 35:264-271.

Jewitt, T. N. 1950. Field nitrates in Gezira soil. J. Agr. Sci. 40: 160-165.

Jewitt, T. N. 1956. Field nitrate in the Gezira soil II. J. Agr. Sci. 47:461-467.

Jewitt, T. N., and Barlow, H. W. B. 1949. Animal excreta in the Sudan Gezira. Empire J. Exp. Agr. 17:1-17.

Jones, E. J. 1951. Loss of elemental nitrogen from soils under anaerobic conditions. Soil Sci. 71:193-196.

Jones, T. 1956. Carbon and nitrogen studies in the arid irrigated soil of the Sudan Gezira. Trans. Intern. Cong. Soil Sci. 6th. Cong. Paris 13:417-426.

Joshi, N. V., and Biswas, S. C. 1948. Does photo-nitrification occur in the soil? Indian J. Agr. Sci. 18:115-129.

Jung, J. 1960. Über die Nährstoffanlieferung aus mit Kunststoff amhüllten Düngergranulaten. Z. Pflanzenern. Düng. Bodenk. 91:122-130.

Jung, J. 1961. Über die Wirkung von Crotonylidendiharnstoff (CD-Harnstoff) als Stickstoffdünger. Plant and Soil 15:284-290.

Kaila, A., Köylijärvi, J., and Kivinen, E. 1953. Influence of temperature upon the mobilization of nitrogen in peat. J. Sci. Agr. Soc. Finland 25:37-46.

Kaila, A., and Soini, S. 1957. Influence of lime on the accumulation of mineral nitrogen in incubation experiments of peat soil. J. Sci. Agr. Soc. Finland 29:229-237.

Kapp, L. C. 1933. Study of rice fertilization. Arkansas Agr. Exp. Sta. Bul. 291:13-14.

Kappen, H., Hofer, J., and Grosse-Brauckmann, E. 1949. Über die Wirkung des Hüttenkalkes auf die Zerstörung der organischen Stoffe des Bodens und über eine einfache Methode zu ihrer Bestimmung. Z. Pflanzenernähr., Düng., Bodenk. 44:6-33.

Kappen, H., Scheng-Tscheng-Jen, Nickolay, W., and Wienhues, W. 1943. Zur Verflüchtigung von Ammoniak aus Lösungen von Ammonsalzen. Bodenkunde, Pflanzenernähr. 31:223-244.

Kellerman, K. F., and Allen, E. R. 1911. Bacteriological studies of the soil of the Truckee-Carson irrigation project. USDA Bur. Plant Ind. Bul. 211. 33 pp.

King, F. H., and Whitson, A. R. 1901. Development and distribution of nitrates and other soluble salts in cultivated soils. Wisconsin Agr. Exp. Sta. Bul. 85. 48 pp.

King, F. H., and Whitson, A. R. 1902. Development and distribution of nitrates in cultivated soils. Wisconsin Agr. Exp. Sta. Bul. 93. 41 pp.

Kirkham, D. 1956. Mathematical aspects of soil nitrogen studies. In: A conference on Radioactive Isotopes in Agriculture. Atomic Energy Commission Rep. N° TJD-7512:349-359.

Kirkham, D., and Bartholomew, W. V. 1955. Equations for following nutrient transformations in soil, utilizing tracer data. I. Soil Sci. Soc. Amer. Proc. 18:33-34. 1954; 19:189-192.

Kivekäs, J., and Kivinen, E. 1959. Observations on the mobilization of peat nitrogen in incubation experiments. J. Sci. Agr. Soc. Finland 31:268-281.

Kivinen, E., and Kaila, A. 1958. Peat as a source of nitrogen for plants in pot culture. J. Sci. Agr. Soc. Finland 30:223-232.

Kluijver, A. J., and Verhoeven, W. 1954. True dissimilatory nitrate reduction. Antonie van Leeuwenhoek 20:241-262; 339-358.

Kohnke, H., Dreibellis, F. R., and Davidson, J. M. 1940. A survey and discussion of lysimeters and a bibliography on their construction and performance. USDA Misc. Pub. 372. 68 pp.

Köhnlein, J., and Vetter, H. 1953a. Ernterückstände und Wurzelbild. Paul Parey, Hamburg-Berlin. 138 pp.

Köhnlein, J., and Vetter, H. 1953b. Die Stalldüngerrotte bei steigender Stroheinstreu. Z. Pflanzenernähr., Düng., Bodenk. 63:119-141.

Kolenbrander, G. J. 1961. Leaching of nitrogen. (In Dutch.) De Fruitteelt 51:602-603.

Koudriawtseva, A. 1925. Accumulation of nitrate in the soil by tillage. (In Russian.) J. Agr. Sci. (Russ.) 2. no 4:261-302.

Krassilnikov, N. A. 1934. Influence of root-secretion on the development of *Azotobacter* and other soil microbes. (In Russian.) Microbiologia (Microbiology) 3:343-359.

Kresge, C. B., and Merkle, F. G. 1957. A study of the validity of laboratory techniques in appraising the available nitrogen producing capacity of soil. Soil Sci. Soc. Amer. Proc. 21:516-521.

Kresge, C. B., and Satchell, D. P. 1960. Gaseous loss of ammonia from nitrogen fertilizers applied to soil. Agron. J. 52:104-107.

Kuntze, H. 1959. Der Einfluss von Harnstoff-Acetaldehyd-Kondensaten auf die Nährstoffaufnahme der Pflanzen. Z. Pflanzenernähr., Düng., Bodenk. 86:206-214.

Lawes, J. B. 1889. The history of a field newly laid down to permanent grass. J. Royal Agr. Soc. England 2nd ser. 25:1-24.

Leather, J. W. 1909. *In:* Burt, B. C. Experiments under nitrogen investigations. I: Drain gauge—Amount and composition of drainage water collected during the year 1907-08. Cawnpore Agr. Sta. Rep. 1909:22-26.

Leather, J. W. 1911. Records of drainage in India. Drain-gauge records at Cawnpore, 1903-1910, and at Pusa, 1906-1910. Mem. Dep. Agr. India, Chem. Scr. 2:62-140.

Lees, H. 1948. The effect of various organic materials on soil nitrification, Bioch. J. 42:528-531.

Lefevre, G., and Drouineau, G. 1951. Variations saisonnieres de la teneur en azote mineral dans un sol calcaire soumis au climat mediterraneen. Ann. Agron. 21:1-12.

Lefevre G., and Hiroux, G. 1958. Essai de bilan de la production d'azote mineral d'un sol en place. Ann. Agron. Ser. A. 9:23-50.

Lefcvre, G., and Hiroux, G. 1960. Considerations sur la mineralization et l'utilization des reserves azotees du sol. Ann. Agron. Ser. A.: 135-162.

Lehr, J. J. 1950. Differences in the recovery of nitrogen from ammoniacal and nitrate sources in the reclaimed polders of the Zuider Sea. Plant and Soil 2:345-358.

Lehr, J. J. and Veen, B. 1952. Nitrogen economy of the soil in relation to seasonal and periodical climatic variations. Internat. Soc. Soil Sci. Trans. Dublin 1952, II:61-67.

Lehr, J. J. and Wesemael, J. C. 1961. The volatilization of ammonia from lime-rich soils. (In Dutch.). Landbouwk. Tijdschr. 73:1156-1168.

Lehr, J. J., Wijbenga, J. M., and Hoekendijk, J. A. 1962. On the influence of nitrogen on the formation of chlorophyll with special regard to a difference in effect between sodium nitrate and calcium nitrate. Plant and Soil 17:68-86.

Lemmermann, O. 1919. Untersuchungen über verschiedene Düngungsfragen. Arb. Deutsch. Landw. Gesell. Heft 297. 198 pp.

Lemmermann, O., and Fresenius, L. 1913. Beitrag zur Frage der Ammoniakverdunstung aus Boden. Landw. Jahrb. 45:127-154.

Leutenegger, F. 1956. Changes in the ammonia and nitrate contents of a tropical red loam as influenced by manuring and mulching during a period of one year. East Afr. Agr. J. 22:81-87.

Liebig, J. von. 1862. Die Chemie in ihrer Anwendung auf Agricultur und Physiologie. Friedrich Vieweg und Sohn, Braunschweig, Ed. 7 part II 325 pp.

Liechti, P. and Ritter, E. 1910. Über das Entweichen von Ammoniak aus Gülle während und nach dem Ausbringen derselben. Landwirtsch. Jahrb. Schweiz 24:481-525.

Lindhard, A. J. 1954. Investigations on losses of nitrogen by evaporation from samples of cow manure. (In Danish.) Tidsskr. Planteavl 57:108-120. English Summary.

Linser, H., Mayr, H. H., and Unzeitig, H. 1959. Untersuchungen über die Wanderung von Ionen in Bodensäulen. Z. Pflanzenernähr., Düng., Bodenk. 86:57-65.

Lipman, C. B., Burgers, P. S., and Klein, M. A. 1916. Comparison of the nitrifying powers of some humid and some arid soils. J. Agr. Res. 7:47-82.

Livens, J. 1959. Contribution a l'etude de l'azote mineralisable. Agricultura (Louvain) 7:27-44.

Livens, J. 1960. Observations about variations in nitrogen content as influenced by crop rotation. (In Dutch.) Agricultura (Louvain) 8:61-76. English Summary.

Ljones, B. 1958. Experiments on soil cultivation and nitrogen application in orchards, 1951-1956. (In Norwegian.) Forskn. Forsk. Landbr. 9:453-471. English Summary.

Lochhead, A. G. 1958. The soil microflora, the plant, and the root pathogen. Trans. Royal. Soc. Canada 52 Sect. V:17-24.

Loewenstein, H., Englebert, L. E., Attoe, O. A., and Allen, O. N. 1957. Nitrogen loss in gaseous form from soils as influenced by fertilizers and management. Soil Sci. Soc. Amer. Proc. 21:397-400.

Löhnis, F. 1910. Handbuch der landwirtschaftlichen Bakteriologie. Gebrüder Borntraeger, Berlin. 905 pp.

Löhnis, F. 1926a. Nitrogen availability of green manure. Soil Sci. 22:253-290.

Löhnis, F., and Blobel, E. 1908. Die Ursache der Wirkungsunterschiede von schwefelsaurem Ammoniak und Chilisalpeter. Fühlings Landw. Ztg. 57:385-402.

Lyon, T. L., and Bizzell, J. A. 1918. Lysimeter experiments. Records for tanks 1 to 12 during the years 1910 to 1914 inclusive. Cornell Agr. Exp. Sta. Mem. 12. 115 pp.

Lyon, T. L., and Bizzell, J. A. 1936. Lysimeter experiments. IV Records for tanks 17 to 20 during the years 1922-1933 and for tanks 13 to 16 during the years 1913-1928. Cornell Univ. Agr. Exp. Sta. Mem. 194. 59 pp.

Lyon, T. L., Bizzell, J. A., and Wilson, B. D. 1920. The formation of nitrates in a soil following the growth of red clover and of Timothy. Soil Sci. 9:53-64.

Lyon, T. L., Bizzell, J. A., Wilson, B. D., and Leland, E. W. 1930. Lysimeter experiments III. Records for tank 3 to 12 during the years 1910 to 1924 inclusive. Cornell Agr. Exp. Sta. Mem. 134. 70 pp.

Lyon, T. L., and Wilson, J. R. 1921. Liberation of organic matter by roots of growing plants. Cornell Agr. Exp. Sta. Mem. 40. 44 pp.

Maasz, G. 1961. Untersuchungen über den Einfluss von Ammoniak- und Nitratdünger auf den Gehalt an mineralischem Stickstoff im Boden. Z. Pflanzenernähr. Düng., Bodenk. 93:26-38.

Malik, M. N. 1960. The contribution of soil nitrogen to the nitrogen requirements of crops on Florida soils. Ph.D. thesis. University of Florida.

Marggraf. 1761. In Miller, N. H. J. The amounts of nitrogen as ammonia and as nitric acid, and of chlorine in the rainwater collected at Rothamsted. J. Agr. Sci. 1:280-303. 1905-6.

Marshall, T. J. 1959. Relation between water and soil. Commonwealth Bureau of Soils. Harpenden Tech. Commun. 50:51-54.

Martin, A. E. 1949. Nitrification studies in temporary grassland soils using a perfusion technique. J. Brit. Grassland Soc. 4:161-182.

Martin, A. E., and Cox, J. E. 1956. Nitrogen studies on black soils from the Darling Downs, Queensland. II The nitrifying activity of subsurface horizons. Austral. J. Agr. Res. 7:184-193.

Martin, A.P.J., and Synge, R. L. M. 1941. A new form of chromatogram employing two liquid phases. Biochem. J. 35:1358-1368.

Martin, J. P., and Chapman, H. D. 1951. Volatilization of ammonia from surface-fertilized soils. Soil Sci. 71:25-34.

Martin, T. S. 1925. Effect of straw on accumulation of nitrates and crop growth. Soil Sci. 20:159-164.

Martin, W. P., Buehrer, T. F., and Caster, A. B. 1943. Threshold pH value for the nitrification of ammonia in desert soils. Soil Sci. Soc. Amer. Proc. (1942) 7:223-228.

Maschhaupt, J. G. 1938. Lysimeter investigations at Groningen and elsewhere. I Rainfall, drainage and evaporation. (In Dutch.) Versl. Landbouwk. Onderz. 44:1-184. English Summary.

Maschhaupt, J. G. 1941. Lysimeter investigations at Groningen and elsewhere. II. The chemical composition of the drainage-water. (In Dutch.) Versl. Landbouwk. Onderz. 47:165-528. English Summary.

Maschhaupt, J. G. 1949. Lysimeter investigations at Groningen. III Rainfall, drainage and evaporation 1918-1946. (In Dutch.) Versl. Landbouwk. Onderz. 55. 40 pp. English Summary.

McCool, M. M. 1947. Nitrogen availability in soils as measured by growth response of rye-grass and *Cunninghamella Blakesleeana*. Boyce Thompson Inst. Contr. 14:363-368.

McDonald, Iain. 1957. The influence of some crops and crop residues on the organic matter status of certain North Carolina soils. Ph.D. thesis. North Carolina State College, Raleigh, N. C.

McGarity, J. W., Gilmour, C. M., and Bollen, W. B. 1958. Use of electrolytic respirometer to study denitrification in soil. Canadian J. Microbiol. 4:303-316.

McIntosh, T. H., and Frederick, L. R. 1958. Distribution and nitrification of anhydrous ammonia in a Nicollet sandy clay loam. Soil Sci. Soc. Amer. Proc. 22:402-405.

Meiklejohn, Jane. 1953a. The microbiological aspects of soil nitrification with special reference to the Kawanda experiment on nitrate accumulation. East Afr. Agr. J. 19:54-56.

Meiklejohn, Jane. 1953b. The nitrifying bacteria: a review. J. Soil Sci. 4:59-68.

Micah, W. M. L. 1960. Determinations of potentially available nitrogen in soil by acid hydrolysis. Ph.D. thesis. Rutgers Univ.

Michniewicz, M. 1951. The processes of nitrification and denitrification in the soils of Bialowieza Wilds. (In Polish.) Ann. Univ. Mariae Curie-Sklodowska. Lublin, Polonia 6, Sect. C: 19-75.

Miller, N. H. J. 1906. The amount and composition of the drainage through unmanured and uncropped land, Barnfield, Rothamsted. J. Agr. Sci. 1:377-399.

Mills, W. R. 1953/'54. Nitrate accumulation in Uganda soils. East African Agr. J. 19:53-54.

Minderhoud, J. W. 1960. Growth of grass and ground-water level. (In Dutch.) Ph.D. thesis, Wageningen. English Summary.

Mokin, N. N. 1926. Observations about accumulation and displacement of nitrate in a 4-crop rotation. (In Russian.) Proc. Agr. Exp. Sta. for the Don- and Northern Caucasus-Area. no. 9.

Molen, W. H. van der. 1956. Desalinization of saline soils as a column process. Soil Sci. 81:19-27.

Molen, W. H. van der. 1958. The exchangeable cations in soils flooded with sea water. Ph.D. thesis, Wageningen.

Mooers, C. A., MacIntire, W. H. and Young, J. B. 1927. The recovery of soil nitrogen under various conditions as measured by lysimeters of different depths. Tennessee Agr. Exp. Sta. Bul. 138. 30 pp.

Moore, D. G. 1960. Nitrogen movement in soil as affected by time of application, form of nitrogen and fixation. Ph.D. thesis, University of Wisconsin. 100 pp.

Morrill, L. G. 1959. An explanation of the nitrification patterns observed when soils are perfused with ammonium sulphate. Ph.D. thesis, Cornell University.

Munson, R. D., and Stanford, G. 1955. Predicting nitrogen fertilizer needs of Iowa soils. IV Evaluation of nitrate production as a criterion of nitrogen availability. Soil Sci. Soc. Amer. Proc. 19:464-468.

Muzychkin, E. T. 1959. Perennial herbage as a means of restoring the fertility of irrigated Cis-caucasian chernozems. (In Russian.) Pochvovedenië (Pedology) no. 12:13-23. English Summary.

Najjar, V. A., and Allen, M. B. 1954. Formation of nitrogen, nitrous oxide and nitric oxyde by extracts of denitrifying bacteria. J. Biol. Chem. 206:209-214.

Nelson, C. E. 1953. Methods of applying nitrate fertilizer on field corn and a study of the movement of NH_4^+—and NO_3^-—nitrogen in the soil under irrigation. Agron. J. 45:154-157.

Neubauer, H. 1946. Die Ausdehnung der Keimpflanzenmethode auf die Stickstoffbestimmung im Boden und in Komposterden. Z. Pflanzenernähr., Düng., Bodenk. 37 (82):97-110

Newton, J. D., Joung, R. S., and Malloch, J. G. 1939a. Nitrification under and after alfalfa, brome, timothy, and Western rye-grass. I Nitrogen absorption of hay crops and succeeding wheat crops. Canadian J. Res. 17 C:212-231.

Newton, J. D., Wyatt, F. A., Ignatieff, V., and Ward, A. S. 1939b. Nitrification under and after alfalfa, brome, timothy and Western rye-grass. II Soil microbiological activity. Canadian J. Res. 17 C:256-293.

Nightingale, G. F. 1948. The nitrogen nutrition of green plants. Botan. Rev. 14:185-221.

Nõmmik, H. 1956. Investigations on denitrification in soil. Acta Agr. Scand. 6:195-228.

Nõmmik, H. 1957. Fixation and defixation of ammonium in soils. Acta. Agr. Scand. 7:395-436.

Nõmmik, H., and Varlin, B. 1960. Volatilization losses of ammonia as a result of surface application of ammonium nitrate limestone. Kungl. Lantbr. Högsk. Ann. 26:303-316.

Norman, A. G. 1943. Problems in the chemistry of soil organic matter. Soil Sci. Soc. Amer. Proc. (1942) 7:7-15.

Norman, A. G., and Werkman, C. H. 1943. The use of the nitrogen isotope N^{15} in determining nitrogen recovery from plant materials decomposing in soil. J. Amer. Soc. Agr. 35:1023-1025.

Ogata, G., and Caldwell, A. C. 1960. Nitrate content of soils and nitrogen content of oat plants as affected by rates of liming. Agr. J. 52:65-68.

Olden, E. van. 1940. Manometric investigations on bacterial denitrification. Proc. Koninkl. Acad. Wetensch. 43:635-644.

Owens, L. D. 1960. Nitrogen movement and transformations in soils as evaluated by a lysimeter study utilizing isotopic nitrogen. Soil Sci. Soc. Amer. Proc. 24:372-376.

Paauw, F. van der. 1959. Nitrogen requirement of crops in dependence on rainfall in the preceding winter. (In Dutch.) Landbouwk. Tijdschr. 71:679-689. English summary.

Paauw, F. van der. 1962a. Effect of winter rainfall on the amount of nitrogen available to crops. Plant and Soil 16:351-380.

Paauw, F. van der. 1962b. Periodic fluctuations of soil fertility, crop yields, and of responses to fertilization effected by alternating periods of low or high rainfall. Plant and Soil 17:155-182.

Palmer, E. F., and Haarlem, J. R. van. 1944. Orchard soil management. Ontario Dep. Agr. Bul. 437, 15 pp.

Panganiban, E. H. 1925. Temperature as a factor in nitrogen changes in the soil. J. Amer. Soc. Agr. 17:1-32.

Parbery, N. H. 1945. The effect of dolomite on nitrification in strongly acid red basaltic soils. Agr. Gaz. New South Wales 56:543-544.

Pathak, A. N., and Schrikhande, J. G. 1953. Optimum temperature for nitrification and nitrogen fixation. J. Indian Soc. Soil Sci. 1:131-136.

Payne, T. M. B., Rouatt, J. W., and Katzelson, H. 1956. Detection of free amino acids in soil. Soil Sci. 82:521-524.

Peevy, W. J., and Norman, A. G. 1948. Influence of composition of plant materials on properties of the decomposed residues. Soil Sci. 65:209-226.

Penman, F. 1949. Effects on Victorian soils of various crop rotation systems with particular reference to changes in nitrogen and organic matter under cereal cultivation. Brit. Commonwealth Sci. Off. Conf. Australia, Session D. 11 pp.

Peterson, L. A., Attoe, O. J., and Ogden, W. B. 1960. Correlation of nitrogen soil tests with nitrogen uptake by the tobacco plant. Soil Sci. Soc. Amer. Proc. 24:205-209.

Pfeiffer, Th. 1906. Die Wirkung des Ammoniakstickstoffs als Düngemittel. Fühlings Landw. Ztg. 55:153-159.

Prescott, J. A. 1919. Nitrification in Egyptian soils. J. Agr. Sci. 9:216-236.

Prescott, J. A. 1934. The nitrogen problem in the Australian wheat belt. Proc. 5th Pacific. Sci. Congr. Pacific Sci. Assoc. 4:2657-2667.

Prescott, J. A., and Piper, G. R. 1930. Nitrate fluctuations in a South Australian soil. J. Agr. Sci. 20:517-531.

Pritchett, W. L., Black, C. A., and Nelson, L. B. 1948. Mineralizable nitrogen in soils in relation to the response of oats to nitrogen fertilization. Soil Sci. Soc. Amer. Proc. (1947) 12:327-331.

Pritchett, W. L., Malik, M. N., and Eno, C. F. 1960. Relationships of soil nitrogen to crop response from fertilizer nitrogen applied to mineral soils. Soil and Crop Sci. Soc. Florida Proc. 20:393-403.

Prostakow, P. E. 1960. Methods for regulating nitrification processes on the Cis-Caucasian calcareous chernozems during irrigation. (In Russian.) Pochvovedeniĕ (Pedology) no 1:74-80. English Summary.

Purvis, E. R., and Micah, W. M. L. 1961. Rapid procedure for estimating potentially available soil nitrogen under greenhouse conditions. J. Agr. Food Chem. 9:15-17.

Rahn, O. 1919. Die schädliche Wirkung der Strohdüngung und deren Verhütung. Z. Techn. Biol. 7:172-186.

Rao, G. G., and Dhar, N. R. 1931. Bildung von Stickstoffverbindungen in Luft und im Boden unter dem Einfluss des Lichtes. Z. Anorg. Allgem. Chemie 199:422-426.

Rappe, G. 1950. Seasonal variations observed in the nutritive substances of a cultivated sphagnum peat soil. Trans. Intern. Cong. Soil Sci. 4th Cong. Amsterdam 1:155-160.

Ray, H. E., McGregor, J. M., and Schmidt, E. L. 1957. Movement of ammonium nitrogen in soils. Soil Sci. Soc. Amer. Proc. 21:309-312.

Rebour, H. 1962. Effect du climat et du sol sur la fumure azotee de printemps. Compt. Rend. Acad. Agr. (Paris) 48:831-837.

Reed, F. J., and Sturgis, M. B. 1937. A study of the fertilization of rice. Lafayette Agr. Exp. Sta. Bul. 292, 25 pp.

Reed, F. J., and Sturgis, M. B. 1939. Chemical characteristics of the soils of the rice area of Louisiana. Lafayette Agr. Exp. Sta. Bul. 307, 36 pp.

Remy, Th. 1902. Bodenbakteriologische Studien; A. Die Ausnutzung des Düngerstick-stoffs und das bakterielle Verhalten des Bodens. Centralbl. Bakteriol., Parasitenk., Infektionskrankh. Abt. II 8:657-662.

Rheinwald, H. 1933. Die Nitratkonzentration der Bodenlösung und die ihre Höhe bestimmenden Faktoren. Z. Pflanzenernähr., Düng., A 30:82-98.

Ribble, J. M., and Davis, L. E. 1955. Ion exchange in soil columns. Soil Sci. 79:41-47.

Richardson, H. L. 1938. The nitrogen cycle in grassland soils. With especial reference to the Rothamsted Park grass experiment. J. Agr. Sci. 28:73-121.

Richardson, H. L. 1952. Verbal communication at the session on "Organic matter and nitrogen." Trans. Intern. Soc. Soil Sci. Joint meeting comm. II and IV. Dublin 2:28 pp.

Robinson, J. B. D. 1957. The critical relationship between soil moisture content in the region of the wilting point and the mineralization of natural soil nitrogen. J. Agr. Sci. 49:100-105.

Rogers, W. S., Raptopoulos, T., and Greenham, D. W. P. 1948. Cover crops for fruit plantations. J. Hort. Sci. 24:228-283.

Romell, L. G. 1924. Das Zusammenwirken verschiedener Produktionsfaktoren. (In Swedish.) Skogsvärdsförcn. Tidsskr. 3:89-120. German summary.

Roo, H. C. de, and Wiersum, L. K. 1963. Root training by plastic tubes. Agronomy J. 55:402-405.

Rosselet, F. 1953. Nitrogen in citrus soils under permanent grass. Farming S. Africa 28:275-286.

Rousselle, V. 1913. Le movement de nitrates dans le sol et les consequences relatives a l'emploi du nitrate du soude. Ann. Sci. Agron. 1:97-115.

Rubins, E. J., and Bear, F. E. 1942. Carbon-nitrogen ratios in organic fertilizers in rela-tion to the availability of their nitrogen. Soil Sci. 54:411-423.

Russell, E. J. 1914. The nature and amount of the fluctuations in nitrate contents of arable soils. J. Agr. Sci. 6:18-57.

Russell, E. J. 1937. Soil Conditions and Plant Growth. 8th Ed. Longmans, New York. 635 pp.

Russell, E. J., and Richards, E. H. 1920. The washing out of nitrates by drainage water from uncropped and unmanured land. J. Agr. Sci. 10:22-43.

Russell, J. C., Jones, E. G., and Bahrt, G. M. 1925. The temperature and moisture fac-tors in nitrate production. Soil Sci. 19:381-398.

Sabey, B. R., Bartholomew, W. V., Shaw, R., and Pesek, J. 1956. Influence of tempera-ture on nitrification in soil. Soil Sci. Soc. Amer. Proc. 20:357-360.

Sacks, L. E., and Barker, H. A. 1949. The influence of oxygen on nitrate and nitrite reduction. J. Bacteriol. 58:11-22.

Sacks, L. E, and Barker, H. A. 1952. Substrate oxidation and nitrous oxide utilization in denitrification. J. Bacteriol. 64:247-252.

Sazanow, W. 1907. Contribution to the problem of the nitrification in the black earth, the influence thereupon of external factors, and the amount of nitrates in the soil in different seasons. (In Russian.) Sjournal Opytnoi Agronomii (J. Exp. Agron.) 8:1-38. German summary.

Schachtschabel, P. 1953. Reaktion und Kalkbedarf von Hochmoorböden. Z. Pflanzen-ernähr., Düng., Bodenk. 60:21-27.

Schachtschabel, P. 1961. Vergleich zwischen der Austauschermethode nach Tepe und anderen Methoden der Bodenuntersuchung. Landw. Forschung 14: 136-147.

Scheffer, F., Kloke, A., and Grummer, H. J. 1957. Gefäsz- und Feldversuche mit gekörnten Stickstoffdüngern. Z. Pflanzenernähr., Düng., Bodenk. 78(123):97-107.

Schloesing, Th., and Müntz, A. 1879. Recherches sur la nitrification. Compt. Rend. Acad. Sci. (Paris) 89:1074-1076.

Schmuck, A. A. 1924. Observation about absorption of nitrates by the "Chernozem"-soil. (In Russian). J. Agr. Sci. (Russ.). 1 no 2:142-153.

Schneidewind, W. 1904. Fünfter Bericht über die Versuchswirtschaft Lauchstädt. Landw. Jahrb. 33:165-334.

Schofield, J. L. 1945. A comparison of soil nitrate nitrogen values under bare fallow and after ploughing in various perennial tropical legumes and cowpeas. The Queensland J. Agr. Sci. 2:170-189.

Schreven, D. A. van. 1950. Loss of nitrogen from ammonium containing fertilizers applied to calcareous soils of the Zuider-Sea polders. Trans. Intern. Congr. Soil Sci. Amsterdam 1:259-261.

Schreven, D. A. van. 1955. Loss of nitrogen from ammonium containing fertilizers applied to calcareous soils of the Zuiderzeepolders. (In Dutch.) Van Zee tot Land. no 11. 41 pp. English Summary.

Schreven, D. A. van. 1956a. The effect of some ammonium containing fertilizers on the loss of nitrogen after application to a calcareous soil of the Northeastern Polder. Rapp. Cong. Intern. Sci. du Sol, Paris D:65-73.

Schreven, D. A. van. 1956b. Nitrogen metabolism in soil and determination of soil nitrogen for estimating the need of nitrogen. (In Dutch.) Meded. Dir. Tuinb. 19:641-655. English Summary.

Schreven, D. A. van. 1957. Nitrogen metabolism in soil and nitrogen mineralization in relation to the response of winter wheat to nitrogen fertilization in the North-Eastern Polder. (In Dutch.) Van Zee tot Land no 22:35 pp. English Summary.

Schreven, D. A. van. 1958. Experiments on nitrogen mineralization in soil. (In Dutch.) Van Zee tot Land. no 26:26-52. English Summary.

Schreven, D. A. van. 1963. Nitrogen transformations in the former subaqueous soils of polders recently reclaimed from lake Yssel. Plant and Soil 18:143-174.

Sen, Abhiswar, and Asija, G. L. 1954. A study of the action of tank silts on soils. Indian J. Agr. Sci. 23:223-232. 1953; 24:51-63.

Sen, Abhiswar, and Rewari, R. B. 1958. Seasonal variation in nitrogen content of Indian soils. Science and Culture 23:624-626.

Shishelova, N. A. 1936. The possibility of determining the content of assimilable nitrogen in soil by means of the fungus *Cunninghamella*. (In Russian.) Trudy Inst. Selsk. Choz. Microbiol. (Rep. Inst. Agr. Microbiol.) 8:83-93.

Simpson, J. R. 1960. The mechanism of surface nitrate accumulation on a bare fallow soil in Uganda. J. Soil Sci. 11:45-60.

Smeding, S. 1935. The reclamation of the Zuider-Sea in olden times and now. (In Dutch.) Landbouwk. Tijdschr. 47:797-826.

Smirnow, V. N. 1958. The dynamic of nutrient elements and the biological activity of podzolic soils of the southern belt of the forest zone. (In Russian.) Pochvovedenië (Pedology) no. 7:58-65. English Summary.

Smith, F. B. 1940. Factors affecting the decomposition of organic matter in soils under Florida conditions. Soil Sci. Soc. Florida Proc. 2:125-128.

Smith, G. E. 1952. Soil fertility and corn production. Minnesota Agr. Exp. Sta. Bul. 583. 67 pp.

Smith, H. V. 1944. A lysimeter study of the nitrogen balance in irrigated soils. Arizona Agr. Exp. Sta. Tech. Bul. 102. 259-308.

Smith, J. B. 1928. Distribution of nitrates in three layers of fallow soil. Soil Sci. 26:347-350.

Snow, O. W., and Greene, H. 1935. The nitrate profile in an arid soil. Trans. Intern. Cong. Soil Sci. 3rd. Cong. Oxford I:360-363.

Sobornikowa, I. G. 1959. The effect of irrigation on the terrace cis-Caucasian chernozems of the Rostov region. Pochvovedenië (Pedology) no. 2:65-74. English Summary.

Solberg, P., and Braadlie, O. 1957. The nitrate and ammonia content of cultivated soil with and without plant cover. Preliminary investigations. (In Norwegian.) Forskn. Fors. Landbr. 8:329-367. English Summary.

Soubies, L., Gadet, R., and Maury, P. 1952. Migration hivernale de l'azote nitrique dans un sol limoneux de la region toulousaine. Ann. Agron. 3:365-384.

Soulides, D. A., and Clark, F. E. 1958. Nitrification in grassland soils. Soil Sci. Soc. Amer. Proc. 22:308-311.

Sprengel, C. 1839. Die Lehre vom Dünger. J. Müller, Leipzig. 456 pp.

Sreenivasan, A., and Subrahmanyan, V. 1934. Loss of nitrogen from swamp soils. Current Science India 2:432-433.

Sreenivasan, A., and Subrahmanyan, V. 1935. Biochemistry of water-logged soils. IV. Carbon and nitrogen transformations. J. Agr. Sci. 25:6-21.

Stanford, G., and Hanway, J. 1955. Predicting nitrogen fertilizer needs of Iowa soils: II A simplified technique for determining relative nitrate production in soils. Soil Sci. Soc. Amer. Proc. 19:74-77.

Starkey, R. L. 1929. Some influences of the development of higher plants upon the microörganisms in the soil: I, II, III. Soil Sci. 27: 319-334, 355-378, 433-444.

Starkey, R. L. 1958. Interrlations between microorganisms and plant roots in the rhizosphere. Bacteriolog. Rev. 22:154-172.

Steenbjerg, F. 1944. Loss of ammonia from nitrogenous artificial fertilizers when spread on arable soil. I Sulphate of ammonia. (In Danish). Tidsskr. Planteavl. 48:516-543. English Summary.

Stevenson, I. L., and Chase, F. E. 1953. Nitrification in an orchard soil under three cultural practices. Soil Sci. 76:107-114.

Stewart, R., and Peterson, W. 1915. The origin of the "nitre spots" in certain western soils. J. Amer. Soc. Agron. 6:241-248.

Stewart, R., and Peterson, W. 1916. The origin of the "nitre spots" in certain western soils. Science 43:20-24.

Stöckli, A. 1949. Der Einfluss der Mikroflora und Fauna auf die Beschaffenheit des Bodens. Z. Pflanzenernähr. Düng., Bodenk. 45:41-53.

Stoklasa, J. 1892. Studie über die Frage ob man den Chilisalpeter durch das Ammoniumsulfat ersetzen kann. Österr.-Ungar. Z., Zuckerind. und Landw. 21:426-433.

Stoklasa, J. 1908a. Beitrag zur Kenntniss der Stickstoffanreicherung des Bodens durch Bakterien und ihre Bedeutung für die Pflanzenernährung. Deutsche Landw. Presse 35:297-298.

Stoklasa, J. 1908b. Wann kann das schwefelsaure Ammoniak die Erträge unserer Kulturpflanzen erhöhen? Landw. Monatshefte 1:278-283.

Stoklasa, J., and Ernest, A. 1909. Beiträge zur Lösung der Frage der chemischen Natur des Wurzelsekretes. Jahrb. Wissensch. Bot. 46:55-102.

Stotzky, G., and Mortensen, J. L. 1957. Effect of crop residues and nitrogen additions on decomposition of an Ohio muck soil. Soil Sci. 83:165-174.

Subbiah, B. V., and Asija, G. L. 1956. A rapid procedure for the estimation of available nitrogen in soils. Current Sci. India 25:259-260.

Süchting, H. 1933. Über Forstdüngungsversuche. Mitteil. Forstwirtsch. Forstwissensch. 4:96-114.

Süchting, H. 1950. Über die Stickstoffdynamik der Waldböden und die Stickstoffernährung des Waldbestandes. Z. Pflanzenernähr. Düng., Bodenk. 48 (93):1-37.

Süchting, H., John, G., Deines, G., and Maurmann, G. 1933. Untersuchungen über die Wirkung der Düngung auf Waldböden. Mitteil. Forstwirtsch. Forstwissensch. 4:439-493.

Synghal, K. N. 1960. A simpler and more accurate procedure than the Iowa method for determining nitrification in soil. J. Indian Soc. Soil Sci. 8:219-222.

Tacke, Br. 1910. Bemerkung zu der Abhandlung: "Bildung und Verbrauch von Stickoxydul durch Bakterien" von M. W. Beijerinck mit Mitwirkung von D. C. J. Minkman. Centralbl. Bakteriol., Parasitenk., Infektionskrankh. Abt II 26:236.

Tandon, S. P., and Dhar, N. R. 1934. Influence of temperature on bacterial nitrification in tropical countries. Soil Sci. 38:183-189.

Tepe, W. 1956. Die Bestimmung der Bodenleistung mit Ionenaustauchern im Hinblick auf die Ernährung der Pflanzen. Landw. Forschung S. H. 7:83-89.

Tepe, W. 1958. Die Abhängigkeit der Nährstoffleistung des Bodens von dem Kalk- und

Kolloidgehalt. Trans. Intern. Soc. Soil Sci. commission II en IV Hamburg 2:147-154.

Tepe, W., and Leidenfrost, E. 1960. Ein Vergleich zwischen pflanzen-physiologischen, kinetischen und statischen Bodenuntersuchungswerten. Landw. Forschung 11:217-229. 1958; 13:96-113.

Theron, J. J. 1951. The influence of plants on the mineralization of nitrogen and the maintenance of organic matter in the soil. J. Agr. Sci. 41:289-296.

Theron, J. J., and Haylett, D. C. 1953. The regeneration of soil humus under a grass lay. Empire J. Exp. Agr. 21:86-98.

Thomas, B., and Elliott, F. J. 1932. The effect of manurial treatment on nitrogen fixation and nitrification in certain experimental plots. J. Soc. Chem. Ind. 51:332-336.

Thompson, F. B., and Coup, M. R. 1940. Studies of nitrate and ammonia in soils under permanent pasture. II The variability of distribution of nitrate. New Zealand J. Sci. Tech. Agr. Section 22. no. 2A: 72-78.

Thornton, G. D. 1947. Greenhouse studies of nitrogen fertilization of Soybeans and Lespedeza using isotopic nitrogen. Soil Sci. Soc. Amer. Proc. (1946) 11:249-251.

Tovborg-Jensen, S., and Kjaer, Betsy. 1948. Loss of ammonia by evaporation from ammonium sulfate applied to soils. (In Danish.) Tidsskr. Planteavl 51:666-711. English Summary.

Tovborg-Jensen, S., and Kjaer, Betsy. 1950. Stickstoffverluste aus Böden durch Ammoniakverdampfung bei Düngung mit schwefelsaurem Ammoniak. Z. Pflanbenernähr., Düng., Bodenk. 50:25-38.

Tyler, K. B., and Broadbent, F. E., and Hill, G. N. 1959. Low temperature effects on nitrification in four California soils. Soil Sci. 87:123-129.

Valera, C. L., and Alexander, M. 1961. Nutrition and physiology of denitrifying bacteria. Plant and Soil 15:268-280.

Vanstallen, R. 1959. The variability of soluble nitrogen in loam soil. (In Dutch.) Agricultura (Louvain) 7:45-60. English Summary.

Vanstallen, R. 1960. Losses of nitrogen through volatilization of ammonia. (In Dutch.) Agricultura (Louvain) 8:91-102. English Summary.

Várallyay, G. 1937. Veränderungen im Ammoniak-und Nitrat-Gehalt des Bodens. Bodenk. Pflanzenernähr. 2:192-198.

Vault, D. de. 1943. The theory of chromatography. J. Amer. Chem. Soc. 65:532-540.

Verhoeven, W. 1952. Aerobic sporeforming nitrate reducing bacteria. Ph.D. thesis. Delft.

Verhoeven, W. 1956. Studies on true dissimilatory nitrate reduction. V Antonie van Leeuwenhoek 22:385-406.

Viets, Frank G. 1960. Recovery of fertilizer nitrogen on irrigated and dry land soils of the Western United States. 7th Int. Cong. of Soil Sci. II:486-493.

Vine, H. 1953. Experiments on the maintenance of soil fertility at Ibadan, Nigeria 1922-1951. Emp. J. Exp. Agr. 21:65-85.

Volk, G. M. 1959. Volatile loss of ammonia following surface application of urea to turf or bare soil. Agron. J. 51:746-749.

Volk, G. M. 1961. Gaseous loss of ammonia from surface applied nitrogenous fertilizers. J. Agr. Food Chem. 9:280-283.

Wagner, P. 1892. Die Stickstoffdüngung der landwirtschaftlichen Kulturpflanzen. Paul Parey, Berlin. 441 pp.

Wagner, P. 1898. Ammoniaksalz order Chilisalpeter? Deutsche Landw. Presse 25:327, 336-337.

Wagner, P. 1901. Versuche über den relativen Düngewert des Ammoniaksalzes. Mitteil. Deutsch. Landw. Ges. 16:55-60.

Wagner, P. 1903a. Die Düngung mit schwefelsaurem Ammoniak und organischen Stickstoffdüngern im Vergleich zu Chilisalpeter. Arb. Deutsch. Landw. Ges. 80. 335 pp.

Wagner, P. 1903b. Unter welchen Umständen und durch welche Mittel ist der Ammoniakstickstoff zu höchstmöglicher Wirkung zu bringen? Jahrb. Deutsch. Landw. Ges. 18:37-49.

Wagner, P. 1907. Versuche über die Stickstoffdüngung der Kulturpflanzen unter Verwendung von Chilisalpeter, Ammoniaksalz und Kalkstickstoff. Arb. Deutsch. Landw. Ges. 129. 286 pp.

Waksman, S. A. 1917. The influence of available carbohydrates upon ammonia accumulation by microorganisms. J. Amer. Chem. Soc. 39:1503-1512.

Waksman, S. A. 1923a. Microbiological analysis of soil as an index of soil fertility. IV Ammonia accumulation (ammonification). Soil Sci. 15:49-65.

Waksman, S. A. 1923b. Microbiological analysis of soil as an index of soil fertility. VI Nitrification. Soil Sci. 16:55-67.

Waksman, S. A. 1927. Principles of Soil Microbiology. Baillière, Tindall and Cox. London. 897 pp.

Waksman, S. A., and Tenney, F. G. 1927. The composition of natural organic materials and their decomposition in the soil. Soil Sci. 24: 275-282, 317-332.

Walker, F. W., Adams, A. F. R., and Orchiston, H. D. 1956. Fate of labeled nitrate and ammonium nitrogen when applied to grass and clover grown separately and together. Soil Sci. 81:339-351.

Warington, R. 1892. Six lectures on the investigations at Rothamsted Experiment Station. Lecture III: Nitrification. USDA Exp. Sta. Bul. 8. 50 pp.

Warington, R. 1900. The comparative value of nitrate of sodium and sulphate of ammonium as manures. J. Roy. Agr. Soc. England 3rd series II part 2:300-346.

Wark, D. C. 1938. A method for testing nitrogen deficiency. J. Austr. Inst. Agr. Sci. 4:208-210.

Webster, R., and Gasser, J. K. R. 1958. Leaching of nitrate from soils. Rothamsted Exp. Sta. Rep. 1957:58.

Webster, R., and Gasser, J. K. R. 1959. Soil nitrogen. V Leaching of nitrate from soils in laboratory experiments. J. Sci. Food Agr. 10:584-585.

Wetselaar, R. 1960. Capillary movement of nitrate towards tropical soil surfaces. Nature 186:572-573.

Wetselaar, R. 1961. Nitrate distribution in tropical soils. I Possible causes of nitrate accumulation near the surface after a long dry period. Plant and Soil 15:110-120.

Wetselaar, R. 1962. Nitrate distribution in tropical soils. III. Downward movement and accumulation of nitrate in the subsoil. Plant and Soil 16:19-31.

Wetselaar, R., and Hutton, J. T. 1963. The ionic composition of rainwater at Katherine, N. T., and its part in the cycling of plant nutrients. Austr. J. Agr. Res. 14:319-329.

White, J. W., Holben, F. J., Jeffries, C. D., and Richer, A. C. 1949. Correlation of microbiological and chemical soil data with crop yields of the Jordan soil fertility plots. Soil Sci. 67:279-285.

Wijler, J., and Delwiche, C. C. 1954. Investigations on the denitrifying process in soil. Plant and Soil 5:155-169.

Wiley, H. W. 1896. Soil ferments important in agriculture. USDA Yearbook Agr.

Willis, W. H., and Green, V. E. Jr. 1949. Movement of nitrogen in flooded soil planted to rice. Soil Sci. Soc. Amer. Proc. (1948) 13:229-237.

Wilson, J. K. 1943. Nitrous acid and the loss of nitrogen. Cornell Agr. Exp. Sta. Mem. 253. 36 pp.

Wilson, J. N. 1940. A theory of chromatography. J. Amer. Chem. Soc. 62:1583-1591.

Winnik, M. 1935. Ten years of lysimeter studies on some soils of Palestine. Trans. Intern. Cong. Soil Sci. 3rd Cong. Oxford I: 212-214.

Winsor, G. W. 1958. Mineralization and immobilization of nitrogen in soil. J. Sci. Food Agr. 9:792-801.

Winsor, G. W., and Pollard, A. G. 1956. Carbon-nitrogen relationships in soil. I The immobilization of nitrogen in the presence of carbon compounds. J. Sci. Food Agr. 7:134-141.

Winter, H. 1894. Possible losses of nitrogen when applying sulphate of ammonia or "boenkil." (In Dutch.) Archief Java Suikerindustrie 2, 1st part:373-384.

Wittich, W. 1952. Der heutige Stand unseres Wissens vom Humus und neue Wege zur Lösung des Humusproblems im Walde. Schriftenreihe der Forstlichen Fakultät der Universität Göttingen 4, Sauerländers Verlag, Frankfurt a.M.

Wlodek, J. von. 1911. Beiträge zur Frage der Ammoniakverdunstung und Umwandlung im Boden. Ph.D. thesis. Berlin. 89 pp.

Woldendorp, J. 1962. The quantitative influence of the rhizosphere on denitrification. Plant and Soil 17:267-270.

Woldendorp, J. 1963. The effect of plants on denitrification. Ph.D. thesis. Wageningen,

Woodruff, C. M. 1950. Estimating the nitrogen delivery of soil from the organic matter determination as reflected by Sanborn field. Soil Sci. Soc. Amer. Proc. (1949) 14:208-212.

Wright, R. C. 1915. The influence of certain organic materials upon the transformations of soil nitrogen. J. Amer. Soc. Agron. 7:193-208.

Yankovitch, L. 1933. Contribution a la meilleure comprehension du problème de l'azote dans les terres Nord-Africaines. Ann. Serv. Bot. Agron. 10:1-86.

Yankovitch, L., and Yankovitch, J. 1953. Nitrification dans les terres salées. Compt. Rend. Acad. Agr. France 39:321-323.

Yee, J. Y., and Love, Katharine, S. 1947. Nitrification of urea-formaldehydr reaction products. Soil Sci. Soc. Amer. Proc. (1946) 11:389-392.

Yuen, Q. H., and Hance, F. E. 1939. Nitrogen in the cane leaf. Hawaii Plant. Rec. 43:163-207.

Zöttl, H. 1960a. Dynamik der Stickstoffmineralization im organischen Waldbodenmaterial. I, II, III Plant and Soil 13:166-182, 183-206, 207-223.

Zöttl, H. 1960b. Methodische Untersuchungen zur Bestimmung der Mineralstickstoffnachlieferung des Waldbodens. Forstwissensch. Centralbl. 79:72-90.

Zöttl, H. 1960c. Die Mineralstickstoffanlieferung in Fichten- und Kiefernbeständen Bayerns. Fortwissensch. Centralbl. 79:221-236.

Chapter 3

Organic Nitrogen in Soils

J. M. BREMNER

Iowa State University
Ames, Iowa

I. INTRODUCTION

Most of the nitrogen in surface soils is organically combined. The importance of this organic nitrogen from the standpoint of soil fertility has long been appreciated, and numerous studies concerning the nitrogenous organic complexes in soils have been reported. Research on the nature of the organic nitrogen in soils dates back more than 90 years to the work of Detmer (1871), who concluded that much of this nitrogen is in the form of proteins. The gradual accumulation of knowledge concerning the forms, amounts, transformations, and importance of organic nitrogen in soils has been traced in reviews by Tyurin (1937), Waksman (1938), Ensminger and Pearson (1950), Bremner (1951, 1952, 1956), Harmsen and van Schreven (1955), Scheffer (1958), Scheffer and Ulrich (1960), Konova (1961), and Russell (1961). The distribution, transformations, and importance of organic nitrogen in soils are discussed elsewhere in this monograph, and no attempt will be made to review these topics here. The main purpose of this chapter is to review and summarize present knowledge concerning the nature of the organic nitrogen in soils.

II. DETERMINATION

Until about 1954 it was generally assumed that only a small proportion (<2%) of the nitrogen in soils is in inorganic forms of combination and that organic soil nitrogen can therefore be estimated reasonably accurately by determination of total soil nitrogen. It is now well established, however, that some soils contain significant amounts of fixed (nonexchangeable) ammonium which is not determined by the methods normally used for estimation of inorganic forms of nitrogen in soils (Rodrigues, 1954; Dhariwal and Stevenson, 1958; Bremner, 1959; Bremner and Harada, 1959; Stevenson, 1959; Stevenson and Dhariwal, 1959; Schachtschabel, 1960; Walsh and Murdock, 1960; Young, 1962). The proportion of soil nitrogen in the form of nonexchangeable ammonium is rarely greater than 8% in surface soils, but it can exceed 40% in subsoils. Since no direct method of determining organic soil nitrogen is available, this means that, for accurate estimation of this nitrogen, it is necessary to determine total soil nitrogen by a method which effects quantitative recovery of both organic and inorganic forms of nitrogen and to subtract total inorganic soil nitrogen as determined by methods that permit quantitative determination of (exchangeable ammonium + nonexchangeable ammonium + nitrate + nitrite)-N.

Two methods are available for determination of total nitrogen in soils and other complex materials containing several forms of nitrogen: the Kjeldahl method, which is essentially a wet-oxidation procedure; and the Dumas method, which is fundamentally a dry-oxidation technique. In the Kjeldahl method, the nitrogen in the sample is converted to ammonium by digestion with concentrated sulfuric acid containing substances which promote this conversion, and is determined from the amount of ammonia liberated by distillation of the digest with alkali. In the Dumas method, the sample is heated with copper oxide (usually above 600°C) in a stream of purified carbon dioxide, and the gases liberated are led over hot copper to reduce nitrogen oxides (mainly N_2O) to N_2, and then over copper oxide to convert CO to CO_2. The N_2-CO_2 mixture thus obtained is collected in a nitrometer containing concentrated alkali, which absorbs the CO_2, and the volume of N_2 gas is measured.

The Kjeldahl methods universally favored for determination of total nitrogen in soils fail to recover nitrogen in refractory compounds such as nicotinic acid and pyridine and in certain compounds containing N-N and N-O linkages (see Bremner, 1965a). This raises serious doubt concerning the accuracy of these methods, because, as shown below, the chemical nature of a considerable fraction of soil nitrogen is still obscure. However, numerous modifications of conventional Kjeldahl methods have been developed which permit inclusion of virtually all combined forms of nitrogen, and in recent work involving application of a selection of these modified Kjeldahl procedures to a variety of soils containing from 0.03 to 2.7% nitrogen, Bremner (1960) found that with each of the soils analyzed, the results by the various modified methods were identical, and in close agreement with the results obtained by conventional Kjeldahl methods. This is good evidence that the Kjeldahl method is satisfactory for determination of total nitrogen in most soils, because there are few, if any, naturally-occurring combined forms of nitrogen which cannot be determined by one or another of the Kjeldahl procedures used in this work.

The classical Dumas method is a rather complicated procedure and it has rarely been used for determination of total nitrogen in soils. However, Dyck and McKibbin (1935) analyzed 26 organic soils by Dumas and Kjeldahl methods and found that with every sample tested the Dumas method gave a considerably higher nitrogen value. Similar results were obtained in comparative work reported by Bremner and Shaw (1958), but they found that Dumas and Kjeldahl methods gave practically identical results with mineral soils (compare Bremner, 1965a). These findings have been confirmed by Stewart et al. (1963). They studied the reliability of an automated micro-Dumas apparatus (Coleman Nitrogen Analyzer, Model 29) for determining total nitrogen in soils and concluded that the Dumas procedure was satisfactory for soils containing up to 0.3% nitrogen, but gave erroneously high results with plant materials and with soils rich in organic matter. They also showed that these high values were due to formation of methane during Dumas combustion. In subsequent work, Stewart et al. (1964) developed a modified Dumas procedure which eliminated the formation of methane during Dumas combustion of organic soils and found that the total nitrogen values obtained by this procedure with soils containing from 0.06 to 1.31% nitrogen were in close agreement with those obtained by Kjeldahl analysis. Taken with the results obtained in Bremner's evaluation of Kjeldahl procedures, these findings by Stewart and his associates leave very little doubt that the total nitrogen content of most soils can be determined satisfactorily by both Kjeldahl and Dumas procedures provided certain precautions are observed. However, some doubt exists concerning the reliability of these procedures for determination of total nitrogen in soils containing appreciable amounts of fixed ammonium. Bremner (1959, 1960) investigated the possibility that Kjeldahl procedures may give low results with these soils, but could obtain no evidence that Kjeldahl digestion failed to recover ammonium trapped in the lattices of clay minerals (see also Bremner and Harada, 1959). For example, he found that the values obtained in Kjeldahl analysis of soils containing native fixed ammonium were not increased by pretreatment of these soils with hydrofluoric acid to destroy clay minerals and release fixed ammonium before Kjeldahl digestion. However, Stewart and Porter (1963) subsequently found that this pretreatment led to a significant increase in the values obtained in Kjeldahl analysis of three clay soils containing large amounts of native fixed ammonium, which indicates that the native fixed ammonium in some soils is not recovered quantitatively by the Kjeldahl method. Since no studies of the reliability of Dumas procedures for determination of total nitrogen in soils containing significant amounts of native fixed ammonium have been reported, the possibility that both Dumas and Kjeldahl methods give low results with some of these soils cannot be excluded.

The Kjeldahl methods generally used for determination of total nitrogen in soils do not effect quantitative recovery of nitrate or nitrite. Modified methods which include these forms of nitrogen are available (see Bremner, 1965a), but the amounts of nitrate and nitrite in soils are usually so small that the total-N values obtained by these modified methods are not significantly different from those obtained using conventional Kjeldahl methods. Stewart et al. (1964) found that their modification of the Dumas procedure recovered nitrate-N.

For accurate determination of organic nitrogen in soils, it is clearly necessary to have methods which permit quantitative determination of total inorganic soil nitrogen as well as total soil nitrogen. Quantitative determination of (ammonium + nitrate + nitrite)-N in soils presents many difficulties, but recent work has led to development of a relatively simple procedure which appears satisfactory for determination of (exchangeable ammonium + nitrate + nitrite)-N. However, considerable doubt exists concerning the accuracy of the methods currently available for determination of nonexchangeable ammonium in soils, and use of these methods in determination of total inorganic soil nitrogen may lead to serious error when organic nitrogen in soils containing large amounts of fixed ammonium is calculated from determinations of total-N and total inorganic-N. For a discussion of the methods available for determination of inorganic forms of nitrogen in soils see Bremner, 1965c.

To summarize, present knowledge indicates that organic nitrogen in soils containing small amounts of fixed ammonium can be estimated accurately from determinations of total soil nitrogen and total inorganic soil nitrogen by methods currently available for these determinations. Improvements in these methods may be required for accurate estimation of organic nitrogen in soils containing large amounts of fixed ammonium.

III. AMOUNTS

Current information concerning the amounts of organic nitrogen in soils is based on the assumption that more than 98% of the nitrogen in soils is organically combined and that Kjeldahl analysis of soil for total nitrogen therefore provides a good estimate of organic nitrogen. The fact that recent work discussed in the previous section has rendered this assumption invalid does not seriously detract from the value of conclusions from Kjeldahl data concerning the distribution of organic nitrogen in surface soils, because present knowledge indicates that well over 90% of the total nitrogen in most surface soils is organically combined. However, the finding that more than 40% of the total nitrogen in certain subsoils is in the form of fixed ammonium means that any conclusions concerning the distribution of organic nitrogen in subsurface soils which are based on Kjeldahl data must be treated with some reserve.

The total nitrogen content of soils ranges from less than 0.02% in subsoils to more than 2.5% in peats; the plowed layer of most cultivated soils contains between 0.08 and 0.4% nitrogen. The amount of nitrogen present in a particular case is determined by a variety of factors, including climate, type of vegetation, topography, parent material, and activities of man. Jenny (1930) demonstrated the great importance of climatic factors and concluded that the order of importance of soil-forming factors in determining the nitrogen content of medium textured soils in the United States is as follows: climate > vegetation > topography and parent material > age. The literature on factors affecting the nitrogen content of soils is reviewed in chapter 1 (see also Jenny, 1941; Ensminger and Pearson, 1950; Black, 1957).

Studies of the vertical distribution of nitrogen in soil profiles indicate that the amount of organic nitrogen ordinarily decreases gradually with depth except in soils having pronounced horizon differentiation or in soils derived from recent sediments, where irregularities may occur (Byers et al., 1935; Brown and Byers, 1935; Pearson and Simonson, 1940; Brown and Thorpe, 1942; Stevenson, 1957c, 1959). In most soils, the bulk of the organic nitrogen occurs in the surface 2 feet of the profile. The profile distributions of nitrogen in soils representative of various great soil groups are discussed in chapter 1.

Determinations of the C/N ratios of soils have shown that the amount of organic nitrogen in soil tends to be related to the amount of organic carbon (for a review of the early literature on C/N ratios, see Anon., 1945). The C/N ratio of the organic matter in the surface layer of soils of temperate regions is usually about 10 or 11, but large variations in this ratio have been observed (see Russell, 1961; Young, 1962). For example, Anderson and Byers (1934) found that the C/N ratio of the organic matter in various surface soils ranged from about 9 with a chernozem to about 22 with a podzol. The C/N ratio usually decreases with depth in the profile and it is as low as 5 in certain subsoils. Recent work indicates that this is at least partly due to the fact that a substantial amount of the nitrogen in some subsurface soils is in the form of fixed ammonium (see section II).

The amount of organic nitrogen in soil tends to be related to the amounts of organic phosphorus and sulfur as well as to the amount of organic carbon. Work reviewed by Black and Goring (1953) indicated that the organic matter of mineral soils contains carbon, nitrogen, and phosphorus in roughly the ratio 110:9:1 by weight. Subsequent work has shown that the phosphorus content of soil organic matter is rather variable and that correlations between organic nitrogen and organic sulfur are much better than those between organic nitrogen and organic phosphorus (for a review of this work, see Barrow, 1961). Walker and Adams (1958) found that the average carbon: nitrogen: sulfur: organic phosphorus ratio of 20 grassland soils in New Zealand was 120:10:1.3:2.7, and Williams et al. (1960) obtained a similar average ratio (140:10:1.4:2.4) from analyses of 50 Scottish soils.

IV. FORMS

Present knowledge concerning the nature of the organic nitrogen in soils is based largely on studies involving identification and estimation of the forms of nitrogen released by treatment of soils with hot acids. These hydrolysis studies have shown that from 20 to 40% of the total nitrogen in most surface soils is in the form of bound amino acids (Kojima, 1947a; Bremner, 1949a; Stevenson, 1954, 1956b; Sowden, 1956; Young and Mortensen, 1958; Keeney and Bremner, 1964) and that from 5 to 10% is in the form of combined hexosamines (Bremner and Shaw, 1954; Stevenson, 1957a, b, c; Sowden, 1959; Keeney and Bremner, 1964). The amino acids and hexosamines liberated by acid hydrolysis of soils have been identified, but their modes of linkage in soils have not been established. Purine and pyrimidine derivatives have been detected, but current evidence indicates that they do not account for more than about 1% of the total nitrogen in surface soils (Adams et al., 1954; Anderson, 1958, 1961). Other organic nitrogen compounds, including choline, creatinine, and allantoin, have been isolated from soils, but the quantities detected have been very small, and there is no evidence to suggest that these compounds account for a significant amount of the organic nitrogen in soils. Many theories have been advanced concerning the nature of the organic soil nitrogen which has not been identified. For example, it has been postulated that some of this nitrogen is in the form of lignin-ammonia, quinone-ammonia, quinone-amino acid, or carbohydrate-amino acid condensation products. However, there is very little evidence to support these theories, and the chemical nature of about half of the organic nitrogen in soils remains obscure.

A. Nitrogen Distribution

Until recently, the methods used to characterize the organic nitrogen compounds in soils were essentially modifications of the Hausmann (1899) and Van Slyke (1911-12, 1915) methods of protein analysis. In these methods, the material under analysis is hydrolyzed by hot, strong mineral acid, and the nitrogen distribution after acid hydrolysis is determined by a procedure involving separation and estimation of humin-N, ammonia-N (amide-N), basic and nonbasic nonamino-N, and basic and nonbasic amino-N (see Stevenson, 1965b). Phosphotungstic acid is used to separate basic and nonbasic forms of nitrogen, and amino-N is estimated by the Van Slyke (1911, 1929) nitrous acid method, which is based on the finding that aliphatic amines react with nitrous acid to liberate N_2 ($R.NH_2 +$ $HNO_2 = R.OH + H_2O + N_2$). Use of these methods for characterization of the organic nitrogen in soils was stimulated by the belief that most of this nitrogen is in the form of proteins; and it was encouraged by the findings that a large proportion (usually 60 to 80%) of the total nitrogen in surface soils is dissolved by the treatments used for acid hydrolysis of proteins and that soil hydrolysates obtained by these treatments contain the various types of nitrogen distinguished by the methods used for analysis of protein hydrolysates (ammonia-N, basic and nonbasic amino-N, etc.). The limitations of these methods became obvious with the findings that only 24 to 37% of the total nitrogen in surface soils could be definitely accounted for as amino acid-N (Kojima, 1947a; Bremner, 1949a) and that from 5 to 10% of surface soil nitrogen is in the form of hexosamines (Bremner and Shaw, 1954). In recent years, therefore, attention has been directed toward development of hydrolytic methods of characterization which will provide reliable estimates of the amounts of amino acid-N and hexosamine-N in soils. The reliability of analyses of soil hydrolysates for amino acid-N has been increased by the adoption of the ninhydrin method of determining α-amino acids developed by Van Slyke et al. (1941), which involves estimation of the CO_2 evolved by treatment of amino acids with ninhydrin (Fig. 1). This ninhydrin-CO_2 method of determining α-amino-N is highly specific, because it requires the presence, in the free unconjugated state, of both a carboxyl and an adjacent NH_2 or $NH\text{-}CH_2$ group. In contrast, the nitrous acid method previously used for estimation of amino acids is relatively unspecific and is subject to interference by many nonnitrogenous compounds (e.g., phenols, tannins, lignins, ethanol, acetone, pyruvic acid). Results obtained in nitrogen distribution analyses of two organic soils using the ninhydrin-CO_2 method for estimation of α-amino-N are given in Table 1.

Recent work has led to development of a relatively simple method of nitrogen distribution analysis which permits both estimation and isotope-

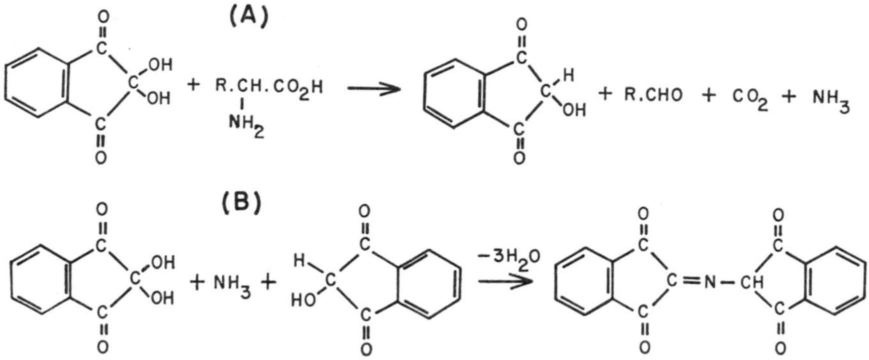

(A)

(B)

Fig. 1. Reactions of α-amino acids with ninhydrin.

ratio analysis of total-N, ammonium-N, hexosamine-N, (serine + threo-nine)-N (hydroxyamino acid-N), and amino acid-N in soil hydrolysates (see Bremner, 1965b). In this procedure, the soil hydrolysate is neutralized without prior removal of the acid used for hydrolysis, and the different forms of nitrogen in the neutralized hydrolysate are converted to, and estimated as, ammonia, which is readily oxidized to nitrogen gas for mass-spectrometer assay of N^{15}. Some of the data obtained by this procedure in a recent survey of the isotopic composition of soil nitrogen (Bremner et al., 1964) are presented in Table 2. They illustrate the finding that there is variation in the abundance of N^{15} in soils and in different forms of soil nitrogen. This variation cannot be attributed to analytical errors and is apparently due to nitrogen isotope-fractionation during nitrogen transformations in soils.

The defects of the nitrogen fractionation achieved by application of modifications of the Hausmann or Van Slyke methods of protein analysis to soils have been pointed out in several publications (e.g., Morrow and Gortner, 1917; Shorey, 1930; Kojima, 1947a; Bremner, 1949a; Stevenson, 1965b), and the significance of most of the terms used to describe nitrogen

Table 1. Nitrogen distribution analyses of soils.*

Fraction	Percentage of total soil N	
	Muck soil	Fen soil
Total acid-soluble N	72.8	68.1
Total α-amino-N	36.8	36.1
Ammonia-N (amide-N)	10.2	17.9
Total humin-N	33.2	31.9
Acid-insoluble humin-N	27.2	27.2
Acid-soluble humin-N	6.0	4.7
Total basic-N	20.8	11.6
Basic α-amino-N	3.8	5.0
Basic nonamino-N	17.0	6.6
Total nonbasic-N	37.2	33.4
Nonbasic α-amino-N	33.0	31.1
Nonbasic nonamino-N	4.3	2.3

* Data of Kojima (1947a) and Bremner (1949a).

Table 2. N^{15}-content of various forms of nitrogen in soils.[*]

Form of nitrogen	N^{15} -content (atom $\% N^{15}$)			
	Grundy silt loam	Colo peat	Austin clay	Glencoe silty clay loam
Total	0. 3719	0. 3671	0. 3680	0. 3666
Hydrolyzable:				
Total	0. 3725	0. 3678	0. 3687	0. 3675
Ammonium	0. 3686	0. 3681	0. 3670	0. 3700
Hexosamine	0. 3750	0. 3668	0. 3656	0. 3647
Amino acid	0. 3718	0. 3680	0. 3726	0. 3700
Hydroxyamino acid	0. 3751	0. 3729	-	-
Nonhydrolyzable	0. 3650	0. 3647	0. 3657	0. 3642

* Bremner, Cheng, and Edwards (1964).

fractions distinguished by these procedures (humin-N, amide-N, etc.) and of the fractionation achieved by phosphotungstic acid are now generally questioned. In recent years, most workers have favored fractionation procedures involving estimation of the total-, ammonium-, hexosamine- and amino acid-N liberated by hydrolysis of soils with 6N HCl. These hydrolysis procedures have several limitations, the most obvious being that they do not characterize a considerable proportion of the nitrogen released by hydrolysis and provide no information concerning the nature of the nonhydrolyzable (acid-insoluble) nitrogen, which constitutes from 20 to 40% of the total nitrogen in most surface soils. Nevertheless, they have provided valuable information concerning the nitrogen compounds in soils and have proved very useful in studies of the distribution of various forms of nitrogen in soil profiles (Stevenson, 1957c; Sowden, 1958; Bremner, 1958b, 1959) and of the effects of cultivation and other treatments on the nitrogen compounds in soils (Rendig, 1951; Stevenson, 1956b; Young and Mortensen, 1958; Cheng and Kurtz, 1963; Keeney and Bremner, 1964; Porter et al., 1964).

One of the most interesting results of nitrogen distribution analyses of soils has been the finding that a large proportion of soil nitrogen is released as ammonium by acid hydrolysis. The amount of ammonium-N liberated by hydrolysis of surface soils with 6N HCl increases markedly with time of hydrolysis, and the amount liberated in 12 hours usually represents 15 to 25% of the total soil nitrogen (Bremner, 1949a; Keeney and Bremner, 1964). The validity of the early assumption that this ammonium-N is derived from amide-N in proteins has long been questioned, and the origin of the ammonium released by hot acid treatment of soils has been the subject of much speculation (Shorey, 1930; Kojima, 1947a; Bremner, 1949a, 1955d, 1959; Bremner and Shaw, 1954; Stevenson, 1954, 1956b, 1957c, 1959; Sowden, 1958; Stevenson et al., 1958). There is now evidence that at least some of this ammonium is formed by hydrolysis of amide (glutamine and asparagine) residues in soil organic matter (Sowden, 1958), but calculations based on the assumption that the glutamic acid and aspartic acid in soils occur entirely in the form of glutamine and asparagine show that much of the ammonium liberated by acid hydrolysis of soils cannot be derived from these amides. There is no doubt that some of this ammonium is formed by decomposition of hydroxyamino acids (serine and threonine) and amino sugars, and it seems likely that some is formed by deamination of other amino compounds known to occur in soils (see Bremner, 1949a; Bremner and Shaw, 1954). The amount derived by deamination of purines and pyrimidines is probably very small, because present knowledge indicates that not much more than about 1% of the total nitrogen in soils is in the form of purine or pyrimidine derivatives. Recent findings concerning the occurrence and distribution of fixed ammonium in soils have led several workers to deduce that a significant amount of the ammonium released by acid hydrolysis of mineral soils may be derived from ammonium trapped in the lattices of clay minerals (Stevenson, 1957c, 1959; Sowden, 1958; Stevenson et al., 1958; Bremner, 1959) and this deduction has been confirmed by the finding that from 50 to 90% of the native fixed ammonium in surface and subsurface soils is released by hydrolysis with 6N HCl for 12 hours (Bremner, 1959; cf. Cheng and Kurtz, 1963). The release of clay-fixed ammonium during acid hydrolysis of soils provides an explanation of the observation that the proportion of soil nitrogen liberated as ammonium by acid hydrolysis increases with depth in the profile (Stevenson, 1957c; Sowden, 1958; Bremner, 1959), because the proportion of soil nitrogen as fixed ammonium also increases with depth. It also helps to account for the finding that the proportion of soil nitrogen released as ammonium by acid hydrolysis is usually highest with soils containing large amounts of clay. However, even if allowance is made for ammonium derived from clay minerals, the amount of ammonium liberated by acid hydrolysis of soil is usually considerably greater than the amount which can be satisfactorily accounted for by present knowledge concerning the forms of nitrogen in soils. The possibility that soil hydrolysates contain organic nitrogen compounds which are converted to, or estimated as, ammonium in the alkaline distillation procedures used for determination of ammonium in soil hydrolysates cannot be excluded, but there is evidence that very little, if any, of the nitrogen determined in ammonium-N analyses of soil hydrolysates is derived from alkali-labile organic nitrogen compounds during these analyses or is in the form of volatile amines (Bremner, 1949a, 1955d; Bremner and Shaw, 1954). Several workers (e.g., Bremner, 1955d; Stevenson, 1957c, 1960a; Sowden, 1958; Bremner and Führ, 1964) have suggested that some of the ammonium liberated by acid hydrolysis of soils may be derived from complexes formed by reaction of lignins or sugars with organic or inorganic nitrogen compounds (e.g., lignin-ammonia, lignin-nitrite, or sugar-amino acid reaction products), but the origin of a considerable fraction of the ammonium released by acid hydrolysis of soils is still obscure. De (1956) and Stevenson (1959, 1960a) have found that most of the nitrogen in the fulvic fraction of soil organic matter is converted to ammonium by acid hydrolysis, and Stevenson (1960a) has obtained evidence that the nitrogenous fulvic constituents which are readily deaminated by acid hydrolysis are largely associated with pigments.

Before concluding this section, attention should be drawn to the finding that the nitrogen distributions of alkali hydrolysates of soils are not greatly different from those of acid hydrolysates (Kojima, 1947a; Bremner,

1949a). More ammonium is liberated by alkali than by acid hydrolysis, but the amounts of total-N and amino acid-N released by the two methods of hydrolysis are similar. The finding that the proportion of nonhydrolyzable nitrogen is essentially the same whether hydrolysis is performed with acid or alkali is of considerable interest in relation to theories concerning the nature of the nonhydrolyzable nitrogen in soils (see Kojima, 1947a; Bremner, 1949a), but it appears to have led to the assumption that a considerable fraction of the nitrogen in soils is in complexes which are not hydrolyzed or dissolved by hot acid or hot alkali. There is no basis for this assumption, because several workers have shown that some of the nitrogen which is not dissolved by acid hydrolysis of soils is readily dissolved by cold alkali (e.g., Kobo et al., 1956; Johnston, 1959).

B. Amino Acids

Most of the information now available concerning the amounts and forms of amino acid-N in soils has emerged from studies involving hydrolysis of soils or soil organic matter preparations with strong mineral acid (usually 6N HCl). The hydrolysis techniques adopted in these studies for release of bound amino acids are adaptations of methods used for hydrolysis of proteins, and few studies of the conditions of hydrolysis required to achieve maximal release of amino acid-N from soils have been reported. Bremner (1949a) found that when 6N HCl was used for hydrolysis of surface soils, maximal release of amino acid-N was obtained by hydrolysis under reflux for about 12 hours, and this procedure, or modifications involving longer periods of hydrolysis, has been adopted in almost all recent investigations concerning the amounts and forms of amino acid-N in soils. Most amino acids are stable toward hydrolysis with 6N HCl, and Bremner (1949a) found that hydrolysis of surface soils with 6N HCl beyond the time required to obtain maximal amino acid-N values did not lead to a marked decrease in these values. Laatsch and Schlichting (1953) found that amino acids are destroyed when heated with 6N HCl in the presence of MnO_2, the destruction being caused by the chlorine gas produced during this treatment ($MnO_2 + 4HCl = MnCl_2 + 2H_2O + Cl_2$). Since most soils contain MnO_2, this observation suggests that serious destruction of amino acids may occur when soils are heated with 6N HCl. However, recent work indicates that this MnO_2-HCl reaction causes very little destruction of amino acids during 6N HCl hydrolysis of soils (see Bremner, 1965b).

Several methods have been used for estimation of amino acid-N in hydrolysates of soils or soil organic matter preparations, but most workers have adopted the nitrous acid or ninhydrin-CO_2 methods described above. The results using the ninhydrin-CO_2 method are probably more accurate than those obtained by the nitrous acid method, but no detailed studies of the reliability of these methods have been reported (for discussions and comparisons of these methods, see Kojima, 1947a; Bremner, 1949a). Recent work has led to development of a simple method of determining amino acid-N (α-amino-N) in soil hydrolysates which involves estimation of the ammonia liberated by oxidation of amino acids with ninhydrin (Bremner, 1965b). This ninhydrin-NH_3 method is based on the finding that the condensation reaction which interferes with the determination of α-amino acids from the ammonia liberated in their reaction with ninhydrin (see reaction B in Fig. 1) is suppressed if the reaction with ninhydrin is performed at pH 2.5 and the reaction products are steam distilled with phosphate-borate buffer at pH 11.2. This method has high specificity, and it gives quantitative recovery of amino acid-N added to soil hydrolysates (for analyses of virgin and cultivated soils using this procedure, see Keeney and Bremner, 1964). A simple method of determining (serine + threonine)-N (hydroxyamino acid-N) in soil hydrolysates has also been described (Bremner, 1965b).

Present data concerning the amounts of α-amino-N or amino-N liberated by hydrolysis of soils indicate that from 20 to 40% of the total nitrogen in most surface soils is in the form of amino acids (Kojima, 1947a; Bremner, 1949a, 1959; Rendig, 1951; Parker et al., 1952; Wittich, 1952; Laatsch and Schlichting, 1953; Schlichting, 1953a; Stevenson, 1954, 1956b; Sowden, 1955, 1956; Kobo et al., 1956; Cornfield, 1957; Young and Mortensen, 1958; Keeney and Bremner, 1964). The proportion of soil N present as amino acids is low in podzols and heath soils and high in rendzinas (Wittich, 1952; Schlichting, 1953a). It decreases with depth in the profile (Sowden, 1956, 1958; Stevenson, 1957c; Bremner, 1958b, 1959) and is affected by cropping, cultivation, and fertilization (Rendig, 1951; Stevenson, 1956b; Cornfield, 1957; Young and Mortensen, 1958; Keeney and Bremner, 1964; Porter et al., 1964). Estimates of the proportion of soil nitrogen in the form of bound amino acid-N from determinations of the amino acid-N released by acid hydrolysis of soils must be regarded as minimal, because some destruction of amino acids occurs during hydrolysis (see Bremner, 1949a). Moreover, Sowden (1958) has shown that some of the ammonium liberated by hydrolysis of soils is derived from amide (glutamine and asparagine) residues in proteins or other amino-acid complexes.

Early attempts to identify the amino acids in soils were hindered by the lack of satisfactory methods for separation and characterization of amino acids, but by 1950, the following ten amino acids had been detected: leucine (Suzuki, 1906-8; Robinson, 1911; Lathrop, 1917; Kojima, 1947b), isoleucine (Robinson, 1911; Kojima, 1947b), valine (Kojima, 1947b), alanine and proline (Suzuki, 1906-8), arginine and histidine (Schreiner and Shorey, 1910a, c; Lathrop, 1917; Tokuoka and Dyo, 1937), lysine (Shorey, 1913; Lathrop, 1917), aspartic acid (Suzuki, 1906-8; Kojima, 1947b), and tyrosine (Lathrop, 1917). Since 1950, studies of the amino acids in soils have been simplified by the development of chromatographic methods of identifying and estimating amino acids, and many investigations involving application of these methods to acid hydrolysates of soils or soil organic matter preparations have now been reported (Bremner, 1950a, b, 1952, 1955a, c, d; Davidson et al., 1951; Parker et al., 1952; Stevenson, 1954, 1956a, b, 1960b; Okuda and Hori, 1954, 1955, 1956; Pavel et al., 1954, 1955; Black et al., 1955; Sowden, 1955, 1956, 1958; Kononova and Aleksandrova, 1956; Turchin, 1956; Biswas and Das, 1957; Davies et al., 1957;

Carles et al., 1958; Young and Mortensen, 1958; Coulson et al., 1959a; Jenkinson and Tinsley, 1959, 1960; Sowden and Ivarson, 1959; Carles and Decau, 1960a, b; Scharpenseel and Krausse, 1962; Grov, 1963b; Yamashita and Akiya, 1963).

Bremner (1950b) studied the amino-acid composition of acid hydrolysates of a wide variety of soils by paper chromatography, and found that the following 20 amino acids were present in every hydrolysate examined: phenylalanine, leucine, isoleucine, valine, alanine, glycine, serine, threonine, aspartic acid, glutamic acid, arginine, histidine, lysine, proline, hydroxyproline, α-amino-n-butyric acid, γ-aminobutyric acid, α,ε-diaminopimelic acid, β-alanine, and tyrosine. Semiquantitative analyses indicated that the first 14 amino acids listed accounted for most of the amino acid-N in the hydrolysates studied. Methionine sulfoxide was found in most of the hydrolysates; tryptophan could not be detected.

The findings in this investigation concerning the amino-acid composition of soils have been confirmed by Stevenson (1954, 1956a, b, 1960b) and other workers, and they have been extended by the detection of cystine, cysteic acid, methionine, methionine sulfone, ornithine, and 3:4-dihydroxyphenylalanine in hydrolysates of soils or soil organic matter preparations (see Table 3). Many unidentified ninhydrin-reacting sub-

Table 3. Amino acids isolated from soils or detected in acid hydrolysates of soils or soil organic matter preparations.

Amino acid	References	Amino acid	References
Basic:		Neutral:	
Arginine	Schreiner & Shorey(1910a, c)	Serine	Bremner (1950a, b)
Histidine	Schreiner & Shorey(1910a, c)	Threonine	Bremner (1950a, b)
Lysine	Shorey (1913)	Proline	Suzuki (1906-8)
Ornithine	Stevenson (1956a, b)	Hydroxyproline	Bremner (1950a, b)
Acidic:		Methionine	Bremner (1955d)
Aspartic acid	Suzuki (1906-8)	Methionine sulfoxide	Bremner (1950b)
Glutamic acid	Bremner (1950a, b)	Methionine sulfone	Pavel et al. (1954)
Neutral:			
Glycine	Bremner (1950a, b)	Cystine	Okuda & Hori (1955)
Alanine	Suzuki (1906-8)	Cysteic acid	Bremner (1952)
Valine	Kojima (1947a)	α-Amino-n-butyric acid	Bremner (1950a, b)
Leucine	Suzuki (1906-8)		
Isoleucine	Robinson (1911)	γ-Aminobutyric acid	Bremner (1950a, b)
Phenylalanine	Bremner (1950a, b)	β-Alanine	Bremner (1950a, b)
3:4-Dihydroxy-phenylalanine	Pavel et al. (1954)	α, ϵ-Diamino-pimelic acid	Bremner (1950b)
Tyrosine	Lathrop (1917)		

stances have also been detected in these hydrolysates (e.g., Pavel et al., 1954; Stevenson, 1954, 1956a, b, 1960b; Bremner, 1955d; Young and Mortensen, 1958). For example, Young and Mortensen (1958) detected more than 50 ninhydrin-reacting substances in desalted hydrolysates of several Ohio soils, and could identify only 23 of these substances. However, the amounts of unidentified ninhydrin-reacting compounds detected have been very small, and there is no evidence to indicate that these compounds account for a significant fraction of the amino acid-N in soils or that they are even amino compounds.

The detection of α,ε-diaminopimelic acid, β-alanine, α-amino-n-butyric acid, γ-aminobutyric acid, ornithine, and 3:4-dihydroxyphenylalanine in soil hydrolysates is of considerable interest, because these amino acids do not occur in proteins. Some of these "nonprotein" amino acids may be artifacts produced during hydrolysis of soils. For example, ornithine could arise from arginine, α-amino-n-butyric acid from threonine, and γ-aminobutyric acid from glutamic acid. However, there is evidence to indicate that the γ-aminobutyric acid and ornithine detected in soil hydrolysates are not artifacts (Bremner, 1955d; Stevenson, 1956a), and the occurrence of most of these "nonprotein" amino acids in natural products is now well established. The detection of α,ε-diaminopimelic acid in soil hydrolysates is of special interest, because this amino acid appears to be confined to bacteria. Cystine and methionine are unstable towards acid hydrolysis, and the cysteic acid, methionine sulfoxide, and methionine sulfone detected in soil hydrolysates are probably artifacts formed by oxidation of cystine and methionine during hydrolysis of soils. Failure to detect tryptophan in acid hydrolysates of soils does not mean that this amino acid is absent from soil, because tryptophan is destroyed by acid hydrolysis. However, the failure of attempts to detect tryptophan in alkaline hydrolysates of soils (Kojima, 1947a; Bremner, 1949a, 1950b) indicates that this amino acid does not occur in more than trace amounts in soils because tryptophan is reasonably stable towards alkaline hydrolysis.

The data obtained by chromatographic analysis of soil hydrolysates indicate that the amino-acid composition of soils is reasonably constant and that variations in this composition are quantitative rather than qualitative (Bremner, 1950a, b; Parker et al., 1952; Sowden, 1955, 1956; Stevenson, 1954, 1956b; Biswas and Das, 1957; Carles et al., 1958; Young and Mortensen, 1958; Sowden and Ivarson, 1959; Carles and Decau, 1960a, b; Yamashita and Akiya, 1963). Carles and his associates studied the distribution of amino acids in French and African soils and concluded that the amino-acid composition of soil is influenced by climate and by the addition of organic matter (Carles et al., 1958; Carles and Decau, 1960a, b). Their work indicated that an increase in soil temperature promotes the growth and activity of bacteria which decarboxylate amino acids (ethanolamine and histamine were detected in several soil hydrolysates). Sowden (1956) studied the amino-acid distribution in several soil profiles and observed no significant difference between various soil types or between various horizons of the same profile. However, Coulson et al. (1959a) found that the surface layers of upland peat soils were characterized by the presence of "nonprotein" amino acids (β-alanine, α-amino-n-butyric acid, 3:4-dihydroxyphenylalanine, etc.).

Ion-exchange chromatography is superior to paper chromatography for quantitative determination of amino acids, and studies by Stevenson (1954, 1956b) and Young and Mortensen (1958) using this technique have provided the best data thus far obtained concerning the amounts of different amino acids released by hydrolysis of soils. Some calculations from the averages of data obtained by these workers in analyses of a Flanagan silt loam containing 0.32% nitrogen (Stevenson, 1956b) and of a Hoytville clay loam containing 0.55% nitrogen (Young and Mortensen, 1958) are given in Table 4. It can be seen that about two-thirds of the amino acid-N

Table 4. Distribution of amino acid-N in soil hydrolysates.*

Amino acid	N in amino acid as % of total amino acid-N	Amino acid	N in amino acid as % of total amino acid-N
Basic:	19.1	Neutral:	66.4
Lysine	10.1	Alanine	11.0
Arginine	3.6	Glycine	10.9
Histidine	2.0	Serine	8.2
Ornithine	3.4	Threonine	7.3
		Valine	6.4
Acidic:	14.5	Leucine	5.0
		Isoleucine	3.4
Glutamic acid	6.3	Proline	4.7
Aspartic acid	8.2	Hydroxyproline	1.2
		Tyrosine	1.2
		Phenylalanine	1.8

* Calculated from data obtained by Stevenson (1956b) and Young and Mortensen (1958).

liberated by hydrolysis of these soils was in the form of neutral amino acids and that about 95% of the amino acid-N so released was accounted for by the amino acids listed. The amino acids not listed include cystine and methionine (or their oxidation products), β-alanine, and γ-amino-butyric acid.

A major difficulty in quantitative estimation of amino acids in soil hydrolysates by ion-exchange chromatography is that the methods available for desalting these hydrolysates before chromatographic analysis can lead to significant (> 20%) loss of amino acid-N (see Young and Mortensen, 1958). Another difficulty is that recovery of amino acid-N from the resin column used for chromatography is not quantitative (see Stevenson, 1956b; Lynch et al., 1959). The importance of desalting soil hydrolysates before amino-acid analysis by ion-exchange chromatography is illustrated by comparison of the results obtained by Sowden (1955, 1956) with undesalted hydrolysates and by Stevenson (1954, 1956a, b) with desalted hydrolysates.

It is commonly assumed that the bound amino acids in soils are in the form of proteins or peptides. Attempts to isolate proteins from soils have not thus far been successful, but many workers have reported the isolation or detection of substances with some of the properties of peptides (e.g., Walters, 1915; Hobson and Page, 1932b, c; De and Mukherjee, 1951; Goulden and Jenkinson, 1959; Jenkinson and Tinsley, 1959, 1960; Scharpenseel and Krausse, 1962; Ladd and Butler, 1964). The failure of attempts to isolate or detect proteins has led many workers to suggest that some of the amino acid-N in soils may be in complexes formed by reaction of quinones or phenolic compounds with amino acids or peptides (see Kononova, 1951, 1961; Flaig, 1955, 1959, 1960; Mason, 1955; Swaby, 1957; Rinderknecht and Jurd, 1958; Coulson et al., 1959c; Kononova and Aleksandrova, 1959; Stein and Tendeloo, 1959; Burges, 1960; Moore and Murphy, 1960; Swaby and Ladd, 1962; Ladd and Butler, 1964), and recent work has shown that some of the nitrogen in polymers formed by reaction of catechol or benzoquinone with glycine or alanine is released as amino acid-N by acid hydrolysis (Swaby, 1957; Coulson et al., 1959c; Ladd and Butler, 1964). The possibility that some of the amino acid-N released by acid hydrolysis of soils is derived from complexes formed by reactions of phenols or quinones with amino acids or peptides clearly cannot be excluded, but there is currently no evidence to indicate that such complexes occur in soils.

It seems very likely that some of the bound amino acid-N in soils is in the form of mucopeptides (amino acid-amino sugar complexes) and teichoic acids (ribitolphosphate or glycerophosphate polymers containing ester-linked alanine), because recent work has shown that these polymers are important constituents of bacterial cell walls (see Salton, 1960). Mucopeptides have several interesting features. For example, they contain an amino sugar not previously detected in natural substances (muramic acid) and only a few (3-5) amino acids. Their amino acid-N is largely in the form of alanine, glutamic acid, and lysine or diaminopimelic acid, and a considerable proportion of the alanine and glutamic acid is in the D-form of these amino acids. Diaminopimelic acid (a "nonprotein" amino acid) and D-amino acids have been detected in soil hydrolysates (Bremner, 1950b), but the small amounts of D-amino acids detected could have arisen by racemization of L-amino acids during hydrolysis. Teichoic acids are major cell wall constituents of Gram-positive bacteria and account for as much as 50% of the material in some bacterial cell walls.* Several types of teichoic acids have been recognized, but all contain ester-linked alanine. On hydrolysis, they yield alanine, ribitol or glycerol, inorganic phosphate, and usually a sugar (glucose) or amino sugar (glucosamine). The detection of ester-linked alanine in these bacterial polymers is of considerable interest, because this type of linkage of an amino acid has not previously been observed in natural products.

Until recently, there was no reliable evidence for the occurrence of free amino acids in soils. Some evidence was provided by the isolation of arginine, histidine, and lysine from extracts obtained by treatment of soils with dilute alkali (2% NaOH) at room temperature (Schreiner and Shorey, 1910a, c; Shorey, 1913; Tokuoka and Dyo, 1937) and by work reported by Kivekäs (1939), but this evidence could be criticized on the grounds that the isolation or identification techniques used in these studies may have caused hydrolysis of peptides. However, recent chromatographic studies of soil extracts obtained by mild treatments which are not likely to cause release of amino acids from peptides or other organic substances containing bound amino acids have provided good evidence for the occurrence of small amounts of free amino acids in soils (Bremner, 1952; Dadd et al., 1953; Simonart and Peeters, 1954; Dhar and Roy, 1955;

---

* The possibility that a significant proportion of the organic phosphorus in soils may be in the form of teichoic acids seems to deserve consideration, because research on the nature of this phosphorus has indicated that not more than one-third of it can be accounted for as nucleic acids, nucleotides, inositol phosphates, or phospholipids.

Putnam and Schmidt, 1959; Paul and Schmidt, 1960, 1961; Grov, 1963a; Grov and Alvsaker, 1963). The amino acids detected in these studies include most of the amino acids found in acid hydrolysates of soils (e.g., glycine, alanine, valine, leucine, isoleucine phenylalanine, tyrosine, serine, threonine, aspartic acid, glutamic acid, lysine, arginine, histidine, β-alanine, γ-aminobutyric acid, cystine, and proline). The occurrence of glutamine and asparagine in soil extracts has also been reported.

Several difficulties have been encountered in attempts to detect and estimate free amino acids in soils. One is that the amounts present are so small that highly sensitive methods of analysis are required for their investigation. Putnam and Schmidt (1959) found that microbiological assay techniques did not have the sensitivity required, but that the presence of free amino acids could be readily demonstrated by elution chromatography of concentrated ethanolic extracts of soils. Another difficulty is that extensive loss of amino acids can apparently occur when soil extracts are concentrated by relatively mild treatments. Payne et al. (1956) found that ninhydrin-reacting substances were readily detectable in cold aqueous extracts of soils when the extracts were concentrated by freeze-drying, but were not detectable when the extracts were concentrated *in vacuo* at 40°C. Bremner (1950b) was unable to detect amino acids or other ninhydrin-reacting substances on paper chromatograms of cold aqueous extracts of several neutral clay loams and fen soils which had been concentrated *in vacuo* at 40°C before analysis. A third, and major, difficulty is that although soils contain amino acids which are free in the sense that they are not combined with other organic substances, these amino acids do become sorbed to soil surfaces (Putnam and Schmidt, 1959; Paul and Schmidt, 1960; Schmidt et al., 1960). This sorption complicates the extraction of free amino acids from soils, and no quantitative method of extraction has been developed. The reagents which have been used for extraction include water, ethanol (70-80%), and barium hydroxide and ammonium acetate solutions. Paul and Schmidt (1960) studied the efficiency of various reagents and confirmed other evidence (Putnam and Schmidt, 1959; Schmidt et al., 1960) that water and ethanol are very inefficient. They found that 0.1N barium hydroxide and neutral 0.5N ammonium acetate were much more effective than water or ethanol, and that extracts obtained using these reagents contained a greater variety, and much greater amounts, of amino acids than did ethanol extracts. In subsequent work, they analyzed neutral ammonium acetate extracts of rhizosphere and nonrhizosphere soils by elution chromatography and found that these extracts contained about 15 amino acids totaling 2 to 4 μg per g of soil and numerous unidentified substances at concentrations estimated as 0.1 to 0.5 μg per g of soil (Paul and Schmidt, 1961). They also confirmed previous evidence (Putnam and Schmidt, 1959; Paul and Schmidt, 1960) that incubation of soil after addition of glucose and nitrate to stimulate microbial activity leads to a marked increase in the concentration of free amino acids and that soils treated with glucose and nitrate contain a greater variety of free amino acids than untreated soils (i.e., that the forms and amounts of free amino acid-N are related to the level of microbial activity). Other investigations of the effects of microbial activity on the free amino acid content of soils have been reported (Simonart and Buysse, 1954; Simonart et al., 1957).

The ammonium acetate extraction procedure used by Paul and Schmidt has the disadvantage that it does not effect quantitative recovery of neutral or acidic amino acids and gives only 30 to 50% recovery of basic amino acids (Paul and Schmidt, 1960). Nevertheless, this procedure is the most effective thus far developed for extraction of free amino acids in soils, and the data obtained by Paul and Schmidt (1960, 1961) using this extraction technique leave very little doubt that the total amount of free amino acid-N in soils rarely exceeds about 2 μg per g of soil. The occurrence of more than trace amounts of free amino acids in soils seems unlikely, because most amino acids are rapidly decomposed when added to soils (Quastel and Scholefield, 1949; Bremner, 1949a; Greenwood and Lees, 1956; Wheeler and Yemm, 1958; Putnam and Schmidt, 1959; Schmidt et al., 1960).

C. Amino Sugars

The first evidence for the presence of amino sugars in soils was provided by the finding that soil hydrolysates gave positive tests for 2-amino sugars (hexosamines) and by the detection of glucosamine on paper chromatograms of soil hydrolysates (Bremner, 1949a, 1950a, b). There is now good evidence that both D-glucosamine (2-deoxy-2-amino-D-glucose) and D-galactosamine (2-deoxy-2-amino-D-galactose) occur in soils and that from 5 to 10% of the nitrogen in most surface soils is in the form of hexosamines.

The presence of both glucosamine (chitosamine) and galactosamine (chondrosamine) in soils has been established by chromatographic analysis of soil hydrolysates (Stevenson, 1954, 1956a, b; Bremner, 1958a; Young and Mortensen, 1958; Sowden, 1959) and by isolation of these compounds as their hydrochlorides (Bremner, 1958a). The presence of acetylated 2-amino sugars (N-acetyl-D-glucosamine or N-acetyl-D-galactosamine) in soil hydrolysates has been reported (Stevenson, 1954, 1956a, b; Young and Mortensen, 1958), but these reports have not been confirmed (Bremner, 1958a; Stevenson, 1960b). No other amino sugars have been detected in soils, and the hexosamine-N released by acid hydrolysis of soils appears to be largely, if not entirely, in the form of glucosamine and galactosamine (Bremner, 1958a; Sowden, 1959).

Sowden (1959) determined the ratio of glucosamine to galactosamine in soil hydrolysates by a modification of Moore and Stein's (1951) chromatographic method of determining basic amino acids and found that the ratio varied from 1.6 to 4.1 being highest with podzol soils and lowest with prairie soils. His data supported previous indications that this ratio tends to increase with decrease in soil pH and to be higher where fungi are relatively more important than bacteria (Sowden and Ivarson, 1959).

The methods used for determination of amino sugars in soils involve hydrolysis with 6N HCl at 100°C for 6 to 9 hours to release bound amino sugars, and analysis of the hydrolysate by colorimetric, distillation, or chromatographic techniques. The hydrolysis procedure used is essentially that adopted by Smithies (1952) for hydrolysis of amino-sugar complexes in fungal mycelium, and the methods used for analysis of the hydrolysate are modifications of those developed by Elson and Morgan (1933), Tracey (1952), and Eastoe (1954) for estimation of 2-amino sugars.

The determination of amino sugars in soils and other biological materials is complicated by the fact that significant decomposition of hexosamines occurs under the conditions required for hydrolysis of the amino-sugar complexes present in these materials. Bremner and Shaw (1954) found that the recoveries of hexosamine-N after hydrolysis of glucosamine and chitin with 6N HCl at 100°C for 6 hours were 86.9 and 80.3%, respectively, and that these recoveries were not significantly affected by the presence of soil during the hydrolysis. They concluded that use of a correction factor to allow for decomposition of hexosamines during acid hydrolysis of soils was justified, and they applied a correction factor of 1.25 to the hexosamine-N values obtained using a 6-hour period of hydrolysis. Stevenson (1957a) also found that the recoveries of hexosamine-N after hydrolysis with 6N HCl at 100°C were not significantly affected by the presence of soil during the hydrolysis. From the recoveries he obtained with glucosamine (87.5% after 6 hours, and 84.1% after 9 hours), he concluded that the appropriate correction factors for the results obtained in analysis of soil hydrolysates were 1.143 using a 6-hour period of hydrolysis, and 1.19 using a 9-hour period. Sowden (1959) corrected for loss of hexosamine-N during hydrolysis of soils with 6N HCl by determining the amount of hexosamine-N present after different periods of hydrolysis, plotting the log of the amount against time of hydrolysis, and extrapolating to zero time to estimate the 'true' hexosamine value. He found that the average factors necessary to correct 8-hour hydrolysis data were 1.25 for glucosamine, 1.26 for galactosamine, and 1.21 for total hexosamine. These correction factors are similar to those used by Bremner and Shaw and by Stevenson, and there appears little doubt that the application of correction factors to allow for decomposition of hexosamines during acid hydrolysis of soils is justified. Bremner (1965b) has recently described a simple distillation method of determining hexosamine-N in soils in which hydrolysis is effected by heating the soil sample with 6N HCl under reflux for 12 hours. This hydrolysis procedure causes greater decomposition of hexosamines than the methods previously used for hydrolysis of amino-sugar complexes (the correction factor required is about 1.4), but has the advantage that it also serves for determination of amino acid-N in soils.

The colorimetric and distillation methods used for determination of hexosamines in soil hydrolysates give similar results (Bremner and Shaw, 1954) and appear to be reliable (for descriptions and discussions of these methods, see Bremner and Shaw, 1954; Bremner, 1965b; Stevenson, 1957a, 1965a). The chromatographic method adopted by Sowden (1959) also appears satisfactory, and the results obtained by this method in studies of the distribution of hexosamine-N in soils are similar to those obtained using colorimetric and distillation procedures. Cessi and Piliego (1960) and Cessi and Serafini-Cessi (1963) have recently described methods of determining amino sugars which appear very suitable for analysis of soil hydrolysates, but no estimations of hexosamine-N in soils by these methods have been reported.

Present estimates indicate that from 5 to 10% of the nitrogen in most surface soils is in the form of hexosamines (Bremner and Shaw, 1954; Stevenson, 1957a, b, c; Sowden, 1959; Singh and Singh, 1960; Cheng and Kurtz, 1963; Keeney and Bremner, 1964). Stevenson (1957a, b, c) studied the distribution of amino sugars in soil profiles representative of several great soil groups and found that from 5 to 13% of the nitrogen in the surface soils examined was hexosamine-N. He also found that with a number of soils the proportion of nitrogen in the form of amino sugars increased with depth in the profile, usually reaching a maximum in the B horizon (see also Sowden, 1959; Cheng and Kurtz, 1963). The maximal accumulation of hexosamine-N observed was in the B horizon of Cisne silt loam (a planosol developed under grass vegetation) where 24% of the total nitrogen was in the form of hexosamines. Studies of the effects of drainage, vegetation, and cultivation on the amounts of hexosamine-N in soils have been reported (Stevenson, 1957a, b; Keeney and Bremner, 1964).

No free amino sugars have been detected in soils, and the amino sugar nitrogen in soils appears to be largely, if not entirely, in the form of high-molecular substances. The nature of these substances is still obscure. The presence of chitin (a polymer of N-acetylglucosamine) in soils has been reported (see Waksman, 1938), but the material referred to as 'chitin' in these reports was not adequately characterized, and the occurrence of chitin in soils has not been demonstrated. Nevertheless, it seems very likely that some of the hexosamine-N in soils is in the form of chitin, because this substance occurs in most fungi and in the exoskeletons of soil-inhabiting insects. Amino sugars occur in many substances synthesized by microorganisms (e.g., polysaccharides, teichoic acids, mucopeptides, antibiotics), and most of the amino sugar nitrogen in soils is probably of microbial origin. It is relevant in this connection that amino sugars have been detected in several apparently microbially-derived polysaccharides isolated from soils (e.g., Whistler and Kirby, 1956; Parsons and Tinsley, 1961) and that studies of nitrogen transformations during the biological decomposition of plant materials have shown that microbial decomposition of straws and forest litters is accompanied by synthesis of hexosamines (Bremner, 1955b; Sowden and Ivarson, 1959). Bremner (1955d) detected both glucosamine and galactosamine in acid hydrolysates of humic acid preparations isolated from alkali and neutral pyrophosphate extracts of various soils, and found that from 3 to 10% of the nitrogen in these preparations was hexosamine-N. This confirmed previous evidence (Bremner, 1949a) that soils contain amino sugar complexes which, unlike chitin, are soluble in alkali or neutral pyrophosphate. Further evidence that soils contain amino sugar complexes besides chitin has been provided by the detection of hexosamines in hydrolysates of the fulvic fraction of soil organic matter (Stevenson, 1960a) and of aqueous and neutral pyrophosphate extracts of soils (Coulson et al., 1959a; Waldron and Mortensen, 1961).

Recent work has shown that several substances synthesized by microorganisms contain amino sugars other than glucosamine and galactosamine (see Stacey and Barker, 1960, 1962; Salton, 1960), and some of these amino sugars probably occur in soils. For example, it seems very likely that muramic acid (3-O-carboxyethyl-D-glucosamine) occurs in soils, because, like glucosamine, it has been detected in all bacterial cell walls thus far examined (see Salton, 1960). However, there is evidence to indicate that, if this 2-amino sugar occurs in soils, the amount present is much smaller than the amounts of glucosamine or galactosamine (Bremner, 1958a; Sowden, 1959; Sowden and Ivarson, 1959).

D. Purines and Pyrimidines

Four purine derivatives (adenine, guanine, xanthine, hypoxanthine) and three pyrimidine derivatives (cytosine, uracil, thymine) have been isolated from soils or soil preparations (Table 5). Adenine, guanine,

Table 5. Purine and pyrimidine derivatives in soils.

Derivative	References
Purine:	
Adenine	Schreiner and Lathrop, 1912; Shorey, 1913; Lathrop, 1917; Bottomley, 1919; Wrenshall and McKibbin, 1937; Anderson, 1957, 1958, 1961.
Guanine	Lathrop, 1912; Schreiner and Lathrop, 1912; Bottomley, 1919; Wrenshall and Dyer, 1941; Anderson, 1957, 1958, 1961.
Xanthine	Schreiner and Shorey, 1910a,b; Schreiner and Lathrop, 1912.
Hypoxanthine	Schreiner and Shorey, 1910a,b; Schreiner and Lathrop, 1912.
Pyrimidine:	
Cytosine	Schreiner and Shorey, 1910a,b; Schreiner and Lathrop, 1912; Lathrop, 1917; Bottomley, 1919; Anderson, 1957, 1958, 1961.
Uracil	Bottomley, 1919; Wrenshall and McKibbin, 1937; Anderson, 1957, 1958, 1961.
Thymine	Anderson, 1957, 1958, 1961.

cytosine, thymine, and uracil are components of nucleic acids. Xanthine and hypoxanthine are products of microbial decomposition of nucleic acids, xanthine being formed by enzymatic deamination of guanine, and hypoxanthine by enzymatic deamination of adenine.

Most of the information currently available concerning the occurrence of purine and pyrimidine derivatives in soils has emerged from work designed to elucidate the nature of soil organic phosphorus. During the period 1910-1920, evidence that some of this phosphorus is in the form of nucleic acids (or nucleotides) was provided by the isolation of purine and pyrimidine derivatives from soil extracts and by the detection of hydrolysis products of nucleic acids (phosphoric acid, pentose sugars, purine and pyrimidine bases) in hydrolysates of phosphorus-rich fractions of soil organic matter (Schreiner and Shorey, 1910a, b; Shorey, 1911, 1912a, 1913; Schreiner and Lathrop, 1912; Lathrop, 1912, 1917; Bottomley, 1919). As interest in the nature of soil organic phosphorus increased, efforts were made to obtain quantitative estimates of the amounts of nucleic acid phosphorus in soils, and by 1950 there was evidence to indicate that between one-third and two-thirds of the organic phosphorus in soils is nucleic acid phosphorus (Wrenshall and McKibbin, 1937; Sokolov, 1948; Bower, 1949). However, recent work by Adams et al. (1954) and Anderson (1957, 1958, 1961) indicates that these estimates of the amounts of nucleic acid phosphorus in soils are much too high. Adams et al. (1954) used ion-exchange chromatography and spectrophotometric methods to estimate ribonucleic acid phosphorus in soil extracts. Their results indicated that a Carrington soil containing 575 ppm of organic phosphorus, and a Webster soil containing 327 ppm, contained not more than 1 ppm and 6 ppm, respectively, of ribonucleic acid phosphorus. Moreover, they were unable to detect purine bases in soil hydrolysates. They concluded that neither ribonucleic acid (RNA) nor deoxyribonucleic acid (DNA) exists in the soil in appreciable quantities.

Anderson (1957, 1958) detected guanine, adenine, cytosine, thymine, and uracil in hydrolysates of humic acid fractions of three Scottish agricultural soils. The quantities of guanine, adenine, cytosine, and thymine were of the same order; uracil was present in only trace amount. Since RNA would be almost completely degraded to acid-soluble derivatives by the method used to separate the humic acid fractions examined in this work, Anderson concluded that the purines and pyrimidines detected in these fractions were largely in the form of DNA. The relative proportions of guanine, adenine, cytosine, and thymine in the humic acid fraction of one soil indicated that the DNA present was unlike that usually found in plants and animals, but like that found in some bacteria. The pyrimidine 5-methylcytosine, which is found in DNA from plant sources, was not detected. Only 0.6% of the total organic phosphorus in one soil could be accounted for as DNA phosphorus. Anderson (1961) later developed an improved method of estimating purine and pyrimidine bases in soil humic acids and applied this method to a variety of soils. The results indicated that these bases accounted for only 0.06 to 0.88% of the total nitrogen in the soils examined. The proportions of guanine, adenine, cytosine, and thymine indicated that these bases were probably in the form of polynucleotides derived mainly from bacterial DNA.

To summarize, the occurrence of purine and pyrimidine bases in soils is well established, but present information indicates that the proportion of soil nitrogen in the form of these bases is very small and probably does not exceed about 1%

E. Other Identified Forms

In addition to the organic nitrogen compounds discussed above, the following have been detected in soils or soil products:

1. Trimethylamine (Shorey, 1913)
2. Ethanolamine (Carles and Decau, 1960a; Grov, 1963a; Grov and Alvsaker, 1963; Hance and Anderson, 1963)

   3. Histamine (Carles and Decau, 1960a)

   4. Choline (Aso, 1905; Shorey, 1913; Hance and Anderson, 1963)

   5. Creatinine (Schreiner et al., 1911; Shorey, 1912b)

   6. Allantoin (Shorey, 1938)

   7. Cyanuric acid (Walters and Wise, 1917; Wise and Walters, 1917; Ichikawa, 1936)

   8. α-Picoline-γ-carboxylic acid (Shorey, 1907; Schreiner and Shorey, 1908, 1909)

   9. Urea (Fosse, 1916)

Trimethylamine was detected by Shorey (1913) in the products obtained when a Georgia salt marsh soil was made alkaline and distilled under reduced pressure. This compound occurs in plant and animal products added to soils and may be produced in soils through microbial decomposition of compounds such as choline.

Carles and Decau (1960a) detected ethanolamine and histamine in soil hydrolysates and concluded that these compounds are formed in soils by decarboxylation of amino acids.

Grov (1963a) and Grov and Alvsaker (1963) detected ethanolamine in aqueous extracts of the F-, H-, and A-layers of a pine forest soil profile.

Hance and Anderson (1963) detected both ethanolamine and choline in the products liberated by acid hydrolysis of a phosphorus-rich fraction of soil organic matter. The amount of choline detected was much greater than the amount of ethanolamine. Since the fraction examined was separated by a procedure used for isolation of lipids and yielded glycerophosphate when subjected to alkaline hydrolysis, Hance and Anderson concluded that it contained phospholipids and that phosphatidyl choline was one of the predominant lipid components. The most common phospholipids in plants and microorganisms are the glycerophosphatides, which often contain choline or ethanolamine. Choline had previously been isolated from alkali extracts of soils (Aso, 1905; Shorey, 1913). It occurs in plants not only as lipids but as the free base and in such compounds as acetylcholine.

Creatinine has been isolated from both alkali and aqueous extracts of soils in concentrations equivalent to several parts per million of dry soil (Schreiner et al., 1911; Shorey, 1912b) and allantoin has been isolated in similar amounts from aqueous soil extracts (Shorey, 1938). Creatinine occurs in stable manure, urine, and leguminous plants.

Shorey and Walters (1914) isolated a compound they called tetracarbonimid from the fulvic fraction of an alkali extract of soil, but later work by Walters and Wise (1917) showed that this compound was actually cyanuric acid. Cyanuric acid has been detected in a variety of soils (Wise and Walters, 1917), and Ichikawa (1936) found that it accounted for 0.30% of the total nitrogen in one soil he examined. It may be formed in soils by decomposition of uric acid.

A pyridine derivative identified as α-picoline-γ-carboxylic acid was isolated from a Hawaiian soil by Shorey (1907) and from other soils by Schreiner and Shorey (1908, 1909). Schreiner and Shorey (1909) have suggested that this compound may be formed in soils by decomposition of tryptophan.

Urea has been detected in forest soils and other soils rich in organic matter (Fosse, 1916), but its occurrence in mineral soils has not been reported.

Baudisch and Euler (1935) obtained some evidence for the presence of chlorophylls and related substances in soils, and Kamoshita (1942) concluded that the reddish fluorescence of acetone extracts of soils was due to the presence of "chlorophylls.' Chlorophyll derivatives have been detected in lake and marine deposits (Vallentyne, 1957) and in woodland soils (Gorham, 1959), and recent work indicates that they are present in grassland and cultivated soils (Hoyt and Cooke, 1963; Hoyt, 1964). However, studies of the decomposition of chlorophylls and related substances in soils indicate that very little of the organic nitrogen in arable soils is in the form of chlorophyll-type compounds (see Hoyt and Cooke, 1963; Hoyt, 1964).

Shmuk (1924) and Flaig and Breyhan (1956) have reported the occurrence of heterocyclic nitrogen compounds in alkaline fusion products of soil humic acids. Shmuk (1924) detected pyrrole and indole derivatives (e.g., skatole) in alkaline fusion products of chernozem humic acids, and Flaig and Breyhan (1956) detected substances which gave color tests for indole derivatives in products obtained by alkaline fusion of the nonhydrolyzable fraction of black earth humic acids. However, alkali fusion is a drastic treatment, and detection of pyrrole or indole derivatives in alkali fusion products of soil organic matter does not mean that these derivatives occur in soils. Also, Steclink et al. (1960) have detected resorcinol and other phenolic compounds in alkali fusion products of podzol humic acids and have shown that several phenols give the color tests used by Flaig and Breyhan (1956) for detection of indole-type compounds. Substances with auxin activity similar to that of indole-3-acetic acid have been detected in soils (see Vallentyne, 1957), but there is no evidence that indole derivatives, or any of the other forms of nitrogen discussed in this subsection, account for a significant amount of the organic nitrogen in soils.

F. Unidentified Forms

Numerous theories have been advanced concerning the nature and mode of formation of the nitrogenous organic complexes in soils, and a detailed discussion and evaluation of these theories is beyond the scope of this review. It may be pointed out, however, that, to merit attention, any theory concerning the nature of the unidentified organic nitrogen in soils must help to account for the finding that most of this nitrogen is either not dissolved by treatment of soils with hot acid or is converted to ammonium by this treatment. Also, any theory concerning the nature of the organic nitrogen complexes in soils should provide some explanation of other well-established properties of these complexes, e.g., their high resistance to mineralization by soil microorganisms (see section VI).

The lignin-protein theory of humus formation advanced by Hobson and Page (1932b) and Waksman and Iyer (1932) to account for the biological and chemical properties of the organic nitrogen complexes in soils has the merit that it provides some explanation of the resistance of these complexes to mineralization by soil microorganisms (see section VI) and there is now some evidence to indicate that lignin-protein complexes may occur in soils (Tinsley and Zin, 1954; Jenkinson and Tinsley, 1959, 1960; Goulden and Jenkinson, 1959). However, the limitations of this theory have long been apparent, and these have been emphasized in recent years by the failure of attempts to demonstrate the occurrence of substantial amounts of protein material in soils and by the finding that only about one-third of the organic nitrogen in surface soils can be definitely accounted for as combined amino acid-N. Also, there is now a considerable amount of evidence to support Gottlieb and Hendrick's (1946) conclusion that if a major fraction of soil organic matter is lignin-derived, the amount in the form of unaltered lignin is not appreciable. For example, it has been found that whereas plant lignins give substantial yields (as much as 25%) of phenolic aldehydes (e.g., vanillin, syringaldehyde) when oxidized with nitrobenzene in alkaline solution, the corresponding yields by alkaline nitrobenzene oxidation of soil organic matter usually do not exceed about 1% (Bremner, 1955c; Morrison, 1958, 1963). An obvious criticism of the lignin-protein theory is that it does not account for the finding that a considerable proportion of the organic nitrogen in soils is not dissolved by acid hydrolysis and that a substantial amount of the nitrogen released by hydrolysis is in the form of ammonium. The same criticism applies to theories that most of the organic nitrogen in soils is in complexes formed by reactions of proteins with quinones or with phenolic substances besides lignins (e.g., tannins), because Laatsch and Schlichting (1953) found that the proportions of protein-N converted to acid-insoluble forms or to ammonium by hydrolysis of gelatin with 6N HCl for 12 hours were not significantly increased if the gelatin hydrolyzed was in the form of a complex with lignin, tannin, catechin, or quinone humic acid.

Early workers assumed that most of the organic nitrogen in soils occurred as proteins and that much of the nitrogen in residues from treatment of soils with hot acid was in the form of acid-insoluble humin produced during acid hydrolysis of proteins. The acid-insoluble humin formed when purified proteins are hydrolyzed with acid usually contains only a few per cent of the total protein-N, but humin formation during protein hydrolysis is greatly increased by the presence of carbohydrates. This is believed to be due to condensation of the amino acids (particularly tryptophan) and furfural liberated during acid hydrolysis of protein-carbohydrate mixtures. Since soil organic matter contains a substantial amount of carbohydrate material, including pentosans and other substances that yield furfural on acid hydrolysis, the possibility that a large amount of the organic nitrogen in residues from treatment of soils with hot acid may be in humin-like material formed by reactions of amino acids (or other amino compounds) with furfural (or other carbohydrate derivatives) liberated during acid hydrolysis of soils clearly cannot be excluded. However, Kojima (1947a) and Bremner (1949a) have obtained several indications that the amount of acid-insoluble humin-N formed by such reactions during acid hydrolysis of soils is probably very small. For example, they found that when hydrolysis of soil was carried out with alkali or with alkali or acid under reducing conditions, the amount of nonhydrolyzable nitrogen was not greatly different from the amount found using acid hydrolysis, and it is known that humin formation during protein hydrolysis is greatly reduced if hydrolysis is performed with alkali or with acid or alkali under reducing conditions. Also, they found that tryptophan, which is destroyed by acid hydrolysis but not by alkali hydrolysis, could not be detected in alkali hydrolysates of soils. It seems unlikely, therefore, that a significant amount of the nitrogen in residues from treatment of soils with hot acid is in the form of humin material produced by condensation of tryptophan and furfural liberated during this treatment. Kojima (1947a) found that the amount of acid insoluble-N obtained when a casein-soil mixture was hydrolyzed with 6N HCl was not significantly greater than the amount obtained when the constituents of this mixture were hydrolyzed separately.

Many workers have postulated that some of the nitrogen in soil organic matter is in the form of complexes produced in soils by reactions of phenolic substances or quinones with amino acids (e.g., Laatsch, 1948; Laatsch et al., 1950, 1951, 1952; Kononova, 1951, 1961; Flaig, 1955, 1959, 1960; Swaby, 1957; Coulson et al., 1959c; Kononova and Aleksandrova, 1959; Swaby and Ladd, 1962; Ladd and Butler, 1964). These theories clearly merit attention, because there is little doubt that the reactants and the enzymes required for these reactions are produced during the decomposition of plant materials in soils and because the dark-colored substances produced by these reactions exhibit some of the properties of the humic substances found in soils (Hackman and Todd, 1953; Mason, 1955; Swaby, 1957; Rinderknecht and Jurd, 1958; Coulson et al., 1959c; Stein and Tendeloo, 1959; Ladd and Butler, 1964). For example, recent work has shown that some of the nitrogen in polymers formed by reaction of catechol or benzoquinone with glycine or alanine is not dissolved by hydrolysis with 6N HCl and that a considerable amount of the nitrogen released by this treatment is amino acid-N and ammonium-N (Ladd and Butler, 1964). Work by Sørensen (1962) has suggested that reactions between oxidized lignins and amino acids may occur during the biological decomposition of plant materials in soils.

Studies by Mattson and Koutler-Andersson (1942, 1943) have suggested that some of the nonhydrolyzable organic soil nitrogen may be present as nitrogenous complexes formed in soils by reaction of oxidized lignins with ammonia. They prepared such complexes by autoxidation of lignin in ammonium hydroxide and showed that part of the nitrogen fixed by lignin in this reaction was resistant towards strong acid and alkali. They also studied the fixation of ammonia by organic compounds of known constitution and concluded that fixation of ammonia by lignin takes place at phenolic hydroxyl groups and is preceded by oxidation of these groups. Some support for this conclusion was provided by Bennett's (1949) finding that methylation of lignin markedly reduced the ammonia-fixing capacity of this material. The lignin-ammonia theory of humus formation advanced by Mattson and Koutler-Andersson helps to account for the biological stability of the organic nitrogen in soils and for the finding that a significant proportion of this nitrogen is released as ammonium by acid hydrolysis, because it has been found that the organic nitrogen in complexes formed by reaction of lignin with ammonia is highly resistant to mineralization by soil microorganisms and that a considerable amount of this nitrogen is liberated as ammonium by hydrolysis with 6N HCl (Bremner, 1955d; Bremner and Shaw, 1957). Considerable support for this theory has been provided by the finding that soil organic matter and various organic substances added to soils have the ability to fix substantial amounts of ammonia and that significant fixation of ammonia-N by soil organic matter can occur when soils are treated with ammonium or ammonium-yielding fertilizers (Sohn and Peech, 1958; Jansson, 1960a, b; Broadbent et al., 1960; Burge and Broadbent, 1961; Nõmmik and Nilsson, 1963). Since current knowledge and theories concerning the mechanism of ammonia fixation by soil organic matter are reviewed in chapters 5 and 6, this topic will not be discussed here. However, attention may be drawn to the fact that there is very little evidence to support the present assumption that the lignin or lignin-derived fraction of soil organic matter is primarily responsible for this fixation. It is relevant in this connection that Chang et al. (1961) recently found that the hemicellulose fraction of sugar cane bagasse was largely responsible for ammonia fixation by this material and that the lignin fraction had little capacity to fix ammonia. The most obvious defect of the lignin-ammonia theory is that it does not account for the finding that more than 40% of the organic nitrogen in most surface soils is in the form of combined amino acids and amino sugars.

Führ and Bremner recently found that a chemical reaction between soil organic matter and nitrite can occur when soils are treated with nitrite, and that this reaction leads to conversion of nitrite-N to gaseous forms of nitrogen and to fixation of nitrite-N by soil organic matter (Bremner and Führ, 1964; Führ and Bremner, 1964a, b). They also found that the nitrogen fixed by soil organic matter in its reaction with nitrite is not readily mineralized by soil microorganisms, that only about half of this nitrogen is released by hydrolysis with 6N HCl for 12 hours, and that about three-quarters of the nitrogen released by acid hydrolysis is in the form of ammonium. These observations suggest that some of the organic nitrogen in soils may be in the form of nitroso or other types of nitrogenous groups formed by reaction of soil organic matter with nitrite. However, soils rarely contain significant amounts of nitrite, and it is doubtful if this reaction occurs to any significant extent under normal field conditions.

Several workers (e.g., Maillard, 1912, 1917; Enders, 1942; Schuffelen and Bolt, 1950; Bremner, 1956; Dawson, 1956; Stevenson, 1960a; Konogova, 1961) have suggested that some of the organic nitrogen in soils may be in complexes formed by reactions of carbohydrates or their derivatives (sugars, methyl glyoxal, etc.) with amino compounds (amino acids, amines, proteins, etc.). Maillard (1912, 1917) studied the reactions of sugars with amino compounds and concluded that the brown materials (melanoidins) formed by these reactions were similar to soil humic acids. These so-called Maillard or browning reactions have been studied intensively in recent years because of their importance in food technology, and they have been found to involve formation of N-substituted glycosylamines by addition reactions and subsequent Amadori rearrangement of these glycosylamines to products which polymerize with formation of the brown nitrogenous substances described as melanoidins. Sugar recovery by hydrolysis apparently ceases after the Amadori rearrangement and only about half of the amino-N can be recovered at this point. The polymerization reactions are extremely complex and their mechanisms have not been fully elucidated (for reviews of the chemistry of these reactions, see Hodge, 1953, 1955; Ellis and Honeyman, 1955; Ellis, 1959). Enders (1942) considered that the formation of humic substances in soils has much in common with the formation of melanoidins during the manufacture of beer and advanced the theory that both humic acids and melanoidins are formed by condensation of amino acids with methyl glyoxal produced by autolysis of microorganisms. He postulated that when the metabolic processes of microorganisms are disturbed by autolysis the decomposition products of proteins (amino acids) and carbohydrates (methyl glyoxal) are no longer used up in normal metabolism and condense to form humic substances. Support for this theory has been provided by the finding that methyl glyoxal will react with amino acids to produce humic substances under physiological conditions and that methyl glyoxal-amino acid condensation products have properties similar to those of soil humic acids (Enders and Sigurdsson, 1947; Schuffelen and Bolt, 1950). Further support has been provided by the detection of methyl glyoxal in soils, in humified materials from various sources, and in products of autolysis of microorganisms (for references to this work and to other literature concerning Enders's methyl glyoxal theory see Bremner, 1954; Dawson, 1956).

The reactants required for browning reactions are undoubtedly formed during the microbial decomposition of plant materials in soils, and the products of these reactions exhibit some of the properties of the organic nitrogen complexes in soils. For example, part of the nitrogen in browning products is not dissolved by acid hydrolysis and some of the nitrogen released by this treatment is in the form of ammonium. Stevenson (1960a) has suggested that the readily deaminated nitrogenous pigments in the fulvic fraction of soil organic matter may be formed by browning reactions, and much geochemical importance has been attributed to the Maillard reaction in recent research concerning the biogeochemistry of organic matter. However, as Vallentyne (1964) has pointed out, there is very little evidence to indicate that this reaction occurs in soils or sediments.

Several workers (e.g., Kojima, 1947a; Bremner, 1949a; Flaig, 1950, Flaig and Breyhan, 1956) have suggested that some of the nonhydrolyzable nitrogen in soils may be in the form of heterocyclic nitrogen compounds (e.g., indole, pyrrole, or pyridine derivatives), but there is no evidence to support this suggestion (see section IV, E). Flaig (1950) found that when hydroquinone was oxidized in ammonium hydroxide solution the product contained about 6% of apparently heterocyclically bound nitrogen which was resistant to distillation with concentrated alkali, and several workers have postulated mechanisms whereby heterocyclic nitrogen compounds may be formed in soils by reactions of phenolic substances or quinones with ammonia, amines, or amino acids (e.g., Laatsch, 1948; Flaig, 1950, 1960; Jansson, 1960b; Murphy and Moore, 1960). If, as Laatsch (1948) and other workers have suggested, quinone-ammonia reactions are important in the formation of humic substances in soils, then there is a possibility that some of the organic nitrogen in soils is in the form of amino groups attached to quinone rings, because it has been demonstrated that extended quinones react readily with ammonia to yield amino derivatives (Brown et al., 1952).

The possibility that heterocyclic nitrogen compounds (pyridine derivatives) may be formed in soils by the reactions outlined in Fig. 2 appears

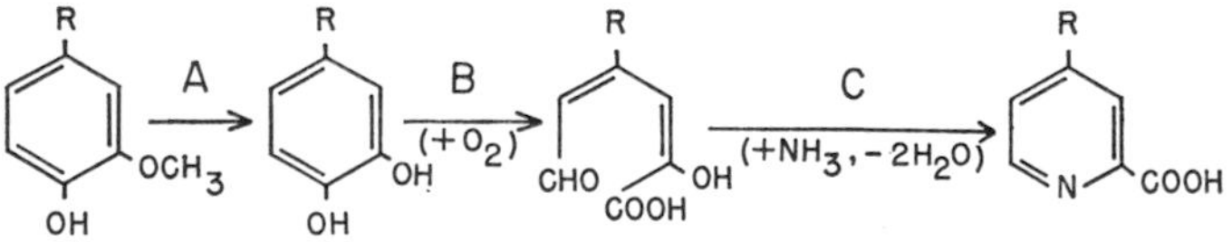

Fig. 2. Possible mode of formation of pyridine derivatives from lignins and other phenolic substances in soils. A, demethylation (enzymatic); B, oxidative ring fission (enzymatic); C, ring closure (nonenzymatic). I, lignin; II, o-dihydroxyphenol; III, pyridine derivative.

to deserve serious consideration, because recent work (Dagley et al., 1960; Cain, 1962; Ribbons and Evans, 1962) has shown that soil microorganisms (pseudomonads) produce aromatic ring-splitting enzymes (catechol-2:3-oxygenase and protocatechuic acid-4:5-oxygenase) which effect reaction B and that oxidation of catechol and protocatechuic acid by these enzymes in the presence of ammonium can lead to the formation of pyridine derivatives by reaction C. Some support for the theory that the microbial decomposition of plant lignins in soils may involve the reactions outlined in Fig. 2 has been provided by studies of the lignin-like material in soils and of the biological decomposition of plant lignins, because these studies indicate that plant lignins entering the soil are decomposed by microbial reactions which lead to loss of methoxyl and hydroxyl groups and to introduction of carboxyl and nitrogenous groups (see Bremner, 1954). The formation of α-picolinic acid derivatives in soils as outlined in Fig. 2 would help to account for the finding that soil organic matter has the ability to chelate metals, because the literature indicates that these derivatives have chelating properties.

The possibility that some of the organic nitrogen in soils which is not dissolved by acid hydrolysis may be trapped in the lattices of clay minerals deserves consideration, because it has been shown that a considerable amount of the clay-fixed amonium in soils is not released by hydrolysis with 6N HCl (Bremner, 1959; Cheng and Kurtz, 1963) and there are indications that mineral soils may contain significant quantities of clay-bound organic nitrogen. For example, Bremner and Harada (1959) found that some mineral soils contained a considerable amount of organic nitrogen which was not extractable by alkaline or neutral reagents but was dissolved when these soils were treated with hydrofluoric acid to destroy clay minerals and release clay-fixed ammonium. Also, Bremner (1959) found that from 9 to 45% of the organic nitrogen in soil profile samples was dissolved by cold N HF: N HCl, and that when calculated as a percentage of total soil nitrogen, both the amount of ammonium-N and the amount of organic-N released by this reagent increased markedly with depth in the profile. The deduction from these studies that some soils, particularly subsoils, may contain significant amounts of clay-bound organic-N as well as clay-fixed ammonium-N is supported by Stevenson's (1959) finding that nearly half of the organic nitrogen in the B_3 and C horizons of a Cisne silt loam was insoluble in 0.5N KOH but soluble in N HF. Bremner (1959) has suggested that for characterization of soil nitrogen by acid hydrolysis procedures, it may be profitable to pretreat the soil sample with HF to release ammonium and organic nitrogen compounds held by clay minerals, but no work using this technique has been reported. Studies of the sorption of organic nitrogen compounds by clay minerals suggest that it is not unlikely that soils may contain low-molecular nitrogen compounds (e.g., amino acids, amino sugars) within the expanding layer lattices of clay minerals.

Few attempts have been made to characterize the nitrogen in residues from treatment of soils with hot acid and identification of the organic nitrogen compounds in these residues seems likely to prove difficult. However, work by Kobo et al. (1956) indicates that extraction of these compounds for characterization studies may not be a serious problem, because they found that the organic matter in residues from hydrolysis of soils with 6N HCl was almost completely dissolved by cold 0.125N NaOH. Johnston (1959) separated two components by paper electrophoresis of the 'humic' (acid-insoluble) fraction of 2% NaOH extracts of residues from hydrolysis of soils with 6N HCl. One component was a yellow fluorescent substance, the other a dark-colored nonfluorescent material. Analysis of the dark-colored component isolated from a Xenia silt loam showed that it had a high methoxyl content (6.7%) and contained 52.5% carbon,

38.4% oxygen, 4.65% hydrogen, and 1.98% nitrogen. The dark-colored components separated from other soils had similar nitrogen contents (1.8 to 2.0%).

As noted in part A of this section, a considerable amount (usually about 30%) of the nitrogen released by acid hydrolysis of soils cannot be accounted for as amino acid-, ammonium-, or hexosamine-N. Some of this nitrogen is in the form of purine and pyrimidine bases (see part D), and a small amount is probably in the form of choline and other nitrogen compounds discussed in part E, but the chemical nature of most of this nitrogen is still obscure.

V. CHARACTERIZATION OF ORGANIC NITROGEN COMPLEXES

Although much useful information concerning the organic nitrogen complexes in soils has been obtained by the hydrolytic studies discussed in the previous section, isolative studies are clearly essential for characterization of these complexes. Many new methods of characterizing organic substances have been developed in recent years, but before these methods can be used profitably to study the organic nitrogen complexes in soils, the latter must first be extracted and then suitably fractionated.

Research on the nature and properties of the organic nitrogen complexes in soils has been greatly hindered by the lack of satisfactory methods of separating organic and inorganic soil constituents. The classical method of separation involving extraction of the organic constituents with strong alkali (usually 0.5N NaOH) dissolves a considerable amount of organic matter, but has the disadvantage that the material so dissolved is partially oxidized and hydrolyzed and probably otherwise modified during extraction (see Shorey, 1930; Bremner and Lees, 1949; Bremner, 1950c; Choudhri and Stevenson, 1957; Evans, 1959; Stevenson, 1960a; Tinsley and Salam, 1961a). Attempts have been made to develop milder methods of extracting soil organic matter, and methods involving the use of complexing or chelating reagents, particularly sodium pyrophosphate, have gained some popularity in recent years. The first serious attempt to develop mild extraction procedures has been attributed to Simon (1929), who recommended the use of sodium fluoride and oxalate solutions. Bremner and Lees (1949) surveyed the extractive powers of various neutral reagents, particularly the sodium salts of organic and inorganic acids, and found that sodium pyrophosphate, sodium oxalate, sodium fluoride, and sodium citrate were the most effective of the reagents tested. Their results showed that the most effective neutral extractants were those with the ability to complex or chelate polyvalent metals and indicated that the solubility of organic soil constituents in neutral reagents is largely determined by the nature and extent of their association with these metals. Sodium pyrophosphate was found to be the most generally useful of the neutral reagents tested, and the optimal conditions for extraction by this reagent were investigated. Bremner (1949b) subsequently compared the amounts of carbon and nitrogen extracted from various soils by sodium pyrophosphate, sodium hydroxide, sodium carbonate, and sodium fluoride and found that under the influence of any one of these reagents organic carbon was dissolved only along with, and in proportion to, organic nitrogen (cf. Hobson and Page, 1932a). He also found that the relative proportions of carbon and nitrogen extracted by these reagents varied with both the soil and the extractant and that sodium hydroxide extracted more nitrogen in relation to carbon than did the milder reagents.

Hamy and Leroy (1952a, b) compared the extractive powers of ammonium salts of organic acids and found that oxalate, malonate, and salicylate were much more efficient than succinate, adipate, maleate, acetate, trichloracetate, or phthalate. They also compared the ammonium and metal salts of malonic acid and found that the extractive power of these salts decreased in the order: lithium > sodium > ammonium > potassium > magnesium. They pointed out that the most effective neutral extractants are those capable of forming complexes with iron.

Evans (1959) compared the efficiencies of various neutral and alkaline reagents, including pyrophosphate, citrate, oxalate, fluoride, carbonate, and bicarbonate, and obtained results similar to those reported by Bremner and Lees (1949). His data showed that the amount of organic matter extracted and the proportion of humic (acid-insoluble) material in the extract tended to increase with increase in the pH of the extractant solution. He suggested that the extractive power of pyrophosphate may be related to the ability of this reagent to complex iron.

Tinsley and Salam (1961b) compared the abilities of various sodium and potassium salts and alkali solutions to extract organic nitrogen from a calcareous meadow soil and a sodium-saturated sample of this soil and confirmed that sodium pyrophosphate, citrate, and oxalate are more efficient than noncomplexing reagents. They also showed that sodium sulfite is as effective as sodium pyrophosphate at comparable concentrations and pH values and that potassium salts are less effective than sodium salts when extraction is performed at room temperature.

The finding in these investigations that the most effective neutral extractants are those with the ability to complex or chelate polyvalent metals has provided support for the theory (Bremner et al., 1946) that much of the organic matter in mineral soils occurs as metal-organic matter complexes formed by reaction of organic soil constituents with polyvalent metals such as calcium, iron, and aluminum. However, this theory does not account for several findings in studies of the effectiveness of various treatments for extraction of soil organic matter and dispersion of soil particles, and recent work (Edwards and Bremner, 1963, 1964, 1965) has provided considerable support for the theory that much of the humified organic matter in mineral soils is in the form of water-stable micro-aggregates (generally less than 250 microns in diameter) which consist largely of clay-metal-organic matter complexes in which clay and organic matter are bonded by strong (probably covalent) linkages with polyvalent metals. This clay-polyvalent metal-organic matter theory is in harmony with many of the findings in studies of the solubility of soil organic matter in different reagents and of the mechanisms of soil aggregation and dispersion. For example, it helps to account for the observations that reagents found to be effective for extraction of soil organic matter are also effective for dispersion of clay colloids and that the organic matter in extracts obtained using these reagents is intimately associated with fine clay and cannot be separated from this clay without use of reagents which decompose clay minerals (Edwards and Bremner, 1963). Also, it provides an explanation of the recent findings that it is possible to effect complete dispersion of the clay fraction of soils without use of oxidants, acids, or soluble peptizing reagents, that soils containing large amounts of clay can be dispersed effectively by a sonic vibration technique which does not lead to dissolution of more than trace amounts of organic or inorganic material, and that fine grinding or sonic vibration of soils leads to a marked increase in the susceptibility of their organic matter to decomposition by soil microorganisms (Edwards and Bremner, 1963, 1964, 1965; Waring and Bremner, 1964).

The organic matter in the B horizons of podzolic soils is much more readily extracted than the organic matter in surface soils and can largely be dissolved by acidic as well as neutral and alkaline reagents (Gallagher, 1942; Martin and Reeve, 1955; Schnitzer and Wright, 1956, 1957; Schnitzer et al., 1958; Wright et al., 1958; Sowden and Deuel, 1961). For example, Martin and Reeve (1955) found that organic complexing reagents such as cupferron, oxime, and acetylacetone dissolved large amounts of organic matter from podzol B horizons, whereas Choudhri and Stevenson (1957) found that these reagents were relatively ineffective for extraction of organic matter from surface soils. Schnitzer and Wright (1956, 1957) found that dilute inorganic acids extracted very little of the organic matter in the A_0 horizons of podzol profiles but extracted more than 90% of the organic matter in the B horizons of these profiles. Schnitzer et al. (1958) compared the effectiveness of 15 reagents for extraction of organic matter from the A_0 and B_{21} horizons of a podzol profile and found that whereas $Na_4P_2O_7$, Na_3PO_4, NaF, Na_2CO_3, NaOH, HF, and EDTA-Na_2 extracted more than 80% of the organic matter in the B_{21} horizon of this profile, only one of these reagents (NaOH) extracted appreciable amounts of organic matter from the A_0 horizon. The ease of extraction of the organic matter in podzol B horizons has stimulated research on the nature of this organic matter and several valuable studies of the illuvial organic matter in podzolic soils have been reported in recent years. Unfortunately there is no reason to believe, or evidence to indicate, that the organic matter in podzol B horizons is similar to the organic matter in surface soils.

Rather (1917) found that organic matter in soil could be estimated by a method in which the soil sample is treated with dilute hydrofluoric and hydrochloric acids to remove hydrated mineral matter before determination of loss on ignition, and modifications of this HF-HCl treatment have been used to separate material containing a high percentage of organic matter from mineral soils (e.g., Broadbent and Bradford, 1952). However, recent work (Bremner, 1959; Bremner and Harada, 1959; Stevenson, 1959) has shown that some mineral soils, particularly subsoils, contain a considerable amount of organic nitrogen which is not extractable by neutral or alkaline reagents but is dissolved when these soils are treated with HF or HF-HCl solutions to decompose clay minerals (see section IV F). This suggests that some soils contain clay-bound organic nitrogen compounds and that modifications of Rather's method of removing hydrated mineral matter may prove valuable for extraction and characterization of these compounds.

Tinsley and Parsons found that formic acid dissolves significant amounts of soil organic matter and that from 27 to 43% of the total nitrogen in 5 soils they examined was extracted by hot formic acid containing 0.2N LiBr (Tinsley, 1956; Parsons and Tinsley, 1960). This extraction procedure has proved useful for investigation of the polysaccharide material in soils (Parsons and Tinsley, 1961), but its value for studies of the organic nitrogen complexes in soils appears dubious.

Whitehead and Tinsley (1964) recently found that more than half of the organic matter in four soils they examined was dissolved by boiling dimethylformamide containing oxalic, boric, hydrofluoric, or fluoroboric acid. This extraction technique seems unsuitable for studies of the organic nitrogen complexes in soils, because it could lead to hydrolysis of these complexes and the reagents used contain both carbon and nitrogen.

Other methods of extracting soil organic matter with organic and inorganic solvents have been described but they have no apparent value for studies designed to characterize the organic nitrogen complexes in soils (for discussions of these methods, see Bremner, 1954; Tinsley and Salam, 1961a).

The major defect of the pyrophosphate extraction technique introduced by Bremner and Lees (1949) and of other mild methods of extraction discussed above is that their virtue of mildness is offset by their inefficiency compared with the classical method of extraction with strong alkali. This defect would not be serious if it could be argued that the organic matter extracted by mild procedures is reasonably representative of the whole, but there is no evidence to support this argument. Methods involving the use of nitrogenous or organic reagents have little attraction because these reagents increase the difficulties encountered in characterization of the organic material extracted and may cause complications by reacting chemically with this material.

In addition to other defects mentioned, the various methods of extracting soil organic matter discussed have the disadvantage that they yield extracts containing the reagent used for extraction. This complicates investigation of the organic material extracted, particularly if the extractant used contains carbon or nitrogen. Where effective methods of removing the extractant from the extract are available, they are usually tedious and time-consuming and often lead to some loss or degradation of organic material. Bremner and Ho (1961) investigated the possibility that this problem could be eliminated by use of water-insoluble cation-exchange resins for extraction of soil organic matter and found that considerable amounts of organic matter were dispersed by shaking aqueous suspensions of soils with the Na+ or K+ forms of several synthetic cation-exchange resins now available commercially. They also found that very little of the organic matter extracted by this resin treatment was dialyzable through cellophane and that, unlike the organic material extracted by sodium hydroxide and other reagents now commonly used for extraction of soil organic matter, the material dissolved by resins was not precipitated at pH 3 (cf. Yuan, 1964). The extractive power of the resins tested was found to be related to their selectivity for polyvalent cations and to decrease in the order: iminodiacetic acid type (e.g., Dowex A-1) > carboxylic acid type (e.g., Amberlite IRC-50) > sulfonic acid type (e.g., Dowex 50). Comparison of the amounts of organic carbon and nitrogen dissolved by a single treatment of 8 mineral and organic soils with Na^+ Dowex A-1 and with 0.5M NaOH at room temperature for 15 hours showed that, on the average, there was not much difference in the percentage of soil organic nitrogen extracted by the two methods (resin, 33%; alkali, 34%), but that the resin method extracted a considerably higher percentage of soil organic carbon (resin, 37%; alkali, 26%). Subsequent work (Edwards and Bremner, unpublished) has shown that more than half of the organic matter in surface soils can be extracted by resins if several treatments with resin are performed and the residue from each extraction is finely ground before further treatment with resin. This method of extraction appears to merit further attention, because besides having the important advantage of yielding an extract which is not contaminated by extractant, it is considerably more effective than methods involving extraction with aqueous solutions of complexing reagents such as sodium pyrophosphate and does not involve the risks associated with the use of strong alkali.

Many methods of fractionating the organic matter in soils or soil extracts have been described, but very few of these have shown any promise of being useful for characterization of the organic nitrogen complexes in soils (for literature on these methods, see Bremner, 1954; Davies et al., 1957; Coulson et al., 1959b; Sowden and Deuel, 1961). It is obvious that any material as complex as soil organic matter can be fractionated by a wide variety of methods. The problem is to devise fractionation techniques which serve some useful purpose, e.g., permit separation of a relatively homogeneous fraction of soil organic matter or remove substances that complicate characterization of the particular fraction under investigation. In recent years several attempts have been made to fractionate soil organic matter by chemical methods (e.g., Davies et al., 1957; Bromfield et al., 1959; Sowden and Deuel, 1961) and by chromatographic or electrophoretic techniques (e.g., Forsyth, 1947b; Stevenson et al., 1952; Coulson et al., 1959b; Johnston, 1959; Stevenson, 1960a; Sowden and Deuel, 1961; Waldron and Mortensen, 1961, 1962), but these have met with very little success. For example, Coulson et al. (1959b) attempted to fractionate the humic fraction of soil organic matter by a variety of techniques, including ascending and descending paper chromatography, high and low voltage paper electrophoresis, gel diffusion, and column and ion exchange chromatography, but found that none of these techniques gave useful fractionations. Few attempts have been made to develop methods of fractionating the organic nitrogen complexes in soil extracts and in most work designed to characterize these complexes the classical acidification method of fractionation has been used. Studies of the organic nitrogen complexes in the so-called humic (acid-insoluble) and fulvic (acid-soluble) fractions distinguished by this method are discussed below.

The humic fraction of soil organic matter has been extensively investigated, but relatively little progress has been made in attempts to characterize the nitrogenous complexes in this fraction. However, it has been established that 20 to 50% of the nitrogen in most humic acid preparations is amino acid N (Bremner, 1952, 1955a, d; Wittich, 1952; Schlichting, 1953c; Scharpenseel and Krausse, 1962), that 3 to 10% is amino sugar (hexosamine) N (Bremner, 1955d), and that a small amount is purine or pyrimidine N (Anderson, 1961).

Bremner (1955d) studied the chemical nature of the nitrogen in humic preparations isolated from 0.5M sodium hydroxide and 0.1M sodium pyrophosphate (pH 7) extracts of mineral and organic soils and found that alkali-extracted and pyrophosphate-extracted preparations from the same soil differed markedly in total nitrogen content and in nitrogen distribution after acid hydrolysis, the alkali-extracted preparations having a higher nitrogen content and a higher proportion of acid soluble N and α-amino N (cf. Stevenson et al., 1958). He also found that 20 to 60% of the nitrogen in these preparations was not released by acid hydrolysis and that 48 to 70% of the nitrogen dissolved by hydrolysis was amino acid N. His data showed that at least 31 to 48% of the nitrogen in the alkali-extracted preparations and 20 to 35% of the nitrogen in the pyrophosphate-extracted preparations was amino acid N and that from 3 to 10% of the nitrogen in these preparations was amino sugar N. The finding that the nitrogen contents of alkali-extracted preparations are higher than those of pyrophosphate-extracted preparations is in harmony with the observations that alkali extracts more nitrogen in relation to carbon from soil than does neutral pyrophosphate, and that there is little difference between the C/N ratio of a soil extract and the C/N ratio of its humic fraction (Bremner, 1949b).

Waksman and Iyer (1932) and Hobson and Page (1932b) postulated that humic acids are formed by reaction between lignin and protein material in soils and that humic nitrogen is largely protein (see section VI and section IV F). This lignin-protein theory is open to a variety of criticisms (see Mattson and Koutler-Andersson, 1942, 1943; Forsyth, 1947a; Sowden and Atkinson, 1948; Parker et al., 1952; Sowden et al., 1952; Bremner, 1955d; Kononova, 1961) and has several rather obvious defects. For example, numerous studies have shown that the nitrogen distribution of humic acid hydrolysates is markedly different from that of protein hydrolysates (e.g., Hobson and Page, 1932b; Sowden and Atkinson, 1949; De and Mukherjee, 1951; Parker et al., 1952; Sowden et al., 1952; Wittich, 1952; Schlichting, 1953c; Bremner, 1955a, d; Stevenson et al., 1958; Stevenson, 1959; Ladd and Butler, 1964), and even if it is assumed that the amino acid N released by acid hydrolysis of humic acid preparations is derived exclusively from proteins, only about one-third of the total nitrogen in most humic preparations can be accounted for as protein N. Although it seems likely to some investigators that some of the combined amino acid nitrogen in humic acids is in the form of peptides (see Hobson and Page, 1932b; De and Mukherjee, 1951; Bremner, 1955c; Scharpenseel and Krausse, 1962; Ladd and Butler, 1964), attempts to isolate proteins or peptides from humic acid preparations have not thus far been successful. Several workers have suggested that some of the nitrogen in humic acids is in the form of complexes produced in soils by reactions of phenolic substances or quinones with amino acids, but there is no evidence to support these suggestions (see section IV F). Mattson and Koutler-Andersson (1942, 1943) advanced the theory that humic acids are derived from lignin by autoxidation and ammonia fixation and that humic nitrogen is largely in the form of nitrogenous complexes produced by reaction of oxidized lignins with ammonia. This lignin-ammonia theory has some attractions (see section IV F) but has the obvious defect that it does not account for the finding that at least 20 to 50% of the nitrogen in most humic acid preparations is in the form of combined amino acids and amino sugars. For other theories concerning the mode of formation of soil humic acids and the nature of humic nitrogen see section IV F.

Chromatographic studies of the amino-acid composition of acid hydrolysates of humic acid preparations have been reported (Bremner, 1952, 1955a, c, d; Parker et al., 1952; Okuda and Hori, 1954, 1955, 1956; Pavel et al., 1954, 1955; Kononova and Aleksandrova, 1956; Davies et al., 1957; Coulson et al., 1959a; Scharpenseel and Krausse, 1962). The data obtained in these investigations indicate that humic acid preparations from different soils do not differ markedly in amino-acid composition. Bremner (1952, 1955d) analyzed acid hydrolysates of 15 humic acid preparations from a variety of soils by paper chromatography and observed little variation in their amino-acid composition. He also found that the amino-acid composition of hydrolysates of alkali-extracted preparations was similar to that of pyrophosphate-extracted preparations and not greatly different from that of soil hydrolysates. The following amino acids were detected in every hydrolysate examined: phenylalanine, leucine, isoleucine, valine, glycine, threonine, serine, aspartic acid, glutamic acid, lysine, arginine, histidine, proline, hydroxyproline, α-amino-n-butyric acid, β-alanine, γ-aminobutyric acid, tyrosine, cysteic acid, and methionine sulfone. Semi-quantitative analyses indicated that most of the amino acid N in the hydrolysates studied was in the form of the first 10 amino acids listed. Methionine, methionine sulfoxide, α,ε-diaminopimelic acid, and unidentified ninhydrin-reacting substances were detected in some of the hydrolysates examined. The findings in this work have been confirmed by other chromatographic studies cited above and they have been extended by the detection of cystine (Okuda and Hori, 1955, 1956; Kononova and Aleksandrova, 1956), 3:4-dihydroxyphenylalanine (Pavel et al., 1954; Davies et al., 1957; Coulson et al., 1959a), and ornithine (Scharpenseel and Krausse, 1962). The occurrence of methylhistidine in humic acid hydrolysates has also been reported (Scharpenseel and Krausse, 1962), but this report has not been confirmed. It is noteworthy that humic acid hydrolysates, like soil hydrolysates, contain several "nonprotein" amino acids (see section IV B) and that the small qualitative variations observed in the amino-acid composition of humic acid hydrolysates have largely been confined to these amino acids (see Bremner, 1955d; Coulson et al., 1959a; Scharpenseel and Krausse, 1962).

The hexosamine N in humic acid preparations appears to be largely, if not entirely, in the form of glucosamine and galactosamine (Bremner,

1955d). The occurrence of amino sugars in these preparations suggests that some of the acetyl groups detected by Gillam (1940) and other workers in humic acids may be in the form of N-acetyl amino sugars.

Anderson (1957, 1958, 1961) detected purine and pyrimidine bases (guanine, adenine, cytosine, thymine, and uracil) in acid hydrolysates of humic acid preparations and obtained indications that these bases were probably in the form of polynucleotides derived mainly from bacterial deoxyribonucleic acid (see section IV D). However, his data indicated that very little of the nitrogen in the preparations examined was in the form of purine or pyrimidine bases.

The presence of heterocyclic nitrogen compounds in alkali fusion products of humic preparations has been reported (Shmuk, 1924, Flaig and Breyhan, 1956), but there is no evidence to indicate that a significant amount of humic nitrogen is in heterocyclic compounds (see section IV E).

Several attempts have been made to determine how much of the nitrogen in the humic fraction of soil organic matter is in the form of free amino groups, because an estimate of these groups is required for evaluation of theories concerning the chemical nature of soil humic acids and the mechanisms by which they may complex metals and react with clay colloids (see Bremner, 1954, 1957; Brydon and Sowden, 1959). Bremner (1952, 1955c, 1957) found that when humic acids isolated from alkali and pyrophosphate extracts of soils were analyzed for free amino N by the Van Slyke (1929) nitrous acid method (see section IV A), the results indicated that 10 to 30% of the total nitrogen in these preparations occurred as free amino groups. This estimate could not be verified by checking that the nitrogen contents of the preparations analyzed decreased on treatment with nitrous acid by the amount expected from the equation $R.NH_2 + HNO_2 = R.OH + H_2O + N_2$, because it was found that treatment of humic preparations with nitrous acid led to fixation of nitrite-N as well as liberation of N_2 and/or N_2O. Since it appears unlikely that 10 to 30% of the nitrogen in humic preparations occurs as free amino groups, Bremner deduced that these preparations contain material which interferes with the estimation of amino groups by the Van Slyke method. He found that lignin interferes with this method by reacting with nitrous acid to liberate N_2 and/or N_2O (cf. Stevenson and Swaby, 1964) and that the reaction of lignin with nitrous acid resembles the reaction of humic acid with nitrous acid in that it is accompanied by fixation of nitrite-N and by the destruction of methoxyl groups. He also found that only about one-third of the nitrogen fixed by lignin in its reaction with nitrous acid was released by prolonged hydrolysis with 6N HCl, and that most of the nitrogen so released was in the form of ammonium. The deduction from these observations that lignin-derived or other phenolic material may be largely responsible for the high apparent amino-N values obtained in analysis of humic preparations by the Van Slyke method is supported by recent tracer studies of the reaction of soil organic matter with nitrite (Bremner and Führ, 1964; Führ and Bremner, 1964a, b). For example, these studies have shown that only about half of the nitrogen fixed by soil organic matter in its reaction with nitrous acid is released by hydrolysis with 6N HCl for 12 hours and that most of the fixed nitrogen released by this treatment is liberated as ammonium. Edwards and Bremner (unpublished work) recently attempted to determine the isotopic composition of the N_2 liberated in the reaction of humic acid preparations with N^{15}-enriched nitrous acid in the hope that isotope-ratio analysis of this gas would reveal how much, if any, of the N_2 liberated in this reaction is derived from amino groups in these preparations. They found, however, that N^{15}-analysis of the N_2 liberated by treatment of humic preparations with acidified $NaN^{15}O_2$ was vitiated by other gases released during this treatment and were unable to eliminate this interference.

Sowden and Parker (1953), Okuda and Hori (1954) and Bremner (1955c, 1957) were unable to detect free amino groups in humic acid preparations by Sanger's (1945) fluorodinitrobenzene (FDNB) method. Failure to detect free amino groups by this method is not conclusive evidence that such groups are absent, because the FDNB technique was designed for characterization and estimation of terminal amino groups in proteins or peptides, and humic acids may contain other types of amino groups. Also, there is a possibility that failure to detect free amino groups by this technique may be due to steric factors affecting the reactivity of amino groups in humic acids towards FDNB (see Bremner, 1957). Work by Sowden (1957) and Brydon and Sowden (1959) suggests that humic acids as normally isolated from soils may contain amino groups which are combined with metals or metal oxides, because they found that although free amino groups could not be detected in humic acids by the FDNB technique or by Edman's (1950) phenylisothiocyanate method of studying the terminal amino groups in peptides, amino groups were detectable by these methods when humic preparations were 'demineralized' by treatments with acid, dithionite, or EDTA before analysis.

The fulvic fraction of soil organic matter has received much less attention than the humic fraction and very few studies of the chemical nature of fulvic nitrogen have been reported. However, there is evidence that 20 to 30% of the nitrogen in the fulvic fraction of alkali and pyrophosphate extracts of soil is amino acid N (Bremner, 1952; Stevenson, 1960a) and that 8 to 10% is amino sugar N (Stevenson, 1960a). The remainder of the nitrogen in this fraction appears to be largely in the form of nitrogenous complexes which are readily deaminated by hot acid (De, 1956; Stevenson, 1959, 1960a).

Hobson and Page (1932c) and Forsyth (1947b) found that the fulvic fraction of alkali extracts of soils did not give tests for proteins, but several workers have reported the detection in this fraction of substances resembling peptides (e.g., Walters, 1915; Hobson and Page, 1932c; De and Mukherjee, 1951). Bremner (1952) studied the amino-acid composition of acid hydrolysates of the nondialyzable material in fulvic fractions by paper chromatography and found that it was similar qualitatively to that of humic acid hydrolysates but differed quantitatively, particularly with respect to β-alanine and basic amino acids (cf. Kononova and Aleksandrova, 1956).

A considerable proportion of fulvic nitrogen is dialyzable through cello-

phane (see Stevenson, 1960a), and several low-molecular nitrogen compounds, including arginine, histidine, lysine, xanthine, hypoxanthine,
cyanuric acid, and creatinine, have been isolated from the fulvic fraction
of alkali extracts of soils (see section IV). Hobson and Page (1932c) and
Stevenson (1960a) found that a considerable proportion (12 to 15%) of
the nitrogen in this fraction was ammonium N. Stevenson (1960a) also
showed that the fulvic fraction of soil organic matter contains nitrogenous
organic compounds which are deaminated by 0.5N NaOH at room temperature and confirmed previous evidence (De, 1956; Stevenson, 1959) that
a considerable proportion of fulvic nitrogen is in complexes which are
readily deaminated by hot acid. He found that about half of the nitrogen
in the fulvic fractions of alkali and pyrophosphate extracts of Elliott silt
loam was converted to ammonium by acid or base hydrolysis, and that
when these fractions were hydrolyzed with 6N HCl, about one-fourth of
their nitrogen was liberated as amino acid N and about one-tenth was
liberated as amino sugar N. He also fractionated the fulvic constituents
of Elliott silt loam by a modification of Forsyth's (1947b) selective adsorption technique and showed that the components separated by this
technique contained amino acids and that several contained amino sugars.
He further observed that the nitrogenous fulvic complexes readily deaminated by acid hydrolysis are largely associated with pigments and postulated that these pigments are formed in soils through condensation of
carbonyl compounds with amino derivatives by mechanisms similar to
those proposed for the browning reactions which occur during storage of
food (see section IV F).

The amino sugars in the fulvic fraction of soil organic matter have not
been identified, but it seems very likely that both glucosamine and galactosamine are present. Bremner (1949a) found that the fulvic fractions of
alkali and pyrophosphate extracts of soils gave the Müller color test for
acetylated 2-amino sugars.

Research on the nature of soil organic phosphorus has involved many
studies of the phosphorus compounds in the fulvic fraction of alkali extracts of soils and these investigations have provided evidence that some
of the nitrogen in this fraction is in the form of nucleotides or their
derivatives. However, work by Adams et al. (1954) indicates that the
proportion of fulvic nitrogen in the form of purine or pyrimidine derivatives is probably very small (see section IV D).

Several chemical and chromatographic methods of fractionating the
fulvic constituents of soil organic matter have been described (e.g., Hobson and Page, 1932c; Forsyth, 1947b; De and Mukherjee, 1951; Schlichting, 1953b; Stevenson, 1960a; Sowden and Deuel, 1961), but their value
for studies of the chemical nature of fulvic nitrogen seems very limited.

Characterization of the organic nitrogen complexes in the fulvic fraction of soil organic matter has been greatly complicated by the fact that
the methods normally used to separate this fraction yield preparations
which are grossly contaminated by the reagent used for extraction of
fulvic constituents. This difficulty can be eliminated by use of the cation-
exchange resin method of extracting soil organic matter described by

Bremner and Ho (1961) and adoption of this method of extraction should permit much more detailed studies of fulvic nitrogen complexes than have hitherto been possible.

VI. STABILITY

One of the major contributions of soil organic matter to soil fertility is that it supplies a considerable quantity of nitrogen for crop growth and acts as a natural storehouse for this important plant nutrient. The organic nitrogen in soils is not directly available to plants, but some of it is mineralized by soil microorganisms during the growing season, and this mineralization process supplies a substantial amount of plant-available nitrogen. Nevertheless, the organic nitrogen in soils displays a high resistance to microbial decomposition and the amount mineralized during the growing season usually represents only 1 to 3% of the total amount present. It is difficult to account for this, because the organic nitrogen compounds added to soils in the form of plant and animal residues are not particularly resistant to decomposition. Moreover, although present knowledge indicates that more than 40% of the organic nitrogen in most surface soils is in the form of amino-acid, amino-sugar, and purine-pyrimidine complexes, nitrogenous substances considered to be models of these complexes (e.g., proteins, chitin, nucleic acids) are rapidly mineralized when added to soils (see Bremner and Shaw, 1954, 1957).

The resistance of the organic nitrogen complexes in soils to microbial decomposition has considerable practical significance, and several theories have been advanced to account for the stability of these complexes.

One explanation of the unavailability of soil organic nitrogen is that the organic nitrogen compounds in soils are stabilized by reaction with other organic soil constituents. As early as 1892, Hebert and Dehérain suggested that proteins may be stabilized in soils by association with lignins (see Russell, 1961). Forty years later this theory was revived independently by Waksman and Iyer (1932) and by Hobson and Page (1932b). Waksman and Iyer (1932) postulated that lignin-protein complexes are formed in soils by a gradual process involving reaction of carbonyl groups in lignins with amino groups in proteins, and they showed that nitrogen in complexes formed by acidification of alkaline solutions of lignin and protein was highly resistant to mineralization. Their findings concerning the stabilizing effect of lignin on proteins have been confirmed by several workers (e.g., Bremner and Shaw, 1957; Lynch and Lynch, 1958; Estermann et al., 1959), and recent work by Sørensen (1962) has shown that oxidized lignins react readily with nitrogenous compounds present in peptone. However, there is good evidence that a considerable fraction of the amino acid-N in soils is not associated with lignins, and the lignin-protein theory clearly does not account for the stability of the nonprotein nitrogen in soils. Several workers have suggested that organic soil nitrogen may be stabilized by other reactions which have been postulated to occur during the decomposition of plant materials in soils, e.g., by re-action of amino compounds (amino acids, peptides, etc.) with sugars, phenols, or quinones (see section IV F), but there is currently no evi-dence to support these suggestions. Handley (1954, 1961) has postulated that tannins present in the leaves of some plant species react with cyto-plasmic proteins to form rather resistant tannin-protein complexes which protect the mesophyll tissue from rapid decomposition, and that this reaction is of fundamental importance in the formation of the mor type of humus found in acid soils developed under coniferous or heather vegetation. The reactions of lignin with ammonium and nitrite (see sec-tion IV F) deserve consideration in speculation concerning the stability of soil nitrogen, because it has been demonstrated that the nitrogen fixed by lignin in its reactions with ammonium and nitrite is not readly min-eralized by soil microorganisms (Bremner and Shaw, 1957). The possibility that inorganic forms of nitrogen in soils may be converted to relatively stable organic forms by reaction with organic soil constituents clearly cannot be ignored, because recent work has shown that both ammonium and nitrite can react with soil organic matter under field conditions and that the nitrogen fixed by soil organic matter in these reactions is highly resistant to mineralization by soil microorganisms (Broadbent et al., 1960; Burge and Broadbent, 1961; Nõmmik and Nilsson, 1963; Bremner and Führ, 1964; Führ and Bremner, 1964a, b).

Another explanation of the biological resistance of the organic nitrogen compounds in soils is that these compounds are stabilized through adsorp-tion by clay minerals. This theory originated from work by Ensminger and Gieseking (1942), who found that the enzymatic hydrolysis of proteins (albumin and hemoglobin) by proteolytic enzymes (pepsin and pancrea-tin) was markedly reduced by the presence of clay minerals. They also found that the effect of clay on protein hydrolysis depended upon the base-exchange capacity of the clay. Where the latter was high, as in the case of bentonite, the effect was very marked; where it was low, as in the case of kaolinite, the effect was insignificant. Ensminger and Gieseking suggested two explanations of their findings: (1) that adsorption of pro-teolytic enzymes by clays inactivates the enzymes; (2) that adsorption of proteins by clays orients the protein molecules in such a way that their active groups are inaccessible to enzymes.

Ensminger and Gieseking's findings concerning the protective effect of clays on proteins have been confirmed and extended by several workers (Pinck and Allison, 1951; Pinck et al., 1954; Birch and Friend, 1956; Lynch and Cotnoir, 1956; Estermann et al., 1959). Pinck and his associates found that the rate of decomposition of gelatin by soil microorganisms is much reduced if the gelatin is mixed with bentonite, and still further re-duced if the gelatin is in the form of a complex with bentonite (Pinck and Allison, 1951; Pinck et al., 1954). They also noted that the protective ef-fect of bentonite on gelatin varied with the protein-clay ratio, and that when gelatin-bentonite complexes contained more than about 30% pro-tein, the rate of decomposition was about the same as when no clay was present (Pinck et al., 1954). Birch and Friend (1956) confirmed the protective effect of bentonite on gelatin and found that kaolinite did not have a similar effect. Lynch and Cotnoir (1956) showed that montmorillonite reduced the rate of decomposition of casein and gelatin by soil microorganisms, but that kaolinitic and illitic clays exhibited very little protective effect. Estermann et al. (1959) found that protein in dried, rewetted protein-montmorillonite complexes was considerably more resistant than protein merely adsorbed on montmorillonite. They further observed that silica as well as montmorillonite reduced the rate of decomposition of proteins, and that bacterial digestion of protein-montmorillonite complexes was accompanied by a decrease in the (001) X-ray diffraction spacing of these complexes (see also Estermann and McLaren, 1959).

Support for the theory that clay minerals may play an important role in the stabilization of organic nitrogen compounds in soils has been provided by the finding that clays have a protective effect on plant residues (Allison et al., 1949; Lynch and Cotnoir, 1956) and organic phosphorus compounds (Bower, 1949; Goring and Bartholomew, 1950; Mortland and Gieseking, 1952) as well as proteins. Allison et al. (1949) found that clays can have an important effect upon the rate of decomposition of organic materials in sand culture. The effect was very marked with readily decomposable materials but not with sawdust, peat, and cellulose. It depended largely upon the amount and type of clay added, bentonite having the greatest effect and kaolinite the least. For example, in one experiment with soybeans and corn stover plus urea, the average carbon-retention percentages after 12 months were: sand, 23; sand plus 10% kaolin, 26; sand plus 30% kaolin, 31; sand plus 10% bentonite, 41. Lynch and Cotnoir (1956) found that bentonite reduced the rate of decomposition of crop residues and other organic substances by soil microorganisms, but observed very little protective effect with illite or kaolinite. Studies by Bower (1949), Goring and Bartholomew (1950) and Mortland and Gieseking (1952) have demonstrated that clays retard the enzymatic hydrolysis or microbial decomposition of organic phosphorus compounds (nucleic acids, phytin, glycerophosphate, lecithin, etc.). In each of these studies, the protective effect of bentonite was found to be much greater than that of kaolinite.

It is worthy of note that in all investigations thus far reported concerning the protective effect of clays, the effect of montmorillonite (Wyoming bentonite) has been found to be greater than that of other clay minerals tested. Lynch et al. (1957) found that attapulgite had no effect on the decomposition of gelatin by soil microorganisms and, in most investigations, kaolinite has been found to exhibit little, if any, protective effect. Estermann and McLaren (1959) found that kaolinite actually increased the rate of protein decomposition by bacteria and concluded that this mineral acted as a concentrating surface for adsorbed substrate and exoenzymes and thereby promoted more rapid breakdown of substrate (see also Estermann et al., 1959). There seems little doubt that the protective action of expanding layer lattice clays involves factors besides adsorption of substrates or inactivation of enzymes or bacteria by adsorption (see Estermann and McLaren, 1959; Estermann et al., 1959), and the mechanism of the protection effected by these clays is still rather obscure (for a recent study of the mechanism of adsorption of protein by bentonite see Armstrong and Chesters, 1964).

The theory that organic nitrogen compounds in soils are stabilized by clay minerals is supported by the finding that soil texture has an important effect on the nitrogen content of soil in local areas, the nitrogen content increasing as the texture becomes finer (for an example of this effect, see Table 6). It also helps to account for the common observation that it is

Table 6. Average nitrogen contents of upland soils of different texture in northeastern Iowa.*

Soil texture	Average nitrogen content of soil (%)
Sand	0.027
Fine sand	0.042
Sandy loam	0.100
Fine sandy loam	0.107
Loam	0.188
Silt loam	0.230

* Walker and Brown (1936).

much easier to build up, or maintain, the nitrogen content of fine-textured soils than it is to increase, or stabilize, the nitrogen content of coarse-textured soils. Also, this theory provides some explanation of the findings in recent work by Waring and Bremner (1964). They studied the effect of soil mesh-size on the results obtained in estimation of mineralizable nitrogen in soils by incubation techniques and found that a decrease in soil mesh-size resulted in a marked increase in the amount of nitrogen mineralized under aerobic or waterlogged conditions. For example, they found that with 52 soils examined, a decrease in mesh size from <10 to <80 led to a 25 to 124% increase in the amount of nitrogen mineralized during incubation under waterlogged conditions at 30°C for 2 weeks. This work indicates that some of the organic nitrogen in soil aggregates is not susceptible to microbial decomposition until the aggregates are disrupted by grinding or other processes that render this nitrogen physically accessible to microorganisms. The findings in this work are explicable if some of the organic nitrogen in soils is rendered inaccessible to microbes by clay barriers which can be ruptured by grinding. Rovira and Greacen (1957) found that disruption of soil aggregates increased the activity of soil microorganisms.

An entirely different explanation of the stability of the organic nitrogen in soils was provided by tracer work reported by Broadbent and Norman (1947) and Broadbent (1948), which showed that decomposition of soil organic matter and mineralization of soil organic nitrogen are greatly accelerated by the addition of plant materials. For example, Broadbent (1948) studied the effects of adding Sudan grass enriched with C^{13} and N^{15} to a Clarion silt loam and found that mineralization of organic soil nitrogen during incubation of this soil for 32 days was approximately doubled, and that carbon-dioxide evolution from the soil was increased about threefold, by addition of this energy-rich plant material. Broadbent and Norman (1947) concluded that the stability of the organic nitrogen in soils is more apparent than real and results largely from the absence of enough energy material to support a vigorous microbial population, i.e., that the unavailability to crops of organic soil nitrogen is due to the normally low level of microbial (enzymatic) activity in soils rather than to the formation of resistant complexes.

Each of the theories discussed above is supported by experimental observations, and a combination of these theories provides a reasonably satisfactory explanation of the stability of the organic nitrogen complexes in soils. The possibility that the stability of organic soil nitrogen may be due to the occurrence of a substantial amount of this nitrogen in viable tissue can be discounted, because it seems unlikely that much more than about 2% of the organic matter in arable soils is in the form of living bacteria or fungi (Russell, 1961). The possibility that a large amount of the organic nitrogen in soils is in microbial cell substances which are not readily decomposed would appear to deserve some consideration, because it has been estimated that from one-third to one-half of the organic matter in soils may be microbially derived (Norman, 1943) and it is known that many microbial cell walls are not attacked by proteolytic and other enzymes that rapidly degrade intracellular constituents (see Salton, 1960). However, studies of the decomposition of microbial tissue in soils have provided no indications that microbial cell walls or other substances elaborated by microbes are particularly resistant to degradation by soil microorganisms.

The striking increases in crop yields resulting from the recent rapid expansion in the use of nitrogen fertilizers have made it obvious that the amount of nitrogen made available by mineralization of organic soil nitrogen during the growing season is rarely sufficient to meet the demand for this nutrient in current cropping practices. This has emphasized the need for a laboratory test which will provide an index of the availability of soil nitrogen and permit reasonably accurate prediction of the amount of fertilizer nitrogen required to produce a desired crop yield.

The practical value of a method providing an index of the availability of soil nitrogen has long been appreciated, and many biological and chemical methods have been proposed (see Bremner, 1965d). Attempts to develop chemical methods of assessing "available" soil nitrogen have been encouraged by the experience that chemical methods of analysis are generally more rapid and convenient than biological methods, and a variety of chemical tests involving estimation of the total- or ammonium-N released by treatment of soil with various reagents have been proposed. Most of these methods appear to have very limited value, and all are open to the criticism that they are completely empirical and make no allowance for the fact that the nitrogen mineralization-immobilization cycle in soils is controlled by the supply of energy for microbial processes. Attempts to develop more rational chemical methods have been hindered by lack of knowledge concerning the relationships between the composition of the organic matter and the availability of the nitrogen in different soils and by lack of information concerning the chemical nature of the organic soil nitrogen that is readily mineralized and is the source of the nitrogen made available for plant growth by soil microorganisms. Some information concerning the nature of the readily mineralizable nitrogen in soils has been provided by recent studies of the effect of cultivation on the nitrogen distribution in soils (Keeney and Bremner, 1964; Porter et al., 1964). Porter et al found that cultivation and cropping led to loss of acid-insoluble (nonhydrolyzable) N, nondistillable acid-soluble N, and distillable acid-soluble N and to changes in the relative proportions of these forms of nitrogen, the percent loss of nondistillable acid-soluble N being greater than the percent loss of acid-insoluble N or distillable acid-soluble N. Keeney and Bremner (1964) found that cultivation led to a marked decrease in all forms of soil nitrogen excepting nonexchangeable ammonium N, but that, on the average, it did not cause marked changes in the relative proportions of hydrolyzable and nonhydrolyzable forms of nitrogen, i.e., that the decrease in total N on cultivation was accompanied by a roughly proportional decrease in hydrolyzable and nonhydrolyzable forms of nitrogen (see Fig. 3). Their results showed that the average

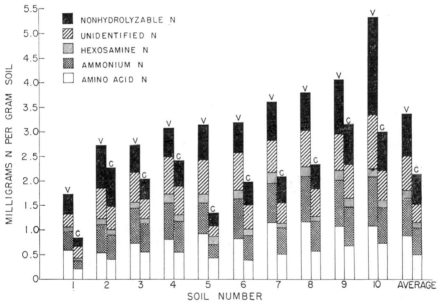

Fig. 3. Nitrogen distributions of virgin (V) and cultivated (C) soils. (Keeney and Bremner, 1964).

percent losses of different forms of nitrogen on cultivation decreased in the order: amino acid N (43.0%) > nonhydrolyzable N (39.4%) > total N (36.2%) > total hydrolyzable N (35.2%) > unidentified hydrolyzable N (34.5%) > hydrolyzable ammonium N (28.6%) > hexosamine N (27.6%) > nonexchangeable ammonium N (0.2%). These results do not permit any definite conclusions concerning the nature of the readily mineralizable forms of nitrogen in soils because the effects of nitrogen immobilization processes, crop residues, and ammonium fixation on the changes in nitrogen distribution resulting from cultivation cannot be assessed. However, they indicate that the native nonexchangeable ammonium N in soils is practically unavailable to plants or microorganisms and that there are no very marked differences in the susceptibilities of the various forms of organic nitrogen in soils to mineralization. These indications have been confirmed by recent work in the author's laboratory (Keeney and Bremner, unpublished) in which the nature of the readily mineralizable nitrogen in soils was studied by analyzing a wide variety of soils before and after incubating them at 30°C for 12 months under conditions conducive to mineralization of soil nitrogen. The results obtained in this work indicate that the amino acid N in soils may be more susceptible to mineralization than other forms of organic soil nitrogen and that native nonexchangeable ammonium N is essentially unavailable to soil microorganisms. However, they show that, with the exception of nonexchangeable ammonium N, the amounts of different forms of soil nitrogen mineralized during incubation are roughly proportional to the amounts present before incubation. It seems likely, therefore, that any chemical method of assessing the availability of soil nitrogen based solely on determination of a particular fraction of soil N will prove unsatisfactory.

VII. LITERATURE CITED

Adams, A. P., Bartholomew, W. V., and Clark, F. E. 1954. Measurement of nucleic acid components in soil. Soil Sci. Soc. Am. Proc. 18:40-46.

Allison, F. E., Sherman, M. S., and Pinck, L. A. 1949. Maintenance of soil organic matter: I. Inorganic soil colloid as a factor in retention of carbon during formation of humus. Soil Sci. 68:463-478.

Anderson, G. 1957. Nucleic acid derivatives in soils. Nature 180:287-288.

Anderson, G. 1958. Identification of derivatives of deoxyribonucleic acid in humic acid. Soil Sci. 86:169-174.

Anderson, G. 1961. Estimation of purines and pyrimidines in soil humic acid. Soil Sci. 91:156-161.

Anderson, M. S., and Byers, H. G. 1934. The carbon-nitrogen ratio in relation to soil classification. Soil Sci. 38:121-138.

Anonymous. 1945. Carbon-nitrogen and other ratios. Soils and Fertil. 8:135-137.

Armstrong, D. E., and Chesters, G. 1964. Properties of protein-bentonite complexes as influenced by equilibration conditions. Soil Sci. 98:39-52.

Aso, K. 1905. On organic compounds of phosphoric acid in the soil. Tokyo Imp. Univ. Coll. Agr. Bull. 6:277-284.

Barrow, N. J. 1961. Phosphorus in soil organic matter. Soils and Fertil. 24:169-173.

Baudisch, O., and Euler, H. V. 1935. Über den Gehalt einiger Moor-Erdarten an Caratinoiden. Arkiv. Kemi, Mineral Geol. 11A. No. 21.

Bennett, E. 1949. Fixation of ammonia by lignin. Soil Sci. 68:399-400.

Birch, H. F., and Friend, M. T. 1956. Humus decomposition in East African soils. Nature 178:500-501.

Biswas, T. D., and Das, N. B. 1957. Amino acids in soils growing berseem. J. Indian Soc. Soil Sci. 5:31-37.

Black, C. A. 1957. Soil-Plant Relationships. John Wiley & Sons, Inc., New York.

Black, C. A., and Goring, C. A. I. 1953. Organic phosphorus in soils. In W. H. Pierre and A. G. Norman, ed. Soil and Fertilizer Phosphorus in Crop Nutrition. pp. 123-152. Academic Press, Inc., New York.

Black, W. A. P., Cornhill, W. J., and Woodward, F. N. 1955. A preliminary investigation on the chemical composition of sphagnum moss and peat. J. Appl. Chem. 5:484-492.

Bottomley, W. B. 1919. The isolation from peat of certain nucleic acid derivatives. Proc. Roy. Soc. (London) 90B:39-44.

Bower, C. A. 1949. Studies on the forms and availability of soil organic phosphorus. Iowa Agr. Exp. Sta. Res. Bull. 362.

Bremner, J. M. 1949a. Studies on soil organic matter. Part I. The chemical nature of soil organic nitrogen. J. Agr. Sci. 39:183-193.

Bremner, J. M. 1949b. Studies on soil organic matter. Part 3. The extraction of organic carbon and nitrogen from soil. J. Agr. Sci. 39:280-282.

Bremner, J. M. 1950a. Amino-acids in soil. Nature 165:367.

Bremner, J. M. 1950b. The amino-acid composition of the protein material in soil. Biochem. J. 47:538-542.

Bremner, J. M. 1950c. Some observations on the oxidation of soil organic matter in the presence of alkali. J. Soil Sci. 1:198-205.

Bremner, J. M. 1951. A review of recent work on soil organic matter. Part I. J. Soil Sci. 2:67-82.

Bremner, J. M. 1952. The nature of soil-nitrogen complexes. J. Sci. Food Agr. 3:497-500.

Bremner, J. M. 1954. A review of recent work on soil organic matter. II. J. Soil Sci. 5:214-232.

Bremner, J. M. 1955a. Nitrogen distribution and amino-acid composition of fractions of a humic acid from a chernozem soil—(Hildesheimer Schwarzerde). Z. Pflanzernähr. Düng. Bodenk. 71:63-66.

Bremner, J. M. 1955b. Nitrogen transformations during the biological decomposition of straw composted with inorganic nitrogen. J. Agr. Sci. 45:469-475.

Bremner, J. M. 1955c. Recent work on soil organic matter at Rothamsted. Z. Pflanzernähr. Düng. Bodenk. 69:32-38.

Bremner, J. M. 1955d. Studies on soil humic acids. I. The chemical nature of humic nitrogen. J. Agr. Sci. 46:247-256.

Bremner, J. M. 1956. Some soil organic-matter problems. Soils and Fertil. 19:115-123.

Bremner, J. M. 1957. Studies on soil humic acids. II. Observations on the estimation of free amino groups. Reactions of humic acid and lignin preparations with nitrous acid. J. Agr. Sci. 48:352-360.

Bremner, J. M. 1958a. Amino sugars in soil. J. Sci. Food Agr. 9:528-532.

Bremner, J. M. 1958b. Distribution of the forms of nitrogen in soil profiles. Rep. Rothamsted Exp. Sta. 1957. p. 57.

Bremner, J. M. 1959. Determination of fixed ammonium in soil. J. Agr. Sci. 52:147-160.

Bremner, J. M. 1960. Determination of nitrogen in soil by the Kjeldahl method. J. Agr. Sci. 55:11-33.

Bremner, J. M. 1965a. Total nitrogen. In Agronomy 9. C. A. Black, ed. Methods of Soil Analysis. American Society of Agronomy, Madison, Wis. pp. 1149-1178.

Bremner, J. M. 1965b. Organic forms of nitrogen. In Agronomy 9. C. A. Black, ed. Methods of Soil Analysis. American Society of Agronomy, Madison, Wis. pp. 1238-1255.

Bremner, J. M. 1965c. Inorganic forms of nitrogen. In Agronomy 9. C. A. Black, ed. Methods of Soil Analysis. American Society of Agronomy, Madison, Wis. pp. 1179-1237.

Bremner, J. M. 1965d. Nitrogen availability indexes. In Agronomy 9. C. A. Black, ed. Methods of Soil Analysis. American Society of Agronomy, Madison, Wis. pp. 1324-1345.

Bremner, J. M., and Führ, F. 1964. Tracer studies of the reaction of soil organic matter with nitrite. Rept. FAO-IAEA Technical Meeting on the Use of Isotopes in Soil Organic Matter Studies, Braunschweig, 1963. In press.

Bremner, J. M., and Harada, T. 1959. Release of ammonium and organic matter from soil by hydrofluoric acid and effect of hydrofluoric acid treatment on extraction of soil organic matter by neutral and alkaline reagents. J. Agr. Sci. 52:137-146.

Bremner, J. M., and Ho, C. L. 1961. Use of ion-exchange resins for extraction of soil organic matter. Agron. Abstr., p. 15. American Society of Agronomy.

Bremner, J. M., and Lees, H. 1949. Studies on soil organic matter. Part II. The extraction of organic matter from soil by neutral reagents. J. Agr. Sci. 39:274-279.

Bremner, J. M., and Shaw, K. 1954. Studies on the estimation and decomposition of amino sugars in soil. J. Agr. Sci. 44:152-159.

Bremner, J. M., and Shaw, K. 1957. The mineralization of some nitrogenous materials in soil. J. Sci. Food Agr. 8:341-347.

Bremner, J. M., and Shaw, K. 1958. Denitrification in soil. I. Methods of investigation. J. Agr. Sci. 51:22-39.

Bremner, J. M., Cheng, H. H., and Edwards, A. P. 1964. Assumptions and errors in

N^{15}-tracer research. Rept. FAO-IAEA Technical Meeting on the Use of Isotopes in Soil Organic Matter Studies, Braunschweig, 1963.

Bremner, J. M., Heintze, S. G., Mann, P. J. G., and Lees, H. 1946. Metallo-organic complexes in soil. Nature 158:790.

Broadbent, F. E. 1948. Nitrogen release and carbon loss from soil organic matter during decomposition of added plant residues. Soil Sci. Soc. Am. Proc. (1947) 12:246-249.

Broadbent, F. E., and Bradford, G. R. 1952. Cation-exchange groupings in the soil organic fraction. Soil Sci. 74:447-457.

Broadbent, F. E., and Norman, A. G. 1947. Some factors affecting the availability of the organic nitrogen in soil—a preliminary report. Soil Sci. Soc. Am. Proc. (1946) 11:264-267.

Broadbent, F. E., Burge, W. D., and Nakashima, T. 1960. Factors influencing the reaction between ammonia and soil organic matter. Trans. 7th Internat. Congr. Soil Sci. 2:509-516.

Bromfield, A. R., Coulson, C. B., and Davies, R. I. 1959. Humic acid investigations: fractionation studies. Chem. Industr. 601-602.

Brown, I. C., and Byers, H. G. 1935. The chemical and physical properties of dryland soils and of their colloids. U. S. Dept. Agr. Tech. Bull. 502.

Brown, I. C., and Thorpe, J. 1942. Morphology and composition of some soils of the Miami family and the Miami catena. U. S. Dept. Agr. Tech. Bull. 834.

Brown, B. R., Johnson, A. W., MacDonald, S. F., Quayle, J. R., and Todd, A. R. 1952. Colouring matters of the Aphididae. Part VII. Addition reactions of Erythroaphin-fb. J. Chem. Soc. 4928-4935.

Brydon, J. E., and Sowden, F. J. 1959. A study of the clay-humus complexes of a chernozemic and a podzol soil. Canad. J. Soil Sci. 39:136-143.

Burge, W. D., and Broadbent, F. E. 1961. Fixation of ammonia by organic soils. Soil Sci. Soc. Am. Proc. 25:199-204.

Burges, A. 1960. The nature and distribution of humic acid. Sci. Proc. Roy. Dublin Soc., Ser. A1:53-58.

Byers, H. G., Alexander, L. T., and Holmes, R. S. 1935. The composition and constitution of the colloids of certain of the great groups of soils. U. S. Dept. Agr. Tech. Bull. 484.

Cain, R. B. 1962. New aromatic ring-splitting enzyme, protocatechuic acid-4:5-oxygenase. Nature 193:842-844.

Carles, J., and Decau, J. 1960a. Variations in the amino acids of soil hydrolysates. Sci. Proc. Roy. Dublin Soc., Ser. A1:177-182.

Carles, J., and Decau, J. 1960b. (Some conditions likely to modify the proportion of amino acids in soil.) Ann. Agron. Paris 11:557-575.

Carles, J., Soubiés, L., and Gadet, R. 1958. Les acides aminés du sol et leurs variations. C. R. Acad. Sci. Paris 247:1229-1232.

Cessi, C., and Piliego, F. 1960. The determination of amino sugars in the presence of amino acids and glucose. Biochem. J. 77:508-510.

Cessi, C., and Serafini-Cessi, F. 1963. A method for the determination of D-galactosamine in the presence of D-glucosamine. Biochem. J. 88:132-136.

Chang, C. D., Kononenko, O. K., and Herstein, K. M. 1961. The ammoniation of sugar cane bagasse. J. Sci. Food Agr. 12:687-693.

Cheng, H. H., and Kurtz, L. T. 1963. Chemical distribution of added nitrogen in soils. Soil Sci. Soc. Am. Proc. 27:312-316.

Choudhri, M. B., and Stevenson, F. J. 1957. Chemical and physiochemical properties of soil humic colloids: III. Extraction of organic matter from soils. Soil Sci. Soc. Am. Proc. 21:508-513.

Cornfield, A. H. 1957. Effect of 8 years fertilizer treatment on the 'protein-nitrogen' content of four cropped soils. J. Sci. Food Agr. 8:509-511.

Coulson, C. B., Davies, R. I., and Khan, E. J. A. 1959a. Chemical studies on upland peat in North Wales. J. Sci. Food Agr. 10:209-217.

Coulson, C. B., Davies, R. I., and Khan, E. J. A. 1959b. Humic-acid investigations. II. Studies in the fractionation of humic acids. J. Soil Sci. 10:271-283.

Coulson, C. B., Davies, R. I., and Khan, E. J. A. 1959c. Humic acid investigations: 3. Studies on the chemical properties of certain humic acid preparations. Soil Sci. 88:191-195.

Dadd, C. C., Fowden, L., and Pearsall, W. H. 1953. An investigation of the free amino-acids in organic soil types using paper partition chromatography. J. Soil Sci. 4:69-71.

Dagley, S., Evans, W. C., and Ribbons, D. W. 1960. New pathways in the oxidative metabolism of aromatic compounds by micro-organisms. Nature 188:560-566.

Davidson, D. I., Sowden, F. J., and Atkinson, H. J. 1951. Application of paper chromatography to identification and quantitative estimation of amino acids in soil organic matter fractions. Soil Sci. 71:347-352.

Davies, R. I., Coulson, C. B., and Luna, C. 1957. Humic acid investigations. Chem. Industr. 1544-1545.

Dawson, J. E. 1956. Organic soils. Advanc. Agron. 8:377-401.

De, P. K. 1956. Soil organic matter with special reference to nitrogen compounds in rice soils. J. Proc. Inst. Chemists (India) 28:353-360.

De, P. K., and Mukherjee, M. B. 1951. The nature of the organic nitrogen compounds of rice soils. Indian J. Soil Sci. 21:77-92.

Detmer, W. 1871. Die näturlichen Humuskörper des Bodens und ihre landwirtschaftliche Bedeutung. Landw. Vers. Sta. 14:248-300.

Dhar, N. R., and Roy, T. B. G. 1955. Chromatographic detection of amino acids in soils. Proc. Natl. Acad. Sci. India 24A:341-342.

Dhariwal, A. P. S., and Stevenson, F. J. 1958. Determination of fixed ammonium in soils. Soil Sci. 86:343-349.

Dyck, A. W. J., and McKibbin, R. R. 1935. The non-protein nature of a fraction of soil organic nitrogen. Can. J. Res. 13B:264-268.

Eastoe, J. E. 1954. Separation and estimation of chitosamine and chondrosamine in complex hydrolysates. Nature 173:540-541.

Edman, P. 1950. Method for determination of the amino acid sequence in peptides. Acta Chem. Scand. 4:283-293.

Edwards, A. P., and Bremner, J. M. 1963. Studies of the mechanisms of soil aggregation and dispersion using cation exchange resins and sonic vibration for the separation of soil particles. Paper presented at 9th Annual Meeting of the Canadian Society of Soil Science, Banff, Alberta.

Edwards, A. P., and Bremner, J. M. 1964. Use of sonic vibration for separation of soil particles. Canad. J. Soil Sci. 44:366.

Edwards, A. P., and Bremner, J. M. 1965. Dispersion of mineral colloids in soils using cation exchange resins. Nature 205:208-209.

Ellis, G. P. 1959. The Maillard reaction. Advanc. Carboh. Chem. 14:63-134.

Ellis, G. P., and Honeyman, J. 1955. Glycosylamines. Advanc. Carboh. Chem. 10:95-168.

Elson, L. A., and Morgan, W. T. J. 1933. A colorimetric method for the determination of glucosamine and chondrosamine. Biochem. J. 27:1824-1828.

Enders, C. 1942. Über den Chemismus der Huminsäurebildung unter physiologischen Bedingungen. I. Biochem. Z. 312:339-348.

Enders, C., and Sigurdsson, S. 1947. Über den Chemismus der Huminsäurebildung unter physiologischen Bedingungen. VII. Biochem. Z. 318:44-46.

Ensminger, L. E., and Gieseking, J. E. 1942. Resistance of clay-adsorbed proteins to proteolytic hydrolysis. Soil Sci. 53:205-209.

Ensminger, L. E., and Pearson, R. W. 1950. Soil nitrogen. Advanc. Agron. 2:81-111.

Estermann, E. F., and McLaren, A. D. 1959. Stimulation of bacterial proteolysis by adsorbents. J. Soil Sci. 10:64-78.

Estermann, E. F., Peterson, G. H., and McLaren, A. D. 1959. Digestion of clay-protein, lignin-protein, and silica-protein complexes by enzymes and bacteria. Soil Sci. Soc. Am. Proc. 23:31-36.

Evans, L. T. 1959. The use of chelating reagents and alkaline solutions in soil organic-matter extraction. J. Soil Sci. 10:110-118.

Flaig, W. 1950. Zur Kenntnis der Huminsäuren. I. Zur chemischen Konstitution der Huminsäuren. Z. Pflanzernähr. Düng. Bodenk. 51:193-212.

Flaig, W. 1955. Zur Bildungsmöglichkeit von Huminsäuren aus Lignin. Holzforschung 9:1-4.

Flaig, W. 1959. Über die biochemische Bildung von Humusstoffen aus Lignin. Fourth International Congress of Biochemistry. Vol. II Biochemistry of Wood. Pergamon Press, New York.

Flaig, W. 1960. Comparative chemical investigations on natural humic compounds and their model substances. Sci. Proc. Roy. Dublin Soc., Ser. A1:149-162.

Flaig, W., and Breyhan, T. 1956. Über das Vorkommen von Indolverbindungen in Schwarzerdehuminsauren. Z. Pflanzernähr. Düng. Bodenk. 75:132-135.

Forsyth, W. G. C. 1947a. The characterization of the humic complexes of soil organic matter. J. Agr. Sci. 37:132-138.

Forsyth, W. G. C. 1947b. Studies on the more soluble complexes of soil organic matter. I. A method of fractionation. Biochem. J. 41:176-181.

Fosse, M. R. 1916. Origine et distribution de l'urée dans la nature. Ann. de Chimie, 9e série, 6:13-96.

Führ, F., and Bremner, J. M. 1964a. Beeinflussende Faktoren in der Fixierung des Nitrit-Stickstoffs durch die organische Masse des Bodens. Atompraxis 10:109-113.

Führ, F., and Bremner, J. M. 1964b. Untersuchungen zur Fixierung des Nitrit-stickstoffs durch die organische Masse des Bodens. Landw. Forsch. 18:43-51.

Gallagher, P. H. 1942. The mobile colloidal humus of podsolic soils and its relationship to the process of podsolisation. Proc. Roy. Irish Acad. 48B:213-229.

Gillam, W. S. 1940. A study on the chemical nature of humic acid. Soil Sci. 49:433-453.

Gorham, E. 1959. Chlorophyll derivatives in woodland soils. Soil Sci. 87:258-261.

Goring, C. A. I., and Bartholomew, W. V. 1950. Microbial products and soil organic matter: II. The effect of clay on the decomposition and separation of the phosphorus compounds in microorganisms. Soil Sci. Soc. Am. Proc. (1949) 14:152-156.

Gottlieb, S., and Hendricks, S. B. 1946. Soil organic matter as related to newer concepts of lignin chemistry. Soil Sci. Soc. Am. Proc. (1945) 10:117-125.

Goulden, J. D. S., and Jenkinson, D. S. 1959. Studies on the organic material extracted from soils and compost. II. The infra-red spectra of lignoproteins isolated from compost. J. Soil Sci. 10:264-270.

Greenwood, D. J., and Lees, H. 1956. Studies on the decomposition of amino acids in soils: I. Plant and Soil 7:253-262.

Grov, A. 1963a. Amino acids in soil. II. Distribution of water-soluble amino acids in a pine forest soil profile. Acta Chem. Scand. 17:2316-2318.

Grov, A. 1963b. Amino acids in soil. III. Acids in hydrolysates of water-extracted soil and their distribution in a pine forest soil profile. Acta Chem. Scand. 17:2319-2324.

Grov, A., and Alvsaker, E. 1963. Amino acids in soil. I. Water-soluble acids. Acta Chem. Scand. 17:2307-2315.

Hackman, R. H., and Todd, A. R. 1953. Some observations on the reaction of catechol derivatives with amines and amino acids in the presence of oxidizing agents. Biochem. J. 55:631-636.

Hamy, A., and Leroy, G. 1952a. L'extraction de l'humus par les solutions salines. Ann. Agron. 3:939-946.

Hamy, A., and Leroy, G. 1952b. Sur l'extraction de l'humus par les solutions salines. C. R. Acad. Agric. Fr. 38:553-554.

Hance, R. J., and Anderson, G. 1963. Identification of hydrolysis products of soil phospholipids. Soil Sci. 96:157-161.

Handley, W. R. C. 1954. Mull and mor formation in relation to forest soils. Bull. For. Comm. Lond. No. 23.

Handley, W. R. C. 1961. Further evidence for the importance of residual leaf protein complexes in litter decomposition and the supply of nitrogen for plant growth. Plant and Soil 15:37-73.

Harmsen, G. W., and van Schreven, D. A. 1955. Mineralization of organic nitrogen in soil. Advanc. Agron. 7:299-398.

Hausmann, W. 1899. Ueber die Vertheilung des Stickstoffs im Eiweissmolekül. Z. Physiol. Chem., Hoppe-Seyler's, 27:95-108.

Hobson, R. P., and Page, H. J. 1932a. Studies on the carbon and nitrogen cycles in the soil. VI. The extraction of the organic nitrogen of the soil with alkali. J. Agr. Sci. 22:297-299.

Hobson, R. P., and Page, H. J. 1932b. Studies on the carbon and nitrogen cycles in the soil. VII. The nature of the organic nitrogen compounds of the soil: "humic" nitrogen. J. Agr. Sci. 22:497-515.

Hobson, R. P., and Page, H. J. 1932c. Studies on the carbon and nitrogen cycles in the soil, VIII. The nature of the organic nitrogen compounds of the soil: "non-humic" nitrogen. J. Agr. Sci. 22:516-526.

Hodge, J. E. 1953. Chemistry of browning reactions in model systems. J. Agric. Food. Chem. 1:928-943.

Hodge, J. E. 1955. The Amadori rearrangement. Advanc. Carboh. Chem. 10:169-205.

Hoyt, P. B. 1964. Decomposition in soils of chlorophyll-type compounds. Rep. Rothamsted Exp. Sta. 1963. pp. 43-44.

Hoyt, P. B., and Cooke, G. W. 1963. Decomposition of chlorophyll-type compounds in soil. Rep. Rothamsted Exp. Sta. 1962. p. 45.

Ichikawa, C. 1936. (Isolation of cyanuric acid from the soil of Kagamigahara.) J. Agr. Chem. Soc., Japan 12:898-899. (C.A. 31:1139).

Jansson, S. L. 1960a. On the humus properties of organic manures. I. Actual humus properties. Kgl. Lantbruks-Högskol. Ann. 26:51-75.

Jansson, S. L. 1960b. On the humus properties of organic manures. II. Potential humus properties. Kgl. Lantbruks-Högskol. Ann. 26:135-172.

Jenkinson, D. S., and Tinsley, J. 1959. Studies on the organic material extracted from soils and compost. Part I. The isolation and characterization of ligno-protein from compost. J. Soil Sci. 10:245-253.

Jenkinson, D. S., and Tinsley, J. 1960. A comparison of the ligno-protein isolated from a mineral soil and from a straw compost. Sci. Proc. Roy. Dublin Soc., Ser. A1:141-147.

Jenny, H. 1930. A study on the influence of climate upon the nitrogen and organic matter content of the soil. Missouri Agr. Exp. Sta. Res. Bull. 152.

Jenny, H. 1941. Factors of Soil Formation. McGraw-Hill Book Co., New York.

Johnston, H. H. 1959. Soil organic matter: I. Electrophoretic separation of acid-resistant components. Soil Sci. Soc. Am. Proc. 23:293-295.

Kamoshita, Y. 1942. (The fluorescence of soils.) J. Sci. Soil Manure, Japan 16:136-140. (C.A. 46:3691)

Keeney, D. R., and Bremner, J. M. 1964. Effect of cultivation on the nitrogen distribution in soils. Soil Sci. Soc. Am. Proc. 28:653-656.

Kivekäs, J. 1939. Studies on the organic N-compounds of soil. Preliminary communication. 1: Water-soluble fraction. Acta Chem. Fenn. 12B:1.

Kobo, K., Tatsukawa, R., and Oba, Y. 1956. The nitrogen distribution of soil organic matter and its relation to the type of humus. Rapports VIe Congrès International de la Science du Sol, Paris. Volume B. Commission II. pp. 485-491.

Kojima, R. T. 1947a. Soil organic nitrogen: I. Nature of the organic nitrogen in a muck soil from Geneva, New York. Soil Sci. 64:157-165.

Kojima, R. T. 1947b. Soil organic nitrogen: II. Some studies on the amino acids of protein material in a muck soil from Geneva, New York. Soil Sci. 64:245-252.

Kononova, M. M. 1951. (The problem of soil humus and contemporary aims of its study.) Akad-Nauk SSSR: 1-386.

Kononova, M. M. 1961. Soil Organic Matter. Translated by T. Z. Nowakowski and G. A. Greenwood. Pergamon Press, New York.

Kononova, M. M., and Aleksandrova, I. V. 1956. (The use of paper partition chromatography for a study of the forms of nitrogen in humic substances.) Pochvovedenie No. 5, 86-92.

Kononova, M. M., and Aleksandrova, I. V. 1959. The biochemistry of humus formation and some problems of plant nutrition. Soils and Fertil. 22:77-83.

Laatsch, W. 1948. Untersuchungen über die Bildung und Anreichung von Humusstoffen. Ber. Landtech. No. 4, pp. 31.

Laatsch, W., and Schlichting, E. 1953. Zur Bestimmung der α-Amino-N-haltigen Komplexe im Boden. Z. Pflanzernähr. Düng. Bodenk. 62:50-63.

Laatsch, W., Bauer, I., and Bieneck, O. 1950. Die Bildungsweisen der Huminsäuren. Landw. Forsch. 2:38-50.

Laatsch, W., Hoops, L., and Bauer, I. 1951. Über Huminsäuren mit Aminostickstoff. Z. Pflanzernähr. Düng. Bodenk. 53:20-29.

Laatsch, W., Hoops, L., and Bieneck, O. 1952. Über Huminsäuren des Pilzes Spicaria elegans. Z. Pflanzernähr. Düng. Bodenk. 58:258-268.

Ladd, J. N., and Butler, J. H. A. 1964. Comparison of properties of synthetic and natural humic acids. Rept. FAO-IAEA Technical Meeting on the Use of Isotopes in Soil Organic Matter Studies, Braunschweig, 1963. (In press)

Lathrop, E. C. 1912. Guanine from a heated soil. J. Am. Chem. Soc. 34:1260-1263.

Lathrop, E. C. 1917. The organic nitrogen compounds of soils and fertilizers. J. Franklin Inst. 183:169-206, 303-321, 465-498.

Lynch, D. L., and Cotnoir, L. J. 1956. The influence of clay minerals on the breakdown of certain organic substrates. Soil Sci. Soc. Am. Proc. 20:367-370.

Lynch, D. L., and Lynch, C. C. 1958. Resistance of protein-lignin complexes, lignins and humic acids to microbial attack. Nature 181:1478-1479.

Lynch, D. L., Hughes, D. H., and Rhodes, Y. E. 1959. Pressure and gradient elution in ion exchange chromatography of the amino acids in soils. Soil Sci. 87:339-344.

Lynch, D. L., Wright, L. M., and Cotnoir, L. J. 1957. Breakdown of cellulose dextrin and gelatin in the presence of attapulgite. Nature 179:1131.

Maillard, L. C. 1912. Action des acides aminés sur les sucres; formation des mélanoidines par voie méthodique. C. R. Acad. Sci. Paris 154:66-68.

Maillard, L. C. 1917. Identité des matières humiques de synthèse avec les matières humiques naturelles. Ann. de Chimie, 9e série, 7:113-152.

Martin, A. E., and Reeve, R. 1955. The extraction of organic matter from podzolic B horizons with organic reagents. Chem. Industr. 356.

Mason, H. S. 1955. Comparative biochemistry of the phenolase complex. Adv. Enzymol. 16:105-184.

Mattson, S., and Koutler-Andersson, E. 1942. The acid-base condition in vegetation, litter, and humus: V. Products of partial oxidation and ammonia fixation. Kgl. Lantbruks-Högskol. Ann. 10:284-332.

Mattson, S., and Koutler-Andersson, E. 1943. The acid-base condition in vegetation, litter, and humus: VI. Ammonia fixation and humus nitrogen. Kgl. Lantbruks-Högskol. Ann. 11:107-134.

Moore, S., and Stein, W. H. 1951. Chromatography of amino acids on sulfonated polystyrene resins. J. Biol. Chem. 192:663-681.

Morrison, R. I. 1958. The alkaline nitrobenzene oxidation of soil organic matter. J. Soil Sci. 9:130-140.

Morrison, R. I. 1963. Products of the alkaline nitrobenzene oxidation of soil organic matter. J. Soil Sci. 14:201-216.

Morrow, C. A., and Gortner, R. A. 1917. The organic matter of the soil: V. A study of the nitrogen distribution in different soil types. Soil Sci. 3:297-331.

Mortland, M. M., and Gieseking, J. E. 1952. The influence of clay minerals on the enzymatic hydrolysis of organic phosphorus compounds. Soil Sci. Soc. Am. Proc. 16:10-13.

Murphy, D., and Moore, A. W. 1960. A possible structural basis of natural humic acid. Sci. Proc. Roy. Dublin Soc., Ser. A1:191-195.

Nõmmik, H., and Nilsson, K. 1963. Fixation of ammonia by the organic fraction of the soil. Acta Agr. Scand. 13:371-390.

Norman, A. G. 1943. Problems in the chemistry of soil organic matter. Soil Sci. Soc. Am. Proc. (1942) 7:7-15.

Okuda, A., and Hori, S. 1954. Chromatographic investigation of amino acids in humic acid and alkaline alcohol lignin. Trans. 5th Internat. Congr. Soil Sci. 2:255-258.

Okuda, A., and Hori, S. 1955. Identification of amino acids in humic acid. Soil Plant Food 1:39-40.

Okuda, A., and Hori, S. 1956. Identification of amino acids in humic acid. J. Sci. Soil Tokyo 26:346-348.

Parker, D. I., Sowden, F. J., and Atkinson, H. J. 1952. The nitrogen distribution and amino acid content of certain soil organic matter fractions. Sci. Agr. 32:163-169.

Parsons, J. W., and Tinsley, J. 1960. Extraction of soil organic matter with anhydrous formic acid. Soil Sci. Soc. Am. Proc. 24:198-201.

Parsons, J. W., and Tinsley, J. 1961. Chemical studies of polysaccharide material in soils and composts based on extraction with anhydrous formic acid. Soil Sci. 92:46-53.

Paul, E. A., and Schmidt, E. L. 1960. Extraction of free amino acids from soil. Soil Sci. Soc. Am. Proc. 24:195-198.

Paul, E. A., and Schmidt, E. L. 1961. Formation of free amino acids in rhizosphere and nonrhizosphere soil. Soil Sci. Soc. Am. Proc. 25:359-362.

Pavel, L., Koloušek, J., and Šmatlák, V. 1954. (Humic substances. II. Amino acids in the hydrolysates of humic acids of some genetic soil types.) Sborn. Čsl. Akad. Zemed. Věd. 27A:207-212.

Pavel, L., Koloušek, J., and Šmatlák, V. 1955. (Amino acids in hydrolysates of humic acids of some genetic soil types.) Sborn. Čsl. Akad. Zemed. Věd. 28: 249-250.

Payne, T. M. B., Rouatt, J. W., and Katznelson, H. 1956. Determination of free amino acids in soil. Soil Sci. 82:521-524.

Pearson, R. W., and Simonson, R. W. 1940. Organic phosphorus in seven Iowa soil profiles: distribution and amounts as compared to organic carbon and nitrogen. Soil Sci. Soc. Am. Proc. (1939) 4:162-167.

Pinck, L. A., and Allison, F. E. 1951. Resistance of a protein-montmorillonite complex to decomposition by soil micro-organisms. Science 114:130-131.

Pinck, L. A., Dyal, R. S., and Allison, F. E. 1954. Protein-montmorillonite complexes, their preparation and the effects of soil microorganisms on their decomposition. Soil Sci. 78:109-118.

Porter, L. K., Stewart, B. A., and Haas, H. J. 1964. Effects of long-time cropping on hydrolyzable organic nitrogen fractions in some Great Plains soils. Soil Sci. Soc. Am. Proc. 28:368-370.

Putnam, H. D., and Schmidt, E. L. 1959. Studies on the free amino-acid fractions of soils. Soil Sci. 87:22-27.

Quastel, J. H., and Scholefield, P. G. 1949. Influence of organic nitrogen compounds on nitrification in soil. Nature 164:1068.

Rather, J. B. 1917. An accurate loss-on-ignition method for determination of organic matter in soils. Arkansas Agr. Exp. Sta. Tech. Bull. 140.

Rendig, V. V. 1951. Fractionation of soil nitrogen and factors affecting distribution. Soil Sci. 71:253-267.

Ribbons, D. W., and Evans, W. C. 1962. Oxidative metabolism of protocatechuic acid by certain soil pseudomonads: a new ring-fission mechanism. Biochem. J. 83:482-492.

Rinderknecht, H., and Jurd, L. 1958. A novel non-enzymatic browning reaction. Nature 181:1268-1269.

Robinson, C. S. 1911. Two compounds isolated from peat soils. J. Am. Chem. Soc. 33:564-568.

Rodrigues, G. 1954. Fixed ammonia in tropical soils. J. Soil Sci. 5:264-274.

Rovira, A. D., and Greacen, E. L. 1957. The effect of aggregate disruption on the activity of microorganisms in the soil. Aust. J. Agr. Res. 8:659-673.

Russell, E. W. 1961. Soil Conditions and Plant Growth. Ed. 9. Longmans, Green and Co., Ltd., London.

Salton, M. R. J. 1960. Microbial Cell Walls. John Wiley & Sons, Inc., New York.

Sanger, F. 1945. The free amino groups of insulin. Biochem. J. 39:507-515.

Schachtschabel, P. 1960. Fixierter Ammoniumstickstoff in Löss und Marschböden. Trans. 7th Internat. Congr. Soil Sci. 2:22-27.

Scharpenseel, H. W., and Krausse, R. 1962. Aminosäureuntersuchungen an verschiedenen organischen Sedimenten, besonders Grau- und Braunhuminsäurefraktionen verschiedener Bodentypen (einschliesslich C14- markierter Huminsäuren). Z. Pflanzernähr. Düng. Bodenk. 96:11-34.

Scheffer, F. 1958. Der organisch gebundene Stickstoff des Bodens, seine Verwertbarkeit (auch Harnstoff). In W. Ruhland, ed. Handbuch der Pflanzenphysiologie 8:179-200. Springer-Verlag, Berlin.

Scheffer, F., and Ulrich, B. 1960. Humus and Humusdüngung. Ferdinand Enke. Stuttgart.

Schlichting, E. 1953a. Zur Kenntnis des Heidehumus. I. Fraktionierung und Untersuchung des ganzen Humuskörpers. Z. Pflanzernähr. Düng. Bodenk. 61:1-12.

Schlichting, E. 1953b. Zur Kenntnis des Heidehumus. II. Die Fulvosäurefraktion. Z. Pflanzernähr. Düng. Bodenk. 61:97-107.

Schlichting, E. 1953c. Zur Kenntnis des Heidehumus. III. Die Huminsäurefraktion. Z. Pflanzernähr. Düng. Bodenk. 61:193-204.

Schmidt, E. L., Putnam, H. D., and Paul, E. A. 1960. Behaviour of free amino acids in soil. Soil Sci. Soc. Am. Proc. 24:107-109.

Schnitzer, M., and Wright, J. R. 1956. Note on the extraction of organic matter from the B horizon of a podzol soil. Canad. J. Agr. Sci. 36:511-512.

Schnitzer, M. and Wright, J. R. 1957. Extraction of organic matter from podzolic soils by means of dilute inorganic acids. Canad. J. Soil Sci. 37:89-95.

Schnitzer, M., Wright, J. R., and Desjardins, J. G. 1958. A comparison of the effectiveness of various extractants for organic matter from two horizons of a podzol profile. Canad. J. Soil Sci. 38:49-53.

Schreiner, O., and Lathrop, E. C. 1912. The chemistry of steam heated soils. J. Am. Chem. Soc. 34:1242-1259.

Schreiner, O., and Shorey, E. C. 1908. The isolation of picoline carboxylic acid from soils and its relation to soil fertility. J. Am. Chem. Soc. 30:1295-1307.

Schreiner, O., and Shorey, E. C. 1909. The isolation of harmful organic substances from soils. U. S. Dept. Agr. Bur. Soils Bull. 53.

Schreiner, O., and Shorey, E. C. 1910a. Chemical nature of soil organic matter. U. S. Dept. Agr. Bur. Soils Bull. 74.

Schreiner, O., and Shorey, E. C. 1910b. Pyrimidine derivatives and purine bases in soils. J. Biol. Chem. 8:385-393.

Schreiner, O., and Shorey, E. C. 1910c. The presence of arginine and histidine in soils. J. Biol. Chem. 8:381-384.

Schreiner, O., Shorey, E. C., Sullivan, M. X., and Skinner, J. J. 1911. A beneficial organic constituent of soils: creatinine. U. S. Dept. Agr. Bur. Soils Bull. 83.

Schuffelen, A. C., and Bolt, G. H. 1950. Some notes on the synthesis of humus compounds. Landbouwk. Tijdschr. 62:333-338.

Shmuk, A. A. 1924. The chemistry of soil organic matter. Trudy Kuban S.-Kh. Inst. 1:2.

Shorey, E. C. 1907. Organic nitrogen in Hawaiian soils. Hawaii Agr. Exp. Sta. Ann. Rept. 1906. pp. 37-59.

Shorey, E. C. 1911. Nucleic acids in soils. Biochem. Bull. 1:104.

Shorey, E. C. 1912a. Nucleic acids in soils. Science 35:390.

Shorey, E. C. 1912b. The isolation of creatinine from soils. J. Am. Chem. Soc. 34:99-107.

Shorey, E. C. 1913. Some organic soil constituents. U. S. Dept. Agr. Bur. Soils Bull. 88.

Shorey, E. C. 1930. Some methods for detecting differences in soils. U. S. Dept. Agr. Tech. Bull. 211.

Shorey, E. C. 1938. The presence of allantoin in soils. Soil Sci. 45:177-184.

Shorey, E. C., and Walters, E. H. 1914. A nitrogenous soil constituent: tetracarbonimid. J. Agr. Res. 3:175-178.

Simon, K. 1929. Über die Herstellung von Humusextrakten mit neutralen Mitteln. Z. Pflanzernähr. Düng. Bodenk. 14A:252-257.

Simonart, P., and Buysse, R. 1954. (Bacteria and free amino acids in the soil.) Trans. 5th Internat. Congr. Soil Sci. 3:136-140.

Simonart, P., and Peeters, F. 1954. (Free amino acids in humus.) Trans. 5th Internat. Congr. Soil Sci. 3:132-135.

Simonart, P., Poffé, R., and Mayaudon, J. 1957. (Quantitative determinations of free amino acids in the soil.) Pédologie 7:284-289.

Singh, S., and Singh, P. K. 1960. Distribution of hexosamines in some soils of Uttar Pradesh: J. Indian Soc. Soil Sci. 8:125-128.

Smithies, L. R. 1952. Chemical composition of a sample of mycelium of Penicillium griseofulvum Dierckx. Biochem. J. 51:259-263.

Sohn, J. B., and Peech, M. 1958. Retention and fixation of ammonia by soils. Soil Sci. 85:1-9.

Sokolov, D. F. 1948. (The presence of certain organic phosphorus compounds in soils.) Pochvovedenie 1948, 503-513.

Sørensen, H. 1962. Decomposition of lignin by soil bacteria and complex formation between autoxidized lignin and organic nitrogen compounds. J. Gen. Microbiol. 27:21-34.

Sowden, F. J. 1955. Estimation of amino acids in soil hydrolysates by the Moore and Stein method. Soil Sci. 80:181-188.

Sowden, F. J. 1956. Distribution of amino acids in selected horizons of soil profiles. Soil Sci. 82:491-496.

Sowden, F. J. 1957. Note on the occurrence of amino groups in soil organic matter. Canad. J. Soil Sci. 37:143-144.

Sowden, F. J. 1958. The forms of nitrogen in the organic matter of different horizons of soil profiles. Canad. J. Soil Sci. 38:147-154.

Sowden, F. J. 1959. Investigations on the amounts of hexosamines found in various soils and methods for their determination. Soil Sci. 88:138-143.

Sowden, F. J., and Atkinson, H. J. 1949. Composition of certain soil organic matter fractions. Soil Sci. 68:433-440.

Sowden, F. J., and Deuel, H. J. 1961. Fractionation of fulvic acids from the B horizon of a profile. Soil Sci. 91:44-47.

Sowden, F. J., and Ivarson, K. C. 1959. Decomposition of forest litters. II. Changes in the nitrogenous constituents. Plant and Soil 11:249-261.

Sowden, F. J., and Parker, D. I. 1953. Amino nitrogen of soils and of certain fractions isolated from them. Soil Sci. 76:201-208.

Sowden, F. J., Parker, D. I., and Atkinson, H. J. 1952. Comparison of organic matter fractions from three soil types. Sci. Agr. 32:127-134.

Stacey, M., and Barker, S. A. 1960. Polysaccharides of microorganisms. Clarendon Press, Oxford.

Stacey, M., and Barker, S. A. 1962. Carbohydrates of living tissues. Van Nostrand, London.

Steelink, C., Berry, J. W., Ho, A., and Nordby, H. E. 1960. Alkaline degradation products of soil humic acid. Sci. Proc. Roy. Dublin Soc., Ser. A1:59-67.

Stein, H. N., and Tendeloo, H. J. C. 1959. The oxidation of phloroglucinol as a model for humification processes. Plant and Soil 11:131-138.

Stevenson, F. J. 1954. Ion exchange chromatography of the amino acids in soil hydrolysates. Soil Sci. Soc. Am. Proc. 18:373-377.

Stevenson, F. J. 1956a. Isolation and identification of some amino compounds in soils. Soil Sci. Soc. Am. Proc. 20:201-204.

Stevenson, F. J. 1956b. Effect of some long-time rotations on the amino acid composition of the soil. Soil Sci. Soc. Am. Proc. 20:204-208.

Stevenson, F. J. 1957a. Investigations of aminopolysaccharides in soils: I. Colorimetric determination of hexosamines in soil hydrolysates. Soil Sci. 83:113-122.

Stevenson, F. J. 1957b. Investigations of aminopolysaccharides in soils: II. Distribution of hexosamines in some soil profiles. Soil Sci. 84:99-106.

Stevenson, F. J. 1957c. Distribution of the forms of nitrogen in some soil profiles. Soil Sci. Soc. Am. Proc. 21:283-287.

Stevenson, F. J. 1959. Carbon-nitrogen relationships in soil. Soil Sci 88:201-208.

Stevenson, F. J. 1960a. Chemical nature of the nitrogen in the fulvic fraction of soil organic matter. Soil Sci. Soc. Am. Proc. 24:472-477.

Stevenson, F. J. 1960b. Some aspects of the distribution of biochemicals in geologic environments. Geochim. Cosmochim. Acta. 19:261-271.

Stevenson, F. J. 1965a. Amino sugars. In Agronomy 9. C. A. Black, ed. Methods of Soil Analysis. American Society of Agronomy, Madison, Wis. pp. 1429-1436.

Stevenson, F. J. 1965b. Amino acids. In Agronomy 9. C. A. Black, ed. Methods of Soil Analysis. American Society of Agronomy, Madison, Wis. pp. 1437-1451.

Stevenson, F. J., and Dhariwal, A. P. S. 1959. Distribution of fixed ammonium in soils. Soil Sci. Soc. Am. Proc. 23:121-125.

Stevenson, F. J., Dhariwal, A. P. S., and Choudhri, M. B. 1958. Further evidence for naturally occurring fixed ammonium in soils. Soil Sci. 85:42-46.

Stevenson, F. J., Marks, J. D., Varner, J. E., and Martin, W. P. 1952. Electrophoretic and chromatographic investigations of clay-adsorbed organic colloids: II. Preliminary investigation. Soil Sci. Soc. Am. Proc. 16:69-73.

Stevenson, F. J., and Swaby, R. J. 1964. Nitrosation of soil organic matter. I. Nature of gases evolved during nitrous acid treatment of lignins and humic substances. Soil Sci. Soc. Am. Proc. 28:773-778.

Stewart, B. A., and Porter, L. K. 1963. Inability of the Kjeldahl method to fully measure indigenous fixed ammonium in some soils. Soil Sci. Soc. Am. Proc. 27:41-43.

Stewart, B. A., Porter, L. K., and Beard, W. E. 1964. Determination of total nitrogen and carbon in soils by a commercial Dumas apparatus. Soil Sci. Soc. Am. Proc. 28:366-368.

Stewart, B. A., Porter, L. K., and Clark, F. E. 1963. The reliability of a micro-Dumas procedure for determining total nitrogen in soil. Soil Sci. Soc. Am. Proc. 27:377-380.

Suzuki, S. 1906-1908. Studies on humus formation. Bull. Coll. Agr. Tokyo 7:95-101, 419-425, 513-529.

Swaby, R. J. 1957. Fractionation of soil humus. 9th Ann. Rept. C.S.I.R.O. p. 18. Government Printers, Canberra.

Swaby, R. J., and Ladd, J. N. 1962. Chemical nature, microbial resistance and origin of soil humus. Internat. Soil Conf. N.Z. 197-202.

Tinsley, J. 1956. The extraction of organic matter from soils with formic acid. Trans. Intern. Congr. Soil Sci. 6th Congr. Paris 2:541-546.

Tinsley, J., and Salam, A. 1961a. Extraction of soil organic matter with aqueous solvents. Soils and Fertil. 24:81-84.

Tinsley, J., and Salam, A. 1961b. Chemical studies of soil organic matter. I. Extraction with aqueous solutions. J. Soil Sci. 12:259-268.

Tinsley, J., and Zin, M. K. 1954. The isolation of lignoprotein from soil. Trans. 5th Internat. Congr. Soil Sci. 2:324-347.

Tokuoka, M. and Dyo, S. 1937. (Organic constituents of humus in Formosa from the viewpoint of social plants. II. Organic constituents accompanying humus in the soils.) J. Soc. Trop. Agr., Taihoku Imp. Univ. 9:26-33. (C. A. 31:8784)

Tracey, M. V. 1952. The determination of glucosamine by alkaline decomposition. Biochem. J. 52:265-267.

Turchin, F. V. 1956. (The role of mineral and biological nitrogen in the agriculture of the U.S.S.R.) Pochvovedenie No. 6,15-29.

Tyurin, I. V. 1937. Organicheskoe Veshchesto Pochv (Soil Organic Matter). Moscow.

Vallentyne, J. R. 1957. The molecular nature of the organic matter in lakes and oceans, with lesser reference to sewage and terrestrial soils. J. Fish Res. Bd. Canada 14:33-82.

Vallentyne, J. R. 1964. Biogeochemistry of organic matter. II. Thermal reaction kinetics and transformation products of amino compounds. Geochim. Cosmochim. Acta 28:157-188.

Van Slyke, D. D. 1911. A method for quantitative determination of aliphatic amino groups. J. Biol. Chem. 9:185-204.

Van Slyke, D. D. 1911-12. The analysis of proteins by determination of the chemical groups characteristic of the different amino-acids. J. Biol. Chem. 10:15-55.

Van Slyke, D. D. 1915. Improvements in the method for analysis of proteins by determination of the chemical groups characteristic of the different amino-acids. J. Biol. Chem. 22:281-285.

Van Slyke, D. D. 1929. Manometric determination of primary amino nitrogen and its application to blood analysis. J. Biol. Chem. 83:425-461.

Van Slyke, D. D., MacFadyen, D. A., and Hamilton, P. 1941. Determination of free amino acids by titration of the carbon dioxide formed in the reaction with ninhydrin. J. Biol. Chem. 141:671-680.

Waksman, S. A. 1938. Humus. Ed. 2. Rev. The Williams and Wilkins Co., Baltimore.

Waksman, S. A., and Iyer, K. R. N. 1932. Contributions to our knowledge of the chemical nature and origin of humus. Soil Sci. 34:43-69.

Waldron, A. C., and Mortensen, J. L. 1961. Soil nitrogen complexes: II. Electrophoretic separation of organic components. Soil Sci. Soc. Am. Proc. 25:29-32.

Waldron, A. C., and Mortensen, J. L. 1962. Soil nitrogen complexes: III. Distribution and identification of nitrogenous constituents in electrophoretic separates. Soil Sci. 93:286-293.

Walker, T. W., and Adams, A. F. R. 1958. Studies on soil organic matter: I. Influence of phosphorus content of parent materials in accumulations of carbon, nitrogen, sulfur and organic phosphorus in grassland soils. Soil Sci. 85:307-318.

Walker, R. H., and Brown, P. E. 1936. The phosphorus, nitrogen and carbon content of Iowa soils. In Brown, P. E. Soils of Iowa. Iowa Agr. Exp. Sta. Spec. Rept. 3.

Walsh, L. M., and Murdock, J. T. 1960. Native fixed ammonium and fixation of applied ammonium in several Wisconsin soils. Soil Sci. 89:183-193.

Walters, E. H. 1915. The presence of proteoses and peptones in soils. J. Ind. Eng. Chem. 7:860-863.

Walters, E. H., and Wise, L. E. 1917. The identity of cyanuric acid with so-called "tetracarbonimid." J. Am. Chem. Soc. 39:2472-2477; J. Agr. Res. 10:85-91.

Waring, S. A., and Bremner, J. M. 1964. Effect of soil mesh-size on the estimation of mineralizable nitrogen in soils. Nature 202:1141.

Wheeler, B. E. J., and Yemm, E. W. 1958. The conversion of amino acids in soils. I.

Amino-acid breakdown and nitrification in cultivated and natural soils. Plant and Soil 10:49-77.

Whistler, R. L., and Kirby, K. W. 1956. Composition and behaviour of soil polysaccharides. J. Am. Chem. Soc. 78:1755-1759.

Whitehead, D. C., and Tinsley, J. 1964. Extraction of soil organic matter with dimethylformamide. Soil Sci. 97:34-42.

Williams, C. H., Williams, E. G., and Scott, N. M. 1960. Carbon, nitrogen, sulfur, and phosphorus in some Scottish soils. J. Soil Sci. 11:334-346.

Wise, L. E., and Walters, E. H. 1917. Isolation of cyanuric acid from soil. J. Agr. Res. 10:85-92.

Wittich, W. 1952. Der heutige Stand unseres Wissens vom Humus und Neue Wege zur Lösung der Rohhumusproblems im Walde. Schrift. Forstl. Fak. Univ. Göttingen 4.

Wrenshall, C. L., and Dyer, W. J. 1941. Organic phosphorus in soils: II. The nature of the organic phosphorus compounds. A. Nucleic acid. B. Phytin. Soil Sci. 31:235-248.

Wrenshall, C. L., and McKibbin, R. R. 1937. Pasture studies. XII. The nature of the organic phosphorus in soils. Canad. J. Res. 15B:475-479.

Wright, J. R., Schnitzer, M., and Levick, R. 1958. Some characteristics of the organic matter extracted by dilute inorganic acids from a podzolic B horizon. Canad. J. Soil Sci. 38:14-22.

Yamashita, T., and Akiya, T. 1963. (Amino-acid composition of soil hydrolysates.) J. Sci. Soil Tokyo 34:255-258.

Young, J. L. 1962. Inorganic soil nitrogen and carbon:nitrogen ratios of some Pacific Northwest soils. Soil Sci. 93:397-404.

Young, J. L., and Mortensen, J. L. 1958. Soil nitrogen complexes: I. Chromatography of amino compounds in soil hydrolysates. Ohio Agr. Exp. Sta. Res. Circ. 61.

Yuan, T. L. 1964. Comparison of reagents for soil organic matter extraction and effect of pH on subsequent separation of humic and fulvic acids. Soil Sci. 98:133-141.

Chapter 4

Sorption of Inorganic Nitrogen Compounds by Soil Materials

M. M. MORTLAND AND A. R. WOLCOTT

Michigan State University
East Lansing, Michigan

I. INTRODUCTION

The nature of complexes formed when inorganic nitrogen compounds are adsorbed on clay and organic matter in soils is of interest from both a practical and theoretical point of view. Large quantities of nitrogen in the form of ammonia, ammonium, and nitrate are being used to increase crop production. Ammonia and several oxides and acids of nitrogen are also products of microbial activity in the soil. It is imperative then, that the reactions of ammonia and other inorganic nitrogen compounds in soils be clearly understood.

A good deal of literature exists on the nature of ammonia-clay and ammonia-organic matter complexes but relatively little about the nature of other inorganic nitrogen complexes with clays and organic matter. Mortland (1958) reviewed the reactions of ammonia in soils. A small number of publications have dealt with the reactions of lignin with various oxides of nitrogen but the literature is almost devoid of work concerning the reactions of these compounds with clays. The purpose of this chapter is to review current concepts regarding the nature of inorganic nitrogen complexes with clays and organic matter. Of necessity, it will be concerned primarily with ammonia.

The nature of ammonia adsorption by clays, organic matter, and other adsorbents can range from the purely physical to purely chemical with a complete gradation within these extremes. Theoretically, physical adsorption is characterized by easy reversibility, low heat of adsorption, and does not require any specific adsorption sites. The energies involved are similar to those in condensation phenomena. Thus, any compound that is physically adsorbed by a colloid is quite easily removed upon reduction in the pressure or concentration of the adsorbate in question. On the other hand, compounds that are chemically adsorbed are characterized by a degree of irreversibility and high heat of adsorption and they require specific adsorption sites on the colloid with which they can react. The energies involved in chemical adsorption are then similar to those appearing in ordinary chemical reactions. Compounds that are chemically adsorbed cannot easily be removed from the colloid merely by a reduction in pressure or concentration of the compound in the gas or liquid phase. In an adsorbent possessing a heterogenous group of adsorption sites, there will be a wide spectrum of adsorption energies ranging from the most to the least energetic. On the other hand, even if homogenous adsorption sites were present, there could be a general decrease in adsorption energies as adsorption proceeds, due to interaction of molecules already adsorbed with those in the process of being adsorbed.

Organic matter can react with ammonia and oxides of nitrogen with the resulting formation of various amides, imides, amines, and nitro or nitroso compounds in which the bond with the nitrogen group is covalent in character. Of course, ammonia will also react with protons provided by carboxyl groups to form the ammonium ion. Naturally, physical adsorption will occur once chemical adsorption sites are satisfied and the pressure of ammonia is increased.

The nature of inorganic nitrogen complexes with clays and organic matter are discussed in the following sections.

II. NATURE OF CLAY MINERAL-INORGANIC NITROGEN COMPLEXES

A. Clay Mineral-Ammonia

There are a variety of kinds of bonding possible when ammonia is adsorbed on clay minerals. Cook (1935) found that an acid clay was formed when bentonite partly saturated with ammonium ions was heated at 450°C for 48 hours. This, of course, suggested that the ammonium ions were being split into ammonia and hydrogen ions and further suggested that, if acid clay were reacted with ammonia, the ammonium ion would be formed. This last reaction was established by Buswell and Dudenbostel (1941) using infrared absorption techniques. That this was not the only kind of chemisorption was established by Barrer and MacLeod (1954) and Mortland (1955), who found ammonia irreversibly adsorbed by sodium and calcium montmorillonite, respectively. Stone and Wild (University of Reading, personal communication) demonstrated that ammonia adsorbed on Mg-vermiculite could not all be extracted by 2N HCl, fixation as ammonium undoubtedly being responsible. Reactions of ammonia with residual water molecules (Cornet, 1943; Jackson and Chang, 1947; Mortland, 1955; Brown and Bartholomew, 1962) between the clay platelets or with exposed hydroxyl groups (Cornet, 1943; Jenny et al., 1945; Mortland, 1955) have been suggested as possible mechanisms of adsorption. Other types of suggested reactions of ammonia with clay minerals are coordination type complexes with exchangeable bases (Barrer and MacLeod, 1954; Mortland, 1958; James and Harward, 1962), and hydrogen bonding between the hydrogens of ammonia and oxygens of the clay mineral surface (Mortland, 1955). Young and McNeal (1964) suggest the possibility of a hydrogen bond between the nitrogen of NH_3 and the OH groups of the clay lattice. Rynders and Schuit (1950) have suggested that a hydrogen bond is operating when ammonia is adsorbed on the surface of metal oxides. The least energetic bonding would be adsorption of the Van der Waal type and could be classified as physical in nature.

1. X-RAY DIFFRACTION PROPERTIES

Ammonia can penetrate the interlamellar surfaces of montmorillonite and cause it to swell. This is not surprising; in view of the similarities of ammonia and water, one would expect similar effects. Cornet (1943) observed this phenomenon when he exposed dry acid montmorillonite to ammonia gas. Mortland et al. (1963) confirmed this observation and showed that great hysteresis occurred in the lattice spacing as a pressure of ammonia was first advanced and then reduced. Even K- and Cs-montmorillonites were observed to expand in the presence of NH_3 gas. It was also observed by X-ray diffraction techniques that the magnitude of swelling was related to the hydration properties of the exchangeable cation. Following adsorption and degassing, varying quantities of chemically adsorbed ammonia were found, depending on the nature of the exchangeable cation and the rigor of the degassing procedure. Young and Cattani (1962) also suggest that dry montmorillonite will swell upon exposure to ammonia as a result of the penetrating power and cation-hydrating property of ammonia.

Cloos and Mortland (unpublished data) have obtained results on the expansion of montmorillonite in ammonia atmosphere over the whole relative pressure range up to saturation. Figs. 1, 2, 3 show these results. The influence of exchangeable cation on the expanding properties of the clay mineral is obvious. All the experiments where the montmorillonite was saturated with alkali metal and alkaline earth cations showed expan-

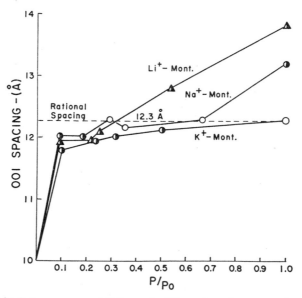

Fig. 1. Effect of relative pressure of NH_3 on the 001 spacing of montmorillonite saturated with Li+, Na+, or K+. Open symbols represent rational, non-interstratified systems, and half-shaded symbols indicate presence of random interstratification.

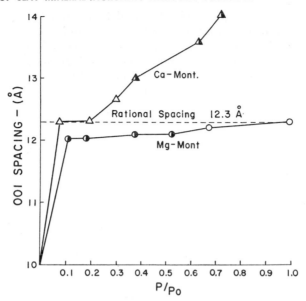

Fig. 2. Effect of relative pressure of NH₃ on the 001 spacing of montmorillonite saturated with Ca⁺⁺ or Mg⁺⁺. Open symbols represent rational, non-interstratified systems, and half-shaded symbols indicate presence of random interstratification.

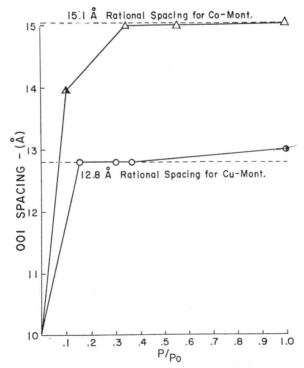

Fig. 3. Effect of relative pressure of NH₃ on the 001 spacing of montmorillonite saturated with Co⁺⁺ or Cu⁺⁺.

sion but to different degrees. The Mg- and K-clay never exceeded a spacing of 12.3Å even at saturation, while Ca, Li, and Na montmorillonite expanded to higher levels as saturation was approached. The 001 spacing of 12.3Å undoubtedly represents one layer of NH_3 molecules in the interlamellar positions of the clay mineral and the 15Å spacing indicated at higher relative pressures for the Ca-, Li-, and Na-clays represents two layers of NH_3, although the latter spacing was observed only in randomly interstratified systems of one and two layers. In the case of Ca- and Na-montmorillonites a rather stable homogenous system containing one layer of ammonia was established, which after increasing pressure, began to yield a two layer system. In the case of Li-clay, however, a stable one-layer system was never established and a continuous swelling of the clay occurred over the whole pressure range.

The results for the Cu- and Co-montmorillonites can be interpreted in terms of coordination complex formation, verification of these having been obtained by infrared. The spacing of Cu-montmorillonite (12.8Å) may result from the observed complex formation having probably a coordination number of 4 and a planar configuration. A coordination complex may be expected in the Co-clay which would have a coordination number of 6 and an octahedral geometry. The difference in spacing between the Cu- and Co-montmorillonites may thus be explained on the basis of their coordination numbers and the geometry of the resulting complex ions. It is of interest to note the formation of non-interstratified layers in the Cu- and Co-clays at low pressures and the stability of these layers up to saturation pressure $(P/P_0 = 1)$. The complexes are apparently quickly formed at low pressure and further adsorption found upon increase in pressure may be NH_3 molecules filling in the spaces around the complex ions.

Mortland et al. (1963) have found that a dehydrated vermiculite, whether saturated with calcium or sodium, would not expand in the presence of ammonia. They found no change in the C-axis spacing after several increments of ammonia pressure. The spacing remained rational, indicating little, if any, interstratification of expanded layers with non-expanded. However, it was found that, after degassing, the vermiculite had retained considerable ammonia of the order of one-third to one-half the cation exchange capacity. Apparently the first ammonia molecules to penetrate the lattice are not in large enough numbers to cause noticeable expansion as indicated by X-ray diffraction. They then react with residual water molecules to form the ammonium ion, and resulting fixation prevents swelling. Infrared studies by Mortland et al. (1963) clearly show that NH_4^+ ions exist in the base-saturated vermiculite after adsorption of NH_3. That residual water is present in apparently dehydrated (heated to 105°C) vermiculite and montmorillonite is clearly evident in infrared absorption data. These observations suggest that there is a difference in the swelling properties of "dry" vermiculite and montmorillonite upon exposure to ammonia. Undoubtedly, these differences are related primarily to charge density and, perhaps, charge location, whether tetrahedral or octahedral. Just as the swelling of vermiculite with water is restricted by its charge, its swelling with ammonia is also restricted. Data shown here in Fig. 1, 2, and 3 indicate that montmorillonite does not expand as much in the presence of NH_3 as other workers have observed with H_2O.

The influence of adsorption of ammonia by hydrated vermiculite was studied by Young and Cattani (1962). They found that some soil minerals collapsed from a 14Å spacing to near 10Å upon adsorption of ammonia. Similar observations were made by them on soil montmorillonites. James and Harward (1964) and Russell and Farmer (personal communication) have also shown that ammonia and water compete for adsorption sites, with the former the most effective. Mortland et al. (1963) found that hydrated calcium vermiculite collapsed to near 10Å upon adsorption of ammonia, while hydrated calcium montmorillonite contracted almost one angstrom unit upon ammonia adsorption. The almost complete dehydration of vermiculite and the partial dehydration of montmorillonite upon ammonia adsorption may be the result of ammonium ion formation followed by fixation, aided by low pressure which would promote dehydration. Young and McNeal (1964) have shown lattice contraction of a number of hydrated expanding minerals upon treatment with ammonia. They also point out differences in effects between minerals of supposedly similar structures.

The behavior of expanding clays will vary somewhat, depending on the environment provided. For example, Stone and Wild (personal communication) found a basal spacing of about 12.2Å for Mg-vermiculite which had been fully hydrated, then exposed to ammonia. In their systems, however, the mineral was not subjected to less than atmospheric pressure, a stream of ammonia gas having been passed over the sample. This is in contrast to the work of Mortland et al. (1963) which was done at relatively low pressures. Stone and Wild found that, when the Mg-vermiculite was only partially hydrated, with a basal spacing of 11.6Å, there was no change upon treatment with ammonia. Stone and Wild also observed contraction of the lattice when hydrated Cu^{2+}- and Na^+-vermiculites were exposed to ammonia gas. Young and McNeal (1964) were able to show reversibility of the lattice contraction of hydrated montmorillonite upon ammoniation by wetting the clay with water. The lattice expanded to 001 spacings greater than 18Å. The ammoniated vermiculites which they studied showed little or no re-expansion on wetting.

The influence of ammonia adsorption by non-swelling minerals on their X-ray diffraction properties would be expected to be small, since it would all be on external surfaces with no alteration of the basic crystal structure.

2. ADSORPTION ISOTHERMS

The nature of adsorption isotherms of ammonia on minerals has been studied by Cornet (1943), Barrer and MacLeod (1954), Mortland (1955), Zettlemoyer et al. (1955), Slabaugh and Siegel (1956), Chao and Kroontje (1960), Brown and Bartholomew (1962), Mortland et al. (1963), and James and Harward (1962). The adsorption isotherms of ammonia on charcoal were studied by Titoff (1910) and on silica gel by Stober (1956). Apparently only physical adsorption took place on the charcoal, even at elevated temperatures, while chemical adsorption was observed on the silica gel.

The magnitude of ammonia adsorption by clay minerals is a function of two main factors: the extent of surface area and the nature of the exchangeable cation. Stone and Wild (personal communication) have shown that ammonia adsorption by hydro-biotite and vermiculite is proportional to cation exchange capacity, but this property is, of course, also a function of surface area. That different clay minerals adsorb more or less ammonia, depending on their specific surface has been clearly shown by Cornet (1943), Mortland (1955), and Brown and Bartholomew (1962). Ammonia can penetrate the interlayer surfaces of dry montmorillonite, thus giving rise to tremendous adsorption by this clay mineral. However, in the case of another dry swelling clay mineral, vermiculite, some ammonia penetrates the interlayer spaces and is chemically adsorbed, but the lattice does not swell and adsorption involving less than chemical adsorption energy does not occur (Mortland et al., 1963). This probably results from the fact that once chemical adsorption takes place, the fixation of the ammonium ion occurs, thus removing the internal surface as a locale for further chemical and physical adsorption. Since one of the main differences between montmorillonite and vermiculite is total charge, there is undoubtedly a critical charge lying somewhere between the extremes of these two minerals where the internal surfaces do become available for physical adsorption. Nature of the exchangeable cation, as shown by Dennis and Ellis (1962) for potassium fixation, and particle size may also play a part in determining the point where the internal surface becomes available for adsorption.

Minerals which do not possess large surface areas such as kaolinite, illite, and gibbsite have correspondingly lower magnitudes of ammonia adsorption. Brown and Bartholomew (1962) have shown that the internal surface of halloysite is not available for ammonia adsorption. However, since the mineral was evidently in the dehydrated state, it is still possible that ammonia may be able to penetrate the internal surface of the hydrated form. Young and McNeal (1964) observed considerably more retention of NH_3 by air-dry halloysite than by kaolinite. The data of Brown and Bartholomew indicate that gibbsite does not chemically adsorb ammonia. However, they and James and Harward (1962) suggest that ammonia can react with weakly acidic hydroxyl groups at the edge of a clay mineral lattice. Presumably these must be associated with the tetrahedral rather than the octahedral layer. Stober (1956) observed chemical adsorption of NH_3 on silica gel, thus at the edge of a clay mineral lattice the silica layer might react in a similar manner.

The shapes of adsorption isotherms have been interpreted in terms of classical theories. Mortland (1955), Mortland and Erickson (1956), Zettlemoyer et al. (1955b), and Slabaugh and Siegel (1956) have described ammonia adsorption isotherms in terms of the Brunauer, Emmet, and Teller theory of multimolecular adsorption. Chao and Kroontje (1960) have utilized the Langmuir and Fruendlich adsorption isotherms. Problems exist in applying the classical theories to ammonia adsorption by clay minerals—the expanding ones like montmorillonite, particularly. This is because of the extremely heterogenous nature of the adsorption phenomenon, ranging from pure chemical adsorption at one end to pure physical adsorption at the other. The application of the classical theories to ammonia adsorption by clay minerals appears to be only partially successful at best.

The influence of exchangeable cation on the adsorption isotherm is quite marked. Cornet (1943) observed that H-bentonite (probably mostly Al) adsorbed more ammonia than K-bentonite, which he associated with a lack of lattice expansion by the latter. That K-montmorillonite and even Cs-montmorillonite expand to a limited extent in the presence of ammonia gas, has been demonstrated by Mortland et al. (1963). Mortland (1955) found that the effect of exchangeable cations on adsorption by montmorillonite followed the sequence H > Ca > Na > K. Brown and Bartholomew (1962) in a detailed study on the effect of exchangeable cations on adsorption by montmorillonite found the sequence H > Al > Ca > NH_4 > Na > K in the first isotherms. They obtained an identical series for halloysite. However, after allowing the montmorillonite samples to equilibrate in ammonia gas, then evacuating and obtaining isotherms again, they found less ammonia adsorption and little difference between samples, with the possible exception of K-montmorillonite. Their data suggest that the large differences in isotherms observed in the initial experiments are due to chemical adsorption.

Chemical adsorption of ammonia by H-clays was demonstrated by Buswell and Dudenbostel (1941). The reaction between ammonia and exchangeable protons, or protons provided by hydrolysis of exchangeable aluminum, is to be expected. However, Barrer and MacLcod (1954) demonstrated hysteresis in adsorption-desorption isotherms of ammonia on sodium bentonite. Mortland (1955) showed by the irreversibility of the isotherm and high heats of adsorption, that calcium-saturated montmorillonite chemically adsorbed ammonia.

Brown and Bartholomew (1963) have shown, by means of adsorption isotherms, the competition between water and ammonia for adsorption sites on clay minerals. They observed a great interaction between ammonia adsorption and moisture levels of clays. At ammonia pressures below 10 to 100 mm of mercury, "dry" bentonite and halloysite adsorbed more ammonia than comparable moist clays. However, at higher ammonia pressures, moist clays adsorbed more than dry clays. The kind of exchangeable cation on the exchange complex was observed to affect ammonia adsorption by moist clays in the same order as for dry clays Al > Ca > K. Apparently, one effect of the exchangeable cation is an influence on the quantity and nature of water of hydration. The most reasonable picture of water-ammonia competition is that, at finite pressures of H_2O and NH_3, they compete (1) for hydration or ammination* of the exchangeable cation, and (2) for hydrogen bonding to the surface oxygen atoms of the silicate layer.

---

* The term "ammine" is applied here to all complexes in which ammonia is coordinated to a cation, independent of the type of cation involved and the nature of the coordinate bond.

Young and McNeal (1964) observed that NH_3 which was strongly adsorbed by clay minerals and retained under vacuum degassing conditions could be readily displaced by atmospheric water. James and Harward (1964) have studied the competition of NH_3 and H_2O for adsorption sites on clay minerals and describe it by the law of mass action:

$$M(NH_3)_n Clay + mH_2O \rightleftarrows M(H_2O)_m Clay + nNH_3$$

where M represents an exchangeable metal cation.

Russell and Farmer (personal communication) determined total nitrogen ($NH_3 + NH_4^+$) by chemical analysis, and estimated ammonium content from its 1440 cm^{-1} absorption band in ammonia-treated, base-saturated montmorillonite. The results in Table 1, obtained immediately

Table 1. Amounts of NH_3 and NH_4^+ retained on montmorillonite after treatment with dry NH_3, followed by evacuation at 0.03-0.05 mm Hg for 30 minutes. (Unpublished data of Russell and Farmer)

Ion on clay	$NH_3 + NH_4^+$, me./100 g (by chemical methods)	NH_4^+, me./100 g (estimated from infrared)
Li	160	17
Na	102	27
K	·28	9
NH_4	107	103
Mg	102	80
Ca	123	70
Al	103	·86
Cu	137	16

following treatment and vacuum degassing, show that the ammonium content of Ca-, Mg-, and Al-clays is close to the exchange capacity. They ascribe this to the mechanism postulated by Mortland et al. (1963), e.g.,

$$Ca(H_2O)_x^{2+} + 2\,NH_3 \rightarrow Ca(OH)_2 + 2\,NH_4^+ + (X - 2)H_2O \qquad [1]$$

They consider it uncertain to what extent this mechanism contributes to the lower ammonium contents in clays saturated with monovalent ions. The excess NH_3 indicated by chemical analysis is considered to be principally coordinated to the ions and support for this was given by the infrared spectra. The large amount of NH_3 retained by Li ion is in accord with its known complexing power. This is also true to a lesser degree of Na, while the K-montmorillonite retains little. The low NH_3 content of the Al-montmorillonite shows that the hydroxides formed inhibit complex formation with NH_3.

When these systems were exposed to air, loss of coordinated NH_3 was rapid and was essentially complete within an hour due to displacement by water. Ammonium ion content also decreased, rapidly in the case of Ca where two-thirds was lost in 17 minutes, and more slowly, over several days, with Mg. This was ascribed to a reversal of equation [1], i.e.:

$$Ca(OH)_2 + 2\,NH_4^+ + (X - 2)H_2O \rightarrow Ca(H_2O)_x^{2+} + 2\,NH_3 \qquad [2]$$

Only 10 meq/100 g remained after 4 months. The ammonium content of the system containing monovalent ions decreased slowly over several days; 4-10 meq/100 g remained after 4 months. The hydroxide formed in Al-montmorillonite was stable, and the NH_4^+ content remained high (76 meq/100 g after 4 months). With copper montmorillonite, the ammonium content increased from 16 meq to 74 meq in 5 days by the reaction:

$$[Cu(NH_3)_x]^{2+} + 2 H_2O \rightarrow Cu(OH)_2 + 2 NH_4^+ + (X - 2)NH_3$$

Thus, in montmorillonite, as in aqueous solution, the copper ammine complex is only stable in the presence of excess ammonia, loss of which leads to hydrolysis with the formation of the hydroxide and the ammonium ion.

3. HEAT OF ADSORPTION OF AMMONIA ON CLAY MINERALS

The heat of adsorption of ammonia on clay minerals has been measured indirectly, using adsorption isotherms obtained at different temperatures and applying the Clausius-Clapeyron equation, by Mortland (1955) and James and Harward (1962). Direct measurements of the heat involved have been made with a calorimeter by Mortland et al. (1963). Ellis (1961) has measured the heat of desorption of ammonia from ammonium montmorillonite with differential thermal analysis. Surprisingly good agreement was obtained between the different methods.

If the calorimetric differential heats of adsorption are plotted with respect to n, the number of adsorbed molecules, different curves are obtained, depending on the nature of the saturating cation and treatment. If, however, one extrapolates the linear portion of the isotherms to zero pressure and obtains the figure n_0 and then plots the ratio n/n_0 versus the same calorimetric results, the experimental points fit a single function, as shown in Fig. 4.

The value of n_0 is the "point A" of Brunauer and for S-shaped isotherms should be closely related to the monolayer content. However, X-ray diffraction data show that the lattice of ammoniated montmoril-

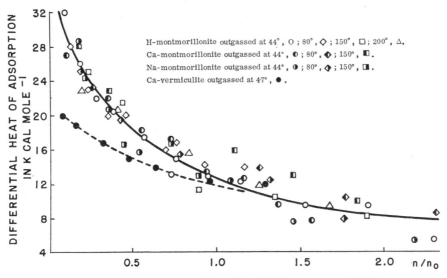

Fig. 4. Calorimetric differential heat of adsorption of NH_3 on montmorillonite.

lonites is far from being completely expanded under these conditions. Furthermore, if one takes the value of n_0 together with the cross-sectional area of the ammonia molecule (13Å^2) and compares the area covered by ammonia with the theoretical surface area of montmorillonite, one finds that, for Ca-montmorillonite, n_0 amounts to only 17% of the whole specific surface. Also, for H-montmorillonite the value of n_0 corresponds very well with the cation exchange capacity of about 100 me/100 g. The conclusion is that n_0 does not represent the monolayer content. In fact, it apparently gives a reasonable estimate of the magnitude of the chemical adsorption.

The most important observations to be made from Fig. 4 are that: (1) when $n = n_0$, the same differential heat of adsorption (i.e., 12.7 kcal) is obtained in all cases; (2) regardless of the nature of the exchangeable cation and the pretreatment, the same thermodynamic processes are involved for the three kinds of cation saturation studied here and these samples differ in the adsorption capacity only. Results obtained for Ca-vermiculite are definitely lower as shown in Fig. 4. This may be explained by the energy consumed by diffusion processes which for several reasons are more important in vermiculite than in montmorillonite. Much larger particle size, and lack of expanding character in the presence of ammonia are the main ones. For example, vermiculite required twice as much time for reaching thermal equilibrium as montmorillonite did.

Conversion of gaseous ammonia into ammonium ions on the clay surface will produce a heat effect of the order 30-35 kcal. If an ammine complex is formed with the adsorbed cation, the heat effect would be something less than the heat of formation of the ammonium ion and would depend upon the nature of the coordinating cation. When $n < n_0$, chemisorption of NH_3 as ammonium ion or as ammine complex occurs. When $n > n_0$, the observed heat effect corresponds with hydrogen bonding and physical adsorption processes. The high initial heats of adsorption (higher than 30 kcal) as shown in Fig. 4 together with infrared studies, show that the initial chemisorption is the formation of the ammonium ion, even in the case of base-saturated clay. The mechanism for this reaction is believed to involve the donation of a proton from residual water molecules and is discussed in detail elsewhere. Rynders and Schuit (1950) found that ammonia was adsorbed relatively firmly on the surfaces of metal oxides. They obtained heats of adsorption of about 10 kcal per mole and suggested that the ammonia was hydrogen-bonded to the oxygen atoms of the oxides. More recently, Blyholder and Richardson (1962) obtained a heat of adsorption of NH_3 on α Fe_2O_3 of 11.5 kcal per mole. They attribute only 4 to 6 kcal of this to hydrogen bonding and the rest to ion-dipole interaction of Fe^{+++} and NH_3.

Ellis (1961) found that as NH_4^+-montmorillonite was heated there was a mole-for-mole loss of NH_3 and H_2O in the temperature range from 200° to 450°C. Using differential thermal techniques, he observed an average heat of desorption of 35 kcal per mole of NH_3. Stone and Wild (personal communication) have shown by D.T.A. that NH_3 sorbed by Mg- and Cu-vermiculite is held rather firmly. Some NH_3 was evolved in the high temperature range of 500 to 850°C. James and Harward (1962) have interpreted differences in heat of adsorption of NH_3 on calcium- and ammonium-montmorillonite as indicating the formation of ammine complexes on the calcium-clay.

4. INFRARED ABSORPTION CHARACTERISTICS

The infrared spectra of NH_4-montmorillonite were first examined by Buswell and Dudenbostel (1941). They found that when acid montmorillonite was treated with dry gaseous ammonia the infrared spectra indicated that the chemisorbed ammonia was present as the ammonium ion. Since it is now known that the method they used to prepare the so-called H-montmorillonite results in obtaining an almost pure aluminum-clay, their data suggest that hydrated aluminum ions are able to convert NH_3 to $NH_4{}^+$. Undoubtedly, the hydrolysis of exchangeable hydrated aluminum ions is able to provide the necessary protons for the reaction, and the results of Russell and Farmer in Table 1 verify this idea. Eischens and Pliskin (1958) have been able to characterize the state of ammonia adsorbed on cracking catalysts by means of infrared absorption. Fripiat et al. (1962) have reported extensively on the infrared spectra of organic amine-clay complexes.

Mortland et al. (1963) have studied in detail the infrared spectra of ammonia chemisorbed on montmorillonite and vermiculite. Basically, there was little difference in the spectra of ammonia chemisorbed on acid-, sodium-, or calcium-montmorillonite. In every case the molecule appeared to exist as the ammonium ion. Stone and Wild (personal communication) have come to the same conclusion from infrared studies of ammonia adsorbed on Mg-vermiculite. Table 2 reports the infrared bands

Table 2. Observed and reported infrared and Raman frequencies (in cm^{-1}).

	Species	$NH_4 Cl*$	$ND_4 Cl*$		NH_3 chemisorbed by:		ND_3 chemisorbed by:	
					H-mont.	Ca-mont.	H-mont.	Ca-mont.
ν_1	A_1	3048	2214	R				
ν_2	E	1710	1215	R				
ν_3	F_2	3138	2350	R, IR	3280	3280	2469	2481
ν_4	F_2	1403	1066	R, IR	1427	1428		

* E. L. Wagner and D. F. Hornig (1950) Journ. Physical Chemistry 18:296.

for NH_3 and ND_3 on H- and Ca-montmorillonites. The frequencies quoted for NH_3 chemisorbed on H-montmorillonite in Table 2 are identical with those given by degassed ammonium saturated montmorillonite.

The formation of $NH_4{}^+$ in acid clay after exposure to NH_3 obviously results from the reaction of NH_3 with exchangeable protons or protons provided by hydrated aluminum ions. In base-saturated montmorillonite, only water or constitutional hydroxyl can supply the proton necessary for the transformation of NH_3 to $NH_4{}^+$.

Experiments have been conducted with ND_3 (deuterated ammonia) to study the rate of exchange of protons from lattice OH groups and the chemisorbed ND_3 (Mortland et al., 1963). The kinetics of this particular isotopic exchange should provide an insight into the availability of the constitutional OH to provide the necessary protons. It was found that only above 200°C did the reaction rate between ND_3 and lattice OH become appreciable. It was found to follow a first order rate law and had an activation energy of about 6 kcal. It was also observed that chemisorbed ND_3 reacted rapidly with residual water to form D_2O and NH_3. Data in this work and that of Faucher and Thomas (1955) have shown a rapid isotopic exchange between D_2O and lattice OH. In the first instance it was found that the extent of lattice OH exchange with D_2O was about 50% in 10 minutes at 20°C. Under similar conditions no noticeable exchange took place with ND_3. Of course, if ND_3 was applied to a relatively moist clay film, D_2O was formed, resulting again in a relatively rapid deuteration of the lattice OH groups. From this work it is apparent that the lattice OH groups (with the possible exception of those on the very edge) are not available as proton donors to ammonia for the formation of the ammonium ion. This conclusion is supported by the work of Stone and Wild (personal communication) on reaction of vermiculite with ND_3 and D_2O.

The most likely source of protons for the formation of ammonium ion in base-saturated clays is residual water molecules. They are water molecules which are strongly polarized in the vicinity of exchangeable cations at the clay surface and are characterized by an appreciable increase in dissociation constant. Ordinary water could not provide nearly enough protons for the observed ammonium ion formation. The reaction would be:

$$(H_2O)_{residual} + NH_3 \longrightarrow NH_4^+ + OH^-$$

The following observations on base-saturated montmorillonite support this viewpoint:

a) The absorbance of the deformation band of residual H_2O is inversely proportional to the absorbance of NH_4^+ deformation band. When higher chemisorption levels are obtained, the amount of residual water seen with infrared absorption decreases. Similar results were obtained with Ca-vermiculite.

b) The amount of chemisorbed ammonia is higher, the more hydrated the exchangeable cation.

Work of Ducros and Dupont (1962) with nuclear magnetic resonance has also indicated that water adsorbed by montmorillonite has a higher degree of dissociation than usual. The average "life" of a proton in any particular molecule is thought to be several orders of magnitude less than in ordinary water.

Infrared studies not only give information on the presence of ammonium ions in montmorillonite, but also provide information on their environment. The frequencies quoted in Table 2 are those obtained for degassed specimens. The presence of interlayer water perturbs the vibrations of NH_4^+ by hydrogen bonding: subsidiary bands then appear in the NH stretching region at 2860 and 3080 cm^{-1}, and the deformation frequency shifts from 1430 cm^{-1} to 1440 cm^{-1} (Mortland et al., 1963). Interlayer ammonia forms still stronger hydrogen bonds with NH_4^+ and causes larger frequency shifts. These perturbed bands can be seen in the infrared spectra of Ca-montmorillonite which had been exposed to liquid NH_3 and evacuated two hours with a mechanical pump (Curve A, Fig. 5). The peaks at 3405 cm^{-1} (v_3) and 1628 cm^{-1} (v_4) prove the presence of some NH_3, the band at 3285 cm^{-1} corresponds to unperturbed $NH_4{}^+$, and those at 3050, 2960 and 2840 cm^{-1} are NH stretching vibrations of $NH_4{}^+$ perturbed by hydrogen bonding with NH_3. The two peaks at 1460 and 1428 cm^{-1} represent the deformation band (v_4) of $NH_4{}^+$, the first perturbed by hydrogen bonding with NH_3, the second unperturbed. Upon heating (curves B and C), the NH_3 is largely driven off giving only unperturbed vibrations of $NH_4{}^+$ at 1428 cm^{-1} and at 3285 cm^{-1}. Upon rehydration in the air (curve D) perturbation of the $NH_4{}^+$ deformation and stretching bands can again be seen, this time by hydrogen bonding with water.

Recent infrared studies have provided evidence for ammine in addition to ammonium formation in base-saturated montmorillonites. Infrared studies by Stone and Wild (personal communication) on copper-vermiculite treated with NH_3 showed the presence of both $NH_4{}^+$ and NH_3, the latter in a Cu^{2+} ammine complex. The formation of this complex gave a steely blue color. Similar complexes on Cu^{2+}-montmorillonite have also been observed by Russell, Farmer, and Mortland (unpublished data). Cloos and Mortland (unpublished) have found that when evacuated Co^{+2}-montmorillonite film is exposed to NH_3, in addition to $NH_4{}^+$, coordinated NH_3 is formed with a band at 1368 cm^{-1} which suggests a CoIII complex. Upon heat treatment, the coordinated NH_3 band shifted to 1245 cm^{-1}, a position characteristic of CoII ammine complexes. Thus, an oxidation-reduction reaction is also indicated. Chaussidon et al. (1962) have shown with infrared studies that CoIII hexammine-saturated montmorillonite decomposes catalytically when the mineral is dehydrated and that the ammonium ion is formed. They suggest that protons are available from residual water for the ammine ligands and the complex is consequently destroyed.

The formation of coordination complexes with transition metal ions is not surprising. Similar complexes with alkali metal and alkaline earth ions are much less stable. Nevertheless, Russell and Farmer (personal communication) have observed coordinated NH_3 on saponite under anhydrous conditions. The deformation band for coordinated NH_3 appeared at 1130 cm^{-1} for Li-, 1185 cm^{-1} for Ca-, and 1218 cm^{-1} for Mg-saponite. This region of the spectrum is obscured in montmorillonite by silicate absorption, but amounts of NH_3 retained by base-saturated montmorillonite (Table 1) strongly suggest the presence of such complexes in that mineral, particularly with Li and Na. On exposure to air, the NH_3 was displaced by H_2O in 15 to 30 minutes, according to the infrared spectra.

The persistence of the NH_3 bands on Ca-montmorillonite in Figs. 5 and 6 suggests the treatment with liquid NH_3 created considerable ammine complex which was relatively stable to the two-hour evacuation procedure. Cloos and Mortland (unpublished) have noted that Li-montmorillonite treated with liquid NH_3, retained NH_3 even after heating for $2\frac{1}{2}$ hours at 105°C as indicated by the continued presence of the 3404 cm^{-1}

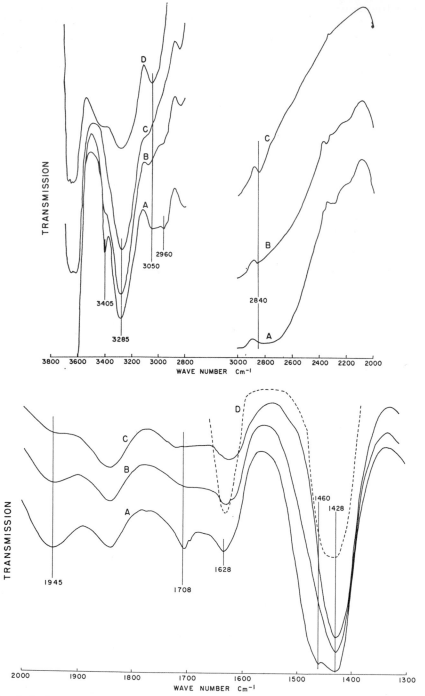

Fig. 5. A. Ca montmorillonite film treated with liquid NH_3, then evacuated 2 hours and scanned immediately. B. Same film after heating at 105°C for 1 hour. C. After heating at 105°C for 60 hours. D. Rehydration in the air after heat treatment.

band. No other cation-montmorillonite system retained NH_3 under this treatment. It may be this is NH_3 which is trapped in the interlayer areas after Li ions have dropped into the empty holes in the octahedral layer thus neutralizing charge and reducing the expansion properties of the clay. It is also possible that the $Li-NH_3$ complex on the clay might be stable under these conditions. It is unlikely that Li amide or any metal amide could account for infrared absorptions that have been observed in NH_3 work since the reaction $2\ NH_3 \rightleftarrows NH_4{}^+ + NH_2{}^-$ has a dissociation constant of the order of 10^{-33}.

5. DISCUSSION

The nature of the first ammonia chemisorbed by hydrogen- or base-saturated montmorillonite or vermiculite has been shown by infrared absorption to be in the ammonium state. This is to be expected for the acid-clay where protons from exchange sites, dissociation of hydrated aluminum ions, or weakly acidic hydroxyl groups at the edge are available for ammonium formation. In the case of base-saturated clays, residual water molecules are believed to be the source of protons. The residual water between the platelets of swelling clays like montmorillonite and vermiculite must be different chemically from ordinary water in order to provide the number of protons necessary for ammonium formation. The exchangeable bases plus the effects of the clay surface itself are believed to exert polarization forces on the residual water molecules of a magnitude such that these molecules dissociate more readily than ordinary water molecules. The amount of NH_3 chemisorbed as ammonium by base-saturated montmorillonite is approximately in proportion to the hydration properties of the cation following the series $Al > Mg > Ca > Na > Li > K$ (Table 1).

Reaction of ND_3 with very dry swelling clays indicate that the deuteration of lattice hydroxyls is a slow reaction except at elevated temperatures, and, with the exception of those at the very edge, it is believed that they do not take direct part in the transformation of chemisorbed NH_3 into $NH_4{}^+$.

Apparently, in $NH_4{}^+$-montmorillonite prepared by saturation of the clay with an ammonium salt, the $NH_4{}^+$ ion is the same as that formed by reaction of acid-clay with NH_3 gas. Additional adsorption bands in the infrared region in moist clays suggest that $NH_4{}^+$ ions are hydrogen bonded to physically adsorbed water. Hydrogen bonding of $NH_4{}^+$ to NH_3 has also been observed with infrared absorption.

It is possible that certain polar organic compounds, such as amino acids, peptides, proteins, and other amine-bearing material, are capable of accepting a proton from residual water molecules in a manner similar to that described for NH_3. This has been confirmed for ethylamine on montmorillonite by Farmer and Mortland (unpublished). Apparently base-saturated clays like montmorillonite and vermiculite possess certain acidic properties in spite of their base saturation. This may be an acidic property that, while not reflected in pH measurements, exerts considerable influence in the space immediately next to the clay surface. Such influence might be important in the reaction with amine-type compounds, as previously discussed, and also in any other reaction involving protons such as certain catalytic reactions and microbiological processes.

The formation of complexes of ammonia with the exchangeable cations of clay minerals certainly plays a part in the adsorption of ammonia. James and Harward (1962, 1964) have interpreted adsorption isotherm data and enthalpy calculations in terms of the formation of such complexes on clay minerals. Direct proof of their formation and that of the ammonium ion has come, however, from infrared studies described previously. The nature of these complexes will vary greatly with the kind of cation. Complexation with the transition metal ions produces systems which are often quite stable. On the other hand, the reactions of ammonia with other cations of the alkaline earth and alkali metal series are less distinct. While the alkaline earth metals form many compounds with ammonia, as for example $CaCl_2 \cdot 2 NH_3$, the stability is a great deal less than that of compounds such as $Co(NH_3)_6Cl_3$, a cobalt ammine complex. The alkali metals K^+, Rb^+, and Cs^+ are even more reluctant to form covalent compounds but Li^+ and Na^+ react to a degree with ammonia to form such compounds as $LiI \cdot 4 NH_3$. The stability of most of the alkali metal complexes with ammonia is relatively low. This suggests that any ammonia complexation with the alkali metal or alkaline earth ions on clay surfaces would be more analogous to "hydrates" rather than complexes of the cobalt hexammine type. As a matter of fact, ion-dipole interaction results in complexes having great variation in stability and energy of formation depending on the nature of the ion in question. The above comments are based on the properties of known salts. It is possible that where the clay is the anion, the stability might be a great deal different but the results of Russell and Farmer (personal communication), Young and McNeal (1964), and of James and Harward (1964) indicate that water can easily displace the coordinated NH_3 in such systems.

Aluminum, on the other hand, is more receptive to electrons furnished by donor groups such as ammonia and so would be expected to more nearly approach a true coordinate bonding. Thus, exchangeable aluminum was suggested by James and Harward (1962) to react with ammonia to form ammine-type complexes. As a matter of fact NH_4^+ formation is extensive as shown in Table 1, the resulting hydroxyl preventing much complex formation with NH_3.

Ammonia is adsorbed on clay minerals by other mechanisms, once the most energetic chemisorption as ammonium is satisfied. In fact, it is clear from Fig. 4 that there is no sharp break in energy of adsorption and that the processes merge one into the other. The last ammonia adsorbed is by physical forces, the energy being only slightly greater than the heat of vaporization. Ammine formation with exchangeable cations followed by hydrogen bonding to surface oxygens of the clay lattice represent reactions of intermediate energy in the spectrum of heats of adsorption on montmorillonite. When there is considerable moisture present there is a competition for the ligand positions on the exchangeable cations and for hydrogen bonds to surface oxygen atoms of the clay lattice.

The discussion here has been concerned primarily with the actual mechanisms of ammonia reactions with clay minerals with suggestions as to relative bonding energies. In the soil after an injection of anhydrous ammonia as in fertilizer application, all these processes will be operative to varying degrees from the point of injection to the periphery of the diffusion zone and amounts of ammonia adsorbed by these mechanisms will change in magnitude with time and conditions. Thus, rapid changes in the status of the adsorbed ammonia on clay minerals may occur as concentration is reduced in the vapor phase by diffusion away from the point of injection and by competition with water. A competition for ammonia by the organic matter and the clay fraction will also be a factor.

B. Clay Mineral-Nitrogen

Adsorption of nitrogen (N_2) gas on clay minerals has been utilized by many workers as an estimate of the specific surface. Adsorption isotherms are obtained at liquid nitrogen temperatures and the specific surface determined using the Brunauer, Emmett and Teller theory of multimolecular adsorption. While it is an excellent method for surface area determination of non-expanding clay minerals, it measures only the external surface of such clay minerals as montmorillonite and vermiculite. The N_2 molecule cannot penetrate the interlamellar surfaces in these clays.

The mechanism of N_2 adsorption on clays can be described as completely physical in nature. The energy of adsorption is near the heat of vaporization and the adsorption process is completely reversible. It is not likely that this particular adsorption has any great influence on soil processes.

C. Clay Mineral-Nitric Oxide

Nothing was found in the literature on this subject; however, Terenin and Roev (1959) have studied NO-metal oxide interactions. Chemical adsorption of NO has recently been found not to occur on clay minerals saturated with either alkali metal or alkaline earth cations by Mortland (unpublished data) using vacuum and infrared techniques. However, if transition metal ions such as Fe^{++}, Fe^{+++}, or Co^{++} are on the exchange complex, chemical adsorption occurs by the formation of coordination complexes, examples of which appear in Fig. 6. For coordinated NO, the position of the stretching vibration depends on the nature of the metal ion, being at 1888 and 1830 cm^{-1} for the iron-clay systems. The band at 2265 cm^{-1} is the ν_3 vibration of adsorbed N_2O and the ν_1 vibration of this molecule was found near 1300 cm^{-1}. Nitrosonium cation (NO^+) formation was indicated by a weak band at 1940 cm^{-1} on the Fe^{++}-nontronite system. Montmorillonite saturated with Co^{++}, Fe^{++}, Fe^{+++}, and Cu^{++} adsorbed NO on the external surfaces which, on the admittance of air, is immediately oxidized to nitrite in a coordinated structure, as indicated by infrared absorption. In the case of Co-montmorillonite and -nontronite, the NO molecule is able to penetrate the interlamellar surfaces as shown by the increase in intensity of the NO bands with time.

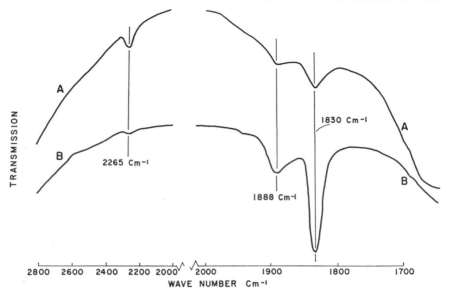

Fig. 6. A. Fe^{+++}-nontronite after exposure to 28 cm Hg pressure of NO followed by degassing. B. F^{++}-nontronite after exposure to 35 cm Hg pressure of NO followed by degassing.

Upon introduction of air, oxidation of the NO takes places at a rate dependent upon the diffusion of the NO to edge of the particle where oxidation to nitrite takes place. Up to 24 hours has been required to oxidize all of the nitric oxide.

D. Clay Mineral-Nitrogen Dioxide

There is almost a complete absence of papers in the literature on this subject. Aldrich and Buchanan (1955) injected NO_2 into soils and observed that it was readily adsorbed and that losses to the atmosphere were small. Mechanisms and the nature of any adsorption process on the clay or organic fraction of the soil were not included in the discussion.

III. NATURE OF ORGANIC MATTER-INORGANIC NITROGEN COMPLEXES

The reactions of ammonia or ammonium with clay minerals described above have far reaching implications; theoretical, geochemical and practical. In natural soil systems, reactions of these and other mineral forms of nitrogen with organic matter are at least equally significant. Reactions of ammonia with organic materials found or expected in soils have received the most attention. Reactions of nitrogen oxides and acids with soil and plant materials have been reported, and these have important implications for a number of unsolved problems of nitrogen transformation in soils.

A. Physical Sorption of Ammonia by Organic Materials

As pointed out in an earlier review (Mortland, 1958), the fixation of NH_3 by organic materials involves both physical and chemical processes. Mortland (1955), applying the BET equation to NH_3 adsorption data, calculated a specific surface of 661 sq m/g for a calcium-saturated muck soil. This compared with an area of 572 sq m/g calculated for calcium bentonite. In spite of the rather similar surfaces, the muck sorbed about twice as much NH_3 as the clay at atmospheric pressure. Marked hysteresis in the adsorption—desorption isotherm indicated that part of the NH_3 had been fixed irreversibly by chemical bonding.

There was no evidence in the absorption isotherms for muck, reported in the above paper, of inflexions or plateaus such as were found by Junker (1941) in the adsorption isotherms for lignin. Junker ascribed these plateaus to chemical fixation by specific active groups on the lignin. After these sites were satisfied, adsorption proceeded with increasing pressure in a manner characteristic for physical adsorption by charcoal.

The lack of characteristic inflexions in the adsorption isotherms of muck is to be understood in terms of the heterogeneity and overlapping polarities of active groups in soil organic matter. The point to be noted is that while initial sorption of NH_3 may be physical, rapid conversion to irreversible or difficultly reversible combinations continues until the more energetic groups responsible for chemical fixation are used up. Extensive chemical fixation takes place, even in dry systems. Mattson and Koutler-Andersson (1941) found little difference in the quantities of nitrogen fixed chemically by air dry materials from NH_3 vapors or by the same materials suspended in aqueous solutions of NH_3.

Physically sorbed ammonia is readily removed by reduction in pressure. With simple aeration at atmospheric pressure, some physically sorbed NH_3 may be retained in the form of semi-stable ammoniates (Zettlemoyer et al., 1955a). The formation of semi-stable ammoniates may be involved in the adsorption of ammonia from the atmosphere by relatively inert materials, such as cellulose, or in the initial adsorption by dry surface soil layers, since the sorbed ammonia is readily leached (deRossi, 1947; Ingham, 1950; Malo and Purvis, 1964). However, it is probable that the bulk of the NH_3 sorbed or retained on exposure to air at atmospheric pressures is chemically bound although there is no sharp energetic delineation between chemical and physical adsorption.

B. Chemical Fixation of Ammonia by Organic Materials

1. FORMS OF FIXED AMMONIA

The Committee on Terminology of the Soil Science Society of America[*] has defined ammonia fixation as "the adsorption of ammonium ions by soils or minerals in such form that they are neither water soluble

[*] Glossary of terms approved by the Soil Science Society of America. 1962. Soil Sci. Soc. Amer. Proc. 26:305-317.

nor readily exchangeable." There are ambiguities in the strict application of this definition to the products of chemical reaction of NH_3 or NH_4^+ with organic materials. Whether NH_3 or NH_4^+ is the reacting form is, of course, a function of pH. Both react with carboxyl groups to form dissociable ammonium salts. Reactions of either NH_3 or NH_4^+ with other active groups, such as carbonyl, phenolic or enolic hydroxyls, or unsaturated carbon groupings, lead to the formation of covalent compounds and are essentially reactions of NH_3, regardless of pH. Many such compounds are soluble in water or exchange extractants, but the contained nitrogen is not ammonium.

Ammoniation by exposure to NH_3 in gaseous or solution form characteristically leads to an increase in water solubility of organic materials (Burge and Broadbent, 1961; Davis and Scholl, 1933, 1939; Jansson, 1960; Jung, 1959; Lisk, 1957; Mattson and Koutler-Andersson, 1954; Sohn and Peech, 1958). Feustel and Byers (1933) found that 35 to 48% of peat materials was solubilized by ammoniation at elevated temperature. A major part of the retained N appeared in the water-soluble fraction, and of this only about 30% was distillable with MgO. McIntosh (1962) found that, of the total nitrogen retained by the organic fraction of prairie soils after treatment at room temperatures with NH_4OH solutions, 20 to 37% was water-soluble. Such increases in solubility of soil organic matter are observed soon after ammoniation. Their persistence in soils after dissipation of excess NH_3 has not been investigated.

Much of this water-soluble nitrogen is precipitable by acid at low pH. However, Mattson and Koutler-Andersson (1943) observed that its precipitability decreased as the degree of decomposition or oxidation of the material ammoniated increased.

In order to minimize losses of dissolved organic materials in ammonia fixation studies, acid treatments or acidified extractants for exchangeable NH_4^+ have been used (Sohn and Peech, 1958; Broadbent et al., 1960; Burge and Broadbent, 1961). Depending upon the analytical and computational methods employed, organically combined nitrogen in the acid-soluble fraction may or may not be included in the total. Where fixed nitrogen is determined in the extracted residue, acid-soluble organic nitrogen is excluded. Where fixation is calculated by difference between total N and NH_4^+-N determined by distillation or nesslerization of the extract, soluble forms of organic N will be included in "fixed N."

Interest has principally centered on the products insoluble in dilute acids because of their relevance to the lignin-NH_3 complex theory of humus formation proposed by Mattson and Koutler-Andersson (1941, 1942, 1943, 1954, 1955). These authors found that, of the nitrogen fixed by leaves or soil humus in forms insoluble in dilute acid, less than 10% was removed by 24-hour digestion with 4N HCl or by distillation with Mg $(OH)_2$. Fifty percent or more was retained after distillation with 2N NaOH or after digestion for 3 hours in 72% H_2SO_4 followed by dilution and boiling for 5 hours. Davis et al. (1935) subjected the water-insoluble fraction of ammoniated peat to exhaustive serial extraction with ether, water, alcohol, 2% HCl and 1:1 HCl and found that the residue still contained 47% of the original N. Broadbent et al. (1960) observed that some of the fixed NH_3 in peat soils which could not be extracted with $N/10$ HCl or with acidified N NaCl was resistant to refluxing for 16 hours with 6N HCl. Nitrogen fixed by peat and by hydroquinone was stable to heating up to 400°C. Most of the exchangeable ammonium was removed below 200°C.

This chemical resistance suggests resistance to biological decomposition and low availability of fixed NH_3 to plants. Few systematic studies of this nature have been reported. Davis et al. (1935) found that the water-soluble fraction of ammoniated peat was nitrified about as fast as $(NH_4)_2SO_4$, but the water-insoluble fraction nitrified at about the same low rate as native soil organic matter. Exhaustive extraction of the water-insoluble portion (described in the preceding paragraph) did not appreciably alter the nitrifiability. The acid-insoluble fraction of ammoniated lignin was similarly resistant to mineralization, as has been shown also by Bremner and Shaw (1957). Using $(^{15}NH_4)_2SO_4$, Burge and Broadbent (1961) were able to fix up to 350 ppm N in acid-insoluble form on a peaty muck subsoil in the presence of $Ca(OH)_2$ at pH 10.0. Only 4.29% of the tagged nitrogen was removed by a first crop of sudangrass, 1.31% by a second, and a third cutting could not be taken because low availability of N allowed no appreciable growth.

The declining recoveries of fixed nitrogen obtained by Burge and Broadbent suggested progressive reversion to more resistant compounds, or that not all of the fixed N was in the same form of chemical combination. Both factors may have been involved. The heterogeneity of acid-insoluble fixed N is attested by data of Violanda (1958). After exposure for 24 hours to anhydrous NH_3, peat soils were H-saturated with N HCl. After thorough washing and air drying, they were extracted with phosphate buffer (pH 7.0). In a newly developed acid muck (pH 3.8), 13% of the fixed nitrogen appeared in the extract. In a long-cultivated muck with pH 5.8, 68% of the fixed nitrogen was extractable. The nitrifiability of the H-saturated ammoniated and non-ammoniated soils was directly related to their solubility in the buffer and their apparent amino-N content as determined with HNO_2. Nitrate formed during the period of rapid nitrification (25 to 27 days) was only of the order of $\frac{1}{3}$ to $\frac{1}{2}$ of the soluble nitrogen, however.

Soils have large capacities for retaining ammonia by chemical adsorption. Figures of Young and Cattani (1962) for 65 horizons from 17 Pacific Northwest soils ranged from 820 to 9,190 ppm. Similar figures calculated from Sohn and Peech (1958) ranged from 660 to 8,100 ppm for 14 mineral soils and from 8,400 to 17,600 ppm for 3 muck soils from New York. Of the total retained in the latter study, $\frac{1}{6}$ to $\frac{1}{4}$ was fixed in non-exchangeable form by clay minerals or in non-ammoniacal form by organic matter. Even in the mineral soils, the non-ammoniacal organic forms accounted for $\frac{1}{2}$ to $\frac{3}{4}$ of the total fixation. Since fixed NH_3 was determined by difference between total-N and NH_3-N distilled from the extracts, it would have included soluble covalent organic compounds in which the N cannot be considered "fixed" by strict adherence to the S.S.S.A. definition.

There is obvious need, as pointed out by McIntosh (1962), for considering both the soluble and the insoluble products in studies of NH_3 fixation by soils. The tremendous capacity for chemical retention of NH_3 by soil

organic matter represents a comfortable safety factor in the initial retention of nitrogen from fertilizers which contain or release NH_3. It is of
practical significance to problems of effective placement of such fertilizers
(Baker et al., 1959; Goring and Martin, 1959; Humbert, 1957; McDowell
and Smith, 1958; Ray et al., 1957; Volk, 1959). The short term and residual effectiveness of the added nitrogen will be influenced, however, by
the extent to which soluble and insoluble reaction products are formed
and how long they persist in the soil. Leaching losses of soluble nitrogen
compounds may be as significant in reducing effectiveness under certain
conditions as is the initial fixation in insoluble forms or later reversion
of soluble to insoluble forms.

For the purposes of this review, the term "fixed ammonia" as applied
to organic materials will refer to nitrogen (retained) in combinations
which share with humic acid the property of insolubility in acid media.
This will include materials which may be soluble at alkaline pH but are
precipitated by acidification. The balance of chemically retained nitrogen
will include organic compounds or complexes with properties of fulvic
acids.

2. pH RELATIONSHIPS

A very extensive literature dealing with reactions of model compounds
indicates that the principal chemical reactions to be expected under natural conditions between NH_3 or NH_4^+ and organic materials involve
oxygen-containing groups: carboxyls, carbonyls, enolic, phenolic, or quinonic hydroxyls, or unsaturated carbon sites associated with these groups
(Brown et al., 1952; Burge and Broadbent, 1961; Flaig, 1950; Hasek et al.,
1960; Hough et al., 1952; Lindbeck and Young, 1964; Mattson and
Koutler-Andersson, 1942, 1943; Murphy and Moore, 1960; Scheffer and
Ulrich, 1960; Sprung, 1940). The reactions which may occur are strongly
dependent upon pH. In the acid range, in addition to the carboxyl
groups, the sites most likely to react with ammonia are carbonyls, hy-
droxls, and unsaturated carbons associated with rather highly oxidized
structures such as quinones, unsaturated enols, and diketones. Simple,
dissociable ammonium salts are formed with the carboxylic acids. With
the other groups, addition reactions are to be expected which are con-
densatory in nature, leading to ring closure and polymerization. The concentration of appropriately reactive structures in the soil at any given
time is limited and the capacity to fix ammonia in non-exchangeable form
in the acid range is low. A continuing slow fixation is possible by reason
of the continuing production of suitably oxidized structures by enzymatic
or chemical catalysis (see section 5-a).

With increasing alkalinity, these structures become increasingly polarized and reactive. In addition, new reactive configurations are exposed by
peptization of iron or calcium humates, by hydrolysis, and by inter- or
intramolecular disproportionations. Thus, in addition to the formation of
dissociable ammonium salts by reaction of NH_3 with newly exposed carboxyl groups, an increasing incorporation of ammonia nitrogen in
heterocyclic combinations is to be expected with increasing pH.

Both the number of reactive groups and their reactivity increase rapidly in the alkaline range. Accordingly, Mattson and Koutler-Andersson (1943), Shoji (1958), Broadbent et al. (1960), and McIntosh (1962) found a small but measurable fixation of ammonia at pH as low as 3.0 by lignin, organic soils, or organic fractions of mineral soils. Fixation increased slowly with pH or $NH_4{}^+$ concentration below pH 7.0, but then increased abruptly above neutrality.

3. ROLE OF OXYGEN IN CHEMICAL FIXATION

Mattson and Koutler-Andersson (1941, 1942, 1943, 1954) observed that NH_3 fixation by organic materials in alkaline media involves two distinct processes. The first represents fixation at an intermediate stage of oxidation by groups which are already present or which are activated by alkaline pH. This process takes place rapidly in the absence of air, is essentially complete in 24 hours, and is accompanied by minimal losses of CO_2. It is directly related to the content of non-dialyzable acidoids which dissociate below pH 10. The second process requires the presence of oxygen or chemical oxidants and involves the simultaneous reaction of NH_3 with reactive groups as they reach the appropriate stage of oxidation. It is accompanied by rapid uptake of O_2 and by somewhat enhanced evolution of CO_2. It is at least equally as rapid as the anaerobic fixation, but it continues over a period of several days leading to several-fold greater fixation of NH_3. The uptake of NH_3 from aerated ammoniacal solutions was found to be essentially equivalent to the formation in aerated alkali solutions of new acidoids dissociable below pH 10. Prior oxidation, whether in nature or by alkaline autoxidation, suppressed both anaerobic and aerobic fixation of NH_3, except in vegetation and slightly decomposed litter where anaerobic fixation was enhanced by pre-oxidation.

Broadbent et al. (1960) found that fixation by air-dry California peats during a 24-hour exposure to anhydrous NH_3 was but little affected by partial pressures of oxygen ranging from 0 to 0.5. With 7-day exposures, fixation was greater in the presence of oxygen. In a later report (Burge and Broadbent, 1961), fixation with 7-day exposures was shown to be linearly related to carbon content in a series of peats and HF-treated peat preparations covering a range from 14 to 57% C content. Fixation capacities calculated from the regression coefficients were 106 meq per 100 g organic matter in the absence of oxygen and 161 meq when the gas mixture contained 25% O_2 and 75% NH_3.

Flaig (1950) found that the incorporation of NH_3 into synthetic humic acids by alkaline autoxidation of hydroquinone was directly related to O_2 uptake. The humic acids formed by autoxidation in NaOH no longer had the capacity to fix NH_3. Incorporation of NH_3 in acid-insoluble structures could only take place during the course of oxidation and polymerization.

4. OTHER FACTORS AFFECTING CHEMICAL FIXATION

In addition to pH and aeration, the extent of chemical fixation by soil organic materials is influenced by the concentration of NH_3 or $NH_4{}^+$ (Broadbent et al., 1960; McIntosh, 1962; Shoji, 1958), reaction temperature and pressure (Broadbent et al., 1960; Davis and Scholl, 1933, 1939; Feustel and Byers, 1933; Sohn and Peech, 1958), reaction time (Davis and Scholl, 1933, 1939; Mattson and Koutler-Andersson, 1943; McIntosh, 1962), the nature of associated cations (Shoji, 1958) or anions (Stojanovic and Broadbent, 1960), and the initial pH or base status of the soil and its degree of weathering (Mattson and Koutler-Andersson, 1943; Sohn and Peech, 1958).

In general, it may be said that fixation increases with temperature and pressure, and with the concentration of NH_3 or NH_4^+. In the absence of oxygen, whether at atmospheric or elevated temperatures and pressures, reaction at high pH is essentially complete in 24 hours, although fixation at a greatly reduced rate continues over considerable periods of time. In the presence of oxygen at atmospheric temperatures and pressures, and where a high pH is continuously maintained, fixation, initially rapid, continues at a declining rate for periods up to a week. The pH drops rapidly during aerobic ammoniation in alkaline media, due to the oxidative formation of strongly acidic groups. The period of active fixation and the total fixation is reduced accordingly. Extended aerobic exposure to NH_3 at high pH leads to the formation of an increasing proportion of soluble compounds by hydrolytic and oxidative degradation of high molecular weight polymers.

Shoji (1958) found that the aerobic fixation of nitrogen by mucks and lignin from NH_4Cl suspensions at pH 7.5 was much greater when NaOH was used to adjust the pH than when $Ca(OH)_2$ was used. It is known that the autoxidative uptake of O_2 by lignin and soil humic materials in alkaline media is promoted to different degrees by different basic ions (Bremner, 1950; Junker, 1941; Mattson and Koutler-Andersson, 1942). It is to be expected that ammonia fixation will be similarly affected, since it is intimately associated with oxidative processes. Stojanovic and Broadbent (1960) found that a small but consistently greater proportion of the ammonium added to soils as $(NH_4)_2HPO_4$ or as NH_4NO_3 could be recovered by acidified salt solutions after air drying or oven drying for 3 days than where the ammonium was added as NH_4OH or NH_4Cl. Thus, the nature of associated nutrients and carriers may influence the extent to which fertilizer nitrogen enters into fixation reactions with soil organic matter.

Prior oxidation reduces the proportion of potentially oxidizable groups in soil organic matter and, consequently, the capacity for fixing NH_3. As a result, relationships between NH_3-fixation and native soil cations and pH are the reverse of those found during the fixation process itself. Mattson and Koutler-Andersson (1943, 1954) found that acid high-moor peats were less highly oxidized and fixed considerably more NH_3 from ammoniacal solutions or from anhydrous NH_3 than low-moor peats developed under conditions of high base status and neutral pH. Further, more nitrogen had been incorporated into humus under high base conditions, so that a part of the potential NH_3-fixing sites in the parent plant residues had already been satisfied prior to ammoniation. The sum of initial plus fixed N in a group of 20 profile samples varying rather widely in base status and N content was found to be a constant 8% of the ligninous fraction—in which 50% or more of the fixed N was recovered.

Sohn and Peech (1958) also observed that NH_3 fixing capacity of a group of New York soils, as determined by short periods of exposure to anhydrous NH_3, was greatest in soils of low pH and high organic matter content.

It is to be expected that the extent to which native or added NH_3 or NH_4^+ nitrogen enters into fixation reactions with soil organic matter will be influenced by the extent to which pH or aeration conditions associated with treatment differ from equilibrium conditions established prior to treatment. Thus, drainage of poorly drained soils, liming of acid soils, cultivation of soil previously under perennial cover, would promote the oxidative reactions associated with NH_3 fixation. The activating effect on soil organic matter of increased pH resulting from addition of fertilizers containing or releasing NH_3 would be expected to promote fixation maximally in acid soils, to a lesser extent in calcareous soils and minimally in alkali soils. These pH effects would be subject to the specific influence of associated cations and anions. Their net effect on fixation would vary with fertilizer concentrations and diffusion volumes as determined by rates and methods of application and by soil physical and chemical properties which influence the mobility of NH_3 and the activity of associated ionic species.

5. MECHANISMS FOR CHEMICAL FIXATION

Groups capable of reacting with NH_3 are present in the phenols and quinones which arise by hydrolysis, demethylation, and oxidation during the decomposition of lignin. Because lignin is so widely distributed in plant materials, it has been commonly inferred that lignin derivatives are primarily responsible for fixation of NH_3 and NH_4^+ in acid-resistant combinations (Broadbent et al., 1960; Flaig, 1955, 1960a; Mattson and Koutler-Andersson, 1942, 1943, 1954).

Phenols and quinones with *ortho* and *para* configurations similar to lignin derivatives are to be expected also in degradation products of essential oils, tannins, and proteins, in pigments of microbial and insect origin and, together with *meta* structures, in degradation products of plant leaf pigments (Brown et al., 1952; Davies et al., 1960; Fieser and Fieser, 1956; Green and Steelink, 1962). Aromatic structures in fungal autolysates have been shown to arise as products of glucose metabolism (Kononova, 1961). The possibility that aromatic and quinonic structures may arise by non-enzymatic alteration of inositol or reducing sugars has been proposed (Flaig, 1950; Flaig and Schulze, 1952).

It is unlikely that large polymers, as cellulose or proteins, are involved directly in chemical fixation of NH_3 (Jansson, 1960; Mattson and Koutler-Andersson, 1942, 1943). However, the fixation of NH_3 in an electrophoretically mobile polysaccharide fraction in muck soils has been observed (Violanda, 1958). It is possible that this may have involved reactions with polyuronides. However, reactions of NH_3 with reducing sugars, amino sugars, intermediates of sugar metabolism and intermediates in the Maillard browning reactions have been observed (Hodge, 1953; Hough et al., 1952; Taufel et al., 1958; Weygand and Bergmann, 1947).

Thus a large number of biological materials have been implicated in fixation of NH_3 by the organic fraction of soils. Views on mechanisms for reaction of ammonia with soil organic materials are inferred from observed reactions with simple model compounds. Of primary interest to the present review are model reactions with aromatic or alicyclic compounds and with sugars or products of degradation of sugars. Only a very few of the very great number of possible reactions can be considered here. These have been selected to illustrate what appear to the authors to be important fundamental principles.

a. Reactions with Aromatic and Unsaturated Alicyclic Compounds

It is a general consensus that, regardless of origin, aromatic compounds and their unsaturated alicyclic counterparts, the quinones, are primary building blocks in the synthesis of humus (Davies et al., 1960; Kononova, 1961; Scheffer and Ulrich, 1960). It is considered that these condense oxidatively among themselves and with nitrogen compounds, primarily amino acids, to form heterogeneous complexes which are the essential framework of humic acids. There is controversy regarding the nature of the oxidative reactions involved in condensation. They may be strictly chemical: autocatalytic or catalyzed by mineral ions or oxides. Or they may involve the action of microbial phenol oxidases. More likely both chemical and biological oxidations are involved.

As noted by Mattson and Koutler-Andersson (1943), monosubstituted benzenes, such as phenol, are not readily oxidized, nor do they fix ammonia. According to Sprung (1940), the carbonyl group of the aromatic aldehydes (I) will react with NH_3 at room temperature to form "hydroamides" (II), which are high-melting crystalline substances. Certain hydroamides when heated for a few hours at 130°C undergo cyclization to the corresponding 2, 4, 5 triaryldihydroimidazoles (III). Heating to a higher temperature results in dehydrogenation to the corresponding triarylimidazoles (IV). Winans and Adkins (1933) noted that the unsaturated configuration of the cinnamaldehyde side chain (V) permits this compound to go directly at room temperature, to the tristyryl analogue of III (VI).

Without further modification of the benzene ring, these substituted imidazoles are terminal polymers. According to Flaig (1950), extensive chemical fixation of NH_3 by aromatic compounds is dependent upon extensive polymerization. Active polymerization requires the presence on the aromatic ring of substituents which permit conversion to alicyclic quinone or orthoquinone configurations. Thus, the first step in the polymerization in alkali of the dihydroxybenzenes, catechol (VII) and hydroquinone (VIII), is their oxidation to the corresponding alicyclic compounds, o-quinone (VII-A) and p-quinone (VIII-A). Both pass, by hydration and further oxidation, through the benzenetriol (IX) to

o-hydroxyquinone (X), which in later studies (Flaig, 1955) was shown to be in tautomeric equilibrium with p-hydroxy-o-quinone (XI). These latter structures readily undergo extensive polymerization with the formation of amorphous precipitates with characteristics very similar to soil humic acids.

In the presence of NH_3, the polymerization of X was visualized by Flaig (1950) as proceeding with the simultaneous incorporation of nitrogen into bridging structures of the type depicted in the central elements of XII and XIII. This heterocyclic linkage is analogous to that in the phenoxazine dyes.

These postulated structures were based on the "nuclear nitrogen" content of humic acids synthesized from hydroquinone or catechol in the presence of NH_3 at pH 10. "Nuclear nitrogen" was defined as nitrogen resistant to distillation in concentrated NaOH. The fraction soluble in 2N HCl of products for which the nuclear structure XIII was calculated contained 12.29 percent N. This represented the maximum fixation of NH_3 and the maximum uptake of O_2 (2 moles per mole of hydroquinone) which could occur before carbonate appeared as the result of ring rupture and rapid degradation of exposed side chains.

Murphy and Moore (1960) observed the fixation of nitrogen in proportions approximating XII when 4-methyl catechol was oxidized with sodium iodate in the presence of NH_3. The incorporation of nitrogen in phenoxazine rings was consistent with the disappearance of ring hydrogens subject to chlorination. They found no evidence, however, for the quinoid elements postulated in XII and XIII.

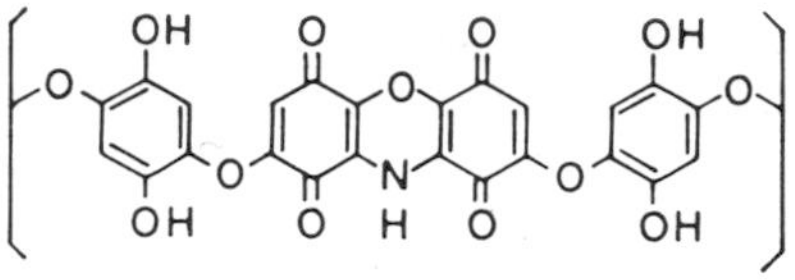

XII

(2.75% N)

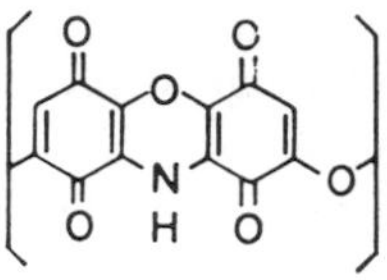

XIII

(5.45% N)

Polyhydroxybenzenes with *meta* configurations, such as phloroglucinol (XIV) and orcinol (XV), are not readily oxidized or polymerized in alkali solutions, but they are in ammoniacal solutions (Eller, 1923a; Musso, 1957). According to Scheffer and Ulrich (1960), this is due to the resonance afforded by —N= bridges, as in the phenoxazone chromophore (XVI) described by Musso (1957) in the products of reaction of orcinol and NH_3.

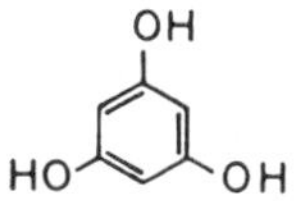

XIV 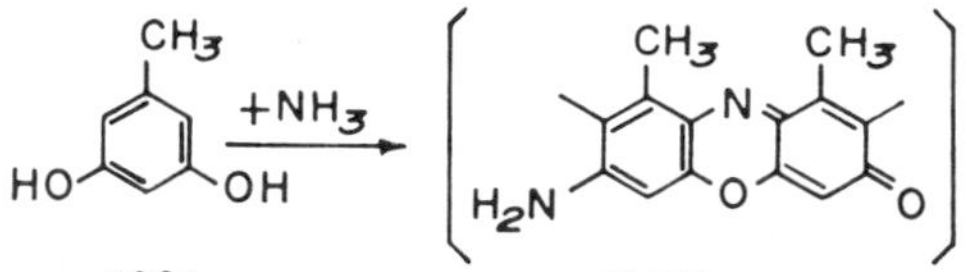   XV   XVI

Musso described a series of products of increasing degree of polymerization with the phenoxazone chromophore as a nucleus, and noted their susceptibility to further oxidation. The significance of resonating structures in promoting oxidative polymerization of polyphenols with *meta* configurations is evident from the fact that phloroglucinol (XIV) is readily oxidized in the presence of compounds such as styrene, asparagine, tryptophane and ammonia, but not in the presence of amino acids such as glycine, proline, or lysine (Stein and Tendeloo, 1959).

The reactivity of polyphenols and quinones is to be understood in terms of their tendency to form semiquinone free radicals by univalent oxidation or reduction (Fieser and Fieser, 1956; Flaig, 1960a, b; Gould, 1959; Scheffer and Ulrich, 1960). The free radical character resonates mesomerically between substituted oxygen atoms and unoccupied *ortho*- or *para*-oriented carbons in the ring. Patterns of reaction are randomly determined by the possible mesomeric forms and by the relative stabilities of their reaction products. The nitrogen in NH_3 (and in aliphatic and aromatic amines and in amino acids) is nucleophilic and reacts with the carbon radicals rather than the oxygen (Katritsky, 1960).

It is to be noted that fixation of NH_3 does not necessarily involve addition at the site of existing phenolic hydroxyls as envisioned by Mattson and Koutler-Andersson (1942, 1943) and Bennett (1949). The sites of addition are, however, potential hydroxyl sites.

The semiquinone anion (XVII) is formed, at alkaline pH, by intermolecular disproportionation, whether one starts with hydroquinone or *p*-quinone (VIII or VIII-A). On adding water, a third hydroxyl may appear in *ortho* position to form 1,2,4-benzenetriol (IX), which is at the same stage of oxidation as *p*-quinone (Erdtmann, 1955). In the presence of NH_3, the 2-aminohydroquinone (XVIII) will also be formed. Starting with catechol or *o*-quinone, both *ortho* and *para* addition products are found (Flaig, 1960a).

The addition of water to form IX and the addition of NH_3 to form XVIII are both the result of the greater stability associated with cyclic conjugated double-bond systems (Gould, 1959). This tendency to aromaticity leads to cyclic regeneration of phenolic hydroxyls during progressive oxidation of phenols, as in the sequence VIII $\xrightarrow{-2e}$ (VIII-A $\rightleftarrows$ IX $\rightleftarrows$ XVIII). The equilibrium products are at an equivalent stage of oxidation but decrease in energy content and increase in stability from left to right (Fieser and Fieser, 1956).

Addition reactions of phenols and quinones with peptides, amino acids, and primary and secondary amines follow similar principles (Flaig, 1960b). The *para*-substituted amines formed by reaction of amino acids with *o*-quinones are unstable, the aliphatic side chain of the amino acid breaking off in what is essentially a transamination (Scheffer and Ulrich, 1960).

Lindbeck and Young (1964) obtained polarographic evidence for the sequential formation of XVIII and XIX in *p*-quinone-ammonia systems. Halfcell potentials were observed for quinhydrone (XVII) and for the semi-quinone systems involving XVIII and its corresponding 2-amino-quinone and XIX and its corresponding 2,5-diaminohydroquinone. The rate of reaction increased with pH from 7.1 to 9.9. Controlled potential oxidation and reduction showed the reversibility of all reactions through the formation of the postulated initial condensation product (XX). Reversibility decreased on standing in air, presumably due to further condensations permitted by dissociable protons in the amino groups in XX. The humic-acid-like product which precipitated at pH 9.9 had a nitrogen content of 11.37%, comparable to that found by Flaig at pH 10.0 (cf. XIII and text).

Scheffer and Ulrich (1960) have noted that aminophenols readily undergo polymerization with the formation of phenoxazine rings (as in XII and XIII) or phenazine rings (as in XX), depending on the orientation of the amino groups. This polymerization very likely proceeds by intermediate oxidation to aminoquinones, as depicted above. Polymerization continues as long as structures capable of forming stable free radicals are formed by oxidation.

Under conditions where free radicals are stable in the presence of their oxidized and reduced forms, reversibility is high and activation energies of possible oxidation-reduction reactions are greatly reduced (Kalckar, 1946; Michaelis, 1946). Where an unpaired electron is free to distribute itself over a large number of positions in compounds with extensively conjugated double bond structure, very stable free radicals are formed (Gould, 1959). Because of the highly resonant structures which can be postulated for soil humic acids, Ploetz (1955) suggests that they may be looked upon as polymeric semiquinones—"giant quinhydrone molecules." Steelink and Tollin (1962) obtained paramagnetic resonance spectra for soils and humic acid preparations suggestive of two semiquinone free radical species, one of a quinhydrone type, the other possibly involving a resorcinol type copolymer. Calculated electron spin concentrations ranged from 0.2 to 15.0×10^8 per gram. Assuming one unpaired electron per molecule, these corresponded to molecular weights of 40,000 for ethanol-soluble fractions and 270,000 for insoluble humic materials.

Semiquinones are more stable in their highly polarized anionic form, hence at alkaline pH. The greatly enhanced capacity of soil organic matter to fix NH_3 in the alkaline range is readily understood in terms of the formation and polarization of free radicals and accelerated autocatalytic oxidation and polymerization.

In the upper acid range, similar autocatalytic mechanisms may involve free radicals stabilized in large, resonant molecules. The reduced forms of these radicals likely include the more acidic phenolic groups in humus.

In addition, oxides and hydroxides of iron can catalyze the polymerization of hydroquinones over the entire pH range from 3.0 to 7.0 (Scheffer and Ulrich, 1960). Béres and Király (1959) found that the ratio Fe^{++}/Fe^{+++} in solutions of peat fulvic acids increased with pH in the acid range. Michaelis (1946) noted the frequent catalytic involvement of reducible cations such as Fe III or Cu II in oxidation reactions and explained it by their ready univalent valence change and the formation of free radical coordination complexes as intermediates. Numerous instances of catalytic involvement in the oxidative polymerization of polyhydroxybenzenes are cited by Scheffer and Ulrich (1960) for other reducible cations, as well as for amorphous silica. The catalytic action of silica was observed by Ziechmann and Pawelke (1959) in the synthesis of humic acids from soluble fractions extracted from peat.

The catalytic oxidation of hydroquinone in acid media in the presence of iron oxides and hydroxides was found to be much slower than the autoxidation in alkali (Scheffer and Ulrich, 1960). The catalytic effect declined with pH and was less under anaerobic than aerobic conditions. These relationships to pH and aeration parallel those already described for ammonia fixation.

Free radicals are also formed by the action of microbial phenoloxidases and dehydrogenases. As noted by Flaig (1960), these may appear as a first step in the oxidation of the phenylpropene units of lignin, as well as later, after the complete degradation of the propenol side chains. In the semiquinones arising from polyhydroxybenzenes, the unpaired electron may appear mesomerically on a substituted oxygen atom or on a ring carbon in *para* or *ortho* position to an oxygen atom. In the semiquinones formed enzymatically from phenylpropene derivatives of lignin, Freudenberg (1956, 1957) showed that the mesomerism involves the oxygen of the phenolic hydroxyl, a ring carbon in *ortho* position, and the *beta*-carbon of the side chain. Reactions of coniferyl alcohol, syringenin, and *p*-hydroxycinnamyl alcohol with ammonia do not appear to have been investigated.

In acid soil systems, free radicals formed by enzymatic action from aromatic compounds may form coordination complexes with reducible cations such as Fe^{+++} and thereby achieve the stability requisite for reversibility and lowered activation energies. However, it is likely that their slow but continuing production as transient intermediates by extracellular oxidases and dehydrogenases is more relevant to the slow fixation of NH_3 by soil under field conditions in the acid range (cf. Mattson and Koutler-Andersson, 1954, 1955; Andersson, 1960; Broadbent et al., 1960).

b. Reactions with Carbohydrates

The possibility that carbohydrates may participate in nonbiological processes of humus formation under natural soil conditions is receiving renewed attention (Bremner, 1954; Dawson, 1956; Stevenson, 1960; Scheffer and Ulrich, 1960).

Mattson and Koutler-Andersson (1943) found that reducing sugars fixed NH_3 actively from ammoniacal solutions. Sucrose was essentially inactive.

The reactions of NH_3 with reducing sugars in the alkaline range appear to follow a course very similar to the browning reactions, described in the extensive review by Hodge (1953), which lead to the formation of melanoidin pigments in mixtures of sugars and amino acids in acid media.

On paper chromatograms of reducing sugars, developed with ammoniacal solvents, Bayly et al. (1952) and Raacke-Fels (1953) observed the formation of glycosylamine and diglycosylamine. The latter corresponds to the N-substituted glycosylamines which are formed in the first of the browning reactions. Hough et al. (1952) observed an early rapid epimerization of glucose to mannose and fructose in aqueous ammonia solutions. C-2 epimerization is a consequence of the reversible "Schiff's base" reactions which precede the irreversible Amadori rearrangement in the initiating sequence of browning reactions.

Gradual color development was observed by Hough et al. (1952) as the sugars were degraded and polycondensation products were formed. Typical heterocyclic melanoidin components were identified among the products, including imidazoles, such as 4(5) methyl-glyoxaline (XXIII), and pyrazines, such as 2-methyl-5-(tetrahydroxybutyl) pyrazine (XXV). The former would have been formed by the polycondensation of 2 moles of NH_3 with one of formaldehyde (XXI) and one of pyruvaldehyde (XXII), the latter, by polycondensation with pyruvaldehyde and aldehydo glucose (XXIV).

Aldehydo glucose (XXIV) and pyruvaldehyde (XXII) are reduced and oxidized representatives, respectively, of a heterogeneous group of extremely reactive compounds—the reductones and dehydro-reductones —which appear as fission products of sugars during the browning reactions. According to Scheffer and Ulrich (1960), these dienols and diketones partake of many of the characteristics of polyphenols and quinones. They are acidic, and they form reversible redox systems in which the intermediate diradicals correspond in reactivity to the semiquinone free radicals.

The fission of reducing sugars proceeds autocatalytically at alkaline pH. Whether NH_3 acts as a catalyst in these reactions or is merely caught up in polycondensation reactions with the highly reactive fission products is not clear.

In the acid range, amino acids act as catalysts in the browning reactions of sugars (Hodge, 1953; Scheffer and Ulrich, 1960). This catalytic role is expressed in the fission reactions by which the sugars are broken down, as well as in subsequent aldol condensations of the fission products. The NH_4^+ ion does not appear to have this catalytic capability. In later reactions, the amino nitrogen is incorporated into polymeric complexes in various ways. The secondary amines formed by reaction with diketonic fission products may be broken down by Strecker degradation of the amino acid. This is essentially a transamination reaction, since the amino group is transferred to the diketone, and is comparable to reactions of amino acids with o-quinones. In subsequent polycondensations, this transferred amino nitrogen appears in heterocyclic structures, such as pyrroles, imidazoles, pyridines, and pyrazines. Or the secondary amines may be stabilized in combinations which permit recovery of the unaltered amino acids by hydrolysis. Hydrolyzable ester linkages involving the carboxyl of the amino acid are also possible.

In many respects, melanoidins are very similar to natural soil humic acids, although, as Dawson (1956) points out, there are important differences. Enders et al. (1948) attribute these differences to artifacts of structural orientation in the synthetic polymers. Patterns of incorporation of amino nitrogen observed in the browning reactions are consistent with the presence in soil humic acids of both hydrolyzable amino acids and resistant nitrogen compounds (cf. Savage and Stevenson, 1961; Murphy and Moore, 1960).

The transaminations observed in reactions of amino acids with browning intermediates, as well as with quinones, make it clear that prior ammonification of proteins is not essential for the entry of amino nitrogen into pathways leading to resistant heterocyclic combinations. It is unlikely that ammonia fixation represents a major process in humus formation in nature, as has been suggested (Mattson and Koutler-Andersson, 1942, 1943, 1954; Jansson, 1960; Broadbent et al., 1960; Burge and Broadbent, 1961). Nevertheless, mechanisms for the fixation of NH_3 by aromatic compounds and carbohydrates have been demonstrated in the alkaline pH range. Mechanisms operable in the acid range may be inferred from the nature of known intermediates and from the possibilities which exist for both enzymatic and mineral catalysis. Such reactions undoubtedly play a role in the reversion to slowly available forms of ammonia released by microbial ammonification or applied in fertilizers, as well as in the sorption from the atmosphere of ammonia released by the combustion of fuels or formed by electrical discharges in the atmosphere.

According to data of a number of investigators (Malo and Purvis, 1964; Mattson and Koutler-Andersson, 1954; deRossi, 1947), sorption of ammonia from the atmosphere by soils may represent an annual increment of as much as 20 to 40 pounds of N per acre (cf. Ingham, 1950; Dhar, 1960). Allison (1955) suggests that these figures are unrealistic because they do not appear to be reflected in crop response. However, if, as appears likely, the sorbed ammonia is quickly reverted to slowly available forms, it would have little effect on current crop response. Current uncertainties regarding nitrogen balances in soils makes practical evaluation difficult (Allison, 1964).

C. Reactions of Oxides and Acids of Nitrogen

Interactions between soil organic matter and oxides and acids of nitrogen are receiving renewed attention because of their relevance to gaseous losses of nitrogen from soils (Clark et al., 1960; Clark and Beard, 1960; Führ and Bremner, 1964; Tyler and Broadbent, 1960) and to problems involved in the quantitative determination of forms of nitrogen in soils (Bremner, 1957). Also, the possible use of nitrogen dioxide as a fertilizer for injection application (Aldrich and Buchanan, 1955) raises questions regarding mechanisms for its retention and stabilization in soils.

1. REACTIONS WITH SOIL AND ORGANIC MATERIALS

In recent reviews, Allison (1963, 1964) has discounted the significance under field conditions of the Van Slyke reaction, strictly defined as the reaction of nitrous acid with α-amino groups to release N_2. The laboratory reaction is carried out in glacial acetic acid in an atmosphere of nitric oxide and involves the undissociated acid, or more likely the nitrosonium cation, NO^+ (Heslop and Robinson, 1960).

From studies with nitrite-amended soils, Smith and Clark (1960) concluded that reaction between HNO_2 and NH_4^+ at acid pH to give N_2 is unlikely. They confirmed the observation of others that, as soil pH is lowered, there is a greater tendency for nitrous acid to decompose to NO and HNO_3 than for it to react with NH_4^+. In the presence of atmospheric oxygen, the NO in turn had a greater tendency to convert to nitric acid than to diffuse from the soil. Nevertheless, added nitrite was extensively reduced to N_2 and N_2O at acid pH by interaction with some soil component, apparently present in the organic fraction.

In later studies, Clark and Beard (1960) established more definitely that organic matter plays a specific role in promoting mineral nitrogen deficits in nitrite-amended acid soil. The reactions involved were shown to be chemical, since loss of nitrogen by air drying or by heating for 1 hour at 75 to 80°C was equivalent to the loss after a week's incubation at room temperature. Nitrite-reactive components were present in peptone and alfalfa leaf meal, but not in dextrose, although reactive materials stable to heating appeared quickly during incubation of soil amended with dextrose.

These results tend to support a minority view, reaffirmed as recently as 1957 by Gerretsen and de Hoop, that a Van Slyke type reaction is involved in losses of nitrogen from soils at low pH. However, nitrous acid is known to react with other than amino groups to release N_2 or N_2O, leading to spurious amino nitrogen values in the Van Slyke determination (Bremner, 1952; Carter and Dickman, 1943; Hulme, 1935).

Bremner (1955, 1957) obtained anomalous amino nitrogen values for lignin and soil humic acids by the Van Slyke procedure. In addition to the vigorous evolution of N_2 or N_2O and detectable quantities of HCN, there was a simultaneous fixation of nitrogen in the residual organic materials. Of the fixed nitrogen, about one-third was released as NH_3 by hydrolysis with acids or alkali. There was a reduction in methoxyl groups in the residue, and detectable quantities of hydroxylamine were released along with ammonia during acid hydrolysis. The release of hydroxylamine was consistent with the view that nitrous acid reacts initially with methylene groups to form oximino groups or with aromatic lignin derivatives to form nitrosophenols, which tautomerize to quinone oximes.

In later work (Führ and Bremner, 1964), lignin was found to fix nitrite-N more actively than chitin, casein, or xylan. Only traces were fixed by nucleic acids and essentially none by cellulose. Reactions with simple model compounds indicated the probable formation of nitroso compounds. The fixation of ^{15}N-labelled nitrite by soils increased with nitrite concentration and with soil carbon content. Up to 28% of added nitrite-N was fixed at pH 3.0. The percentage fixation declined rapidly to pH 7.0, although measurable fixation occurred at pH 9.0.

In studies reported by Führ and Bremner (1964), nitrite fixation by sterilized soils in the range from pH 3.0 to 7.0 was accompanied by losses of 33 to 79% of the added nitrite-N. Losses of this magnitude occurred when soils were air dried immediately after addition of nitrite solutions. Losses were sharply reduced in moist soil and the associated fixation by the soil was somewhat greater. However, additions of water in excess of saturation strongly inhibited both fixation and loss in sterilized soils. Nitrogen in these studies was lost presumably as N_2, N_2O, and NO.

These gases were identified by Stevenson et al. (1963, 1964) in the gaseous products of reaction of nitrous acid with soil humic acids, lignin, and model lignin derivatives at pH's up to 7.0. Methyl nitrite was also found in the products of reaction with lignin and with model compounds containing the syringyl group (2, 6-dimethoxyphenol).

Highly reactive aromatic compounds, such as phenols and aromatic amines, are readily nitrated. The nitration by nitric acid is accelerated by nitrous acid in moderately acid media (Gould, 1959). A nitroso group (R-NO) formed initially is oxidized by nitric acid to the nitro group (R-NO$_2$).

In the scheme depicted by Brauns (1952) for the nitrosation of phenolic structures (XXVI) in lignin, nitrous anhydride (N_2O_3) was represented as the source of NO+ and NO$_2^-$ for the formation of the nitrosite (XXVII). By addition of water, HNO$_2$ is split off to yield a hydrated nitroso ketone (XXVIII). Dehydration yields the nitroso phenol (XXIX), which is in tautomeric equilibrium with the corresponding quinone oxime (XXX). The latter grouping yields NH$_3$ and HCN by action of acids. Bremner (1957) noted that the action of nitrous acid on quinone oximes results in the formation of N_2 and N_2O.

| XXVI | XXVII | XXVIII | XXIX | XXX |

According to Gould (1959), the formation of nitroso groups (R-NO) is unlikely in the presence of nitrate at the high acid concentrations where nitrous anhydride could serve as a source of the nitrosonium cation ($N_2O_3 \rightleftharpoons NO^+ + NO_2^-$). This is due to the greater reactivity of the nitronium cation (NO$_2^+$), which arises from nitric acid and reacts to form nitro groups (R-NO$_2$).

At lower acid concentration and lower polarity associated with moderately acid pH, N_2O_4 appears to be the principal source of NO+ ($N_2O_4 \rightleftharpoons NO^+ + NO_3^-$). With decreasing polarity associated with increasing pH, as well as in nonpolar solvents and in the dry gas, molecular dissociation of N_2O_4 into its monomer, NO_2, also occurs. Nitrogen dioxide is a free radical and an active nitrating agent.

Freudenberg and Durr (1930) investigated the nitration of lignin by dry NO_2 gas. The initial absorption of NO_2 (or N_2O_4) was very rapid, apparently complete in a matter of minutes. Secondary reactions leading to the formation of NO were observed after one-half hour. In the phase of rapid NO_2 absorption, the main reaction appeared to involve the initial formation of a dinitro compound (XXXI). This decomposed spontaneously to yield nitrous acid and the stable nitro compound (XXXII), normally substituted *ortho* or *para* to the methoxyl group. However, there was evidence for loss of methoxyl as methyl nitrite. Because of resonance in the NO_2 (and N_2O_4) molecules, the initial addition can involve one of the oxygen atoms to form a nitrite ester (XXXIII). Spontaneous decomposition of this would yield methyl nitrite and a nitroquinol (XXXIV), which tautomerizes to a nitrophenol (XXXV).

XXXI   **XXXII**

XXXIII   **XXXIV**   **XXXV**

XXXVI   **XXXVII**

Nitro derivatives are readily reduced to the corresponding amino derivatives (XXXVI). Further action of nitrous acid on the aromatic amines leads to numerous nitroso and diazo compounds which are readily decomposed by reduction or hydrolysis to release N_2 or NH_3 (Fieser and Fieser, 1956). Ring closure to heterocyclic configurations (XXXVII) may also occur (Brauns 1952).

The proposed reaction sequences for lignin are speculative but are based on well-documented reactions with simpler model compounds. They represent types of reactions which can lead from nitrite to reduced nitrogen gases, as well as to organically fixed nitrogen.

Conditions closely approaching the conditions of the Van Slyke procedure or of usual laboratory nitrations are not to be expected in normal soils. However, the reactions cited for NO_2 (N_2O_4) and lignin occurred under conditions not drastically different from those which may obtain during normal air-drying of soils. Since N_2O_4 is an equilibrium product of the decomposition of nitrous acid at pH's below neutrality, it appears a likely key intermediate in reactions of nitrous acid with soil organic matter.

Recent rapid advances in the chemist's understanding of nitration reactions have derived from more precise identification of reactive nitrogen species through a combination of spectrographic and kinetic evidence (Gould, 1959). The results of such studies lead to speculations regarding the nature of dominant species arising from nitrite nitrogen in normal soil environments.

2. PROBABLE REACTIVE SPECIES FROM TRIPOSITIVE

NITROGEN IN SOIL

The forms that tripositive nitrogen can take and the reactions which they undergo are strongly dependent upon pH, aeration, and moisture content (Cady and Bartholomew, 1960, 1961; Chao and Kroontje, 1963; Thorne and Roberts, 1954; Gould, 1959; Heslop and Robinson, 1960).

In the alkaline range, the nitrite ion is stable. Its oxidations and reductions, in general, require catalysis, although its spontaneous reaction with ammonium may lead to extensive losses of N_2 from soils with pH up to 8.5 or 9.0 (Allison, 1963, 1964; Wahhab and Uddin, 1954). Reactions of NH_3 with HNO_2 or of NH_4^+ with NO_2^- become increasingly less probable at more alkaline pH because of changes in proportionate distribution of these species.

The decomposition of HNO_2 in the acid range leads to a number of ionic and molecular equilibrium products. Depending upon pH, acid concentration, and aeration, chemical equilibria involving the following species may be expected: HNO_2, NO, NO_2, N_2O_4, N_2O_3, N_2O_5, NO^+, NO_2^+, NO_3^-, and NO_2^- (Gould, 1959; Heslop and Robinson, 1960; Thorne and Roberts, 1954).

The anhydrides (N_2O_3, N_2O_5) are promoted by high acid concentrations. Their ionic dissociation (NO^+ NO_2^- and NO_2^+ NO_3^-) is promoted by high polarities associated with low pH. At lower polarities associated with moderately acid pH and lower acid concentrations, the reactions of nitrous acid appear to involve primarily the equilibrium species, N_2O_4, NO_2, and NO^+. In nonpolar solvents, nitrous acid decomposes principally to N_2O_4 and NO_2 (Gould, 1959).

The nature of these equilibria over the range of pH and moisture contents to be expected in soils under field conditions has not been defined. The above relationships to solvent polarity and acid concentration suggest that the dominant species in acid soils may be N_2O_4, its ionic dissociation product, the nitrosonium cation (NO^+), or its molecular dissociation product, nitrogen dioxide (NO_2).

Nitric oxide (NO) is frequently cited as a key intermediate in gaseous losses of nitrogen from soils (Allison, 1963, 1964; Cady and Bartholomew, 1960; Clark et al., 1960). However, in the presence of O_2, NO is immediately converted to NO_2 by a reaction which is detectably reversed only at temperatures above $150°C$ (Thorne and Roberts, 1954). As shown by

Mortland (section II C above) NO is readily oxidized to nitrite (NO_2^-) in the presence of clay systems containing reducible cations.

Both NO and NO_2 are free radicals and enter into addition or substitution reactions with compounds which can act as electron donors. However, Cady and Bartholomew (1963) have shown that NO equilibrates only slowly with denitrifying acid soil systems in the absence of oxygen. Equilibration of NO with nitrous and nitric acids in equation [1] requires the presence of NO_2 in the intermediate equilibrium [2]. In the absence of oxygen, NO_2 can arise only by [3] or the reversal of [2].

$$3\ HNO_2 \rightleftharpoons HNO_3 + 2\ NO + H_2O \tag{1}$$

$$NO + NO_2 \rightleftharpoons N_2O_3 \underset{}{\overset{+H_2O}{\rightleftharpoons}} 2\ HNO_2 \tag{2}$$

$$HNO_2 + HNO_3 \underset{}{\overset{-H_2O}{\rightleftharpoons}} N_2O_4 \rightleftharpoons 2\ NO_2 \tag{3}$$

The delay in equilibration of NO observed by Cady and Bartholomew (ibid.) suggests that NO_2 was depleted by more rapid reactions of NO_2 (or of N_2O_4 or NO^+) with organic compounds in the decomposing alfalfa meal which was supplied as energy source for the denitrifiers. The delay continued during the period when low concentrations of NO were maintained by reversal of [2] in a parallel system to which no extraneous NO was supplied. In both systems, N_2O and N_2 appeared only after conditions were favorable for rapid equilibration of NO, at which time NO quickly disappeared.

It would seem, therefore, that NO is an equilibrium by-product, rather than an intermediate, in reactions of tripositive nitrogen in acid soils. A fair inference from these theoretical considerations is that the dominantly reactive species arising from decomposition of HNO_2 under normally encountered soil conditions are N_2O_4, NO_2, and NO^+.

This inference would be consistent with reaction sequences such as the following between nitrite and organic matter in acid soils:

(1) Initial nitration of aromatic or unsaturated aliphatic compounds by N_2O_4 or NO_2 to form nitrite esters and reducible nitro groups.

(2) Biological or chemical reduction of nitro groups to amines.

(3) Reaction of NO^+ with primary or secondary amines formed by (2) to yield nitrosoamines, themselves unstable or reacting further to form diazo compounds which are decomposed by reduction or hydrolysis to release N_2 or NH_3.

(4) Reaction of NO^+ with quinone oximes formed by tautomerization of nitrophenols arising in (1) to yield N_2O, in addition to N_2.

(5) Chelation of suitably oriented amino groups by ring closure to give heterocyclic nitrogen resistant to hydrolysis.

Reactions involving NO^+ would be enhanced by moderate increases in polarity and acid concentration associated with air drying. Losses of nitrogen in gaseous forms would be greatly enhanced.

Overall reactions of NO^+ which lead to N_2 are essentially similar to the Van Slyke reaction. However, the likelihood of the Van Slyke reaction as strictly defined by Allison (1963) would decrease as the isoelectric point of specific α-amino groups is approached from the acid side (Fieser and Fieser, 1956; Heslop and Robinson, 1960).

D. Discussion

That chemical sorption by soils of NH_3 from the atmosphere may play a significant role in the nitrogen cycle was proposed as early as 1847 by Liebig (Malo and Purvis, 1964). The possibility that equally significant immobilization, accompanied by volatile losses, may arise by strictly chemical reactions involving nitrite and soil organic matter has been proposed only recently (Bremner, 1957; Führ and Bremner, 1964). Both processes greatly complicate the problem of calculating soil nitrogen balances. Their evaluation under conditions corresponding to natural field situations demands a high priority in research on soil nitrogen transformations.

There are parallels and dissimilarities between probable mechanisms for fixation and volatilization of nitrite and those involved in fixing NH_3. Similar organic compounds at comparable stages of oxidation have been implicated in both processes. Both appear to involve free radical intermediates and the formation of amines with potentialities for condensing oxidatively to form humic acid-like polymers.

However, the reactions of NH_3 are addition reactions, whereas those of HNO_2 or its decomposition products are substitution reactions. Polarities conducive to the former are promoted by increasing pH, the latter by decreasing pH.

The initial fixation of HNO_2 or its decomposition products by organic materials likely involves the formation of nitro and nitroso compounds and nitrite esters. Considering the heterogeneous nature of soil organic matter, a large number of such compounds are possible. The subsequent fate of these initial products will vary with the stability and reactivity of specific compounds, as well as with the concentration and supply of reactive nitrogen species as determined by pH, aeration, moisture content, and microbial activity.

To the extent that nitro groups are reduced to amines, oxidative condensations should lead to polymeric structures similar to those formed in reactions with NH_3. Where stable nitro substitutions are retained, rules for orientation in subsequent reactions are altered. Distinct differences in the nature of resulting polymers would be expected. Mattson and Koutler-Andersson (1942) found that nitration of soil humic materials increased their exchange capacity, while ammoniation decreased it. Bremner and Shaw (1957) found that nitrogen fixed by lignin from nitrous or nitric acids was more readily nitrified than that in ammoniated lignin.

Of intriguing interest for diagnostic purposes is the observation by Violanda (1958) that there was a close linear relationship between the nitrifiability of acid-washed ammoniated and non-ammoniated mucks and the apparent Van Slyke nitrogen content of their phosphate buffer extracts.

Under the conditions of the Van Slyke reaction, nitrosation by NO^+ appears to be the dominant reaction. Losses of N_2 and N_2O may arise by reaction with amines already present or with oximes formed by nitrosation of phenols or methylene groups.

At lower acid concentrations, nitration by NO_2 (N_2O_4) may be a major mechanism for initial fixation of nitrite nitrogen. The extent of initial fixation and the subsequent fate of the fixed nitrogen can be expected to vary with the oxidation-reduction status of reacting organic matter as affected by microbial activity or by changes in aeration or pH.

Changes in pH are always associated with the formation of nitrite in nature. Microbial reduction of nitrate to nitrite under anaerobic conditions is associated with increasing pH, whereas the first step of nitrification is associated with decreasing pH (Hiltbold and Adams, 1960; Patrick, 1960). Conflicting reports in the literature dealing with soil nitrogen transformations may derive from as yet unknown or unappreciated effects of *changing* pH.

Thus, Clark et al. (1960) and Gerretson and de Hoop (1957) observed large losses of nitrogen as soil pH declined during nitrification. The pH ranges for maximum loss were different in the two investigations, however. In the latter study, the extent of loss varied with C/N ratio and content of soil organic matter, and in some acid soils losses occurred only after addition of $CaCO_3$. The effect of $CaCO_3$ may have been to increase microbial activity, as the authors suggest. On the other hand, increasing pH would have tended to shift oxidation-reduction equilibria in soil organic matter in the direction of promoting the reduction of nitro groups and the accelerated oxidative condensation of resulting aromatic amines. Increases in organic nitrogen attributed to microbial assimilation may have included nitrogen immobilized chemically.

While nitration by NO_2 (N_2O_4) may be a prime mechanism in the fixation of nitrite by organic materials, losses of nitrogen as N_2 or N_2O likely involve nitrosation by NO^+ of previously formed amines and oximes. The ionic dissociation of N_2O_4 (NO^+ NO_3^-) occurs under the polarizing influence of moderately low pH or of close approach to polar groups. The latter would be promoted by air drying. Major losses of nitrite nitrogen from acid soils occur during air drying (Clark and Beard, 1960; Führ and Bremner, 1964; Wahhab and Uddin, 1954).

The nitrosonium cation may arise also from the ionic dissociation of N_2O_3 (NO^+ NO_2^-). However, equilibrium concentrations of the acid anhydrides are very low except at acid strengths unlikely to be found in soils even after air drying. It should be noted, however, that the nitrite ion (NO_2^-) can arise by this mechanism in the acid pH range. Thus, the reaction of NH_4^+ with NO_2^- to form N_2 can occur in acid soils and its likelihood increases with decreasing pH (Allison, 1963, 1964; Gerretson and de Hoop, 1957; Thorne and Roberts, 1954).

Losses of nitrogen by decomposition of ammonium nitrite in the range of acid pH to be found in agricultural soils will doubtless prove to be minor when compared with losses by more probable reactions involving NO^+ and nitrogen immobilized chemically or biologically in the organic fraction.

Numerous opportunities for chemical catalysis by polarizing effects of clay minerals and reducible cations appear from studies with NH_3 and NO cited in earlier sections of this review. The direct oxidation of NO to NO_2^- observed by Mortland is very probably reversible, as appears from work of Wullstein et al. (1963) who observed losses of NO or NO_2 proportional to kind and concentration of heavy metal salts added with nitrite to sand systems.

Thus, oxidative and reductive transformations of nitrogen in soils probably involve both chemical and biological mechanisms. In some cases, as in the fixation of NH_3 or the reduction of nitro groups, biological processes may be involved only incidentally. Here, strictly chemical changes would follow as a consequence of changes in polarity resulting from enzymatic transfer of electrons to active groups on the surface of humic acid polymers. Similar changes in polarity could occur by disproportionation in response to an increase in pH resulting from anaerobic metabolism or from the addition of alkalizing fertilizer materials.

IV. SUMMARY

The sorption of inorganic nitrogen compounds by soil materials may be very complex. A wide variety of reactions are possible with clay minerals and organic matter, the active components of soils. Most of the published work has been concerned with the sorption of ammonia by clays and organic matter.

Studies of ammonia-clay mineral complexes have been made using absorption isotherms, X-ray diffraction, calorimetry, and infrared absorption. The conclusions from these studies are: (1) The ammonium ion is formed when ammonia is adsorbed by acid clay minerals. (2) The ammonium ion is also formed when certain base-saturated clay minerals adsorb ammonia. The source of the proton for the latter reaction is thought to be provided by water molecules which have been altered in their dissociation properties by polarization effects of exchangeable cations augmented by the clay mineral surface itself. (3) Ammine type (coordination) bonds may be formed upon ammonia adsorption if appropriate cations are present on the exchange complex. This ion-dipole interaction varies greatly in stability depending on the nature of the ion. Hydrogen bonding of ammonia to surface oxygen atoms of clay lattices and of various oxides existing in soils is another adsorption mechanism. Hydrogen bonding between NH_3 and NH_4^+ and between H_2O and NH_4^+ also takes place. (4) Pure physical adsorption of ammonia represents the least energetic adsorption mechanism. The preceding complexes are listed in the apparent order of reaction energy from the greatest to the least.

Nitric oxide is adsorbed on clay minerals as coordinated NO and sometimes as the NO^+ cation when transition metal ions saturate the complex. The complexes of clay minerals with other inorganic nitrogen compounds is a subject which has received little attention in the past and is certainly worthy of study in the future.

Complexes involving less than chemically energetic bonding between inorganic nitrogen compounds and soil organic materials probably exist only transiently in nature. Chemical reactions of ammonia or of oxides and acids of nitrogen are closely related to the oxidation-reduction status of the organic matter. These reactions lead to immobilization of nitrogen in combinations that range in stability from dissociable ammonium salts to extremely stable heterocyclic compounds. By convention, nitrogen which is retained in forms insoluble in dilute acids is referred to as "fixed nitrogen."

The fixation of NH_3 (or NH_4^+) appears to involve, principally, its circumstantial entrapment during the course of oxidative condensation reactions leading to polymerization of aromatic or unsaturated alicyclic compounds or of fission products arising during the degradation of sugars. These reactions are largely autocatalytic in the alkaline pH range. They are rapid and, in the presence of oxygen, lead to extensive fixation of ammonia. The rate of fixation declines with pH and is markedly reduced below neutrality. Continued slow fixation, even at low pH, appears to involve the continuing slow exposure by enzymatic or mineral catalysis of oxidized groups (free radicals) which can enter into condensation reactions. The fission of sugars may be catalyzed by amino acids through the sequence of the so-called "browning reactions." The ability of NH_4^+ to react with sugar fission products in the acid range has not been shown but may be inferred.

Extensive losses of nitrite as N_2 or N_2O from nitrifying acid soils has recently been linked to the organic fraction. As in parallel reactions of nitrous acid with lignin or soil humic materials under more drastic laboratory conditions, a portion of the nitrite nitrogen is retained in the organic fraction. From theoretical considerations and parallels drawn from well-documented reactions in organic chemistry, it appears that N_2O_4 or its ionic and molecular dissociation products are key intermediates in these reactions at acidities encountered in soils.

The numerous possibilities for free radical formation and for both mineral and enzymatic catalysis in soil systems leads to the expectation that reactions covering a wide range of activation energies may be available for organic matter-inorganic nitrogen interactions. Thus, reactions which are possible under drastic laboratory conditions may reasonably be found to proceed under soil conditions.

REFERENCES

Aldrich, D. G., and Buchanan, J. R. 1955. Laboratory studies of reactions between injected nitrogen dioxide and various soils, with special reference to its possible use as a fertilizer. Soil Sci. Soc. Amer. Proc. 19:42-47.

Allison, F. E. 1955. The enigma of soil nitrogen balance sheets. Adv. in Agron. 7:213-250.

Allison, F. E. 1963. Losses of gaseous nitrogen from soils by chemical mechanisms involving nitrous acid and nitrites. Soil Sci. 96:404-409.

Allison, F. E. 1964. The soil nitrogen balance sheet—a continuing enigma. In Soil and Fertilizer Nitrogen Research. Proc. Nitrogen Research Symposium, Wilson Dam, Ala.,

Tennessee Valley Authority, Div. of Agr. Development, Soils and Fert. Res. Branch:1-17.

Andersson, E. K. 1960. Geochemistry of a raised bog. III. Correlation between total nitrogen and ash alkalinity in bog peats. Ann. Agr. Coll. Sweden 26:33-40.

Baker, J. H., Peech, M., and Musgrave, R. B. 1959. Determination of application losses of anhydrous ammonia. Agron. J. 51:361-362.

Barrer, R. M., and MacLeod, D. M. 1954. Intercalation and sorption by montmorillonite. Trans. Faraday Soc. 50:980-989.

Bennett, E. 1949. Fixation of ammonia by lignin. Soil Sci. 68:399-400.

Béres, T., and Király, I. 1959. Investigations on the reducing effect of peat fulvic acid on ferric iron and iron compounds of fulvic acid. Z. Pflanzenernähr. Düng. Bodenk. 87:16-26.

Blyholder, George, and Richardson, Edwin. 1962. Infrared and volumetric data on the adsorption of ammonia, water, and other gases on activated iron. III. Oxide. J. Phys. Chem. 66:2597-2602.

Brauns, F. E. 1952. *The Chemistry of Lignin.* Academic Press, Inc., New York. pp. 339-358.

Bremner, J. M. 1950. Some observations on the oxidation of soil organic matter in alkali. J. Soil Sci. 1:198-204.

————. 1952. The nature of soil-nitrogen complexes. J. Sci. Food Agric. 3:497-500.

————. 1954. A review of recent work on soil organic matter. II. J. Soil Sci. 5:214-232.

————. 1955. Recent work on soil organic matter at Rothamsted. Z. Pflanzenernähr. Düng. Bodenk. 69:32-38.

————. 1957. Studies on soil humic acids; observations on the estimation of free amino groups; reactions of humic acid and lignin preparations with nitrous acid. J. Agr. Sci. 48:352-360.

————, and Shaw, K. 1957. The mineralization of some nitrogenous materials in soil. J. Sci. Food Agric. 8:341-347.

Broadbent, F. E. 1953. The soil organic fraction. Adv. in Agron. 5:153-183.

————, Burge, W. D., and Nakashima, T. 1960. Factors influencing the reaction between ammonia and soil organic matter. Trans. Intern. Congr., Soil Sci. 7th Congr. Madison II: 509-516.

Brown, B. R., Johnson, A. W., McDonald, S. F., Quayle, J. R., and Todd, A. R. 1952. Colouring matters of the Aphididae: Part VII. Addition reactions of erythroaphin-fb. J. Chem. Soc. London: 4928-4935.

Brown, James M., and Bartholomew, W. V. 1962. Sorption of anhydrous ammonia by dry clay systems. Soil Sci. Soc. Amer. Proc. 26:258-262.

————, and Bartholomew, W. V. 1963. Sorption of gaseous ammonia by clay minerals as influenced by sorbed aqueous vapor and exchangeable cations. Soil Sci. Soc. Amer. Proc. 27:160-164.

Burge, W. D., and Broadbent, F. E. 1961. Fixation of ammonia by organic soils. Soil Sci. Soc. Amer. Proc. 25:199-204.

Buswell, A. M., and Dudenbostel, B. F. 1941. Spectroscopic studies of base exchange materials. J. Amer. Chem. Soc. 63:2554-2559.

Cady, F. B., and Bartholomew, W. V. 1960. Sequential products of anaerobic dentrification in Norfolk soil material. Soil Sci. Soc. Amer. Proc. 24:477-482.

————, and Bartholomew, W. V. 1961. Influence of low pO_2 on dentrification processes and products. Soil Sci. Soc. Amer. Proc. 25:362-365.

————, and Bartholomew, W. V. 1963. Investigations of nitric oxide reactions in soils. Soil Sci. Soc. Amer. Proc. 27:546-549.

Carter, H. E., and Dickman, S. R. 1943. Anomalous amino nitrogen values. J. Biol. Chem. 149:571.

Chao, T. T., and Kroontje, W. 1960. Ammonia adsorption phenomena in soils. Trans. 7th Int. Congr. Soil Sci. II:517-522.

————, and Kroontje, W. 1963. Inorganic nitrogen oxidations in relation to associated changes in free energy. Soil Sci. Soc. Amer. Proc. 27:44-47.

Chaussidon, J., Calvet, R. Helsen, J., and Fripiat, J. J. 1962. Catalytic decomposition of cobalt III. Hexammine cations on the surface of montmorillonite. Nature 196:161-162.

Clark, F. E., and Beard, W. E. 1960. Influence of organic matter on volatile loss of nitrogen from soil. Trans. Intern. Congr., Soil Sci. 7th Congr., Madison II:501-508.

———, ———, and Smith, D. H. 1960. Dissimilar nitrifying capacities of soils in relation to losses of applied nitrogen. Soil Sci. Soc. Amer. Proc. 24:50-54.

Cook, R. L. 1935. Divergent influence of degree of base saturation of soils on the availability of native soluble and rock phosphates. J. Amer. Soc. Agron. 27:297-311.

Cornet, I. 1943. Sorption of ammonia on montmorillonite clay. J. Chem. Phys. 11:217-226.

Davies, R. I., Coulson, C. B., and Lewis, D. A. 1960. Polyphenols in soil profile development. Sci. Proc. Roy. Dublin Soc. Ser. A, 1(4):183-189.

Davis, R. O. E., Miller, R. R., and Scholl, W. 1935. Nitrification of ammoniated peat and other nitrogen carriers. J. Amer. Soc. Agron. 27:729-737.

———, and Scholl, W. 1939. Ammoniated peat. Effect of varying the conditions of ammoniated treatment on nitrogen quality. Ind. Eng. Chem. 31:185-189.

Dawson, J. E. 1956. Organic soils. Adv. in Agron. 8:378-401.

Delwiche, C. C. 1956. Denitrification. *In* Ed. W. D. McElroy and B. Glass, *Inorganic Nitrogen Metabolism*. John Hopkins, Baltimore. pp. 233-259.

Dennis, E. J., and Ellis, R. Jr. 1962. Potassium ion fixation, equilibria and lattice changes in vermiculite. Soil Sci. Soc. Amer. Proc. 26:230-233.

Dhar, N. R. 1960. Role of organic matter in soil fertility. Trans. Intern. Congr., Soil Sci. 7th Congr., Madison II:314-320.

Ducros, Pierre, and Dupont, Marcel. 1962. Etude par resonance magnetique nucléaire des protons dans les argiles. Compt. rend. 254:1409-1410.

Eischens, R. P., and Pliskin, W. A. 1958. The infrared spectra of adsorbed molecules. *Adv. in Catalysis* 10:1. Academic Press.

Eller, W. 1923a. Studien über Huminsäuren IV. Darstellung und Eigenschaften künstlicher und natürliche Huminsäuren. Liebigs Ann. Chem. 431:133-161.

———, Meyer, H., and Saenger, H. 1923b. Studien über Huminsäuren. V. Einwirkung von Salpetersäure auf Huminsäuren. Liebig's Ann. Chem. 431:162-177.

Ellis, B. G. 1961. The measurement of heats of reactions of soil components with a differential thermal analysis apparatus. Ph.D. Thesis, Michigan State University, E. Lansing.

———, and Mortland, M. M. 1963. Heats of desorption of NH_3 and simple organic materials from bentonite. Soil Sci. Soc. Amer. Proc. 27:21-25.

Enders, C., Tschapek, M., and Glawe, R. 1948. Vergleichende Untersuchung einiger kolloider Eigenschaften von naturlichen Huminsäuren und synthetischen Melanoidinen. Kolloid Z. 110:240-244.

Erdtman, H. 1955. Die Reaktion von Benzochinon mit Alkali. Z. Pflanzenernähr. Düng. Bodenk. 69:38-43.

Faucher, J. A., and Thomas, H. C. 1955. Exchange between heavy water and clay minerals. J. Phys. Chem. 59:189.

Feustel, I. C. 1939. The acidic properties of peat and muck. U.S.D.A. Tech. Bul. 690.

———, and Byers, H. G. 1933. The decomposition of hydrolytic peat products including ammoniated peat. U.S.D.A. Tech. Bul. 389.

Fieser, L. F., and Fieser, M. 1956. Organic Chemistry. Reinhold Publishing Co., New York.

Flaig, W. 1950. Zur Kenntnis der Huminsäuren: I. Zurchemischen Konstitution der Huminsäuren. Z. Pflanzenernähr. Düng. Bodenk. 51:193-212.

Flaig, W. 1955. Chinone als Modellsubstanzen von Huminsäurevorstufen. Z. Pflanzenernähr. Düng. Bodenk. 69:43-50.

Flaig, W. 1960. Comparative chemical investigations on natural humic compounds and their model substances. Sci. Proc. Roy. Dublin Soc. Ser. A, 1(4):149-162.

Flaig, W., and Schulze, H. 1952. Über den Bildungsmechanismus der Synthese-Huminsäuren. Z. Pflanzenernähr. Düng. Bodenk. 58:59-67.

Freudenberg, K. 1957. Structure and formation of lignin. Ind. Eng. Chem. 49:1384.

Freudenberg, K. 1956. Lignin in Rahmen der polymeren Naturstoffe. Angewandte Chemie 68:84-92.

Freudenberg, K., and Dürr, W. 1930. Lignin und Stickstoffdioxyd. Ber. Deut. Chem. Gesellsch. 63:2713-2720.

Fripiat, J. J., Chaussidon, J., and Touillaux, R. 1960. Study of dehydration of montmorillonite and vermiculite by infrared spectroscopy. J. Phys. Chem. 64:1234.

Fripiat, J. J., Servais, A., and Leonard, A. 1962. Etude de l'adsorption des amines par les montmorillonites. III. La nature de la liason aminemontmorillonite. Bul. Soc. Chim. Fr. 617, 625, 635.

Führ, F., and Bremner, J. M. 1964. Beeinflussende Faktoren in der Fixierung des Nitrit-Stickstoffs durch die organische Masse des Bodens. Atompraxis 10(2):109-113.

Gerretson, F. C., and de Hoop, H. 1957. Nitrogen losses during nitrification in solutions and sandy soils. Can. J. Microbiol. 3:359-380.

Goring, C. A. I., and Martin, R. T. 1959. Diffusion and sorption of aqua ammonia injected into soils. Soil Sci. 88:336-341.

Gould, E. S. 1959. Mechanism and Structure in Organic Chemistry. Henry Holt and Company, New York.

Green, Gisele, and Steelink, C. 1962. Structure of soil humic acid. II. Some copper oxidation products J. Org. Chem. 27:170-174.

Hasek, R. H., Elam, E. U., and Martin, J. C. 1960. Reaction of secondary and tertiary aldehydes with ammonia. J. Org. Chem. 26:1822-1825.

Heslop, R. B., and Robinson, P. L. 1960. Inorganic Chemistry. Elsevier Publ. Co., New York.

Hiltbold, A. E., and Adams, F. 1960. Effects of nitrogen volatilization on soil acidity changes due to applied nitrogen. Soil Sci. Soc. Amer. Proc. 24:45-47.

Hodge, J. E. 1953. Chemistry of browning reactions in model systems. J. Agr. Food Chem. 1:928-943.

Hough, L., Jones, J. K. N., and Richards, E. L. 1952. The reaction of amino-compounds with sugars. Part 1. The action of ammonia on D-glucose. J. Chem. Soc. London 1952:3854-3857.

Hulme, A. C. 1935. Biochemical studies in the nitrogen metabolism of the apple fruit: I. The estimation of amino-nitrogen by the Van Slyke method in the presence of tannin. Bioch. J. 29:263-271.

Humbert, R. P., and Ayres, A. S. 1957. The use of aqua ammonia in the Hawaiian sugar industry: II. Injection studies. Soil Sci. Soc. Amer. Proc. 21:312-316.

Ingham, G. 1950. Effect of materials absorbed from the atmosphere in maintaining soil fertility. Soil Sci. 70:205-212.

Jackson, M. L., and Chang, S. C. 1947. Anhydrous ammonia retention by soils as influenced by depth of application, soil texture, moisture content, pH value, and tilth. J. Amer. Soc. Agron. 39:623-633.

James, D. W., and Harward, M. E. 1962. Mechanism of NH_3 adsorption by montmorillonite and kaolinite. Clays and Clay Minerals 11:301-320.

James, D. W., and Harward, M. E. 1964. Competition of NH_3 and H_2O for adsorption sites on clay minerals. Soil Sci. Soc. Amer. Proc. 28:636-640.

Jansson, S. L. 1960. On the humus properties of organic manures. I. Actual humus properties. II. Potential humus properties. Ann. Agr. Coll. Sweden (Uppsala) 26:51-75; 135-172.

Jenny, H., Ayers, A. S., and Hosking, J. S. 1945. Comparative behavior of ammonia and ammonium salts in soils. Hilgardia 16:429-457.

Jung, J. 1959. Vergleichende Überprüfung verschiedener Stickstoffverbindungen auf ihre chemische Reaktion mit Rohhumus und die photometrische Erfassung dieses Reaktionseffektes. Z. Pflanzenernähr. Düng. Bodenk. 85:104-112.

Junker, E. 1941. Zur Kenntnis der kolloidchemischen Eigenschaften des Humus. Kolloid Z. 95:213-250.

Kalckar, H. M. 1946. Mesomeric concepts in the biological sciences. In Ed. D. E. Green, Currents in Biochemical Research. Interscience Publishers, Inc., N. Y. pp. 229-240.

Katritzky, A. R., and Lagowski, Jeanne M. 1960. Heterocyclic Chemistry. John Wiley & Sons, N. Y. pp. 274.

Kononova, M. M. 1961. Soil Organic Matter. Pergamon Press, N. Y.

Lindbeck, M. R., and Young, J. L. 1964. Polarography of intermediates in the fixation of nitrogen by para-quinone-aqueous ammonia systems. Anal. Chim. Acta (in press).

Lisk, D. J. 1957. Chemical composition of soil solution. Diss. Abstr. 17:457.

Lunt, O. R., Sciaroni, R. H., and Kofranek, A. M. 1962. Ion exchange fertilizers and ammoniated organic matter. California Agr. Exp. Sta. Cal. Agr. 16(4):13-14.

McDowel, L. L., and Smith, G. E. 1958. The retention and reactions of anhydrous ammonia on different soil types. Soil Sci. Soc. Amer. Proc. 22:38-42.

McIntosh, T. H. 1962. Fixation of added ammonium by the clay and organic fractions of soil. Ph.D. Thesis, Iowa State University, Ames, Iowa.

Malo, B. A., and Purvis, E. R. 1964. Soil absorption of atmospheric ammonia. Soil Sci. 97:242-247.

Mattson, S., and Koutler-Andersson, E. 1941. The acid-base condition in vegetation, litter and humus. IV. The strength of the acidoids and the relation to nitrogen. Ann. Agr. Coll. Sweden 9:57-73.

Mattson, S., and Koulter-Andersson, E. 1942. The acid-base condition in vegetation, litter and humus. V. Products of partial oxidation and ammonia fixation. Ann. Agr. Coll. Sweden 10:284-332.

Mattson, S., and Koutler-Andersson, E. 1943. The acid-base condition of vegetation, litter and humus. VI. Ammonia fixation and humus nitrogen. Ann. Agr. Coll. Sweden 11:107-134.

Mattson, S., and Koutler-Andersson, E. 1954. Geochemistry of raised bog. I. Ann. Agr. Coll. Sweden 21:321-366.

Mattson, S., and Koutler-Andersson, E. 1955. Geochemistry of raised bog. II. Ann. Agr. Coll. Sweden 22:219-224.

Michaelis, L. 1946. Fundamentals of oxidation and reduction. *In* Ed. D. E. Green, Currents in Biochemical Research, Interscience Publishers, Inc., N. Y. pp. 207-227.

Mortland, M. M. 1955. Adsorption of ammonia by clays and muck. Soil Sci. 80:11-18.

Mortland, M. M., and Erickson, A. E. 1956. Surface reactions of clay minerals. Soil Sci. Soc. Amer. Proc. 20:476-479.

Mortland, M. M. 1958. Reactions of ammonia in soils. Adv. in Agron. X:325-348.

Mortland, M. M., Fripiat, J. J., Chaussidon, J., and Uytterhoeven, J. 1963. Interaction between ammonia and the expanding lattices of montmorillonite and vermiculite. J. Phys. Chem. 67:248-258.

Murphy, D., and Moore, A. W. 1960. A possible structural basis of a natural humic acid. Sci. Proc. Roy. Dublin Soc. Ser. A, 1(4):191-195.

Musso, H., Matthies, H. G., Beecken, H., and Kramer, H. 1957. Zur Konstitution der Orceinfarbstoffe. Angew. Chem. 69:178.

Patrick, W. H. 1960. Nitrate reduction rates in a submerged soil as affected by redox potential. Trans. Intern. Congr., Soil Sci. 7th Congr. Madison II:494-500.

Ploetz, Th. 1955. Polymere Chinone als Huminsäuremodelle. Z. Pflanzenernähr. Düng. Bodenk. 69:50-58.

Raacke-Fels, I. D. 1953. Reaction of carbohydrates with ammonia as studied by paper chromatography. Arch. Biochem. Biophys. 43:289-298.

Ray, H. E., McGregor, J. M., and Schmidt, E. L. 1957. Movement of ammonium-nitrogen in soils. Soil Sci. Soc. Amer. Proc. 21:309-312.

de'Rossi, G. 1947. Absorption of ammonia by soil from the atmosphere. Ital. Agr. 84:201.

Rynders, G. W. A., and Schuit, G. C. A. 1950. Adsorption of ammonia on surfaces of oxides. Rec. Chim. des Pay-Bas 69:668-670.

Savage, S. M., and Stevenson, F. J. 1961. Behavior of soil humic acids towards oxidation with hydrogen peroxide. Soil Sci. Soc. Amer. Proc. 25:35-39.

Scheffer, F., and Schlüter, H. 1959. Über Aufbau und Eigenschaften der Braunund Grau-huminsäuren. Z. Pflanzenernähr. Düng. Bodenk. 84:184-193.

Scheffer, F., and Ulrich, B. 1960. Humus und Humusdüngung. Ferdinand Enke, Stuttgart. pp. 39-125.

Scholl, W., and Davis, R. O. E., 1933. Ammoniation of peat for fertilizers. Ind. Eng. Chem. 25:1074-1078.

Shoji, S. 1958. The fixation of ammonia and nitrate by organic materials. M. S. Thesis, Michigan State University, E. Lansing.

Slabaugh, W. H., and Siegel, Richard H. 1956. Sorption of ammonia by homoionic bentonites. J. Phys. Chem. 60:1105-1108.

Smith, D. H., and Clark, F. E. 1960. Volatile losses of nitrogen from acid or neutral soils or solutions containing nitrite and ammonium ions. Soil Sci. 90:86-92.

Sohn, J. B., and Peech, M. 1958. Retention and fixation of ammonia by soils. Soil Sci. 85:1-9.

Sprung, M. M. 1940. A summary of the reactions of aldehydes with amines. Chem. Revs. 26:297-338.

Steelink, C., and Tollin, G. 1962. Stable free radicals in soil humic acid. Bioch. Biophys. Acta 59:25-34.

Stein, H. N., and Tendeloo, H. J. C. 1959. Oxidation of phloroglucinol as a model for humification processes. Plant and Soil 11:131-138.

Stevenson, F. J. 1960. Chemical nature of the nitrogen in the fulvic fraction of soil organic matter. Soil Sci. Soc. Amer. Proc. 24:472-477.

Stevenson, F. J., and Kirkman, M. A. 1964. Identification of methyl nitrite in the reaction product of nitrous acid and lignin. Nature 201(4914):107.

Stevenson, F. J., and Swaby, R. J. 1963. Occurrence of a previously unobserved nitrogen gas in the reaction product of nitrous acid and lignin. Nature 199(4888):97-98.

Stober, W. 1956. Adsoptionseigenschaften und Oberflachenstruktur von Quarzpulvom. Kolloid Zeit. 145:17.

Stojanovic, B. J., and Broadbent, F. E. 1956. Immobilization and mineralization rates of nitrogen during decomposition of plant residues in soil. Soil Sci. Soc. Amer. Proc. 20:213-217.

Stojanovic, B. J., and Broadbent, F. E. 1960. Recovery of ammonium nitrogen from soils. Soil Sci. 90:93-97.

Täufel, K., Romminger, K., and Rudolph, I. 1958. Maillard reaction. V. Behavior of glucosamine and acetyl-glucosamine towards ammonia, amines, and amino acids. Ernahrungsforschung 3:373-385.

Terenin, A., and Roev, L. 1959. Infrared spectra of nitric oxide adsorbed on transition metals, their salts and oxides. Spectrochim. Acta 11:946-957.

Thorne, P. C. L., and Roberts, E. R. 1954. Inorganic Chemistry. (Fritz Ephraim) Interscience Publishers, New York.

Titoff, A. 1910. Die Adsorption von Gasen durch Kohle. Z. Phys. Chem. 74:641.

Tyler, K. B., and Broadbent, F. E. 1960. Nitrite transformations in California soils. Soil Sci. Soc. Amer. Proc. 24:279-282.

Violanda, A. T. 1958. Ammonia fixation by soil organic matter: Some relationships between forms of nitrogen and components of soil organic matter. Ph.D. Thesis, Cornell University, Ithaca, N. Y.

Volk, G. M. 1959. Volatile loss of ammonia following surface application of urea to turf or bare soils. Agron. J. 51:746-749.

Wahhab, A., and Uddin, F. 1954. Loss of nitrogen through reaction of ammonium and nitrite ions. Soil Sci. 78:119-126.

Waldron, R. D., and Hornig, D. F. 1953. Infrared spectra and structure of crystalline ammonia hydrates. J. Amer. Chem. Soc. 75:6079.

Weygand, F., and Bergmann, A. 1947. Über N-Glykoside: VI. Katalysche Oxidation von Aryl-isoglycosaminen. Chem. Ber. 80:261-263.

Winans, C. F., and Adkins, H. 1933. The preparation of amines by catalytic hydrogenation of derivatives of aldehydes and ketones. J. Amer. Chem. Soc. 55:2051-2058.

Wullstein, L. H., Gilmour, C. M., and Bollen, W. B. 1963. Gaseous losses of soil nitrogen by chemical and microbial pathways. Agron. Abstr. 1963:34.

Young, J. L. 1964. Ammonia and ammonium reactions with some Pacific Northwest soils. Soil Sci. Soc. Amer. Proc. 28:339-345.

Young, J. L., and Cattani, R. A. 1962. Mineral fixation of anhydrous NH_3 by air-dry soils. Soil Sci. Soc. Amer. Proc. 26:147-152.

Young, J. L., and McNeal, B. L. 1964. Ammonia and ammonium reactions with some layer-silicate minerals. Soil Sci. Soc. Amer. Proc. 28:334-339.

Zettlemoyer, A. C., Chessick, J. J., and Chand, A. 1955a. Sorption by organic substances: II. Effect of functional groups on ammonia sorption. J. Phys. Chem. 59:375-378.

Zettlemoyer, A. C., Young, G. J., and Chessick, J. J. 1955b. Studies of the surface chemistry of silicate minerals. III. Heats of immersion of bentonite in water. J. Phys. Chem. 59:962-966.

Ziechmann, W., and Pawelke, G. 1959. Zum Vergleich natürlicher und synthetischer Huminsaüren und ihrer Vorstufen. Z. Pflanzenernähr. Düng. Bodenk. 84:174-184.

Chapter 5

Ammonium Fixation and Other Reactions Involving a Nonenzymatic Immobilization of Mineral Nitrogen in Soil

HANS NÕMMIK

Royal College of Forestry
Stockholm, Sweden

I. INTRODUCTION

According to the classical view, which is still widely accepted among practical agronomists, the inorganic forms of nitrogen, unlike several other nutrient elements, are of almost unlimited solubility in the soil and thus indefinitely available to the plants. Ammonium, nitrite, and nitrate nitrogen are generally considered not to be involved in any chemical reactions which may result in the formation of products of decreased solubility and of reduced biological availability. The only reactions earlier considered of practical significance in reducing the effectiveness of inorganic nitrogen in soil were those which lead to direct losses of the nitrogen, i.e., losses by leaching and by formation of gaseous nitrogenous compounds. Efforts recently made in the fields of soil chemistry and soil fertility have, however, revealed that this is not entirely correct. Considerable evidence has been accumulated that in some soils and under certain conditions a nonenzymatic transformation of inorganic nitrogen to slightly soluble and biologically only slowly available nitrogen forms may occur. This is especially true of the ammonium (ammonia) form of nitrogen. The process of greatest current interest in this respect is unquestionably that of ammonium fixation by inorganic soil materials and the fixation of ammonia by soil organic matter. Both of these topics are discussed and reviewed in the present paper. In addition, mention is made of some other reactions which under special conditions may result in a more or less permanent withdrawal of assimilable mineral nitrogen from the biological nitrogen cycle in the soil. The non-enzymatic reactions, which lead to the formation of gaseous nitrogenous compounds, such as nitrite dissimilation and ammonia volatilization, are excluded, as they are treated elsewhere in this monograph. The present discussion covers the literature through February 1964.

II. FIXATION OF AMMONIUM NITROGEN
IN SOILS AND CLAY MINERALS

It is well known that some soils have the ability to bind added ammonium, NH_4, and also potassium, K, in such a manner that it will not be readily replaced by other cations. As regards the NH_4 ion, the first observations on its binding in difficultly exchangeable form in soils seem to have been made by McBeth (1917). He demonstrated that in some soils the added NH_4 nitrogen could not be completely recovered by extraction with 10% hydrochloric acid solution or by alkaline distillation. He called the unrecovered portion of the added NH_4 "fixed" NH_4. McBeth was probably also the first to study the effect of various factors on the rate and magnitude of NH_4 fixation, coming to the conclusion that fixation was increased by temperature, reaction time, and concentration of the added NH_4 salt solution. It was, on the other hand, independent of the kind of anion and, what is very important, it was markedly reduced by Al, Fe, and K salts added to the soil prior to the addition of NH_4. McBeth was at that time not able to give any satisfactory explanation of the mechanism involved in the NH_4 fixation.

The results of this pioneer work by McBeth, which was carried out more than 40 years ago, have since been carefully checked by other investigators and found at most points to be entirely correct. It is remarkable that this excellent study and the suggestions made by McBeth were not immediately followed up by other workers. Disregarding the fundamental studies on the analytical methods of determination of NH_4 in soils by Bengtsson (1924) and Olsen (1929), the next reports on NH_4 fixation did not appear until about 20 years later, namely, those by Chaminade and Droineau (1936) and Chaminade (1940). Most of the available information is, however, of recent origin, i.e., within the last 10 to 15 years.

In comparison with the literature on fixation of NH_4, that on K is considerably more extensive. Several well-documented surveys have covered various aspects of the question (Agarwal, 1960; Kardos, 1955; Reitemeier, 1951; Schuffelen, 1955; and Wiklander, 1954). Much of the information available on NH_4 fixation, its mechanism, and its effects on plant production originates from basic studies on the fixation of K. In order to minimize the scope of this review the author has been compelled to exclude most of the voluminous information on K fixation and to limit the survey to the question of NH_4 fixation only. References to the literature on K fixation are made only in cases in which it is desired to draw parallels between the fixation of these two cations or in which the experimental results obtained in K fixation may help to explain some of the phenomena in NH_4 fixation.

A. Theories on the Mechanism of Ammonium Fixation

A number of theories have been advanced to explain the phenomena of K and NH_4 fixation in soils. They were, however, rather unsuccessful as long as we lacked the basic information about the mineralogical composition of the mineral fraction of the soil. Decisive progress in this respect was made when Hadding (1923) and Hendricks and Fry (1930), were able in the 1920's to demonstrate with the aid of X-ray diffraction analyses that soil materials, even in their finest size fractions, are crystalline in nature, and that the number of different crystalline minerals likely to be found is limited. Some years later Volk (1934) found that in soil samples taken in connection with a long-term field experiment from a plot which had been fertilized yearly for 50 years with K fertilizers the clay fraction $(0.3 - 2\mu)$ gave stronger second-order diffraction lines of muscovite on X-ray analysis than did the soil from the corresponding untreated plot. He concluded that a portion of the added K had reacted with silica and alumina-gel to form muscovite. According to Gorbunov (1936), K is fixed in soil gels by an occlusion process which depends primarily on the electrokinetic conditions in the soil. About the same time, Chaminade and Drouineau (1936) found that not only K but also NH_4 and Mg could be fixed, but not Ca and Na. They suggested that the fixation resulted from a migration of cations into the crystal nuclei of the colloids, but were not able to give any explanation of why some cations are fixed and others not. Chaminade (1940) suggested additionally that, if K ions were in excess of 4% of the total exchange capacity of the soil, fixation of applied K would not occur.

The reaction mechanism of cation fixation was further clarified when it was proved that the fixation of K was accompanied by a corresponding decrease in the cation-exchange capacity of the soil (Hoagland and Martin, 1933; Joffe and Levine, 1939; Karlsson, 1952; Troug and Jones, 1938). This gave a strong indication that the exchange sites were involved in the fixation reaction. Since in the layer-lattice minerals such as montmorillonite a part of the exchangeable ions are considered to be located in the interplanar spaces of the expanded lattice, Joffe and Kolodny (1939) suggested that the fixation of K, which in montmorillonite takes place as a result of heating, was caused by the contraction of the mineral lattice.

Further progress in the field of cation fixation was made possible mainly by successful X-ray diffraction studies on the structure of the clay minerals. As this information is of great importance for a correct understanding of the cation-fixation and release reactions, a brief description of the idealized structure of the layer-lattice minerals will be given below. For more detailed information on this subject the reader is referred to the textbooks and the excellent reviews available on the structure of silicate minerals (Gieseking, 1949; Grim, 1953; Mackenzie, 1955; Marshall, 1949; Rich and Thomas, 1960; Schachtschabel, 1952; Schuffelen and Marel, 1955).

According to current views, clay minerals are secondarily formed alumino-silicates, having a layer-lattice crystal structure. They are generally divided into two categories on the basis of their silica-alumina ratio. The first category, the two-layer or 1:1 type of clay minerals, includes those in which a tetrahedral Si-O sheet (Si^{4+} surrounded by 4 O^{2-} ions) is combined with a single octahedral Al-O-OH sheet (Al^{3+} surrounded by 6 O^{2-} or OH^- ions), forming together a unit layer (Grim, 1953). Kaolinite and halloysite are two minerals belonging to this group. It is characteristic of these minerals that they do not show any expansion of the interlayer distance by hydration and that all the exchangeable cations are bound on the external surface of the crystal particles. They are unable to fix NH_4 or K in difficultly exchangeable form.

The second group, known as the three-layer or 2:1 type of clay minerals, involves a number of minerals containing "mica" units, each of which consists of an octahedral sheet "sandwiched" between two tetrahedral Si-O sheets. If the octahedral positions are filled exclusively with Al^{3+} ions and the tetrahedral positions with Si^{4+} ions, we have a crystal lattice which is characteristic of the rather uncommon mineral pyrophyllite. In micas and micaceous clay minerals generally a part of the octahedral Al^{3+} ions is isomorphously substituted by Mg^{2+} or Fe^{2+}, and a part of the Si^{4+} in the octahedral layer by Al^{3+}, Fe^{3+}, etc. Such substitution of a positive ion of higher valency by one of lower valency leads to the development of a negative charge in the lattice. This charge can be neutralized in two ways (Mackenzie, 1955), by substituting an ion of higher valency for one of lower valency elsewhere in the lattice or by the presence of positive ions at the surface of the unit layers. The second type of neutralization is by far the more important. Three-layer minerals differ from each other as regards the type of cation present in the interlayer positions, the total magnitude of charge in the lattice, and the origin of the negative charge of the lattice.

In an idealized mica the lattice charge is balanced by K ions, occupying the positions between the mica sheets. On the other hand, in clay minerals, among which may be mentioned illites, vermiculites, and montmorillonites, the interlayer K is partly or totally replaced by other cations. In illites about half of the K is replaced by Ca^{2+}, Mg^{2+}, Na^+, H^+, etc., in vermiculites the predominant interlayer cation is Mg^{2+}, and in montmorillonites mainly Ca^{2+}, Na^+, and H^+ (Grim, 1953; Rich and Thomas, 1960; Schachtschabel, 1952; Schachtschabel et al., 1961). The interlayer cations in the above minerals are to varying extents exchangeable for other cations.

X-ray diffraction analyses have revealed that the basal spacing of the clay minerals is largely dependent on the type of cations occupying the interlayer positions. Thus Hendricks et al. (1940) found for a K-saturated bentonite a maximum basal spacing of 12 Å, whereas for Ca-, Mg-, Na- and H-saturated samples the corresponding figure was about 16 Å. According to Jackson and Hellman (1942), a K-saturated montmorillonite, when dried at 30°C, showed a basal spacing of 12.3 Å, the corresponding figures for Na- and Ca-saturated samples being as high as 14.6 and 15.1 Å, respectively.

More recently, Barshad (1948, 1950, 1951) showed by X-ray diffraction studies that the basal spacing of montmorillonite, saturated with Mg, Ca,

Ba, Na, Li, or H and afterwards air-dried, was considerably increased when re-wetted, whereas with K, NH_4, and Rb as interlayer cations the lattice structure remained contracted. As regards an air-dried vermiculite, Barshad (1948) demonstrated that the basal spacing with K and NH_4 as interlayer cations was 10.4 and 11.2 Å, respectively, whereas Na, Mg, and Ca provided spacing of 12.6, 14.3, and 15.1 Å, respectively.

The investigations cited above and also several others (Dyal and Hendricks, 1952; van der Marel, 1954) indicate that the saturation of vermiculite and degraded illite (under special conditions also montmorillonite) with NH_4 and K may lead to a contraction of the crystal lattice. The K and NH_4 ions are thereby "trapped" between the silica sheets, being in this position largely withdrawn from exchange reactions. A number of theories have been proposed to explain the specificity of the different cations as regards their ability to contract or expand the mica lattice, and thus their readiness to be fixed between the silica sheets. One of these is the "lattice hole" theory, proposed by Page and Baver (1940). According to this, cation fixation is related to the size of the cation as well as to the kind of fixing material. In explanation it may be mentioned that, according to the generally accepted idea, the exposed surface between the sheets of 2:1 lattice-type minerals consists of oxygen ions, arranged hexagonally. The opening within the hexagon is equal to the diameter of an oxygen ion, i.e., ca. 2.8 Å. Page and Baver consider that ions having a diameter of the above magnitude (e.g., NH_4 and K) will fit snugly into the lattice holes, and that such ions will be held very tightly as they come closer to the negative electrical charges within the crystal. Owing to this, the layers are allowed to approach and be bound together, thus preventing the rehydration and re-expansion of the lattice. The cations larger than 2.8 Å, according to this theory, cannot enter the cavities and will therefore remain more loosely held between the layers and be more accessible for re-exchange (or redisplacement). Smaller cations (e.g., Na, Mg, Ca) may be able to enter the cavities but are too small to contact and bind the layers tightly together. As indirect evidence that the interlayer distance is critical in the fixation of cations it was mentioned that the K fixation by montmorillonite was considerably decreased by placing large organic cations between the Si-O sheets. These large ions prevented the lattice from contracting and made the K ions situated in interlayer positions accessible for exchange with other cations present in external solution.

As regards the different 2:1 type clay minerals, the vermiculites have the greatest capacity to fix K and NH_4. Illite may fix or may not, depending on the degree of weathering and the K saturation of the lattice. Montmorillonites do not fix NH_4 under moist conditions. This differential behavior of clay minerals, according to Wear and White (1951) and Bailey (1942), depends on whether the main part of the negative charge of the

Table 1. Crystal ionic radii of some cations (Pauling, 1940).

Cation	Li	Na	K	NH_4	Rb	Cs	Mg	Ca	Ba
Radius, Å	0.60	0.95	1.33	1.48	1.48	1.69	0.65	0.99	1.35

lattice originates from the hexagonal layer or from the tetrahedral layer. These authors emphasize that the force of attraction between the positively charged interlayer cations and the negative charges in the crystal lattice will be greatest when the negative charge results from an isomorphous substitution of Al for Si in the tetrahedral layers, giving a shorter distance between the interlayer cations and the negative sites of the lattice. It may be noted that in vermiculites about 80-90% of the total substitution is located in the tetrahedral Si-O sheets, whereas the corresponding value for illites is approximately 65% or higher. For montmorillonites the tetrahedral substitution makes less than 20%, explaining the incapacity of K and NH_4 under moist conditions to contract and hold together the sheets (Schachtschabel, 1961a).

According to Barshad (1954a), it is most likely the magnitude of the interlattice charge, rather than its origin, that determines the K and NH_4 fixation. Barshad considers that, if all of the cavities in the interlayer oxygen sheets of the mica minerals were occupied by a monovalent cation, the total interlayer charge in the mineral would range from 240 to 260 me. per 100 g. A mineral which has a smaller charge than this would have empty hexagonal cavities. Likewise, in the case of a divalent cation only one-half or fewer of the cavities would be occupied. Barshad suggests that the empty cavities will act as ports of entry to and departure from the interior of the particle. Therefore, the greater the number of these empty cavities, the greater is the chance of replacement of interlayer cations by other cations in extraneous solution, and, consequently, the less would be the capacity of the mineral to fix NH_4 and K.

On the basis of available information it seems evident that the ability of soils to fix NH_4 may be ascribed to the occurrence of micaceous minerals, the lattice of which has been impoverished in K. Chemical weathering and the activity of the plant roots are the processes primarily responsible for it (Ghildyal, 1961; Reichenbach, 1958). Thus Bray (1937) found that the clay fraction of some Illinois soils showed a tendency to become lower in K content with increasing age. The observation made by Schreven (1963), according to which the old marine clays fixed considerably more NH_4 than the young polder soils, seems to support the above finding. Interesting in this connection is the observation made by Swedish workers that the highly fixing, mainly illitic soils, are generally characterized by a low content of exchangeable K in relation to their content of clay (Nõmmik, 1957) and the proportion of total K released by treating the soils with N HCl is inversely proportional to the fixation capacity (Ståhlberg, 1960). Furthermore, according to Karlsson (1952), the primary mica minerals, muscovite and biotite, which normally did not fix K, were kept fixing after a partial removal of their lattice-bound K by means of electrodialysis. Similarly, Mortland et al. (1956) have shown that an extraction of K by continuous wheat cropping resulted in an alteration of biotite to vermiculite.

To explain the phenomenon of fixation and release of K in clay minerals, it has been suggested that there exists a kind of dynamic equilibrium between the potassium dissolved in the soil solution, K_s, the exchangeable potassium, K_e, and the fixed potassium, K_f (Bartholomew and Janssen,

1931; Chaminade, 1934; Schachtschabel, 1937). A similar equilibrium may occur between the different forms of ammonium in the soil:

$$(NH_4)_{soluble} \rightleftarrows (NH_4)_{exchangeable} \rightleftarrows (NH_4)_{fixed}$$

According to this equation, a change in any of the above forms of NH_4 will affect the other forms of NH_4 involved in the equilibrium reaction. When the concentration of $(NH_4)_s$ exceeds the equilibrium value (e.g., after the addition of NH_4-containing fertilizers), the reaction proceeds to the right, leading ultimately to a fixation of some of the added NH_4. On the other hand, the fixed ammonium, $(NH_4)_f$, will be released when $(NH_4)_e$ falls below the actual equilibrium value. In view of the generally overwhelming predominance of K^+ vs. NH_4^+ in soil systems and the similarity of these ions with respect to fixation reactions, it is often more realistic to introduce into the equilibrium equation the sum of NH_4 and K ions, rather than NH_4 alone (Nõmmik, 1957):

$$(NH_4 + K)_s \rightleftarrows (NH_4 + K)_e \rightleftarrows (NH_4 + K)_f$$

With the aid of tracer techniques Wiklander (1950) and Nõmmik (1957) showed that only a fractional part of the fixed K or fixed NH_4 participates in a real equilibrium with the exchangeable ions, indicating that the last stage of the equilibrium reaction is strongly hysteretic.

A schematic picture illustrating the different forms of NH_4 on illite is given in Fig. 1.

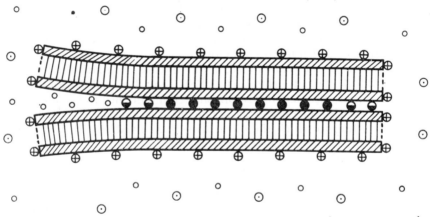

⊟ Si-O layer;   ▥ Al-O-OH layer;   ● Lattice-bound K^+;   ◓ Fixed NH_4^+;
⊕ Exchangeable NH_4^+;   ⊙ NH_4^+ in soils solution;   ○ Ca^{2+}, Mg^{2+}, Na^+, H^+.

Fig. 1. Schematic picture showing the different forms of NH_4 on illite (modified after Wiklander, 1958, and Schachtschabel, 1961).

Though considerable effort has been made to elucidate the nature of cation fixation, it must be confessed that our knowledge of the mechanism of the fixation reaction is still defective on some fundamental points. It is thus apparent that such characteristics as ionic radius, valency, and entropy of hydration are not always enough to explain why one ion is susceptible to fixation but another is not. Additional information is needed, *inter alia,* on the problems of the hydration phenomenon in charged ions, the geometry of the distribution of the charges, and, not least, the energy relationships in the fixation process (cf. Kardos, 1955).

More recent work on the K exchange reactions in illites and illitic soils has yielded information which enables us to approach the fixation-defixation phenomena from a rather different angle. Thus it has been found that the exchange-displacement behavior of K can be explained by accepting the existence of several types of exchange positions, each with an exchange constant specific of this type of site (Bolt et al., 1963; Schouwenburg and Schuffelen, 1963). Roughly three types of exchange sites have been identified with an illite mineral: planar sites on the external surfaces of the lattice, edge sites, and interlattice sites situated between the layers of the mineral. The edge and especially the interlattice sites show a very marked preference for K. This explains why, for example, Na ions and Ca ions are extremely ineffective in removing K from these sites as long as the released K ions are not removed from the system. NH_4 ions are, in contrast, highly effective in displacing the interlayer K. Their action, however, is kept within bounds owing to the circumstance that the mineral lattice remains fairly well contracted during the penetration of NH_4 ions (Schouwenburg and Schuffelen, 1963). The existence of specific edge sites with high preference for K is undoubtedly supported by results of some recent isotopic exchange studies by Sumner and Bolt (1962), according to which an extraction of illite with 0.5 N $NaNO_3$ removed less K than was exchangeable against K^{42}.

B. Methods of Determination of Ammonium Fixation

As was previously noted, the basal spacing of 2:1 lattice clay minerals is dependent on the type of cation occupying the interlayer exchange positions. When Ba, Ca, Mg, Na, Li, or H supplies the interlayer cation, the crystal lattice is, at ordinary temperature, in an expanded and hydrated state. With K, Rb, or Cs in interlayer positions, the crystal lattice becomes contracted and non-expansible, even when immersed in water, being in this respect identical with potash mica. Barshad (1951) and other workers have shown that the exchangeability of the interlayer cations depends on their accessibility to the replacing cation. Thus the cations present in an expanded crystal lattice are readily replaced by other cations which leave the lattice in an expanded state, but more slowly by cations which cause the lattice to contract. Likewise, the cations present in a contracted crystal lattice (e.g., NH_4, K) may be slowly replaced by those which bring about an expansion of the lattice, but not by cations which contract it. Thus the interlayer NH_4 in a contracted lattice of vermiculite, illite, or montmorillonite can be slowly replaced by cations such as Ca, Mg, and Na, but hardly by K. It is evident from this that the concept of cation fixation is somewhat arbitrary, the magnitude of fixation being dependent on the character of the replacing cation. The definition of cation fixation must necessarily include information as to the method used to replace the cation in question.

In studying the NH_4-fixing properties of soils and minerals, it is desirable from several points of view to find a procedure which enables a sharp separation of the readily exchangeable NH_4 and the NH_4 in interlattice positions. The cation used to remove the water-soluble and the easily exchangeable NH_4 should, if possible, not replace the NH_4 ions from interlattice positions, even on prolonged extraction and leaching. Otherwise the fixation values will be dependent on the time and intensity of the extraction and will therefore not be reproducible. In considering the ability of different cations to expand the lattice of three-layer clay minerals, Barshad (1951) proposed that the fixed NH_4 should be defined as NH_4 which is not replaceable by prolonged extraction and leaching of the soil with K-salt solutions, and inversely, that the fixed K may be defined as the K which is not replaced by NH_4. The term "fixed NH_4" is used in the same sense in the present paper. It must, however, be pointed out that the term "fixed" in the above sense does not imply anything about the biological availability of this NH_4 fraction.

In studying the ability of soils to fix NH_4, two fundamentally different methods can be used. The first involves a treatment of the soil with a known amount of dilute NH_4-salt solution and, after prolonged contact, a determination of the easily exchangeable portion of the added NH_4, using the KCl-leaching procedure. The difference between the NH_4 added and that recovered represents the NH_4 fixed, giving a fairly sensitive measure of the ability of the soil to fix NH_4 from diluted solutions. When working under identical conditions, the method gives fully reproducible results. For the purpose of removing the soluble and exchangeable NH_4 a special aeration procedure has been proposed by Leggett and Moodie (1962).

The other method involves an estimation of the maximum capacity of the soil to fix NH_4. In this case the soil is treated with excessive amounts of relatively concentrated NH_4 solution in order to achieve complete saturation of the fixing minerals with NH_4. Owing to the large amounts of NH_4 added, the estimation of the fixation from the difference between the added NH_4 and the NH_4 recovered by KCl leaching, as described above, would be an extremely insensitive procedure, especially in soils with low NH_4-fixing capacity. For this reason a number of other procedures have been proposed, some of which are described below.

1. TOTAL-NITROGEN PROCEDURE

The soil sample, previously saturated with NH_4, is extracted and leached with a N KCl solution until the last drops of the filtrate do not give any noticeable reaction for NH_4. The leached soil is then analyzed for its content of total N by Kjeldahl's digestion method. The increase in the N content over the control soil, which was not treated with NH_4 salts but was extracted and leached with KCl in exactly the same way as the other sample, represents the quantity of NH_4 fixed (Allison et al., 1951). This procedure has been applied with a number of different modifications, generally yielding fully reproducible results (Dhariwal and Stevenson, 1958; Nõmmik, 1957). For soils with a high total N content and a low NH_4-fixing capacity the method appears, however, to be rather insensitive. Moreover, Leggett and Moodie (1962) have pointed out that with some soils a greater leaching loss of organic N occurs from the NH_4-treated than from the untreated samples during the KCl extraction, giving erroneously low fixation figures.

2. N[15] TECHNIQUES

In principle this is the same procedure as described previously, with the difference that in this case the soil is treated with an ammonium salt solution containing an excess of nitrogen isotope N^{15}. After leaching with KCl, the soil sample is analyzed both for its total-N content and for the atomic percentage of N^{15} in the total-N fraction. From the above data, and from the known N^{15} content of the NH_4 salt used for saturation of the soil, the fixed amount of NH_4 can be calculated. If an NH_4 salt with a high content of N^{15} is used, the method is unquestionably very sensitive and gives fully reproducible results (Nõmmik, 1957). Owing to the high cost of the N^{15} preparations, however, the applicability of this procedure is limited.

3. HYDROFLUORIC-ACID PROCEDURE

In this method the NH_4-saturated and KCl-leached soil sample is treated with a mixture of hydrofluoric acid and mineral acid to disintegrate the clay minerals and to liberate the NH_4 from interlayer positions. The difference between the NH_4-N released in the control and that released in the NH_4-treated samples (in both samples the exchangeable NH_4 is removed by leaching with N KCl) corresponds to the soil content of fixed NH_4, exclusive of the native fixed NH_4 (Dhariwal and Stevenson, 1958; Nõmmik, 1957). A disadvantage of this procedure is that it is rather tedious and time-consuming.

4. THE ALKALINE DUPLICATE-DISTILLATION PROCEDURE

In this procedure, which was proposed by Barshad (1951), the fixed NH_4 and the NH_4-fixing capacity of the soil are estimated from the difference between the amounts of NH_4 released by distilling the NH_4-treated soil (excessive amounts of NH_4 salt removed by leaching with alcohol) with NaOH and KOH, respectively. It is assumed that the distillation with NaOH will remove both the exchangeable and the interlattice NH_4, but the distillation with KOH will remove the exchangeable NH_4 only. The method involves, furthermore, the assumption that the amount of NH_3 released by the decomposition of the organic N compounds in the soil during the distillation is exactly the same for the NaOH and KOH treatments (cf. Bremner, 1959). This assumption is probably quite correct (Nõmmik, unpublished data); a conclusive proof of it is, however, lacking.

The Barshad procedure has been used in a number of investigations, giving generally satisfactory results (Hanway and Scott, 1956; Nõmmik, 1957). In some cases an incomplete recovery of fixed NH_4 has been recorded, however. This may be due to (a) the blocking effect of K released from the fixing material or present in the added reagents as an impurity, and (b) the fixation of NH_3 by the soil organic matter during the alkaline distillation (Allison and Roller, 1955a, 1956; Hanway and Scott, 1956; Hanway et al., 1957; Leggett, 1958; Leggett and Moodie, 1963; Nõmmik, 1957). A shortcoming of the procedure is that the amount of NH_3 released from the organic matter of the soil during the alkaline distillation is dependent on the rate and duration of distillation (Dhariwal and Stevenson, 1958). It is to be considered, furthermore, that the alkaline distillation procedure includes also a part of the native fixed NH_4 in the soil. In estimating the NH_4-fixing capacity of the soil, a correction should therefore be made for this (see section H below).

C. Factors Affecting the Rate and Magnitude of Ammonium Fixation

It has been demonstrated that, besides the mineralogical composition of the soil, several other factors are of significance for the capacity of the soil to fix added NH_4. A brief discussion of them follows.

1. CONCENTRATION AND VOLUME OF THE AMMONIUM SALT SOLUTION ADDED

The amount of NH_4 fixed has been generally found to increase with increasing amounts of NH_4 added (Allison et al., 1951; Harada and Kutsuna, 1954; van den Hende, 1962; Jansson, 1958; Leggett and Moodie, 1962; Mela Mela, 1962; Nõmmik, 1957). This is in accordance with the idea that there exists some form of equilibrium between the fixed and the exchangeable NH_4 ions. As regards the percentage fixation, this generally decreases with an increase in the amount of NH_4 added (cf. Table

Table 2. Relation between the amounts of NH_4 added and NH_4 fixed in a vermiculite-containing surface soil from central Sweden (Nõmmik, 1957).

NH_4 added, me./100 g soil	NH_4 fixed, me./100 g soil	Fixed NH_4 in % of added NH_4
1	0.83	83
2	1.39	70
5	2.17	43
10	3.18	32
20	3.85	19
40	4.48	11

Soil:water ratio 1:1

2). Jansson (1958) demonstrated that the amount of the added NH_4 fixed was appreciably decreased by an increase in the water-soil ratio.

2. RATE OF FIXATION

Fixation is a relatively rapid process, the rate of which is determined mainly by ion diffusion. The fixation rate is highest in the periods immediately after the NH_4 addition and gets lower as the equilibrium point is approached (Harada and Kutsuna, 1954; van den Hende, 1962; Jansson, 1958; Leggett, 1958; Leggett and Moodie, 1962; Nõmmik, 1957; Stanford and Pierre, 1947). Under certain conditions about 60-90% of the total fixation can occur within a few hours (cf. Fig. 2).

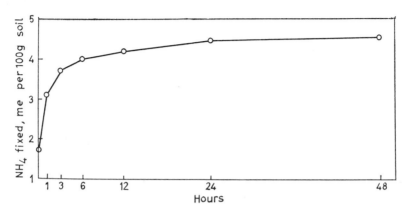

Fig. 2. Influence on fixation of time of reaction between ammonium nitrogen and soil. 7.4 me. NH_4 added per 100 g soil (Harada and Kutsuna, 1954).

3. TEMPERATURE

The temperature, which influences the rate of ion diffusion, is a factor affecting the rate of NH_4 fixation. In short-term fixation tests Harada and Kutsuna (1954) and Nõmmik (1957) demonstrated that within the temperature interval of 0-60°C fixation was increased with increasing temperature (cf. Aomine and Wada, 1952a). It has not been shown, however, whether the absolute magnitude of fixation (at equilibrium) is affected by temperature.

4. DRYING VERSUS ALTERNATE WETTING AND DRYING

Generally, the capacity of the surface soil to fix NH_4 under moist conditions has been found to be rather low. Only a few investigators have reported finding surface soils which had the ability to fix appreciable amounts of added NH_4 under moist conditions (Allison et al., 1951; Harada and Kutsuna, 1954; Jansson, 1958; Kaila, 1962; Leggett, 1958; and Nõmmik, 1957). Drying the soil after the addition of NH_4 salt solution (either air-drying or drying in the oven) has been shown to increase the rate as well as the magnitude of fixation. Two different reactions seem to be responsible for this. In the first place, the drying implies removal of water and consequently an increase in the concentration of NH_4 in the soil solution. This may, as has been shown previously, lead to an additional fixation of the NH_4 added. In soils in which the fixing material consists of the minerals vermiculite or illite, this increase in NH_4 fixation by drying is generally observed only when the soil is in contact with relatively dilute NH_4-salt solutions. When concentrated NH_4 solutions are applied, e.g., in determining the NH_4-fixing capacity of the soil, the effect of drying is often limited. For montmorillonites and the montmorillonite-containing soils, on the other hand, drying is a condition necessary to get the NH_4 fixed at all. Drying results in this case in a dehydration of the interlayer spacing of the lattice, thereby making possible a partial contraction of the lattice. In montmorillonite-containing soils the amount of fixation is thus increased by drying.

The effect of drying may be illustrated by the experimental results reported by Allison et al. (1951), according to which a Harpster clay loam (the predominating clay mineral being montmorillonite) was able to fix 1.1, 3.5, and 6.2 me.NH_4 per 100 g soil under moist, air-dried, and oven-dried conditions, respectively. The temperature of drying is evidently a factor of significance. It is likely, furthermore, that the rate of drying may also influence the extent of fixation. Alternate drying and wetting may be especially effective in increasing the fixation. Thus, Jansson (1958) showed that in a sandy loam from southern Sweden (probably illitic) the soil fixed under moist conditions ca. 50% of the 10 mg NH_4-N added per 100 g soil. After a single drying of the moistened soil at 30°C the fixation increased to 63%, and after three wettings and dryings to 77%.

Walsh and Murdock (1960) investigated a large number of montmorillonite-containing Wisconsin soils and found that under moist conditions the surface horizons of some gray-brown podzolic soils fixed 0.08 me.NH_4 per 100 g on the average, the corresponding figure after oven-drying being 0.68 me.(2.0 me.NH_4 added per 100 g of soil). Similar trends in fixation values have been obtained by several other workers (Aomine, 1951; Bower, 1950; Harada and Kutsuna, 1954; Ivanov, 1962; Jansson, 1958; Legg and Allison, 1959; Stojanovic and Broadbent, 1960).

In some papers the effect of drying on the fixation has been studied by measuring the difference between the added NH_4 and the NH_4 recovered by KCl leaching. The results of these investigations may be of questionable value, as volatilization losses of NH_3 may have occurred, especially from soils of high base saturation (pH > 7.0).

5. FREEZING AND THAWING

Since freezing, like drying, removes water from the system, it may very likely influence the amount of NH_4 fixed. Information on this point is, however, meager. Walsh and Murdock (1960) showed that a treatment for 5 days at −15°C increased the fixation of a number of podzolic soils from 0.08 to 0.14 me. per 100 g soil on the average (cf. Ivanov, 1962; Walsh and Murdock, 1963). According to Nõmmik (unpublished data), the fixation of NH_4 in a vermiculite-containing clay soil was increased from 3.08 to 3.42 me. per 100 g soil by freezing the moist soil for 24 hours at −17°C (10 me.NH_4 added).

6. PARTICLE SIZE OF THE FIXING MATERIAL

The fixation capacity is in general positively correlated with the particle size of the fixing minerals. Barshad (1954a) demonstrated that in most of the vermiculitic samples a decrease in particle size, obtained either by grinding or exfoliation, brought about a decrease in NH_4 fixation, measured by the KCl-leaching procedure. It may be noted also that, according to McDonnell et al. (1959) nearly all the fixed NH_4 in an NH_4-saturated vermiculite, amounting to 69 me. per 100 g, was released from the mineral by prolonged ball milling. Barshad (1954a) suggested that this increase in the accessibility of the fixed NH_4, accompanying a decrease in particle size, is the result of a conversion of the internal surfaces of a particle to external ones and of an increase in edge surfaces and fractures, through which the replacing and the adsorbed cations can enter or leave the interior of the particles. Thus, the smaller the particle and the more numerous the ports of entry into the particle, the smaller would be the contracted zone of the unit cells and the more easily the exchange reaction would be completed.

In soils an inverse relationship to particle size is often observed. Fixation capacity is in several areas associated with the clay fraction of the soil. After analyzing a large number of Swedish surface soils, Nõmmik (1957) found that the NH_4 fixation tended to increase with the increasing clay content of the soils (cf. also van den Hende, 1962; MacLean and Brydon, 1963; Schachtschabel, 1961; Wiklander, 1960). The correlation was nevertheless not very close, as even clayey silt and fine sand soils often showed considerable fixing capacity. These results have been confirmed by Jansson and Ericsson (1961) for soils in the province of Scania in Sweden, and by Kaila (1962) and Smirnov and Fruktova (1963) for the Finnish and Russian soils, respectively. According to the above Russian workers, the Chernozems fix considerably more NH_4 than the soddy-podzolic soils.

The relationship found between the clay content and the soil's capacity to fix NH_4 undoubtedly argues in favor of a uniform mineralogical composition of the clay fraction of the soils studied. Since no data regarding the mineralogical make-up of the coarser fractions of the soils were included, however, the results give no information as to the effect of the particle size of the fixing material on the capacity to fix NH_4. The low fixation figures usually found in the sand and fine sand fractions of the soil are most likely due to the predominantly non-micaceous mineral composition of these fractions.

The capacity of the silt and fine sand fractions of the soil to fix NH_4 under moist conditions has been demonstrated by Harada and Kutsuna (1957) and Nõmmik, who investigated two vermiculite-containing clay soils from Japan and Sweden, respectively:

Fractions, μ	NH_4-fixing capacity, me./100 g	
	Harada and Kutsuna (1951)	Nõmmik (Unpub.)
<2	8.57	7.51
2-20	13.74	4.64
20-200	9.99	1.83
200-2 mm	6.02	0.19

It may be noted that in the soil analyzed by Harada and Kutsuna the silt and even the fine sand fraction showed a higher NH_4-fixing capacity than the clay fraction (cf. Aomine and Wada, 1953; Mortland et al., 1956). This is often explained by the accumulation of montmorillonite in the finest clay fraction as the vermiculite is rather easily weathered and its stability decreases substantially with decreasing size of the mineral particles.

Thus no general correlation can be expected between the clay content and the ability of the soil to fix NH_4.

7. OTHER CATIONS INCLUDING POTASSIUM

From the previous discussion it was evident that not only NH_4 but also K, Rb, and Cs may be subject to fixation in 2:1 layer clay minerals. It is therefore likely that the last-mentioned cations, if present, will compete with NH_4 for the fixation positions in the minerals. This may result in a reduction of the fixation of NH_4. The depressive effect of K on the fixation of NH_4, and vice versa, is also well known and has been demonstrated by several workers. Stanford and Pierre (1947) and later Bower (1950), Nõmmik (1957), Jansson (1958), and Wiklander and Andersson (1959) showed that there was a highly significant correlation between the ability of soils to fix NH_4 and K, when added in equivalent amounts. It was established, furthermore, that the fixation of NH_4 was reduced by K added prior to the addition of NH_4, and that this reduction was proportional to the amount of K previously fixed (Fig. 3). A

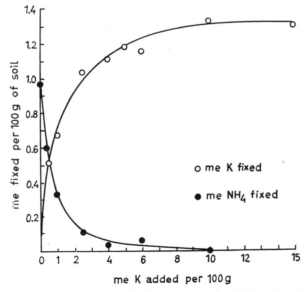

Fig. 3. Reduction in NH_4 fixation in relation to the levels of K previously fixed. 10 me. NH_4 added per 100 g soil. Fixation period for each cation 30 minutes (Stanford and Pierre, 1947).

similar relationship has been found for bentonite (Joffe and Levine, 1947) and for vermiculite (Barshad, 1951).

Even if in most soils the capacity to fix NH_4 and K is nearly the same, in some cases diverging results have been reported. Nõmmik (1957) thus found that a vermiculite-containing clay soil fixed 10-15% more NH_4 than K, and that this was valid for a fairly wide concentration interval.

Wiklander and Andersson (1959) likewise demonstrated that in a soil profile the surface horizon fixed about the same amounts of NH_4 and K, whereas in the subsoil the fixation of NH_4 was considerably greater than for K. No reasonable explanation could be adduced for this.

According to Nõmmik (1957), the higher fixability for NH_4 might be due to the small difference in interlayer space of the contracted mineral, depending on whether K or NH_4 occupies the interlayer positions. As concerns vermiculite, Barshad (1954b) showed that the interlayer space of the NH_4-saturated lattice was about 0.8 Å greater than for the lattice saturated with K. Because of the small expansion of the lattice brought about by replacing the interlayer K with NH_4, the fixed K will possibly be more accessible to a replacement by NH_4 than vice versa.

The relationship between NH_4 and K has been the subject of several investigations. One important finding from these investigations is that the effect of K on the fixation of NH_4 is not only dependent on the amount of K added but also on the time when K is added, in relation to the addition of NH_4. The magnitude of the depressive effect of K on the fixation of NH_4 has been shown to be different, depending on whether K is added simultaneously, prior to or after the addition of NH_4. In accordance with the discussion above, the addition of K prior to the addition of NH_4 will depress the fixation of the NH_4. An addition of K after the addition of NH_4 will, on the other hand, not appreciably influence the amount of NH_4 fixed. Results obtained by Jansson (1958) may illustrate this (Table 3).

Table 3. Influence of the time of K addition, in relation to the addition of NH_4, on the fixation of NH_4 (Jansson, 1958).

Addition, me./100 g soil	% of added NH_4 fixed
0.714 me. NH_4	42.7
0.714 me. NH_4 + 0.714 me. K (simultaneously)	50.0
0.714 me. NH_4 + 0.714 me. K (added 2 h after the addition of NH_4)	50.4
0.714 me. K + 0.714 me. NH_4 (K added 2 h before the addition of NH_4)	28.3

When NH_4 and K are added simultaneously, various results can be obtained, depending, *inter alia*, on the type of fixing mineral, the concentration level and the ratio between NH_4 and K. Joffe and Levine (1947) found that when equivalent amounts of K and NH_4 were added simultaneously to a H-saturated montmorillonite it fixed more K than NH_4 at lower concentrations, the relation being reversed at higher concentrations.

The above question has been investigated more thoroughly by Nõmmik (1957), who studied the effect of increasing amounts of simultaneously added K on the fixation of NH_4 in a vermiculitic clay. He found that, when equivalent amounts of NH_4 and K (1 me./100 g soil) were simultaneously added, the soil fixed them in the proportion of 3.4:1. Thus, considerably more NH_4 than K was fixed. One interesting and somewhat unexpected consequence of this preferential fixation of NH_4 was that at the concentration level in question the simultaneous addition of K led to a small but significant increase in the fixation of NH_4 (Fig. 4). More recently Nõmmik (unpub. data) demonstrated that the preferential fixation of NH_4 was not characteristic only of the rela-

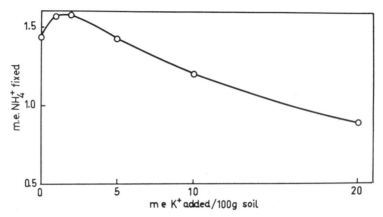

Fig. 4. Effect of simultaneously added K on the fixation of NH_4 in a vermiculite-containing heavy clay. 2 me. NH_4 and varying amounts of K added per 100 g soil in the form of mixed solutions (Nõmmik, 1957).

tively low concentration levels, but also of considerably larger additions of NH_4 and K (Table 4).

From numerous investigations it is evident that not only K, Rb, and Cs but also other cations which do not contract the crystal lattice may influence the capacity of the minerals to fix NH_4. This may very likely be explained by a competition between NH_4 and other cations for the

Table 4. Fixation of NH_4 and K in a vermiculite-containing clay, when added singly and when added simultaneously as mixed solutions (Nõmmik, unpub. data).

NH_4 resp. K added/100 g soil	NH_4 fixed, me.	K fixed, me.	$\dfrac{NH_4 \text{ fixed}}{K \text{ fixed}}$
1.0 me. NH_4	0.80		
1.0 me. K		0.69	
1.0 me. NH_4 + 1.0 me. K	0.89	0.30	3.0
2.5 me. NH_4	1.61		
2.5 me. K		1.37	
2.5 me. NH_4 + 2.5 me. K	1.60	0.49	3.3
10.0 me. NH_4	3.36		
10.0 me. K		3.13	
10.0 me. NH_4 + 10.0 me. K	2.78	0.98	2.8

exchange positions, influencing thereby the equilibrium between the exchangeable and fixed NH_4 (section II A). The addition of a cation of high replacing power will, according to this, lead to a decrease of the exchangeable NH_4 in the soil and consequently to a lower fixation of the added NH_4 or, alternatively, to a release of some of the already fixed NH_4. From this it is apparent that the greatest depressive effect on NH_4 fixation may be exerted by the di- and tri-valent cations and by the hydrogen ion. According to Nõmmik (1957), the depressive effect of

Table 5. Fixation of NH_4 by a residual soil from Japan saturated with different cations under moist conditions (Harada and Kutsuna, 1954).

Treatment*	NH_4 fixed	
	me.	% of added
Untreated	11.9	39.9
Na-saturated	11.2	37.4
K-saturated	0.7	2.3
Ca-saturated	12.2	40.7
Ba-saturated	9.7	32.3
Al-saturated	0.5	1.7
H-saturated	1.7	5.6

* 30 me. NH_4 added per 100 g soil

different cations increased in the following order: Na < Mg < Ca < Ba < La < H. Approximately the same trend was reported by Aomine and Wada (1953), Harada and Kutsuna (1954), and by Wiklander (1950) for fixation of K.

8. pH AND DEGREE OF BASE SATURATION

The significance of the degree of hydrogen saturation of soils and clay minerals on their capacity to fix NH_4 and K has been the subject of several investigations. Most of the available information originates from studies with K. Stanford (1948) investigated the fixation of K by Wyoming bentonite and illite under moist conditions and showed that bentonite did not fix K over the pH range of 4 to 10. For illite a slight constant rise in fixation was observed with increasing pH. When dried at $100°C$, even bentonite fixed K, the fixation being greatest at the lowest pH interval. Stanford considered that the effect of the addition of NaOH, $Ca(OH)_2$, and even of phosphate and fluoride, in increasing the moist fixation of K by illite, could be attributed to their ability to remove H, Fe, and Al ions from the interlayer positions. Wiklander and Andersson (1959) analyzed the soil from a liming experiment 22 years after the application of lime and were able to demonstrate that the ability of the soil to fix NH_4 and K was measurably increased by liming (Table 6).

Table 6. Effect of liming on the capacity of the surface soil to fix NH_4 and K. The analyses of soil performed 22 years after the application of lime (Wiklander and Andersson, 1959).

Lime added, kg CaO/ha	pH_{H_2O}	NH_4 fixed, me.	K fixed, me.
0	6.0	1.28	1.31
3000	6.1	1.24	1.47
6000	6.4	1.45	1.60
12000	7.0	1.46	1.69

4 me. NH_4 and K, respectively, added per 100 g soil.

A statistical analysis of the fixation figures of more than 200 surface soils from Sweden showed, according to Nõmmik (1957), that there was a tendency for NH_4 fixation to increase with increasing pH of the soils.

The soils with a pH value lower than 5.5 showed, in general, low fixation values. A weak positive correlation between the pH and the soil capacity to fix NH_4 was found also by Kaila (1962). This is in accordance with the observations that in the H-saturated soils the fixation capacity is as a rule insignificant (Barshad, 1954; Ghildyal and Singh, 1961; Harada and Kutsuna, 1954; Hauser, 1941; Karlsson, 1952; Nõmmik, 1957; Wiklander, 1950). The relationship between the soil acidity and the NH_4-fixing capacity is, nevertheless, not very pronounced. This is shown by the fact that the majority of Scandinavian clay soils which contain free $CaCO_3$ are classified as low-fixing. In the Swedish surface soils the highest fixation figures (4-6 me.NH_4 per 100 g) are, in fact, found in the pH class 6.0-6.5 (Nõmmik, 1957).

Karlsson (1952) and Nõmmik (1957) demonstrated that a long-term extraction and leaching of H-treated soils with calcium acetate resulted in a partial restoration of their original capacity to fix K and NH_4.

The extraordinarily marked effect of the low pH and of H treatment on the fixability of NH_4 and K is not fully understood. The high relative replacing power of the H ions is presumably one of the factors of importance, influencing the state of equilibrium between $(NH_4)_e$ and $(NH_4)_f$. Barshad (1954) considered, however, that the decrease of NH_4 fixation in the presence of exchangeable H^+ may be due to the somewhat expanded state in which the adsorbed H^+ leaves the crystal lattice and which therefore renders the interlattice NH_4 more accessible to a replacing cation.

The most plausible explanation of this phenomenon is given by recent investigations, according to which the incapacity of the crystal lattice of expanded 2:1 layer minerals to contract on K treatment is related to occurrence of non-exchangeable Al in the interlayer space (Rich, 1960; Rich and Obenshain, 1955; Rich and Thomas, 1960; Sawhney, 1960; Scheffer et al., 1961). Rich and Obenshain (1955) and Rich (1960) thus showed that a partial filling of the interlayer space of vermiculite and montmorillonite with hydroxy-Al groups reduced the collapsibility of the lattice and as a result of this, the fixation of NH_4 by these minerals. The aluminum interlayers in vermiculite and montmorillonite, when produced experimentally, were found to result in stable 14-Å spacing and to reduce the cation exchange capacity of the original minerals (1960). It seems likely that this "propping" action of the hydroxy-Al groups offers a conceivable explanation of the low NH_4-fixing capacity of H-treated soils and of soils "weathered" in acid milieu, containing 2:1 type clay minerals (Scheffer et al., 1961).

9. EFFECT OF DIFFERENT ANIONS

The nature of the anion associated with NH_4 has been found to influence the capacity for NH_4 fixation. This may be ascribed, *inter alia,* to the effect of the anion on the pH of the soil. The effect of the anion on the adsorption capacity of the associated cation is possibly also to be considered. From the Paneth-Fajans-Hahn rule it is to be expected that an anion which is strongly adsorbed by the soil may increase the adsorption of the cation. In this respect the effect of phosphate ions has been given the greatest attention. Thus, Joffe and Kolodny (1937) reported that a soil which had been treated for 20 years with phosphate fertilizers fixed more K than the corresponding untreated soil. Leggett (1958) also showed that in a number of different NH_4 salts tested the highest fixation was obtained with diammonium phosphate.

As it has been found that the fixation may be blocked by prior treatment of the soil with Fe or Al (McBeth, 1917; Reitemeier, 1951; Rich, 1960; Stanford, 1948) and since compounds of these cations with phosphate are characterized by extremely low solubility, the fixation capacity may be increased by removal of these cations by precipitation as phosphates. Malquori and Radaelli (1960) suggested, on the other hand, that fixed NH_4 in soil may be released in the zone of high phosphate concentration occurring in the immediate surroundings of the granules of soluble phosphate fertilizers.

It may be noted that Harada and Kutsuna (1954) found that the NH_4 fixation was the same, independent of whether NH_4 was added as sulphate or as chloride. The fixation was, however, somewhat lower when it was added in the form of dihydrophosphate (cf. Stojanovic, 1960).

D. Influence of Fixation of Ammonium on the Cation-Exchange Capacity of the Fixing Material

It has been observed that in some soils the sum of different bases replaceable with NH_4 may exceed the cation exchange capacity of the same soil, determined according to the conventional NH_4-saturation procedure (Bower, 1950; Kelley and Brown, 1924, 1927; McGeorge, 1945). This discrepancy was particularly marked in many semihumid soils, which did not contain either soluble salts or $CaCO_3$. An acceptable explanation of this phenomenon was given by Bower (1950), who demonstrated that in some saline and alkaline California soils the observed excess of exchangeable Na over the amounts of NH_4 maximally sorbed by the soils depended on the inability of the other cations to replace all of the NH_4 present in exchange positions. In a subsoil sample Bower found that its content of exchangeable Na was more than 30% greater than its cation exchange capacity, determined by the conventional, neutral, N ammonium-acetate procedure.

For Dutch soils, characterized by a high K-fixing capacity, Marel (1954) found that the ratio between the total exchangeable cations and the cation exchange capacity (according to the NH_4-saturation procedure) in some cases was as high as 1.30. The same author also noticed that there was a definite correlation between the above ratio and the capacity of the soil to fix K.

Barshad (1951) showed that a pretreatment of the soils with NH_4 depressed their Ba^{2+}-exchange capacity (Table 7). Several other workers have reported that the fixation of K by a soil is accompanied by a decrease in its cation exchange capacity (Allison et al., 1953; Buehrer et al.,

Table 7. Ba-exchange capacity of natural soils and of soils pretreated with NH_4 (Barshad, 1951).

Soil	Ba-exchange capacity of natural soil, me. /100 g	Ba-exchange capacity of soils pretreated with NH_4, me. /100 g
Sheridan 0-6 in.	32. 2	27. 8
Sheridan 18-24 in.	25. 9	18. 0
Cayneos 0. 6 in.	24. 0	20. 2

1949; Joffe and Kolodny, 1939; Joffe and Levine; 1939; Karlsson, 1952; Peterson and Jennings, 1938; Troug and Jones, 1938; Wear and White, 1951).

E. Release of Fixed Ammonium from Soils and Minerals by Different Extraction and Distillation Procedures

As previously noted, considerable evidence has been accumulated, which indicates that there exists some form of dynamic equilibrium between the fixed and exchangeable NH_4. According to this, NH_4 fixation occurs when the concentration of exchangeable NH_4 exceeds the equilibrium value for the soil in question and, vice versa, the fixed NH_4 is released when the exchangeable NH_4 drops below this equilibrium value. Theoretically, therefore, all of the fixed NH_4 might be gradually liberated from the soils and clay minerals if the NH_4 released is continuously removed from the system and if no other influencing ions or materials are present. It was shown, furthermore, that the different cations may differ as regards their ability to replace and thus release the fixed NH_4 from interlattice positions. This was ascribed to differences in the effectiveness of the cations to expand the collapsed mineral lattice and thus make a cation exchange possible. It was demonstrated that cations which are not fixed under the same conditions as NH_4 (e.g., Na, Mg, Ca) are capable of releasing fixed NH_4, whereas the others are not (e.g., K, Rb, Cs).

With regard to the effect of the type of clay minerals on the readiness of release of fixed NH_4 the information is extremely meager and inconsistent. As concerns the K, it has been reported, *inter alia,* by Mortland et al. (1957) that fixed K is released comparatively easily from montmorillonites and vermiculites, but not from illites. This is in variance with the findings of Marel (1959), according to which the interlattice K was held only weakly by the illite, being thus readily available to crops.

The following section of this chapter deals with the effectiveness of different cations, and different extraction and distillation procedures in releasing fixed NH_4. Special attention has been given to the effect of K on this replacement reaction.

1. RELEASE BY LEACHING WITH DIFFERENT SALT AND ACID SOLUTIONS

In determining the NH_4 fixation of soils by the total-N procedure, Allison et al. (1953b, 1955) found that the results might differ a great deal, depending on whether the exchangeable NH_4 was removed by leaching with N KCl or $CaCl_2$ solution. Leaching with KCl resulted in consistently higher fixation values than leaching with $CaCl_2$. On considering the effectiveness of the two cations in expanding the NH_4-saturated lattice of the minerals, the authors suggested that $CaCl_2$, unlike KCl, will remove not only the soluble and exchangeable fractions of the soil NH_4 but also significant amounts of the fixed NH_4 (Table 8.)

Table 8. Comparison of N KCl and N $CaCl_2$ as extractants for removing exchangeable NH_4 in determining the NH_4-fixing capacity of the soil (Allison et al., 1953).

Soil	NH₄ fixation capacity, me./100 g			
	Moist		Air-dried	
	KCl	CaCl₂	KCl	CaCl₂
Miami silt loam, 9-13 in.	1.7	1.1	2.6	2.0
Clarence silt loam, 15-23 in.	1.8	1.3	2.8	1.9
Harpster clay loam, 14-20 in.	1.5	1.1	2.3	1.5
Yolo silt loam, 10-21 in.	1.1	0.4	1.4	0.3
Traver fine sandy loam, 24-60 in.	3.4	3.1	3.6	3.4
Pachappa fine sandy loam, 27-33 in.	3.5	2.5	3.7	2.5
Mountain soil, Colorado, 39-54 in.	3.6	2.8	4.0	3.3

As regards K, Barashad (1954a) demonstrated that fixed as well as native K in different mica minerals was replaced much more easily by leaching with neutral Mg than with NH_4 salt solutions.

The release of NH_4 from NH_4-saturated Montana vermiculite and Wyoming bentonite by treating the samples with NaCl solutions was studied by Hanway et al. (1957). The experimental procedure involved boiling the minerals with NaCl solutions of different concentrations and different volumes, and afterwards determining the amount of NH_4 present in the equilibrium solution. They found that the amount of NH_4 extracted from the vermiculite increased as the amount of NaCl in the extraction solution, calculated per gram of vermiculite, was increased. At the highest NaCl mineral ratio not less than 98% of the fixed NH_4 was replaced by treatment with the boiling NaCl solution (Table 9).

Table 9. NH_4 extracted from NH_4-saturated Montana vermiculite by boiling for 1 hour in NaCl solutions (Hanway et al., 1957).

Vermiculite, g	Normality of NaCl	Volume of NaCl solution, ml	NH₄ extracted, me./100 g
1	0.1	100	14.4
1	1	100	49.0
1	1	200	60.8
1	2	100	61.1
1	5	100	73.0
1	5	250	80.5

The same authors found, furthermore, that the addition of only small amounts of K exerted a blocking effect on the release of fixed NH_4. At a sufficiently high concentration of K the release of NH_4 was entirely blocked. At intermediate K concentrations the replacement of fixed NH_4 proceeded until the sum of the two fixable cations, i.e., of NH_4 and K, reached a sufficiently high level to form a new equilibrium with the fixed

NH_4 ions and to stop a further release of the NH_4. The K level, at which a certain reduction of NH_4 release was attained was to a large extent dependent on the K:Na ratio. At the same K level the amount of fixed NH_4 released increased as the K:Na ratio decreased. A similar blocking effect has been reported for exchangeable NH_4 ions, when accumulated in the soil-water system during equilibration of NH_4-saturated soils in various volumes and concentrations of NaCl solutions (Leggett and Moodie, 1963).

According to Scott et al. (1958), more fixed NH_4 was removed from vermiculite when the pH of the extracting solution either increased or decreased from the neutral point. When the accumulation of released NH_4 in the extracting solution was prevented by using alkaline solutions or the successive extraction technique, more fixed NH_4 was released than by a single equilibrium extraction.

The interfering effect of K on the release of fixed NH_4 from soils by leaching with different neutral salt solutions has also been studied by Nõmmik (1957) and Jansson (1958). By using the N^{15} technique, these authors were able to confirm the results presented above, though it appeared that for soils a prolonged leaching was not as effective as for the clay minerals in replacing fixed NH_4. They showed, additionally, that when K was present in the system, a reduction in the concentration of exchangeable NH_4 alone, leaving the concentration of K unaltered, was not sufficient to make a release of the fixed NH_4 possible.

It is interesting to note in this connection that the blocking effect of K on the release of fixed NH_4 seems to be of a mutual character. Nõmmik (1957) thus demonstrated that the release of fixed and native K from soils by leaching with neutral salt solutions was markedly inhibited by the presence of NH_4 ions in the extraction solution. Barshad (1954a) and Peech (1948) had earlier shown that NH_4 was the least effective cation in replacing the native K from soils and minerals.

2. RELEASE BY ALKALINE DISTILLATION PROCEDURE

The alkaline distillation procedure is unquestionably a more effective method of releasing the fixed NH_4 from soils than is the leaching procedure. This is due to the fact, as pointed out previously, that by distillation the NH_4 released from the internal surfaces is continuously removed from the system, leaving the exchangeable NH_4 at a low level. In investigating the replacing effect of different diluted hydroxide solutions, Barshad (1954) found that, with the exception of KOH, this effect was of approximately the same magnitude for all the hydroxides tested. The relative order of effectiveness was, however, Ba >Li, Na >Mg, Ca. The low solubility of several of the hydroxides mentioned limits their applicability for analytical purposes.

As previously noted, Barshad (1951) has proposed a method for the determination of fixed NH_4 by means of a duplicate distillation procedure (see section II B4). In this procedure the separate samples of the soil or clay mineral are distilled with KOH and NaOH, respectively. The difference in the amounts of NH_4 released will show the amount of fixed NH_4 present in the sample. The method presumes that the KOH distillation removes only the water-soluble and exchangeable NH_4, whereas the NaOH distillation releases also the fixed, interlayer NH_4. Barshad has not given sufficient information concerning the limitations and the applicability of the procedure. The method has been tested, however, by several other workers. In comparing it with the KCl-extraction procedure, Allison and Roller (1955a) found that the alkaline distillation method gave too low results on heated, NH_4-treated soils, and too high results on moist soils. The low results on heated soils were ascribed by these authors to the failure of NaOH to remove all of the fixed NH_4 present and the high results on the moist soils to fixation of some of the readily exchangeable NH_4 during the KOH distillation. Allison and Roller (1955 a, b), therefore, considered the distillation procedure unsatisfactory when determining fixed NH_4 at levels below fixation capacity and when large amounts of exchangeable NH_4 are simultaneously present in the system. The distillation procedure was also found to be unsatisfactory on soils which had been extracted previously with the chlorides of K, Ca, Mg, Na, and H.

Contrary to Allison et al., Hanway and Scott (1956) demonstrated that the duplicate distillation procedure was as satisfactory as the KCl-leaching procedure (total-N procedure), both methods giving nearly the same results (Nõmmik, 1957). These authors showed, however, that the presence of fairly small amounts of K interfered with the replacement of fixed NH_4 in soils by NaOH distillation. This question was later studied extensively by Hanway et al. (1957) and Leggett (1958). According to these authors, the release of fixed NH_4 on NaOH distillation was decreased by increasing the K/Na ratio in the system. The K/Na ratio required to bring about a certain reduction of the NH_4 release was shown to be different in different minerals and soils. According to Leggett (1958), approximately ten times as great a K/Na ratio was required for vermiculite as for the soils to produce the same percentage effect.

Hanway and Scott (1956) found that small amounts of nonexchangeable K were released from the soils during NaOH distillation. According to them, these amounts of K were not, however, high enough to interfere with the replacement of fixed NH_4 by Na in determining the fixation capacity of the soil, as in this case the exchangeable K of the soil was removed by leaching with NH_4 salts. In determining the content of naturally occurring fixed NH_4 in soils, the water-soluble and exchangeable K are, on the other hand, not removed from the sample, being present during the NaOH distillation. Until adequate methods have been developed to overcome this blocking effect of K, the alkaline distillation procedure could not, according to the above authors, be recommended for determining native fixed NH_4 in soils.

Studying the release of fixed NH_4 by alkaline distillation and aeration procedures, respectively, Leggett and Moodie (1963) showed that when no K was added to NH_4-saturated, air-dried soils, 86 to 98% of the fixed NH_4 were recovered. When small amounts of K were added, the release was markedly decreased. At a K/Na ratio of 0.005 only 14 to 35% of the fixed NH_4 was released. It may be mentioned that Nõmmik (unpublished data), testing the effectiveness of different methods of recovering fixed

NH$_4$ from a N^{15}H$_4$-saturated vermiculitic clay, found that the blocking effect of K could be considerably reduced by the addition of large quantities of solid NaCl to the distilling solutions (in both NaOH and KOH treatments) (Fig. 5).

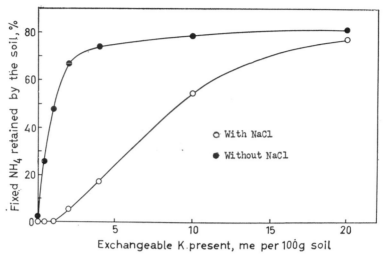

Fig. 5. The percentage of fixed N^{15}H$_4$ retained by a vermiculite-containing clay after treatment with boiling 0.5 N NaOH solution as affected by different levels of exchangeable K and by addition of NaCl (10 gramequi. per 100 g soil). The fixed NH$_4$ refers to NH$_4$ not liberated as ammonia by distillation with 0.5 N KOH (The soil-hydroxide solution ratio 1:60). The soil content of fixed NH$_4$ 4.2 me. per 100 g. The exchangeable NH$_4$ of the soil removed by leaching with 1 N CaCl$_2$ (Nõmmik, unpublished results).

Using the aeration procedure to remove the exchangeable NH$_4$, Leggett and Moodie (1963) found a linear relationship between the time of aeration and the logarithm of the rate of NH$_4$ release, indicating that the release of fixed NH$_4$ by Na is an apparent first-order reaction. As a diffusion-controlled process (Mortland and Ellis, 1959; Scott and Reed, 1962), the release of fixed NH$_4$ is expected to be affected by factors such as the concentration gradient across the diffusion path, concentration of replacing cations, size of particles and temperature (Leggett and Moodie, 1963).

3. RELEASE BY TREATMENT WITH CATION-EXCHANGE RESINS

If a clay mineral of a soil containing fixed NH$_4$ is placed in contact with a cation-exchange resin, this may result in a decrease of the water-soluble NH$_4$ fraction as well as the NH$_4$ adsorbed on the external surfaces of the soil particles. This displacement of the equilibrium would reasonably lead to a release of some of the fixed NH$_4$. A procedure based on the above principle is frequently used for determining the K-supplying power of the soils. As regards the effect of cation-exchange resin on the release of fixed NH$_4$, the question has been studied by Scott et al. (1960). In this case the NH$_4$-saturated vermiculite, bentonite, and illite were equilibrated at room temperature by shaking the samples for periods of 2 to 8 days with both cation-exchange resin (Amberlite IR-120) and with Na and K chloride solutions. The mineral-resin ratio was 1:20. The water-soluble and exchangeable NH_4 were determined in the KCl extract. They found that, as regards the vermiculite, both the H- and Na-saturated resins, and to a lesser extent the NaCl equilibrium extraction, were effective in releasing fixed NH_4 (Table 10). As expected, the K resin was

Table 10. Amounts of NH_4 removed from NH_4-saturated clay minerals by various treatments, me. per 100 g (Scott et al., 1960).

Treatment	Ammonium vermiculite	Ammonium bentonite	Ammonium illite
Kjeldahl digestion	81.4	50.4	25.3
Hydrogen resin*	80.5	36.7	23.9
Sodium resin*	80.5	36.3	23.2
Sodium chloride, 1N	66.5	33.0	22.4
Potassium resin*	10.7	9.0	22.7
Potassium chloride, 1N	8.1	5.7	22.1
Potassium hydroxide distillation	2.8	24.6	22.6

* Mineral: resin ratio 1:20. Mineral: salt solution ratio varied between 1:40 and 1:100. The NH_4 not liberated as ammonia by distillation with KOH was considered as fixed.

ineffective in this respect. The effectiveness of the resin treatment in the release of fixed NH_4 was considerably higher for vermiculite than for illite and bentonite.

Nõmmik (unpub. data), working with a heavy clay soil containing 4.91 me. fixed $N^{15}H_4$ (the main part of the exchangeable $N^{15}H_4$ was removed by leaching with $CaCl_2$), was able to demonstrate that the cation-exchange resin (Amberlite IR-120), when mixed with the soil in the proportion of 10:1 and with a contact period of 4 days, released 9.2 and 38.1% of the fixed NH_4 on treatment with Na and H resins, respectively.

4. RELEASE BY TREATMENT WITH SODIUM TETRAPHENYLBORON

Analogously to the effect of treatment with cation-exchange resins, an addition of a reagent which will reduce the concentration of exchangeable K and NH_4 by precipitation may very likely lead to a release of some of these cations from fixed positions. Recently, sodium tetraphenylboron ($NaBPh_4$) has been suggested as a precipitant for K and NH_4 (Gloss, 1953). Scott et al. (1960b) used this precipitant for investigating the ease with which the non-exchangeable K was released on soils and clay minerals. They found that essentially all of the K in vermiculite, 12% of the K in muscovite, and as much as 47% of the K in illite was extracted by the $NaBPh_4$ solution, even though most of the K in these materials was otherwise non-exchangeable with Na and NH_4. It was concluded that the $NaBPh_4$ reduced the blocking effect of accumulated exchangeable K by precipitation. According to Scott and Reed (1962), the $NaBPh_4$ treatment of a sample of Grundite-illite resulted in an increase of its capacity to fix NH_4 by ca. 35 me. per 100 g.

In experimenting with a strongly fixing Washington soil and a special alkaline aeration procedure, Leggett (1958) demonstrated that the addition of NaBPh$_4$ interfered with the removal of NH$_4$ from the alkaline soil-water suspension. The more NaBPh$_4$ was added, the less was the recovery of NH$_4$. It was found, furthermore, that the use of NaBPh$_4$ could not facilitate the removal of fixed NH$_4$ from soils with the special technique used by the author.

F. Availability of Fixed Ammonium to the Soil Microflora

According to the preceding information, NH$_4$ fixation is a rather common reaction in arable soils. Although interesting in itself, the fixability of NH$_4$ may not have any practical importance in the N economy of our arable soils if it does not interfere with the biological availability of the NH$_4$ form of N. On the basis of information on the release of fixed NH$_4$ by different procedures of leaching and distillation, the possibility is not excluded that the activity of microbes and higher plants, which involves consumption of the exchangeable NH$_4$ in the soil, may exert an influence on the extent and rate of release of fixed NH$_4$ in soils. A large number of investigations have aimed at elucidating this agronomically important question.

In an uncropped soil mainly two microbial processes are responsible for the consumption and removal of the NH$_4$ form of N: (1) nitrification and (2) immobilization. As these processes are of fundamentally different natures, their relationships to the release of fixed NH$_4$ will be treated separately.

1. AVAILABILITY OF FIXED AMMONIUM TO NITRIFIERS

As has been pointed out previously, fixation and defixation are to be considered as two opposed reactions in an equilibrium system. Thus the fixed NH$_4$ will be released from the soil when the concentration of the exchangeable and water-soluble NH$_4$ falls below a certain value characteristic of the system. From these considerations it seems likely that the nitrification process, which involves a consumption of the exchangeable and water-soluble NH$_4$ in the soil may bring about a release of NH$_4$ from fixed positions. Several investigators have shown that this is the case.

The first research workers to study thoroughly the question of the availability of fixed NH$_4$ to nitrifying organisms were Bower (1951) and Allison and co-workers (Allison et al., 1951, 1953a, b. c; Allison and Roller, 1955b). For his investigations Bower used two subsoils saturated with NH$_4$, and the exchangeable portion of the NH$_4$ was removed by leaching with a mixed CaCl$_2$-MgCl$_2$ solution. The NH$_4$-fixation capacity of the two soils was estimated to be 3.5 and 4.0 me. NH$_4$ per 100 g respectively. The incubation test revealed that after a nitrification period of 14 days only 13 to 28% of the difficultly exchangeable (fixed) NH$_4$ was nitrified. Prolonged incubation did not result in any further release of fixed NH$_4$. Of the readily exchangeable NH$_4$ (added to the soil after saturating it with K) 78 to 87% was nitrified in the same time interval. The fixed NH$_4$ thus showed a considerably lower availability to nitrifiers than the exchangeable NH$_4$.

The results of other workers are in good agreement with those of Bower. Allison and co-workers have treated this question in several publications and have shown that in most of the soils tested not more than 10% of the fixed NH_4 was nitrified during the incubation. In examining soils of different mineralogical compositions, the same workers found that the availability of fixed NH_4 was lowest in vermiculite-containing soils and highest in those containing montmorillonite as the fixing mineral (Allison et al., 1953a). They studied also the effect on the availability of residual fixed NH_4 of leaching the soils with KCl and $CaCl_2$ to remove excess amounts of NH_4. It was concluded that the treatment with $CaCl_2$ not only left less NH_4 in the crystal lattice of clay minerals, but also that the NH_4 left seemed to be more available to nitrifiers than after a pretreatment with KCl. The leaching of soils with KCl to remove the exchangeable NH_4, a technique used by some workers (Smirnov and Fruktova, 1963), thus exerts a blocking effect on the availability of the fixed NH_4 to nitrifying organisms.

Low availability of added NH_4 to nitrifiers in highly fixing Swedish soils has been reported also by Nõmmik (1957) and Jansson (1958) (see Fig. 6). According to Nõmmik, the percentage availability of fixed NH_4

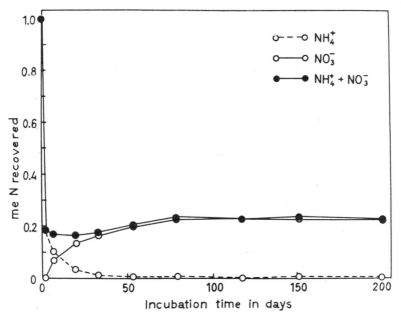

Fig. 6. Availability of ammonium nitrogen to nitrifying organisms in a highly fixing heavy clay. 1.0 me. NH_4 added per 100 g of soil (Nõmmik, 1957).

was dependent, among other things, on the degree to which the total fixing capacity of the soil was saturated by NH_4. The availability showed a tendency to increase with increasing NH_4 saturation of the soil.

In geological specimens of vermiculite the fixed NH_4 has been shown to be nearly as available to nitrifying organisms as the NH_4 of neutral

NH$_4$ salts (Allison et al., 1953c; Welch and Scott, 1960). According to Allison et al. (1953c), the different types of vermiculite appeared, however, to behave rather differently in this respect. In a South African vermiculite the availability to nitrifiers was thus only 11 to 16%.

Axley and Legg (1960) have investigated the availability of added NH$_4$ nitrogen to nitrifiers in soils with different NH$_4$-fixing capacity (both surface soils and subsoils). They concluded that the percentage of the added NH$_4$ nitrified during the incubation showed an unmistakable tendency to decrease with increasing NH$_4$-fixing capacity of the soil. In highly fixing soils only 10-15% of the added NH$_4$ was recovered as nitrate nitrogen after an incubation period of 50 days (Table 11). Similar results

Table 11. Nitrification of ammonium added to soils with varying fixation capacities (Axley and Legg, 1960).

Soil	NH$_4$-fixing capacity, me./100 g	% of added NH$_4$ nitrified*
Meyersville A	1.18	46.0
Meyersville B$_2$	7.07	13.5
Meyersville C	8.93	9.6
Chester B$_2$	0.58	57.1
Sassafras B$_2$	0.57	41.8
Hagerstown surface soil	0.70	94.4

* Added at the rate of 100 ppm N.

were obtained by Aomine and Higashi (1953b), who studied the nitrification of added NH$_4$ in Japanese soils having various fixing capacities. Thus in a nonfixing soil practically 100% of the added NH$_4$ was converted to NO$_3$ during an incubation of 4 weeks, whereas in fixing soils the amounts of nitrified N after incubation for 11 weeks were only about 40 to 75% (cf. Wanstallen, 1960). Investigating an ammonium-fixing Belgian soil, Baert-de Bièvre et al. (1961) made the observation that only NH$_4$ extractable with KCl and NaCl was susceptible to nitrification.

The low availability of fixed NH$_4$ to nitrifiers, reported by several workers, may be considered as unexpected and not fully consistent with the theory of the reversibility of the fixation-defixation reaction. If the ammonium were the only fixable ion in the system, the above results would be rather anomalous. In a soil system the situation is also more complicated, owing primarily to the presence of K, which has been shown to interfere with the release of fixed NH$_4$. The interfering effect of K is evidenced by the fact that in K-free clay minerals, such as vermiculite and montmorillonite the fixed NH$_4$ has appeared to be nearly as available to nitrifiers as the exchangeable NH$_4$. The mechanism of this interference is at present not fully understood. It might be considered possible that the removal of exchangeable NH$_4$ by nitrification results not only in a release of fixed NH$_4$ but also in a simultaneous liberation of small amounts of the lattice-bound K. If this really is the case, the content of exchangeable K will gradually increase in the soil during the course of nitrification. As a consequence of this the defixation of NH$_4$ may not be complete but may cease at a stage where the concentration of exchangeable K is high enough to balance both the lattice-bound K and the NH$_4$ at a new equilibrium level. On analyzing the control and the NH$_4$-treated soils after an incubation period of 6 months, Nõmmik (1957) found that the content of exchangeable K was indeed somewhat higher in the NH_4-treated soils than in the control soils. The difference was, however, rather small and it was considered unlikely that this accumulation of K alone could explain the low release of fixed NH_4 in the nitrification process (cf. Welch and Scott, 1960).

As another conceivable explanation for the incomplete release of fixed NH_4 during nitrification, there is the possibility that the availability of fixed NH_4 to nitrifiers will gradually decrease as the incubation proceeds, possibly as a consequence of a migration of NH_4 from the outermost cavities to the interior of the mineral particles. No experimental evidence supporting this hypothesis is available, however. Observations made by the author in greenhouse experiments, which showed an extremely low residual effect of the fixed NH_4 not removed by the crop during the first vegetation period, seem to some extent to argue in favor of this supposition.

The effect of K on the availability of fixed NH_4 to nitrifying organisms has been studied in some detail under laboratory conditions by Welch and Scott (1960). The experiments were carried out in clay mineral-water suspensions, which were inoculated with a low-K culture of nitrifying organisms. The nitrifying system was aerated and mixed with a stream of water-saturated air. The results obtained in these investigations clearly demonstrate that K does interfere with the nitrification of fixed NH_4 in the clay minerals tested. When only small amounts of K were present in the system, a substantial part of the fixed NH_4 in vermiculite and montmorillonite was available for nitrification. As the level of exchangeable K was increased, the amount of fixed NH_4 nitrified was markedly decreased. In a nutrient solution, which did not contain any clay minerals, an addition of K did not affect the nitrification results obtained with $(NH_4)_2SO_4$ (Fig. 7). These findings of Welch and Scott thus indicate that most of the divergent results obtained as concerns the availability of fixed NH_4 to nitrifiers can be attributed to varying levels of exchangeable K in the soils and clay minerals used.

2. AVAILABILITY OF FIXED AMMONIUM TO HETEROTROPHIC SOIL MICROFLORA

For their growth and activity, nitrifying organisms evidently have an extremely low requirement for K in the nutrient medium (Welch and Scott, 1959). On this account it is supposed that the level of K in soil or other nutrient medium is not significantly altered during the process of nitrification. This is probably one of the explanations of the relatively low availability of fixed NH_4 to these organisms. On this point the heterotrophic microorganisms and higher plants differ considerably from the nitrifiers. They have, in comparison with nitrifiers, a high requirement also for the nutrient element K. It therefore appears likely that the two groups of organisms in question may behave differently as regards their ability to utilize fixed NH_4 from soils.

As concerns the heterotrophic soil microflora, their requirement for

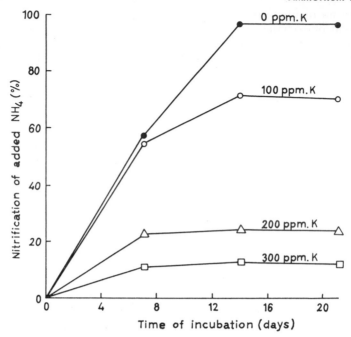

Fig. 7. Nitrification of NH_4 in air-dried, NH_4-saturated South Carolina High vermiculite as affected by added K. The experiments carried out in vermiculite-water suspensions inoculated with nitrifying organisms. Total NH_4 content of vermiculite $= 79.5$ me. per 100 g, 2.8 me. in exchangeable form (Welch and Scott, 1960).

assimilable N and also for K are highly dependent on the supply of available energy, i.e., readily oxidizable organic material. The higher the level of decomposable organic matter, the greater the amounts of available N and K taken up by the organisms. In a soil containing abundant amounts of available energy the exchangeable K and NH_4 are generally held at a low level, a condition favorable for the release of fixed NH_4 and K from clay minerals.

The simplest and perhaps the most convenient way of studying the availability of fixed NH_4 to mixed heterotrophic microflora is to incubate a moist soil with a high content of oxidizable organic matter at varying levels of N and to measure the CO_2 production. When other nutrient elements are present in optimum amounts, the supply of assimilable N will be the limiting factor for the activity of microbes. The addition of only small amounts of mineral N may in this case result in a marked increase in the CO_2 production. By comparing the effect of a known amount of fixed NH_4 with that of varying amounts of NO_3-N on CO_2 production, an approximate measure of the availability of fixed NH_4 may be obtained.

The experimental technique described above has been used by some investigators to study the availability of NH_4 to heterotrophic microflora in highly fixing soils. Using a vermiculite-containing, heavy clay soil, which under moist conditions fixed about 80-90% of the NH_4 added

(0.5 to 2.0 me.NH_4 per 100 g soil), and glucose as the source of energy, Nõmmik (1957) found that the fixed NH_4 was approximately two-thirds as effective a source of N for the microorganisms as NO_3. By adding K to the soil, in addition to NH_4 nitrogen (1 me. per 100 g soil), the ability of the microbes to utilize NH_4 was markedly reduced. It could be estimated that in the latter case only about 10% of the fixed NH_4 was available to the organisms. In combination with NO_3 no such inhibiting effect of K was obtained (Fig. 8).

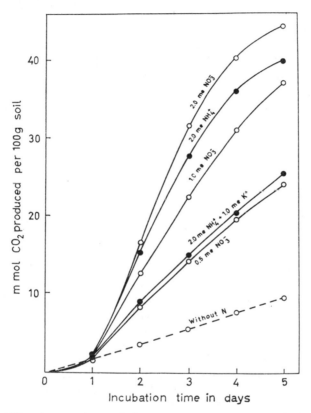

Fig. 8. Availability of ammonium and nitrate sources of nitrogen to mixed heterotrophic microflora on a highly fixing vermiculite-containing surface soil. 2 g of glucose added per 100 g soil as the source of energy (Nõmmik, 1957).

Using another highly fixing vermiculitic surface soil from Central Sweden and applying the same CO_2-measurement technique, Nõmmik (unpub. data) carried out some experiments on the availability of fixed NH_4 in different textural fractions of the soil. For this purpose the clay (particles less than 0.002 mm in diameter), silt (0.002-0.02 mm) and fine sand (0.02-0.2 mm) fractions of the above soil were saturated with NH_4 and the exchangeable NH_4 was afterwards removed by leaching with 0.5 N $CaCl_2$ solution. The different textural fractions, having different NH_4-fixing capacities, were then mixed with the untreated, unfractionated soil in such proportions that the final sample contained exactly 1 me. fixed NH_4 per 100 g. Glucose was used as a source of energy. The experimental results indicated that the availability of the fixed NH_4 to the heterotrophic organisms decreased with increasing particle size of the NH_4-bearing material. In comparison with nitrate, the availability of fixed NH_4 in clay, silt, and fine sand fractions was 89, 70, and 50% respectively.

Similar availability tests, using ground cereal straw instead of glucose as the source of energy, have been extensively carried out by Jansson (1958). He reported that the fixation markedly reduced the ability of the heterotrophic microflora to utilize the added NH_4 nitrogen. According to his investigations, the heterotrophic microflora of the soil appeared to be a rather weak and ineffective extractant of fixed NH_4, being in some cases equivalent to, and in other cases even weaker than a N KCl solution. As a general conclusion from these experiments, Jansson stated that extraction with N KCl gives a fairly good estimate of the amounts of NH_4-N available to heterotrophic microflora in the soil. He found also that in some cases nitrifiers seemed to be more effective utilizers of NH_4-N than heterotrophic organisms.

On hasty consideration, Jansson's results may seem to conflict with those of this reviewer. This is, however, not the case. The low availability of NH_4 in fixing soils reported by Jansson is fully understandable when we bear in mind that in these studies the organic material was added in the form of cereal straw. In comparison with the glucose used by Nõmmik, straw is considerably less readily decomposable by the microorganisms and, what is more important, the straw used by Jansson contained ca. 1.0% K. An application of 2.5 g straw per 100 g soil will thus involve a simultaneous addition of 0.64 me.K. With the knowledge of the blocking effect of K on the release of fixed NH_4 the above results are fully explainable and in accord with the previous observations. Control experiments carried out by Jansson with K-free straw indicated that the above interpretation was correct.

G. Availability of Fixed Ammonium to Field Crops

From the previous discussion it is evident that the question of NH_4 fixation has been subjected to intensive study in both soil chemistry and mineralogy. Considerable information has thus been accumulated on the nature of the fixation reaction and on the conditions of release of fixed NH_4 by cation exchange. On the practical consequences of the fixation process the literature is, however, rather sparse. Notwithstanding the fact that NH_4 fixation is relatively widespread and common reaction in many arable soils, our knowledge of its significance for the availability of added NH_4 nitrogen to field crops is extremely deficient. The information available is, moreover, rather inconsistent in several important points. It is likewise to a large extent based upon results obtained in pot experiments, and is therefore not directly applicable to field conditions.

The first attempt to elucidate this question seems to have been made by Bower (1951), who studied the availability of fixed and easily exchangeable NH_4 to barley seedlings by a modified Neubauer technic. Nitrate was used as a source of N for comparative purposes. The experiments showed that only small amounts of non-exchangeable NH_4 were recovered by the barley plants. In soils inoculated with nitrifying organisms, the recovery of fixed NH_4 amounted to 14 and 25% in two soils containing 3.5 and 4.0 me. fixed NH_4 per 100 g, respectively. These values agreed closely with the maximum nitrification obtained for the above soils in the incubation test. The findings led Bower to conclude that bacteria were more effective in removing fixed NH_4 from soils than higher plants.

Extremely low availability for fixed NH_4 has been reported also by Allison et al. (1953a). They demonstrated that millet, grown in the greenhouse, was capable of utilizing only 7% of the non-exchangeable NH_4 fixed by air-drying and 12% of that fixed by heating. These figures were only slightly higher than those obtained in nitrification tests, showing, according to the authors, that "under the experimental conditions nitrate formation is a rather accurate measure of availability" (for millet). In the related availability test the experimental soil was pretreated with N KCl to remove the exchangeable NH_4, which may, of course, have influenced the accessibility of the fixed NH_4 to the plants. The same objection may be made to the pot experiments carried out by Smirnov and Fruktova (1963), though in both cases the excess of K was subsequently removed from the soil by leaching with $CaCl_2$ or $MgCl_2$.

Aomine and Higashi (1953a) studied the availability of added NH_4-N to crops on soils with different capacities for fixing NH_4. They reported that in general rice and wheat plants were able to utilize more NH_4 from a soil which had a low fixing power than from the one with a high fixing power. It was found, however, that the fixed NH_4 was in part recovered by the crop, the degree of its accessibility being mainly dependent on the nature of the fixing material (cf. Peterburgskii and Korchagina, 1963).

In more recent greenhouse experiments considerably higher availability of fixed NH_4 to higher plants has been recorded. Using a highly fixing, vermiculite-containing, heavy clay, Nõmmik (1957) found that the growth response of oats to NH_4-N was only insignificantly ($<10\%$) lower than that of NO_3-N. The same was valid also for the total amount of N taken up by the crop. Since analysis of the soil 1 week after the start of the experiment indicated that only 10-20% of the added NH_4 nitrogen could be recovered as exchangeable NH_4 or NO_3, it was concluded that in this soil the oat plants were highly effective in utilizing the fixed NH_4 nitrogen. Analysis of the crop at an early stage of development (approximately 10 days before the beginning of earing) indicated, however, that there was a marked difference in the rate of uptake of N, when added either as NO_3 or as NH_4. Nitrogen added as $Ca(NO_3)_2$ was thus absorbed considerably more rapidly than N added in the form of $(NH_4)_2SO_4$. In the treatments with $(NH_4)_2SO_4$ the oat plants absorbed large amounts of N at later stages of development, whereas in the $Ca(NO_3)_2$-treated pots the uptake of N was almost completed before the beginning of earing. Evidently fixation may result in a delayed uptake of added NH_4 nitrogen.

In the same pot experiment the author also studied the effect of the addition of K on the uptake of fertilizer nitrogen. It could be demonstrated that the addition of fairly large doses of K_2SO_4 did not significantly influence the yield and uptake of N by oats, when the N was applied in the form of nitrate. When K was added in combination with $(NH_4)_2SO_4$ (in the same solution), the effect of NH_4-N was markedly decreased. It was shown that the degree of reduction of the N effect was greatly dependent on the rate of K addition (Table 12).

Table 12. Yield of oats and amount of N taken up per pot at different nitrogen and potassium applications on a highly NH_4-fixing surface soil from central Sweden (Nõmmik, 1957).

Treatment	Yield, g/pot		N taken up by crop	
	Grain	Straw	mg/pot	Increase over control
Untreated	9. 1	15. 0	161	
0. 2 g N as $Ca(NO_3)_2$*	16. 3	31. 3	308	+147
0. 4 g N as "	26. 3	36. 3	470	+309
0. 8 g N as "	33. 7	36. 1	748	+587
0. 2 g N as $(NH_4)_2SO_4$*	15. 2	31. 0	299	+138
0. 4 g N as "	26. 0	34. 3	476	+315
0. 8 g N as "	33. 1	32. 8	690	+529
0. 2 g N as $(NH_4)_2SO_4$ + 4g K_2SO_4*	6. 4	12. 4	121	- 40
0. 4 g N as " + "	8. 7	17. 0	157	- 7
0. 8 g N as " + "	14. 2	25. 7	232	+ 71
4 g K_2SO_4 + 0. 2 g N as $(NH_4)_2SO_4$†	15. 5	25. 6	256	+ 95
4 g K_2SO_4 + 0. 4 g N as "	22. 8	31. 6	390	+229
4 g K_2SO_4 + 0. 8 g N as "	33. 6	36. 1	658	+497
Least significant difference, 5% level	2. 8	3. 1		

* The fertilizers mixed into the soil immediately before the sowing.   † Potassium mixed into the soil immediately before the sowing and the ammonium nitrogen added 3 weeks after the sowing.

An interesting finding from the above experiment was that the negative effect of K was almost entirely eliminated when the K_2SO_4 was added three weeks before the addition of NH_4 salt. This is in accordance with the previous observations on the influence of the application time of K on the fixation and release of NH_4. About the same time Jansson (1961) and Jansson and Ericsson (1961) published results from their investigations on the effect of K on the response of different crops to NH_4 and NO_3 forms of N in a highly fixing subsoil from the province of Scania in Sweden. The results obtained are in good agreement with those of the present author.

It is of interest to note that, conversely, a blocking effect of NH_4 on the release of non-exchangeable K from the soil has been reported by Welch and Scott (1961). According to these authors, the uptake of non-exchangeable K by corn plants in short-term greenhouse experiments was inversely related to the amount of NH_4 salts added. This blocking effect of fertilizer NH_4 on the release of non-exchangeable soil K may possibly be of practical significance in soils with a low nitrification capacity.

The results obtained by the above Swedish workers have more recently been confirmed by investigations carried out in the U.S.A. Thus, Legg and Allison (1959), using soils of different horizons, showed that the uptake of added NH_4 nitrogen by sudangrass in two NH_4-fixing subsoils was of approximately the same order as that in a nonfixing surface soil. They found in addition that the uptake of N from $NaNO_3$ and banded $(NH_4)_2SO_4$ was higher than that from $(NH_4)_2SO_4$ uniformly mixed in the soil; the difference could not, however, be ascribed entirely to NH_4 fixation.

In studying the availability of NH_4 in Maryland soils of different NH_4-fixing capacities Axley and Legg (1960) reported that the plant uptake of N from $(NH_4)_2SO_4$ or urea was not greatly affected by the capacity of the soil to fix NH_4, unless sufficient K was present to block the release of fixed NH_4. Addition of K with $NaNO_3$ had little effect on yields or uptake of N. With an NH_4 source of N, however, a similar addition of K severely depressed the yields and the nitrogen uptake by oats from soils having appreciable fixing capacities. The authors therefore suggested that NH_4 should not be applied with K to soils of the latter type. The above recommendation is in harmony with the results of greenhouse studies by Walsh and Murdock (1963), according to which the recovery of N by a corn crop was measurably higher when K and NH_4 were applied in separate layers of soil, than when the nutrients were applied in the same layer.

The high availability of fixed NH_4 reported above was obtained with cereal crops. The possibility cannot be excluded that different plant species may behave differently in this respect. It is well known that the ability of different plant species to absorb monovalent cations from a nutrient solution varies considerably and, according to some workers, this is probably due to differences in the cation-exchange capacity of the plant roots. The roots of graminaceous plants generally show comparatively low values of cation exchange capacity, and they are therefore considered effective in absorbing monovalent cations from highly diluted nutrient solutions in the presence of a great excess of divalent cations (Drake et al., 1951; Elgabaly and Wiklander, 1949). Dicotyledons, the roots of which have a higher cation-exchange capacity, may, according to this view, be less effective in absorbing K and NH_4 from the minerals. Some observations made in greenhouse tests argue in favor of this assumption. Jansson (1958) thus found that an oat crop, grown after a mustard crop on a fixing soil, was able to take up significant amounts of the tagged fertilizer NH_4 not recovered by the first mustard crop. No such residual effect of the applied NH_4-N was recorded for an oat crop following another cereal crop. In a later report Jansson and Ericsson (1961) gave further support to the above findings. They demonstrated that oats were most effective in utilizing added NH_4 on a fixing soil and that mustard was least effective. Sugar beet and potatoes took an intermediate position in this respect. According to unpublished results obtained by the author, the NH_4 form of N was approximately 70% as effective as NO_3 for a rape crop on a highly fixing surface soil. For an oat crop, on the other hand, $(NH_4)_2SO_4$ was practically as good a source of N as $Ca(NO_3)_2$.

It is to be expected that the ability of plants to utilize non-exchangeable NH_4 will depend on such characteristics as the rate of growth, root habit, and K requirement. In this connection the findings by Evans and Attoe (1948) may be noted. Comparing the utilization of non-exchangeable K of six soils by oats and ladino clover respectively, they reported that the clover extracted more from the four soils with relatively high exchange levels, whereas oats removed more from the soils with low levels of exchangeable K. According to the authors, the difference was attributable to the ability of oats to grow well at low levels of available K.

The experimental results mentioned above indicate that in fixing soils under certain conditions, substantial amounts of added NH_4 nitrogen are not removed by the first crop. This may be particularly true of crops which are ineffective in utilizing fixed NH_4 and especially when large amounts of K fertilizer are simultaneously applied. The question arises whether this residual NH_4 is released by the succeeding crops and to what extent. Information on this point is unfortunately rather inadequate. In the previously cited investigations of Jansson and Ericsson (1961) the authors report, without giving any numerical data, that in pot experiments a marked residual effect was obtained in treatments in which NH_4 nitrogen had been combined with only a little dose of K. No such residual effect was recorded where a large dose of K was given to the first crop. In succeeding crops a positive residual N effect was also obtained, however, for treatments with a fairly heavy dressing of K. The release of fixed NH_4 occurred rather slowly, however, and even five successive crops were not sufficient to remove all of the fixed NH_4 left in the soil. These results clearly demonstrate that removal of the added K is an absolute condition for a complete release of fixed NH_4 to crops.

The information obtained in pot experiments on the availability of NH_4 nitrogen to crop plants in NH_4-fixing soils is certainly of considerable interest. It cannot, however, be used uncritically for drawing conclusions regarding the availability of fertilizer NH_4 under field conditions. The readiness with which the cereal plants have been found to utilize fixed NH_4 in pot experiments need not *a priori* be valid for crops grown under field conditions. The conditions for the two cultivation techniques are quite different and therefore do not justify direct comparison of the results. It should only be mentioned that in the field the density of plant roots per volume of soil is usually much lower than in pots, implying that a considerably smaller part of the exchangeable and even of the non-exchangeable K is removed by the activity of the plant roots during the vegetation period. This may certainly influence the rate on which the fixed NH_4 is released from the clay minerals. Furthermore, the extent of NH_4 fixation under field conditions may be considerably different from that induced under laboratory or greenhouse treatment conditions.

Available information on the relative effectiveness of NH_4 nitrogen on fixing soils under field conditions appears extremely defective. In Sweden, where the surface soils in several of the best agricultural districts show a rather high NH_4-fixing capacity, experimental work on this question has recently been started (Jansson, 1961; Nõmmik, 1961; Nõmmik, unpub. data). The results so far show that the response of spring cereals to the NH_4 form of N was rather different in the different years concerned. In 1960 the $Ca(NO_3)_2$, when applied in amounts of 31 kg N per hectare, was thus significantly superior to the corresponding amount of N added as $(NH_4)_2SO_4$, the effect of $(NH_4)_2SO_4$ being on the average only 63% of that of $Ca(NO_3)_2$. In 1961 and 1962, when the trials were carried out on similar NH_4-fixing soils in the same district, no such difference in effect between these two N sources could be recorded. The K when added in combination with N had no appreciable influence on the size of the yields, either in 1960 or in 1961-62. The exceedingly variable results obtained in the three years have not been satisfactorily explained. They may possibly be ascribed to differences in the amount and distribution of the precipitation during the spring and early summer. The drying conditions shortly after the application of N materials seem to exert an unfavorable influence on the uptake and recovery of the NH_4 form of N by the crop. Of interest in this respect is the finding by Jansson (1958), showing that the fixation in the air-dried soil was about 40% higher than in the same soil pre-incubated under moist conditions for 30 days. According to Schachtschabel (1961), the general experience in German agricultural practice is that the soil N is more available to the plants in wet than in dry summers. Schachtschabel suggests that this may be due to easier release of fixed NH_4 from the soil during a wet season. According to him, the moisture content influences the degree of expansion of the "degraded" illites and thus also the readiness with which the interlattice K and NH_4 can migrate from the interior of the crystal to the peripheral zones of the mineral particle.

In moderately fixing soils Jansson and Ericsson (1961) recorded only small and inconsistent differences in the effect of $(NH_4)_2SO_4$ and $Ca(NO_3)_2$ on spring wheat and sugar-beet, the tendency being for the NO_3 form of N to be superior. According to observations by Kaila and Hänninen (1961), the yield increase obtained by the application of ammonium nitrate limestone to NH_4-fixing Finnish soils was not significantly lower than that produced by an equal amount of N as $Ca(NO_3)_2$.

Summarizing the discussion above, it may be concluded that the question of the availability of fixed NH_4 to field crops and the significance of the fixing capacity of the soil on the relative effectiveness of NH_4-fertilizers is not yet sufficiently clear. Many more field studies are necessary to elucidate this complicated problem. It is evident, however, that neither the nitrification test nor the chemical laboratory test for determining the NH_4-fixing capacity of the soil provides a fully reliable measure of the availability and effectiveness of the applied NH_4-N to field crops. As the great majority of arable surface soils evidently fix much less NH_4 than many of the Scandinavian and Japanese soils described in this paper (cf. Allison et al., 1953b; Axley and Legg, 1960; Hanway and Scott, 1956; Kaila, 1962; Rich, 1960; Schuffelen and van der Marel, 1955; Smirnov and Fruktova, 1963; Walsh and Murdock, 1960), the fixation figures only exceptionally exceeding 1 me. per 100 g soil, the agronomic significance of fixation on the availability of fertilizer NH_4 nitrogen should not be overestimated. A high fixing capacity, frequently reported for subsoils, would not substantially influence the effectiveness of NH_4 applied with fertilizers. In this connection we may note that there are practical measures which make it possible to reduce the fixability of fertilizer NH_4. Here we need only mention the use of granulated materials and their band application.

Although fixation most likely involves a reduction in the availability of applied NH_4-N to crops, the phenomenon may possibly not be considered as entirely unfavorable from the agronomic point of view (Karlsson, 1952; van der Marel, 1954; Mela Mela, 1962; Nõmmik, 1957). Thus, fixation under certain soil and climatic conditions may be a factor of significance in preventing losses through leaching of excessive amounts of fertilizer N. It will, furthermore, ensure a more continuous supply of N throughout the growing season.

H. Occurrence of Native Fixed Ammonium in Soils and Minerals

The capacity of many arable soils to fix added NH_4 nitrogen makes it reasonable to suppose that the soils may contain some NH_4 in fixed form. The results of recent research work give evidence that this is actually the case. Thus Rodrigues (1954) found that in tropical soils a considerable portion of the total N is resistant to hydrogen peroxide oxidation, chromicsulphuric acid oxidation at $100°C$, and boiling 10% sulphuric acid treatment, but is readily released in the form of NH_4 by treatment of the soil with hydrofluoric acid. Rodrigues concluded that this NH_4-N was derived from NH_4 ions situated on the interplanar surface of certain clay minerals. According to him, no less than 14 to 78% of the total-N in the soils investigated occurred in the form of fixed NH_4. He concluded, furthermore, that the pronounced decrease in the C:N ratio with depth, observed in some of the soil profiles examined, could largely be explained by the presence of native fixed NH_4.

The findings of Rodrigues have given rise to several new research projects for the purpose of elucidating this interesting phenomenon. The most urgent and also the most difficult task of these studies has been to find a reliable method for the quantitative determination of the fixed NH_4 naturally occurring in the soils. Unlike the analytical procedures for the estimation of the NH_4-fixing capacity of the soil, the determination of the native fixed NH_4 is considerably more complicated and the reliability of the methods is difficult to check. The analytical procedure proposed by Rodrigues, involving a treatment of the soil with a 4:1 (v/v) mixture of 40% hydrofluoric acid and 50% sulphuric acid has been criticized by several workers as being too drastic a procedure (Bremner, 1959; Bremner and Harada, 1959; Dhariwal and Stevenson, 1958; Schachtschabel, 1960; Schachtschabel 1961). It is considered likely that treatment of the soil in this way may result in a release of not only the fixed NH_4 but also some of the organically bound N, which is then included in the analysis as fixed NH_4. It may be noted that acid-labile organic N compounds, such as amides (glutamine, asparagine) and hexosamines, are relatively readily deaminated by the acid treatment described. Asparagine and glutamine *per se* have not been positively identified in soils, but the presence of hexosamines has been definitely established (Bremner, 1949; Bremner and Shaw, 1954; Stevenson, 1957a, b).

The duplicate distillation procedure of Barshad (1951), proposed for the determination of the NH_4-fixing capacity of the soil, has also been used by several workers for the estimation of naturally occurring fixed NH_4. The applicability of Barshad's procedure for the latter purpose has been questioned, however, as the NaOH distillation appears to be ineffective in producing a complete removal of the native fixed NH_4 in the presence of small amounts of exchangeable K. The figures obtained by the alkaline distillation procedure are in general substantially lower than those obtained by procedures involving treatment with HF (Bremner, 1959; Hanway and Scott, 1956; Nõmmik, unpub. data). In comparing the methods of Rodrigues and Barshad, Hanway and Scott (1956) noted that the results were of approximately the same order for soil samples from B and C horizons, but they differed markedly for samples of surface soil. The HF-treatment procedure, according to Rodrigues, here gave considerably higher figures, possibly owing to the higher humus content of the samples.

Recently, several new procedures for the determination of native fixed NH_4 have been proposed. In order to reduce the analytical error caused by the NH_3 released in the decomposition of soil organic N compounds during HF treatment, some of the procedures involve a partial removal of the organic matter by pretreating the soil with either hot KOH (Dhariwal and Stevenson, 1958) or with H_2O_2 in the presence of an excess of K salts (Schachtschabel, 1960, 1961b). In others the workers have aimed at reducing the interference of the organic matter in the soil by treating the samples with reagents as mild as possible and by carrying out the extraction at room temperature (Bremner, 1959; Bremner and Harada, 1959; Walsh and Murdock, 1960). In examining the ability of several hydrofluoric acid-mineral acid mixtures to remove fixed NH_4 from an exfoliated vermiculite, Walsh and Murdock (1960) found that the Bremner (N HF:N H_2SO_4) and the Dhariwal and Stevenson (5 N HF:0.75 N HCl:0.65 N H_2SO_4) extraction procedures were equally effective in this respect, both producing a complete release of fixed NH_4. Schachtschabel (1960) reported, however, that the Bremner extraction procedure was ineffective in removing all of the fixed NH_4 present in the soil. Nõmmik (unpub. data), using a vermiculite-containing, heavy clay soil, which was saturated with N^{15}-labelled NH_4, likewise failed to recover the fixed NH_4 completely by the HF-treatment procedures mentioned above. This observation is in accordance with the finding of Bremner (1959) and Rich (1960) that in some soils a longer period of treatment and a larger volume of extracting solution per unit of soil was sometimes required than what was prescribed in the analytical procedure proposed.

The interference of organic N compounds in the soil can be reduced, as was pointed out previously, by a pretreatment of the soil with hot KOH or H_2O_2. Neither of the above treatments results, however, in a complete removal of the organic matter in the soil. When investigating this question, Dhariwal and Stevenson (1958) considered, however, that organic matter which resists extraction with hot KOH probably does not interfere with the estimation of fixed NH_4 by HF extraction. In Schacht-schabel's method a correction for the possible interference of the organic N, not removed by treatment with H_2O_2, is made on the basis of the residual carbon content of the soil. Of interest is the observation made by Stewart and Porter (1963), according to which some soils contain a form of indigenous fixed NH_4 that was not quantitatively removed by the standard Kjeldahl digestion procedure. This fixed NH_4 was released by treatment with HF.

Notwithstanding the inability to check the accuracy of the different analytical procedures used, considerable information has been accumulated on the question of the occurrence of native fixed NH_4 in different soils as well as in minerals and rocks. These studies indicate that most of the soils appear to contain significant amounts of NH_4 in a fixed form. According to Stevenson (1959a), 3.5 to 7.9% of the N in the surface soils of the central region of the United States occurs as fixed NH_4. The relative amount of N occurring as fixed NH_4 increased with increasing depth in the soil. In many cases, this may explain the narrowing of the C:N ratio with increasing depth, an observation made also by several other workers (Hanway and Scott, 1956; Ivanov, 1962; Nõmmik, 1957; Rich, 1960; Rodriguez, 1954; Smirnov and Fruktova, 1963; Stevenson et al., 1958).

On analyzing soils from Great Britain, Bremner (1959) found that 3 to 8% of the N in the surface soils and 9 to 44% in the subsoils examined was fixed NH_4. For Wisconsin soils Walsh and Murdock (1960) give a content of fixed NH_4 of 0.5 to 1.0 me. per 100 g. According to Young (1962) the inorganic fraction of total N in individual horizons of 17 Pacific Northwest (U.S.A.) soils varied from 1.7 to 47.2%, the values being highest for subsurface horizons. The author emphasizes the necessity of using organic N rather than total N for characterizing soil organic matter by C/N ratios.

As regards the significance of the mineralogical composition of the clay fraction Stevenson et al. (1958) demonstrated that a silt loam, in which illite was the predominating clay mineral, contained a larger amount of fixed NH_4 than a silt loam in which montmorillonite was the predominating mineral. In another investigation Stevenson and Dhariwal (1959) found that, with respect to clay mineral type and the content of native fixed NH_4, the order was illite > montmorillonite > kaolinite. Drainage, type of cover, and extent of leaching of the profile by percolating water were of little significance as regarded the occurrence of native fixed NH_4 in the soil. An interesting finding was that cropping decreased the amount of fixed NH_4 present in the surface soils, an observation confirmed also by Walsh and Murdock (1963). The experimental results of the last-mentioned authors indicate, however, that even under the most advantageous conditions very little of the native fixed NH_4 is available to crops. The extent of the release was supposed to be dependent on the K level in the soil.

Here reference should be made to investigations by Smirnov and

Fruktova (1963), who found that the content of native fixed NH_4 was especially high in the intensively cultivated and regularly fertilized soils.

Investigating a number of Virginia soil profiles, Rich (1960) showed that the amounts of native fixed NH_4 increased with depth. He assumed that the fixed NH_4 in the parent materials (predominantly muscovite) substituted isomorphously for K and that for any soil there was a constant ratio between total K and fixed NH_4 in the parent material. The parent material of the soils studied contained 4% K and the average NH_4/K ratio in the C horizon was 1 NH_4 ion to 58 K ions.

In German soils Schachtschabel (1961) found that the content of native fixed NH_4 in loess soils varied between 0.57 and 1.50 me. per 100 g. The corresponding figures for marsh soils were 1.1 to 6.1 me. According to the same author, the content of native fixed NH_4 was negatively correlated with the size of the soil particles. In a loess soil the content of fixed NH_4 in the textural fractions <2 μ, 2-20 μ, and >20 μ was 2.02, 0.72, and 0.25 me. per 100 g, respectively. The content of native fixed NH_4 in the soil was thus greatly dependent on the clay content of the soil. The latter finding has been confirmed by a number of other workers (Blanchet et al., 1963; Gouny et al., 1960; Schreven, 1963). No such relationship was, however, found by Young and Cattani (1962) for the soils of the Pacific Northwest.

Of considerable interest is the finding of Stevenson (1959b) according to which not only soils but also rocks may contain appreciable amounts of native fixed NH_4. The content of fixed NH_4 in shales varied between 330 and 420 μg N/g, and that in granite rocks between 5 and 27 μg N/g. The above figures indicate that from one-fourth to one-half of the total nitrogen in granite rocks and up to two-thirds of that in some paleozoic shales occurs as fixed NH_4. On the basis of these data Stevenson calculated that the quantity of nitrogen present as fixed NH_4 in the earth's crust will exceed that present as molecular nitrogen in the atmosphere.

Schachtschabel (1961) also analyzed a number of different silicate minerals and found the following content of native fixed NH_4: illite 2.1-6.4, muscovite 3.7, biotite 0.6, and adular 1 me. per 100 g. As concerns the biological availability to plants, Schachtschabel considered that the native fixed NH_4 in feldspar and muscovite is probably very difficultly available.

The origin of the native fixed NH_4 is a subject for speculation. Owing to the fact that even rocks are reported to contain appreciable amounts of fixed NH_4 and that the mica minerals in the granite rocks generally have a K-saturated, contracted lattice, being incapable of taking up NH_4 from their environment, it is held to be likely that the NH_4 may have been built into the crystal lattice at the time of synthesis of the minerals (Stevenson, 1959b). In soils and sedimentary rocks some of the native fixed NH_4 may, of course, originate from more recent fixation reactions. Of interest is the suggestion of Goldschmidt (1954), according to which the most likely nitrogen compound in magmatic rocks would be the titanium nitride, TiN, which by reaction with water vapor is easily decomposed to form NH_3.

III. FIXATION OF AMMONIA BY THE ORGANIC FRACTION OF THE SOIL

A number of investigators have demonstrated that the organic fraction of the soil has the capacity to fix considerable amounts of ammonia (NH_3) and that the ammonia-organic matter complex is extraordinarily resistant to decomposition. The mechanism of the latter reaction and its agronomic consequences are only imperfectly understood. Owing to the increasing consumption of N materials containing free NH_3 (e.g., anhydrous ammonia and nitrogen solutions) and of materials which in soil decompose to form NH_3 (e.g., urea), the question of NH_3 fixation has become increasingly important. The literature on this subject up to 1957 has been summarized by Mortland (1958).

The term "fixed NH_3," as used in the present paper, refers to this fraction of added NH_3, which is retained by the soil organic matter after intensive extraction and leaching with acid (Broadbent et al., 1961; Burge and Broadbent, 1961; Nõmmik and Nilsson, 1963a) or neutral salt solutions (Nõmmik and Nilsson, 1963b).

A. The Nature of and Conditions for the Fixation Reaction

The first information on the ability of soil organic matter to fix NH_3 originates from the experimental work carried out with the intention of producing organic N material appropriate for use as commercial fertilizers. Several patents have been issued for processes involving the use of NH_3 in treating peat and other materials of plant origin. Thus Erasmus (1928) heated carbohydrates of plant origin such as sugar, cellulose, etc. with NH_3 under pressure and obtained a product containing up to 20% N. Ehrenberg and Heimann (1932) suggested a process by which they fixed NH_3 in peat soils in the presence of oxygen and various catalysts. Feustel and Byers (1933) treated peat with NH_3 at different temperatures and for different periods of time, and reported that only a fractional part of the total amount of NH_3 sorbed by the peat was ammoniacal in form. They did not find any relationship between the amount of N originally present in the peat and the amount of NH_3 taken up in the treatment. An extensive study of the fixation of NH_3 in peat under varying conditions of temperature, pressure, length of treatment and moisture content has been presented by Scholl and Davis (1933). The authors reported that the NH_3 treatment of a moss peat at 300°C resulted in a product which showed a nitrogen content of 21.7%. Only about one-fifth of this N was in water-soluble form. Scholl and Davis found no correlation between the pH of the original peat and the amount of NH_3 sorbed. Economic considerations indicated, according to the authors, that commercial production of ammoniated peat was possible.

Extensive studies, important from the agronomical point of view, have been carried out on NH_3 fixation by Mattson and Koutler-Andersson

(1941, 1942, 1943, 1954a, b, 1956). In treating peat, litter, humus, and lignin, they found that the amount of NH_3 fixed in nonexchangeable form was proportional to the acidoid content of the material. They were able to demonstrate that, owing to the reduction of acidoid strength, the pH at the isoelectric point was raised as a consequence of NH_3 fixation. This finding is in accordance with the observation that a high N content in the natural litter is associated with a weak acidoid. They also showed (Mattson and Koutler-Andersson, 1942) that the fixation of ammonia was associated with a simultaneous oxidation reaction, indicated by an uptake of oxygen from the flask atmosphere (Jansson, 1960; Junker, 1941; Nõmmik and Nilsson, 1963b). This autoxidation of organic matter, and consequently also the fixation of NH_3, was favored by an alkaline reaction. It could be demonstrated that there exists a definite relationship between the oxidation status of the organic material and its capacity to fix NH_3. Thus a simultaneous oxidation favored fixation, whereas a pre-oxidation of the organic matter reduces its capacity to react with NH_3. Mattson and Koutler-Andersson (1954b) reported that the NH_3-fixing capacity of the peats was intimately correlated with their degree of humification and thus with their total N content. The higher the original N content, the lower was their capacity to fix NH_3. They concluded that a high N content of the peat reflected a high state of oxidation of the lignin and that NH_3 fixation is a measure of its non-saturation with N. A weak tendency to a decreased NH_3 fixation capacity with increasing total-N content of peat was shown also by Nõmmik and Nilsson (1963b), who studied the NH_3 fixation in peats of about the same botanical composition but of different states of humification. Violanda (1958) also reported that a less oxidized muck fixed more NH_3 than a more oxidized muck. This finding is, however, at variance with the work of Feustel and Byers (1933) and Shoji and Matsumi (1961), who found no relationship between the amount of N originally present in the peat and the amount of N taken up in the treatment with NH_3.

Mattson and Koutler-Andersson (1943) consider that NH_3 fixation most likely occurs also under natural soil conditions, and that most of the N in humus originates from a fixation reaction with ammonia (Laatsch et al., 1950; Swaby and Ladd, 1962).

The exact nature of the ammonia-organic matter complex is not known. The information available as to the reaction of NH_3 with known organic compounds and groups gives us, however, an insight into the possible reactions of NH_3 with the soil organic matter. Mattson and Koutler-Andersson (1942) suggested that the NH_3-fixing group is fairly stable, because it exists in the natural materials. According to the same authors (1943), the ammoniated complex was extremely stable toward acid treatment. Digestion of the NH_3-treated beech leave humus with 4.0 N HCl for 24 hours thus removed only 10% of the fixed NH_3. By distillation with 2 N NaOH, however, nearly half of the NH_3 was removed. They reported, furthermore, that the autoxidized and ammoniated litter and humus is much less soluble in acetyl bromide than the original materials (Pinck et al., 1935).

On the basis of results obtained in investigations of humus material and of di- and tri-hydric phenols and poly-hydric aromatic carbonic acids, Mattson and Koutler-Andersson (1943) suggested that in soils the oxidative NH_3 fixation was related to the lignin fraction, and that it required the presence of aromatic rings with two or more OH groups. The above suggestion of Mattson and Koutler-Andersson is supported by the findings of Bennett (1949), who reported that the treatment of lignin with NH_3 reduced its capacity to form methoxyl groups upon treatment with dimethyl sulphate. The methylation, conversely, reduced the NH_3-fixing capacity of the material. This is in accordance with the more recent findings of Burge and Broadbent (1961), giving further evidence that the phenolic hydroxyl groups are involved in the fixation reaction. When investigating if other functional groups might be responsible for the fixation reaction, the latter authors reported that the ammoniation did not decrease the number of aldehyde groups, indicating that aldehyde-ammonia products were not formed. They suggested furthermore that the formation of amides through the action of anhydrous ammonia on carboxylic esters might play a minor role in NH_3 fixation. An interesting finding of Burge and Broadbent (1961) was that the treatment of the organic soils with ammonia usually resulted in a decrease in the capacity of the soil to retain Ba^{2+} and Ca^{2+}. There was, however, no quantitative relationship between the amount of NH_3 fixed and the decrease in the cation retention capacity.

As reported by Mattson and Koutler-Andersson (1942), the NH_3 fixation involves a simultaneous oxidation reaction, indicated by absorption of oxygen. Recent investigations by Broadbent et al. (1961), show, however, that the presence of oxygen is not critical for the NH_3 fixation in soils. Substantial quantities of NH_3 were fixed also under anaerobic conditions. In short-term experiments (exposure period 24 hours) no influence of varying partial pressure of oxygen was indicated. In this respect the soil organic matter behaved distinctly differently from that of pure polyphenolic compounds, e.g., orcinol, hydroquinone and pyrogallol, which were found not to fix NH_3 in the absence of oxygen. From these results Broadbent et al. (1961), concluded that polyphenolic compounds must undergo partial oxidation before NH_3 fixation can occur. They suggested, furthermore, that the reactive groupings capable of fixing NH_3, possibly quinones produced by oxidation of polyphenols (Flaig, 1950), are obviously normally present in the soil, explaining the fixation under anaerobic conditions. When these active groups were consumed, a further fixation of NH_3 should, according to this, be possible only when new groupings were produced by oxidation. The correctness of this suggestion was supported by the fact that in long-term experiments lasting seven days, the reaction performed in the presence of oxygen resulted in a more extensive NH_3 fixation than the same reaction carried out in the absence of oxygen.

In studying the NH_3 fixation and oxygen consumption during autoxidation of cow dung, farmyard manure and sewage sludge, Jansson (1960) considered that the biological humus formation has important features in common with the chemical autoxidation of ligninous complexes in strongly alkaline media. The biological oxidation proceeds, however, much more slowly than the reaction of chemical autoxidation in a strongly alkaline medium. As regards the mechanism of NH_3 fixation, Jansson suggested that NH_3 may primarily be bound to the phenolic hydroxyl groups under the formation of amino phenols, which by oxidation are converted to quinonoimines. These compounds are rather unstable, and, referring to Laatsch (1948), Jansson considered that the imino groups may easily react with adjacent groups or chains under formation of heterocyclic rings. The ring formation would give a satisfactory explanation of the resistance of the fixed NH_3-N to treatment with strong acids and alkalies.

Of great agronomical interest is the observation made by Burge and Broadbent (1961), according to which NH_3 fixation in organic soils was shown to be linearly correlated with their content of carbon (Fig. 9).

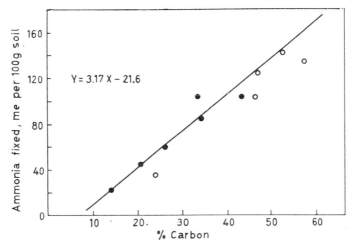

Fig. 9. Relationship between carbon content and ammonia fixation in organic soils under aerobic conditions (Burge and Broadbent, 1961).

The higher the carbon content, the more NH_3 was generally fixed by the soil (Mendez, 1963; Nõmmik and Nilsson, 1963b; Sohn and Peech, 1958). Under the experimental conditions applied, 1 molecule of NH_3 was fixed for every 29 atoms of C under aerobic conditions and 1 for every 45 atoms of C in the absence of oxygen. According to Sohn and Peech (1958), the greatest NH_3-fixing capacity was found in acid soils containing large amounts of organic matter.

Owing to the fact that free NH_3 and not the NH_4 ion is involved in the fixation reaction, it is evident that the pH of the medium may be of decisive significance for the extent of NH_3 fixation. This relationship has been elucidated in several investigations. Mattson and Koutler-Andersson (1943) demonstrated that the NH_3-fixing capacity of the humus was negligible at pH 7 and that it was increased by increasing the pH of the ammoniated sample. The variation in pH was obtained in this investigation by varying the amount of NH_3 added. Thus, not only the pH but also the total NH_3 concentration was varied.

The influence of pH on NH_3 fixation at a fixed level of ammonium salts has been studied in organic soils by Shoji and Matsumi (1961) and by Nõmmik and Nilsson (1963b). According to these investigations, the capacity of the soil to fix NH_3 is highly dependent on the H-ion concentration in the treated samples. At pH < 7 the fixation was insignificant and in general not measurable analytically. This is in agreement with the results of Themlitz (1956a), who studied nitrogen fixation by an acid raw humus treated with $(NH_4)_2SO_4$ and found that a significant increase of the organic N content was obtained only in samples in which the pH of the humus material was increased by liming over the neutral point. A strong pH dependence of the fixation reaction was demonstrated also by Broadbent et al. (1961). Calculating the extent of fixation from N^{15}-recovery data, they concluded that the fixation occurred to a large extent only above the neutral point, becoming almost a linear function of pH at the higher values (Fig. 10). Contrary to the

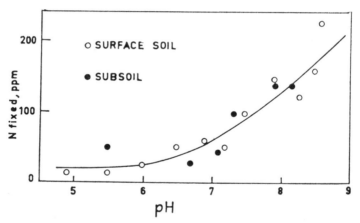

Fig. 10. Relation of ammonia fixation to pH of a peaty muck. The variation in pH obtained by applying increasing amounts of $Ca(OH)_2$ (Broadbent et al., 1960).

investigators cited previously, Broadbent et al. (1961) found a small but still measurable fixation of added NH_3 even at pH 6 and lower.

As previously suggested, not only anhydrous ammonia and aqua ammonia but also the N in materials which decompose in the soil to form NH_3, e.g., urea and calcium cyanamide, may be fixed by the organic fraction of the soil. This has been shown to be true for urea, the application of which resulted, according to Jung (1959), in a NH_3 fixation which was of about the same order as with corresponding amounts of NH_3 gas. Similar results were obtained by Nõmmik and Nilsson (1963b) who reported, however, that this was valid only for low and moderate application rates. At high doses considerably more N was fixed from added aqua ammonia than from urea. The latter finding was explained by the fact that the activity of enzyme urease is markedly suppressed when the pH of the medium rises above 8. At pH 8.5 the enzymatic breakdown of urea will, as a rule, cease entirely (Howell and Sumner, 1934). In urea-treated soils, even at extremely high rates of application, the pH therefore never exceed the above level. In treatment with NH_3 considerably higher alkalinity may be reached.

When investigating the NH_3 fixation of a pine raw humus, Themlitz (1956a, 1958) found that the application of calcium cyanamide led to a higher N fixation than the treatment of the humus material with a corresponding amount of NH_3. This is in accordance with the findings by Nõmmik and Nilsson (1963b), who reported that in a muck soil the extent of N fixation was more than twice as high for calcium cyanamide as for aqua ammonia. The authors suggested that the higher fixability of N in calcium cyanamide is probably explained by the fact that in this case not ammonia but the undecomposed cyanamide molecule was involved in the fixation reaction.

From the methodological point of view it is important to note that in mineral soils the determination of the ammonia fixation capacity of the organic fraction is generally more complicated than in peat soils. The mineral fraction may thus participate in the fixation reaction. An increase in the soil's content of nonexchangeable N on NH_3 treatment represents in a mineral soil the sum of the NH_3 fixed by organic matter and the NH_4 fixed in clay minerals. Several procedures have been proposed to eliminate the interfering effect of the soil mineral fraction. For this purpose Sohn and Peech (1958) analyzed the soil as regards its capacity to fix K and suggested that the difference between the amounts of NH_3 and K fixed by the soil would represent a conservative estimate of the NH_3-fixing capacity of the soil that can be attributed to the organic matter. Burge and Broadbent (1961) pre-treated the soil with a mixture of HF to remove the clay minerals. The simplest, even if not the most effective, way to overcome interference by the mineral fraction is probably to saturate the soil with K prior to treatment with NH_3 (Nõmmik and Nilsson, 1963b).

In this connection it should be noted that the procedure of estimating the NH_3-fixing capacity of the soil by measuring the increase in the soil's content of non-exchangeable N on treatment with NH_3 may not always give a completely correct measurement of the absolute magnitude of the fixation reaction. This is due to the fact that the treatment of the soil with NH_3 results not only in an incorporation of NH_3 into the humus substances but generally also in a simultaneous deamination of some of the organic N compounds, which are unstable at the high pH levels in question (e.g., amides, amino-sugars). It has been shown that considerable amounts of organically bound soil N are released as NH_3 by moderate alkali treatment (Bremner, 1949; Bremner and Shaw, 1954; Cornfield, 1960). The procedure of measuring the difference in the soil's content of organic N prior to and after the treatment with NH_3 evidently gives erroneously low values for the amounts of NH_3 really fixed by the organic fraction of the soil. The figures for NH_3-fixation capacity obtained in this way represent actually net effects between two reactions, one of which consumes and the other releases ammonia. The above relationship has been illustrated by experimental data by Nõmmik and Nilsson (1963b) using $N^{15}H_3$ as a tracer.

B. Biological Availability of Ammonia Fixed by the Organic Fraction of the Soil

As concerns the biological availability of N in the ammonia-organic matter complexes, our information is rather inadequate. According to recent observations, these complexes seem to be fairly stable compounds, being only slowly mineralized by soil microflora. In studying the properties of ammonia-lignin complexes, Bremner and Shaw (1957) found that they were remarkably resistant to microbial decomposition. Burge and Broadbent (1961) studied the availability of N to higher plants in ammonia-soil organic matter complexes, using for this purpose tagged N. They reported that in an organic soil the fixed N, though not removable by leaching with dilute HCl, was to a small but significant extent available to sudangrass. In the first cutting the plants utilized 4.29% of the tagged, fixed N present in the soil, whereas the corresponding figure for nontagged, native organic N was only 0.14%. The fixed N was thus considerably more readily available to plants than the bulk of the soil organic N. In the second cutting, however, the sudangrass absorbed only 1.31% of the remaining, tagged soil N, indicating that the fixed N was not present in the same form of chemical combination or that the tagged N was gradually transformed into compounds of greater resistance to microbial attack.

In a pot experiment Jung (1961) studied the response of rye-grass, poplar cuttings and seedlings of oak and sycamore to different forms of N, added to small samples of raw humus and then mixed with a sandy soil. The author reported that virtually all of the added N from NH_4 salts of strong acids was immediately available to the plants. Ammonia, urea, and formamide, on the other hand, had partly reacted with the raw humus, resulting in a lower uptake of N by the plants during an experimental period of two years.

C. Agronomic Significance of Ammonia Fixation

In the literature reviewed considerable evidence has been accumulated to show the capacity of the soil organic matter to react with NH_3 and to bind it in a difficultly hydrolyzable form. Biological tests show that fixed N is only slowly available to soil microflora and higher plants. It may be asked whether nonenzymatic ammonia fixation is likely to occur under natural soil conditions and whether it may significantly influence the effectiveness of the NH_3 form of fertilizer nitrogen. According to Mattson and Koutler-Andersson (1943), "the ammonia fixation can and must occur under soil conditions." These authors further consider that the nitrogenous humus complex in the soil is a chemical product resulting from

autoxidation and NH_3 fixation. Burge and Broadbent (1961) and Broadbent et al. (1961) consider it not unlikely that the NH_3 released by
breakdown of the plant and animal residues, in which most of the nitrogen is in the α-amino form, may be fixed by reaction with lignin derivatives and will thereby be rendered less available. Stevenson (1957), on
the other hand, suggested that the evidence for the presence of lignin-
ammonia complexes is rather presumptive, as there is no proof that large
quantities of soil nitrogen occur in this form (Laatsch et al., 1950, 1951;
Swaby and Ladd, 1962).

The presence of ammonia-organic matter complexes might unquestionably be more likely in a soil to which nitrogenous fertilizers are
being applied than in untreated soil, where normally no accumulation of
NH_3 occurs. The experimental evidence for the correctness of this statement is, however, lacking. The information available on the extent of
NH_3 fixation is thus almost exclusively based on data from laboratory
investigations. These data likewise give us some possibilities of estimating
the degree of probability of NH_3 fixation under field conditions. These
studies indicate that, when applying NH_3 at a rate of 100 kg of N per
hectare and with 100 cm beween the applicator knives, the concentration of NH_3 in the center of the retention zone may only for short
periods exceed 2000 ppm (Blue and Eno, 1954; McDowell and Smith,
1958; McIntosh and Frederick, 1958; Nõmmik and Nilsson, 1963a). In
most cases the concentration is considerably lower and decreases rapidly
with increasing distance from the point of injection. The pH of the soil
in the center of the retention zone may only exceptionally exceed 9.0.
The initial pH and the buffering capacity of the soil are two of the factors determining the NH_3 distribution and the pH level in the retention
zone. It is thus primarily on the calcareous, light-textured soils that the
highest pH values are expected to occur after NH_3 application. With
heavy applications and large spacings the pH of the soil in the center
of the injection zone may not seldom reach values of about 8.5 to 9
and exceptionally still higher (McDowell and Smith, 1958; McIntosh
and Frederick, 1958; Nõmmik and Nilsson, 1963a). Under these conditions some fixation of ammonia will certainly occur. The extent of
fixation will to a large extent be dependent on the type and amount of
organic matter in the soil and, of course, on the time of reaction. The
latter condition is markedly influenced by factors influencing the rate
of NH_3 diffusion and nitrification in the soil.

Owing to the fact that in row application the NH_3 is generally distributed only through a fractional part of the top soil (an estimated
1/10 to 1/30 of the top-soil volume) and that only in the center of the
retention zone will a sufficiently high pH and NH_3 concentration be
reached, it seems highly probable that in mineral soils and at moderate
rates of application only a fairly small part of the applied NH_3 will be
inactivated by reaction with the soil organic matter. The correctness of
this assumption is demonstrated by the findings that in field experiments
in general no significant difference in the effectiveness of nitrogen is obtained between the solid NH_4 salts and anhydrous ammonia. It is, however, not excluded that in organic soils the fixation may be a factor of

greater significance in determining the effectiveness of the NH_3 source of N for field crops. In the last case, especially, when it concerns the acid raw humus soils, the NH_3 application may in addition induce an increased biological immobilization of the mineral nitrogen. Evidently considerably more information is needed about the fertility aspect of the problem and its agronomic implications.

As regards urea and calcium cyanamide which decompose in the soil to form ammonia, it is conceivable that under certain conditions the pH and the ammonia concentration round the fertilizer granules may reach such values that a reaction with the organic matter may be possible. A localized placement of these fertilizers may reasonably increase the risk of ammonia fixation. In this connection it is of interest to note that, according to Wittich (1961), a uniform incorporation of 200 kg of N as ammonia gas per hectare did not result in any fixation of ammonia by the raw humus. In applying the same amounts of ammonia with a special applicator roller, it was found that after a period of one year the soil content of nonhydrolyzable nitrogen was markedly increased at the points of ammonia injection, whereas no such increase was observed in the soil between the injection points. The same author reported furthermore that the ammonia treatment of the soil brought about a peptization of the humus colloids, resulting in an increased leaching of the colloids to deeper soil horizons.

IV. OTHER REACTIONS

Besides the two fixation reactions described above, there are some other processes, which under certain conditions might be responsible for a more or less permanent withdrawal of inorganic forms of N from the biological N cycle of the soil. Here we may mention especially the formation of NH_4 taranakites and the reaction between nitrite and soil organic matter.

In general, the inorganic salts of ammonium, nitrite, and nitrate are characterized by high water solubility. Regarding the NH_4 form of N, the formation of some slightly soluble compounds should, however, not be excluded under soil conditions. Thus, fixation of added NH_4 has been demonstrated in some Hawaiian amorphous soils free of layer-lattice silicates (Tamimi, 1963). These soils contain large amounts of colloidal hydrated oxides of Fe and Al, and they show a high capacity to fix phosphate. In a recent leaching study with these types of soils Kanehiro et al. (1960) found that sorption of NH_4 ion was higher when applied as $NH_4H_2PO_4$ or $(NH_4)_2HPO_4$ than when applied as $(NH_4)_2SO_4$ or NH_4Cl. In treating soils with acidic phosphate solutions, containing NH_4 or K, formation of several slightly soluble crystalline products, *inter alia*, *ammoniam taranakite*, $H_6(NH_4)_3Al_5(PO_4)_8 \cdot 18\ H_2O$, and its potassium analogue, $H_6K_3Al_5(PO_4)_8 \cdot 18\ H_2O$, has been reported by a number of investigators (Birrell, 1961; Lindsay et al., 1962; Lindsay and Taylor, 1960; Tamimi et al., 1963; Wada, 1959). Several workers have studied the mineralogical characters and the solubility of taranakites under varying conditions (Haseman et al., 1950; Kittrick and Jackson, 1956; Smith and Brown, 1959; Taylor and Gurney, 1961).

As follows from the chemical formula, the prerequisites for the formation of ammonium taranakite are the presence of NH_4, Al, P, moisture, and an acid reaction. Tamimi et al. (1963) consider, consequently, that the formation of tarankite under field conditions is possible primarily in the hydrol humic and humic latosols, when these soils are treated with fertilizers containing both NH_4 and P. It seems logical that the higher the PO_4:NH_4 ratio in the fertilizer, the higher the proportion of the added NH_4 that would be precipitated as taranakite. Thus it seems likely that on the above soils the monoammonium phosphate may be a less effective source of N than the diammonium phosphate. There are no experimental data available, however, illustrating this relationship. In general, at the present time no statements can be made regarding the possible significance of the reaction of taranakite formation. Owing to the fact that there is a tendency for NH_4 phosphates to become more important as sources of N and P in commercial fertilizers, it seems highly desirable that the research work on this subject should be intensified substantially.

Recent work by Bremner and co-workers (Bremner and Führ, 1963; Bremner and Shaw, 1957; Führ and Bremner, 1964) has directed attention to a possible reaction between the nitrite form of N and the soil organic matter. Using N^{15}-labeled $NaNO_2$, they found that during a reaction time of 24 hours under the conditions in question a considerable part of the applied NO_2^--N was fixed by the soil, the amount of fixation being linearly correlated with the soil content of organic matter. A mineral soil, containing 2.2% organic C, fixed 25% of the 12.5 ppm NO_2^--N added (pH-5.1). When added in quantities of 500 ppm N, the fixation percentage fell to 7. An interesting observation was that the fixation was promoted by acidic conditions and by sterilization. The reaction occurs even in neutral soils, the amount of fixation at pH 7 being, however, about 3 to 4 times lower than at pH 4. It was shown that during the fixation reaction 33 to 79% of the added NO_2^--N was changed into gaseous N_2, N_2O, and NO. Only 55 to 60% of the fixed NO_2^--N was released from the soil by boiling with 6 N HCl for 12 hours (the corresponding figure for the total soil N being ca. 80%), and of this N about 45 to 50% was recovered as NH_4 (Führ and Bremner, 1964). Studies on the mechanism of the nitrite-soil organic matter reaction indicated that the lignin-derived fraction of soil organic matter was mainly responsible for the fixation of NO_2^--N (Bremner and Führ, 1963). This conclusion was supported by results obtained in experiments with model substances, showing, e.g., that lignin had the highest capacity to fix NO_2^-, whereas cellulose did not fix it at all. On the basis of these observations it was suggested that the reaction of nitrite with soil organic matter involves the formation of aromatic nitroso compounds.

The results of Bremner and Führ (1963) and Führ and Bremner (1964) certainly reveal new prospects as to the possible pathways of mineral nitrogen immobilization and losses in arable soils. They also indicate an occurrence of nitroso groups in the soil organic matter. Nevertheless, the significance of the reaction is still difficult to decide. As we know, no accumulation of nitrite occurs generally in arable soils. High nitrite levels have been reported only in soils treated with large amounts of N materials containing free ammonia or organic forms of nitrogen, e.g., liquid ammonia, aqua ammonia, urea, and calcium cyanamide. In these cases nitrite concentrations of up to several hundred ppm N may be found in the central zones of ammonia retention or in the vicinity of fertilizer granules (Broadbent et al., 1957; Chapman and Liebig, 1952; Cornfield, 1960; Nõmmik and Nilsson, 1963a). Since the accumulation of nitrite is intimately related to a high ammonia concentration, and thus to pH values above neutral point, the percentage fixation under these conditions would not be very high. The significance of the reaction of nitrite fixation presumably increases with the increasing organic matter content of the soil (Bremner and Führ, 1963; Führ and Bremner, 1964). A more accurate evaluation of the reaction must evidently await the acquisition of considerably more basic data.

REFERENCES

Agarwal, R. R. 1960. Potassium fixation in soils. Soils and Fert. 23:375-378.

Allison, F. E., Doetsch, J. H., and Roller, E. M. 1951. Ammonium fixation and availability in Harpster clay loam. Soil Sci. 72:187-200.

Allison, F. E., Doetsch, J. H., and Roller, E. M. 1953a. Availability of fixed ammonium in soils containing different clay minerals. Soil Sci. 75:373-381.

Allison, F. E., Kefauer, M. and Roller, E. M. 1953b. Ammonium fixation in soils. Soil Sci. Soc. Am. Proc. 17:107-110.

Allison, F. E., Roller, E. M., and Doetsch, J. H. 1953c. Ammonium fixation and availability in vermiculite. Soil Sci. 75:173-180.

Allison, F. E., and Roller, E. M. 1955a. A comparison of leaching and distillation procedures for determining fixed ammonium in soils. Soil Sci. 80:349-362.

Allison, F. E., and Roller, E. M. 1955b. Fixation and release of ammonium ions by clay minerals. Soil Sci. 80:431-441.

Aomine, S. 1951. Studies on the fixation of ammonium in soils. I. Ammonium fixing power of some soils in the Southwestern provinces of Japan. J. Sci. Soil Man. Japan 22:83-87.

Aomine, S., and Higashi, T. 1953a. Studies on the fixation of ammonium in soils. V. Availability of fixed ammonia by crops. J. Sci. Soil Man. Japan 23:105-108.

Aomine, S., and Higashi, T. 1953b. Studies on the fixation of ammonium in soils. VI. Nitrification of fixed ammonium. J. Sci. Soil Man. Japan 23:185-188.

Aomine, S., and Wada, K. 1952a. Studies on the fixation of ammonium in soils. II. Manner of ammonium fixation. J. Sci. Soil Man. Japan 22:227-230.

Aomine, S., and Wada, K. 1952b. Studies on the fixation of ammonium in soils. III. Fixation of ammonium in Fukuma sandy soil. J. Sci. Soil Man. Japan 22:315-318.

Aomine, S., and Wada, K. 1953. Studies on the fixation of ammonium in soils. IV. Fixation of ammonium in homoionic soils. J. Sci. Soil Man. Japan 23:1-4.

Axley, J. H., and Legg, J. O. 1960. Ammonium fixation in soils and the influence of potassium on nitrogen availability from nitrate and ammonium sources. Soil Sci. 90:151-156.

Baert-de Bièvre, M., Hende, A. van den, and Lox, F. 1961. Étude de la fixation d'ammonium dans deux sols argileux à l'aide de N[15]. Pédologie. Symp. intern. 2, Appl. sc. nucl. ped., 104-118.

Bailey, T. A. 1942. Mechanism of potassium fixation by various clays. Ph.D. Thesis, University of Wisconsin, Madison.

Barshad, I. 1948. Vermiculite and its relation to biotite as revealed by base exchange reactions, x-ray analyses, differential thermal curves, and water content. Amer. Mineral. 33:655-678.

Barshad, I. 1950. The effect of the interlayer cations on the expansion of the mica type of crystal lattice. Amer. Mineral. 35:225-238.

Barshad, I. 1951. Cation exchange in soils: I. Ammonium fixation and its relation to potassium fixation and to determination of ammonium exchange capacity. Soil Sci. 72:361-371.

Barshad, I. 1952. Factors affecting the interlayer expansion of vermiculite and montmorillonite with organic substances. Soil Sci. Soc. Am. Proc. 16:176-182.

Barshad, I. 1954a. Cation exchange in micaceous minerals: I Replaceability of the interlayer cations of vermiculite with ammonium and potassium ions. Soil Sci. 77:463-472.

Barshad, I. 1954b. Cation exchange in micaceous minerals: II. Replaceability of ammonium and potassium from vermiculite, biotite, and montmorillonite. Soil Sci. 78:57-76.

Bartholomew, R. P., and Janssen, G. 1931. Rate of absorption of potassium by plants and its possible effect upon the amount of potassium remaining in soils from applications of potassium fertilizers. Arkansas Agr. Exp. Sta. Bul. 265.

Bengtsson, N. 1924. The determination of ammonia in soil. Soil Sci. 18:255-278.

Bennett, E. 1949. Fixation of ammonia by lignin. Soil Sci. 68:399-400.

Birrell, K. S. 1961. Ion fixation by allophane. New Zealand J. Sci. 4:393-414.

Blanchet, R., Studer, R., Chaumont, C., and LeBlevenec, L. 1963. Principaux facteurs influencant la rétrogradation de l'ammonium dans les conditions naturelles des sols. C. R. Acad. Sci. Paris 256:2223-2225.

Blue, W. G., and Eno, C. F. 1954. Distribution and retention of anhydrous ammonia in sandy soils. Soil Sci. Am. Proc. 18:420-424.

Bolt, G. H., Sumner, M. E., and Kamphorst, A. 1963. A study of the equilibrium between three categories of potassium in an illitic soil. Soil Sci. Soc. Am. Proc. 27:294-299.

Bower, C. A. 1950. Fixation of ammonium in difficultly exchangeable form under moist conditions by some soils of semiarid regions. Soil Sci. 70:375-382.

Bower, C. A. 1951. Availability of ammonium fixed in difficultly exchangeable form by soils of semiarid regions. Soil Sci. Am. Proc. (1950) 15:119-122.

Bray, R. H. 1937. Chemical and physical changes in soil colloids with advancing development on Illinois soils. Soil Sci. 43:1-14.

Bremner, J. M. 1949. Studies on soil organic matter. I. The chemical nature of soil organic nitrogen. J. Agr. Sci. 39:183-193.

Bremner, J. M. 1959. Determination of fixed ammonium in soil. J. Agr. Sci. 52:147-160.

Bremner, J. M., and Führ, F. 1963. Tracer studies of the reaction of soil organic matter with nitrite. FAO, IAEA Technical Meeting on the Use of Isotopes in Soil Organic Matter Studies, Braunschweig.

Bremner, J. M., and Harada, T. 1959. Release of ammonium and organic matter from soil by hydrofluoric acid and effect of hydrofluoric acid treatment on extraction of soil organic matter by neutral and alkaline reagents. J. Agr. Sci. 52:137-146.

Bremner, J. M., and Shaw, K. 1954. Studies on the estimation and decomposition of amino sugars in soil. J. Agr. Sci. 44:152-159.

Bremner, J. M., and Shaw, K. 1957. The mineralization of some nitrogenous materials in soil. J. Sci. Food Agr. 8:341-347.

Broadbent, F. E., Burge, W. D., and Nakashima, T. 1961. Factors influencing the reaction between ammonia and soil organic matter. Trans. 7th Int. Congr. Soil Sci. 2:509-516.

Broadbent, F. E., Tyler, K. B., and Hill, G. N. 1957. Nitrification of ammoniacal fertilizers in some California soils. Hilgardia 27:247-267.

Buehrer, T. F., Robinson, D. O., and Deming, J. M. 1949. The mineral composition of the colloidal fraction of some Southwestern soils in relation to field behavior. Soil Sci. Soc. Am. Proc. (1948) 13:157-165.

Burge, W. D., and Broadbent, F. E. 1961. Fixation of ammonia by organic soils. Soil Sci. Soc. Am. Proc. 25:199-204.

Carter, D. L., Harward, M. E., and Young, J. L. 1963. Variation in exchangeable K and relation to intergrade layer silicate minerals. Soil Sci. Soc. Am. Proc. 27:283-287.

Chaminade, R. 1934. Étude des équilibres entre le complexe absorbant et les solutions des sols. Ann. Agron. 4:781-792.

Chaminade, R. 1940. Fixation de l'ion NH$_4$ par les colloides argileux des sols sous forme non exchangeable. Compt. Rend. Acad. Sci. 210:264-266.

Chaminade, R., and Drouineau, G. 1936. Recherches sur la mecanique chemique des cations exchangeables. Ann. Agron. 6:677-690.

Chapman, H. D., and Liebig, G. F. 1952. Field and laboratory studies of nitrite accumulation in soils. Soil Sci. Soc. Am. Proc. 16:276-282.

Cornfield, A. H. 1960. Ammonia released on treating soils with N sodium hydroxide as a possible means of predicting the nitrogen-supplying power of soils. Nature 187:260-261.

Court, M. N., Stephen, R. C., and Waid, J. S. 1962. Nitrite toxicity arising from the use of urea as a fertilizer. Nature 194:1263-1265.

Davey, C. B. 1953. Decomposition of hard maple (Acer saccharum) sawdust by treatment with anhydrous ammonia and inoculation with Coprinus Ephemerus. Wis. Acad. Arts & Let. Trans. 42:177-181.

Dhariwal, A. P. S., and Stevenson, F. J. 1958. Determination of fixed ammonium in soils. Soil Sci. 86:343-349.

Drake, N., Vengris, J., and Colby, W. G. 1951. Cation exchange capacity of plant roots. Soil Sci. 72:139-147.

Dyal, R. S., and Hendricks, S. B. 1952. Formation of mixed layer minerals by potassium fixation in montmorillonite. Soil Sci. Soc. Am. Proc. 16:45-48.

Ehrenberg, C., and Heimann, H. 1932. German Patent 545,923. November, 1930, issued March, 1932.

Elgabaly, M. M., and Wiklander, L. 1949. Effect of exchange capacity of clay mineral and acidoid content of plant on uptake of sodium and calcium by excised barley and pea roots. Soil Sci. 67:419-424.

Erasmus, P. 1928. German Patent 514,510, November 7, 1928.

Evans, C. E., and Attoe, O. J. 1948. Potassium-supplying power of virgin and cropped soils. Soil Sci. 66:323-334.

Feustel, I. C., and Byers, H. G. 1933. The decomposition of hydrolytic peat products including ammoniated peat. USDA Tech. Bul. 389.

Flaig, W. 1950. Zur Kenntnis der Huminsäuren. I. Zur chemischen Konstitution der Huminsäuren. Z. Pflanzenern. Düng. Bodenk. 51:93-212.

Führ, F., and Bremner, J. M. 1964. Beeinflussende Faktoren in der Fixierung des Nitrit-Stickstoffs durch die organische Masse des Bodens. Atompraxis 10:109-113.

Ghildyal, B. P., and Singh, P. N. 1961. Ammonium fixation in cultivated and afforested alluvial soil. Soil & Plant Food 6:164-169.

Gieseking, J. E. 1949. The clay minerals in soils. Advances in Agron. 1:159-204.

Gloss, G. H. 1953. Sodium tetraphenylboron: A new analytical reagent for potassium, ammonium, and some organic nitrogen compounds. Chemist Analyst 42:50-55.

Goldschmidt, V. M. 1954. Geochemistry. Ed. by A. Muir. Clarendon Press, Oxford, 730 pp.

Gorbunov, N. I. 1936. The nature of potassium fixation in non-exchangeable form. (Russ.) Chemisation Socialist Agr. 2-3:82-90.

Gouny, P., Mériaux, S., and Grosman, R. 1960. Importance de l'ion ammonium a l'état non échangeable dans un profil de sol. C. R. Acad. Sci. Paris 351:1418-1420.

Grim, R. E. 1953. Clay Mineralogy. McGraw-Hill Book Co., Inc., New York, 384 pp.

Hadding, A. 1923. Eine röntgenographischeMethode kristalline und kryptokristalline Substanzen zu identifizieren. Z. Krist. 58:108-112.

Hanway, J. J., and Scott, A. D. 1956. Ammonium fixation and release in certain Iowa soils. Soil Sci. 82:379-386.

Hanway, J. J., Scott, A. D., and Stanford, G. 1957. Replaceability of ammonium fixed in clay minerals as influenced by ammonium or potassium in the extracting solution. Soil Sci. Soc. Am. Proc. 21:29-34.

Harada, T., and Kutsuna, K. 1954. Ammonium fixation by residual soil from crystalline schists at Yahatahama. Bull. Nat. Inst. Agr. Sci. Japan Ser. B No. 3:17-41.

Haseman, J. F., Lehr, J. R., and Smith, J. P. 1950. Mineralogical character of some iron and aluminum phosphates containing potassium and ammonium. Soil Sci. Soc. Amer. Proc. 15:76-84.

REFERENCES

Hauser, G. F. 1941. Die nichtaustauschbare Festlegung des Kalis im Boden Diss. Wageningen, 171 pp.

Hende, A. van den. 1962. Premiers résultats obtenus à l'aide de l'isotope d'azote lourd N^{15} concernant la fixation des ions ammoniaques. C. A. Rech. I. R. S. I. A. 28:125-137.

Hendricks, S. B., and Fry, W. H. 1930. The results of X-ray and microscopical examinations of soil colloids. Soil Sci. 29:457-479.

Hendricks, S. B., Nelson, R. A., and Alexander, L. T. 1940. Hydration mechanism of the clay mineral montmorillonite saturated with various cations. J. Am. Chem. Soc. 62:1457-1464.

Hoagland, D. R., and Martin, J. C. 1933. Absorption of potassium by plants in relation to replaceable, non-replaceable, and soil solution potassium. Soil Sci. 36:1-33.

Howell, S. F., and Sumner, J. B. 1934. The specific effects of buffers upon urease activity. J. Biol. Chem. 104:619-626.

Hudig, F. and Reesema, N. H. S. van. 1940. Het probleem van de stabiliteit der humusstoffer. Landbouwk. Tijdschr. 52:371-398, 529-634.

Ivanov, P. 1962. Ammonium fixation in certain soils. (Bulg.) Izv. Dobrudzh. s. -stop. nauch. -iszled. Inst. Tolbukhin 3:5-19.

Jackson, M. L., and Hellman, N. N. 1942. X-ray diffraction procedure for positive differentiation of montmorillonite from hydrous mica. Soil Sci. Soc. Am. Proc. (1941) 6:133-145.

Jansson, S. L. 1958. Tracer studies on nitrogen transformations in soil with special attention to mineralisation-immobilization relationships. Kungl. Lantbrukshögsk. Ann. 24:101-361.

Jansson, S. L. 1960. On the humus properties of organic manures. II. Potential humus properties. Kungl. Lantbrukshögsk. Ann. 26:135-172.

Jansson, S. L. 1961. Einige Erfahrungen über Ammonium- und Kaliumfixierung in südschwedischen Böden. Kungl. Skogs- och Lantbruksakad. Tidskr., Suppl. 5:40-45.

Jansson, S. L., and Ericsson, J. 1961. Kväve- och kaliumproblem i skånsk växtodling. En preliminär redogörelse. Socker, Handlingar I, 17, 2, 9-21.

Joffe, J. S., and Kolodny, L. 1937. Fixation of potassium in soils. Soil Sci. Soc. Am. Proc. (1936) 1:187-192.

Joffe, J. S., and Kolodny, L. 1939. The effect of alternate drying and wetting on the base-exchange complex, with special reference to the behavior of the potassium ion. Soil Sci. Soc. Am. Proc. (1938) 3:107-111.

Joffe, J. S., and Levine, A. K. 1939. The relation of potassium fixation to the exchange capacity of soils. Soil Sci. Soc. Am. Proc. 4:157-161.

Joffe, J. S., and Levine, A. K. 1947. Fixation of potassium in relation to exchange capacity of soils: II. Associative fixation of other cations, particularly ammonium. Soil Sci. 63:151-158.

Jung, J. 1959. Vergleichende Überprüfung verschiedener Stickstoffverbindungen auf ihre chemische Reaktion mit Rohhumus und die photometrische Erfassung dieses Reaktionseffektes. Z. Pflanzenern. Düng. Bodenk. 85:104-112.

Jung, J. 1961. Wirkung und Ausnutzung des bei der Behandlung von Rohhumus zugeführten Düngerstickstoffs. Landw. Forschung 14:168-176.

Junker, E. 1941. Zur Kenntnis der kolloidchemischen Eigenschaften des Humus. Kolloid Z. 95:213-250.

Kaila, A. 1962. Fixation of ammonium in Finnish soils. Maataloust. Aikak. 34:107-114.

Kaila, A., and Hänninen, P. 1961. Fertilizer nitrogen in soil. Maataloust. Aikak. 33:169-184.

Kanehiro, Y., Nagasako, L. K., and Hadano, M. F. 1960. Leaching loss of nitrogen fertilizers. Hawaii Farm Sci. 9:6-7.

Kardos, L. T. 1955. Soil fixation of plant nutrients. In F. E. Bear, ed. Chemistry of the Soil. Reinhold Publishing Corporation, New York, pp. 177-199.

Karlsson, N. 1952. Kalium i marken. Kungl. Lantbruksakad. Tidskr. 91:297-329.

Kelley, W. P., and Brown, S. M. 1924. Replaceable bases in soils. California Agr. Exp. Sta. Tech. Paper 15.

Kelley, W. P., and Brown, S. M. 1927. Base unsaturation in soils. Proc. First Intern. Congr. Soil Sci. 2:491-507.

Kittrick, J. A., and Jackson, M. L. 1956. Electronmicroscope observations of the reaction of phosphate with minerals, leading to a unified theory of phosphate fixation in soils. J. Soil Sci. 7:81-89.

Laatsch, W. 1948. Untersuchungen über die Bildung und Anreicherung von Humusstoffen. KTL Schriftenreihe "Berichte über Landtechnik." IV. München.

Laatsch W., Baur, I., and Bieneck, O. 1950. Die Bildungsweisen der Huminsäuren. Landw. Forschung 2:38-50.

Laatsch, W., Hoops, L., and Baur, I. 1951. Über Huminsäuren mit Aminostickstoff. Z. Pflanzenern. Düng. Bodenk. 53:20-29.

Legg, J. O., and Allison, F. E. 1959. Recovery of N^{15}-tagged nitrogen from ammonium-fixing soils. Soil Sci. Soc. Am. Proc. 23:131-134.

Leggett, G. E. 1958. Ammonium fixation in soils and minerals. State College of Washington, Project 1253, Dept. Agron., 85 pp.

Leggett, G. E., and Moodie, C. D. 1962. The aeration-recovery method for determining ammonium fixation by soils under moist conditions. Soil Sci. Soc. Am. Proc. 26:160-163.

Leggett, G. E., and Moodie, C. D. 1963. The release of fixed ammonium from soils by sodium as affected by small amounts of potassium or ammonium. Soil Sci. Soc. Am. Proc. 27:645-648.

Levine, A. K., and Joffe, J. S. 1947. Fixation of potassium in relation to exchange capacity of soils: IV. Evidence of fixation through the exchange complex. Soil Sci. 63:329-335.

Lindsay, W. L., Frazier, A. W., and Stephenson, H. F. 1962. Identification of reaction products from phosphate fertilizers in soils. Soil Sci. Soc. Am. Proc. 26:446-452.

Lindsay, W. L., and Taylor, A. W. 1960. Phosphate reaction products in soil and their availability to plants. Trans. 7th Int. Congr. Soil Sci. 3:580-589.

Mackenzie, R. C. 1955. Potassium in clay minerals. In Potassium Symposium. International Potassium Institute, Rome, pp. 123-143.

MacLean, A. J., and Brydon, J. E. 1963. Release and fixation of potassium in different size fractions of some Canadian soils as related to their mineralogy. Canad. J. Soil Sci. 43:123-134.

Malquori, A., and Radaelli, L. 1960. Fosfatolisi e ammonio fissato nel terreno. Agrochimica 4:288-298.

Marel, H. W. van der. 1954. The amount of exchangeable cations of K-fixing soils. Trans. 5th Intern. Congr. Soil Sci. Congr. Leopoldville 2:300-307.

Marel, H. W. van der. 1959. Potassium fixation, a beneficial soil characteristic for crop production. Z. Pflanzenern. Düng. Bodenk. 85:51-63.

Marshall, C. E. 1949. The Colloid Chemistry of the Silicate Minerals. Academic Press, New York, 195 pp.

Mattson, S., and Koutler-Andersson, E. 1941. The acid-base condition in vegetation, litter and humus: IV. The strength of the acidoids and the relation to nitrogen. Lantbrukshögsk. Ann. 9:57-73.

Mattson, S., and Koutler-Andersson, E. 1942. The acid-base condition in vegetation, litter and humus: V. Products of partial oxidation and ammonia fixation. Lantbrukshögsk. Ann. 10:284-332.

Mattson, S., and Koutler-Andersson, E. 1943. The acid-base condition in vegetation, litter and humus: VI. Ammonia fixation and humus nitrogen. Lantbrukshögsk. Ann. 11:107-134.

Mattson, S., and Koutler-Andersson, E. 1954a. Geochemistry of a raised bog. Kungl. Kantbrukshögsk. Ann. 21:321-366.

Mattson, S., and Koutler-Andersson, E. 1954b. The acid-base condition in vegetation, litter and humus. XI. Acid and base in decomposing litter. Kungl. Lantbrukshögsk. Ann. 21:389-400.

Mattson, S., and Koutler-Andersson, E. 1956. Geochemistry of a raised bog. II. Some nitrogen relationships. Kungl. Lantbrukshögsk. Ann. 22:219-224.

McBeth, I. G. 1917. Fixation of ammonia in soils. J. Agr. Res. 9:141-155.

McDonnell, P. M., Stevenson, F. J., and Bremner, J. M. 1959. Release of fixed ammonium from soil by ball milling. Nature 183:1414-1415.

McDowell, L. L., and Smith, G. E. 1958. The retention and reaction of anhydrous ammonia on different soil types. Soil Sci. Soc. Am. Proc. 22:38-42.

McGeorge, W. T. 1945. Base exchange pH relations in semiarid soils. Soil Sci. 59:271-275.

REFERENCES

McIntosh, T. H., and Frederick, L. R. 1958. Distribution and nitrification of anhydrous ammonia in a Nicollet sandy loam. Soil Sci. Soc. Am. Proc. 22:402-405.

Mela Mela, P. 1962. Fixation of ammonium by clay minerals in relation to some probable effects on the vegetative development of plants. Soil Sci. 93:189-194.

Mendez, J. 1963. Fijación de amonio en suelos pratenses de Galicia. Trabajos Jard. Bot., Santiago de Compostela No. 30:41-48.

Mortland, M. M. 1958. Reactions of ammonia in soils. Advances in Agron. 10:325-348.

Mortland, M. M., and Ellis, B. 1959. Release of fixed potassium as a diffusion controlled process. Soil Sci. Soc. Am. Proc. 23:363-364.

Mortland, M. M., Lawton, K., and Uehara, G. 1956. Alteration of biotite to vermiculite by plant growth. Soil Sci. 82:477-481.

Mortland, M. M., Lawton, K., and Ueahara, G. 1957. Fixation and release of potassium by some clay minerals. Soil Sci. Soc. Am. Proc. 21:381-384.

Nõmmik, H. 1957. Fixation and defixation of ammonium in soils. Acta Agric. Scand. 7:395-436.

Nõmmik, H. 1961. Kalium- und Ammoniumfixierung in schwedischen Ackerböden. Kungl. Skogs-och Lantbruksakad. Tidskr. Suppl. 5:28-39.

Nõmmik, H., and Nilsson, K. O. 1963a. Nitrification and movement of anhydrous ammonia in soil. Acta Agric. Scand. 13:205-219.

Nõmmik, H., and Nilsson, K. O. 1963b. Fixation of ammonia by the organic fraction of the soil. Acta Agric. Scand. 13:371-390.

Olsen, C. 1929. Analytical determination of ammonia in soil and the absorption power of soil for ammonia. C. R. Trav. Lab. Carlsberg 17(15):1-18.

Page, J. B., and Baver, L. D. 1940. Ionic size in relation to fixation of cations by colloidal clay. Soil Sci. Soc. Am. Proc. (1939) 4:150-155.

Pauling, L. 1940. The Nature of the Chemical Bond. Ed. 2, Cornell University Press, Ithaca, New York. 450 pp.

Peech, M. 1948. Chemical methods for assessing soil fertility. In H. B. Kitschen, ed. Diagnostic Techniques for Soils and Crops. Am. Potash Inst., Washington, D. C. pp. 1-52.

Pennington, R. P., and Jackson, M. L. 1948. Segregation of clay minerals of polycomponent soil clays. Soil Sci. Soc. Am. Proc. (1947) 12:452-457.

Peterburgskii, A. V., and Korchagina, Yu. I. 1963. The utilization of ammonium nitrogen with respect to its exchange and fixation by soils. (Russ.), Izv. Timiryazevsk. Selśkokhoz. Akad. No. 2:47-61.

Peterson, J. D., and Jennings, D. S. 1938. A study of the chemical equilibrium existing between soluble salts and base-exchange compounds. Soil Sci. 45:277-292.

Pinck, L. A., Howard, L. B., and Hilbert, G. E. 1935. Nitrogenous composition of ammoniated peat and related products. Ind. Eng. Chem. 27:440-445.

Reichenbach, H. 1958. Graf v. Über die Beziehung zwischen Kaliumnachlieferung und Kaliumfestlegung des Bodens. Trans. Int. Soc. Soil Sci. II & IV Comm. 2:188-193.

Reitemeier, R. F. 1951. Soil potassium. Advances in Agron. 3:113-164.

Rich, C. I. 1960. Ammonium fixation by two red-yellow podzolic soils as influenced by interlayer-Al in clay minerals. Trans. 7th Int. Congr. Soil Sci. 4:468-475.

Rich, C. I., and Obenshain, S. S. 1955. Chemical and clay mineral properties of a Red-Yellow Podzolic soil derived from muscovite schist. Soil Sci. Soc. Am. Proc. 19:334-339.

Rich, C. I., and Thomas, G. W. 1960. The clay fraction of soils. Advances in Agron. 12:1-39.

Rodrigues, G. 1954. Fixed ammonia in tropical soils. J. Soil Sci. 5:264-274.

Sawhney, B. L. 1960. Weathering and aluminum interlayers in a soil catena: Hellis-Charlton-Sutton-Leicester. Soil Sci. Soc. Am. Proc. 24:221-226.

Schachtschabel, P. 1937. Aufnahme von nicht-austauschbarem Kali durch die Pflanzen. Bodenk. u. Pflanzenern. 3:107-133.

Schachtschabel, P. 1952. Aufbau und Kolloidchemische Eigenschaften der Tonminerale. Z. Pflanzenern. Düng. Bodenk. 56:227-238.

Schachtschabel, P. 1960. Fixierten Ammoniumstickstoff in Löss- und Marschböden. Trans. 7th Int. Congr. Soil Sci. 2:22-27.

Schachtschabel, P. 1961a. Bestimmung des fixierten NH_4 im Boden. Z. Pflanzenern. Düng. Bodenk. 93:125-136.

Schachtschabel, P. 1961b. Fixierung und Nachlieferung von Kalium- und Ammonium-Ionen. Beurteilung und Bestimmung des Kaliumversorgungsgrades von Böden. Landw. Forschung, 15. Sonderheft: 29-47.

Scheffer, F., Meyer, B., and Fölster, H. 1961. Dreischicht-Tonminerale mit Aluminium-Zwischenschichtbelegung in mitteldeutschen sauren Braunen Waldböden. Z. Pflanzenern. Düng. Bodenk. 92:201-207.

Scholl, W., and Davis, R. O. E. 1933. Ammoniation of peat for fertilizers. Ind. Eng. Chem. 25:1074-1078.

Schouwenburg, J. Ch. van, and Schuffelen, A. C. 1963. Potassium exchange behavior of an illite. Neth. J. Agric. Sci. 11:13-22.

Schreven, D. A. 1963. Nitrogen transformation in the former subaqueous soils of polders recently reclaimed from Lake Ijssel. I. Water-extractable, exchangeable, and fixed ammonium. Plant and Soil 18:143-162.

Schuffelen, A. C., and Marel, H. W. van der. 1955. Potassium fixation in soils. *In* Potassium Symposium. Intern. Potash Institute, Rome. pp. 157-201.

Scott, A. D., Edwards, A. P., and Bremner, J. M. 1960a. Removal of fixed ammonium from clay minerals by cation exchange resins. Nature 185:792.

Scott, A. D., Hanway, J. J., and Edwards, A. P. 1958. Replaceability of ammonium in vermiculite with acid solutions. Soil Sci. Soc. Am. Proc. 22:388-392.

Scott, A. D., Hunziker, R. R., and Hanway, J. J. 1960b. Chemical extraction of potassium from soils and micaceous minerals with solutions containing sodium tetraphenylboron. I. Preliminary experiments. Soil Sci. Soc. Am. Proc. 24:191-194.

Scott, A. D., and Reed, M. G. 1962. Chemical extraction of potassium from soils and micaceous minerals with solutions containing sodium tetraphenylboron. III. Illite. Soil Sci. Soc. Am. Proc. 26:45-48.

Shoji, S., and Matsumi, S. 1961. Chemical characteristics of peat soils. 2. Non-biological fixation of ammonia by peat soils and availability of the fixed ammonia. Res. Bull. Hokkaido Nat. Agr. Exp. Sta. 76:37-41.

Smirnov, P. M., and Fruktova, N. I. 1963. Nonexchangeable fixation of ammonia by soils. (Russ.) Pochvovedenie No. 3:83-93.

Smith, J. P., and Brown, W. E. 1959. X-ray studies of aluminum and iron phosphates containing potassium and ammonium. Am. Mineralogist 44:138-142.

Sohn, J. B., and Peech, M. 1958. Retention and fixation of ammonia by soils. Soil Sci. 85:1-9.

Soubies, L., Gadet, R., and Lenain, M. 1955. Recherches sur l'évolution de l'ureé dans les sols et sur son utilisation comme engrais azote. I. N. R. A. Ann. Agron., Ser. A., 6:997-1033.

Springer, U. 1942. Einfluss der Ammonisierung auf die organische Substanz von Hochmoortorfen. Bodenk. u. Pflanzenern. 28:160-186.

Ståhlberg, S. 1960. Studies on the release of bases from minerals and soils. III. The release of potassium by boiling normal hydrochloric acid. Acta Agric. Scand. 10:185-204.

Stanford, G. 1948. Fixation of potassium in soils under moist conditions and on drying in relation to type of clay mineral. Soil Sci. Soc. Am. Proc. (1947) 12:167-171.

Stanford, G., and Pierre, W. H. 1947. The relation of potassium fixation to ammonium fixation. Soil Sci. Soc. Am. Proc. (1946) 11:155-160.

Stevenson, F. J. 1957a. Investigations of aminopolysaccharides in soils. I. Colorimetric determination of hexosamines in soil hydrolysates. Soil Sci. 83:113-122.

Stevenson, F. J. 1957b. Distribution of the forms of nitrogen in some soil profiles. Soil Sci. Soc. Am. Proc. 21:283-287.

Stevenson, F. J. 1959a. Carbon-nitrogen relationships in soil. Soil Sci. 88:201-208.

Stevenson, F. J. 1959b. On the presence of fixed ammonium in rocks. Science 130:221-222.

Stevenson, F. J., and Dhariwal, A. P. S. 1959. Distribution of fixed ammonium in soils. Soil Sci. Soc. Am. Proc. 23:121-125.

Stevenson, F. J., Dhariwal, A. P. S., and Choudhri, M. B. 1958. Further evidence for naturally occurring fixed ammonium in soils. Soil Sci. 85:42-46.

Stewart, B. A., and Porter, L. K. 1963. Inability of the Kjeldahl method to fully measure indigenous fixed ammonium in some soils. Soil Sci. Soc. Am. Proc. 27:41-43.

Stojanovic, B. J., and Broadbent, F. E. 1960. Recovery of ammonium nitrogen from soils. Soil Sci. 90:93-97.

REFERENCES

2 5 7

Sumner, M. E., and Bolt, G. H. 1962. Isotopic exchange of potassium in an illite under equilibrium conditions. Soil Sci. Soc. Am. Proc. 26:541-544.

Swaby, R. J., and Ladd, J. N. 1962. Chemical nature, microbial resistance, and origin of soil humus. Trans. Int. Soc. Soil Sci. Comm. IV and V, 197-202.

Tamimi, Y. N., Kanehiro, Y., and Sherman, G. D. 1963. Ammonium fixation in amorphous Hawaiian soils. Soil Sci. 95:426-430.

Taylor, A. W., and Gurney, E. L. 1961. Solubilities of potassium and ammonium taranakites. J. Phys. Chem. 65:1613-1616.

Taylor, A. W., Lindsay, W. L., Huffman, E. O., and Gurney, E. L. 1963. Potassium and ammonium taranakites, amorphous aluminum phosphate, and variscite as sources of phosphate for plants. Soil Sci. Soc. Am. Proc. 27:148-151.

Themlitz, R. 1955. Zur Frage der Ausnutzung des von Rohhumus aus Ammoniak in fester Bindung aufgenommenen Stickstoff und der Stickstoffaufnahme aus Schwefelsaurem Ammoniak und Kalkammonsalpeter in Gegenwart von Rohhumus durch Nadelholzsämlinge. Z. Pflanzenern. Düng. Bodenk. 70:207-220.

Themlitz, R. 1956a. Die Stickstoffestlegung aus schwefelsaurem Ammoniak durch Fichtenrohhumus bei verschiedener Reaktion. Z. Pflanzenern. Düng. Bodenk 73:202-209.

Themlitz, R. 1956b. Zersetzungsgeschwindigkeit von Kalkstickstoff in Gegenwart von Fichtenrohhumus und Umwandlung desselben durch Cyanamid in Vergleich zu Ammoniak bei verschiedener Reaktion. Z. Pflanzenern. Düng. Bodenk. 75:257-268.

Themlitz, R. 1958. Umsetzung verschiedener N-Dünger mit einem durch voraufgegangene Bestandskalkung bzw. -stickstoffdüngung umgewandelten Fichtenrohhumus. Z. Pflanzenern. Düng. Bodenk. 82:165-174.

Troug, E., and Jones, R. J. 1938. Fate of soluble potash applied to soils. Ind. Eng. Chem. 30:882-885.

Violande, Aurora T. 1958. Ammonia fixation by soil organic matter: relations between forms of nitrogen and components of soil organic matter. Ph.D. Thesis, Cornell University, New York. Dissertation Abstr. 19:35.

Volk, N. J. 1934. The fixation of potash in difficultly available form in soils. Soil Sci. 37:267-287.

Wada, K. 1959. Reaction of phosphate with allophane and halloysite. Soil Sci. 87:325-330.

Walsh, L. M., and Murdock, J. T. 1960. Native fixed ammonium and fixation of applied ammonium in several Wisconsin soils. Soil Sci. 89:183-193.

Walsh, L. M., and Murdock, J. T. 1963. Recovery of fixed ammonium by corn in greenhouse studies. Soil Sci. Soc. Am. Proc. 27:200-204.

Wanstallen, R. 1960. Fiksatie en vervluchtiging van ammoniakale stikstof. Pédologie 10:15-22.

Wear, J. I., and White, J. L. 1951. Potassium fixation in clay minerals as related to crystal structure. Soil Sci. 71:1-14.

Welch, L. F., and Scott, A. D. 1959. Nitrification in nutrient solution with low levels of potassium. Can. J. Bact. 5:425-430.

Welch, L. F., and Scott, A. D. 1960. Nitrification of fixed ammonium in clay minerals as affected by added potassium. Soil Sci. 90:79-85.

Welch, L. F., and Scott, A. D. 1961. Availability of nonexchangeable soil potassium to plants as affected by added potassium and ammonium. Soil Sci. Soc. Am. Proc. 25:102-104.

Welte, E., and Niederbudde, E. A. 1963. Die unterschiedliche Bindungsfestigkeit von fixierten Kalium und ihre mineralogische Deutung. Plant and Soil 18:176-190.

Wiklander, L. 1950. Fixation of potassium by clays saturated with different cations. Soil Sci. 69:261-268.

Wiklander, L. 1954. Forms of potassium in the soil. In Potassium Symposium. International Potash Institute, Zurich. pp. 109-121.

Wiklander, L. 1958. The soil. In W. Ruhland, ed. Handbuch der Pflanzenphysiologie, Band IV, Springer-Verlag, Berlin-Göttingen-Heidelberg. pp. 118-169.

Wiklander, L. 1960. Kalium i skånska åkerjordar. Socker, Handlingar I, 16 (6):51-63.

Wiklander, L., and Andersson, E. 1959. Kalkens markeffekt. III. Kemiska undersökningar av ett långvarigt kalkningsförsök på skifte IV vid Lanna. Grundförbättring 12:1-40.

Wittich, W. 1961. Die Grundlagen der Stickstoffernährung des Waldes und Möglichkeiten für ihre Verbesserung. *In* Der Stickstoff. Seine Bedeutung für die Landwirtschaft und die Ernährung der Welt. Fachverband Stickstoffindustrie e. V. Düsseldorf. pp. 331-369.

Young, J. L. 1962. Inorganic soil nitrogen and carbon:nitrogen ratios of some Pacific Northwest soils. Soil Sci. 93:397-404.

Young, J. L., and Cattani, R. A. 1962. Mineral fixation of anhydrous NH_3 by air-dry soils. Soil Sci. Soc. Am. Proc. 26:147-152.

Chapter 6

Physical Chemistry and Biological Chemistry of Clay Mineral-Organic Nitrogen Complexes

A. D. McLAREN AND G. H. PETERSON

University of California at Berkeley and
California State College at Hayward

I. CLAYS AS ADSORBENTS AND REACTANTS: THERMODYNAMIC CONSIDERATIONS

Complexes between clays and organic materials are of importance from many points of view. Clays are useful as cracking catalysts in the petroleum industry, as adsorbents in the purification of proteins (Zittle, 1953), and in the clarification of industrial products and sewage. Their ubiquity in soil in conjugation with soil organic matter has resulted in the expenditure of countless hours by investigators everywhere (Gieseking, 1949), and much of the mystery that is soil remains as the mystery of the true nature of these complexes.

In the laboratory one can prepare innumerable complexes with clay and products of the organic chemist's art. Some of these are doubtlessly analogous to those in soil. The depth of this analogy, however, has yet to be shown. In this chapter we will discuss clay-organo complexes in the light of recent theories of adsorption and modern polymer chemistry.

Micromolecules. The classical treatment of the adsorption of molecules from the gaseous state by surfaces of solids, is, of course, that of Langmuir (Alexander and Johnson, 1949). In soils we are, however, concerned with the adsorption of solutes onto surfaces from solution. Formally, the treatment is the same; for although water is also adsorbed, it is frequently present in great excess on a molecular basis, and its concentration, or activity, when liquid water is present, may be taken as constant or unity. The diffusion of nonvolatile solutes will be almost nil in the absence of liquid water.

Let the adsorbing surface area of the solid adsorbing phase be A, and let a be the surface of the adsorbent occupied by the single adsorbate under consideration. If the adsorbent is initially in contact with water only, the adsorption of a solute entails an elution of water from the adsorption site on the solid. The rate of adsorption is $k_a(A-a)(S)$, where (S) is the concentration of solute, and $(A-a)$ is the free surface concentration of adsorbent—that is, the hydrated surface not occupied by S. The rate of desorption is given by $k_d(a)$. k_a and k_d are proportionality constants. An equilibrium constant, k_m, is now defined as the ratio of the specific reaction rate constants, k_a/k_d. The basis for this treatment is that the mass law applied; i.e., the adsorbate does not interact with itself on the surface to form dimers, trimers, etc. at high surface concentrations so as to change the value of k_d and the affinity of all surface sites for the solute is the same.

At equilibrium, the fraction of adsorbent covered by adsorbate S is given by equating the rates; i.e.,

$$a/A = K_m(S)/1 + K_m(S). \qquad [1]$$

As an approximation, this equation holds for many combinations of solute and solid (Alexander and Johnson, 1949). At high values of (S), $a \to A$ and the solid may be said to be saturated. At intermediate values of (S), it can readily be shown that $a/A \approx K(S)^{1/p}$, where K is the Freundlich coefficient and p is a number greater than unity; this is the Freundlich equation for the adsorption equilibrium. It may also be derived from geometric considerations (Gyani, 1945).

Macromolecules. Frisch and co-workers have extended this line of thinking to the situation in which the solute consists of macromolecules such as polyvinyl alcohol and others having structures of the type

$$\left[\begin{array}{c} \text{H} \quad \text{H} \\ | \quad\; | \\ -\text{C}-\text{C}- \\ | \quad\; | \\ \text{H} \quad \text{X} \end{array} \right]_n,$$

where X is H, OH, COOH, etc. and n is the degree of polymerization. The degree may be 10^2 to 10^4 or more. The monomer unit is

$$\left[\begin{array}{c} \text{H} \quad \text{H} \\ | \quad\; | \\ -\text{C}-\text{C}- \\ | \quad\; | \\ \text{H} \quad \text{X} \end{array} \right].$$

In proteins the monomer unit is

$$\begin{array}{c} \text{H} \quad\;\; \text{H} \\ | \quad\;\;\; | \\ -\text{N}-\text{C(R)}-\text{CO}- \end{array}$$

and R may be ionizable.

Let A consist of N equivalent, uniformly distributed sites each capable of binding one and only one segment of the macromolecule. Let this surface be placed in contact with a dilute solution consisting of N macromolecules in a solvent; let each macromolecule consist of t segments, of which v are deposited on the surface.

At any instant during adsorption $\theta = a/A = vN_s/N$ where N_s is the number of adsorbed macromolecules.

We need a kinetic argument for the following equilibrium:

$$\text{Macromolecules in } \overset{\text{rate of}}{\underset{\underset{\text{re-solution}}{\text{rate of}}}{\text{deposition}}} \text{ Macromolecules adsorbed,}$$
$$\text{solution } (S) \qquad\qquad N_s, \text{ held at } \nu \text{ segments.}$$

In a study of the adsorption of polyvinyl acetate on chrome-plate, it has been found that there is little interaction between adsorbed molecules (Peterson and Kwei, 1961). Therefore, for the rate of deposition the probability of finding an unoccupied site is proportional to $1 - \theta$, and the probability of finding ν sites at random is proportional to $(1 - \theta)\nu$. Thus, the rate of deposition is $K_a(S)(1 - \theta)^\nu$. The rate of desorption is proportional to the number of adsorbed molecules N_s which in turn is proportional to θ/ν, since $N_s = N\theta/\nu$; it is given by $k_d\theta/\nu$.

At equilibrium

$$\theta = K_\nu(S)\nu(1 - \theta)^\nu \qquad\qquad [2]$$

where $K_\nu = k_a/k_d$.

Now a number of special cases exist, depending on the magnitude of ν and the specificity of the segment adsorption. Frisch (1958) gives examples:

Special Case A. For a stiff or a flexible molecule which is completely deposited, $\nu = t$ and the isotherm, Equation [2], becomes

$$\theta = K_t(S)t(1 - \theta)^t. \qquad\qquad [3]$$

If $t = 1, \theta = K(S)/1 + K(S)$: namely, Equation [1].

Special Case B. For a polymer with stiff (e.g., helical) molecules which gives adsorption at a distinguished segment occurring regularly every T segments, $\nu = t/T$ and we have

$$\theta = K_T(S)t(1 - \theta)^{t/T}/T. \qquad\qquad [4]$$

Now it is characteristic of some isotherms of high polymers—for example, the proteins (Fig. 1b)—that the initial adsorption at low (S) is very great. This steep initial rise is determined by the magnitude of ν since by Equation [2]

$$d\theta/d(S)_{\theta\to0} = K_\nu\nu = K_t t/T. \qquad\qquad [5]$$

The equations so far discussed have neglected adsorption of solvents. If each surface site can accommodate one solvent molecule and the solution is sufficiently dilute, the area covered by polymer is

$$\theta = K_\nu(S)(1 - \beta)^\nu\nu(1 - \theta)^\nu \qquad\qquad [6]$$

where $\beta = K_0S_0/(1 + K_0S_0)$. S_0 is the solvent concentration and K_0 is the corresponding constant for the solvent adsorption isotherm. A sophisticated discussion of these equations may be found elsewhere (Frisch and Simha, 1954).

In the structural formulas above, X and R may also contain ammonium, $-NH_3^+$. During the adsorption step, the polyvalent cations can replace monovalent cations from an ionizable surface. Frisch believes that these equations will still apply to electrically charged polymers as long as the counter ion cloud essentially makes the forces involved short ranged.

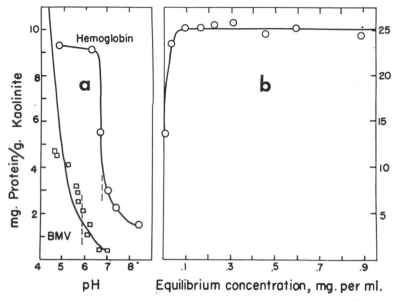

Fig. 1. Adsorption of hemoglobin and southern bean mosaic virus on kaolinite. a: adsorption on 0.0346 g clay from solutions of 0.37 mg hemoglobin in 8 ml suspension and from solutions of virus containing 0.12 mg, both as a function of pH. The dashed vertical lines show the isoelectric points of the adsorbates, respectively. b: adsorption isotherm for hemoglobin in 0.02M phosphate buffer, pH 6.2 ± 0.1.

Frisch and Stillinger (1962) have taken up this difficult problem of the adsorption of polyelectrolytes at planar dielectric surfaces and have computed the Langmuir constants, K, in terms of both the electrical and non-electrostatic contributions to the free energy change of adsorption. By equation [5], at low concentrations $\theta/S = K$; K, the affinity constant, is analogous to an interfacial Henry's law constant. It will be recalled that the free energy change, F, is related to K and the enthalpy, H, and entropy, S, changes of adsorption by

$$K = e(-\exp \Delta F/RT) \quad \text{and} \quad \Delta F = \Delta H - T \Delta S, \qquad [7]$$

where T is absolute temperature. One aspect of this problem which is of importance in attempts to extract organic matter from clays is that of elution. Consider a solid surface with negative charges in contact with a solution of R_n—NH_3^+, where R is an organic moiety containing a number of carbon atoms, n. For $n = $ a small number, let R_n be ethyl; for $n = $ a large number, let R_2 be polyvinyl and R_3 be a protein (ignoring the negative charges on the protein molecules). Let the solution contain equal equivalent weights of polymer and ethylammonium, say 0.001 normal for each species. Let us now consider the adsorption of these species on the solid surface and assume that the heat of binding is the same for an —NH_3^+ group regardless of the size of R_n. The entropy change of adsorption should be greater with R_1 than with R_2 because on R_2 the —NH_3^+ group has less freedom than on R_1: on R_2 it is attached to a polymer chain. With R_2, therefore, the $-NH_3^+$ has less entropy (freedom) to lose on adsorption. Ammonium groups have even less freedom on the relatively non-flexible, cross linked chains of a protein molecule. Thus, for the corresponding free energy changes (decreases) of adsorption, ΔF_3 is greater than ΔF_2 is greater than ΔF_1. By Equation [7], the adsorption from a mixture of $R_1NH_3^+$ and $R_3NH_3^+$ would be greatly in favor of $R_3NH_3^+$ (Ruehrwein and Ward, 1952; McLaren, 1953). We have found with proteins that it takes $0.1MR_1NH_3^+$ solution to elute about 25% of an adsorbed protein at about $10^{-5}M$ total protein concentration.

Irrespective of the mechanism of adsorption, phenomenologically the free energy change is given by

$$dF_{T,P,A} = \mu' dn' + \mu'' dn''$$
$$= -(\mu^0 + RT \ln 1) dn' + (\mu^0 + RT \ln a) dn'' \qquad [8]$$

for the transfer of dn' moles of solute from the solution state at unit activity to the adsorbed state at an activity a. μ^0 is the chemical potential of solute at unit activity, dn'' is the moles of adsorbed solute and $dn'' = -dn'$; i.e., the solution loses dn moles as the adsorbent gains dn moles. By Equation [8], $dF = RT \ln (S) \, dn$ and

$$\int dF = nRT \ln (S) + RT \int_S^0 nd \ln (S). \qquad [9]$$

We have substituted concentration for activity since, at low concentrations, polymer solutions, such as proteins, do not differ much from ideality (Bull, 1956). The first term gives the free energy change on going from a solution of unit concentration of solute to one of concentration (S) in equilibrium with adsorbed solute, and the second term gives the energy change in covering the adsorbent surface as this equilibrium is reached. Bull (1957) has found that the free energy of adsorption of one mole of egg albumin from a hypothetical one molal solution on Pyrex glass is -6829 cal/mole, a quite substantial quantity. (Since the molecular weight of albumin is 45,000, a 1 molal solution is fractional.) It is difficult to remove the protein from the glass with acetate buffer. By contrast, ΔF for replacement of sodium by aliphatic amines of the formula $C_nH_{2n+1}NH_2^+$ on bentonite varies from only -350 to -2740 calories (Slabaugh, 1954).

We can say that nature has utilized three ways of rendering organic materials less accessible to digestive processes: *polymerization* (cellulose is less readily digestible by enzymes and microorganisms than glucose); *adsorption* of the material on surfaces (proteins adsorbed on clays are less digestible than in solution for a given amount of protease in a unit volume of materials); and *crystallization* (e.g., quasi-crystalline cellulose is less easily digested than amorphous starch, and the phosphorus in minerals is less readily available to fungi and bacteria than it is as superphosphate).

It is well known that following a drying and rewetting of soil there is a burst of microbial activity, and this could mean that adsorbed organic material has been eluted and solubilized by exchange with salts which become concentrated in the soil solution during drying. As far as we know, no one has been able to elute soil enzymes from soil particles. Perhaps, in addition to physical adsorption to clays, enzymes are chemically attached to the soil humus. If so, however, this humus must be that fraction which is not eluted by the usual extractive solvents.

II. SORPTION OF MICROMOLECULAR NITROGEN COMPOUNDS

A. Amines

By titrating kaolinite suspensions with cetyltrimethylammonium bromide in the acid range, Cashen (1959) found that the negative charge of the clay is reduced. At the same time, the pH of the external solution was reduced. Evidently the organic cation neutralizes negative sites on the clay. The surface charge density of exchangeable cations on kaolinite (and margarite) has been calculated to be greater than on montmorillonite, vermiculite or mica, however, and is so great that quantitative exchange with large quaternary ammonium ions is not obtained. This phenomenon is known as a "cover up effect" (Hendricks, 1941; Weiss, 1959; White and Cowan, 1960). With kaolinite, illite and montmorillonite, the relatively small butylamine is sorbed up to the exchange capacity, and Grim et al. (1947) report that sorption of dodecylamine can exceed the exchange capacity (e.c.); presumably Van der Waals' attraction must be invoked to account for the additional affinity.

This association of amines with clays is sufficiently strong to reduce the capacity of clays to adsorb water and to swell (Grim et al., 1947; Gieseking, 1939).

Gieseking (1939) did not find any correlation between d(001) interplanar spacings of montmorillonite clay-salts and molecular dimensions of the organic cation. Both Hendricks (1941) and Gieseking noted the apparent d(001) spacings may be constant over a wide range of sorption, even from 0.1 to 0.7 me./g with o-phenylenediamine and montmorillonite. Other examples are shown in Fig. 2. Hendricks also found that some weak bases—e.g., nitroaniline—do not form clay-salts, whereas others—e.g. benzidine and naphthylamine—were sorbed in amounts equivalent to the exchange capacity of the clay used (0.92 me./g). Alkaloids were found to neutralize less of the hydrogen on the clay than benzidine, but the remaining hydrogen was only partially replaceable by barium, indicating a "cover-up effect" of theoretically replaceable hydrogen by these organic bases. A naphthylamine salt swelled at 70% relative humidity of water, but the phenylenediamine salts did not, indicating that the diamine acts as a cross-linking agent which holds the clay sheets together.

In interpreting his work, Hendricks pointed out that the variable distance between sheets will be determined, for any given organic cation, by a combination of Coulombic and Van der Waals forces acting in such a way as to obtain a maximum total force of attraction. "In other words, the maximum number of atoms possible within the molecule would, consistent with the characteristic separation of the ionic portion, approach

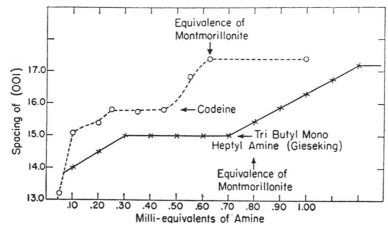

Fig. 2. Interplanar spacing for (001) of codeine and heptyltributylammonium montmorillonites as a function of amine content. (Hendricks, 1941).

the oxygen surface of the silicate layer. This distance of approach would be determined by Van der Waals' radii for the various atoms." For example, between an ammonium content of 0.3 and 0.7 me./g, a single layer [d(001) = 15 Å] of heptyltributyl ammonium ion is formed. Below 0.3 me./g a single layer is not present between all sheets, and above 0.7 me./g double layers of amines are formed. Above 1 me. additional ammonium salt is formed by Van der Waals' adsorption, as no further ion exchange is possible (cf. Kurilenkod and Mikhalyuk, 1959). Aromatic compounds have to be oriented so that the rings are in planes parallel to the sheets in order that the spacings found be consistent with known atomic radii of adsorbate atoms.

As saturation of bentonite is approached by the addition of complex bases such as the alkaloids, flocculation occurs. Water washing of the clay-salt removes some base; 1% NaCl removes considerably more (Smith, 1939).

Thus far we can see that we are dealing with the conceptually inexact domain of colloid chemistry. From a physical chemical point of view we can say that with clay colloids we have added *form* to the chemical *functions* of classical chemistry. This is to say, although clays have some properties similar to those of soluble acids (binding of hydrogen ions, negative charges) they also have a gross geometry not found markedly manifest in simple acids such as butyric and sulfuric. The geometry may so bias stoichiometry as to lead to "cover-up effects," and Van der Waals' association, as well as to ion exchange and flocculation.

Clays, as cationic salts, must also be thought of as specific entities; by illustration, sodium in montmorillonite is replaced stoichiometrically upon the addition of long chain aliphatic amines, whereas calcium and magnesium clays require greater than stoichiometric amounts of the organic bases for replacement during titration (McAtee, 1959). Polyamine bases give a more complicated result (Mortland and Gieseking, 1949). With paraphenylenediamine and diethylenetriamine, complexes are formed with bentonite which have residual amino groups for anion sorption and exchange. A reaction may be written as follows:

$$H—Clay + NH_3^+—R—NH_3^+(H_2PO_4^-)_2 \rightarrow$$
$$Clay—NH_3—R—NH_3^+(H_2PO_4^-) + H_3PO_4.$$

Upon drying of these complexes, a "mechanical trapping" of the organic moiety and phosphate occurs, and the sorbed phosphate exhibits reduced exchangeability with sulfuric acid.

In an effort to sort out some of the structural chemistry of the sorption process, Palmer and Bauer (1961) exposed dry Wyoming bentonite (93 me. Na+, 2 me. K+, 9 me. Ca²⁺ per 100 g) to dry amines and measured the rates of adsorption. The relative rates are given in Table 1. An

Table 1. Rates of sorption of amines by bentonite.

Amine	Relative rate	Activation energy (Kcal)	Me. adsorbed (max.)/g
Methyl	1	1.4	2.7
Ethyl	0.79	1.3	1.5
Dimethyl	0.76	1.4	1.4
Trimethyl	0.21	5	0.5

analysis of the initial relative rates showed that sorption was a linear function of time of sorption to the one-half power, which is typical of many diffusion controlled processes, for the first three amines. The activation energy for diffusion was about the same for the amines with a nitrogen proton. Trimethylamine diffused much slower and entailed a higher activation energy for diffusion. For this the authors assume that the clay has two kinds of internal sorption sites: one at the internal oxide surface where amines with N-protons can adsorb through hydrogen bonding and the other at cation sites where amines could sorb through ion-dipole interaction. The latter type sites would be the ion exchangeable sites for the same clay in water solutions of these bases. In the gaseous system, a small amount of dry amine seemed to adsorb instantaneously; this was probably amine sticking to the external surfaces of the clay particles. The explanation offered accounts for the fact that the same amount of the isomers ethylamine and dimethylamine are sorbed by the clay (Table 1). Since the metal cation exchange capacity is ca.[1] me./g, about 0.6 me. of these amines would be held by the first mechanism, as could 1.8 me. of methylamine. The latter amine is smaller than the isomers, and more equivalents could be held by hydrogen bonding. The fourth amine, trimethyl, has 4 carbons, as compared with 2 for the isomers, so that the 0.5 me. found is comparable with 0.6 for that portion of the isomers held only by hydrogen bonding.

It would be very nice to see if that portion of the amines held by the first mechanism would be eluted if the corresponding adsorbents (complexes) were placed in gaseous or liquid water.

Slabaugh and Kerpka (1958) have calculated heats of exchange and the corresponding free energies and entropies for the exchange of calcium on montmorillonite by the isomers n-butylamine and diethylamine and by n-octylamine. They also concluded that two hydrogens on nitrogen provides for a greater affinity of an amine for the oxygen silicate layer than one, and an increase in the length of the carbon chain results in a greater affinity because of a greater Van der Waals' attraction between the surface and the hydrocarbon moiety. In fact, these Van der Waals' forces are sufficient to allow intercalation of monomethylammonium montmorillonites by the hydrocarbons iso-butane, cyclohexane and benzene (Barrer and MacLeod, 1955; Barrer and Kelsey, 1961a). By contrast, however, dimethyldioctadecyl ammonium bentonite shows no such porosity. Evidently the large alkyl groups of this cation take up all the possible space into which other hydrocarbons might go. Heats of adsorption of these liquids are very small, much too small to "melt" the clay structure so that additional layers of molecules might be sorbed.

The sorption of urea by montmorillonite salts of Na, Mg, Ca, Ba, and Al must take place with the formation of hydrogen bonds only since urea has an exceedingly low dissociation constant as a cation. The sorption can lead to at least a double layer of urea, except with K and NH_4 clay (Shiga, 1961).

Amines sorbed at the ionic sites in water have been studied by Cowan and White (1958). n-Heptylamine completely saturates the cation exchange positions, whereas amounts of longer chain amines in excess of the e.c. can be taken up. Short chain amines can be washed out of the complex salts with water, but not all of the longer amines are so elutable (cf. Jordan, 1949). Cowan and White also reached the conclusion that the amine adsorbed in excess of the e.c. was in the free form $(RNH_2{}^+)$ and not in the cationic form $(RNH_3{}^+)$. It is no wonder that mass action quotients do not give consistent values; as no simple sorption mechanism applies, no simple exchange equilibrium equation will be valid. Likewise, a Langmuir sorption isotherm cannot be applied since sorption sites of more than one energy occur, and multilayers of amine, or perhaps rearrangements of sorbed amine molecules, also seem possible (Palmer and Bauer, 1961). In addition to the release of monovalent ions by clays as amines are adsorbed, aluminum ions may also be liberated (Sieskind and Wey, 1958b). The liberation of aluminum increases as the pH is lowered.

From the standpoint of hydrocarbon cracking catalysts, the acidity of clays is of importance. This is a generalized acidity and may be studied with Hammet indicators by titration with butyl amine in non-aqueous systems. As this is out of the present interest, the reader is merely referred to Benesi (1957) for details.

Other clays have, of course, also been studied, with results similar to those discussed with kaolin and montmorillonite. Aminex in ionic form penetrates between layers of micas and vermiculite (Weiss et al., 1956). Sutherland and MacEwan (1961) found a linear relationship between X-ray spacings and number of carbon atoms per alkyl chain sorbed a slope of 2.3Å/carbon atom suggested orientation of the alkyl chains perpendicular to the sheets.

Illite has been reported as showing no base-exchange capacity with several cations. Potassium does exchange with alkylammonium ions with the production of an organophilic illite capable of being extracted by benzene from a benzene-water suspension (Weiss et al., 1956b).

At this point we will summarize some available data on dimensions of some clay-amine complexes. In a gross sense one can certainly expect to find an increase in X-ray d(001) spacings of individual montmorillonite particles which have taken up amines since the amounts taken up by clay would amount to an improbably large number of multilayers if adsorption took place only on external particulate surfaces. In fact, as the uptake of amines approaches the e.c. of bentonite, the gel volume of suspensions of alkylammonium clay in nitrobenzene approaches a maximum (Jordan, 1949a) and then declines as the e.c. is exceeded, which indicates a change in orientation of alkyl chains at an amount of sorption for which no reason could be found if sorption were only external to the particles of adsorbent.

Following the early observations of Hendricks and of Gieseking, Bradley (1945) analyzed the spacings of amine-montmorillonite complexes, He found d(001) to be from 13.1-13.4 Å and interpreted the figures to mean that center to center distances between the aliphatic chain and oxygen was 3.3 to 3.6 Å. These distances are about those expected from Van der Waals' radii for $O—CH_2$. Since, however, the complexes are stable even in water, the energies of attraction must be strong enough for hydrogen bounding between O and CH. This notion was extended by MacEwan (1948) to explain the shorter than normal radii of CH_3 in methanol adsorbed on halloysite—namely, 4Å in the free state and 3.4Å in the adsorbed state.

A fundamental difficulty with all such studies is to know exactly how much sorbed amine must be present to have exactly an intracrystalline monolayer. Adsorption isotherms are not always helpful as they do not always level off to an apparent saturation (Cowan and White, 1958), and when they do, with the short chain amines, the maximal sorption can exceed the exchange capacity of the clay. It then becomes difficult to decide whether the X-ray spacings found correspond to the presence of mixtures of monolayers and double layers or to reordering and repacking of the alkyl chains. Further, a study of fifteen montmorillonites selected on the basis of minor differences in X-ray diffraction and differential thermal analysis and treated with ethylene glycol, piperidine, and dodecylamine lead to the following conclusions (Byrne, 1954):

(a) All the clays had mixed-layer sequences; i.e., adjacent layers differ from one another in composition or structure, and (b) the organo-clay complexes show differences ascribable to differences in the clays. For these reasons, we feel that X-ray data is a powerful tool for detecting and measuring inter-layer expansion but that it may be pressing the technique too far to write about slight variations in bond lengths of the adsorbates *in situ*. Although it is probably safe to conclude that aromatic rings lie planar to intracrystalline sheets—for example, with clays which have been immersed in solutions of pyridine, nitro phenol and the like (Green-Kelley, 1955)—to conclude that an observed spacing is really significantly less than a Van der Waals' thickness observed in organic crystals is neglecting the probable presence of *average* clay-salt spacings in the diffraction patterns. The average can be lower than a monolayer spacing if the clays are not perfectly regular and if some spacings are empty. As an added example of an *ad hoc* explanation, Franzen's observation of a spacing of 38.6Å for cetyltrimethylammonium bromide may be cited. This spacing corresponds to the uptake of 2.4 times the e.c., and Franzen concluded that the chains were arranged at an angle of approximately 45° to the clay surfaces (Franzen, 1955).

Heat has an interesting effect. Up to 180°C, a reversible expansion of the basal spacing of a dimethyldioctadecylammonium bentonite takes place. During heating, an increase in the intensity of the diffraction peaks is found, suggesting to the authors (McAtee and Concilio, 1959) that a certain amount of untangling of alkyl chains takes place which allows for a more uniform packing. At higher temperatures, amines are burned out; this is accompanied by a decline in spacing to 9.8Å (Allaway, 1948; Ramachandran et al., 1961).

In addition to the stepwise hydration of bentonite, up to four monolayers, and the stepwise sorption of organic molecules, one may also encounter the stepwise hydration of an organic-clay complex. Five discrete hydrates of picoline-clay and two of pyridine-clay salts have been observed (Van Olphen and Deeds, 1962).

Jordan et al. have examined some of the physical properties of amine-bentonite salts (Jordan, 1949a, b; Jordan et al., 1950). Ease of filtration with dodecyl-clay complexes was best at 100 to 150 me. base/100 g clay but above 100 mc. the retention of the amine was poor, showing that the free energy decrease of sorption of water exceeds that of part of the amine, probably that part held by Van der Waals' attraction. The purified clay had a cation exchange capacity of about 100 me./100 g, and at this base/clay ratio the viscosity of a 1.9% clay suspension was a maximum for octadecylammonium (ca. 24 centipoise). At this ration, the clay-salt in an organic liquid gives a gel with the greatest strength as measured with an A.S.T.M. grease cone. Stronger gels were obtained as the alkyl chain was increased from 12 to 18 carbons. In the range below 50 me., the d(001) spacing was 9.6 + 4.0Å; between 60 and 100 me. the spacing was 9.6 + 8.0Å and above 155 me./100 g clay, the spacing was 9.6 + 23.5Å. The data with these salts has been interpreted to mean that at first one and two layers of amine are adsorbed with chains parallel to the internal plane sheets of clay micro-crystals; and eventually, in order for large amounts of amine to be sorbed, the aliphatic chains must pack perpendicularly to the planes.

In passing, it may be cited that alkylammonium bentonite complexes have been utilized to separate benzene from cyclohexane in a gas chromatographic procedure (Barrer and Hampton, 1957; White and Cowan, 1958).

Among 77 amines tested, those of the aniline type give color reactions with bentonite; oxygen is not implicated (Hauser and Leggett, 1940), but traces of iron may be causative (Turner, 1955). Nutman has noted color development in bentonite near growing clover roots, which may come from exuded indole compounds (Nutman, 1951). Ferric ethylenediaminetetraacetate can sorb to clays, presumably via EDTA-Fe-clay linkage. The chelates do not enter the montmorillonite particles (Wallace and Lunt, 1956).

B. Amino Acids and Nucleotides

Simple amino acids have three possible ionic forms in water: namely, $NH_3^+CH(R)COOH$, $NH_3^+CH(R)CO_2^-$, and $NH_2CH(R)CO_2^-$, and the relative amounts of each depend on the pH. At low pH, the first form is comparable to aliphatic amines in acid medium. In such media, Sieskind and Wey (1958b) found that as the chain of an amine increases in length (C_2, C_4, C_6) the amount which adsorbs to H-montmorillonite increases; but with each amine H^+ competes with RNH_3^+ for the surface. Sieskind (1960) also found that at pH 2 only those amino acids with a K_b greater than 3×10^{-11} are sorbed sufficiently to achieve saturation of the clay by an isotherm of the Langmuir type and commensurate with the e.c. of the clay. These include beta- and gamma-amino-butyric acids. Alanine and alpha-aminobutyric acid were sorbed only slightly from solutions containing as much as 6 equivalents of acid per 100 g clay. From X-ray data he concluded that the sorbed amino acids separated the clay platelets by $2.8 - 3.3Å$ [$d(001) = 12.4 - 12.9Å$]. Similarly, Talibudeen (1955) found a spacing of $3.6Å$ for alanine and $3.1Å$ for glycine as compared with $5.6Å$ and $4.1Å$ for the Van der Waals' thickness of the amino acids and concluded in the usual way (Bradley, 1945; Grimm et al., 1947) that the discrepancies of about $1Å$ are "attributed to H-bonding to the oxygen sheets on either side of the adsorbed molecule." As we have shown (1958), this is inadmissible, since values up to $4.5Å$ can be found which are not linear functions of the amount of sorption, and which occur when only 3.1 me. of alanine is adsorbed per 100 g clay (Fig. 3). X-ray data do not seem to be available for the region of saturation of clays by amino acids, and without having sorption isotherms and X-ray data on the same materials, attempts to interpret spacings are premature. As we will see, the case with proteins is not so bleak.

The influence of pH on the relative uptake of alanine by montmorillonite has also been studied. Adsorption of alanine shows a maximum of pH 1 to pH 2, a decline beyond pK_a and a further decline above pH 9 at pK_b (McLaren et al., 1958).

Two types of swelling of vermiculite with sorbed amino acids have been observed (Walker and Garrett, 1961). With ornithine, lysine, and gamma-aminobutyric acid, swelling resembles that with butylammonium-vermiculite complexes and occurs after the amino-acid has replaced magnesium by cation exchange, up to 120 to 180 me./100 g. Presumably by osmosis, subsequent dilution of the system with water brings about swelling of single crystals. Separation of the silicate layers to some hundreds of angstroms occurs. If the clay is placed in concentrated solutions of amino acids (e.g., beta-alanine, epsilon-amino caproic) in the dipolar form, ion exchange is not appreciable but the swelling is proportional to concentration. The mechanism is thought to involve a masking of charges of the exchangeable cations within the clay so that attraction between

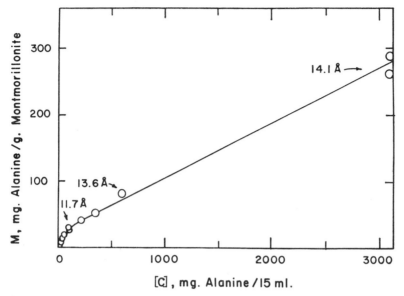

Fig. 3. Adsorption isotherm of alanine on montmorillonite at pH 2. Some d (001) spacings are shown in the figure. (McLaren et al., 1958).

them and the silicate layers is reduced. The dielectric constant of the immersion solution is perhaps the controlling factor (Barshad, 1952).

In an early contribution, Hendricks (1941) decided from X-ray diffraction data that nucleotides sorbed in montmorillonite were oriented with their planar aromatic rings parallel to the silicate sheets. "At equivalent pH values, clay concentrations and organic phosphorus concentrations," mononucleotides were adsorbed to Na-bentonite in amounts in the descending order: 3-adenylic acid > cytidylic acid > guanylic acid; the sorption of guanylic acid to a gram of bentonite was about 12 times that to a gram of kaolinite (Goring and Bartholomew, 1952).

C. Antibiotics and Herbicides

The adsorption of herbicides and other organic compounds by clay minerals has been recently reviewed and studied in some detail by Frissel (1961). The shape of the adsorption isotherm for 3-p-chlorophenyl-1-dimethylurea depends on the salt concentration. At a low salt concentration the isotherm with montmorillonite is linear, and at high salt concentration (3.6 N NaCl, pH 7) the curve is convex to the abscissa: i.e., more of the Raoult than of the Langmuir type in shape. The ureide is practically undissociated at neutral pH. This contrasts with the sorption of methylene blue, which is of the cationic type and somewhat like that expected from Langmuir's equation.

Streptomycin is readily adsorbed by bentonite and illite and by field soils. In bentonite some is found to penetrate the clay with an increase in d(001) spacing (Sminoff and Gottlieb, 1951). By contrast, chloromycetin is weakly sorbed by soil and clay minerals (Gottlieb and Sminoff, 1952). Because of sorption of chloromycetin, terramycin, and aureomycin (Martin and Gottlieb, 1952), *B. subtilis* can grow in the presence of these compounds in soil unless the total concentration is quite high in comparison with the minimal inhibitory quantities required in liquid broth. Of various buffers tested, phosphates are the best eluting agents for basic antibiotics and citrate for amphoteric compounds sorbed on clays (Soulides et al., 1961). Assays that depend on extraction of streptomycin from soil or diffusion from the soil into the assay medium are not adequate. The antibiotic in soil can be assayed by growing a suitable microorganism on an agar medium in which the soil has been dispersed. The sorbed antibiotic is released by the assay procedure; thus, inactivation due to adsorption need not be permanent (Pramer and Starkey, 1962).

D. Discussion

During the nutrition and metabolism of organic nitrogen and phosphorus compounds by plant roots and soil microflora and fauna, intermediate products and byproducts are continuously being shifted from point to point in the soil micro-environment (McLaren, 1962). The nitrogen and phosphorus are distributed among the various phases of soil. Some is found in microbial tissue, a little is in soil solution, but the bulk of the organic forms are attached to and interspersed among soil minerals ranging from the clays to the sands. The attachment is far from that of a simple monolayer, however, and in some instances the attachment of gross material can be seen in soil thin sections, with the aid of the microscope, as an incrustation on soil particles (Russell, 1957). As we have seen, the mechanism of sorption of micromolecules to clays in the laboratory is one to which classical theories of adsorption and ion exchange can be applied as a first approximation. At present it is not known whether the attachment of soil organic matter to clays is entirely via these mechanisms. For example, it is possible to prepare organic derivatives of the clays with acid anhydrides according to the reaction (Chakrravarti, 1959; Slabaugh, 1952):

$$\text{Clay Si-OH} + (\text{RCO})_2\text{O} \rightarrow \text{Clay Si-OCOR} + \text{RCO}_2\text{H};$$

and it is entirely possible that some of the monomolecular layers of soil organic matter at the clay surface are attached by covalent linkages. Furthermore, we have been unable to find any proof that organic matter is found between sheets of the montmorillonites isolated from soil (see below) even though it is stated that ammonium humates will enter these mineral particles under laboratory conditions (Kononova, 1962). In order for an organic molecule to penetrate within a clay particle, it must be soluble in the soil solution. If soluble, it is subject to attack by soil enzymes and microbes and would be taken up by the latter. Once in the clay particle, it is still subject to the action of enzymes (Estermann et al., 1959).

Another thing that is not clear is how the additional organic matter on the soil minerals is built up to microns in thickness. This could be brought about by any of the following mechanisms: (a) breakdown of microbial cells on the soil particles, (b) flocculation of soil organic colloids of microbial and plant origin, (c) accretion of organic matter from the alimentary tracts of mites, worms, etc., (d) condensation of penolic with amino residues of lignins and peptides and (e) polymerization of vinyl compounds and unsaturated esters by means of free radicals normally found in humic acid (Steelink and Tollin, 1962). Polymerization mechanisms, which undoubtedly occur to some extent, can account for the difficultly soluble portions of organic matter which are residual after the most powerful solvents have been used to extract soil.

As a consequence of the various states of organic matter in soil, we are not yet in a position to say exactly where a substance added deliberately to soil will be adsorbed or absorbed preferentially. Any free—i.e., "pure" —clay could certainly act as an absorbent and indirect evidence points to this. For example, in Panama the effective banana-producing lifetime of soils is determined by the rate of spread of *Fusarium* wilt. In an effort to correlate soil lives-time with soil characteristics, Stotzky et al. (1961) investigated soil texture, pH, soluble salts, cation exchange capacity, available phosphorus, organic matter, drainage, and clay mineral content. It was found that only one direct relationship existed: montmorillonite-type clay minerals were present in all the "good" soils (20) and were completely absent in all but 2 out of 14 poor soils. At present it is not known whether the important mechanism involves a clay-host relationship or a clay-pathogen interaction. Montmorillonite is an especially good absorbent for some amino acids, antibiotics, enzymes, and cations in general. It could function either as an absorbent for *Fusarium* toxins or *Fusarium*-stimulating compounds secreted by the plant.

On the other hand, since, as we have shown, high polymeric materials will tend to be adsorbed to surfaces more strongly than micromolecules, in a typical soil little free mineral surface would expectedly be available for the sorption of urea, amines, aliphatic acids, amino acids, and like compounds. Such micromolecules could, of course, be sorbed as solid solutions with macromolecules or be present as mixed salts with them.

The killing of weeds with herbicides has resulted in a group of problems under the heading of persistence of herbicides in soil. The main problem consists in deciding which choice of herbicide to make in terms of whether it is expected to be active long enough to inhibit a second crop of weeds or whether it will persist long enough to spoil a subsequent commercial planting. Factors of influence in persistence are volatility, drainage, covering land with an impenetrable foil, etc. and the nutrition of soil microorganisms. Soils rich in organic matter, and under conditions of high moisture and high temperature, exhibit the most rapid breakdown of organic herbicides. In general, where use is made of the persistence of herbicides in soil, there is a delicate balance between success or failure which is dictated by rainfall, period of fallowness and crop rotation. The addition of borates to soil, along with 2,4-D (2-4-dichlorophenoxyacetic acid), reduces microbial attack of the latter. Another approach is to reduce the volatility of some of the less persistent agents (Woodford and Sagar, 1960).

The effect of herbicides on soil microorganisms has been summarized by W. W. Fletcher (in Woodford and Sagar), and the microbiological breakdown of these substances has been reviewed by L. J. Audus (same reference). At normal field rates of application, nitrifying organisms and proteolytic activity are not suppressed by 2,4-D. Indeed, perfusion of 2,4-D through garden loam shows a rapid rate of disappearance after a lag period of about two weeks. During the first two weeks the soil flora undergo the familiar "enrichment" with respect to those organisms which can adapt to a new substrate. Once adapted, many organisms persist and retain a complement of enzymes active toward this substrate long after the substrate is removed. It is well known that enzymes and microbes are active in the adsorbed state as well as in solution (McLaren, 1962) and that enzymes can act on adsorbed substrates, but how much activity takes place on soil surfaces with herbicides and in soil solution following elution has not been established.

Although a number of workers have tried to find antibiotic activity in unadulterated normal soil, only recently has an example been found. In newly cleared lateritic sandy soils in Western Australia, there can be found a proliferation of certain fungi, notably *Aspergillus* and *Penicillium* species, which produces antibiotics antagonistic toward *Rhizobium trifoli* and to the clover host plants. The normal symbiotic relationship is prevented and the clover fails to establish. Aqueous extracts from such soils have shown toxicity toward the clover bacteria (Holland and Parker, 1962). Evidently these soils are too low in clays of sufficient adsorption capacity to bind all the antibiotics produced.

III. SORPTION OF MACROMOLECULES BY CLAYS

Organic molecules in the hands of chemists can be classified in many ways; one of the obvious is according to molecular size—i.e., weight and dimensions. Practically speaking, those of molecular weights below 1000 may be called micromolecular and those above 10,000, high molecular or macromolecular (Jirgensons and Straumanis, 1954). The latter fall into the range of the classical colloidal particle. By addition polymerization, one tends to get macromolecules with weights much above 10^4, but by condensation nature provides us with the entire range of size, up to millions with nucleic acids for example. Efforts to measure these weights with solutions of soil organic matter have resulted in values in the hundreds of thousands, but we have no idea how close these solutes compare with known structures of natural and synthetic polymers. Again we return to model systems of clays and purified polymers.

Macromolecules which are built up systematically from monomer units are referred to generally as polymers. For example, in polyvinyl acetate (PVA), $CH_2 = CH—O—COCH_3$ (vinyl acetate) is the monomer and $[—CH_2—CH—O—COCH_3—]n$ is the polymer, and n being in the neighborhood of 200 to 2,000 in commercial samples. In any given sample, n is a variable with characteristic mean and most probable numbers. Some of the most recent fundamental work has been done with this material, so we will dwell with it for a moment.

The kinetics of adsorption of PVA on chrome-plate is of the Langmuir type. The polymer coil in benzene solution becomes adsorbed initially with only a few segment-to-surface contacts. This is followed by a reorientation until the polymer has nearly all segments in contact with the surface (Peterson and Kwei, 1961). The fraction of attached segments (monomer units) of polyalkyl-methacrylate on silica has been found to be [v/t] 0.36 and accounts for the fact that in some cases more polymer can be adsorbed on a surface than can be accounted for by a monolayer of fully adsorbed molecular chains of monomer units (Fontana and Thomas, 1961). Contrary to experience with small molecules in which the enthalpy change of adsorption is negative, which leads to a decrease in sorption with increasing temperature, the adsorption of PVA on some surfaces can increase with temperature. Since the free energy change must be negative for adsorption to take place, and since the entropy change over all substances is positive because of the elution of several solvent molecules per polymer molecule adsorbed, the enthalpy is actually positive (Koral et al., 1958).

A. Polyelectrolytes

In the examples just discussed, adsorption involves only Van der Waals' forces. With polycations such as poly-beta-dimethylamino-ethylmethacrylate hydro-acetate (DMAEM), ion exchange is also possible. This linear polymer, consisting of long threadlike molecules, also penetrates montmorillonite particles to give spacings up to 4.4Å (0.67 g/g clay). DMAEM and polyvinylbutylpyridinium bromide (PVBP) flocculate kaolinite suspensions in water at equivalent concentrations only 1/270 that required of sodium and 1/50 that of calcium and aluminum (Ruehrwein and Ward, 1952). Clearly, these polycations attach so closely to the clay surfaces as to suppress almost completely the zeta potentials of such particles.

It is by now well known that polyanions such as polyacrylic acid (where X=COOH) and pectic acid also adsorb to clays, but the sorption is confined to the external surfaces of montmorillonite particles (Ruehrwein and Ward, 1952). Although it has been suggested that sorption is brought about by the formation of ionic linkages of the type Clay—Ca—COO
|
C(H)—CH$_2$—(polymer), divalent metals need not be present as the relatively small amounts of positive charges found on clays and hydrogen bonding seem to be quite sufficient (Emerson, 1956; Warkentin and Miller, 1958; Michaels, 1954; Mortensen, 1957). As the pH of the clay suspensions increases, sorption of the polyanions by kaolinite decreases, especially above pH 7-8 (Michaels and Morelos, 1955; Evans and Russell, 1959). This may be attributed to a repulsion between the increased negative charges of the clay and the polyanion as the clay is titrated.

As might be expected, polycations, although more expensive than commercial polyanions, are also able to affect physical properties of soil and soil suspensions markedly. For example, both poly-4-vinyl-N-n-butylpyridinium bromide and the sodium salt of hydrolyzed polyacrylonitrile improved the crumb stability of a Columbia silt loam soil in the wet-sieving technique (McLaren and Luse, 1955; Yoder, 1936).

B. Enzymes and Other Proteins

The sorption of amphoteric molecules such as the proteins encompasses the same considerations as do the synthetic polyelectrolytes just discussed, with some added features (Neurath and Bull, 1954). Molecules of most soluble proteins are more tightly coiled into structures much more nearly spherical in shape than are molecules of polyelectrolytes in a charged condition. Being preponderantly cationic below the isoelectric point, a protein shows very strong adsorption to clays and can diffuse into the clay particles of montmorillonite. In fact, the clay can be used as a caliper on a molecular scale to give the size of protein molecules (McLaren and Peterson, 1961). For this purpose one must be certain that a complete mono-molecular layer of protein has been adsorbed, and this can be calculated to require 1.3-2.0 g of protein per gram of clay. Details of the experimental procedure follow.

A Wyoming bentonite sample was prepared first by forming a 2% suspension. By sedimentation according to Stokes' Law, the less than 0.5μ fraction was collected. This fine clay was then condensed by extracting the excess water from the suspension with Chamberlin filter candles. To the clay gel enough citric acid solution of an appropriate concentration was added to obtain a 0.5 M citric acid suspension. After washing the clay twice in 0.5 M citric acid solutions, the clay was washed with water to remove any citrate. This hydrogen bentonite was titrated to pH 8.0 with NaOH. Various amounts of protein were added to vials containing clay and buffer. The vials were placed on a vertical wheel; the wheel was placed in a constant temperature bath (25°C) and slowly rotated. Preliminary experiments showed that the length of time before a net increase in adsorption stopped varied between 2 and 5 days. Where it was deemed necessary, experiments were performed to determine the amounts of protein denatured at the liquid-air interface in a given length of time. After rotating the suspension for the desired time, the clay complex was centrifuged down. The protein concentration in the supernatant liquid was determined by use of a spectrophotometer set at 2800Å. In order to obtain the (001) spacing of the clay-protein complex, the clay pellet was removed from the bottom of the cellulose nitrate centrifuge cup and placed on a watch glass. When the sample was air dried, it was ground and passed through a 140-mesh screen. The powder sample was then packed into glass capillaries, and the capillaries then were placed into a glass cylinder which could be evacuated. After evacuation, the glass cylinder was heated to 105°C for a period of 5 hours. (A constant 001 spacing is obtained before the 5-hour period has ended.) After the drying is completed the capillaries are sealed. For X-ray diffraction studies copper $K\alpha 1$ radiation was used.

Assuming that protein molecules are spherical, we have calculated the expected d(001) spacings and compared them with the experimental values found (Table 2); the agreement is moderately good for all but pep-

Table 2. Adsorption of proteins by montmorillonite.

Protein	Mol. wt.	Adsorption (g /g)		Calc. mol. diam., Å	d(001), Theoret- ical	A Experi- mental
		Theoret- ical	Experi- mental			
Lysozyme (native)	14,700	1.3	1.3	32.6	42.2	44
(denatured)	14,700	---	1.3	----	----	46
Chymotrypsinogen	22,500	1.5	1.4	37.2	46.8	40
Lactoglobulin	(17,500)*			(34.8)	(44.4)	--
Pepsin	35,000	1.7	1.0	43.8	53	18
Haemoglobin	63,000	2.0	1.9	53.2	62.8	53
(Human)	(40,000)*			(45.6)	(55.2)	--

* These proteins dissociate under extreme conditions of dilution and/or salt concentration to give the values in parentheses.

sin. Haemoglobin appears to be adsorbed as a monomer, whereas lactoglobulin enters the clay particles as a dimer.

Our results with native pepsin agree with that of Talibudeen (1955): namely, that the d(001) spacing is about 18Å for a wide range of amounts of protein adsorbed; it indicates an unfolding of pepsin molecules into extended polypeptide chains within the clay particles. Pepsin has a distinct tendency to unfold and become a linear molecule because of a high intramolecular electrostatic repulsion; it behaves much like a polyanion in solution (McLaren and Lewis, 1950).

Tobacco mosaic virus (isoelectric point 3.5) was allowed to react with sodium bentonite at pH 3.2 (citrate buffer, ionic strength 0.0375). According to analysis, 1,830 mg of virus was adsorbed per g of clay. At this value, about 15% of the internal surface area of the clay could be covered with the virus. However, X-ray data indicated that internal adsorption had not taken place. Apparently the size of the virus, molecular weight ca. 40,000,000, exceeds the penetrability limit for this clay.

All proteins examined adsorb on the external surface of kaolin below and somewhat above their isoelectric points (Fig. 1a). Tobacco mosaic virus also adsorbs on kaolinite, and electron micrographs show very clearly that no virus particles adhere to the edges of the clay crystals; TMV is clearly discernible on the flat face surfaces. The particles lie flat to the surface in more or less irregular array: i.e., without much two-dimensional order. This is not to suggest that protein cannot absorb to the edges of kaolin at higher pH, provided they have sufficiently high isoelectric points, but it would be very difficult to determine this with the electron microscope, owing to the small size of typical protein molecules. One might be successful with ferritin, which consists of large molecules containing electron dense cores of iron oxide.

The adsorption of a protein by kaolinite seems to follow the Frisch-Langmuir isotherm (Equation 2) rather than the simple Langmuir equation, which points to a relatively large number of points of attachment of a protein to the clay. Even so, probably not all of the exchange sites on kaolinite are involved (McLaren, 1954). At saturation of a Na-clay by lysozyme, only about one-fourth of the sodium is exchanged and eluted. A lysozyme molecule can cover about $834Å^2$, and the area per exchange site averaged over the surface of this clay is only about $80Å^2$, so a protein molecule may cover many surface exchange sites. In fact, by means of sorption studies with fractionated kaolinite, it has been shown that the maximum amount of protein which can be adsorbed is more closely related to surface area than to surface charge of the clay fractions (McLaren et al., 1958).

At low pH where COOH groups in proteins are not ionized, nor are titratable groups on the clay, binding to the clay is probably via hydrogen bonds to OH groups on the clay surface (one face; the other contains O only). At neutral pH, ion exchange, as already illustrated, undoubtedly plays a role in sorption. Far above the isoelectric point of a protein, both the clay and the protein are negatively charged and electrostatic repulsion reduces sorption drastically. Qualitatively, the same story applies to other kinds of clays (Gieseking and Ensminger, 1939), but, by contrast, the sorption of a protein (lysozyme) by sodium montmorillonite in suspension results in the release of essentially all the bound sodium into the aqueous phase.

Some proteins, notably lysozyme and soybean-trypsin-inhibitor, can be eluted from montmorillonite and kaolinite under appropriate conditions of pH and salt concentration and are found to have retained biochemical activity (Sober and Peterson, 1957; Wiklander, 1957). Thus, sorption is a reversible process. Whether the process exhibits hysteresis has not been studied.

C. Nucleic Acids

As with proteins, the rate of sorption of nucleic acids by clays is rapid. The equilibrium amounts of nucleic acid adsorbed are the same at 7° and 45°. Normally, with micromolecules, sorption decreases with increasing temperature; but entropy effects with flexible macromolecules are quite complicated (see above), and the net effect of a rise in temperature over such a narrow range as 38° may be just the opposite or nil (Zittle, 1953). Adsorption of nucleic acids to clays is greater in the presence of divalent ions than with sodium or potassium. Some penetration of bentonite clay crystals takes place, presumably because of the cationic groups on the macromolecules. Since these polymers have low isoelectric points, repulsion between them and clays can only be reduced by suppression of ionization of the clay; as is to be expected, sorption increases with decreasing pH below neutrality (Goring and Bartholomew, 1952).

D. Discussion

There is a great deal of evidence that enzymes in the sorbed state or even attached to solids or gels by covalent linkages are, in many cases, still catalytically active (reviewed by Wiklander, 1957; Kiss, 1958; Sober and Peterson, 1957). The literature has been summarized elsewhere (McLaren, 1962). This evidence is based on two kinds of studies, namely those in which enzymes have been added to clay suspensions and those in which the enzyme activity of clay and silt fractions of soil have been tested with suitable substrates. For example, esterase activity in soil seems to be associated with the clay fraction; all attempts to elute the "enzyme" from the clay failed, however (Haig, 1955). On the other hand, chymotrypsin is active when adsorbed on kaolinite. It is less active if adsorbed directly on the clay than when adsorbed on clay covered first with substrate (McLaren and Estermann, 1956). In the latter case, a striking observation is that the pH optimum for the enzyme action is shifted two pH units toward the alkaline region, reflecting a fact that the pH at the surface of the clays, kaolinite and montmorillonite (Peterson, 1957) is lower than in the ambient buffer solution. As has been shown elsewhere, the enzyme responds to the greater hydrogen ion *concentration* existing near the negatively charged clay (the hydrogen ion activity is the same everywhere in a system at equilibrium) (McLaren and Babcock, 1959).

It has sometimes been found that the adsorption of enzymes by clays reduces enzyme activity. This can indeed be the case (McLaren and Estermann, 1956), but strictly speaking, it is necessary to compare the enzyme at the optimum pH for activity in the adsorbed state with the enzyme at the pH for optimum activity in solution, rather than to compare the enzyme action at a single pH of the liquid phase (McLaren and Estermann, 1957). For example, at pH 6 in suspension, adsorbed chymotrypsin appears to be inactive, but soluble chymotrypsin at this pH is quite active; at pH 9, however, the enzyme is active in either state. This phenomenon may in part explain the apparent suppressing influence of clays on phosphatase (Mortland and Gieseking, 1952). Generally, however, adsorption of an enzyme to a surface leads to a partial reduction of enzyme activity even at corresponding pH optima.

The sorption of proteins between the expanding sheet lattice of montmorillonite or on kaolinite offers little determent to the proteolytic action of chymotrypsin or bacterial enzymes (Skujins et al., 1959; Estermann et al., 1959; Estermann and McLaren, 1959). In order to study the kinetics of the action of a soluble enzyme which will first adsorb upon a solid substrate and then act upon it hydrolytically, one must develop a new equation. This has recently been reported (McLaren, 1962) and has the form:

$$v = k'E_0A/(E_0A_E + A_E/K_m + A - a)$$

where v is the initial velocity of reaction, E_0 is the total amount of enzyme in the system, A is the total surface area of the substrate, A_E is the area occupied per mole by adsorbed enzyme, K_m is the equilibrium constant for the adsorption of the enzyme, a is the area covered by adsorbed enzyme and k' is a proportionality constant. Unlike the classic equations for enzyme action in solution, the rate is not directly proportional to E_0. Although this equation has been tested in model systems, it has yet to be applied to soil organic matter.

Since enzymes are proteins and, like non-enzymatic proteins, are subject to proteolysis by proteolytic enzymes, one would expect to find little free protein in soil, and this is definitely the case (Tinsley and Zin, 1954). Furthermore, nucleotides and amino acids are nutrients for microorganisms so the amounts of these compounds free in soil would also be expectedly small (see, e.g., Paul and Schmidt, 1960; and Adams et al., 1954). Neither silicic acid polymer, lignin nor clays protect proteins from digestion to a significant extent for extended time periods (see, e.g., Estermann et al., 1959, for discussion) and clay-proteins and "ligno-proteins" complexes have not been found in soil in appreciable amounts (Jenkinson and Tinsley, 1960). The quest for the origin of amino acids released by acid digestion of soil organic matter has led to the suggestion of amino acid-polymer complexes quite different than those postulated by Waksman and others (Waksman and Iyer, 1932). The newer theories are summarized by Kononova (1962).

IV. CONCLUDING REMARKS

As we have seen, studies of the adsorption of organic nitrogen compounds by clays is of marked theoretical interest. Advantage of these studies has been taken in the field of protein purification. In field practice, the relevance of these studies is not obvious, and all theories regarding the influence of polymers and clays on the stability of soil nitrogen compounds have been inadequate; the detailed chemical nature of the bulk of the soil organic nitrogen, and, incidentally, phosphorus compounds has yet to be determined. All solvent extraction studies must take into account the possibility of the existence of insoluble, three-dimensional polymeric components in soil of the bakelite type, which, however, intimately tied to clays, are beyond present day analytical procedures. All of these substances serve as sources of soluble nitrogen liberated by the action of microorganisms. Were they completely intractable, soil nitrogen would be continuously building up to staggering amounts. Clearly, microbial enzyme systems are sharper tools for cleavage of soil nitrogen polymers than are the routine chemicals of the laboratory.

Acknowledgment

This work was supported in part by U. S. Atomic Energy Commission Contract AT-(11-1)-34, project 50 and U. S. Public Health Service Grant G-4236.

REFERENCES

Adams, A. P., Bartholomew, W. V., and Clark, F. E. 1954. Measurements of nucleic acid components in soil. Soil Sci. Soc. Am. Proc. 18:40-46.

REFERENCES

Alexander, A. E., and Johnson, P. 1949. Colloid Science. Clarendon Press, Oxford.

Allaway, W. H. 1948. Differential thermal analysis of clays treated with organic cation as an aid in the study of soil colloids. Soil Sci. Soc. Am. Proc. 13:183-188.

Barrer, R. M. and Hampton, M. G. 1957. Gas chromatography and mixture isotherms in alkyl ammonium bentonites. Trans. Faraday Soc. 53:1462-1475.

Barrer, R. M. and Kelsey, K. E. 1961a. Thermodynamics of interlamellar complexes. I. Hydrocarbons in methylammonium montmorillonites. Trans. Faraday Soc. 57:452-462.

Barrer, R. M. and Kelsey, K. E. 1961b. Sorption of dimethyldioctadecylammoniumby bentonite. Trans. Faraday Soc. 57:625-640.

Barrer, R. M. and MacLeod, D. J. 1955. Activation of montmorillonite by ion-exchange and adsorption of tetra-alkyl ammonium montmorillonite. Trans. Faraday Soc. 51:1290-1300.

Barshad, I. 1952. Factors affecting the interlayer expansion of vermiculite and montmorillonite with organic substances. Soil Sci. Soc. Am. Proc. 16:176-182.

Benesi, H. A. 1957. Acidity of catalyst surfaces II. Amine titration using Hammet indicators. J. Phys. Chem. 61:973-975.

Bradley, W. E. F. 1945. Moleculer association between montmorillonite and some polyfunctional organic substances. J. Am. Chem. Soc. 67:975-981.

Bull, H. B. 1956. Adsorption of bovine serum albumin on glass. Biochem. Biophys. Acta. 19:464-471.

Bull, H. B. 1957. Adsorbed monolayers of egg albumin. Archives Biochem. Biophys. 68:102-111.

Bryne, P. J. S. 1954. Some observations on montmorillonite-organic complexes. Proc. Second National Conferences on Clays and Clay Minerals, pp. 241-253.

Casher, G. H. 1959. Electric charges of kaolin. Trans. Faraday Soc. 55:477-486.

Chakravarti, S. K. 1959. Base exchange properties and organophilic characteristic of organic derivatives of clay minerals and their mixture. J. Indian Soc. Soil Sci. 7:27-35.

Cowan, C. T. and White, D. 1958. The mechanism of exchange reactions occurring between sodium montmorillonite and various n-primary aliphatic amine salts. Trans. Faraday Soc. 54:691-697.

Emerson, W. W. 1956. Synthetic soil conditioners. J. Agric. Sci. 47:117-121.

Estermann, E. F. and McLaren, A. D. 1959. Stimulation of bacterial proteolysis by adsorbents. J. Soil Sci. 10:64-78.

Estermann, E. F., Peterson, G. H. and McLaren, A. D. 1959. Digestion of clay-protein, lignin-protein, and silica-protein complexes by enzymes and bacteria. Soil Sci. Soc. Am. Proc. 23:31-36.

Evans, L. T. and Russell, E. W. 1959. The adsorption of humic and fulvic acids by clays. J. Soil Sci. 10:119-132.

Fontana, B. J. and Thomas, J. R. 1961. The configuration of adsorbed alkyl methacrylate polymers by infrared and sedimentation studies. J. Phys. Chem. 65:480-487.

Franzer, P. 1955. X-ray analysis of an adsorption complex of montmorillonite with cetyltrimethylammonium bromide. Clay Minerals Bull. 2:223-225.

Frisch, H. L. 1958. Private Communication.

Frisch, H. L. and Simha, R. 1954. The adsorption of flexible macromolecules. II. J. Phys. Chem. 58:507-512.

Frisch, H. L. and Stillinger, F. H. 1962. On the adsorption of polyelectrolytes at planar dielectric substrates. J. Phys. Chem. 66:823-828.

Frissel, M. J. 1961. The adsorption of some organic compounds, especially, herbicides, on clay minerals. Versl. Lundbouwk. Onderz. NR67.3-Wageningen.

Gieseking, J. E. 1939. The mechanism of cation exchange in montmorillonite-beidellite-nontronite type of clay minerals. Soil Sci. 47:1-14.

Gieseking, J. E. 1949. The clay minerals in soils. Adv. Agronomy 1:159-204.

Gieseking, J. E. and Ensminger, L. E. 1939. Adsorption of proteins by montmorillonitic clays. Soil Sci. 48:467-474.

Goring, C. A. I. and Bartholomew, W. V. 1952. Adsorption of mononucleotides, nucleic acids and nucleoproteins by clays. Soil Sci. 74:149-164.

Gottlieb, D. and Sminoff, P. 1952. The production and role of antibiotics in the soil. II. chloromycetin. Phytopath. 42, 91-97.

Green-Kelly, R. 1955. Sorption of aromatic organic compounds by montmorillonite. I. Orientation studies: Trans. Faraday Soc. 51:412-424.

Grim, R. E., Allaway, W. H. and Cuthbert, F. L. 1947. Reaction of different clay minerals with some organic cations. J. Am. Ceram. Soc. 30:137-142.

Gyani, B. P. 1945. Distribution law, adsorption and chemical reaction. J. Phys. Chem. 49:442.

Haig, A. D. 1955. Some characteristics of esterase-and-urease-like activity in the soil. Ph.D. Thesis, University of California, Davis.

Hauser, E. A. and Leggett. 1940. Color reactions between clays and amines. J. Am. Chem. Soc. 62:1811-1814.

Hendricks, S. B. 1941. Base exchange of the clay mineral montmorillonite. J. Phys. Chem. 45:65-81.

Holland, A. A. and Parkes, C. A. 1962. Microbiol intervention in the establishment of clover pasture. 8th International Congress for Microbiology. Montreal.

Jenkinson, D. S. and Tinsley, G. 1960. A comparison of the ligno-protein isolated from a mineral soil and from a straw compost. Royal Dublin Soc. Scientific Proc. IA:141-148.

Jirgenson, B. and Straumanis, M. E. 1954. A short textbook of colloid chemistry. John Wiley, New York. p. 18.

Jordan, J. W. 1949a. Alteration of the properties of bentonite by reaction with amines. Minerol. Mag. 28:598-605.

Jordan, J. W. 1949b. Organophilic bentonites I. Swelling in organic liquids. J. Phys. Colloid Chem. 53:294-306.

Jordan, J. W., Hooks, J. B. and Finlayson, C. M. 1950. Organophillic bentonites. II. Organic liquid gels. J. Phys. Colloid Chem. 54:1196-1208.

Kiss, I. 1958. Talajenzimek (Soil Enzymes) in Caspo, I. M. Talajtan (Soil Science). State Agro-Silvic Pub. Bucharest, Roumania. Addendum.

Kononova, M. M. 1962. Soil organic matter. Pergamon Press Inc., Cambridge.

Kord, J., Ullman, R. and Eirich, F. R. 1958. The adsorption of polyvinylacetate. J. Phys. Chem. 62:541-550.

Kurilenko, O. D. and Mikhalyik, R. V. 1959. Adsorption of aliphatic amines on bentonite from aqueous solutions. Kolloid Z hur. 21:181-184.

MacEvan, D. M. C. 1948. Complexes of clays with organic compounds. I. Complex formations between montmorillonite and halloysite and certain organic liquids. Trans. Faraday Soc. 44:349-368.

McAtee, J. L. 1959. Inorganic-organic cation exchange on montmorillonite. Am. Mineral. 44:1230-1236.

McAtee, J. L. and Concilio, C. B. 1959. Effect of heat on an organo-montmorillonite complex. Am. Mineral. 44:1219-1229.

McLaren, A. D. 1954. The adsorption and reactions of enzymes and proteins on kaolinite. I. J. Phys. Chem. 58:129-137.

McLaren, A. D. 1963. Enzyme activity in soils sterilized by ionizing radiation and some comments on microenvironments in nature. 8th International Congress for Microbiology, Montreal, 19-25 August 1962. Recent Progress in Microbiology, VIII, University of Toronto Press, Toronto, pp. 221-229.

McLaren, A. D. and Babcock, K. L. and Hayashi, T. 1959. Sub-Cellular Particles. Ronald Press, New York, p. 23.

McLaren, A. D. and Estermann, E. F. 1956. The adsorption and reactions of enzymes and proteins on kaolinite. III. The isolation of enzyme-substrate complexes. Archives Biochem. Biophys. 61:158-173.

McLaren, A. D. and Estermann, E. F. 1957. Influence of pH on the activity of chymotrypsin at a solid-liquid interface. Archives Biochem. Biophys. 68:157-160.

McLaren, A. D. and Lewis, C. 1950. Concerning the inactivation-denaturation of pepsin. J. Polymer Sci. 5:379-381.

McLaren, A. D. and Luse, R. A. 1956. Unpublished information.

McLaren, A. D. and Peterson, G. H. 1961. Montmorillonite as a caliper for the size of protein molecules. Nature. 192:960-961.

McLaren, A. D., Peterson, G. H. and Barshad, I. 1958. The adsorption and reactions of enzymes and proteins on clay minerals: IV. Kaolinite and montmorillonite. Soil Sci. Soc. Am. Proc. 22:239-244.

Martin, N. and Gottlieb, D. 1952. The production and role of antibiotics in soil. III. Terramycin and aureomycin. Phytopath. 42:294-296.

Michaels, A. S. 1954. Aggregation of suspensions by polyelectrolytes. Ind. Eng. Chem. 46:1485-1490.

Michaels, A. S. and Morelos, O. 1955. Polyelectrolyte adsorption by kaolinite. Ind. Eng. Chem. 47:1801-1809.

Mortensen, J. L. 1957. Adsorption of hydrolyzed polyacrylonitrite on kaolinite. I. Effect of exchange cation and anion. Soil Sci. Soc. Am. Proc. 21:385-388.

Mortland, M. M. and Gieseking, J. E. 1952. The influence of clay minerals on the enzymatic hydrolysis of organic phosphorus compounds. Soil Sci. Soc. 16:10-13.

Neurath, H. and Bull, H. B. 1938. The surface activities of proteins. Chem. Revs. 23:391-435.

Nutman, P. S. 1951. Color reactions between clay minerals and root secretions. Nature 167:288.

Palmer, J. and Bauer, N. 1961. Sorption of amines by montmorillonite. J. Phys. Chem. 65:894-895.

Paul, E. A. and Schmidt, E. L. 1960. Extraction of free amino acids from soil. Soil Sci. Soc. Am. Proc. 24:195-198.

Peterson, C. and Kwei, T. K. 1961. The kinetics of polymer adsorption onto solid surfaces. J. Phys. Chem. 65:1330-1333.

Peterson, G. H. 1957. The adsorption and reactions of enzymes and proteins on montmorillonite. Ph.D. Thesis, University of California.

Pramer, D. and Starkey, R. L. 1962. Determination of streptomycin in soil and the effect of soil colloidal material on its activity. Soil Sci. 94:48-54.

Ramachandran, V. S., Garg, S. P. and Kacker, K. P. 1961. Mechanism of thermal decomposition of organo-montmorillonites. Chem. and Ind. 23:790-792.

Russell, E. J. 1962. The World of the Soil. Collins. London. p. 66. 1957.

Ruehrwein, R. A. and Ward, D. W. 1952a. Mechanism of clay aggregation by polyelectrolytes. Soil Sci. 63:485-492.

Ruehrwein, R. A. and Ward, D. W. 1952b. Mechanism of clay aggregation by polyelectrolytes. Soil Sci. 73:485-492.

Shiga, Y. 1961. Studies on the complexes of montmorines with urea and its derivatives. I. The influence of exchangeable cations on the interlayer adsorption of urea by montmorines. Soil and Plant Food. 7:119-124.

Sieskind, O. 1960. Study of adsorption complexes between H-montmorillonite and certain amino acids. Adsorption isotherms at pH 2 and 20°. C. R. Acad. Sci. Paris 250:2228-2230, 2392-2393.

Sieskind, O. and Wey, R. 1958a. Influence on pH on the adsorption of normal aliphatic amines on H-montmorillonite. C. R. Acad. Sci. Paris. 247:74-76.

Sieskind, O. and Wey, R. 1958b. Adsorption of aliphatic amines on montmorillonite. Bull. Groupe franc. argiles. 10:9-14.

Skujins, J. J., Estermann, E. F. and McLaren, A. D. 1959. Proteolytic activity of *bacillus subtilis* in a clay-protein paste system analogous to soil. Can. J. Microbiol. 5:631-639.

Slabaugh, W. H. 1952. The synthesis of organo-bentonite anhydrides. J. Phys. Chem. 56:748.

Slabaugh, W. H. 1954. Cation exchange properties of bentonite. J. Phys. Chem. 58:162-165.

Slabaugh, W. H. and Kupka, F. 1958. Organic cation exchange properties of calcium montmorillonite. J. Phys. Chem. 62:599-601.

Sminoff, P. and Gottlieb, D. 1951. The production and role of antibiotics in the soil. I. The fate of streptomycin. Phytopath. 41:420-430.

Smith, C. R. 1934. Base exchange reactions of bentonite and salts of organic bases. Soil Sci. 56:1516-1563.

Sober, H. A. and Peterson, E. A. 1957. Chromography of proteins and nucleic acids. *In* C. Calmon and T. R. E. Kressman. Ion Exchange in Organic and Biochemistry. Interscience. New York. p. 318.

Soulides, D. A., Pinck, L. A. and Allison, F. E. 1961. Antibiotics in soils. 3. Further studies on release of antibiotics from clays. Soil Sci. 92:90-93.

Steelink, C. and Tollin, G. 1962. Stable free radicals in soil humic acid. Biochem. Biophys. Acta. 59:25-34.

Stotzky, G., Dawson, J. E., Martin, R. T. and Kuile, C. H. H. 1961. Soil minerology as a factor in the spread of Fusarium Wilt of banana. Science 133:1483.

Sutherland, H. H. and MacEwan, D. M. C. 1961. Organic complexes of vermiculite. Clay Minerals Bull. 4:229-233.

Talibudeen, O. 1955. Complex formation between montmorillonoid clays and amino acids and proteins. Trans. Faraday Soc. 51:582-590.

Tinsley, J. and Zin, M. K. 1954. The isolation of lignoprotein from soil. Trans. 5th International Congress of Soil Sci. Leopoldville. 2:342-347.

Turner, E. R. 1955. The reaction between bentonite and certain naturally occurring compounds. J. Soil Sci. 6:319-326.

Van Olphen, H. and Deeds, C. T. 1962. Stepwise hydration of clay-organic complexes. Nature. 194:176-177.

Waksman, S. A. and Iyer, K. R. N. 1932. Contributions to our knowledge of the chemical nature and origin of humus. Soil Sci. 34:43-69.

Walker, G. F. and Garrett, W. G. 1961. Complexes of vermiculite with amino acids. Nature 191:1389.

Wallace, A. and Lunt, O. R. 1956. Reactions of some iron, zinc and manganese chelates in various soils. Soil Sci. Soc. Am. Proc. 20:479-482.

Warkentin, B. P. and Miller, R. D. 1958. Conditions affecting formation of the Montmorillonite-polyacrylic acid bond. Soil Sci. 85:14-18.

Weiss, A., Mehler, A. and Hofman, V. 1956a. Organophile vermiculite. Z. Naturforsch. 11b:431-434.

Weiss, A., Scholy, A. and Hofman, V. 1956b. Trioctahedral illite. Z. Naturforsch. 11b:429-430.

White, D. and Cowan, C. T. 1958. The sorption properties of dimethyldiotadecylammonium bentonite using gas chromatography. Trans. Faraday Soc. 54:557-561.

White, D. and Cowan, C. T. 1960. Aromatic amine derivatives of montmorillonite. Trans. Brit. Ceram. Soc. 59:16-21.

Wiklander, L. 1959. Plant physiology. In C. Calimon and T. R. E. Kressman. Ion Exchange in Organic and Biochemistry. Interscience. New York. p. 473.

Woodford, E. K. and Jager, G. R. 1960. Herbicides and the Soil. Blackwell Scientific Pub. Oxford.

Yoder, R. E. 1936. A direct method of aggregate analysis of soils and a study of the physical nature of erosion losses. J. Amer. Soc. Agron. 28:337-351.

Zittle, C. A. 1953. Adsorption studies with enzymes and other proteins. Adv. Enzymology. 14:319-374.

Chapter 7

Mineralization and Immobilization of Nitrogen in the Decomposition of Plant and Animal Residues

W. V. BARTHOLOMEW

North Carolina State University
Raleigh, North Carolina

I. INTRODUCTION

Nitrogen in organic combination remains associated with, or as an integral part of, plant and animal debris during the course of microbiological decomposition. This tie-up phenomenon, the mechanisms of which are only partially understood, provides an explanation for numerous observations about the cycles of nitrogen in nature and about the fluctuations in the amount of nitrogen available to crop plants in agriculture.

In nature only a small part of the nitrogen associated with the earth is contained in the active biological cycle. It is in the process of going from plant and animal tissue through slow decomposition to mineral forms, nitrate and ammonia, and then back to organic combination through absorption by plants. Through biological fixation and denitrification some nitrogen is taken from and re-enters the atmosphere but the major part of the nitrogen involved in the active cycle channels through decomposition to mineral forms and back to plants and to animals.

Since the decomposition of organic debris in soil is slow, a large segment of the nitrogen in the active biological cycle is found in the decomposing phase. The estimation has been made that about 90×10^{10} tons of nitrogen are currently immobilized in soil humus whereas only about 30.8×10^{10} tons are immobilized in living plants (Clarke, 1924). The latter figure includes the plant life in the seas. Only a small part of the living matter dies each year and is added to the decomposing phases. Likewise, a similar quantity of the nitrogen in the decomposing phase is mineralized each year and is made available to plants (Bartholomew and Kirkham, 1960).

This chapter will be concerned primarily with the nitrogen transformations associated with the decomposing phase and with the natural products and practical implications resulting from these transformation processes.

The practical implications of the nitrogen tie-up (immobilization) and release (mineralization) processes have prompted extensive research. A voluminous literature has accumulated. Unfortunately, much of the data does little more than demonstrate that immobilization and mineralization processes are in operation. However, enough carefully planned and well executed work has been reported so that broad principles have emerged. The reports aptly demonstrate that the transformation processes have many features that are similar regardless of the kind of material undergoing decomposition or the site situations in which the transformations occur. These general observations lend support to the hypothesis that common underlying principles and biological pathways and/or chemical reactions pervade the tie-up and release processes. Some of these processes have been well studied. Others need further investigation.

II. EARLY CONCEPTS

The beginnings of our meager understanding of the immobilization and mineralization processes are lost in antiquity. The very early agriculturists recognized the value of legumes in cropping systems but they did not know that the residual benefits from legumes arose because of fixation and accumulation of nitrogen in the plant and followed by net nitrogen release upon microbiological decomposition of the leguminous residues. Artisans in the middle ages had learned to collect nitrate nitrogen for the manufacture of gunpowder from "nitre-beds" or extensively decomposed accumulations of organic debris. The roll of microbes in the process of liberating and transforming the nitrogen was elucidated at a much later date. The agriculturists in the latter part of the 19th century had concluded that the chief cause of fertility decline in European soils was depletion of the nitrogen supply. This observation provided the incentive for a searching investigation of the nature of "humus" and for diverse studies on the processes of nitrogen tie-up and release.

Doryland (1916) reviewed much of the earlier work on nitrogen tie-up by microbes in growth processes and from his own work concluded that nitrogen immobilization in crop residues resulted from the synthesis of microbial cell tissue containing organic nitrogen. Emphasis on the quantitative aspects of the nitrogen immobilization process was provided first by the work of Hutchinson and Richards (1921) and later by the studies of Richards and Norman (1931) and by Norman (1931a, b, 1933).

The extensive studies by Lohnis (1926a, b) provided a classical example of the early work on the quantitative aspect of mineralization.

III. TERMINOLOGY

A peculiar terminology has evolved relative to nitrogen transformations associated with the decomposition of plant and animal debris. The term "tie-up" frequently has been employed to denote, as a process, the conversion of inorganic nitrogen to the organic form during the microbiological decomposition of organic residues. Nitrogen tie-up has also been employed to denote a condition in which the organic nitrogen tends to remain essentially unchanged in quantity or be not diminished in amount in the later stages of microbial decomposition of organic residues.

"Immobilization" is generally employed to denote the process of conversion of inorganic nitrogen to the organic form during decomposition (Hutchinson and Richards, 1921). Generally accompanying the use of the term is the connotation that the process is microbiological, in which microorganisms use inorganic nitrogen in the synthesis of cell tissue resulting in organic nitrogen which is somewhat resistant to further biological degradation.

The terms "release" and "mineralization" have been employed to denote the microbiological transformation of the organic nitrogen to inorganic form (usually ammonium). This process renders the nitrogen mobile and available, providing secondary soil reactions do not remove the inorganic nitrogen from the field of mobile action.

The opposing processes of "immobilization" and "mineralization" occur continuously and simultaneously in most systems where organic debris is undergoing microbiological decomposition. As a result inorganic nitrogen is continuously transformed to organic and organic to inorganic nitrogen. An interchange process occurs therefore and the term "microbiological interchange" (Hiltbold et al., 1951) has been employed in discussing the combined reactions.

The term "nitrification" of organic nitrogen has been misapplied to the combined processes of mineralization plus the oxidation of the liberated ammonium. However, since the term "nitrification" was originally, and has continued to be, applied to the process of the biological oxidation of ammonium to nitrate, the use of the term in the inclusive sense is perhaps quite inappropriate.

A number of ways have been employed to express the extent of "net immobilization" of nitrogen in partly decomposed residues. Included are composition indices such as percent nitrogen, mg of nitrogen per 100 g residue, and pounds of nitrogen per ton. Such indices show current composition and need to be associated with information on the extent of and/or the time of decay since the nitrogen composition changes with extent of decomposition. To permit some measure of comparison among residues or between periods of decomposition some data are reported as quantity of organic nitrogen per unit of original, undecomposed residue.

Hutchinson and Richards (1921) introduced the term "nitrogen factor" to express the nitrogen needs of plant materials undergoing decomposition. It was defined as the quantity of additional nitrogen needed in decomposition per unit of original plant substance. Data are usually reported as g of nitrogen per 100 g of original plant material.

Another useful index, "nitrogen equivalent" (Richards and Norman, 1931) was defined as the quantity of additional nitrogen needed in decomposition per unit of plant material fermented or consumed in the decomposition process.

Nitrogen changes which accompany microbial decomposition have been expressed by a carbon to nitrogen (C:N) ratio. There is a measure of validity in the use of a C:N ratio first, because trends in C:N ratios reflect immobilization and mineralization of nitrogen and second, because in decomposition of organic residues carbonaceous materials supply the major energy source for microbes and nitrogen is assimilated as protein in the microbial tissues as a function of the growth of the organisms concerned. However, since the computation of the C:N ratio involves the normal errors of determination of both nitrogen and carbon, it is frequently a less reliable index of nitrogen immobilization than is nitrogen percentage. Furthermore the C:N ratio has a serious shortcoming as an index of nitrogen tie-up and release because as stated by Norman (1933) "decomposition depends on the C:N ratio directly, only in the unusual case of all of the carbon and all the nitrogen being readily available." In practice this condition seldom, if ever, occurs.

The C:N ratio has a further shortcoming in that its use is steeped in theory concerning the chemical and biological mechanisms of immobilization of nitrogen in the decay processes. As a consequence, interpretations are frequently made by readers which were not intended by the authors of scientific papers.

IV. METHODOLOGY

Experimental methods need to be closely examined when evaluations are made of nitrogen transformations accompanying the microbiological decomposition processes. Perhaps the most precise method of measuring net nitrogen mineralization or net nitrogen immobilization is to perform the experiment apart from soil and to measure the organic nitrogen both at the beginning and at the conclusion of the decomposition period. This would provide a direct measurement of the net change in organic nitrogen. However, the possible shortcoming in this experimental procedure is that the biological reactions observed apart from soil may be quite different from the biological reactions occurring in a soil system. Thus results obtained apart from soil cannot always be employed to infer soil nitrogen transformations.

When nitrogen transformation studies are performed in a soil system, a determination of the total organic nitrogen before and after incubation generally is not feasible because the total quantity of organic nitrogen is usually large in comparison to the expected net change. This condition makes the error of analysis unduly high. To overcome this error handicap and to simplify the analytical procedures, the general method followed is to analyze only for the changes in inorganic nitrogen. Errors of analysis are smaller for inorganic nitrogen in soil than for organic nitrogen and the procedures for the former are less laborious than for the latter.

Notwithstanding the small errors of determination of inorganic nitrogen, the method may not be as reliable as determining organic nitrogen because of the indirect evaluations of net change. Where only inorganic nitrogen changes have been measured, an evaluation of the organic nitrogen content requires the assumption that no nitrogen was lost from the system and that no nitrogen fixation occurred. This assumption may be largely true in some instances. There is increasing evidence, however, that microbiologically induced nitrogen losses are widespread, even though in most instances they are small (Cady and Bartholomew, 1960b; Hauck and Melsted, 1956).

In a great number of instances only changes in nitrate nitrogen attending the decomposition of organic residues have been followed as an indication of the net immobilization and net mineralization process. In these instances the further assumption was made that the ammonium content of the system underwent no net change during the course of the experiment. Usually such studies have been carried out in soils with known tendencies to rapidly nitrify added ammonium ions.

Greenhouse pot experiments in which growing plants are employed as indicators of changes in nitrogen availability have been extensively employed to indicate both mineralization and immobilization (Hiltbold et al., 1951; Munson and Pesek, 1958). Uptake of nitrogen by plants has been shown to be similar to chemical extraction in reflecting the quantity of inorganic nitrogen in soil (Munson and Pesek, 1958; Rubins and Bear, 1942; Hiltbold et al., 1951). However, since added inorganic nitrogen has seldom been quantitatively recovered by a growing crop, some doubts can be raised about the accuracy of the plant uptake procedure.

Notwithstanding the assumptions involved in the measurement, most studies which provide information on the nitrogen immobilization and mineralization processes have been performed in soil systems and only inorganic nitrogen evaluations made. It is reasonable to conclude, therefore, that in many instances the failure to account for all of the mineralized nitrogen has led to inflated estimations of net immobilization and mineralization.

V. MICROBIAL ORIGIN OF SOIL ORGANIC NITROGEN

Widely accepted among soil microbiologists is the hypothesis that in the early stages of decomposition of fresh plant residues the plant organic nitrogen materials are rapidly attacked and the nitrogen is mineralized and made available for use by the microflora. Moreover, the more stable protein complexes typical of soil organic matter are thought to be formed during the process of decomposition—largely from proteins produced by microorganisms. Considerable evidence has accumulated to support this hypothesis although much of it is indirect.

Isolated plant and animal proteins generally are readily utilized by numerous members of the soil micropopulation (Rubins and Bear, 1942; Bremner and Shaw, 1957; Pearson et al., 1941). That the nitrogen in young succulent green manures is largely available has been aptly indicated by the proportion of the nitrogen appearing in the mineral form in the early stages of decomposition (Lohnis, 1926a).

Indirect evidence is provided in the relationship of the C:N ratio to decomposition rates and to nitrogen release. That this relationship has functioned so well in predicting the tie-up and release of nitrogen in the early stages of decomposition of a variety of plant residues is an indication that a large part or essentially all of the original organic nitrogen in the residues was available to microbes.

The accumulated data on microbiological nitrogen transformations have not demonstrated a biologically resistant fraction of plant organic nitrogen. The nitrogenous materials that remain after extensive decomposition of plant residues are presumed to be synthetic products of soil microorganisms which have accumulated during the processes of decomposition (Doryland, 1916; Pearson et al., 1941). A direct measurement of the extent of utilization of the plant proteins by soil microorganisms awaits the development of methods which will distinguish between plant and microbial proteins. However, a good indirect evaluation of microbial decomposition of plant protein has recently been reported by Kuo and Bartholomew (1965) employing earlier data by Jansson et al. (1955).

In the experimental method, tagged inorganic nitrogen was added to decomposing plant residues in quantities in excess of those required for optimum decomposition. At specified intervals of incubation the organic and inorganic nitrogen phases of the system were analyzed for tracer nitrogen. After short periods of incubation the tag in the organic phase of the system approached closely the concentration of tag in the inorganic phase. A close examination of the data in connection with possible biological mechanisms indicates that this equivalence could take place only if the plant proteins were largely or totally decomposed with the nitrogen therefrom becoming a part of the inorganic pool. The microbes in turn must have used inorganic nitrogen in the synthesis of cell tissue protein.

Other data where tracer techniques have been employed have not been so explicit as those reported by Jansson et al. (1955) in demonstrating the tendency for equivalence of tracer concentration in the organic and inorganic phases during decomposition. These authors report data for the decomposition of alfalfa when excess inorganic nitrogen containing tracer was added at the beginning of decomposition. Although interchange occurred, equivalence in tracer concentration in the organic and inorganic phases was not reached. However, equivalence in tracer concentration in the organic and inorganic phases in such incubation experiments can be expected only where three conditions are met. The first is that all of the plant organic nitrogen be decomposed by the invading microorganisms. The second is that the mineral nitrogen released becomes an integral part of and thoroughly mixed with the added inorganic phase. The third condition is that the microorganisms absorb nitrogen exclusively from the inorganic pool. It is quite conceivable that the plant protein could be all decomposed by the invading microbes without the mineralized protein nitrogen becoming an integral part of the inorganic pool before it was reused by the microflora in the synthesis of new microbial protein. This pattern of tie-up could happen in either of two ways. If the microbes use some organic nitrogen products, complete mineralization would not be effected. Also if the plant protein nitrogen was completely mineralized it might not become intimately mixed with the total pool of inorganic nitrogen before being absorbed by the very active microflora and used in the synthesis of cell tissue. However, the strong tendency toward tracer equivalence in the organic and inorganic phases in studies of this nature, and the occurrence of essential equivalence in at least one instance are strong evidence that plant protein is largely or completely decomposed in the decomposition process and that the organic nitrogen which remains with the residue is microbial in origin.

The general relation between indices reflecting the abundance of the microflora which develops in decomposing residues and the net quantity of organic nitrogen content further support the theory that soil nitrogen materials originated in microbial cells. Jansson and Clark (1952) showed the rate of net nitrogen immobilization to be related to carbon dioxide production in the early stages of decomposition. Nõmmik (1962) demonstrated that the rate of net nitrogen tie-up was related to the rate of decomposition as reflected in loss in weight. Kuo (1955) reported similar results.

VI. THE BIOLOGICAL STABILITY OF SOIL NITROGEN

Notwithstanding the results of experiments which strongly support the thesis that tie-up processes occur through the production of microbial tissue, the perplexing question arises as to why microbial nitrogen products should possess or acquire a measure of stability against further biological decomposition. Moreover, microbial tissues have been found liable to decomposition and the nitrogen materials contained in them to be as susceptible to net mineralization as the nitrogen materials from plant and animal products (Heck, 1929; Jensen, 1932; Norman, 1933). In the studies cited above, the microbial tissues were grown in cultural media and later collected and added to soil to determine the extent to which the nitrogen was mineralized.

If the immobilization of nitrogen in decomposing crop residues involved only the absorption of nitrogen by an invading population of microbes followed in turn by decomposition of their tissues by succeeding generations or populations, owing to the dissipation of the food energy the quantity of microbial cell substance and therefore the amount of organic nitrogen soon would become very small. Each new population would absorb a quantity of nitrogen equivalent to only a part of that contained in the preceding population. After a few generations of microbes had developed and in turn been decomposed not much nitrogen would remain in the organic form.

Rapid net immobilization followed by rather rapid net mineralization has been observed in some instances where readily available carbohydrate substances have been added to soil (Allison and Klein, 1962; Nõmmik, 1961; Peevy and Norman, 1948; Winsor and Pollard, 1956a; Wright, 1915). The use of soluble carbohydrate materials has resulted in higher net nitrogen immobilization per unit of substrate than has the use of normal crop residues (Nõmmik, 1961). This high immobilization has been followed by rapid mineralization such that much of the immobilized nitrogen later reappeared in the inorganic fraction (Allison and Klein, 1962; Nõmmik, 1961; Winsor and Pollard, 1956b; Wright, 1915).

The rapid nitrogen tie-up and release patterns observed when soluble carbohydrates have been added to soil are not typical of the net immobilization and net mineralization changes which occur when plant residues are decomposed. Fig. 1 shows the net immobilization changes for a

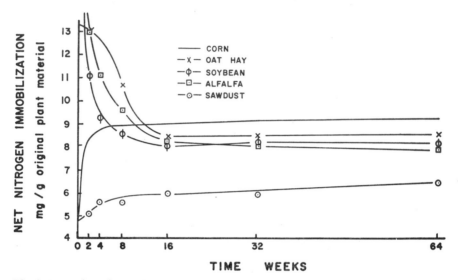

Fig. 1. Rate of net immobilization and/or mineralization of nitrogen in the early stages of decomposition of some crop residues.

number of materials decomposed apart from soil and Fig. 2 gives the changes in materials decomposed in soil. When materials are decomposed in soil the net changes in organic nitrogen in the residue must be evaluated by correcting for the changes in check soils.

Where the fresh residues were low in nitrogen, an initial rapid increase in organic nitrogen was observed. When the fresh residues were high in nitrogen an initial rapid net mineralization occurred. After the first few weeks of decomposition further net changes in organic nitrogen were slow irrespective of the quantity of nitrogen in the original plant residue.

The increases in numbers of microbes in soil resulting from addition of crop residues have coincided closely in time with the changes in organic nitrogen (Clark, 1964; Clark and Thom, 1939; Wilson and Wilson, 1925). Microbial population "explosions" occur soon after the addition of fresh plant residue to soil and generally reach a maximum in numbers in the first or second week after residue addition. The maximum number of microbes may be manyfold greater than the number before the residue addition.

The rapid increase in numbers is followed by a gradual decrease as the readily available food material is dissipated. However, net immobilization of nitrogen does not decline in a similar manner. The data plotted in Fig.

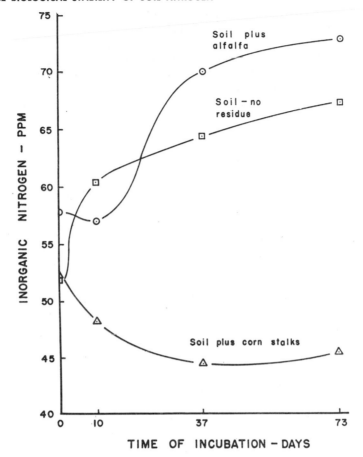

Fig. 2. The influence of alfalfa and corn stalk residues on the available nitrogen in soil.

1 and 2 show net immobilization to reach maximum values at about the time one might expect maximum numbers of microbes. This net immobilization may show a slight decrease during periods when microbial numbers would be expected to decrease but the observed rates of decline in microbial numbers are much greater than the observed decreases in net immobilization. The accumulated data support the hypothesis that, as decomposition processes continue in plant residues, some protective reactions occur which render the microbially produced organic nitrogen more resistant to further decomposition than it would otherwise be if it were apart from the environment of the partially decomposed plant substance. The mechanisms involved are still matters of conjecture. One theory presumes a chemical association of microbial protein or other nitrogen carrying organic materials with non-protein materials resulting from the decomposition of the plant residues. These nonprotein materials have been considered as aromatic, probably polyphenols, either produced by microbes through synthesis or fragmented from the plant resi-

dues through partial decomposition. The nature of the hypothetical chemical associations are discussed in chapter 3.

In a soil system an association of the organic nitrogen with mineral soil colloids can have an influence on biological stability (chapter 6) but since a measure of stability occurs in nonmineral systems apart from soil, factors other than association with mineral colloids are perhaps the more important in stabilizing the nitrogen products against decomposition.

VII. IMMOBILIZATION

As fresh plant materials decompose gross composition changes occur in the residue. Extensive investigations have shown that the carbohydrate fractions are the first parts of the plant to be extensively decomposed and that the lignin components tend to be more resistant. In the course of decomposition, large quantities of microbial tissue are synthesized by the invading microbes so that after the start of decay a distinction between plant origin and microbial origin of residue products is largely impossible. The literature on the subject has given the results of analytical methods applied to the residue mixture as a whole. Some interpretations have been made concerning plant and microbial origin of specific fractions but generally the literature is silent on this aspect.

In regards to the organic nitrogen associated with the decomposing residues, the quantity remaining during the course of decay is of special interest. Fresh residues vary in organic nitrogen content. This variation may range from 0.2 to 0.5% in woods to 1.5 to 3.0% in leguminous hays. Corn stalks, cereal straws and grasses are intermediate in nitrogen having contents which generally range between 0.5 and 1.5%. As fresh materials begin to decompose, changes may occur in the quantity of organic nitrogen. Low nitrogen residues tend to increase in organic nitrogen content if nitrogen is available in excess of that contained in the residues (Fig. 1). High nitrogen residues may decline in organic nitrogen content. In all instances, however, a quantity of organic nitrogen remains associated with the residue during the course of decomposition. Most of the literature on immobilization and mineralization of nitrogen in the decay of crop residues reports or reflects the magnitude of this net immobilization process at some stage in the decay process. The magnitude and nature of the net changes are illustrated in Fig. 1. Corn stalks and sawdust increased in organic nitrogen content during the early stages of decomposition. Oat hay and alfalfa hay, on the other hand, decreased in organic nitrogen content. The major changes occurred early in the decay process. Unless frequent sampling schedules are followed during the early stages of decomposition of organic materials these early organic nitrogen change patterns may be overlooked (Allison and Klein, 1962; Broadbent and Tyler, 1962).

After the initial rapid stages of decomposition of crop residues there remains a product containing organic nitrogen. This organic nitrogen appears to possess a measure of biological stability in that net mineralization is very slow. The quantity thus remaining has been considered as that needed to satisfy the agents of decomposition and has been estimated from 1 to 2% of the weight of the fresh residue (Bal, 1922; Bonnet, 1931; Colom and McCalla, 1952; Iritani and Arnold, 1960; Kuo, 1955; Lockett, 1938; McKenzie, 1958; Munson and Pesek, 1958; Newton and Daniloff, 1927; Nõmmik, 1962; Parbery and Swaby, 1942; Pinck et al., 1946; Richards and Norman, 1931; Rubens and Bear, 1942; Stewart, 1959; Wright, 1915).

The tie-up or immobilization of nitrogen during the decomposition of plant or animal residues has been reported in many instances as a single datum for each material, suggesting that immobilization was a property of the residue which could be expressed by a single number. Some questions have been raised concerning the usefulness of such data since, as immobilization and mineralization are continuous processes, the data are rigidly valid only for the moment of time at which the analyses were made. However, an examination of the data plotted in Figs. 1 and 2 shows that after the initial rapid stages of decomposition the quantity of organic nitrogen associated with the decomposing residue tends to attain a measure of stability and to change slowly thereafter. Observations on the amount of organic nitrogen remaining with the residue in this latter period provide convenient comparisons of net immobilization among residue materials and environmental site situations.

This rapid early biological adjustment in organic nitrogen content which occurs during decomposition has been widely observed (Allison and Klein, 1962; Broadbent and Tyler, 1962; Hiltbold et al., 1951; Kuo, 1955; Norman, 1931b; Richards and Norman, 1931; Viljoen and Fred, 1924; Winsor and Pollard, 1956a). In fact, residues in decomposition exhibit a phenomenon which functions as though the residue possessed a capacity to contain or combine with organic nitrogen such as to hold it in a state or condition in which it is semi-stable against further decomposition. These observed patterns of net change in organic nitrogen content attending decomposition show the usefulness of single indices of immobilization, providing the analyses were made following the initial rapid stages of decomposition.

Table 1 gives a range of values of net nitrogen immobilization by decomposing plant residues. In general these evaluations were made following the initial rapid period of decomposition. Cereal straws and other low nitrogen residues generally tie up from 0.9% to about 1.5% organic nitrogen or 18 to 30 pounds of nitrogen per ton of fresh residue. Legume residues often retain higher amounts but are also more variable.

VIII. ENVIRONMENT AND IMMOBILIZATION

Environmental factors may influence the immobilization of nitrogen either by altering the time at which maximum net immobilization is attained (Nõmmik, 1962) or by modifying the net quantity that remains associated with the residue after extensive decomposition. Although there are numerous publications which report studies on the influences of

Table 1. Net nitrogen immobilization in decomposing plant residues as reported by or calculated from the data of several investigators.

Reference	Residue	Kind of study	%N immobilization*
Allison and Klein (1962)	Straw	Nitrification in soil	1.1
Bonnet (1931)	Sugarcane trash	Incubation - no soil	1.2 - 1.3
Hiltbold et al. (1951)	Straw	Greenhouse incubation	1.45
Hiltbold et al. (1951)	Alfalfa	Greenhouse incubation	2.23
Hutchinson & Richards (1921)	Straw	Incubation - no soil	1.23
Iritani & Arnold (1960)	Vegetable residue	Nitrification in soil	1.7 - 1.9
Jansson (1958)	Straw	Nitrification in soil	1.2 - 1.4
Kuo (1955)	Oat straw	Incubation - no soil	1.0
Kuo (1955)	Alfalfa	Incubation - no soil	0.9 - 1.2
Kuo (1955)	Oat hay	Incubation - no soil	1.7
Kuo (1955)	Sawdust	Incubation - no soil	0.6 - 0.7
Kuo (1955)	Oak leaves	Incubation - no soil	0.9
Kuo (1955)	Soybean straw	Incubation - no soil	0.9 - 1.0
Lockett (1938)	Young clover	Incubation - no soil	1.45
Lockett (1938)	Medium clover	Incubation - no soil	1.04
Lockett (1938)	Mature clover	Incubation - no soil	0.89
Lockett (1938)	Young rye	Incubation - no soil	1.54
Lockett (1938)	Medium rye	Incubation - no soil	1.23
McKenzie (1958)	Sawdust	Incubation - no soil	1.0 - 1.5
Munson and Pesek (1958)	Corn stalk	Greenhouse incubation	1.8
Nommik (1962)	Straw	Mineralization in soil	1.4 - 1.8
Norman (1931b)	Straw	Incubation - no soil	0.7 - 0.9
Parbery and Swaby (1942)	Green manures	Nitrification	1.5
Parker et al. (1957)	Corn stalk	Mineralization in soil	0.9
Pinck et al. (1946)	Straw	Mineralization in soil	1.37 - 1.56
Richards and Norman (1931)	Oat straw	Incubation - no soil	1.1
Richards and Norman (1931)	Flax straw	Incubation - no soil	1.0 - 1.1
Richards and Norman (1931)	Willow peelings	Incubation - no soil	2.3 - 2.6
Richards and Norman (1931)	Esparto grass	Incubation - no soil	1.5
Richards and Norman (1931)	Rice straw	Incubation - no soil	1.0
Richards and Norman (1931)	Maise straw	Incubation - no soil	1.2
Richards and Norman (1931)	Bean husks	Incubation - no soil	3.6
Richards and Norman (1931)	Bean husks	Incubation - no soil	2.8
Richards and Shrinkhande (1935)	Straw	Incubation - no soil	1.1

* Percent of original material.

environmental factors on decomposition, only a few have provided data on the influence of physical and chemical environment on nitrogen immobilization. Nõmmik (1962) and Kuo (1955) found that low temperature slowed down biological activity and thus delayed the time when maximum net immobilization was attained. Suboptimum moisture had a similar effect (Waksman and Gerretsen, 1931; Kuo, 1955). Unfavorable moisture and temperature have had only a minor influence on the magnitude of net immobilization after extensive decomposition. The chief influence has been to slow the rates of biological respiration and microbial reproduction and thus lengthen the time to reach particular stages of decomposition. Data from Kuo (1955) in Fig. 3 illustrate this influence.

Decomposition under anaerobic conditions results in much lower quantities of net immobilization than decomposition under aerobic conditions (Karim, 1948; Acharya, 1935a, b). The natural effect of this phenomenon is seen in the low nitrogen content of peats. Causes for the observed results are not known. However, the kinds of organisms which predominate

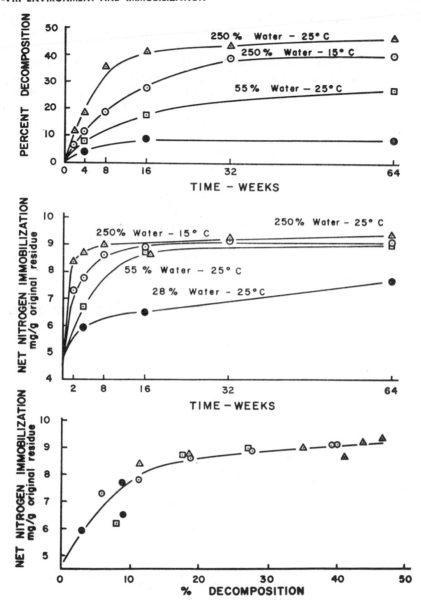

Fig. 3. Influence of moisture and temperature on net immobilization of nitrogen in crop residues.

under anaerobic conditions differ from those under aerobic conditions. Also the rates of decay are generally slower in the former than in the latter conditions. Norman (1931b) found a slight tendency for slower decomposition under acid conditions than under neutral to alkaline conditions. Net immobilization followed the same trend. Differences in the makeup of the microflora would be expected to accompany changes in pH. This might account for the differences in nitrogen tie-up. However, since many biological and chemical reactions are very sensitive to pH changes, causes for the observed differences in net immobilization are matters of speculation.

The position on or in the soil in which plant residues decompose also has an influence on the rate of decomposition and the rate and extent of nitrogen immobilization (Parker et al., 1957; Parker, 1962). Surface residues are subject to rapid drying and thus tend to decompose more slowly than residues which are buried by discing or plowing. Thus decomposition of residues on the soil surface would result in slower rates of immobilization and mineralization. Moreover, surface mulch materials, if low in nitrogen, may not contain sufficient nitrogen to supply the maximum needs for decomposition. The only natural way for nitrogen to be added would be for upward movement of water in which nitrate would be carried and deposited in the residue by evaporation. That this mechanism can function to carry nitrogen to surface residues has been shown by Parker et al. (1957). Residues which are buried and are surrounded by soil are supplied with supplemental nitrogen much more readily than residues on the surface of the soil.

IX. INFLUENCE OF AVAILABLE NITROGEN ON IMMOBILIZATION

Many investigators have concluded that increases in the supply of nitrogen during the decomposition processes result in increased nitrogen immobilization and more "humus" formation per unit of decomposed residue (Salter, 1931; Brown and Allison, 1916; Holtz and Vandecaveye, 1938). The concept was to the effect that in the decomposition process there was an association of carbon with nitrogen resulting in a measure of stabilization to both.

When nitrogen is limiting to the development of the decomposing microflora an increase in inorganic nitrogen will result in an increase in net immobilization (Allison, 1955; Bartholomew, 1955; Kuo, 1955; Richards and Norman, 1931). However, when the needs of the microflora have been met, additional nitrogen remains unused in the system and may, if the concentration is high enough, cause a reduction in the rate of microbial activity (Kuo, 1955; Bartholomew, 1955; Allison, 1955).

X. NITROGEN IN ASSOCIATION WITH PHOSPHORUS, CARBON AND SULPHUR

Phosphorus and nitrogen are closely associated in many compounds important in metabolism and reproduction. This relationship is so widespread that in living tissue there is found a consistent relationship between the content of the two elements. This relationship carries over into the well decomposed organic fractions in soil (Thompson et al., 1948; Thompson and Black, 1950; Thompson et al., 1954; Birch, 1961; Chang, 1939, 1940; Barrow, 1961; Kaila, 1949; Pearson et al., 1939; Schollenberger, 1920; Walker and Adams, 1958). The two elements and also carbon and sulphur apparently are stabilized together in soil. An increase or decrease in one has always been found to be accompanied by a parallel increase or decrease in the other elements (Walker and Adams, 1958). Such a relationship suggests that the measure of biological stability exhibited by soil organic matter must be achieved through reactions of large organic aggregates or molecules containing carbon, nitrogen, phosphorus, and sulphur in approximately the same proportion as these elements are found in microbial tissues.

XI. MINERALIZATION

Nitrogen which is immobilized in the decomposition of crop residues is slow to undergo biological mineralization (Broadbent and Tyler, 1962; Stewart, 1959; Jansson, 1958, 1963; Jansson et al., 1955; Pinck et al., 1948; Richards and Shirkhande, 1935; McKenzie, 1958). Jansson (1963) by the use of tracer nitrogen, found that between 2.6 and 4.0% of the nitrogen immobilized from nitrate and between 1.4 and 3.7% of that immobilized from ammonium treatments were mineralized and recovered each year in a growing crop of oats. Similar small recoveries of immobilized tagged nitrogen were reported by Broadbent and Tyler (1962).

Soil organic nitrogen is mineralized at rates roughly comparable to those reported for newly immobilized nitrogen. Mineralization rates have been estimated from below 2% per year to as high as 10% (Bartholomew and Kirkham, 1960). In short time nitrate production studies even higher release rates of soil organic nitrogen have been observed.

That mineralization of immobilized nitrogen is slow is further demonstrated in the negligible release of nitrogen from crop residues in the field during the second season after application to the soil (Fribourg and Bartholomew, 1956; Schmidt et al., 1959). That single applications of crop residue have had little influence on the nitrogen supply in the soil during a second growing season after application is not surprising when quantitative evaluations are made. For example, a $1\frac{1}{2}$-ton application of legume green manure, containing 75 pounds of nitrogen may release 45 pounds during the early stages of decomposition the first season. Of the 35 pounds of nitrogen remaining associated with the residues, a net mineralization of 3 to 5% during the second season would be so small as to be difficult of detection in the field. Even a net release of 10% would be difficult to measure with field plot techniques. However, the continued or long time treatments with green manure and meadow crops have accumulative effects which often are measurable in the second and third season after turning in the residue (Schmidt et al., 1959; Bartholomew et al., 1957; Allison and Sterling, 1949).

XII. MANURES AND COMPOSTS

Manures and composts are quite different from fresh plant and animal residues in the nitrogen tie-up and release reactions. Manures function much like soil organic matter in that the organic nitrogen is released or mineralized very slowly (Heck, 1931a, b; Barrow, 1961; Lipman and Blair, 1916; Bengtsson and Barthel, 1939; Jensen, 1931; Mann, 1951; Salter and Schollenberger, 1939; Newton and Daniloff, 1927; Mattingly, 1956; Bremner and Shaw, 1957). For the first crop after application, little more than the inorganic nitrogen in animal manure appears to be available (Heck, 1931b; Salter and Schollenberger, 1939). Animal manures and composts have undergone extensive microbial decomposition. The formation mechanisms involve vigorous decay processes. The organic nitrogen which results has acquired a measure of stability to further rapid decomposition.

XIII. IMMOBILIZATION AND MINERALIZATION IN NATURAL PROCESSES AND AGRICULTURAL PRACTICE

The effects of immobilization and mineralization of nitrogen in the decomposition of crop residues are evident in numerous instances in practical agriculture. In fact, the influence of cropping systems and manures on subsequent crop production comes about largely through effects on the available soil nitrogen supply. Moreover, many of the effects of soil management and cultural practices on crop growth also operate in part through influences on available soil nitrogen. The operation of plowing may affect soil available nitrogen through burying the surface deposited residues. Cultivation on other similar operations which kill weeds makes more nitrogen available to the crop because less is immobilized in weeds. Moreover, weeds are frequently high in nitrogen and some net mineralization occurs as a result of their undergoing decomposition.

Cultivation and time of plowing affect subsequent nitrogen supplies through tie-up and release processes. Turning low nitrogen residues well in advance of planting a new crop enhances the available nitrogen supply in that the major decomposition reactions and the accompanying net immobilization processes have been supplied with nitrogen before the season of maximum nitrogen uptake by the crop. Turning under high nitrogen residues too far in advance of planting a subsequent crop may permit nitrogen losses through leaching and denitrification of the rapidly mineralized nitrogen.

In the growth of any crop some residues are returned to the soil. The quantity of residues returned, the chemical make-up of the residues including the nitrogen content, the soil environment and the manner in which the residues are returned all combine to determine the influence of the residues on the soil available nitrogen supply.

Crop residues, if above a critical percentage composition in nitrogen, may supply nitrogen to crops following the addition of such residues to the soil. An application of one ton of the top growth of legume residue containing about two percent nitrogen would supply about 20 pounds of nitrogen during the first season after application. Roots and stubble of legumes contain less nitrogen than the tops and therefore would supply less in the early stages of decomposition. The nitrogen not mineralized in the first season becomes part of the soil organic matter and may decompose slowly over a period of many years. Residues containing from 1 to 1.3% nitrogen may supply little or no mineral nitrogen to the soil during the first season of decomposition because their nitrogen is very near to the critical content. All of the nitrogen contained in the fresh residues could be used by the invading microorganisms.

Corn stover and cereal straws may contain about 0.75% of nitrogen or 15 pounds per ton of residue. In the decomposition process a total of 20 to 25 pounds of nitrogen may be required to satisfy the needs of the microbes which effect the decay. The biological processes, therefore, result in the net tie-up of 5 to 10 pounds of nitrogen from the supply which becomes mineralized from soil organic matter. The nitrogen, absorbed and immobilized in the decay processes is remineralized very slowly.

Nitrogen fertilization of crops may exert two major influences on nitrogen tie-up and release in crop residues. First, it generally increases residue production and second it can increase the nitrogen content of the residue material. With low nitrogen residues these two effects may be compensating in that increase in residue yield accompanied by higher nitrogen contents may have the same affect on the available nitrogen as a lower residue yield and a low nitrogen content. In the fertilization of crops which have high nitrogen residues the effects of higher yields and nitrogen contents complement each other in that both result in greater net nitrogen mineralization when the residues decompose.

Any cropping or cultural practice which affects the production, yield or composition of crop residues and/or which influences the course or conditions of decomposition invariably exerts an effect on the tie-up and release of nitrogen and thus on the supply of nitrogen available to a subsequent crop. Research experience has elucidated the general principles underlying the nitrogen tie-up and release processes. In given circumstances the extent of nitrogen immobilization and mineralization can be anticipated with a reasonable degree of accuracy. Furthermore through soil and crop management operations a large measure of control of net immobilization or net mineralization can be effected and directed toward soil improvement and increased productivity.

REFERENCES

Acharya, C. N. 1935a. Studies on the anaerobic decomposition of plant materials. I. The anaerobic decomposition of rice straw. Biochem. J. 29:528-541.

Acharya, C. N. 1935b. Studies on the anerobic decomposition of plant materials. III. Comparison of the course of decomposition of rice straw under anaerobic, aerobic and partially aerobic conditions. Biochem. J. 29:1116-1120.

Allison, F. E. 1955. Does nitrogen applied to crop residues produce more humus. Soil Sci. Soc. Am. Proc. 19:210-211.

Allison, F. E., and Luann D. Sterling. 1949. Nitrate formation from soil organic matter in relation to total nitrogen and cropping practices. Soil Sci. 67:239-252.

Allison, F. E., and C. J. Klein. 1962. Rates of immobilization and release of nitrogen following additions of carbonaceous materials and nitrogen to soils. Soil Sci. 93:383-386.

Alway, F. J., J. Kittridge, and W. J. Methley. 1933. Composition of the forest floor layers under different forest types on the same soil type. Soil Sci. 36:387-398.

Bal, D. V. 1922. Studies on the decomposition of some common green-manuring plants at different stages of growth, etc. Agr. J. India 17:133-151.

Barrow, N. J. 1961. Mineralization of nitrogen and sulphur from sheep faeces. Aust. J. Agr. Res. 12:644-650.

Bartholomew, W. V. 1955. Fertilization of crop residues. Does it pay? Agr. Chem. 10(8):38-40, 97, 99.

Bartholomew, W. V. 1956. Use of isotopes in following nitrogen transformations in soil. Atomic Energy Comm. Report No. TID-7512.

Bartholomew, W. V., and C. A. I. Goring. 1948. Microbial products and soil organic matter: I. Some characteristics of the organic phosphorus of microorganisms. Soil Sci. Soc. Am. Proc. 12:238-241.

Bartholomew, W. V., and A. E. Hiltbold. 1952. Recovery of fertilizer nitrogen by oats in the greenhouse. Soil Sci. 73:193-201.

Bartholomew, W. V., J. Meyer, and H. Laudelout. 1953. Mineral nutrient immobilization under forest and grass fallow in the yangambi (Belgian Congo) region. INEAC, Serie Scientifique No. 57.

Bartholomew, W. V., W. D. Shrader, and A. J. Englehorn. 1957. Nitrogen changes attending various crop rotations on Clarion-Webster soils in Iowa. Agron. J. 49:415-418.

Bartholomew, W. V., and Don Kirkham. 1960. Mathematical descriptions and interpretations of culture induced soil nitrogen changes. 7th Intern. Cong. Soil Sci. Madison, Wis. Comm. III 2:471-477.

Beavens, E. A., and L. H. James. 1934. The microbial decomposition of successive cuttings of alfalfa hay under aerobic conditions. J. Agr. Res. 48:1121-1126.

Bengtsson, N., and Charles Barthel. 1939. Decomposition of organic compounds in barnyard manure. Int. Soc. Soil Sci. Com. III A:133-136.

Birch, H. F. 1961. Phosphorus transformations during plant decomposition. Plant and Soil 15:347-366.

Bollen, W. B. 1941. Soil respiration studies on the decomposition of native organic matter. J. Sci. 15:353-374.

Bollen, W. B., and K. C. Lu. 1957. Effect of Douglas-fir sawdust mulches and incorporations on soil microbial activities and plant growth. Soil Sci. Soc. Am. Proc. 21:35-41.

Bollen, W. B., and K. C. Lu. 1961. Microbial decomposition and nitrogen availability of reacted sawdust, bagasse and coffee grounds. Agr. and Food Chem. 9:9-15.

Bonnet, J. A. 1931. Nitrogen transformations in the decomposition of sugar cane trash, with special bearing upon Puerto Rico soil problems. J. Puerto Rico Dept. Ag. 15:113-146.

Bremner, J. M., and K. Shaw. 1957. The mineralization of some nitrogenous materials in soil. J. Sci. Food Agr. 8:341-347.

Broadbent, F. E., and K. B. Tyler. 1962. Laboratory and greenhouse investigations of nitrogen immobilization. Soil Sci. Soc. Am. Proc. 26:459-462.

Brown, P. E., and F. E. Allison. 1916. Influence of humus forming material of different nitrogen-carbon ratios on bacterial activities. Iowa Ag. Exp. Sta. Res. Bul. 36.

Cady, F. B., and W. V. Bartholomew. 1960a. Greenhouse recovery of added tracer nitrogen. Soil Sci. Soc. N. C. Proc. 3:44-54.

Cady, F. B., and W. V. Bartholomew. 1960b. Sequential products of anaerobic denitrification in Norfolk soil material. Soil Sci. Soc. Am. Proc. 24:477-482.

Chang, S. C. 1939. The transformation of phosphorus during the decomposition of plant materials. Soil Sci. 48:85-99.

Chang, S. C. 1940. Assimilation of phosphorus by a mixed soil population and by pure culture of soil fungi. Soil Sci. 49:197-210.

Clark, F. E., and Charles Thom. 1939. Effects of organic amendments upon the microflora of the rhizosphere of cotton and wheat. Int. Soc. Soil Sci. Com. III A:94-100.

Clark, Francis E. 1964. Bacteria in soil. In Soil Biology. N. A. Burgess, ed. (in press)

Clarke, F. W. 1924. The Data of Geochemistry. U. S. Geol. Sur. Bul. No. 770.

Coldwell, B. B., and W. A. DeLong. 1950. Studies of the composition of deciduous forest tree leaves before and after partial decomposition. Sci. Ag. 30:456-466.

Colom, Juan, and T. M. McCalla. 1952. The decomposition of partridge pea and its influence on nitrification. Soil Sci. Soc. Am. Proc. 16:208-210.

Doryland, C. J. T. 1916. The influence of energy material upon the relation of soil microorganisms to soluble plant food. North Dakota Agr. Exp. Sta. Bul. 116.

Fribourg, Henry A. 1954. Comparison of leguminous green manure with inorganic nitrogen in rotation with corn. Ph.D. Thesis. Iowa tSate College. Library Ames, Iowa.

Fribourg, H. A., and W. V. Bartholomew. 1956. Availability of nitrogen from crop residues during the first and second seasons after application. Soil Sci. Soc. Am. Proc. 20:505-508.

Goring, C. A. I., and Francis E. Clark. 1948. Influence of crop growth on mineralization of nitrogen in the soil. Soil Sci. Soc. Am. Proc. 13:261-266.

Goswami, N. N., and N. P. Datta, 1961. Tracer studies on the decomposition of C^{14} and P^{32} tagged organic matter and nutrient availability relationships in soils. J. Indian Soc. Soil Sci. 9:269-279.

Guha Sircar, S. S., S. C. De, and H. D. Bhowmick. 1940. Micro-biological decomposition of plant materials. I. Changes in the constituents of rice straw (Kanahtara) produced by micro-organisms present in soil suspension under aerobic, anaerobic and water-logged conditions. Ind. J. Agr. Sci. 10:119-151.

Hauck, R. D., and S. W. Melsted. 1956. Some aspects of the problem of evaluating denitrification in soils. Soil Sci. Soc. Am. Proc. 20:361-364.

Heck, A. F. 1929. A study of the nature of the nitrogenous compounds in fungus tissue and their decomposition in the soil. Soil Sci. 27:1-47.

Heck, A. F. 1931a. Conservation and availability of the nitrogen in farm manure. Soil Sci. 31:335-359.

Heck, A. F. 1931b. The availability of the nitrogen in farm manure under field conditions. Soil Sci. 31:467-481.

Hill, H. H. 1934. The effects of mulched and turned rye in green and mature stages on the liberation of plant nutrients from a silt loam soil. Virginia Ag. Exp. Sta. Tech. Bul. 53.

Hiltbold, A. E., W. V. Bartholomew, and C. H. Werkman. 1951. The use of tracer techniques in the simultaneous measurement of mineralization and immobilization of nitrogen in soil. Soil Sci. Soc. Am. Proc. 15:166-173.

Holtz, H. F., and S. C. Vandecaveye. 1938. Organic residues and nitrogen fertilizers in relation to the productivity and humus content of Palouse silt loam. Soil Sci. 45:143-163.

Hutchinson, C. G., and S. Milligan, 1914. Green manuring experiment, 1912-1913. Agr. Res. Inst. Pusa, Bul. 40.

Hutchinson, H. B., and E. H. Richards. 1921. Artificial farmyard manure. Ministry of Agr. 28:398-411.

Iritani, W. M., and C. Y. Arnold. 1960. Nitrogen release of vegetable crop residues during incubation as related to their chemical composition. Soil Sci. 89:74-82.

Ivarson, K. C., and F. J. Sowden. 1959. Decomposition of forest litters. I. Production of ammonia and nitrate nitrogen, changes in microbial population and rate of decomposition. Plant and Soil 11:237-248.

Jansson, Sven L., and F. E. Clark. 1952. Losses of nitrogen during decomopsition of plant material in the presence of inorganic nitrogen. Soil Sci. Soc. Am. Proc. 16:330-334.

Jansson, Sven L., M. J. Hallam, and W. V. Bartholomew. 1955. Preferential utilization of ammonium over nitrate by micro-organisms in the decomposition of oat straw. Plant and Soil 6:382-390.

Jansson, Sven L. 1958. Tracer studies on nitrogen with special attention to mineralization and immobilization relationships. Kungl. Lantbr. Ann. 24:101-361.

Jansson, Sven L. 1963. A balance sheet and residual effects of fertilizer nitrogen in a 6 year study with N^{15}. Soil Sci. 95:31-37.

Jenkins, S. H. 1935. Organic Manure. Imp. Bur. of Soil Tech Commun. No. 33.

Jensen, H. L. 1929. On the influence of the carbon: nitrogen ratios of organic material on the mineralization of nitrogen. J. Ag. Sci. 19:71-82.

Jensen, H. L. 1931. The microbiology of barnyard manure: I. Changes in the microflora and their relation to nitrification. J. Agr. Sci. 21:38-80.

Jensen, H. L. 1932. The microbiology of farmyard manure decomposition in soil. III. Decomposition of the cells of microorganisms. J. Ag. Sci. 22:1-25.

Kaila, Armi. 1949. Biological adsorption of phosphorus. Soil Sci. 68:279-289.

Karim, A. 1948. Microbiological decomposition of water hyacinth. Soil Sci. 66:401-516.

Karim, A., and M. U. Chowdhury. 1958. Decomposition of organic wastes. Soil Sci. 85:51-54.

Kuo, M. H. 1955. Factors influencing the immobilization of nitrogen during the decomposition of plant residues. M.S. Thesis. Iowa State College Library, Ames, Iowa.

Kuo, M. H., and W. V. Bartholomew. 1963. On the genesis of organic nitrogen in decomposed plant residue. FAO/IAEA Tech. Meet. on Isotopes in Soil Organic Matter Studies. Proc. Braunschweig, Germany.

Landrau, Pablo, Jr. 1953. Influences of cropping and cultural practices on the seasonal trends in nitrification rates of soils used for growing corn in Nebraska. Univ. Puerto Rico Ag. Exp. Sta. Tech. Paper 10.

Lawes, Sir John Bennet, and Joseph Henry Gilbert. 1883. Determinations of Nitrogen in the Soils of Some of the Experimental Fields at Rothamsted. Harrison & Sons. London.

Leukel, W. A., R. M. Barnette, and J. B. Hester. 1929. Composition and nitrification studies on *Crotalaria striata*. Soil Sci. 28:347-371.

Lipman, J. G., and A. W. Blair. 1916. Cylinder experiments relative to the utilization and accumulation of nitrogen. New Jersey Ag. Exp. Sta. Bul. 289.

Lipman, J. G., and A. W. Blair. 1918. Twenty years work on the availability of nitrogen in nitrate of soda, ammonium sulfate, dried blood, and farm manures. Soil Sci. 5:291-301.

Lockett, J. L. 1938. Nitrogen and phosphorus changes in the decomposition of rye and clover at different stages of growth. Soil Sci. 45:13-24.

Lohnis, F. 1926a. Nitrogen availability of green manures. Soil Sci. 22:253-290.

Lohnis, F. 1926b. The effect of growing legumes on succeeding crops. Soil Sci. 22:355-389.

Lunt, Herbert A. 1931. The carbon-organic matter factor in forest soil humus. Soil Sci. 32:27-33.

Lyon, T. L., J. A. Bizzell, and B. D. Wilson. 1923. Depressive influence of certain higher plants on the accumulation of nitrates in soil. J. Am. Soc. Agron. 15:457-467.

McKenzie, W. M. 1958. The effect on nitrogen availability of adding fragmented wood to soil. Aust. J. Agr. Res. 9:664-679.

Mann, H. H., and T. W. Barnes. 1951. The behavior of nitrogenous manures in the soil. I. The loss of manural nitrogen. J. Agr. Sci. 41:309-314.

Mann, H. H. 1958. Field studies in green manuring. Emp. J. Exp. Agr. 26:274-282.

Mattingly, G. E. G. 1956. Studies on composts prepared from waste materials. III. Nitrification in soil. J. Sci. Food & Agr. 7:601-605.

Maynard, L. A. 1917. The decomposition of sweet clover as a green manure under greenhouse conditions. New York Ag. Exp. Sta. Bul. 394.

Millar, H. C., F. B. Smith, and P. E. Brown. 1936. The influence of organic matter on nitrate accumulation and the base exchange capacity of Dickinson fine sandy loam. J. Am. Soc. Agron. 28:856-866.

Munson, Robert D., and John T. Pesek. 1958. The effects of corn residue, nitrogen, and incubation on nitrogen release and subsequent nitrogen uptake by oats: a quantitative evaluation. Soil Sci. Soc. Am. Proc. 22:543-547.

Newton, George A., and Kiril B. Daniloff. 1927. The influence of manures and organic residues on plant growth. Soil Sci. 24:95-101.

Nõmmik, Hans. 1961. Effect of addition of organic materials and lime on the yield and nitrogen nutrition of oats. Acta Agri. Scand. 11:211-226.

Nõmmik, Hans. 1962. Mineral nitrogen immobilization and carbon dioxide production during decomposition of wheat straw in soil as influenced by temperature. Acta Agri. Scand. 12:81-94.

Norman, A. G. 1931a. The biological decomposition of plant materials. IV. The biochemical activities on straws of some cellulose-decomposing fungi. Ann. App. Biol. 18.244-259.

Norman, A. G. 1931b. The biological decomposition of plant materials. VI. The effect of hydrogen ion concentration on the rate of immobilization of nitrogen by straw. Biochem. J. 25:1779-1787.

Norman, A. G. 1933. The biological decomposition of plant materials. VIII. The availability of the nitrogen of fungal tissues. Ann. Appl. Biol. 20:146-164.

Owen, O., and G. W. Winsor. 1950. The nitrogen status of soil. Part I. The nitrification of some nitrogenous fertilizers. J. Agr. Sci. 40:185-190.

Parbary, N. H., and R. J. Swaby. 1942. Organic materials in supplying nitrogen to crops. Agr. Gaz. N.S.W. 53:357-361.

Parker, D. T., W. E. Larson, and W. V. Bartholomew. 1957. Studies on nitrogen tie-up as influenced by location of plant residues in soils. Soil Soc. Soc. Am. Proc. 21:608-612.

Parker, D. T. 1962. Decomposition in the field of buried and surface applied cornstalk residue. Soil Sci. Soc. Am. Proc. 26:559-562.

Pearson, R. W., and R. W. Simonson. 1939. Organic phosphorus in seven Iowa profiles: Distribution and amounts as compared to organic carbon and nitrogen. Soil Sci. Soc. Am. Proc. 4:162-167.

Pearson, R. W., A. G. Norman, and Chung Ho. 1941. The mineralization of the organic phosphorus of various compounds in soil. Soil Sci. Soc. Am. Proc. 6:168-175.

Peevy, W. J., and A. G. Norman. 1948. Influence of composition of plant material on properties of the decomposed residues. Soil Sci. 65:209-226.

Pinck, L. A., F. E. Allison, and V. L. Gaddy. 1946. The nitrogen requirement in the utilization of residues in soil. J. Am. Soc. of Agron. 38:410-420.

Pinck, L. A., F. E. Allison, and V. L. Gaddy. 1948. Utilization of nitrogen in cropping systems with and without green manure in the greenhouse. Soil Sci. 66:39-52.

Richards, E. H., and A. G. Norman. 1931. The biological decomposition of plant materials. V. Some factors determining the quantity of nitrogen immobilized during decomposition. Biochem. J. 25:1769-1778.

Richards, E. H., and J. G. Shrikhande. 1935. The preferential utilization of different forms of inorganic nitrogen in the decomposition of plant materials. Soil Sci. 39:1-8.

Rubins, E. J., and F. E. Bear. 1942. Carbon-nitrogen ratios in organic fertilizer materials in relation to the availability of their nitrogen. Soil Sci. 54:411-423.

Russell, E. W. 1950-52. Report Rothamsted Experimental Sta.

Salomon, Milton. 1953. The accumulation of organic matter from wood chips. Soil Sci. Soc. Am. Proc. 17:114-118.

Salter, F. J. 1931. The carbon : nitrogen ratio in relation to the accumulation of organic matter in soils. Soil Sci. 31:413-430.

Salter, R. M. and C. J. Schollenberger. 1939. Farm Manure. Ohio Ag. Exp. Sta. Bul. 605.

Schmidt, A. R., A. C. Caldwell, and R. A. Briggs. 1959. Effect of various meadow crops. soybeans and grain on the crops which follow. Agron. J. 51:160-162.

Schollenberger, C. J. 1920. The organic phosphorus content of Ohio soils. Soil Sci. 10:127-141.

Sims, John Leonidas. 1961. Nitrogen immobilization and decomposition of crop residue in soil as affected by residue particle size. Dissertation Absts. 21(7):1681-1682.

Sowden, F. J., and K. C. Ivarson, 1959. Decomposition of forest litters. II. Changes in the nitrogenous constituents. Plant and Soil 11:249-261.

Stevenson, F. J. 1959. Carbon-nitrogen relationships in soil. Soil Sci. 88:201-208.

Stewart, Ernest H. 1959. Relative rates of mineralization in soil of organic nitrogen from several forage crops. Agron. J. 51:51-53.

Stojanovic, B. J., and F. E. Broadbent. 1956. Immobilization and mineralization rates of nitrogen during decomposition of plant residues in soil. Soil Sci. Soc. Am. Proc. 20:213-218.

Tenny, F. G., and S. A. Waksman. 1929. Composition of natural organic materials and their decomposition in soil: IV. The nature and rapidity of decomposition of the various organic complexes in different plant materials under aerobic conditions. Soil Sci. 28:55-84.

Thompson, L. M., C. A. Black, and F. E. Clark. 1948. Accumulation and mineralization of microbial organic phosphorus in soil materials. Soil Sci. Soc. Am. Proc. 13:242-245.

Thompson, L. M., and C. A. Black. 1950. The mineralization of organic phosphorus, nitrogen and carbon in Clarion and Webster soils. Soil Sci. Soc. Am. Proc. 14:147-151.

Thompson, L. M., C. A. Black, and J. A. Zoellner. 1954. Occurrence and mineralization of organic phosphorus in soils, with particular reference to associations with nitrogen, carbon and pH. Soil Sci. 77:185-196.

Tyler, K. B., and F. E. Broadbent. 1958. Nitrogen uptake by ryegrass from three tagged ammonium fertilizers. Soil Sci. Soc. Am. Proc. 22:231-234.

Viljoen, J. A., and E. B. Fred. 1924. The effect of different kinds of wood and of wood pulp cellulose on plant growth. Soil Sci. 17:199-211.

Waksman, S. A., and F. G. Tenny. 1927. The composition of natural organic materials and their decomposition in soil. II. Influence of age of plant upon the rapidity and nature of its decomposition—rye plants. Soil Sci. 24:317-333.

Waksman, S. A., and F. C. Gerretsen. 1931. Influence of temperature and moisture upon the nature and extent of decomposition of plant residues. Ecol. 12:33-60.

Walker, T. W. and A. F. R. Adams. 1958. Studies on soil organic matter. I. Influence of phosphorus content of parent materials on accumulations of carbon, nitrogen, sulfur, and organic phosphorus in grassland soils. Soil Sci. 85:307-318.

Whiting, A. L., and T. E. Richmond. 1927. The relative rates of nitrification of different parts of sweet clover plants. Soil Sci. 24:31-37.

Wilson, B. D., and J. K. Wilson. 1925. An explanation for the relative effects of timothy and clover residues in the soil on nitrate depression. Cornell Univ. Ag. Exp. Sta. Mem. 95.

Winsor, G. W., and A. G. Pollard. 1956a. Carbon-nitrogen relationships in soil. I. The immobilization of nitrogen in the presence of carbon compounds. J. Sci. Food and Agr. 7:134-141.

Winsor, G. W., and A. G. Pollard. 1956b. Carbon-nitrogen relationships in soil. II. Quantitative relationships between nitrogen immobilized and carbon added to the soil. J. Sci. Food and Agr. 7:142-149.

Winsor, G. W., and A. G. Pollard. 1956c. Carbon-nitrogen relationships in soil. III. Comparison of immobilization of nitrogen in a range of soils. J. Sci. Food and Agr. 7:613-617.

Wright, R. C. 1915. The influence of certain organic materials upon the transformation of soil nitrogen. J. Am. Soc. Agron. 7:193-208.

Chapter 8

Nitrification

MARTIN ALEXANDER

Cornell University
Ithaca, New York

I. INTRODUCTION

The formation of nitrate by biological agencies has long been of interest in agriculture and biology. From the agronomic viewpoint, the process is of importance because the microbial formation of nitrate is the major means whereby plants are provided with this anion. Moreover, as a result of the transformation, the nitrogen is converted into a form readily lost from soil by leaching or denitrification. The oxidation is of great interest to the microbiologist and the biochemist because of the obligately chemo-autotrophic metabolism of the dominant microbial species concerned in the transformation; further, the concepts of chemoautotrophy and comparative biochemistry were established on a firm footing by considerations of the unique behavior of certain of the nitrifying microorganisms.

Nitrification has often been defined as the reaction or reactions resulting in the production of nitrate and nitrite, with no consideration given to the identity of the specific substrates oxidized by the microflora. Included under the umbrella of this definition are all biochemical steps by which the nitrogen in the native soil organic fraction, crop residues or chemical fertilizers is converted to nitrate or nitrite. Clearly, such a definition, though possibly of operational value, has little to offer to the soil scientist interested in characterizing individual steps catalyzed by the soil microflora. Alternatively, nitrification can be considered as the oxidation of ammonium to nitrate with nitrite as an intermediate in the conversion. Such a definition is rather limiting since it presupposes the identity of the initial substrate, and it eliminates nitrate-forming organisms other than certain well characterized species. That heterotrophic microorganisms can form nitrite and nitrate has now been amply documented, and there is likewise evidence for the existence in soil of organic nitro compounds (Turtschin et al., 1960). Further, there now is precedent for the belief that certain reactions commonly attributed to the activities of autotrophs are largely if not frequently wholly a result of the metabolism of heterotrophic species. Freney (1958), for example, demonstrated that the production of sulfate from cysteine added to soil proceeds by way of an organic sequence rather than through a pathway presumably involving species of *Thiobacillus*. The biological oxidation of manganous ions in soil probably is also a consequence of the activities of heterotrophic microorganisms. In this light, an alternate definition of nitrification has been advanced, namely, the biological conversion of nitrogen in organic or inorganic compounds from a reduced to a more oxidized state (Alexander et al., 1960). Thus, nitrification refers simply to the specific process in which there occurs an increase in the oxidation state of nitrogen.

II. IMPORTANCE

For many years, the nitrifying autotrophs were pointed out as excellent examples of beneficial soil bacteria. The pendulum is now swinging in the opposite direction, and the detrimental consequences of ammonium oxidation are becoming more apparent. An obvious effect of nitrification is upon the nitrogen nutrition of plants, the rates of assimilation by plants of substrate and product of nitrification—ammonium and nitrate—being often quite different. A review of the inorganic nitrogen nutrition of higher plants is beyond the scope of this brief exposition, but it is sufficient to state in the context of the present discussion that plants differ considerably in the rate of uptake of the two forms of nitrogen. Hence, nitrification has a direct bearing upon crop nutrition as it alters the availability of the chief plant nutrient element obtained from the soil. Witness to this fact is the occasional beneficial effects of nitrate as compared with ammonium fertilizer in soils in which nitrification is inhibited by fumigation (McCants et al., 1959).

Nitrification of ammonium salts also results in the conversion of a slowly leached, cationic form of the element to a readily leached, anionic form. If nitrate generated from the reduced nitrogen is not assimilated by the crop or immobilized by the microflora, it is susceptible to downward movement, and the nitrogen may thus in effect be lost to the plants following nitrification. Appreciable nitrogen losses through leaching may thereby occur during periods of active nitrate formation (Baumann and Maass, 1957; Greenland, 1958). Such leaching losses can be appreciable during the winter if ammonium has been applied in the preceding fall and the winter conditions permit nitrate to be formed under circumstances where the roots remove only a portion of the nitrogen oxidized.

Another way in which this element can be lost as an indirect consequence of nitrification is through volatilization. There can be no biological denitrification unless there is an initial oxidation of reduced nitrogen, but once nitrate, nitrite or possibly other intermediates in nitrogen oxidation appear, the denitrifying bacteria have suitable substrates to serve as electron acceptors in respiration. In this sense, nitrification is a necessary prelude to a process which leads to nitrogen disappearance from soil. This obligatory nitrifying overture to the denitrifying finale is clearly demonstrated by the investigations of Hiltbold and Adams (1960) who observed that nitrogen was not volatilized in ammonium sulfate-amended soils too acid for ammonium oxidation, but gaseous loss did take place in high pH soils in which nitrate was formed.

The importance to denitrification of nonbiological reactions involving a product of nitrification is discussed elsewhere in this volume. The pH sensitivity of the nitrifying autotrophs and the pH dependence of these non-enzymatic reactions must be borne in mind in any attempt to assess the significance of nitrification to nitrogen volatilization from acid soils or soils that become acid as nitric and nitrous acid are generated microbiologically. There is, nevertheless, no doubt that nitrogen deficits occur in nitrifying soils in which nitrite accumulates, and the deficit tends to be greatest where the level of nitrite is most pronounced (Clark et al., 1960; Soulides and Clark, 1958).

Nitrification assumes prominence in other ways as a consequence of the acidification of the environment in which these microorganisms live. From ammonium salts, the net reaction is

$$NH_4^+ + 2\ O_2 \rightarrow NO_3^- + H_2O + 2\ H^+$$

Prolonged use of ammonium fertilizers thus leads not only to the self-destruction of the nitrifying autotrophs but also to the appearance in soluble form of a number of cations. The solvent action resulting from the activities of the nitrifiers, without the addition of lime to stem the tide of hydrogen ions, effects the solubilization of potassium, calcium, magnesium, manganese, phosphorus and aluminum (Ames and Boltz, 1919; Blanchet et al., 1960; Pikovskaia, 1948). The repeated use of ammonium fertilizers may also lead to an increase in aluminum toxicity (Leo, 1959).

It is clear, therefore, that nitrification is a mixed blessing and, possibly, a frequent evil. It is consequently not surprising that attention currently is being focused upon means of retarding the responsible microorganisms, a task which may not be difficult to fulfill because of the marked sensitivity of the chemoautotrophs.

III. HISTORY

The history of investigations of nitrification serves as an excellent starting point for inquiry into the history of the meshing of microbiology and soil science. Initial observations of the transformation set the stage for speculation upon the precise nature of the process, particularly whether the oxidation was biological or physico-chemical. The biologists were led naturally to attempts, initially abortive, to obtain the responsible agents in pure culture. Following upon Winogradsky's isolation and description of *Nitrosomonas* and *Nitrobacter,* there appeared a flurry of papers dealing with the ecology and characterization of the organisms. Unfortunately, a similar flurry has been maintained for more than a half-century, and the numbers of definitive inquiries dealing with the ecology, metabolism and precise explanations of soil influences upon the active microorganisms remain surprisingly small. It is to be hoped that greater consideration will be given in the future to establishing new facts about nitrification rather than repeating experiments under conditions not far different from those of earlier observers. Because of the uniqueness of these organisms, their marked sensitivity to environmental change and their importance in soil biochemistry, such studies may contribute much to an understanding of the microorganisms and their metabolic activities in soil.

The harnessing of the nitrifying microorganisms can be traced to the Napoleonic era, during which time the nitrate for gunpowder was reportedly prepared in manure heaps maintained in a moist condition by the addition of water and urine. The nitrate was finally extracted from these piles, this undoubtedly being one of the first instances of microbiological lore being applied to the manly art of destroying one's neighbors. As nitrate production became more the concern of the scientific rather than the military mind, the oxidation became gunfodder in the less destructive warfare then proceeding between chemical and biological schools of thought. The chemical theorists, as was their wont, advanced the concept of a soil catalyst serving in the conversion of ammonium to nitrate. Pasteur (1862) suggested a reevaluation of this view in the light of his evidence that vinegar resulted from a biological oxidation, one apparently similar to nitrification. It remained for Schloesing and Muntz (1877), however, in their classic studies of sewage to resolve between the theories of "organized ferments" and that of a purely chemical reaction between O_2 and nitrogen compounds.

The next task, presumably a simple one, was to obtain the responsible microorganisms in pure culture. Subsequent students of nitrification, to the present day, often attempt the same feat, and rarely do even these modern investigators meet with success. Small wonder, therefore, that the pioneer microbiologists met with considerable difficulties since they had not yet been introduced to the concept of chemoautotrophy. The laboratory media then in vogue were not suited to support the colonial growth of such chemoautotrophs. But, in their failures, these pioneers made many observations which still have agronomic significance; e.g., the toxicity of ammonia to the nitrite oxidizers and the related accumulation of nitrite (Warington, 1891). Finally, in a series of studies which have been described too often to bear repetition, but never sufficiently often to diminish admiration, Winogradsky (1890) obtained the responsible autotrophs in monoculture. The first report of a heterotrophic species which could effect nitrogen oxidation is that of Nelson (1929), almost forty years after the description of autotrophic bacteria.

IV. THE NITRIFYING POPULATION

A. *Nitrosomonas* and *Nitrobacter*

Nearly every soil scientist who has handled a culture flask and possibly an equal percentage of the microbiologists who have used soil as an inoculum into an ammonium-salts medium have observed the ease of initiating enrichments of nitrifying autotrophs. By contrast, comparatively few individuals have isolated in pure culture the organisms carrying out the oxidation. This difficulty in obtaining monocultures extends from the present day back to the first, unsuccessful attempts of Warington and his contemporaries to grow the bacteria in the absence of contaminating microorganisms. Indeed, there have been many studies—possibly in despair—concerned with descriptions of the intruders, the common contaminants in the final enrichments including species of *Pseudomonas, Hyphomicrobium, Mycobacterium, Flavobacterium,* and *Serratia* as well as an occasional myxobacterium (Gundersen, 1955; Stapp, 1940; Ulyanova, 1960). Frequently, a beneficial role is attributed to the contaminant, and it has been proposed that some form of symbiosis takes place in soil to allow the autotroph to grow in an environment not apparently favorable to it. Many, but possibly not all, of these suggestions arise from the inability of the investigator to supply suitable conditions for proliferation of the bacterium, and a large part of the mystique concerning difficulties in isolation of the autotrophs has recently fallen by the wayside.

A number of methods have been devised to separate the autotrophic nitrifier from its aggressive neighbors. In certain of the procedures, the size of the autotrophic population is increased by addition to the inorganic nutrient solution of successive increments of $(NH_4)_2SO_4$. The microbial enrichment is then diluted, and attempts at obtaining pure cultures are made by some single-cell technique, by plating or by transferring aliquots of the dilutions to a large number of tubes of medium in the hope of having one which is free of heterotrophs. Several improved procedures have been devised so that it is no longer a feat in itself to isolate the bacteria. One modification entails bubbling carbon dioxide through the enrichments to remove the cells from the carbonate particles onto which many contaminants adhere (Meiklejohn, 1950). Another technique involves the use of compounds inhibitory to many of the contaminants (Gould and Lees, 1958; Prouty, 1929). Undoubtedly the most effective procedure, however, is that designed by Lewis and Pramer (1958), who bypassed the perennial problem of adsorption of both contaminant and nitrifier by the carbonate particles; this problem was surmounted by means of a solution free of insoluble carbonates in which the pH was maintained relatively constant by regular additions of alkali. Once the ratio of autotrophs to heterotrophs is sufficiently wide, there is no problem in obtaining a heterotroph-free culture of the autotroph.

On the basis of the dominant nitrifiers in enrichments and the frequency of isolation of specific bacteria in pure culture, it appears that only two autotrophic genera are prominent in soil nitrification, *Nitrosomonas* and *Nitrobacter*. These two genera, the former containing ammonium oxidizers, the latter the nitrite oxidizers, are classified in Nitrobacteriaceae, one of the families of the order Pseudomonadales. Most of the ammonium-oxidizing isolates seem to be related to or identical with *Nitrosomonas europaea,* which is a rod-shaped bacterium, $0.9\text{-}1.0 \times 1.1\text{-}1.8$ μ, with a single polar flagellum or occasionally one flagellum at each end of the cell. The common nitrite-oxidizing bacterium appears to be *Nitrobacter winogradskyi,* characterized as a short, gram negative, nonmotile rod, $0.6\text{-}0.8 \times 1.0\text{-}1.2$ μ (Breed et al., 1957). Nelson (1931) described *Nitrosomonas monocella* as a short, ovoid, gram-positive rod which is motile by means of a single polar flagellum; his isolate of *Nitrobacter agilis* was reported to be similar to *N. winogradskyi,* but it had a single polar flagellum as locomotory organelle.

Some differences appear to exist between various isolates. Thus, some strains are gram negative and nonmotile (Lewis and Pramer, 1958), some are gram positive (Heübult, 1929) while others are weakly gram positive to gram negative and motile by a single polar flagellum or occasionally two flagella. The early finding that at least some strains of *Nitrobacter* form buds (Stutzer, 1901) has recently been confirmed, and it appears that *N. winogradskyi* may have, in addition to a budding or a bud-like mechanism, both a flagellated and a nonflagellated stage (Zavarzin and Legunkova, 1959). The differences observed among various early investigators may be more apparent than real because of the suboptimal conditions provided to the cultures, and a reinquiry into the morphology of these bacteria is clearly warranted.

In addition to *Nitrosomonas* and *Nitrobacter,* indisputably the most frequently isolated and hence presumably the most abundant of the autotrophs, five other genera of nitrogen autotrophs are recognized (Breed et al., 1957). These are the ammonium-oxidizing *Nitrosococcus, Nitrosospira, Nitrosogloea* and *Nitrosocystis,* and the nitrite oxidizer, *Nitrocystis.* Strains designated as members of these groups are not commonly encountered, but there are occasional recent reports of the isolation from soil of *Nitrosogloea* (Sims and Collins, 1960), *Nitrosococcus* (Sakai, 1958), *Nitrosospira* and *Nitrosocystis* (Maciejewska, 1959). No attempt will be made here to assess the validity of these genera, an issue first raised by the demonstration of Imshenetsky (1945) and Grace (1951) that myxobacteria occurring as contaminants in *Nitrosomonas* cultures may give rise to forms that appear to be new types of autotrophic nitrifiers. Still in contention, however, is the means by which the purity of such cultures is ascertained. The simple statement that the culture is pure, occasionally together with an almost mystical leaning upon the majesty of the Winogradsky name, is insufficient. Rigid criteria of purity must be established and adhered to, the presence of myxobacteria must be ruled out unequivocally, and the possible presence of slow-growing heterotrophic intruders in cultures of *Nitrosomonas* and *Nitrobacter* must be examined by means of distinctly different organic media.

Considerable attention has been given to the nutrition of the nitrifying chemoautotrophs, in earlier periods in order to characterize this fascinating mode of nutrition in which an organism grew in the complete absence of preformed organic molecules, in more recent times in attempts to explain the equally intriguing inability—or apparent inability—of these bacteria to make use of exogenously supplied organic substances. Notwithstanding occasional claims to the contrary, there is no reason to doubt the capacity of *Nitrosomonas* and *Nitrobacter* spp. to develop in solutions all of whose ingredients are inorganic. The sole energy sources which support growth are nitrogenous, typically ammonium or nitrite salts. The nitrogen of amino acids, amides, proteins or urea is not oxidized by *N. europaea* although some of the nitrogen in certain purines is converted to nitrite, at least by some strains; the purines are likely deaminated prior to nitrification (Ruban, 1958). Hydroxylamine and formic acid are also oxidized by the bacterium (Engel and Alexander, 1960; Silver, 1960), but there is no evidence that these compounds are energy sources for proliferation. As far as presently known, no sugar, organic acid or other organic molecule will serve as sources of either carbon or energy for growth (Delwiche and Finstein, 1965; Ida and Alexander, 1965).

There are few unique features in the mineral nutrition of these bacteria. Magnesium, phosphorus and iron are necessary for the growth of *Nitrosomonas* and *Nitrobacter* strains, but there is no evidence of a requirement for significant quantities of calcium (Aleem and Alexander, 1960; Bomeke, 1950; Lees and Meiklejohn, 1948). The calcium carbonate included in media for cultivation of the ammonium oxidizers provides a source of carbon and a buffer, but the calcium probably can be omitted except when all chemicals have been carefully purified. Potassium (Welch and Scott, 1959) and sulfur are, without question, required also. Because of the small yield of cells even in media which are optimal for development, it is difficult to ascertain the trace mineral requirements, yet molybdenum and copper are stimulatory to *Nitrobacter* (Kiesow, 1962; Zavarzin, 1958b), and iron increases the rate of nitrite oxidation by *N. agilis* enzyme preparations (Aleem and Alexander, 1958). Exogenously supplied B vitamins or amino acids have no beneficial effect upon either of the two important soil genera (Aleem and Alexander, 1960; Gundersen, 1955b). Early but frequently cited reports on stimulation by protein hydrolyzates require verification in the light of the improved cultural conditions now available.

There may be some adaptation of nitrifiers, at least certain strains of *Nitrosomonas,* to their particular environment. This has been suggested by the experiments of Ulyanova (1961, 1962), who found that the optimum pH for activity of the ammonium oxidizers was often similar to that of the environment from which they were isolated; frequently, however, the pH optimum was far removed from that of the original habitat. A bacterial adaptation to the organic matter levels in the original habitat was also suggested, but more definitive work is required before it can be safely stated that these microorganisms truly adapt themselves to their environment.

Much has been made of the role of bacterial adsorption in nitrification, and statements that *Nitrosomonas* requires a solid surface for growth are frequent. True, when calcium or magnesium carbonates are included in culture media to serve as buffers, the *Nitrosomonas* cells adhere tenaciously to the carbonate particles. The use of such media, however, serves no purpose other than honoring the memory of Winogradsky, who propagated his isolates in media of this type, but microbiological techniques have been distinctly improved in the succeeding seven decades. Thus, by providing carbon in the form of a soluble carbonate and by maintaining the pH by additions of alkali, it is not difficult to propagate *N. europaea,* one strain of the bacterium developing in such circumstances with a generation time of 11 hours (Engel and Alexander, 1958b). A generation time of this duration, though it may seem long by comparison with morphologically similar heterotrophs, is one of the shortest reported for members of this genus. Generation times in nutrient solutions will often be as long as approximately 40 hours or as short as 8 hours. For strains of *Nitrobacter,* the minimum generation time appears to be in the vicinity of 7 hours. Parenthetically, the oft-repeated observation that pure cultures nitrify more slowly than mixed cultures must be accepted with considerable caution since, in such investigations, the autotroph is rarely growing at its maximum rate.

In soil receiving large quantities of ammonium or nitrite salts, nitrification is with little question an autotrophic phenomenon, and since for these bacteria nitrogen oxidation is a growth-linked process, the oxidation is logarithmic. From a plot of the logarithm of the quantity of inorganic nitrogen oxidized, the apparent generation time of the ammonium or nitrite oxidizers in soil can be calculated. It is of some interest that the generation time in soil of the nitrite oxidizers is shorter than that of the nitrite formers (Morrill and Dawson, 1962). Moreover, because there rarely occurs an accumulation of nitrite in soils receiving ammonium fertilizers, the rate of oxidation of nitrite would appear to be limited by the availability of the energy substrate for the nitrobacter group.

B. Heterotrophic Microorganisms

There is no known selective enrichment or isolation method for heterotrophic nitrifying microorganisms. Media which support growth of these species must contain organic carbon in addition to nitrogen; such media permit the development of a large segment of the soil microflora, most organisms developing therein being unable to oxidize the nitrogen. In the absence of a selective enrichment method, isolation of the heterotrophic nitrifier in monoculture is achieved by a random selection from colonies developing on some nutrient agar medium, the isolates then being examined for activity in suitable test solutions.

The heterotrophic nitrifier is capable of bringing about an increase in the oxidation state of nitrogen, but the organism cannot use this exothermic reaction as the sole source of energy for cell synthesis. Indeed, there is no evidence that the energy released by ammonium or nitrite-oxidizing heterotrophs is coupled with biosynthetic processes; i.e., that phosphorylation is directly linked with the oxidation. Moreover, some and possibly most of the heterotrophs grow well in conditions which preclude nitrification (Hirsch et al., 1961). It would thus appear that the biochemical mechanisms of the autotrophic and heterotrophic transformations are quite dissimilar in a number of essential regards.

There is no apparent taxonomic relationship among the various heterotrophs. Gram-negative and gram-positive bacteria, spore-formers and non-spore-formers and, surprisingly, even an obligate anaerobe are capable of oxidizing nitrogen compounds. Differing from the autotrophic group, which includes only bacteria, many fungi and actinomycetes nitrify. A summary of the reported nitrogen-oxidizing species is presented in Table 1.

Table 1. Nitrogenous substrates and products of heterotrophic nitrifying microorganisms.

Microorganism	Substrate	Product
Bacteria		
Agrobacterium spp.	Pyruvic oxime	Nitrite
Azotobacter chroococcum	NH_4	Bound NH_2OH
Bacillus sp.	NH_4	Nitrite
Clostridium butyricum	N_2	Nitrate
Corynebacterium simplex	Nitrophenols	Nitrite
Mycobacterium rubrum	NH_4	Nitrite
Pseudomonas spp.	NH_2OH	Nitrite
Pseudomonas methanica	NH_4	Nitrite
Actinomycetes		
Micromonospora spp.	NH_4	Nitrite
Nocardia spp.	NH_4	Nitrite
Nocardia corallina	Pyruvic oxime	Nitrite
Nocardia sp.	p-Nitrobenzoate	Nitrite
Streptomyces spp.	NH_4	Nitrite
Fungi		
Aspergillus flavus	NH_4	Bound NH_2OH, nitrite, β-nitropropionate, nitrate
Aspergillus flavus	Amino	Aspergillic acid
Aspergillus niger	NH_4	NH_2OH
Aspergillus wentii	Nitrite	Nitrate
Cephalosporium sp.	NH_4	Nitrate
Penicillium atrovenetum	NH_4	β-Nitropropionate
Penicillium spp.	Nitrite	Nitrate
Penicillium spp.	Amino	N-formyl hydroxyaminoacetate
Sterigmatocystis nigra	NH_4	NH_2OH

The physiological or biochemical characteristics associated with nitrogen oxidation by heterotrophs are unknown. A single enzyme or a group of related enzymes may serve to catalyze the oxidation of the nitrogenous substrate, but further work is required to determine whether such a physiological similarity exists. Clearly, a number of substances serve as nitrogen sources for these microorganisms, and the products include hydroxamic acids, free and bound hydroxylamine, nitropropionic acid, nitrite and nitrate (Table 1). As the heterotrophic group includes many different microbial types, it is unlikely that there is a common nutritional pattern among the active species. Some attain full growth in the absence of supplemental growth factors (Alexander et al., 1960), but many undoubtedly require one or more vitamins, amino acids or other growth factors. It is possibly of some ecological significance that the oxidized products—nitrite or nitrate—are released into the environs, at least with certain species, only when the supply of nitrogen exceeds the microbial need for that element, i.e., when the C/N ratio is narrow (Hirsch et al., 1961; Jensen, 1951). This suggests that either the formation or the release of oxidized nitrogen occurs only if the organism's demands for assimilatory purposes are satisfied.

The amount of nitrogen oxidized by most heterotrophic nitrifiers is small. A maximum of approximately 5 ppm nitrite-nitrogen is produced from ammonium salts by a spore-forming, thermophilic bacillus, a number of heterotrophic bacteria and a variety of actinomycetes (Campbell, 1932; Eylar and Schmidt, 1959; Hirsch et al., 1961). By contrast with bacteria and actinomycetes, which may form nitrite but rarely nitrate, certain fungi are capable of producing relatively large quantities of nitrate from ammonium salts. Fifteen of the 16 nitrate-forming isolates investigated by Eylar and Schmidt (1959) were fungi. Particularly prominent among the nitrate producers are strains of *Aspergillus flavus* and closely related species, the quantity of nitrate-nitrogen released by the cultures exceeding 100 ppm (Hirsch et al., 1961). Incubation of certain heterotrophs with nitrogen in more highly oxidized states than that in ammonium results in higher yields of nitrite (Gundersen and Jensen, 1956; Jensen, 1951), but as the bulk of the soil nitrogen is in the reduced state, it seems that the high yields from oximes or nitro compounds have little or no relation to natural conditions. Significant amounts of aliphatic or aromatic nitro compounds, however, may be produced from ammonium- or amino-nitrogen, and such nitro compounds might conceivably be substrates for further oxidation.

C. Abundance

A number of methods for estimation of the abundance of nitrifying autotrophs have been described. Although the bacteria form colonies on agar and the suitable selective agar media have been devised, plate counts are not used for the purposes of enumeration because of the long incubation period required for the appearance of colonies of reasonable size. The more widely used procedures of counting rely upon the inoculation of dilutions of a soil suspension into inorganic media containing ammonium or nitrite salts as energy sources; at the end of the incubation period, the presence or absence of the bacteria is assessed by determining whether nitrite has been formed or oxidized. The most-probable-number procedure is then applied to the data thus obtained (Black, 1965).

The population of *Nitrosomonas* and *Nitrobacter* is frequently quite small, and many soils, particularly those which are acid, have fewer than 100 viable cells of one or both genera per gram. As a rule, populations in excess of 10^5 per gram are rare in unfertilized soils. When the soil is treated with manure or an ammonium fertilizer, however, the numbers rise and may reach values in excess of 10^6 and, occasionally, 10^7 cells per gram. Generally, the abundance of the autotrophs declines with increasing soil acidity and increasing depth, and varies with cropping practices, soil treatment and season of year (Eno and Ford, 1958; Walker et al., 1937; Wilson, 1927). The organisms respond to the presence of plant roots, the magnitude of the rhizosphere effect varying with the type of plant (Timonin and Thexton, 1950). The populations of the ammonium and of the nitrite oxidizers are commonly within the same order of magnitude, but there are occasional instances when one group will be appreciably more numerous than the other.

The heterotrophic nitrifiers, representing as they do a number of distinctly different nutritional and physiological types of microorganisms, cannot be enumerated on any of the selective media now known. The only way by which their abundance can be ascertained is by testing a selected percent of random isolates from soil dilution plates for the ability to catalyze some step in nitrogen oxidation. Eylar and Schmidt (1959), for example, reported that 7% of the bacteria, 6% of the fungi and 7% of the actinomycetes produced at least traces of nitrite from reduced nitrogen compounds; nitrate production was largely restricted to the fungi, 3.6% of the isolates liberating nitrate. Using different test media, 30% of the isolates in a collection of Actinomycetales strains produced traces of nitrite (Hirsch et al., 1961). It appears, therefore, that the population of heterotrophs potentially capable of at least some type of nitrogen oxidation is remarkably large.

V. HETEROTROPHY AND AUTOTROPHY IN SOIL NITRIFICATION

There is yet no direct experimental verification of a role for heterotrophic microorganisms in soil nitrification. It is likely that bacteria dominate following the application of sizable quantities of ammonium fertilizers; this is suggested by the logarithmic kinetics of ammonium oxidation in soil (Stojanovic and Alexander, 1958). It is taken for granted, though without specific experimental support, that the responsible bacteria are strains of *Nitrosomonas* and *Nitrobacter* or related chemoautotrophs. It is also of interest to compare the available figures for the abundance of autotrophic nitrifiers with the estimate that approximately 2×10^8 *Nitrosomonas* and 4×10^7 *Nitrobacter* cells must appear for the biosynthesis from ammonium of 1.0 mg nitrate-nitrogen, cell counts equivalent to 10^6 and 2×10^5 cells of ammonium- and of the nitrite-oxidizer per gram of soil to generate 10 pounds of nitrate-nitrogen per acre (Alexander et al., 1960). Comparison of the theoretical and the actual population sizes in various soils during nitrification might provide some of the needed information to resolve whether there are sufficient bacteria to account for the transformation.

Because of the great abundance of the heterotrophic types, it is tempting to postulate a role for them. However, in contrast with the autotrophs, nitrification is not obligately associated with development of the heterotrophs so that the frequency of these microorganisms indicates merely a potential for activity rather than the occurrence of an actual transformation. Despite their capacity for rapid nitrate formation, however, the fungi are of little or no significance in soils where there is a logarithmic oxidation of the nitrogen. Further, nitrogen oxidation in soils fertilized with ammonium salts is markedly inhibited by 2-chloro-6-(trichloromethyl) pyridine (Goring, 1962a, b) a compound which at low concentration affects the autotrophic but not the heterotrophic nitrifiers (Shattuck and Alexander, 1963).

Assessing the types of microorganisms concerned in the generation of nitrate from the soil organic fraction is still more difficult. Frequently, this process may occur in sites containing an insignificantly small number of the autotrophs. The observation that sulfate is formed from organic sulfur by an organic reaction sequence (Freney, 1958) may be a valuable precedent for investigations of the microbiology of the nitrogen cycle. The finding in soil in which nitrification is proceeding of organic compounds containing nitrogen in an oxidized state (Turtschin et al., 1960) may indicate an organic pathway for nitrogen oxidation—which may be either heterotrophic or autotrophic—although such compounds may be produced by nonbiological reactions involving intermediates in the transformation.

The challenge to the unique and essential position of the Nitrobacteriaceae in the nitrogen cycle may be unwarranted, but only careful ecological investigations will provide a basis for resolution of the problem of the dominant genera and species.

VI. BIOCHEMISTRY OF NITRIFICATION

A. Autotrophic Nitrogen Oxidation

Both the conversion of ammonium to nitrite and the transformation of the latter to nitrate are exothermic reactions. For the chemoautotrophic nitrifier, the oxidation is physiologically the equivalent of the heterotrophic conversion of organic carbon to carbon dioxide, both processes providing the respective groups of microorganisms with the energy required for biosynthetic reactions. In addition, a portion of the energy released in the autotrophic oxidation of the nitrogen must be coupled with the reduction of carbon dioxide to the oxidation level characteristic of the protoplasmic constituents of the cell. The heterotroph may put to use part of the energy liberated in its nitrogen oxidation, but it more likely squanders the energy with no appreciable coupling of nitrification with phosphorylation.

Values for the change in free energy (ΔF) in the oxidation of ammonium to nitrite

$$NH_4^+ + 1\tfrac{1}{2} O_2 \rightarrow NO_2^- + 2 H^+ + H_2O$$

have been reported as -65.2 to -84.0 kcal per mole of ammonium. If hydroxylamine is the first product of ammonium oxidation, the change in free energy in this initial step is quite small, namely -0.70 kcal per mole; most of the energy is released in the subsequent steps. The ΔF of the *Nitrobacter* reaction

$$NO_2^- + \tfrac{1}{2} O_2 \rightarrow NO_3^-$$

is reported as -17.5 to -20.0 kcal per mole (Gibbs and Schiff, 1960). The ammonium oxidizer thus has potentially available to it considerably more energy than the nitrite oxidizer per unit of nitrogen undergoing reaction and, assuming similar efficiencies of utilizing the energy liberated for cell synthesis, many more *Nitrosomonas* than *Nitrobacter* cells are formed per unit of ammonium undergoing nitrification in soil.

Kluyver and Donker (1926) established a reasonable basis upon which to develop an experimental approach to studies of the mechanism of nitrification, but serious investigation was hindered because of the lack of a means of culturing the bacteria in such a way that large quantities of active cells free of medium ingredients could be obtained. A persistent superstition dictated that the autotrophic ammonium-oxidizers would not grow unless large quantities of calcium or magnesium carbonate particles were clouding the solution. This fantasy has now vanished, and several techniques for the cultivation of relatively large quantities of *Nitrosomonas* and *Nitrobacter* cells have been developed (Aleem and Alexander, 1958; Engel and Alexander, 1958b; Skinner and Walker, 1961).

The chemical composition of these cells does not appear to be different from cells of heterotrophic species, despite the fact that *Nitrosomonas* and *Nitrobacter* are obligate chemoautotrophs, microorganisms not known to utilize organic nutrients as energy or as carbon sources. One might also anticipate some different protoplasmic constituents in *Nitrobacter* on the grounds that the oxidation-reduction potential of the sole energy substrate used by members of the genus is among the highest known in biology. In the cells of both *Nitrosomonas* and *Nitrobacter* are found the same amino acids, sugars, and organic acids as are reported in heterotrophic bacteria (Engel et al., 1954; Hofman, 1953; Malavolta et al., 1960).

The unique behavior of these obligate chemoautotrophs requires some comment. Although they have much in common with heterotrophs, including an apparently similar cell composition and an analogous mechanism of electron transport, at least in part, they stand apart on the basis of their inability to use exogenously supplied organic molecules as sources of energy or carbon. Several hypotheses can be advanced to account for this unique behavior. The organisms may be impermeable to most of the commonly investigated organic molecules, the autotroph in effect creating a wall between itself and its environment. The barrier need not be at the cell surface for intracellular permeability barriers are known. The organism may, on the other hand, be permeable to a variety of organic compounds, but it may have none of the enzymes required for metabolism of the substrates that penetrate; this seems unlikely in view of the many organic molecules synthesized intracellularly by the enzymes of *Nitrosomonas* and *Nitrobacter* spp. Alternatively, the bacteria may be unable to couple oxidative activities with phosphorylation except in the special cases of those enzymes acting upon ammonium or nitrite. As yet, however, there are few data upon which to build a reasonable explanation for the uniqueness of the obligate chemoautotroph but recent evidence with *Nitrobacter* spp. argues against the concept of permeability barriers and the total absence of enzymes metabolizing exogenously supplied organic molecules (Delwiche and Finstein, 1965; Ida and Alexander, 1965).

The autotrophic nitrification sequence involves a conversion of nitrogen from the -3 to the $+5$ oxidation state, specifically ammonia to nitrate, a span involving the release of 8 electrons. Compounds of nitrogen are known for all of the possible oxidation states between these two extremes; e.g., hydrazine (-2), hydroxylamine (-1), molecular nitrogen (0), hyponitrous acid or nitrous oxide $(+1)$, nitric oxide $(+2)$, nitrous acid $(+3)$, and nitrogen dioxide $(+4)$. For more than three decades, all considerations of the nitrogenous intermediates have had their origin in the monumental paper of Klyver and Donker (1926) entitled *Die Einheit in der Biochemie*. In this communication, which served as a foundation for the concept of comparative biochemistry, it was proposed that nitrification involves a series of sequential oxidations, each representing a loss of two electrons.

$$\begin{array}{c}H\\ \backslash \end{array}\begin{array}{c}H\\ / \end{array} N-OH \xrightarrow[-H_2O]{1/2 O_2} \begin{array}{c}H\\ \backslash \end{array} N-OH \xrightarrow[-H_2O]{1/2 O_2} H-N=O \xrightarrow{H_2O} H-N \begin{array}{c}OH\\ \backslash OH \end{array} \xrightarrow[-H_2O]{1/2 O_2} HO-N=O$$

$$\begin{array}{ccccc} \text{I} & \quad\quad \text{II} & \quad \text{III} & \quad\quad \text{IV} & \quad\quad \text{V} \end{array}$$

Hydroxylamine and hyponitrous acid, $HO—N{=}N—OH$ are reasonably stable, but nitroxyl (III) and dihydroxyammonia (IV) are not. The formation of nitrate by *Nitrobacter* spp. was visualized to consist of an initial hydration followed by an oxidation.

$$HO-N=O \xrightarrow{H_2O} HO-N \begin{array}{c}OH\\ =O\\ OH \end{array} \xrightarrow[-H_2O]{1/2\ O_2} HO-N\overset{=O}{\underset{O}{\downarrow}}$$

At the present time, more than a third of a century after this proposed pathway, there is neither adequate confirmatory evidence nor an experimentally supported, satisfactory alternative.

The initial product of ammonium oxidation is commonly considered to be hydroxylamine. The evidence for the latter as an intermediate rests upon four points.

1. Hydroxylamine is oxidized to nitrite rapidly and stoichiometrically. This activity is not readily lost as the *N. europaea* cell suspension is allowed to age although the rate of ammonium oxidation declines during storage of the cells (Engel and Alexander, 1958a).

2. Ammonium-grown *N. europaea* cells metabolize hydroxylamine with no initial period of induction; that is, cells grown on ammonium contain the enzymes for hydroxylamine oxidation (Engel and Alexander, 1958a). Because the bacterium is only known to utilize ammonium salts as energy sources for growth, it is not possible to use properly the technique of sequential induction.

3. In the presence of hydrazine, which inhibits the oxidation of hydroxylamine, a *Nitrosomonas* sp. incubated with ammonium sulfate accumulates a nitrogenous compound identified as hydroxylamine (Yoshida and Alexander, 1964).

4. *N. europaea* cells contain an enzyme catalyzing the oxidation of hydroxylamine. Neither nicotinamide adenine dinucleotide (NAD) nor nicotinamide adenine dinucleotide phosphate (NADP) is reduced in the reaction. In the presence of some suitable electron acceptor, nitrite is produced, but the quantity of nitrite formed is at best only about three-fourths of the expected value. These enzyme preparations show no detectable oxidation of ammonium (Burge et al., 1963; Engel and Alexander, 1959; Nicholas and Jones, 1960).

The evidence in support of hydroxylamine as an intermediate remains somewhat equivocal. It still remains to be definitely shown that the bacterium has an enzyme which forms hydroxylamine directly from ammonium. When faced by their inquisitors with the shaky evidence used to identify the intermediate of oxidation state -1, those individuals foolish enough to practice the art of intermediary nitrogen metabolism can only answer as another persecuted soul did when facing the judge inquiring whether he would plead innocent or guilty, "What else do you have to offer?"

The identity of the intermediate at the next higher oxidation state remains completely obscure. Because of the instability of hyponitrous acid, a likely candidate, this compound is difficult to use for biological experimentation. Its half-life at pH 7.3 is only about 11 minutes, and even at pH 11.3 the stability in aqueous solutions is not too great. However, in carefully controlled experiments, no microbial conversion of hyponitrite to nitrite is noted with either suspensions of *Nitrosomonas* cells or enzyme extracts prepared from the bacteria (Lees, 1954; Nicholas and Jones, 1960). Early claims that hyponitrite accumulates during nitrification in solution culture have been discredited because of inadequate analytical techniques.

In the absence of oxygen, cytochrome c is reduced during hydroxylamine oxidation; in the process nitrous oxide (N_2O) is evolved. The nitrous oxide is probably a degradation product of the unknown intermediate that is formed between hydroxylamine and nitrite (Falcone et al., 1962). Aleem et al. (1962) proposed that this intermediate is nitrohydroxylamine, $NO_2 \cdot NHOH$. They observed that one mole of nitrite is formed for each mole of nitrohydroxylamine metabolized. It was suggested that nitrohydroxylamine was generated in a reaction between hydroxylamine and endogenous nitrite, and the resulting product was then oxidized by the bacterium to 2 moles of nitrite. The net effect is a conversion of one mole of hydroxylamine to one of nitrite at the expense of a mole of oxygen.

$$NH_2OH + HNO_2 \xrightarrow[-H_2O]{\frac{1}{2}O_2} NO_2 \cdot NHOH \xrightarrow{\frac{1}{2}O_2} 2\ HNO_2$$

This interesting hypothesis requires further study. It is not surprising that nitrohydroxylamine is metabolized rapidly since it is merely a substituted hydroxylamine; other substituted hydroxylamines might work as well. Further, there appears to be an oxidation of hydroxylamine catalyzed by enzymes of *N. europaea* in the absence of oxygen and nitrite (Falcone et al., 1962), reactants which are needed for a process involving nitrohydroxylamine.

Anderson (1964) observed that nitric oxide (NO), as well as nitrous oxide, was produced when extracts of a *Nitrosomonas* sp. were incubated anaerobically with hydroxylamine, provided that methylene blue was present.

There is no reason to believe that any of these intermediates accumulate to a significant extent in soil. All available data indicate that essentially all of the ammonium that has disappeared during nitrification in soil is recovered as either nitrite or nitrate. Indeed, nitrite and nitrate do not appear to be produced biologically in soils amended with hydroxylamine or hyponitrite (Duisberg and Buehrer, 1954). The point at issue is the mechanism by which the bacteria bring about the oxidation, and it is quite likely that the substances formed from ammonium never are released extracellularly under physiological conditions.

Because the initial substrate and the final products of the energy yielding reactions of the ammonium autotrophs are inorganic, there is no *a priori* reason to assume that the intermediates are likewise inorganic. The principle that soil nitrogen exists either in a highly reduced state or in the form of nitrate or occasionally nitrite must be accepted with caution, at least until more is known of the components of the organic fraction. Ample precedent can be found for biological transformations of oximes, hydroxyamino acids and nitro compounds, and some consideration needs to be given to the generation of these during nitrification—as intracellular intermediates, as extracellular products and even as part of the organic fraction of soil.

An enzymatic conversion of nitrite to nitrate has been achieved with extracts of *N. agilis* cells. All the nitrite metabolized by these enzyme preparations is converted to nitrate, and there is no evidence for the accumulation of any nitrogenous intermediates. The O_2 consumed is essentially equal to the theoretical quantity predicted on the basis of the following equation:

$$NO_2^- + \tfrac{1}{2} O_2 \rightarrow NO_3^-$$

Nitrification by enzyme preparations is rapid from about pH 6.5 to 9.5, the optimum being in the vicinity of 7.5 to 8.0. The nitrite-oxidizing system is entirely bound to the particulate constituents of the cell (Aleem and Alexander, 1958). The Michaelis constant, Km, is reported to be 6.7×10^{-4}M at 32°C (Laudelot and van Tiechelen, 1960).

The process of nitrite oxidation may be catalyzed by a single enzyme, the reaction yielding a pair of electrons or hydrogens. Should the transformation be a dehydrogenation, as is common with the energy substrates of lower oxidation-reduction potential, a hydrated nitrite molecule may be the substrate for the dehydrogenase.

$$HNO_2 + H_2O \rightarrow HNO_2 \cdot H_2O \rightarrow HNO_3 + 2\,H$$

$$2\,H + \tfrac{1}{2} O_2 \rightarrow H_2O$$

Reduced cytochrome bands appear at 589, 551 and in the vicinity of 520 mμ when the bacterium is incubated with nitrite, the oxidation of the nitrite being linked with reduction of the cytochromes. *Nitrobacter* also contains a cytochrome oxidase (Butt and Lees, 1958; Lees and Simpson, 1957). Hence, the electrons released in nitrification by this organism flow from nitrite through cytochrome c and cytochrome oxidase to the terminal acceptor, oxygen.

Nitrite oxidation by enzyme preparations of the chemoautotroph is not enhanced by zinc, molybdenum, magnesium or copper ions, but iron is stimulatory, results suggesting a role for iron in the reaction (Aleem and Alexander, 1958). Although added molybdenum is without effect on the enzyme, Zavarzin (1958b) demonstrated that growth of the bacterium is stimulated by small quantities of molybdate. Selective inhibitors of flavin enzymes, such as quinine, reduce the rate of oxidation by *Nitrobacter* cells and by enzyme preparations, but a flavin component has not been specifically characterized in nitrite oxidation per se (Aleem and Nason, 1959; Zavarzin, 1958a).

In view of the role of the nicotinamide adenine dinucleotides (NAD, NADP) in the reduction of nitrate to ammonium, there is a great temptation to postulate that these coenzymes are electron acceptors in the oxidation of inorganic nitrogen. Because of the high equilibrium constants of reactions coupling the nucleotides with ammonium, hydroxylamine and nitrite, however, it would seem unlikely that these coenzymes are directly involved in the oxidation brought about by *Nitrosomonas* and *Nitrobacter* species (Gibbs and Schiff, 1960).

Catalase and peroxidase catalyze the oxidation of nitrogenous compounds, and a role for one or the other of these two enzymes in autotrophic nitrification occasionally has been advanced. *Nitrosomonas* has both catalase and peroxidase activity (Ruban, 1961) while *Nitrobacter* is reported to have neither of the enzymes (Aleem and Nason, 1959), although Zavarzin (1958a) has observed a catalase. Nevertheless, the requirement that nitrogen oxidation provides the bacteria with the energy needed for growth would seem to rule out a peroxidase-catalase type of reaction in favor of a phosphorylative mechanism linked with nitrogen oxidation.

B. Heterotrophic Nitrogen Oxidation

Data upon which to base a working scheme for the biochemical mechanism or mechanisms of nitrification by heterotrophic microorganisms are scarce. Suprisingly little attention has been given to the enzymes that are concerned in catalyzing this transformation among carbon-oxidizing microorganisms. One of the more significant observations is that of Kuznetsov (1950), who noted that all 4 of his heterotrophic nitrifying bacteria possessed peroxidase. Kuznetsov felt that the peroxidative process was a a side-reaction in the course of the bacterial activities. A peroxidase was also found in a nitrate-forming *A. flavus* strain (Marshall and Alexander, 1962). Although plant and animal peroxidase or catalase, an enzyme that may exhibit peroxidative action, catalyze the oxidation of hydroxylamine, nitro compounds, nitrite and azide (Cresswell and Hewitt, 1960; Heppell and Porterfield, 1949; Keilin and Hartree, 1954; Little, 1957), the precise role of one or both of these enzymes in the nitrification reaction sequence remains obscure.

Several possible types of nitrogen compounds may be intermediates in the conversion of ammonium to nitrate. The pathway may involve solely inorganic substances such as hydroxylamine, hyponitrite, and nitrite; alternatively, organic intermediates may be produced during the microbial oxidation of ammonium-, amino-, or amide-nitrogen. Possible substrates or products of nitrogen oxidation include the following:

Inorganic: ammonia (NH_3), hydroxylamine (NH_2OH), hyponitrous acid ($HON=NOH$), nitrous acid (HNO_2), nitric acid (HNO_3),

Organic: amine (RCH_2NH_2), amide ($RCONH_2$), N-alkyl hydroxylamine (RCH_2NHOH), oxime ($RCH=NOH$), hydroxamic acid ($RCONHOH$), nitroalkane (RCH_2NO_2).

An organic pathway may include aromatic or aliphatic intermediates. Chemical precedents for the interconversions of various of these substances are many, and certain oxidizing agents convert nitrogen in organic combination from lower to higher oxidation states; e.g., specific oxidizing agents form N-alkyl hydroxylamines and oximes from amines, nitroalkanes from oximes and hydroxamic acids from amides.

Biological precedents for reactions of the type that may be concerned in heterotrophic nitrification are few. Thus, hydroxamic acids can be formed from hydroxylamine and either amides or fatty acids, and hydroxamic acids may be hydrolyzed with the liberation of free hydroxylamine (De Groot and Lichtenstein, 1960). Peroxidases and catalase, as indicated above, catalyze the oxidation of hydroxylamine, nitrite and nitroalkanes. Oximes of a number of organic acids are rapidly converted to nitrite when perfused through soil, and *Achromobacter* sp. brings about a similar conversion of pyruvic oxime to nitrite in culture (Quastel et al., 1952). Other examples are listed in Table 1.

Bound hydroxylamine (an organic compound which yields hydroxylamine upon acid hydrolysis), β-nitropropionic acid, nitrite, and nitrate appear during nitrification by *A. flavus* in ammonium-containing media. The fungus also contains an enzyme which liberates nitrite from β-nitropropionate, but nitrate is not produced by cell extracts containing the enzyme (Marshall and Alexander, 1962). The sequential formation of an amine, N-alkyl hydroxylamine, oxime, β-nitropropionic acid, nitrite and nitrate is one possible pathway to account for the results. On the basis of such a pathway, one or more carbonaceous substances should serve as carrier of the nitrogen subjected to oxidation. This organic carrier may act in a cyclic sequence that leads to the regeneration of the original carrier molecule; in such a process, only trace quantities of the carrier molecule would be required. On the other hand, if the carbonaceous portion is not recycled and is metabolized parallel with the nitrogen oxidation, then large quantities would be necessary; for example, if propionic acid serves as a nitrogen carrier in the conversion of β-aminopropionic acid (β-alanine) to the β-nitropropionic acid which may be the nitrate precursor, a total of about 0.5 g/L of the propionate must be formed and metabolized to account for 100 ppm nitrate-nitrogen. Needless to say, considerable further study is required to establish the details of the process.

VII. ENVIRONMENTAL VARIABLES

A. Nutrient Supply

Assuming tentatively that nitrification in soil is largely an autotrophic phenomenon, it is likely that rarely would any nutrient other than the energy substrate be limiting for the activity of the population. The quantity of nitrogen turned over relative to the number of cells formed is quite sizable. For example, *Nitrosomonas* spp. commonly oxidize 35 units of nitrogen and *Nitrobacter* spp. in the vicinity of 100 units of nitrogen for each unit of CO_2-carbon assimilated by the cell; those aerobes which live by carbon oxidation, by contrast, oxidize 2 to 10 units of carbon for each one assimilated. Hence, because little cell material is formed as a direct consequence of nitrification, there is but a small demand on the soil's nutrient reserve; and carbon, probably the chief limiting factor for proliferation of heterotrophs, is assimilated in the form of carbon dioxide or bicarbonate, and the supply of carbon dioxide probably far exceeds the biological demand.

The quantity of ammonium-nitrogen that is readily available to microorganisms is rarely appreciable. This may indicate that the rate of oxidation of ammonium exceeds the rate of its formation, and the nitrifiers would consequently be limited in numbers and activities by the supply of energy provided for them by the nitrogen-mineralizing microflora. Similarly, the rarity of finding even 1.0 ppm of nitrite-nitrogen in soil speaks for the limitation of *Nitrobacter* by the availability of its unique energy source. As a rule, therefore, the fastest process is nitrite oxidation, the slowest mineralization; the rate of ammonium oxidation is sandwiched between. If these generalizations are valid, the use of the term nitrification to describe incubation tests involving solely the measurement of nitrate production is grossly inappropriate as the limiting step would be the mineralization sequence.

Nonfixed or chemically extractable ammonium is nitrified readily, and only subsequent to the rapid initial oxidation is there a slow and incomplete transformation of the fixed cation. In their ability to use fixed nitrogen, the nitrifiers do not appear to be as effective as many of the heterotrophic species (Jansson, 1958). The type of clay mineral determines the extent of nitrification; e.g., soils containing montmorillonite exhibit the greatest oxidation followed by soils with illite, while fixed ammonium is nitrified slowly in soils rich in vermiculite (Allison et al., 1953; Nõmmik, 1957). Potassium blocks the release to the nitrifiers of the ammonium fixed on clay (Welch and Scott, 1960).

As nitrite rarely appears in significant quantities during rapid nitrate formation, the organisms of the second step must be particularly active. Under one, not uncommon circumstance, however, *Nitrobacter* development is greatly suppressed while ammonium oxidation remains unaffected; the net effect is an accumulation of the potentially phytotoxic nitrite. This occurs following the application of large quantities of urea, anhydrous ammonia or ammonium salts to soils of high pH or to soils whose pH rises as a result of urea hydrolysis or ammonia additions. Apparently, the extent of nitrite accumulation is related almost entirely to the concentration of ammonium applied to or formed in soil and the alkalinity, the limiting pH below which nitrite fails to appear in significant amounts being ca.pH 7.2 (Morrill, 1959; Stojanovic and Alexander, 1958). This effect of pH on the nitrite-oxidizers undoubtedly accounts for the occasional reports of nitrite in overlimed soils. The toxicity to *Nitrobacter* appears to result from an inhibition of the bacterium by free ammonia rather than ammonium (Aleem and Alexander, 1960). The report of a threshold pH value, 7.7, for nitrification in desert soils (Martin et al., 1942) is undoubtedly in error, resulting from the use of high concentrations of ammonium salts and the failure to take into account the influence of these large dosages on the nitrate-generating bacteria.

The persistence of the nitrite thus formed may be quite prolonged. Chapman and Liebig (1952), for example, reported that Yolo clay loam, pH 7.7, receiving 871 pounds per acre urea-nitrogen in early January contained 31 ppm nitrite-nitrogen in mid-May, and 5 ppm were detected as late as September. These authors could find no phytotoxicity associated with the high nitrite levels, and they pointed out that nitrite was highly inhibitory to plants at low but not at elevated pH. Since nitrite accumulates to appreciable levels only at high pH, it would seem that phytotoxicity from the nitrite produced in nitrification does not often pose a serious agronomic problem. Subsequent investigators (Court et al., 1962), on the other hand, noted that corn showed signs of toxicity and often died 2 to 3 weeks after large amounts of urea were applied to soil, a time coinciding with the appearance of high levels of nitrite.

The concentration of products of nitrification may also alter the rate of the oxidation since both nitrite and nitrate affect the autotrophic bacteria. However, the concentration of nitrate for toxicity is rarely attained in nature, and nitrite, which is toxic for *Nitrosomonas* but not significantly so for *Nitrobacter,* reduces the activity of the microorganisms only at low pH levels (Lewis and Pramer, 1959), and the toxin does not persist in acid soils.

B. Temperature

The effects of two environmental variables, temperature and pH, have been established by some investigators in the field, in the greenhouse, and in the laboratory. In many papers, and in more languages than any mortal agronomist should be expected to comprehend, it has been stated, restated, and again stated that increasing temperatures favor the oxidation. To cite these many references would be superfluous, and it may be taken simply as a principle of faith in microbiological science that increasing temperature stimulates microbial activities and that raising the temperature above a certain level—the optimum—effects a progressive decline in rate until the point of no return. However, it is necessary to state the cardinal values, namely the maximum, the optimum, and the minimum temperatures.

The optimum temperature in both soil and in culture typically falls somewhere between 30° and 35°C. Rarely are there significant quantities of nitrate appearing above 40°C though there are occasional reports of nitrate formed at higher temperatures. The existence of thermophilic nitrifying autotrophs is unknown. The minimum temperature is, to be sure, often an operational rather than an actual minimum since, with longer periods of incubation, some oxidation is often noted, but the operational value is of practical concern because it denotes the lowest point at which significant amounts of the highly leachable, readily denitrifiable anion is generated. There does take place a slow but significant ammonium and nitrite oxidation at 2°C (Frederick, 1956; Gerretsen, 1946), and there is little reason to doubt that there may be a slow nitrification at still lower temperatures. Nitrate therefore continues to appear throughout the autumn, to the time when the soil temperature declines to or falls below the freezing point of water. It is not yet clear whether nitrification in the late autumn in cooler climatic areas is of concern, but at least in some regions there is considerable loss of nitrogen during the cool period of the year, and nitrification at low temperatures in unfrozen soil should be considered as part of any potential mechanism to account for the way in which the nitrogen is lost. It is of interest in this regard that the oxidation of ammonium is more sensitive to low temperature than the mineralization sequence (Tyler et al., 1959).

C. pH

The oft-repeated dicta that nitrification proceeds slowly in acid soil and that the rate is hastened by liming need no amplification. No attempt will be made herein to summarize the many chapters and verses wherein these observations are documented in the literature. For reasons yet totally unclear, nitrogen oxidation stands out among the biological processes in soil by its sensitivity to the hydrogen ion concentration. This is readily apparent in soil receiving nitrogenous amendments and also in liquid media containing either enrichments or pure cultures of the autotrophs.

Considerable care must be taken in ascertaining the pH optimum for *Nitrosomonas* spp. because the energy substrate becomes progressively more toxic with increasing pH. The optimum for most commonly investigated strains tends to fall in the range between pH 7 and 9, and activity is found in even more alkaline solutions. On the other hand, in even slightly acid conditions, proliferation of the bacteria is quite markedly reduced. For *Nitrobacter* strains, the optimum also is often in the neutral to slightly alkaline range, and activity is often detectable from ca.pH 5 to 10. Generalizations concerning a specific optimum hydrogen ion concentration are of little value in view of the fact that the optima vary considerably for different isolates (Ulyanova, 1961). In soil, moreover, the ammonium- and nitrite-oxidizers are recovered from certain sites whose pH is in the vicinity of 4.0 (Boswell, 1955), and nitrate is produced in soil down to similar pH levels (Weber and Gainey, 1962).

The rate of nitrification is closely and directly correlated with the pH, and the optimum reaction in soil for many and possibly most of the ammonium oxidizers is above neutrality, while that for the nitrite oxidizers is close to the neutral point (Morrill and Dawson, 1962). It is quite likely, as recent evidence indicates, that the apparent pH optimum for the bacteria in soil differs somewhat from values noted when the autotrophs are developing in solution (Skujins, 1963). In addition, frequently the bacteria may occupy microecological sites having acidities far different from that suggested by pH determinations made on samples which bulk multitudes of these microenvironments. The bacterium existing in a microecosystem refuses to fit itself into the macroenvironmental methods of the soil chemist.

Because growth of the autotrophs is dependent upon nitrogen oxidation, an influence of the hydrogen ion concentration on the oxidation is *a priori* an effect on proliferation of the microorganisms. By contrast, heterotrophic nitrification is not growth-linked or, more appropriately stated, growth is not obligately linked with nitrification, so that it is simple to differentiate between the effects of this environmental variable on the oxidative mechanism and on cell proliferation. Interestingly, the conversion of ammonium to nitrate by *A. flavus* requires neutral or alkaline conditions, yet the fungus grows well at high acidities. This inhibition of nitrification by acidity is not an artifact arising from the decomposition of an acid-labile nitrogenous intermediate, but rather it is a valid suppression of the enzymes concerned (Hirsch et al., 1961). Other heterotrophs, however, do produce nitrite at pH values below 5.0. Whether nitrate formation in certain acid soils arises from a heterotrophic transformation of ammonium to nitrite followed by a non-biological oxidation of nitrite will require careful scrutiny. A nonbiological reaction of nitrite in acid soils has been studied recently by Tyler and Broadbent (1960).

D. Aeration

The nitrogen autotrophs are obligate aerobes, and all the known heterotrophs with the exception of Willis' (1934) anomalous *Clostridium butyricum* are aerobic. The reduction of nitrate and nitrite, moreover, is favored by a deficiency of oxygen. Hence, it is not surprising that nitrate accumulation is dependent upon adequate aeration, and the absence of oxygen is invariably associated with the absence or immediate loss of oxidized forms of nitrogen. The optimum percentage of oxygen for rapid nitrate production in soil is similar to that found in air (Amer and Bartholomew, 1951; Grechin and Ch'eng, 1960), and low or unnaturally high partial pressures of oxygen suppress the organisms. For the purposes of making enrichments of the active organisms, high rates of effective aeration are not required as suggested by the small amount of oxygen demanded by *Nitrosomonas* and *Nitrobacter* spp., 1.5 and 0.5 moles, respectively, for the oxidation of one mole of their energy substrates.

E. Moisture

The nitrifying autotrophs respond readily to alteration in the soil moisture status. Not all reports on the influence of moisture on nitrate production are pertinent to the present discussion, however, because oxygen deficiency in wet soils favors the nitrate-reducing population, and it is difficult to distinguish between influences on the two microbial groups. The optimum moisture level does not seem to be the same for the nitrifying population in different sites. As a rule, greatest nitrifying activity is noted at about half to two-thirds of the soil's moisture-holding capacity. Nitrate is not formed in air-dry soil nor is it produced at very low moisture levels, although the mineralization of nitrogen may proceed when water is present in sub-optimal amounts, the net effect being a slow rise in the ammonium concentration. In like fashion, the quantity of ammonium increases as the oxidation but not the mineralization of nitrogen is eliminated by excessive water (Robinson, 1957; Slavnina, 1961). Occasional instances of nitrate production, the exceptions that are expected to shake the pillars supporting the established rules, are noted in soils having very little water (Shaw, 1962), but these in no way alter the nebulous generalizations that one must, from the ecological viewpoint at least, advance. An interesting instance of surface nitrate accumulation in a bare fallow latosol has been investigated by Simpson (1960).

Nitrate is produced rapidly in the wet period following a prolonged drought or in the rainy season following a long dry spell (Jacquemin and Berlier, 1956). Irrigation, moreover, favors the oxidation of reduced forms of nitrogen in arid or semi-arid regions. The bacteria do, on the other hand, exhibit a surprising and as yet unaccountable resistance to desiccation, and a few of these organisms remain viable in soils kept for up to 14 to 18 years in the air-dry state (Fraps and Sterges, 1932). There is a slow dying out in time, and Bremner (1956) could find no residual activity in air-dry soils stored for 75 years though denitrification and mineralization did occur when these soil samples were brought to more favorable conditions.

In this connection, it is worthwhile observing that some desert soils receiving little precipitation have autotrophic nitrifying populations in excess of 10^3 cells per gram. Many of these soils, to be sure, have far fewer organisms (Sims and Collins, 1960).

F. Organic Matter

Probably no aspect of the environmental physiology of the autotrophic nitrifiers has been over-emphasized and distorted to such an extent as the effect of organic compounds upon the occurrence and activities of these bacteria. Their sensitivity to many toxic substances and their inability to grow upon exogenously supplied organic compounds have served to stimulate many investigations of the detrimental action of organic molecules. The list of organic compounds which are inhibitory in culture media is now enormous. Coinciding with these cultural studies were investigations designed to account for the fact that nitrification does proceed in environments rich in organic matter. Suggestions of a heterotrophic-autotrophic symbiosis or of a unique behavior of the bacteria in soil as contrasted with their introvert-like behavior in liquid media certainly were not uncommon.

The kinds of organic materials that enter or are formed in soil and in aquatic environments do often reduce and sometimes stop the accumulation of nitrate. Commonly the cessation can be attributed to either an increase in the microbial need for nitrogen for assimilatory purposes—a more rapid immobilization—or to a decline in the partial pressure of oxygen, low oxygen tensions being beneficial to denitrification and detrimental to ammonium oxidation. For cultural studies, due concern needs to be given to the possibility of toxicity arising from organic medium constituents, but there is yet no direct and reasonable evidence to support the contention that the addition of plant residues or the biogenesis in soil of new organic molecules by the subterranean flora has a major influence on the course of nitrogen oxidation *per se.*

G. Season

The season of year is only indirectly a factor influencing the transformation. That which is termed a seasonal influence is rather a compounding of several distinct primary ecological variables, chiefly the availability of nutrients, temperature, moisture status and soil aeration. Only a few meaningful generalizations with regard to season can therefore be made. That a seasonal change occurs is indisputable; often the environmental basis for the change is ignored. Maximum populations have been recorded in the spring and in the early summer (Thorne and Brown, 1937), in spring and autumn (Sakai, 1960a) and in summer (Ross, 1960). The activity is almost invariably low in the dry period of the year, and nitrate is rapidly produced once the rainy season commences. Winter is typically the time of low populations and minimal activities. Whether moisture, temperature, aeration or some other factor is the chief environmental determinant of abundance and activity will, needless to say, depend upon the particular circumstance.

H. Depth

This variable too does not have to be considered in more than a brief fashion. The horizon supporting the most rapid nitrification is determined chiefly by the supply of available nutrients—presumably, the energy substrates—as well as by the aeration, water content, temperature and pH of the particular stratum in question. Rarely does the conversion under field conditions take place more rapidly in subsoil than in the surface layers. Illustrative data giving oxidation rates and population sizes are presented by Eno and Ford (1958), who also reported appreciable numbers of ammonium autotrophs at depths greater than 8 feet. On the other hand, the lack of nitrate formation or the absence of the bacteria has been reported in the lower B horizon. It is perhaps not inappropriate to point out that the pattern of nitrification may not be the same in all horizons, as suggested by Martin and Cox (1956).

I. Inhibitors

Because of the unique physiology of the autotrophs, the ease of measuring their rate of growth and activity, their importance in the nitrogen cycle in nature and their marked sensitivity to toxic compounds, the autotrophic nitrifying bacteria have been the subject of many investigations designed to determine the effect of inhibitory substances. These studies are often of wider than academic interest since various pesticides delay, slow or eliminate the transformation, and such antimicrobial chemicals may thereby influence the nitrogen nutrition of plants and the susceptibility of nitrogen to losses through leaching and denitrification. Quite recently, there have been several intensive surveys designed to find non-phytotoxic chemicals which would, by selectively inhibiting the nitrifying bacteria, diminish nitrogen losses following fertilization; i.e., chemicals which would in effect keep the element in a reduced form for longer periods than could be expected under usual field conditions.

Because of the potential practical value of such inhibitors, a listing of some of these substances is presented in Table 2. The list is not complete, but many of the types of compounds which are active can be seen. Omitted from the list are the pesticides, whose effects on the nitrifiers are discussed below. Among the chemicals known to have a differential effect, chloride is more toxic to ammonium oxidation than to nitrate formation (Hahn et al., 1942), while chlorate and thiocyanate have a greater influence on the latter step (Gleen, 1951; Lees and Quastel, 1946a). Among the inhibitory compounds patented for use in connection with fertilizers containing ammonium or other reduced forms of nitrogen are 2-chloro-6-(trichloromethyl) pyridine, halogenated and nitrophenols, hydrazine salts, o- and m-nitroanalines, several bromo- or chlorosubstituted anilines, halogenated and nitroanilides, halogenated and aminopyridines, 2-amino-5-chloro-2-picoline, acetylene alcohols and dicyandiamide. Undoubtedly, additional promising inhibitors will continue to be revealed.

The most promising of the chemicals designed to retard nitrification and thus to conserve soil nitrogen by keeping it in the reduced form appears to be 2-chloro-6-(trichloromethyl) pyridine. The great interest that this compound has attracted arises from its ability, at least in certain circumstances, to diminish the loss of available nitrogen from the soil through a retardation in the production of nitrate, the highly leachable anion which also is a focal point in nitrogen volatilization. Goring (1962a) has also pointed out that a slowing of nitrogen oxidation may be beneficial because it might (a) reduce the number of nitrogen sidedressings, (b) provide a more uniform release of nitrate with less concern

Table 2. Inhibitors of nitrification in soil and culture.

Inhibitor	Reference
Ammonium oxidation in soil	
Cyanamide	Allison, 1927
Dicyandiamide	Allison et al., 1925
Mercapto compounds	Brown et al., 1954
Chloride	Hahn et al., 1942
Allylthiourea, salicylaldoxime	Lees, 1946
Trichlorisobutanol, ethylurethane, quinhydrone, catechol	Lees & Quastel, 1946a
Hydrazine, hydroxylamine, guanidine, methylamines	Lees & Quastel, 1946b
Methionine sulfoxide, thiourea, p-aminosalicylate	Quastel & Scholefield, 1951
Cysteine, methionine	Quartel & Scholefield, 1949
Nitrite oxidation in soil	
Mercapto compounds	Brown et al., 1954
Thiocyanate	Gleen, 1951
Chlorate	Lees & Quastel, 1945
Nitrosomonas spp.	
Peptone, yeast extract	Buswell et al., 1954
Cyanide, dinitrophenol, hydrazine	Engel & Alexander 1960
Nitrite	Engel & Alexander 1958a
Methionine, cysteine, thiourea, taurine	Jensen & Sorensen, 1952
Arginine, histidine, ethylurethane, allylthiourea	Lees, 1952
Nitrobacter spp.	
Ammonia, nitrite	Aleem & Alexander, 1960
Quinine, quinacrine, rivanol	Zavarzin, 1958a
Nitrophenols, p-nitroaniline	Butt & Lees, 1960a
Nitrate, arsenite, cyanate	Butt & Lees, 1960b
Chlorate	Meiklejohn, 1952
Nitro compounds, amines, heavy metals	Meyerhof, 1916a
Iodoacetate, hydroxylamine, fluoride, 8-hydroxyquinoline	Lundgren & Krikszens, 1959
Peptone, urea, asparagine	Fred & Davenport, 1921

for fertilizer timing than possible when the oxidation rate is determined solely by the microorganisms, (c) permit the use of fall-applied ammonium in areas where such practices are not economical and (d) eliminate concern over possible nitrite accumulation. The concentration of the chemical required to cause a marked inhibition of ammonium oxidation varies from 0.05 to 20 ppm, depending upon the soil; as a rule, higher concentrations are required with increasing soil pH and organic matter content. The chemical, moreover, is neither phytotoxic nor active against many members of the microflora, requirements which must be met by any compound designed for such purposes. When the concentration is expressed as a percentage of the fertilizer-nitrogen, 2% 2-chloro-6-(trichloromethyl) pyridine is needed for urea and ammonium salts in broadcast applications, 0.125% is necessary for band applications and 0.125 to 0.5% is required for aqua ammonia (Goring, 1962a, b). This compound may also be a convenient ecological tool since it suppresses autotrophic but not heterotrophic nitrogen oxidation; and the fact that it acts upon nitrogen autotrophs, but not on sulfur, iron or photoautotrophs, indicates that the inhibition is not associated with the CO_2-fixing mechanism that is unique to autotrophs (Shattuck and Alexander, 1963). Preliminary experiments have demonstrated that this potentially promising chemical, when added together with nitrogen fertilizers, increases the yield of cotton, corn and sugar beets by comparison with standard fertilizer treatments (Swezey and Turner, 1962).

J. Plant Effects

The response of the nitrifying bacteria to plant root excretions and the influence of roots upon the rate of ammonium oxidation have attracted considerable attention. As early as 1913, Lyon and Bizzell (1913) reported that soil samples taken from under alfalfa nitrified more readily than samples taken from the vicinity of the roots of timothy. However, there appear to be no significant differences between the rates of ammonium oxidation in fallow soil and in soil taken from the rhizosphere of certain plants (Reuszer, 1931; Starkey, 1929), and the rhizosphere effect measured in terms of population size does not seem to be too great (Katznelson, 1946). Nevertheless, there often may be a very slow nitrification under grass, and it has been suggested that grass roots may contain a substance toxic to the nitrifiers (Stiven, 1952; Theron, 1951). No evidence for a rhizosphere inhibition was obtained in the soil studies of Molina and Rovira (1964).

VIII. INFLUENCE OF SOME CULTURAL PRACTICES

A. Nitrogenous Fertilizers

The rate of nitrate formation varies not only with soil conditions but it also depends upon the specific ion or molecule carrying the nitrogen. Several factors undoubtedly govern the varying speeds of the transformation of nitrogen supplied in fertilizers, but the chief two appear to be the relative availability of the nitrogen source to nitrifiers and the effect of the fertilizer on soil pH.

Discounting for the present a possible role of heterotrophs in the oxidations of fertilizer-nitrogen, a role for these organisms being unlikely since the rate of application is such as to provide selective enrichment conditions for the autotrophs, the fact that species of *Nitrosomonas* and related genera are limited to the metabolism of ammonium suggests that the susceptibility of the fertilizer-nitrogen to biological oxidation is dependent largely upon the rate at which it is converted to ammonium. Urea, a substrate for the urease-synthesizing microorganisms which are abundant and widely distributed in soil, is hydrolyzed quickly to ammonium so it serves after a short period as an energy source for the autotrophs. The bulk of the nitrogen in ureaformaldehyde, various organic fertilizers, animal manure, green manure and crop residues is mineralized slowly, and nitrate appearance is correspondingly delayed.

The change in soil acidity brought about by the fertilizer, either directly or indirectly through microbial means, also may affect markedly the conversion. When the pH is in the vicinity of neutrality, nitrate is generated more rapidly from $(NH_4)_2SO_4$ than from organic nitrogen compounds. In soils of acid reaction, nitrate appears more rapidly from

NH$_4$OH, anhydrous ammonia, urea and certain organic nitrogen compounds than from (NH$_4$)$_2$SO$_4$ (Eno and Blue, 1957; Fred and Graul, 1916; Tyler et al., 1959); the first two nitrogen carriers raise the pH directly while the last two bring about the same modification as a result of the liberation of ammonia through microbiological agencies. In each instance, the fertilizer raises the pH of the acid habitat to a value more favorable to the autotrophs. In the near neutral environment, a similar increase has little or no effect upon the microorganisms. These pH related differences in nitrate production from various readily available nitrogen sources are eliminated by liming (Eno and Blue, 1957).

Anhydrous ammonia has a number of other microbiological effects. Even when applied at intended rates of 120 pounds per acre, the concentration may reach 1215 ppm ammonium-nitrogen, and the pH may be as high as 9.5 at the site of application, yet the concentration of ammonium and the pH are at the level characteristic of the specific soil several inches away from the point of injection in both horizontal and vertical directions. In such circumstances, nitrification is slow in the region where pH and ammonium levels are high, and the greatest rate of oxidation is found a short distance away (McIntosh and Frederick, 1958). Not only is there an inhibition of nitrate production at the line of ammonia injection, but there is also a distinct rise in nitrite concentration (Duisberg and Buehrer, 1954) and an appreciable killing of nematodes, fungi and bacteria (Eno et al., 1955).

B. Manure and Other Fertilizers

The evidence for a stimulation of the nitrifying population or an increase in its activities by non-nitrogenous fertilizers is equivocal and occasionally conflicting. Phosphorus, on one hand, is stated to increase nitrification by some investigators (Sakai, 1960b; Sinha, 1957; Yankovitch and Yankovitch, 1954). Studies performed by different investigators or in different soil types, on the other hand, reveal no benefit associated with phosphate additions (Fraps and Sterges, 1937; Sakai, 1956). Potassium tends to have a depressing action (Baur, 1934; Munk, 1958; Sinha, 1957), but further definitive work is required. The stimulation reported for inorganic substances is, except in unusual circumstances, likely not nutritional since the phosphorus demand of *Nitrosomonas* for the oxidation of even 1000 pounds of ammonium-nitrogen is probably of the order of 1 pound of phosphorus, a demand easily satisfied without recourse to additional sources of supply. *Nitrobacter* spp. need still less phosphorus for the formation of 1000 pounds of nitrate-nitrogen, and the need by species of both genera for other inorganic nutrients is even smaller.

Manure generally appears to increase the abundance of nitrifiers (Sakai, 1960b; Walker et al., 1937). It may be beneficial merely by providing a source of nitrogen, which, following mineralization, supplies energy for development of the bacteria, but the possibility of an effect on nitrification resulting from a modification of the physical or chemical properties of the environment cannot yet be excluded.

C. Waterlogging

Nitrification is markedly affected by puddling and waterlogging, high water content almost invariably leading to a decline in nitrate production (Abichandi and Patnaik, 1958; Fraps and Sterges, 1947). Of course, the small quantity of nitrate in saturated soils is also associated with reductive processes and denitrification, but the inadequacy of oxygen leaves its expected mark on the ammonium oxidizers. Nevertheless, nitrification does indeed take place in the upper oxidized zone of waterlogged soils, and the nitrate thus produced is particularly subject to loss upon entry into the underlying reduced stratum. At the low O_2 tensions in waterlogged environments, ammonium accumulates as the formation of the cation proceeds much faster than its oxidation. The decline in numbers resulting from flooding is not unique to the nitrifying bacteria, and the abundance of aerobic microorganisms in general is similarly altered (Kaurichev et al., 1959).

D. Inoculation

In contrast with the current concept that the nitrifiers are frequently not paragons of agronomic virtue, their biochemical activities often generating a greater economic loss than gain, numerous attempts have been made to increase the population or to install the autotrophs into soils from which they were absent. The basic premise of such inoculation is that the bacteria will become established, find their own ecological niche and perform the function assigned to them. The organisms must obtain from the soil or be provided by other means the nutrients they require for proliferation; this must be accomplished in the same environment in which the indigenous nitrifying microflora, if such exists, does not or cannot itself perform the activity expected of the inoculum.

Early trials with a "nitrobacter soil vaccine" and a so-called "universal culture" yielded no evidence of significant increases in crop yield or greater biological activity within the soil (Barthel, 1921; Jones, 1921). When lime is added to a site so acid that no nitrification has taken place, the time for the initiation of detectable nitrification is reduced by addition of suitable inocula, but a non-acid soil may serve as the inoculant as well, obviating the need for culturing the bacteria. Recently, there have been some reports of increases in crop yield following inoculation of soil with nitrifying bacteria, often together with other microorganisms (Matsuda and Nagata, 1960; Pikovskaia, 1948). It will be interesting to determine whether these responses are real, significant, reproducible and economically important.

E. Pesticides

The widespread use of selective chemicals for the control or elimination of agricultural pests has created a variety of new agronomic, biological and public health problems. Fungicides, insecticides, nematocides and herbicides are becoming in many regions of the world as standard in the arsenal of agricultural chemicals as $(NH_4)_2SO_4$ and lime. The key position of the nitrifiers in the nitrogen cycle, their role in plant nutrition and nitrogen losses and the great sensitivity of the autotrophs to environmental change make necessary critical examination of the possible deleterious action of these pesticides upon nitrate production. Indeed, because of the surprisingly low concentrations of many substances which retard or eliminate nitrogen oxidation, this transformation is possibly the best indicator of a chemical which may detrimentally affect the biological equilibrium or biochemical changes in the soil.

No attempt will be made to chronicle the numerous investigations of the influences of pesticides. A few examples and generalizations should suffice. As a rule, certain of the fumigants are the most potent of the pesticides as bacteriostatic or bactericidal agents to the nitrifiers, and as a consequence, plants may be compelled to use ammonium-nitrogen, a nutritional alteration which may or may not create difficulties. During the period of inhibition, there will be less nitrogen lost by leaching and/ or denitrification. Eventually the nitrifiers reappear and ammonium is reoxidized, the time elapsing prior to their reappearance being governed by the chemical, the rate of application and the soil type. Among the fumigants which thus affect nitrogen oxidation are chloropicrin, methyl bromide, DD (a mixture of 1,3-dichloropropane and 1,2-dichloropropene), ethylene dibromide, Telone (1,3-dichloropropene) and Vapam (sodium N-methyl dithiocarbamate) (Koike, 1961; Winfree and Cox, 1958). It is noteworthy that nitrate fertilization may be beneficial, for tobacco at least, when nitrification is eliminated by fumigants (McCants et al., 1959). Inhibition has also been recorded for a number of other dithiocarbamate fungicides (Jacques et al., 1959). With few exceptions, herbicides used at the rates recommended for field application exert little influence upon nitrification (Hale et al., 1957). As the danger of suppressing or eliminating important reactions always exists as pesticides are introduced into farm operation, additional tests must be conducted with the new chemicals that are proposed for the control of weeds, plant pathogens, insects and other soil-borne pests.

REFERENCES

Abichandi, C. T., and Patnaik, S. 1958. Nitrogen changes and fertilizer losses in lowland waterlogged soils. J. Indian Soc. Soil Sci. 6:87-93.

Aleem, M. I. H., and Alexander, M. 1958. Cell-free nitrification by *Nitrobacter*. J. Bacteriol. 76:510-514.

Aleem, M. I. H., and Alexander, M. 1960. Nutrition and physiology of *Nitrobacter agilis*. Appl. Microbiol. 8:80-84.

Aleem, M. I. H., Lees, H., Lyric, R., and Weiss, D. 1962. Nitrohydroxylamine: the unknown intermediate in nitrification? Biochem. Biophys. Research Comm. 7:126-127.

Aleem, M. I. H., and Nason, A. 1959. Nitrite oxidase, a particulate cytochrome electron transport system from *Nitrobacter*. Biochem. Biophys. Research Comm. 1:323-327.

Alexander, M., Marshall, K. C., and Hirsch, P. 1960. Autotrophy and heterotrophy in nitrification. Trans. Intern. Cong. Soil Sci. 7th Cong. Madison 2:586-591.

Allison, F. E. 1927. The effect of applications of cyanamid on the nitrate content of field soils. J. Agr. Research 34:657-662.

Allison, F. E., Kefauver, Margaret, and Roller, E. M. 1953. Ammonium fixation in soils. Soil Sci. Soc. Am. Proc. 17:107-110.

Allison, F. E., Skinner, J. J., and Reid, F. R. 1925. Toxicity studies with dicyanodiamide on plants. J. Agr. Research 30:419-429.

Amer, F. M., and Bartholomew, W. V. 1951. Influence of oxygen concentration in soil air on nitrification. Soil Sci. 71:215-219.

Ames, J. W., and Boltz, G. E. 1919. Effect of sulfofication and nitrification on potassium and other constituents. Soil Sci. 7:183-195.

Anderson, J. H. 1964. The metabolism of hydroxylamine to nitrite by *Nitrosomonas*. Biochem. J. 91:8-17.

Barthel, C. 1921. Experiments with Dr. Kuhn's U-cultures. K. Landtbr. Aka. Handl. och Tidskr. 58(2):85-95. 1919 Cited in Exp. Sta. Rec. 45:329.

Baumann, H., and Maass, G. 1957. Über den Verlauf des Nitratgehaltes unter verschiedenen Früchten im Ackerboden. Z. Pflanzernahr. Dung. 79: 155-167.

Baur, A. J. 1934. Effect of composting on the chemical and biological changes in peat and in wheat straw. J. Am. Soc. Agron. 26:820-830.

Black, C. A., ed. 1965. Methods of Soil Analysis. American Society of Agronomy, Madison, Wis.

Blanchet, R., Nadeau, J. C., Chaumont, Colette, and Perigaud, Simone. 1960. Apparition d'aluminium echangeable au cours de l'acidification d'un sol. Compt. Rend. Acad. Sci. Paris 251:1415-1417.

Bomeke, H. 1950. Uber die Erhnahrungs und Wachstumfaktoren der Nitrifikationsbakterien. Arch. Mikrobiol. 14:63-98.

Boswell, J. G. 1955. The microbiology of acid soils. IV. Selected sites in northern England and southern Scotland. New Phytol. 54:311-319.

Breed, R. S., Murrary, E. G. D., and Smith, N. R. 1957. Bergey's Manual of Determinative Bacteriology. Williams and Wilkins, Baltimore.

Bremner, J. M. 1956. Effect of storage on the biological activity of soil. Report Rothamsted Exp. Sta. pp. 52-53.

Brown, W. T., Quastel, J. H., and Scholefield, P. G. 1954. Effect of mercapto compounds on soil nitrification. Appl. Microbiol. 2:235-239.

Burge, W. D., Malavolta, E., and Delwiche, C. C. 1963. Phosphorylation by extracts of *Nitrosomonas europaea*. J. Bacteriol. 85:106-110.

Buswell, A. M., Shiota, T., Lawrence, N., and Van Meter, Irene V. 1954. Laboratory studies on the kinetics of the growth of *Nitrosomonas* with relation to the nitrification phase of the B.O.D. test. Appl. Microbiol. 2:21-25.

Butt, W. D., and Lees, H. 1958. Cytochromes of *Nitrobacter*. Nature 182:732-733.

Butt, W. D., and Lees, H. 1960a. Nitrite oxidation by *Nitrobacter* in the presence of certain nitrophenols. Nature 188:147-148.

Butt, W. D., and Lees, H. 1960b. The biochemistry of the nitrifying organisms. 6. The effect of oxygen concentration on nitrite oxidation in the presence of different inorganic ions. Biochem. J. 76:425-427.

Cain, R. B. 1958. The microbial metabolism of nitro-aromatic compounds. J. Gen. Microbiol. 19:1-14.

Campbell, Eva G. 1932. A thermophil nitrite former. Science 75:23.

Castell, C. H., and Mapplebeck, E. G. 1956. A note on the production of nitrite from hydroxylamine by some heterotrophic bacteria. J. Fish. Research Brd. Canada 13:201-206.

Chapman, H. D., and Liebig, G. F., Jr. 1952. Field and laboratory studies of nitrite accumulation in soils. Soil Sci. Soc. Am. Proc. 16:276-282.

Clark, F. E., Beard, W. E., and Smith, D. H. 1960. Dissimilar nitrifying capacities of soils in relation to losses of applied nitrogen. Soil Sci. Soc. Am. Proc. 24:50-54.

Court, M. N., Stephen, R. C., and Waid, J. S. 1962. Nitrite toxicity arising from the use of urea as a fertilizer. Nature 194:1263-1265.

Cresswell, C. F., and Hewitt, E. J. 1960. Oxidation of hydroxylamine by plant enzyme systems. Biochem. Biophys. Research Comm. 3:544-548.

De Groot, N., and Lichtenstein, N. 1960. The action of *Pseudomonas fluorescens* extracts on asparagine and asparagine derivatives. Biochem. Biophys. Acta 40:99-110.

Delwiche, C. C., and Finstein, M. S. 1965. Carbon and energy sources for the nitrifying autotroph, Nitrobacter. J. Bacteriol. (In Press)

Duisberg, P. C., and Buehrer, T. F. 1960. Effect of ammonia and its oxidation products on rate of nitrification and plant growth. Soil Sci. 78:37-49.

Dulaney, E. L., and Gray, R. A. 1962. Penicillia that make N-formylhydroxyaminoacetic acid, a new fungal product. Mycologia 54:476-480.

Engel, H., Krech, E., and Friederichsen, I. 1954. Beiträge zur Kenntnis der Nitritoxydation durch *Nitrobacter winogradskyi*. Arch. Mikrobiol. 21:96-111.

Engel, M. S., and Alexander, M. 1958a. Growth and autotrophic metabolism of *Nitrosomonas europaea*. J. Bacteriol. 76:217-222.

Engel, M. S. and Alexander, M. 1958b. Culture of *Nitrosomonas europaea* in media free of insoluble constituents. Nature 181:136.

Engel, M. S. and Alexander, M. 1959. Enzymatic activity of *Nitrosomonas* extracts. J. Bacteriol. 78:796-799.

Engel, M. S., and Alexander, M. 1960. Autotrophic oxidation of ammonium and hydroxylamine. Soil Sci. Soc. Am. Proc. 24:48-50.

Eno, C. F., and Blue, W. G. 1957. The comparative rate of nitrification of anhydrous ammonia, urea, and ammonium sulfate in sandy soils. Soil Sci. Soc. Am. Proc. 21:392-396.

Eno, C. F., Blue, W. G., and Good, J. M., Jr. 1955. The effect of anhydrous ammonia on nematodes, fungi, bacteria, and nitrification in some Florida soils. Soil Sci. Soc. Am. Proc. 19:55-58.

Eno, C. F., and Ford, H. W. 1958. Distribution of microorganisms, nitrate production and nutrients in the profile of Lakeland fine sand and related soils. Soil Crops Sci. Soc. Fla. Proc. 18:88-96.

Eylar, O. R., Jr., and Schmidt, E. L. 1959. A survey of heterotrophic microorganisms from soil for ability to form nitrite and nitrate. J. Gen. Microbiol. 20:473-481.

Falcone, A. B., Shug, A. L., and Nicholas, D. J. D. 1962. Oxidation of hydroxylamine by particles from *Nitrosomonas*. Biochem. Biophys. Research Comm. 9:126-131.

Fraps, G. S., and Sterges, A. J. 1932. Causes of low nitrification capacity of certain soils. Soil Sci. 34:353-363.

Fraps, G. S., and Sterges, A. J. 1937. Basicity of some phosphates as related to nitrification. J. Am. Soc. Agron. 29:613-621.

Fraps, G. S., and Sterges, A. J. 1947. Nitrification capacities of Texas soil types and factors which affect nitrification. Texas Agr. Exp. Sta. Bul. 693, 60 pp.

Fred, E. B., and Davenport, Audrey. 1921. The effect of organic nitrogenous compounds on the nitrate-forming organism. Soil Sci. 11:389-407.

Fred, E. B., and Graul, E. J. 1916. Some factors that influence nitrate formation in acid soils. Soil Sci. 1:317-338.

Frederick, L. R. 1956. The formation of nitrate from ammonium nitrogen in soils. I. Effect of temperature. Soil Sci. Soc. Am. Proc. 20:496-500.

Freney, J. R. 1958. Aerobic transformation of cysteine to sulphate in soil. Nature 182:1318-1319.

Gerretsen, F. C. 1946. Enkele waarnemingen betreffende den invloed van de temperatuur op de nitrificatie en vastlegging van de stickstof. Landbouwk. Tijdschr. 54:573-582. 1942. Cited in Soils Fert. 9:96.

Gibbs, M., and Schiff, J. A. 1960. Chemosynthesis: the energy relations of chemoautotrophic organisms. *In* F. C. Steward, ed. Plant Physiology. Academic Press, New York. Vol 1 B, pp. 279-319.

Gleen, H. 1951. Microbiological oxidation of ammonium and thiocyanate ions in soil. Nature 168:117-118.

Goring, C. A. I. 1962a. Control of nitrification by 2-chloro-6-(trichloromethyl) pyridine. Soil Sci. 93:211-218.

Goring, C. A. I. 1962b. Control of nitrification of ammonium fertilizers and urea by 2-chloro-6-(trichloromethyl) pyridine. Soil Sci. 93:431-439.

Gould, G. W., and Lees, H. 1958. The intensive culture of *Nitrobacter*. Biochem. J. 69:38P.

Grace, Joyce B. 1951. Myxobacteria mistaken for nitrifying bacteria. Nature 168:117.

Grechin, I. P., and Ch'eng, H. S. 1960. Influence of various concentrations of gaseous oxygen in the air of the soil on oxidation-reduction conditions. Soviet Soil Sci. 1960:775-778.

Greenland, D. J. Nitrate fluctuations in tropical soils. 1958. J. Agr. Sci. 50:82-92.

Gundersen, K. 1955a. Observations on mixed cultures of *Nitrosomonas* and heterotrophic soil bacteria. Plant and Soil 7:26-34.

Gundersen, K. 1955b. Effects of B-vitamins and amino-acids on nitrification. Physiol. Plantarum 8:136-141.

Gundersen, K., and Jensen, H. L. 1956. A soil bacterium decomposing organic nitro-compounds. Acta Agr. Scand. 6:100-114.

Hahn, B. E., Olson, F. R., and Roberts, J. L. 1942. Influence of potassium chloride on nitrification in Bedford silt loam. Soil Sci. 54:113-121.

Hale, M. G., Hulcher, F. H., and Chappell, W. E. 1957. The effects of several herbicides on nitrification in a field soil under laboratory conditions. Weeds 5:331-341.

Heppell, L. A., and Porterfield, V. T. 1949. Metabolism of inorganic nitrite and nitrate esters. I. The coupled oxidation of nitrite by peroxide-forming systems and catalase. J. Biol. Chem. 178:549-556.

Heübult, J. 1929. Untersuchungen über Nitritbakterien. Planta 8:398-422.

Hiltbold, A. E., and Adams, F. 1960. Effect of nitrogen volatilization on soil acidity changes due to applied nitrogen. Soil Sci. Soc. Am. Proc. 24:45-47.

Hirsch, P., Overrein, L., and Alexander, M. 1961. Formation of nitrite and nitrate by actinomycetes and fungi. J. Bacteriol. 82:442-448.

Hofman, T. 1953. The biochemistry of the nitrifying organisms. 3. Composition of *Nitrosomonas*. Biochem. J. 54:293-295.

Hofman, T., and Lees, H. 1953. The biochemistry of the nitrifying organisms. 4. The respiration and intermediary metabolism of *Nitrosomonas*. Biochem. J. 54:579-583.

Hutton, W. E., and ZoBell, C. E. 1953. Production of nitrite from ammonia by methane oxidizing bacteria. J. Bacteriol. 65:216-219.

Ida, S., and Alexander, M. 1965. Permeability of *Nitrobacter agilis* to organic compounds. J. Bacteriol. (In press)

Imshenetsky, A. A. 1945. Myxobacteria and nitrifying bacteria. (In Russian.) Mikrobiologia 14:177-190.

Iyengar, M. R. S., and Hora, T. S. 1959. Nitrite oxidation by soil fungi. Naturwiss. 46:211.

Jacquemin, H., and Berlier, Y. 1956. Évolution du pouvoir nitrifiant d'un sol de Basse Cote d'Ivoire l'action du climat et de la végétation. Rapports Intern. Cong. Soil Sci. 6th Cong. Paris C:343-347.

Jacques, R. P., Robinson, J. B., and Chase, F. E. 1959. Effects of thiourea, ethyl urethane and some dithiocarbamate fungicides on nitrification in Fox sandy loam. Can. J. Soil Sci. 39:235-243.

Jansson, S. 1958. Tracer studies on nitrogen transformations in soil with special attention to mineralisation—immobilization relationships. Kungl. Lantbrukshogs. Ann. 24:101-361.

Jensen, H. L. 1951. Nitrification of oxime compounds by heterotrophic bacteria. J. Gen. Microbiol. 5:360-368.

Jensen, H. L., and Sorensen, H. 1952. The influence of some organic sulphur compounds and enzyme inhibitors on *Nitrosomonas europaea*. Acta Agr. Scand. 2:295-304.

Jones, D. H. 1921. A bacteriological analysis and cultural test of "nitrobacter soil vaccine." Sci. Agr. 1:266-267.

Katznelson, H. 1946. The "rhizosphere effect" of mangels on certain groups of soil microorganisms. Soil Sci. 62:343-354.

Kaurichev, I. S., Nepomiluyev, V. F., and Poddubnyy, N. M. 1959. The nature of oxidation-reduction processes in solenetzes and solods. Soviet Soil Sci. 1959:403-408.

Keilin, D., and Hartree, E. F. 1954. Reactions of methaemoglobin and catalase with peroxides and hydrogen donors. Nature 173:720-723.

Kiesow, L. 1962. Über den Mechanismus der Chemosynthese. Zeitschr. Naturforschung 17b, 455-465.

Kluyver, A. J., and Donker, H. J. L. 1926. Die Einheit in der Biochemie. Chem. Zelle u. Gewebe 13:134-190.

Koike, H. 1961. The effects of fumigants on nitrate production in soil. Soil Sci. Soc. Am. Proc. 25:204-206.

Kuznetsov, S. I. 1950. Microbiological studies of lakes of the Kokchetov, Kurgan and Tyumen regions. 1. Microbiological characteristics of the mineralization of organic matter in lakes of varying degrees of salinity. (In Russian). Trudy Lab. Sapropel. Othlozhenii, Aka. Nauk S. S. S. R. Inst. Lesa. No. 4, pp. 5-14.

Laudelot, H., and van Tiechelen, L. 1960. Kinetics of the nitrite oxidation by *Nitrobacter winogradskyi*. J. Bacteriol. 79:39-42.

Lees, H. 1946. Effect of copper-enzyme poisons on soil nitrification. Nature 158:97.

Lees, H. 1952. The biochemistry of the nitrifying organisms. 1. The ammonia-oxidizing systems of *Nitrosomonas*. Biochem. J. 52:134-139.

Lees, H. 1954. The biochemistry of the nitrifying bacteria. *In* B. A. Fry and J. L. Peel, eds. Autotrophic Micro-organisms. Cambridge Univ. Press, Cambridge. pp. 84-98.

Lees, H., and Meiklejohn, Jane. 1948. Trace elements and nitrification. Nature 161:398-399.

Lees, H., and Quastel, J. H. 1945. Bacteriostatic effects of potassium chlorate on soil nitrification. Nature 155:276-278.

Lees, H., and Quastel, J. H. 1946a. Biochemistry of nitrification in soil. 1. Kinetics of, and the effects of poisons on, soil nitrification, as studied by a soil perfusion technique. Biochem. J. 40:803-815.

Lees, H., and Quastel, J. H. 1946b. Biochemistry of nitrification in soil. 3. Nitrification of various organic nitrogen compounds. Biochem. J. 40:824-828.

Lees, H. and Simpson, J. R. 1957. The biochemistry of the nitrifying organisms. 5. Nitrite oxidation by *Nitrobacter*. Biochem. J. 65:297-305.

Lemoigne, M., Monguillon, P., and Desveaux, R. 1936. Recherches sur le role biologique de l'hydroxylamine. V. Production de l'hydroxylamine por le *Sterigmatocystis nigra* aux dépens de l'azote nitrique et de l'azote ammoniacal. Bull. Soc. Chem. Biol. 18:1297-1303.

Leo, W. M., Odland, T. E., and Bell, R. S. 1959. Effect on soils and crops of long continued use of sulfate of ammonia and nitrate of soda with and without lime. Rhode Island Agr. Exp. Sta. Bul. 344, 31 pp.

Lewis, R. F., and Pramer, D. 1958. The influence of pH on the inhibition of *Nitrosomonas europaea* by nitrite. Bacteriol. Proc. p. 24.

Lewis, R. F., and Pramer, D. 1959. Isolation of *Nitrosomonas* in pure culture. J. Bacteriol. 76:524-528.

Little, H. N. 1957. The oxidation of 2-nitropropane by extracts of pea plants. J. Biol. Chem. 229:231-238.

Lundgren, D. G., and Krikszens, A. 1959. Bacterial destruction of sodium nitrite in open cooling water systems. Appl. Microbiol. 7:292-300.

Lyon, T. L., and Bizzell, J. A. 1913. The influence of alfalfa and of timothy on the production of nitrates in soil. Cent. Bakteriol., II Abt. 37:161-167.

MacDonald, J. C. 1961. Biosynthesis of aspergillic acid. J. Biol. Chem. 236:512-514.

Maciejewska, Z. 1959. Microbiological studies on sand and peat soils. Torf 3(2):17-18. 1958. Cited in Chem Abst. 53:3567.

Malavolta, E., Delwiche, C. C., and Burge, W. D. 1960. Carbon dioxide fixation and phosphorylation by *Nitrobacter agilis*. Biochem. Biophys. Research Comm. 2:445-449.

Marshall, K. C., and Alexander, M. 1961. Fungi active in heterotrophic nitrification. Can. J. Microbiol. 7:955-957.

Marshall, K. C., and Alexander, M. 1962. Nitrification by *Aspergillus flavus*. J. Bacteriol. 83:572-578.

Martin, A. E., and Cox, J. E. 1956. Nitrogen studies on black soils from the Darling Downs, Queensland. II. The nitrifying activity of subsurface horizons. Austr. J. Agr. Research 7:184-193.

Martin, W. P., Buehrer, T. F., and Caster, A. B. 1942. Threshold pH value for nitrification of ammonia in desert soils. Soil Sci. Soc. Am. Proc. 7:223-228.

Matsuda, K., and Nagata, T. 1960. Microbiological activities of Iwatahara soils, Shizuoka Prefecture, Central Japan. VII. Effect of inoculation of soil with nitrifying bacteria on growth of spinach (In Japanese.) J. Sci. Soil Manure (Tokyo) 31:177-180.

McCants, C. B., Skogley, E. O., and Woltz, W. G. 1959. Influence of certain soil fumigation treatments on the response of tobacco to ammonium and nitrate forms of nitrogen. Soil Sci. Soc. Am. Proc. 23:466-469.

McIntosh, T. H., and Frederick, L. R. 1958. Distribution and nitrification of anhydrous ammonia in a Nicollet sandy clay loam. Soil Sci. Soc. Am. Proc. 22:402-405.

Meiklejohn, Jane. 1950. The isolation of Nitrosomonas europaea in pure culture. J. Gen. Microbiol. 4:185-191.

Meiklejohn, Jane. 1952. Some organic substances and the nitrifying bacteria Soc. Applied Bacteriol. Proc. 15:77-81.

Meyerhof, O. 1916a. Untersuchungen über den Atmungsvorgang nitrifizierender Bakterien. I. Die Atmung des Nitratbildners. Arch. ges. Physiol. 164:353-427.

Meyerhof, O. 1916b. Untersuchungen über den Atmungsvorgang nitrifizierender Bakterien. II. Beeinflussungen der Atmung des Nitratbildners durch chemische Substanzen. Arch. ges. Physiol. 165:229-283.

Molina, J. A. E., and Rovira, A. D. 1964. The influence of plant roots on autotrophic nitrifying bacteria. Can. J. Microbiol. 10:249-257.

Morrill, L. G. 1959. An explanation of the nitrification patterns observed when soils are perfused with ammonium sulfate. Ph.D. Thesis, Cornell University, Ithaca, N.Y.

Morrill, L. G., and Dawson, J. E. 1962. Growth rates of nitrifying chemoautotrophs in soil. J. Bacteriol. 83:205-206.

Munk, H. 1958. Die Nitrifikations von Ammonium salzen in sauren Boden. Landwirtsch. Forsch. 11:150-156.

Nechaeva, N. B. 1947. Mycobacteria which oxidize ammonia to nitrite. (In Russian). Mikrobiologia 16:418-428.

Nelson, D. II. 1929. The isolation of some nitrifying organisms. Iowa State Coll. J. Sci. 3:113-175.

Nelson, D. H. 1931. Isolation and characterization of Nitrosomonas and Nitrobacter. Zent. Bacteriol., II Abt. 83:280-311.

Nicholas, D. J. D., and Jones, O. T. G. 1960. Oxidation of hydroxylamine in cell-free extracts of Nitrosomonas europaea. Nature 185:512-514.

Nommik, H. 1957. Fixation and defixation of ammonium in soils. Acta Agr. Scand. 7:395-436.

Pasteur, L. Études sur les mycodermes. 1862. Role de ces plantes dans la fermentation acétique. Compt. Rend. Acad. Sci. Paris 54:265-270.

Pikovskaia, R. I. 1948. Mobilization of phosphates in soil in connection with the activities of some microbial species. (In Russian). Mikrobiologia 17:362-370.

Prouty, C. C. 1929. The use of dyes in the isolation of a nitrite oxidizing organism. Soil Sci. 28:125-136.

Quastel, J. H., and Scholefield, P. G. 1949. Influence of organic nitrogen compounds on nitrification in soil. Nature 164:1068-1072.

Quastel, J. H., and Scholefield, P. G. 1951. Biochemistry of nitrification in soil. Bacteriol. Rev. 15:1-53.

Quastel, J. H., Scholefield, P. G., and Stevenson, J. W. 1952. Oxidation of pyruvic acid oxime by soil organisms. Biochem. J. 51:278-284.

Raistrick, H., and Stössl, A. 1958. Studies on the biochemistry of micro-organisms. Metabolites of Penicillium atrovenetum G. Smith: β-nitropropionic acid, a major metabolite. Biochem. J. 68:647-653.

Reuszer, H. W. 1931. Microbiological changes occurring in a soil under pasture and bare conditions. J. Am. Soc. Agron. 23:417-428.

Robinson, J. B. D. 1957. The critical relationship between soil moisture content in the region of wilting point and the mineralization of soil nitrogen. J. Agr. Sci. 49:100-105.

Ross, D. J. 1960. Biological studies of some tussock-grassland soils. XVIII. Nitrifying activities of two cultivated soils. New Zeal. J. Agr. Research 3:230-236.

Ruban, Evgeniya L. 1958. Nitrogen metabolism of Nitrosomonas europaea. (In Russian). Mikrobiologia 27:536-541.

Ruban, Evgeniya L. 1961. Physiology and biochemistry of nitrifying microorganisms. (In Russian). Ph.D. Thesis. Akademia Nauk S.S.S.R. Moscow.

Sakai, H. 1956. Studies on the conditions affecting nitrite accumulation in the soil. (In Japanese). Hokkaido Agr. Exp. Sta. Research Bul. 71:21-31. English summary.

Sakai, H. 1958. On a method for isolation of nitrifying organisms. Soil Plant Food 4:81-82.

Sakai, H. 1960a. Studies on nitrification in soils. VIII. Seasonal changes of *Nitrobacter*. (In Japanese). J. Sci. Soil Manure (Tokyo) 31:331-364.

Sakai, H. 1960b. Studies on nitrification in soils. VII. Factors affecting the numbers of *Nitrobacter* in soils. (In Japanese). J. Sci. Soil Manure (Tokyo) 31:281-284.

Saris, N. E., and Virtanen, A. I. 1957. Hydroxylamine compounds in *Azotobacter* cultures. II. The chemical nature of the bound hydroxylamine fraction in *Azotobacter* cultures. Acta Chem. Scand. 11:1440-1442.

Schloesing, T., and Muntz, A. 1877. Sur la nitrification par les ferments organises. Compt. Rend. Acad. Sci. Paris 84:301-303.

Shattuck, G. E., Jr., and Alexander, M. 1963. A differential inhibitor of nitrifying microorganisms. Soil Sci. Soc. Am. Proc. 27:600-601.

Shaw, K. Loss of mineral nitrogen from soil. J. Agr. Sci. 58:145-151.

Silver, W. S. 1960. Exogenous respiration in *Nitrobacter*. Nature 185:555-556.

Simpson, J. R. 1960. The mechanism of surface nitrate accumulation in a bare fallow soil in Uganda. J. Soil Sci. 11:45-60.

Sims, C. M., and Collins, F. M. 1960. The numbers and distribution of ammonia-oxidizing bacteria in some Northern Territory and South Australia soils. Austr. J. Agr. Research 11:505-512.

Sinha, P. 1957. Effects of continuous manuring and cropping on the crop yields, nitrifying power of soil, and nitrogen uptake by plants. J. Indian Soc. Soil Sci. 5:205-211.

Skinner, F. A., and Walker, N. 1961. Growth of *Nitrosomonas europaea* in batch and continuous culture. Arch. Mikrobiol. 38:339-349.

Skujins, J. J. 1963. Enzymatic and microbial activity in radiation sterilized soil. Ph.D. Thesis, Univ. California, Berkeley, California.

Slavnina, T. P. 1961. Effect of soil moisture on the processes of nitrogen mobilization. (In Russian). Nauch. Doklady Vysshei Skholy, Biol. Nauki 1960(4):221-226. 1960. Cited in Chem. Abst. 55:9745.

Soulides, D. A., and Clark, F. E. 1958. Nitrification in grassland soils. Soil Sci. Soc. Am. Proc. 22:308-311.

Stapp, C. 1940. Über Begleitorganismen der Nitrifikationsbakterien. Zent. Bakteriol., II Abt. 102:193-214.

Starkey, R. L. 1929. Some influences of the development of higher plants upon the microorganisms in the soil. III. Influence of the stage of plant growth upon some activities of the organisms. Soil Sci. 27:433-444.

Steinberg, R. A. 1939. Effects of nitrogen compounds and trace elements on growth of *Aspergillus niger*. J. Agr. Research 59:731-748.

Stiven, G. 1952. Production of antibiotic substances by the roots of a grass (*Trachypogon plumosus* (H.B.K.) Nees) and of *Pentanisia variabilis* (E. Mey.) Harv. (Rubiaceae). Nature 170:712-713.

Stojanovic, B. J., and Alexander, M. 1958. Effect of inorganic nitrogen on nitrification. Soil Sci. 86:208-215.

Stutzer, A. 1901. Die Organismen der Nitrifikation. Cent. Bakteriol., II Abt. 7:168-178.

Swezey, A. W., and Turner, G. O. 1962. Crop experiments on the effect of 2-chloro-6-(trichloromethyl) pyridine for the control of nitrification of ammonium and urea fertilizers. Agron. J. 54:532-535.

Theron, J. J. 1951. The influence of plants on the mineralization of nitrogen and the maintenance of organic matter in the soil. J. Agr. Sci. 41:289-296.

Thorne, D. W., and Brown, P. E. 1937. A comparison of the numbers of two species of *Rhizobium* and ammonia-oxidizing organisms in variously treated Iowa soils. J. Am. Soc. Agron. 29:877-882.

Timonin, M. I., and Thexton, R. H. 1950. The rhizosphere effect of onion and garlic on soil microflora. Soil Sci. Soc. Am. Proc. 15:186-189.

Turtschin, F. B., Bersenjewa, S. N., Koritskaja, I. A., Shidkick, G. G., and Lobowikowa,

G. A. 1960. Die Stickstoffumwandlung im Boden nach den Angaben der Untersuchungen unter Anwendung des Isotops N¹⁵. Trans. Intern. Cong. Soil Sci., 7th Cong. Madison. 2:236-245.

Tyler, K. B., Broadbent, F. E. 1960. Nitrite transformations in California soils. Soil Sci. Soc. Am. Proc. 24:279-282.

Tyler, K. B., Broadbent, F. E., and Hill, G. N. 1959. Low-temperature effects on nitrification in four California soils. Soil Sci. 87:123-129.

Ulyanova, O. M. 1960. Isolation and characteristics of pure cultures of *Nitrosomonas* from various natural substrates. (In Russian). Mikrobiologia 29:813-819.

Ulyanova, O. M. 1961. Adaptation of *Nitrosomonas* to existence on various natural substrates. (In Russian). Mikrobiologia 30:236-242.

Ulyanova, O. M. 1962. Adaptation of *Nitrosomonas* ecotypes to concentrations of organic substances in their environment. (In Russian). Mikrobiologia 31:77-84.

Walker, R. H., Thorne, D. W., and Brown, P. E. 1937. The numbers of ammonia-oxidizing organisms in soils as influenced by soil management practices. J. Am. Soc. Agron. 29:854-864.

Warington, R. On nitrification. 1891. Part 4. J. Chem. Soc. 59:484-529.

Weber, D. F., and Gainey, P. L. 1962. Relative sensitivity of nitrifying organisms to hydrogen ions in soils and in solutions. Soil Sci. 94:138-145.

Welch, L. F., and Scott, A. D. 1959. Nitrification in nutrient solutions with low levels of potassium. Can. J. Microbiol. 5:425-430.

Welch, L. F., and Scott, A. D. 1960. Nitrification of fixed ammonium in clay minerals as affected by added potassium. Soil Sci. 90:79-85.

Willis, W. H. 1934. The metabolism of some nitrogen-fixing clostridia. Iowa Agr. Exp. Sta. Research Bul. 173, 32 pp.

Wilson, J. K. 1927. The number of ammonia-oxidizing organisms in soils. Proc. Intern. Cong. Soil Sci. 1st Cong., Washington, 3:14-22.

Winfree, J. P., and Cox, R. S. 1958. Comparative effects of fumigation with chloropicrin and methyl bromide on mineralization of nitrogen in Everglades peat. Plant Disease Reporter 42:807-810.

Winogradsky, S. 1890. Recherches sur les organismes de la nitrification. Ann. Inst. Pasteur 4:213-231, 257-275, 760-771.

Yankovitch, M. L., and Yankovitch, I. 1954. Le role de l'acide phosphorique dans la nitrification. Compt. Rend. Acad. Agr. 40:416-419.

Yoshida, T., and Alexander, M. 1964. Hydroxylamine formation by *Nitrosomonas europaea*. Can. J. Microbiol. 10:923-926.

Zavarzin, G. A. 1958a. The incitant of the second phase of nitrification. I. The participation of respiratory enzymes in nitrification. (In Russian). Mikrobiologia 27:401-406.

Zavarzin, G. A. 1958b. The incitant of the second phase of nitrification. II. The effect of heavy metals on nitrification. (In Russian). Mikrobiologia 27:542-546.

Zavarzin, G. A., and Legunkova, Raisa. 1959. The morphology of *Nitrobacter winogradskyi*. J. Gen. Microbiol. 21:186-190.

Chapter 9

Denitrification

F. E. BROADBENT AND FRANCIS CLARK

University of California at Davis and
Agricultural Research Service, U.S.D.A., Fort Collins, Colo.

I. INTRODUCTION

In nitrogen balance experiments it is commonly found that after careful attempts to account for residual nitrogen, leaching losses, and nitrogen removal by crops on the one hand, and on the other, for nitrogen fixation, fertilizer additions, and nitrate in rainfall or irrigation water, there remains an unaccounted-for loss of nitrogen from the system. Allison (1955) has documented a considerable number of lysimeter experiments in which the nitrogen deficit averaged 15%. Presumably, volatile losses of nitrogen were involved.

In recent years results of several nitrogen balance experiments using the N^{15} tracer have been published, some of which are summarized in Table 1. The tracer experiments permit more precise measurement of nitrogen losses to be made than is possible in conventional lysimeter trials but have the disadvantage of being further removed from actual field conditions. Considering the great variability of soils and experimental conditions represented in Table 1, the data are remarkably consistent.

In some instances, denitrification losses in excess of 50% of the applied nitrogen have been encountered (Gerretsen and de Hoop, 1957; Wagner and Smith, 1958; Soulides and Clark, 1958).

As commonly used, the term denitrification refers to the biological reduction of nitrate and nitrite to volatile gases, usually nitrous oxide and/or molecular nitrogen. In recent years it has been recognized that other mechanisms of nitrogen loss occur in soils, involving a combination

Table 1. Nitrogen losses in greenhouse pot experiments as measured by tracer recovery.

Reference	Source of N	% N loss
MacVicar et al. (1950)	$(NH_4)_2 SO_4$	1-15
Turtschin et al. (1960)	$(NH_4)_2 SO_4$	11-17
Martin et al. (1963)	$NH_4 NO_3$	6
Dilz and Woldendorp (1960)*	KNO_3	11-40
Broadbent and Tyler (1962)	$(NH_4)_2 SO_4$	20-32
" " "	KNO_3	21-35
Jansson (1963)	$(NH_4)_2 SO_4$	9-14
"	$NaNO_3$	13-17

* N recovery from grass sods.

of chemical and biological reactions. In this chapter, the term denitrification is used in a broader sense to include gaseous loss of nitrogen by either biological or chemical mechanisms, but exclusive of ammonia volatilization.

II. GASEOUS LOSS OF NITROGEN THROUGH BIOLOGICAL REDUCTION OF NITRATE

Gayon and Dupetit (1886) are usually credited with being the first to report the reduction of nitrate to nitrous oxide and nitrogen. During the remainder of the 19th century and the early decades of the 20th century other workers discovered many of the important facts about the denitrification process which are known today. It was established that denitrification in soils was favored by the addition or organic materials such as manure (Ferguson and Fred, 1908), that it occurred in wet soils without the addition of organic matter (Oelsner, 1918), and that it proceeds slowly if at all in well-aerated soils (Voorhees, 1902). It was recognized that both nitrate and organic matter are required in combination with poor soil aeration in order for denitrification to occur (van Iterson, 1904).

Although it became widely recognized that denitrification is a common soil process, direct evidence concerning its occurrence in field soils remained limited owing to the formidable experimental difficulties involved in obtaining such evidence. Unconvinced that denitrification was of appreciable economic significance, most soil scientists took little interest in the subject until the discovery in 1946 by the astronomer Adel of nitrous oxide as a constituent of the earth's atmosphere. He observed that the concentration of nitrous oxide is greater near the surface of the earth than high in the atmosphere and suggested that the presence of this gas is due to decomposition of nitrogen compounds in the soil (Adel, 1946, 1951). A few years later Arnold (1954) detected nitrous oxide evolution from soils both in the laboratory and in the field by means of the very sensitive infra-red spectroscopic technique. These observations, coupled with a tremendous increase in use of nitrogen fertilizers in the last decade or so, have led soil scientists to undertake more intensive study of denitrification.

A. The Biochemical Basis of Denitrification

Enzymatic denitrification is a biological process accomplished by facultatively anaerobic bacteria capable of using nitrate in place of oxygen as a hydrogen acceptor. Under aerobic conditions, their oxidation of a simple carbohydrate such as glucose leads to the formation of CO_2 and water:

$$C_6H_{12}O_6 + 6\ O_2 \rightarrow 6\ CO_2 + 6\ H_2O$$

In the absence of oxygen, but in the presence of nitrate, these bacteria are capable of a nitrate respiration which may be expressed as follows:

$$C_6H_{12}O_6 + 4\ NO_3^- \rightarrow 6\ CO_2 + 6\ H_2O + 2\ N_2$$

Jones (1951) established by means of the N^{15} tracer that under anaerobic conditions only a negligible quantity of nitrogen evolved as gas was derived from sources other than nitrate, a finding which was confirmed by Wijler and Delwiche (1954). Several schemes have been proposed (Delwiche, 1956; Kluyver and Verhoeven, 1954) to show a series of biochemical intermediates between nitrate and nitrogen gas. Some of the proposed intermediates, such as hyponitrite, nitramid, and imido-nitric acid have not as yet been identified in denitrifying systems, but there is fairly general agreement that the reduction sequence includes nitrate, nitrite, nitrous oxide, and nitrogen, in that order. Experimental verification of this sequence has been reported by Cady and Bartholomew (1960), who incubated soil samples containing tagged nitrate in a closed glass apparatus designed to provide internal circulation of gases. The initial gaseous denitrification product was found to be nitric oxide in small amounts, which they attributed to decomposition of nitrous acid. Nitrous oxide then appeared and nitric oxide decreased. After an increase in nitrous oxide, molecular nitrogen was produced in amounts that eventually accounted for nearly all of the added nitrate. Recently, Cooper and Smith (1963) reported the distribution of nitrate, nitrite, nitrous oxide, and nitrogen gas as a function of time in soils and their surrounding atmosphere in a closed, anaerobic system in which gas analysis was by means of gas chromatography. In all of the seven soils they examined the sequence $NO_3^- \rightarrow NO_2^- \rightarrow N_2O \rightarrow N_2$ was observed.

There is some disagreement regarding the position of nitrous oxide on the main pathway of denitrification. Allen and van Niel (1952) concluded that nitrous oxide was not the precursor of molecular nitrogen in cultures of *Pseudomonas stutzerii*. Wijler and Delwiche (1954) found nitrous oxide to be the major denitrification product under most soil conditions, but noted that the relative proportions of N_2O and N_2 depended on pH. Above pH 7 nitrous oxide could be readily reduced to nitrogen, but below pH 6 its reduction was strongly inhibited. On the other hand, Schwarzbeck et al. (1961) found that the relative proportions of N_2O and N_2 were markedly influenced by the ratio of ammonium to nitrate in the added source. Where the ratio was 1:1, as in ammonium nitrate, most of the nitrogen lost appeared as N_2O, whereas where only nitrate was supplied, N_2 was the principal product. It seems likely that these last-named authors were dealing with a system in which bacterial denitrification was not solely responsible for the gases produced.

Most of the published evidence is in agreement with Nõmmik's (1956) conclusion that nitrous oxide is an obligatory precursor of molecular nitrogen. However, in field soils it is likely that much of the nitrous oxide produced in denitrification escapes to the atmosphere before it can be further reduced.

When nitric oxide has been detected as a gaseous product in denitrification experiments (Cady and Bartholomew, 1961) it has always been in connection with an acid medium, and probably results from decomposition of nitrous acid rather than from dissimilatory nitrate reduction.

B. Effect of Partial Pressure of Oxygen

The finding of early investigators that denitrification is most likely to occur in waterlogged soils is in full agreement with more modern studies of the denitrifying bacteria which show them to be facultative anaerobes. These prefer oxygen in culture; only when the oxygen supply is very limited will they utilize nitrate as a hydrogen acceptor. The careful work of Skerman and his associates (1951, 1957a, 1957b) in which dissolved oxygen concentrations were measured by a polarographic technique has demonstrated clearly that the threshold oxygen concentration that inhibits nitrate reduction is very low. However, a considerable number of conflicting reports have appeared in the literature in which denitrification has been observed under conditions of apparently adequate oxygen supply. For example Meiklejohn (1940) described two species of *Pseudomonas* capable of denitrification in aerated cultures. Similar findings have been reported by Marshall et al. (1953), Korsakova (1941), and Kefauver and Allison (1957). In a number of instances (Broadbent, 1951; Broadbent and Stojanovic, 1952; Corbet and Wooldridge, 1940 and Allison et al. (1960) denitrification has been observed in aerated soils and in controlled atmospheres containing some oxygen, whereas other investigators have found no evidence of denitrification under aerobic conditions (Sacks and Barker, 1949; Jones, 1951).

It is probable that there is no real contradiction in these apparently conflicting findings. The explanation lies in the different ways in which the terms "aerobic" and "anaerobic" are used. Under conditions where the biological oxygen demand is high, the rate of diffusion of oxygen to denitrifying bacteria may become limiting to the extent that the bacteria must utilize nitrate as a hydrogen acceptor. These conditions may occur where a readily decomposable substrate is undergoing rapid decomposition, and the micro-environment of the bacteria may become essentially anaerobic even though the soil or solution medium is well aerated by ordinary standards. In this connection it is pertinent to repeat the observation of Skerman et al. (1951) that an organism may use two alternative respiratory pathways at the same time, provided conditions are satisfactory for both. In their experiments oxygen diffused into solution and was utilized by cells of *Pseudomonas,* but the oxygen remained at a very low concentration which permitted simultaneous utilization of nitrate.

Obviously, circumstances that permit "aerobic denitrification" of the kind described above will occur more readily in fine-textured soils than in sandy ones. Small pores which are filled with water are particularly prone to the development of anaerobic conditions, even though many of the larger pores are filled with air. In this connection the results of Nommik (1956) are of particular interest. In studying denitrification with different sizes of soil aggregates he made the expected observation that denitrification decreased with increasing size of aggregates. However, when the size of aggregates increased beyond a certain limit there was an increase in rate of denitrification, which he attributed to the longer time required for oxygen to diffuse to the center of the large aggregates.

The rate at which oxygen is supplied to soil microorganisms is obviously more important than partial pressure of oxygen in determining whether or not denitrification will occur although rate is, of course, not independent of pressure. As a practical point, it may be noted that temporary anaerobism is a feature of nearly all soils, whether it results from saturation during or after rainfall or irrigation, or from incorporation of crop residues which impose a heavy oxygen demand. Since denitrification occurs very rapidly, it is likely of significant magnitude in many agricultural soils. Greenland (1962) has observed that nitrification and denitrification can proceed simultaneously in the same soil sample.

In relation to observations of denitrification under apparently aerobic conditions, the findings of Kefauver and Allison (1957) and of Skerman et al. (1958) are pertinent. In the former instance *Bacterium denitrificans* was found to reduce nitrite in the presence of oxygen, and in the latter case, it was reported that reduction of nitrite by *Achromobacter liquefaciens* was essentially independent of oxygen concentration. The importance of aerobic reduction of nitrite as a factor in soil denitrification has not yet been established, but may prove to be of considerable importance, since nitrite may be formed in soils either from reduction of nitrate when oxygen is lacking or from oxidation of ammonium when oxygen is in adequate supply.

C. Effect of Organic Matter

The effect of organic matter on denitrification is twofold: since the free energy change in the reduction of nitrate to nitrous oxide or nitrogen is positive, an oxidizable substrate is required which can furnish energy for growth of the denitrifying bacteria and serve as a hydrogen donor for the denitrification process; and secondly, the rate of organic matter decomposition markedly influences the oxygen demand.

In comparing the effect of several readily and difficultly decomposable organic materials Bremner and Shaw (1958a, b) found that glucose, mannitol, sucrose, and sodium citrate all induced rapid denitrification. In a series of insoluble materials the rate of denitrification varied with their resistance to decomposition, being most rapid with cellulose and least rapid with lignin and sawdust. McGarity (1961) observed that additions of glucose to some Australian soils of low carbon content increased denitrification, but the effect was slight in high carbon soils. He also reported (1962) that freezing and thawing of soils stimulated denitrification, which may have been due to increased availability of organic matter. Mortensen and Martin (1956) observed a temporary sharp increase in soil respiration as a result of freezing and thawing.

In connection with the influence of organic materials on denitrification, the recent investigation of Woldendorp (1962) on the quantitative influence of the rhizosphere on denitrification is of particular interest. He concluded that the effects of living roots on nitrogen losses by denitrification are caused by rhizosphere organisms consuming much oxygen during breakdown of root excretions, thus reducing oxygen tension in the soil solution near the root surface. He also suggested that root excretions may serve as hydrogen donors in denitrification.

D. Effect of pH

Rate of denitrification is profoundly influenced by soil pH, being very slow in acid soils, and very rapid in soils of high pH according to Bremner and Shaw (1958b). Jansson and Clark (1952) reported that in their experiments an alkaline reaction was required for any extensive denitrification and that nitrite toxicity appeared to inhibit denitrification in acid substrates. There is general agreement among several investigators (Delwiche, 1956; Nommik, 1956) that denitrification rates are fairly constant about pH 6. The pH dependence of the relative proportions of N_2O and N_2 as denitrification products has been mentioned previously (Wijler and Delwiche, 1954). Although the reduction of N_2O was found to be strongly inhibited below pH 7, it may be noted that Cady and Bartholomew (1960), working with an acid soil, observed essentially complete reduction of nitrous oxide to nitrogen at the end of their experiments.

E. Effect of Moisture Content

High soil moisture content affects denitrification indirectly by inhibiting the diffusion of oxygen, but in addition, exerts a very pronounced direct effect. Bremner and Shaw (1958b) observed increased losses of nitrogen as a function of moisture content up to 450% of moisture holding capacity, and noted that even when other conditions are very favorable for denitrification, little loss of nitrogen occurs if the moisture content is less than 60% of the water-holding capacity. The direct effect of water has been confirmed by others (Jansson and Clark, 1952; Nommik, 1956).

F. Effect of Temperature

As in the case of other biological processes, denitrification exhibits a temperature dependence. The optimum temperature is surprisingly high, in the range 60-65°C as reported by Nommik (1956) and by Bremner and Shaw (1958b). The relative proportions of N_2O and N_2 in the denitrification gas vary with temperature, nitrous oxide being predominant at the lower temperatures but molecular nitrogen at the higher temperature. This apparently reflects a higher temperature coefficient for the reduction of nitrous oxide than for the other steps in denitrification.

G. Effect of Nitrate Concentration

There is agreement among several workers that denitrification rate is independent of nitrate concentration over a fairly wide range. Nommik

(1956) found that reduction of nitrous oxide to molecular nitrogen did not begin until the greater part of the nitrate was consumed. The curves of Cooper and Smith (1963) also show this to be the case.

H. Redox Potential

After measuring redox potential and nitrate in a number of English soils Pearsall and Mortimer (1939) concluded that above 350 millivolts nitrates would accumulate and below 320 millivolts nitrates would disappear. By using a series of soil samples poised at various potentials Patrick (1960) obtained a value of 338 millivolts for the redox potential at which nitrate in soil becomes unstable. He considered that redox potential, rather than oxygen status, regulated the activity of the nitrate reducing bacteria. Kefauver and Allison (1957), on the other hand, concluded that redox potential is not a limiting factor in nitrite reduction.

Since it is impossible in soil systems to consider redox potential and oxygen status independently, the question as to which governs nitrate stability is academic.

III. GASEOUS LOSSES OF NITROGEN INVOLVING NITROUS ACID OR NITRITES

Within recent years it has become increasingly evident that biological or dissimilatory nitrate reduction, even though it undoubtedly occurs in some soils, does not adequately explain all losses of gaseous nitrogen from soil. Various workers have observed that nitrate nitrogen added to well-aerated fallow soil often can after one to several weeks of incubation be quantitatively recovered, or nearly so, whereas ammonium nitrogen added to similarly incubated replicate lots of soil is not quantitatively recovered. On occasion, the deficit may be of the order of half or more of the nitrogen initially added. Such losses of nitrogen have been shown to be due not to volatilization of ammonia but in part at least to loss of elemental nitrogen. Losses appear especially pronounced in soils in which nitrites have been observed to accumulate following addition of ammonia or ammonium-releasing materials. Because chemical reactions involving nitrous acid or nitrites are variously involved, it appears appropriate to designate these losses as chemo-denitrification (Clark, 1962). This term is not strictly accurate, inasmuch as the formation of nitrite from ammonia is a biological process.

Inasmuch as chemo-denitrification can take place under fully aerobic conditions, this pathway of loss has at times been designated as aerobic denitrification. As noted above, this designation has also been applied to biological denitrification, a process which is basically anaerobic, and although it may occur in apparently well-aerated soil, it does so within an anaerobic microenvironment of the kind postulated to occur in well-aerated soils (Jansson and Clark, 1952; Greenland, 1962). It has also been suggested that in experiments where losses of elemental nitrogen are observed following addition of ammonium nitrogen, nitrification of the added ammonium occurs in aerated portions of the soil, and that the nitrate thus formed then diffuses or is leached into anaerobic pockets within which enzymatic denitrification can take place. This in itself is entirely plausible, but such an explanation ignores the fact that nitrate nitrogen added to soil lots in parallel with the ammonium additions is fully recoverable. If dissimilatory nitrate reduction were involved, it should apply equally to nitrate added initially and to that formed biologically during incubation.

There is extensive evidence that chemo-denitrification occurs in soil (Allison, 1955, 1963; Clark et al., 1960; Clark, 1962; Gerretsen and de Hoop, 1957; Smith and Clark, 1960; Soulides and Clark, 1958; Tyler and Broadbent, 1960; Wahhab and Uddin, 1954; Wijler and Delwiche, 1954). There is considerable disagreement as to the precise chemical pathways that are involved, as well as some confusion in terminology. The discussion in the following paragraphs will briefly discuss four possible pathways of loss in chemo-nitrification and finally it will undertake to evaluate the significance and possible avoidance of chemo-denitrification under field conditions.

A. The Chemical Decomposition of Nitrous Acid at Low pH Values

Under suitably acid conditions nitrous acid decomposes to yield nitric oxide according to the reaction

$$3\,HNO_2 \rightarrow 2\,NO + HNO_3 + H_2O \tag{a}$$

A portion of the nitric oxide formed is in turn oxidized chemically to nitrogen dioxide

$$2\,NO + O_2 \rightarrow 2\,NO_2 \tag{b}$$

This may react with water to form nitric acid

$$3\,NO_2 + H_2O \rightarrow 2\,HNO_3 + NO \tag{c}$$

$$2\,NO_2 + H_2O \rightarrow HNO_3 + HNO_2 \tag{d}$$

Presumably the NO of (c) or the HNO_2 of (d) would again react as in (b) or (a). No gaseous loss would then occur; rather, all nitrous acid would be converted to nitric acid. If so converted, there should be no gaseous loss of nitrogen.

An acidity of at least pH 5 was reported by Allison and Doetsch (1951) to be necessary for appreciable decomposition of nitrous acid. The rate and extent of decomposition were greatly accelerated with further increases in acidity. Gerretsen and de Hoop (1957) have made similar observations. Some of their data are shown in Table 2.

Since nitric oxide is volatile, its escape from the soil could be an important route for losses of soil nitrogen to the atmosphere. Evidence currently available indicates that any appreciable loss by this pathway is improbable. In neutral or alkaline soil, there would be little if any nitric oxide formation. In aerated acid soils, where chemical oxidation of NO

Table 2. Nitrite recoveries at different pH values (Gerretsen and de Hoop, 1957).

pH	mg N loss (measured in KMnO₄ trap)	Percent loss from 37 mg initially present
3.0	9.6	26
3.5	5.5	15
4.0	3.3	9
4.5	1.8	5
5.0	0.9	2.5
5.5	0.3	1
6.0	0	0

proceeds rapidly, it is unlikely that any considerable NO would escape to the atmosphere before oxidation and hydration to HNO_3 could occur.

Quantitative data concerning nitric oxide losses from soils are limited. Wagner and Smith (1958) trapped relatively small quantities of nitric oxide from various soils. Over a period of 58 days, less than 2 mg of NO and/or NO_2 nitrogen was trapped from a silt loam treated initially with 50 mg of urea nitrogen. Tyler and Broadbent (1960) and also Smith and Clark (1960) failed to detect NO in closed atmospheres of soil lots treated with nitrite salts. We consider that large losses of nitrogen from soils as nitric oxide are unlikely except under very unusual conditions.

B. Reactions of Nitrous Acid with α-Amino Acids

Under suitable conditions nitrous acid reacts with amino acids to yield molecular nitrogen according to the reaction

$$RNH_2 + HNO_2 \rightarrow ROH + H_2O + N_2$$

This reaction is commonly known as the Van Slyke reaction. Its possible role in chemo-denitrification processes in soil has been considered by various workers (Gerretsen and de Hoop, 1957; Smith and Clark, 1960) but particularly by Allison and co-workers (Allison and Doetsch, 1951; Allison et al., 1962; Allison, 1955, 1963). The preponderance of work during the past decade indicates that there is small likelihood that this reaction occurs to any significant extent under conditions commonly occurring in soil. At the pH values at which the reaction can occur at an appreciable rate, namely pH 5 or lower, conditions for nitrite formation either by biological oxidation of ammonia or by enzymatic reduction of nitrate are not favorable. Even if nitrous acid were formed, in the presence of air it would at best react only very slowly with amino acids. In the Van Slyke apparatus in which the reaction occurs rapidly, an atmosphere of nitric oxide rather than of air is provided. The writers consider the Van Slyke reaction of little or no importance as a pathway for the volatile loss of nitrogen from soil.

C. Reaction of Nitrous Acid with Ammonia or Urea

In a reaction quite similar to the Van Slyke reaction, ammonia (or ammonia released from urea) may react with nitrous acid to yield molecular nitrogen

$$NH_3 + HNO_2 \rightarrow N_2 + 2 H_2O$$

Many workers (Gerretsen and de Hoop, 1957; Clark, 1962; Reed and Sabbe, 1963) consider this reaction sufficiently similar to the Van Slyke reaction to justify calling it by that name. Allison (1963), however, takes vigorous exception.

Van Slyke (1911) observed that compounds such as ammonia, urea, methylamine, purines and pyrimidines reacted with nitrous acid, even though they did not react as rapidly as did the amino acids. At 20°C in an atmosphere of NO, amino acids reacted completely with nitrous acid in 5 minutes, while ammonia required $1\frac{1}{2}$ to 2 hours to react quantitatively. Urea gave up 50% of its nitrogen in one hour, but required 8 hours for completion. Smith and Clark (1960) observed that nitrous acid and ammonium sulfate reacted much more slowly than did nitrous acid and alanine. Some of their data are given in Table 3.

Table 3. Comparative reaction of amino and ammonium nitrogen with nitrous acid at pH 4.1 (Smith and Clark, 1960).

NaNO$_2$ concentration	N$_2$ evolved during first hour as percent of N source:	
	Alanine	Ammonium sulfate
2.45 mg N/ml.	27	0
61.7 mg N/ml.	92	39

Allison (1963) has emphasized that in the reaction of nitrous acid and ammonia, ammonium nitrite is instantaneously formed and that this product then undergoes decomposition. He writes the reaction as

$$NH_3^+ + HNO_2 \rightarrow NH_4NO_2 \rightarrow N_2 + 2 H_2O$$

He suggests that gaseous losses of nitrogen from soils may well be greater via ammonium nitrite decomposition than by either of the two pathways already discussed above, and that much of the loss of nitrogen that is often attributed to so-called aerobic denitrification is actually the result of the formation and decomposition of ammonium nitrite.

Such data as are available suggest that decomposition of ammonium nitrite is of little or no significance in chemo-denitrification. Fowler and Kotwal (1924) observed that neutral aqueous solutions of ammonium nitrite containing 30 ppm or less of nitrite nitrogen could be kept at room temperature for months without loss of nitrite. Smith and Clark (1960) have presented evidence against the occurrence of ammonium nitrite decomposition in soil. Soil systems treated with ammonium sulfate and potassium nitrite were found to lose the major portion of their nitrite nitrogen but none of their ammonium nitrogen. Indeed, more nitrogen gas was evolved from nitrite-treated Fort Collins silt loam when ammonium sulfate was omitted than when it was added. Most recently, in investigations concerning the requirements for a Van Slyke reaction involving urea and nitrite, Reed and Sabbe (1963) concluded that the pH, reactant concentration, and anaerobic atmosphere requirements made it extremely doubtful that the investigated reaction contributed to chemical denitrification in soils.

We fail to agree with Allison (1963) that ammonium nitrite decomposition may be the major channel for volatile loss of nitrogen apart from ammonia volatilization and biological denitrification.

D. Reactions of Nitrous Acid with Other Soil Constituents

The foregoing paragraphs question whether any reaction of nitrite with amino acids, ammonia or urea, or any decomposition of nitrous acid or ammonium nitrite *per se* can account for any appreciable chemodenitrification in soils that are near neutrality, or at least less acid than about pH 5.

Data of Soulides and Clark (1958) and Clark et al. (1960) show that volatile losses of nitrogen were of much greater magnitude in near-neutral soils than in soils more acid than pH 5.5. Their data suggested to them that the amount of organic matter present in a soil somehow influenced the quantity of gaseous nitrogen lost therefrom. In further work, Clark and Beard (1960) showed that at a given pH value nitrite showed greater instability in the presence of soil than in its absence. This strengthened their belief that some component in soil serves to promote the reactivity of nitrous acid or nitrite. The specific influence in soil was greatly reduced by pre-treatment of soil with hydrogen peroxide, but increased by addition to soil of organic materials such as alfalfa meal. Dextrose as an additive proved to be largely inert, providing there was no interval of pre-incubation to permit the development of microbial activity. Glucose-amended substrates given pre-incubation prior to the addition of nitrite did, however, result in greater nitrite instability and enhanced losses of gaseous nitrogen.

Such work suggests that organic-reducing compounds, probably of microbial origin, accelerate nitrite dismutation (Clark, 1962). Stevenson and Swaby (1962) have also reported that organic matter or constituents thereof are capable of reacting with nitrites at the pH levels found in many soils. They suggested that volatile losses via this pathway may be of greater importance than is generally realized. Some of their data led them to the identification of methyl nitrite as one of the products formed in organic matter—nitrite interactions. Tyler and Broadbent (1960) also concluded that pH is not the sole factor affecting loss of nitrogen from nitrite in soil.

Not only may organic reducing substances be involved, but possibly heavy metal ions as well. Wullstein et al. (1963) noted that sodium chloride extraction of soil reduced volatile losses of nitrogen from soils to which nitrite had been added. They suggested that the exchangeable cations can promote the decomposition of nitrite in soil.

IV. CAN DENITRIFICATION LOSSES BE AVOIDED?

In most field experiments the volatile losses of nitrogen, although highly variable among soils, appear relatively independent of the form of nitrogen applied. There are, of course, a few notable exceptions, such as flooded soils used in rice culture in which ammonium forms are quite stable although nitrates are subject to virtually complete loss through dissimilatory nitrate reduction. In most upland soils it makes little difference whether nitrate or ammonium sources of fertilizer nitrogen are employed insofar as the magnitude of nitrogen loss is concerned. This makes it appear probable that the unexplained volatile losses of nitrogen occur only after the applied nitrogen has entered into biological systems or has been acted upon by soil organisms.

Because of such transformations, chemo-denitrification can occur even following application of nitrate fertilizers. The nitrate initially added may be taken up by soil organisms or plant roots, transformed to protein compounds, and eventually released as ammonia upon decomposition of the proteins. Such ammonia, like applied ammonia, is susceptible to oxidation to nitrite with the subsequent possibility of chemo-denitrification. Alternatively, nitrite arising from dissimilatory reduction of nitrate may undergo loss by this mechanism. Bhat (1964) has observed reduction of nitrate to nitrite by *Pseudomonas stutzerii* in the presence of adequate levels of oxygen, although no production of N_2O or N_2 occurred. Likewise, enzymatic denitrification can occur following use of ammoniacal fertilizers, provided there are suitable conditions for nitrification; nitrate formed by nitrification processes and fertilizer nitrate are equally susceptible.

Gaseous nitrogen losses due to biological reduction of nitrate fall into two categories—losses that are rapid and extensive, and those involving continuing small loss of nitrogen over an extended period of time. The former occur especially when soils containing nitrate and readily decomposable organic material are exposed simultaneously to a warm season temperature and to excessive wetness. This combination does not commonly prevail for arable upland soils during the growing season, but will occur for short periods of time in soils subject to flood irrigation or occasional heavy rains. In paddy or rice soils the appropriate environmental conditions for denitrification do exist, but this fact is well recognized. Nitrate fertilizers are not used on such soils and management practices include precautions to minimize nitrification of ammoniacal fertilizers applied before flooding.

It is sometimes argued that bulk leaching of nitrate from the surface into the deeper portions of the profile can lead to massive denitrification. In most temperate region soils, such leaching does not occur during the warm season. Although movement of nitrate to the deeper profile may occur during the winter, the combination of low temperature and the lack of decomposable organic matter in the subsoil is not conducive to a high biochemical oxygen demand by the soil microorganisms. Therefore, although winter leaching may cause nitrogen loss through removal from the profile, it does not greatly aggravate biological denitrification.

The continuing small losses of nitrogen that occur within small pockets of microbial activity or within the larger-sized soil aggregates in presumably well-aerated soils are probably more serious when taken collectively than the more rapid denitrification that occurs when the entire soil profile becomes anaerobic or nearly so. At the present state of our knowledge, no practical recommendation can be made for controlling these continuing small losses that characterize aerobic denitrification. Although this pathway may remove something like 10 to 15% of the total yearly mineral nitrogen input, this loss is of a magnitude that can be tolerated.

Can the volatile losses of nitrogen associated with nitrite instability be avoided? One approach to this problem has been advocated by Goring (1962) who believed it desirable to inhibit or eliminate the phenomenon of nitrification altogether. This would avoid not only nitrite formation, and thereby chemo-denitrification, but also leaching of nitrates or nitrites, a problem of serious magnitude in some soils. The use of chemicals to restrict nitrification, as suggested by Goring, would appear practical only in connection with applications of fertilizer nitrogen under certain field conditions, and possibly only in certain soils. An alternative avenue of attack in many soils quite probably will be that of achieving rapid and efficient nitrification under conditions that favor neither nitrite accumulation nor dismutation, although just what these conditions should be is not yet clearly established.

A final question that may be raised is whether or not new nitrogen fertilizers can be formulated that will eliminate or minimize denitrification losses. A variety of controlled-release types of fertilizers are already available, but although they may be highly desirable for other reasons, their value as a means of curbing denitrification appears questionable on economic grounds. If, as appears consistent with the experimental data available, denitrification losses are of the order of 10 to 30%, it is cheaper to use compensatory larger quantities of conventional nitrogen fertilizers than it is to turn to special formulations at perhaps twice the cost per pound of nitrogen of the bulk lot fertilizers now in common use.

REFERENCES

Adel, A. 1946. A possible source of atmospheric N_2O. Science 103:280.

Adel, A. 1951. Vertical distribution and origin of atmospheric nitrous oxide. Astron. J. 56:33-34.

Allen, M. B., and van Niel, C. B. 1952. Experiments on bacterial denitrification. J. Bact. 64:397-412.

Allison, F. E. 1955. The enigma of soil nitrogen balance sheets. Advances in Agron. 7:213-250.

Allison, F. E. 1963. Losses of gaseous nitrogen from soils by chemical mechanisms involving nitrous acid and nitrites. Soil Sci. 96:404-409.

Allison, F. E., Carter, J. N., and Sterling, L. D. 1960. The effect of partial pressure of oxygen on denitrification in Soil. Soil Sci. Soc. Am. Proc. 24:283-285.

Allison, F. E., and Doetsch, J. H. 1951. Nitrogen gas production by the reaction of nitrites with amino acids in slightly acidic media. Soil Sci. Soc. Am. Proc. 15:163-166.

Allison, F. E., Doetsch, J. H., and Sterling, L. D. 1952. Nitrogen gas production by interaction of nitrites and amino acids. Soil Sci. 74:311-314.

Arnold, P. W. 1954. Losses of nitrous oxide from soil. J. Soil Sci. 5:116-128.

Bhat 1964. Unpublished Ph.D. thesis, Oregon State University. Corvallis, Oreg.

Bremner, J. M., and Shaw, K. 1958a. Denitrification in soil I. Methods of investigation. J. Agr. Sci. 51:22-39.

Bremner, J. M., and Shaw, K. 1958b. Denitrification in soil II. Factors affecting denitrification. J. Agr. Sci. 51:40-52.

Broadbent, F. E. 1951. Denitrification in some California soils. Soil Sci. 72:129-137.

Broadbent, F. E., and Stojanovic, B. J. 1952. The effect of partial pressure of oxygen on some soil nitrogen transformations. Soil Sci. Soc. Am. Proc. 16:359-363.

Broadbent, F. E., and Tyler, K. B. 1962. Laboratory and greenhouse investigations of nitrogen immobilization. Soil Sci. Soc. Amer. Proc. 26:459-462.

Cady, F. B., and Bartholomew, W. V. 1960. Sequential products of anaerobic denitrification in Norfolk soil material. Soil Sci. Soc. Am. Proc. 24:477-482.

Cady, F. B., and Bartholomew, W. V. 1961. Influence of low pO_2 on denitrification products and processes. Soil Sci. Soc. Am. Proc. 25:362-365.

Clark, F. E. 1962. Losses of nitrogen accompanying nitrification. International Soil Conference Transactions, New Zealand, 1962. pp. 173-176.

Clark, F. E., and Beard, W. E. 1960. Influence of organic matter on volatile loss of nitrogen from soil. Intern. Congr. Soil Sci., 7th Congr. Madison, Comm. III:501-508.

Clark, F. E., Beard, W. E., and Smith, D. H. 1960. Dissimilar nitrifying capacities of soils in relation to losses of applied nitrogen. Soil Sci. Soc. Am. Proc. 24:50-54.

Cooper, G. S., and Smith, R. L. 1963. Sequence of products formed during denitrification in some diverse Western soils. Soil Sci. Soc. Am. Proc. 27:659-662.

Corbet, A. S., and Wooldridge, W. R. 1940. The nitrogen cycle in biological systems 3. Aerobic denitrification in soils. Biochem. J. 34:1036-1040.

Delwiche, C. C. 1956. Denitrification. In Inorganic Nitrogen Metabolism. 233-256, Johns Hopkins Press, Baltimore.

Dilz, K., and Woldendorp, J. W. 1960. Distribution and nitrogen balance of N^{15} labelled nitrate applied on grass sods. 8th Int. Grasslands Cong. (Reading):150-152.

Ferguson, M., and Fred, E. B. 1908. Denitrification: The effect of fresh and well-rotted manure on plant growth. Virginia Agr. Exp. Sta. Ann. Rep. 1908:134-150.

Fowler, G. J., and Kotwal, Y. N. 1924. Chemical factors in denitrification. J. Indian Instit. Sic. 7:29-37.

Gayon, U., and Dupetit, G. 1886. Recherches sur la reduction des nitrates par les infiniments petits. Soc. Sci. Phys. Nat. Bordeaux, Ser. 3, 2:201-307.

Gerretsen, F. C., and de Hoop, H. 1957. Nitrogen losses during nitrification in solutions and in acid sandy soils. Can. J. Microbiol. 3:359-380.

Goring, C. A. I. 1962. Control of nitrification by 2-chloro-6-(trichloromethyl) pyridine. Soil Sci. 93:211-218.

Greenland, D. J. 1962. Denitrification in some tropical soils. Agr. Sci. 58:227-233.

Jansson, S. L. 1963. Balance sheet and residual effects of fertilizer nitrogen in a 6-year study with N^{15}. Soil Sci. 95:31-37.

Jansson, S. L., and Clark, F. E. 1952. Losses of nitrogen during decomposition of plant material in the presence of inorganic nitrogen. Soil Sci. Soc. Am. Proc. 16:330-334.

Jones, E. J. 1951. Loss of elemental nitrogen from soils under anaerobic conditions. Soil Sci. 71:193-196.

Kefauver, M., and Allison, F. E. 1957. Nitrite reduction by Bacterium denitrificans in relation to oxidation-reduction potential and oxygen tension. J. Bact. 73:8-14.

Kluyver, A. J., and Verhoeven, W. 1954. Studies on true dissimilatory nitrate reduction. II. The mechanism of denitrification. Antonie van Leeuwenhoek 20:241-262.

Korsakova, M. P. 1941. Effect of aeration on the process of bacterial nitrate reduction. Mikrobiol. (U.S.S.R.) 10:163-178, 1941. (Abstract in Chem. Abs. 36:4848, 1942).

MacVicar, R., Garman, W. L., and Wall, R. 1950. Studies on nitrogen fertilizer utilization using N[15]. Soil Sci. Soc. Amer. Proc. 15:265-268.

Marshall, R. O., Dishburger, H. J., MacVicar, R., and Hallmark, G. D. 1953. Studies on the effect of aeration on nitrate reduction by *Pseudomonas* species using N[15]. Jour. Bact. 66:254-258.

Martin, A. E., Henzell, E. F., Ross, P. J., and Haydock, K. P. 1963. Isotopic studies on the uptake of nitrogen by pasture grasses I. Recovery of fertilizer nitrogen from the soil:plant system using Rhodes grass in pots. Aust. J. Soil Res. 1:169-184.

McGarity, J. W. 1961. Denitrification studies on some South Australian soils. Plant and Soil 14:1-21.

McGarity, J. W. 1962. Effect of freezing of soil on denitrification. Nature 196:1342-1343.

Meiklejohn, J. 1940. Aerobic denitrification. Ann. App. Biol. 27:558-573.

Mortensen, J. L., and Martin, W. P. 1956. The microbial decomposition and adsorption of synthetic polyelectrolytes in Ohio soils. Conf. on Radioactive Isotopes in Agriculture, Atomic Energy Comm. TID 7512:235-243.

Nommik, H. 1956. Investigations on denitrification in soil. Acta Agric. Scand. VI. 2:195-228.

Oelsner, A. 1918. Uber Nitratreduktion in nassem Ackerboden ohne Zusatz von Energiematerial. Centbl. Bakt. (II) 48:210-221.

Patrick, W. H., Jr. 1960. Nitrate reduction rates in a submerged soil as affected by redox potential. Trans 7th Int. Cong. Soil Sci. 2:494-500.

Pearsall, W. H., and Mortimer, C. H. 1939. Oxidation-reduction potentials in waterlogged soils, natural waters and muds. J. Ecology 27:483-501.

Reed, L. W., and Sabbe, W. E. 1963. Investigations concerning a Van Slyke reaction involving urea and nitrite. Agron. Abstracts 1963, p. 24.

Runov, E. V. 1932. Physiological characteristics of *B. flourescens* as a denitrifier. Proc. 2nd Int. Cong. Soil Sci. 3:160-163.

Sacks, L. E., and Barker, H. A. 1949. The influence of oxygen on nitrate and nitrite reduction. J. Bact. 58:11-22.

Schneider, E. 1932. Investigations on the influence of unbalanced manuring on denitrification in soils. Arch. Pflanzenbau. 8:719-739.

Schwartzbeck, R. A., MacGregor, J. V., and Schmidt, E. L. 1961. Gaseous nitrogen losses from nitrogen fertilized soils measured with infrared and mass spectroscopy. Soil Sci. Soc. Am. Proc. 25:186-189.

Skerman, V. B. D., Carey, B. J., and MacRae, I. C. 1958. The influence of oxygen on the reduction of nitrite by washed suspensions of adapted cells of *Achromobacter liquefaciens*. Can. J. Microbiol. 4:243-256.

Skerman, V. B. D., Lack, J., and Millis, N. 1951. Influence of oxygen concentration on the reduction of nitrate by a *Pseudomonas* species in the growing culture. Austr. J. Biol. Res. 4:511-517.

Skerman, V. B. D., and MacRae, I. C. 1957a. The influence of oxygen on the reduction of nitrate by adapted cells of *Pseudomonas denitrificans*. Can. J. Microbiol. 3:215-230.

Skerman, V. B. D., and MacRae, I. C. 1957b. The influence of oxygen on the degree of nitrate reduction by *Pseudomonas denitrificans*. Can. J. Microbiol. 3:505-530.

Smith, D. H., and Clark, F. E. 1960. Volatile losses of nitrogen from acid or neutral soils or solutions containing nitrite and ammonium ions. Soil Sci. 90:86-92.

Soulides, D. A., and Clark, F. E. 1958. Nitrification in grassland soils. Soil Sci. Soc. Am. Proc. 22:308-311.

Stevenson, F. J., and Swaby, R. J. 1963. Occurrence of a previously unobserved nitrogen gas in the reaction product of nitrous acid and lignin. Nature 199:97-98.

Turtschin, F. B., Bersenjewa, S. N., Koritzkaja, I. A., Shidkick, G. G., and Lobowikowa, G. A. 1960. Die Stickstoffumwandlung im Boden nach den Angaben der Untersuchungen unter Anwendung des Isotops N[15]. Trans. 7th Int. Cong. Soil Sci. II:236-245.

Tyler, K. B., and Broadbent, F. E. 1960. Nitrite transformation in California Soils. Soil Sci. Soc. Am. Proc. 24:279-282.

van Iterson, G., Jr. 1904. Anhaufungsversuche mit denitrifizierenden Bakterien. Centrbl. Bakt. (II) 12:106-115.

Van Slyke, D. D. 1911. A method for quantitative determination of aliphatic amino groups. J. Biol. Chem. 9:185-204.

Voorhees, E. B. 1902. Studies in denitrification. J. Amer. Chem. Soc. 24:785-823.

Wagner, G. H., and Smith, G. E. 1958. Nitrogen losses from soils fertilized with different nitrogen carriers. Soil Sci. 85:125-129.

Wahhab, A., and Uddin, F. 1955. Influence of light on interaction of ammonium and nitrite ions. Soil Sci. 80:121-125.

Wijler, J., and Delwiche, C. C. 1954. Investigations on the denitrifying process in soil. Plant and Soil 5:155-169.

Woldendorp, J. W. 1962. The quantitative influence of the rhizosphere on denitrification. Plant and Soil 17:267-270.

Wullstein, L. H., Gilmour, C. M., and Bollen, W. B. 1963. Gaseous loss of soil nitrogen by chemical and microbial pathways. Agron. Abstracts 1963, p. 34.

Chapter 10

Symbiotic Nitrogen Fixation

P. S. NUTMAN

Rothamsted Experimental Station
Harpenden, England

I. INTRODUCTION

Chapters 1 and 16 describe the origin of the nitrogen cycle, the distribution of nitrogen in the biosphere, and the processes, including fixation, that maintain equilibrium between molecular and combined nitrogen. This chapter will deal with the biology of nitrogen-fixing symbioses, principally in root-nodules of legumes, and particular attention will be paid to the intrinsic factors of host and strain that regulate the efficiency of the fixing process.

A. History of Legume Use

The importance of legumes in building and conserving soil fertility has been recognized since the beginning of agriculture, and their first use is lost in pre-history. Legumes were grown by the bronze-age lake-dwellers of Central Europe, possibly as early as 6000 B.C., they featured in the cropping systems of ancient Egypt, they were often mentioned in the Old Testament, and they found a place in the mythology as well as in the practical agriculture of the Greeks and Romans. Soybean (*Glycine max*) was cultivated in the Far East and Malaya from remote antiquity. The earliest records of legume cultivation in the British Isles come from the pre-Roman lake-dwellings at Glastonbury. The beans (a small-fruited form of *Vicia faba*) found there resemble those buried several millenia earlier in Switzerland.

Alfalfa or lucerne (*Medicago sativa*), indigenous to S. W. Asia, was cultivated in Babylonia from about 700 B.C., whence it spread to the Mediterranean region. In the fourth century B.C. Xenophon referred to alfalfa as the hay of the Medes, hence its generic name. Many centuries later it was introduced into Spain by the Moors.

Legumes were used originally only for human or stock food. The first European reference to green-manuring with beans is by Theophrastus, although the writings of Chia Sza Hsish (fifth century B.C.) suggest that it had an earlier origin elsewhere. The rotational cropping systems first developed by the Romans, employed legumes as green manure, and their agricultural writers, notably Cato, stressed the value of turned-in green crops in improving the soil. The culture of field legumes declined during the Middle Ages, when more reliance was placed upon natural vegetation and bare fallow to restore fertility, and it was not until comparatively recent times that rotations incorporating legumes were brought into general use.

From our own literature and legend we know that the native small clovers, trefoils and vetches were always common, and highly regarded in meadow land; it is from these that most sown pasture-legumes have arisen. In contrast, the progenitors of the earliest cultivated food legumes, *Vicia faba, Pisum sativum,* and *Glycine max,* can no longer be certainly identified among wild plants. In the sixteenth century, red clover (*Trifolium pratense*) was first grown as a crop in the Low Countries and sainfoin (*Onobrychis sativa*) in the south of France. Red clover was introduced into England from Flanders in 1663 at about the same time as alfalfa. The growing of clover spread rapidly but the early spread of alfalfa was restricted because the appropriate nodule organism was lacking. Clover was first used as a sown legume in New England around 1775. Artificial seed inoculation, pioneered by the experimental stations at Hamburg and Connecticut during the 1890's, led to the extended growing of alfalfa in Europe and America. The introduction of legumes into temporary leys was a natural development of these trends towards sown pastures and the increased use of legumes in rotational systems.

The Spaniards brought alfalfa to the New World in the sixteenth century, Chile being the chief center of its cultivation. Later, at the time of the gold rush to California, alfalfa was taken there by the miners and grown successfully, after earlier introductions to the eastern states had failed. Today most of the world production of alfafa is in the U.S.A. and Argentina.

The Maya and Inca agriculturists grew various kinds of beans, of which the lima bean (*Phaseolus lunatus*) is a modern representative, but the peanut or ground-nut (*Arachis hypogea*) is the chief legume of agricultural importance originating in the New World. The Indian potato (*Apios tuberosa*), also a legume and called ground nut, was widely collected by the North American Indians and was eaten by the Pilgrims under the duress of their first winter in Massachusetts.

Soybean, introduced to U.S. agriculture less than half a century ago, has shown phenomenal expansion in production and acreage sown (1917, 50,000; 1945, 10,600,000; 1958, 23,900,000 acres). At 15,960,000 metric tons, the 1958 production in North America exceeded even that of the Far East (11,650,000 metric tons).

The early history of legume use in other continents is conjectural. Indigenous pulses were probably grown in Africa south of the Sahara before European colonizers introduced forage and food legumes, but none has become important in other regions. Polynesian cultivators probably knew no crop legume and the aboriginal Australians had no agriculture. Of Australia's very rich but predominantly shrubby native legume flora, the only ones used in agriculture today are *Trigonella sauveolens,* a valuable fodder plant in restricted areas of Queensland, and some species of *Acacia* and *Leucaena glauca* as reserve browse plants. However, as in

America, introduced European legumes have flourished. Subterranean clover (*Trifolium subterraneum*), which is insignificant in its Mediterranean homeland, is of outstanding importance and is established on about 30 million acres of improved pastures. Much of the earlier work on plant introduction failed because the symbiotic bacteria were not introduced at the same time.

In spite of successes in the full establishment of effectively nodulated legumes in the new pastoral and agricultural regions of America, Australia and to a lesser extent Africa, it nevertheless remains true that the Far East has by far the largest total production of legume food grains. The total 1958 production in metric tons of dry beans of many kinds, peas, lentils, peanuts, and soybean was as follows: Far East, 36,595,000; North America, 17,855,000; Africa, 4,875,000; Latin America, 3,815,000; Europe, 2,590,000; Near East, 1,030,000; Australia, 14,000.

None of the ancient writers seems to have remarked on root nodules. The earliest known references are the herbalists' illustrations in the fifteenth century, and it was not until the early nineteenth century that the special value of legumes was shown to lie in their high nitrogen content. Much controversy centered around the source of this nitrogen until the function of the nodule in fixing nitrogen was finally proved by Hellriegel and Wilfarth and the causative organism isolated by Beijerinck in 1888.

The following references were found useful in writing this section: Beijerinck (1888), De Candolle (1884), FAO Production Yearbook (1959), Fred et al. (1932), Godwin (1956), Gras (1940), Hellriegel and Wilfarth (1888), Morley (1961), and White, Nelssen-Leissner and Trumble (1953).

B. Symbiotic Nitrogen Fixation Under Natural Conditions and in Agriculture

Estimates of the total amount of symbiotically fixed nitrogen that enters the nitrogen cycle each year are subject to very large errors because of difficulties in measurement in the field, and because new nitrogen-fixing and denitrifying agents are still being discovered. It has been estimated that of the 10^8 tons of N_2 fixed annually, by far the largest part comes from symbiotic sources, particularly the nodules of leguminous plants growing in natural associations and in agriculture (Donald, 1960). In number of species the Leguminosae is the second or third largest family of flowering plants; it is of world-wide distribution and includes many major food and forage crops, and plants producing timbers, fibres and other products.

The amounts of atmospheric nitrogen assimilated by legume crops have often been estimated. The following examples indicate the quantities which may be fixed in pounds of nitrogen per acre per crop or season; alfalfa, 50-350; clovers, 50-200; peas, 30-140; peanuts, 88; pastures with legumes, 10-550 (Seeger, 1961; Spector, 1956).

After the legume host dies the fixed nitrogen becomes available to other plants by the normal process of mineralization. There is also evidence that under certain rather ill-defined conditions the living legume root may excrete appreciable amounts of nitrogen (Wilson, 1940). The amounts fixed by individual crops are affected by many factors including the environment (considered in Chapter 11), but the effectively nodulated legume, growing vigorously can provide itself through the activity of its nodules with all the nitrogen it needs, even when none is available from the soil. This also probably applies to the root-nodulated non-legumes, because their maximum rate of fixation per unit volume of nodule tissue is similar to that of legumes (MacConnell, 1957). Also, although their endophytes differ, the nodule symbioses of legume and non-legume have so much in common that their fundamental processes of fixation are likely to be similar.

C. The Widespread Occurrence of Nodules on Legumes

Sample surveys indicate that the nodulating habit among legumes is almost universal. Legumes may fail to produce nodules from a variety of causes (unsuitable conditions or season or absence of endophyte), but a small minority have never been known to form nodules under any conditions. Such non-nodulating legume species occur only in the botanically primitive Caesalpinioideae and Mimosoideae (Allen and Allen, 1961). Among the Papilionateae no species is known that fails to nodulate, but occasional plants of red clover (Nutman, 1949) and soybean (Clark, 1957; Williams and Lynch, 1954) have been described which do not form nodules and from these non-nodulating or resistant lines have been bred. Resistance in both these species is determined by simple recessive host genes, with the additional complication in red clover of a cytoplasmically transmitted component. Resistance in soybean also differs from that in clover in being partially dependent on bacterial strain and being lost when resistant roots are grafted with normal scions. The physiological bases of these kinds of resistance are unknown but resistant soybean plants excrete anti-bacterial factors into the rhizosphere (Elkan, 1962). Resistant and normal lines of soybean are used to study fixation in the field (Lynch and Sears, 1952).

II. THE ROOT-NODULE BACTERIA

A. Cultural and Symbiotic Properties

The bacteria of all leguminous nodules (genus *Rhizobium*) are aerobic, gram-negative, non-sporing rods usually with simple nutritional requirements. Some strains need biotin, thiamin or pantothenic acid or more than one vitamin, others can grow on a simple mineral-salts-sugar medium (Bergersen, 1961). Sucrose is the preferred carbohydrate source for most strains, but many sugars and sugar-alcohols are utilized, usually with the production of slight acid and no gas. In culture, strains differ mostly in growth rate and in flagellation. The nodule bacterium's few characteristic features in culture and variability account for its chequered history of nomenclature; since its isolation by Beijerinck it has been assigned *seriatim* to 5 genera (Fred et al., 1932). Nodule bacteria can live freely in the soil in the absence of their host plant but, as typical rhizosphere organisms, are markedly stimulated by plant roots, particularly legumes. The rhizosphere relations of nodule bacteria are considered in Chapter 13.

In symbiosis, strains can be distinguished by their host range, that is the number of species of plant each can infect, and this character is used to subdivide the genus. The specific epithets used to describe the bacteria of each of the six main "cross inoculation" groups are of doubtful taxonomic validity but are retained for convenience; they are, *R. trifolii, R. meliloti, R. leguminosarum, R. phaseoli, R. lupini* and *R. japonicum.* Fig. 1 gives the botanical composition of the six major cross-inoculation groups (combining the cowpea and soybean groups) with the host tribes arranged phylogenetically (Gams, 1926). Very broadly, host taxonomy and cross-inoculation grouping correspond; nearly related hosts tending to occur together in the same susceptible group.

The most notable feature of the cross-inoculation groups is their very different sizes. The clover group (nodulated by *R. trifolii*) consists only of species of the genus *Trifolium*, (tribe Trifolieae) the medic group (*R. meliloti*) of *Medicago, Melilotus* and *Trigonella* (tribe Trifolieae), the pea group of *Pisum, Vicia, Lathyrus* and Lens (tribe Vicieae). The bean group of some *Phaseolus* species (tribe Phaseoliae); the lupin group of *Lupinus* and *Ornithopus* (tribe Genisteae). By contrast the cowpea group contains hundreds of host genera from each of the remaining subfamilies and tribes of the Leguminosae and from the Phaseoleae and Genisteae. Some plant tribes have species in more than one cross-inoculation group and the genus *Phaseolus* has species in the bean and cowpea groups. The plant species in each group can be further classified into sub-groups on the basis of their nodulation with individual collections of bacterial strains; both "bridging" hosts and "bridging" strains are common.

The bacteria show no absolute correlation between nodulating specificity and morphological or cultural features; the only way to determine the "species" of an isolate is to inoculate a range of leguminous species.

Studies on the mechanism of root-hair infection and on *Rhizobium* genetics suggest that the cross-inoculation group-specificity of bacterial strain depends on its capsular polysaccharide type (as with *Pneumococcus* virulence) and is similarly transformable between the recognized species of *Rhizobium*. Transformation experiments also indicate a close relationship between *Rhizobium* and *Agrobacterium* (Klein and Klein, 1953).

Strains may also be distinguished symbiotically in nitrogen-fixing capacity and in other ways, but these are not regarded as specific characteristics and are better considered in a later section.

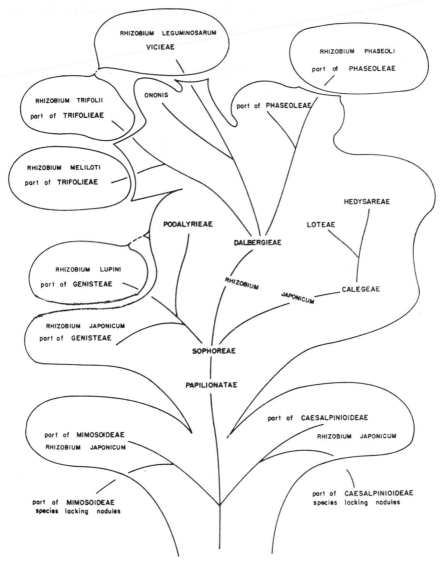

Fig. 1. The relation between taxonomy and cross-inoculation specificity in the Leguminosae.

III. ROOT INFECTION, NODULE INITIATION AND GROWTH

The ways in which legume roots are infected, and nodules develop are so varied, that a full account cannot be given (Allen and Allen, 1958; Fred et al., 1932; Jordan, 1962; Nutman, 1958; Richmond et al., 1954; Wright, 1955). Instead a typical symbiosis of the more highly adapted kind will be described and some examples quoted of the more important departures from this pattern. The chosen symbiosis will be that of red clover (*Trifolium pratense*) associated with a strain of nodule bacteria fully effective in promoting nitrogen fixation in the nodule.

A. Infection

Red clover is infected through its root hairs; the infected hairs usually being locally curled or deformed at the point of infection. The curling is thought to be caused by β-indoleacetic acid (IAA) possibly acting in conjunction with other factors. The source of IAA may be tryptophane, which can be converted to IAA by nodule bacteria (Kefford et al., 1960), and is secreted in small amounts by the root (Rovira, 1959).

Inside the hair the bacteria are confined within a hypha-like structure, the infection thread, which originates at the point of primary infection. Fig. 2A shows a curled and infected hair of white clover. How the bacteria penetrate the hair is unknown. The bacteria themselves do not produce pectinases or cellulases (Davenport, 1960; McCoy, 1932), but the presence of the bacteria in the rhizosphere induces the root to form small amounts of polygalacturonase (PG). Extracellular polysaccharide separated from the bacteria has a similar inducing effect and only those strains of bacteria (or their polysaccharides) able to infect the root can induce PG; induction does not transgress the boundaries of cross inoculation (Fåhraeus and Ljunggren, 1959; Ljunggren and Fåhraeus, 1961). Bacterial "virulence," polysaccharide type and enzyme induction are thus closely connected, suggesting that specificity in the bacterial cross-inoculation group may be determined by polysaccharide constitution, and in the host by susceptibility to the inducing effect of specific polysaccharide. Work on genetic transformation of virulence in *Rhizobium* supports this idea (Balassa, 1960; Lange and Alexander, 1960; Ljunggren, 1961).

The function of the PG in infection is not known. It may act with IAA in altering the plasticity of the primary wall of the young root hair, so that the bacteria can enter, or it may reorientate the growth of the hair wall to form the infection thread by invagination (Nutman, 1959a).

In some clover species all or nearly all primary infections give rise to nodules, but in others many more hairs are infected than nodules formed. The unsuccessful infection threads often fail to grow out of the hair cell into the cortex. Most of the surplus infections arise on the very young seedling before the first nodule is formed, and the number of such infections increases exponentially with time. As soon as the first nodule appears the rate of hair infection declines sharply (Nutman, 1962). Should the initiation of the first nodule be delayed, for example by small additions of nitrate to the medium, hairs continue to be infected and many more infection threads form, although the number of nodules ultimately may be decreased. In the young seedling the distribution of the infections along the root is not at random but tends to be restricted to two or three zones, each beginning with a small group of contiguous infections near to which new infections appear, both above and below the original infections (Nutman, 1962).

The mode of primary infection has been studied in detail with few

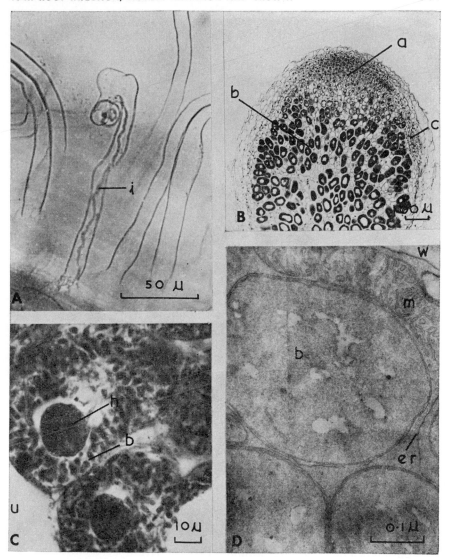

Fig. 2. **A.** An infected root-hair of white clover (*T. repens*): i, infection-thread. **B.** Median longitudinal section of part of an effective nodule of red clover (*T. pratense*): a, apical meristem; b, bacteroid-containing tissue; c, nodule cortex. (Photograph by H. G. Thornton). **C.** Host cells of red clover containing bacteroids: b, bacteroids; h, host nucleus; u, uninfected host cell. (Photograph by H. G. Thornton). **D.** Electron-micrograph of part of bacteroid-containing cell of white clover: b, bacteroid; er, endoplasmic reticulum; m, mitochondrion; w, host wall. (Photograph by B. Mosse).

host species, and in most the routes of infection are still unknown. Some hosts appear to be infected directly through epidermal cells, without the formation of infection threads, others at the points of emergence of lateral rootlets (Allen and Allen, 1940; Arora, 1954; Haack, 1961; Schaede, 1940).

In clovers, the bacteria seem to be wholly distributed within the host by means of infection threads, which branch and ramify throughout the nodule, but in others the bacteria are carried passively from cell to cell by the division of the infected host cells, or their distribution may be partly by one means and partly by another, even in the same host (Milovidov, 1928). The mechanism seems to be host-determined, because there are no records of the presence or absence of threads in any one host being dependent upon bacterial strain.

The growth of the clover infection thread in the root hair and in the cells of root and cortex is controlled in some way by the host cell nucleus, because the thread grows only when near to the nucleus (Fåhraeus, 1957; Nutman, 1959a). The penetration of the thread into the cortex and throughout the nodule is thus associated with the orderly migration of the nuclei of the host cells.

B. Nodule Development

The clover nodule begins as a proliferation of a small group of cells of the inner cortex of the root. These cells are of mixed tetraploid and diploid constitution, the tetraploid cells arising from pre-formed tetraploid initials that are present even in the uninfected root. The stimulus that initiates this development is not known. Although infection threads are always associated with initiation, nodule development does not invariably happen when infection threads penetrate the cortex as noted above. But once the primary stimulation of cell division of the tetraploid initial is initiated, the nodule then differentiates fully by the rapid formation of an organized meristem that produces mainly tetraploid cells basally and diploid cells towards the outside of the root, giving a cortex in which the vascular traces are differentiated. The central tetraploid zone is enclosed within an endodermis continuous with that of the root; separate endodermi also envelop each vascular trace. Individual host cells of the tetraploid region are infected from the extensive system of infection threads originating in an infected root hair. Studies of infection with mixtures of marked strains of bacteria show that a single original infection is usually associated with each nodule, and only rarely does a nodule contain more than one strain of bacteria (Hughes and Vincent, 1942). Fig. 2B shows a median longitudinal section of part of a red clover nodule.

Nodules with a well differentiated apical meristem are cylindrical, but the apex may become laterally compressed, or dichotomise to give flattened or coralloid nodules, especially when conditions restrict infection. Nodules without any clearly defined growing point may be spherical or irregular in form. Nodules also differ in detailed morphology, in colour, texture and sculpturing of their surface. Most nodules are ephemeral and decay at the end of the growing season, but in some species or under certain conditions they show annual zones of growth (Arora, 1955; Harris et al., 1949; Pate, 1961).

In the clover nodule the tetraploid cells of the central region are successively penetrated by the infection threads and then become intracellularly infected. The contiguous zones of invasion and infection are narrowly separated in the actively growing nodule. The bacteria seem to be released from vesicles that form on the thread; the mechanisms of thread penetration and release of the bacteria are not known, but possibly resemble those responsible for the original hair infection. It was long ago shown (McCoy, 1932) that the nodule cells readily separate when the nodule is macerated, so they are not held together by their infection threads. This indicates that the threads may be formed discontinuously, cell by cell, as would be required by an invagination process.

Once in the host cell the bacteria multiply rapidly and then change into the 'bacteroid' condition associated with nitrogen fixation (Fig. 2C). Fine-structure studies on soybean nodules (Bergersen and Briggs, 1958) indicate that each escaping bacterium becomes infolded in the plasma-lemma membrane and then multiplies only two or three times before changing into bacteroids. The mature bacteroids thus come to lie in small groups in a complex system of membrane envelopes of plant origin. In clover and *Vicia* nodules and possibly in lucerne (Dart and Mercer, 1963; Jordan, 1962; Mosse, 1964) the plant membranes surround each bacteroid, as shown in Fig. 2D. The significance of this is further discussed in the next section.

Hosts without infection threads do not have a clearly defined nodular meristem, and the processes of bacterial multiplication and dispersal seem to be simpler, though they have been as yet little studied. The infection thread may have evolved to facilitate orderly infection in nodules with apical growth and acropetal differentiation of tissues.

C. The Bacteroids*

The nodule bacteroids differ from the rod-shaped bacteria of the infection thread (or in culture) in their larger size, pleomorphy and smaller and fragmented nucleus. Bacteroid respiration is marginally higher than that of cultured cells, although the bacteroid has no cytochrome a and is less able to synthesize certain porphyrins (Appleby, 1958; Falk et al., 1959). It is also less sensitive in crushed nodule suspensions to inhibition by fluoride but otherwise both forms are similar metabolically (Richmond et al., 1954). Bacteroids of actively fixing nodules do not contain appreciable carbohydrate reserves, but when fixation is impaired glycogen may accumulate in large amounts, each globule of glycogen being associated with the sites of oxidation-reduction which are demonstrable cytochemically in both bacteroids and cells in culture (Bergersen, 1955). A polymer of β-hydroxy-butyric acid also occurs in bacteria and in the nodule and is presumed to accumulate in the bacteroid (Forsyth and Hayward, 1958; Fred et al., 1932).

In the older part of the nodule the bacteroids autolyse as the host cells degenerate, and thus have no progeny. There is also considerable doubt

* Term originally used by Brunchorst (1885) who thought the bacteroids were host protein granules. Applied by some authors to pleomorphic forms induced in culture by alkaloids, etc. (Golebiowska, 1960). Bacteroid was independently coined to describe endosymbionts of arthropods (Gier, 1947).

about the reproductive capacity of even young bacteroids taken from the nodule and put on media able to support growth of the rod form (Almon, 1933). The nuclear degeneration noted above may explain this apparent inability to multiply.

D. The Infected Host Cell

The bacteroid-containing plant cell has three distinguishing features. First, its nucleus is tetraploid, and while the bacteria are multiplying within the young infected cell the nucleus is large but normal in appearance. Later it becomes compressed and somewhat degenerate. Except for the special examples described later, the vacuolated infected cells do not return to the meristematic condition. The second distinguishing feature of the infected host cell is the absence of starch grains and the presence of platelets of water-soluble dextrin-like carbohydrate (Bergersen, 1957a). In the normal effective nodule this serves as a temporary storage material, disappearing as nitrogen becomes fixed, but in certain ineffective nodules it accumulates to form a continuous sheet around the outer margin of the protoplast and is particularly well developed opposite intercellular spaces; its function is unknown.

The third distinguishing feature is the occurrence of haemoglobin (leghaemoglobin) in solution in the plant sap, or associated with lipoprotein membranes of the endoplasmic reticulum (Bergersen and Wilson, 1959a).

IV. THE SITE OF NITROGEN FIXATION

Nitrogen is fixed by many different micro-organisms living in or on the surface of soil or in association with plants. It has therefore long been assumed that the bacteroids in the nodule fix nitrogen, which then passes to the host plant, and that the special conditions in the nodule stimulate the bacteroids to perform reactions which they are incapable of doing alone. There is no well-authenticated record of fixation by bacteria outside the plant. Fixation by excised nodules, or whole excised roots bearing nodules, stops within a few hours after excision (Aprison and Burris, 1952; Magee and Burris, 1954), and no consistent fixation has yet been achieved with the separated bacteroids or crushed nodules. Fixation therefore requires certain structures or functions, characteristic of the intact nodule attached to the whole plant and for which no substitute has yet been found.

Recent work on isotopic enrichment of the different components of the infected cell after exposure to $^{15}N_2$ has thrown doubt even on the assumption that the bacteroids of the normal nodule fix nitrogen. ^{15}N first appears in the non-bacteroid plant cytoplasmic fraction from crushed nodules (Turchin, 1956), and further separation shows that the fraction probably containing the membranes surrounding the bacteroid first becomes labelled, then the host cytoplasm and lastly the bacteroid (Bergersen and Wilson, 1959a). Nitrogen may thus be fixed on a host structure that is formed only as a consequence of bacterial invasion.

V. BIOCHEMICAL HYPOTHESES OF FIXATION

The early isotopic enrichment of ammonia and glutamate, after exposure of various N-fixing systems to $^{15}N_2$, suggests that fixation is a reductive process (Blom, 1931; Burris, 1956; Virtanen, 1947; Wilson, 1940). Because the reaction $N_2 \rightarrow 2NH_3$ requires the transfer of 6 electrons, there are several possible intermediate compounds. A 2-electron transfer would give a diimide that could exist only transiently in the free state, because it would break down immediately into hydrazine and nitrogen. However, if the diimide group were combined with an organic compound it might be hydrolysed to hydroxylamine, or an oxime, or reduced to hydrazine. Hydrazine might then be further reduced to ammonia, or combine with alpha-ketoglutaric acid to produce dihydropyridazinone-5-carboxylic acid (PCA), which could be directly reduced to glutamine (Bach, 1957). Although there is little evidence for the existence of hydrazine, hydroxylamine or PCA in nodules, these compounds could give rise to ammonia and glutamine by apparently simple chemical pathways.

The agents affecting these hypothetical reactions are even more obscure but various schema have been proposed which coordinate some of the facts of nodule structure and nodule biochemistry (Bauer, 1960; Bergersen, 1960; Roberts, 1959; Virtanen, 1947; Wilson, 1940). One of these involves the redox system: haemoglobin-haemiglobin, which may transfer electrons either directly or through an intermediate carrier to molecular nitrogen to form the first reduced compound. This is thought to take place on the host cytoplasmic membrane with the later transfer of the reduced nitrogen compound to the bacteroid where amino acids and protein may be synthesised. In this process the bacteroid is assigned the function of transferring electrons from its dehydrogenase system to regenerate haemoglobin; this activity may be regarded as a terminal respiratory system in which nitrogen replaces oxygen (Parker and Scott, 1960). The facts which support this scheme are: (1) the fine structural relationships between the host and bacteroid components and their differential enrichment with ^{15}N (Bergersen and Briggs, 1958; Bergersen and Wilson, 1959a); (2) the evidence for the occurrence of respiratory cytochromes on the bacteroid surface (Appleby, 1962; Falk and Appleby, 1959; Fred et al., 1932); (3) the *in vitro* demonstration of the oxidation of haemoglobin by nitrogen and the reduction of haemiglobin by preparations of bacteroids (Bergersen, 1962; Bergersen and Wilson, 1959b). This hypothesis reflects the complex and highly integrated nature of the bacterial-plant interaction in the nodule, but still does not provide a specific role for the Co and Mo known to be necessary for fixation (Anderson, 1956; Delwiche and Johnson, 1961; Nicholas, 1963; Shaukat-Ahmed and Evans, 1961). Spectral changes at different oxygen tensions show that nodule haemoglobin has a very high affinity for oxygen in forming the addition complex (Appleby, 1962). This points to a possible further or alternative function for haemoglobin: the transfer of traces of oxygen from nitrogen-fixing centres, where oxygen might compete with nitrogen for the available reducing power, to the actively respiring bacteroids.

VI. THE PROBLEM OF INEFFECTIVENESS

Not all nodules fix nitrogen efficiently. The maximum rate of fixation per unit of nodular tissue is reasonably constant, but below this fixation can occur at any rate. The extent to which rate is affected by external conditions is considered in Chapter 11. Here only the factors intrinsic to the nodule will be considered.

The problem of ineffectiveness was first met in experiments on cross-inoculation which often showed that strains of bacteria nodulating a common group of hosts fixed nitrogen in association with some species but not others. The cross-inoculation groups may be subdivided on the N-fixing response of their constituent members. In the cowpea-soybean group many different subgroupings seem to be possible, depending on the particular isolates used to do the tests. *Vigna sinensis* itself seems to nodulate effectively with most strains and at the other extreme *Phaseolus lunatus* usually forms an ineffective association with isolates from other hosts (Allen and Allen, 1958).

The lupin group is of particular interest in that it has cross-inoculation links with the cowpea group, some species forming effective symbioses with isolates from the larger group. Thus the blue lupin (*L. digitatus*) is nodulated effectively by isolates from the indigenous W. Australian flora (mainly from the tribe Podalyrieae) whereas the yellow lupin (*L. luteus*) is not (Lange and Parker, 1960, 1961).

The medic group can be provisionally subdivided into four sections (Brockwell and Hely, 1961; Hely, 1957; Vincent, 1954) as shown in Table 1, with most species of *Medicago* and *Melilotus* belonging to the first subgroup. *M. Falcata* responds ineffectively with some, and *M. laciniata* with all strains isolated from the other species. *Trigonella* tends to fall into a separate subgroup. The species in the first group are arranged in a series (a-f) of decreasing effectiveness with strains generally effective on this group.

The clover group divides into two main sections (Table 2), for most strains effective on the white clover subgroup are ineffective on the subterranean clover subgroup, although a few strains are fully effective on

Table 1. Subdivision of the medic cross-inoculation group on the basis of similarity in nitrogen-fixing response.

Group 1
(a) *Medicago minima, M. sativa, Melilotus alba, Mel. officinalis.* (b) *Medicago rigidula* (?) (c) *M. praecox, M. tribuloides,* (d) *M. lupulina,* (e) *M. orbicularis,* (f) *M. arabica, M. denticulata, Melilotus indica.*

Group 2	Group 3	Group 4
Medicago falcata	*Medicago laciniata*	*Trigonella* spp.

Table 2. Subdivision of the clover cross-inoculation group on the basis of similarity in nitrogen-fixing response.

Group 1

Trifolium fragiferum, T. hirtum, T. hydbridum, T. patens, T. pratense, T. procumbens, T. repens. (T. dubium, T. meneghinianum, T. nigrescens, T. resupinatum)

Group 2

T. arvense, T. augustifolium, T. glomeratum, T. incarnatum, T. ornithopodoides, T. parviflorum, T. scabrum

Group 3

T. cheranganiense, T. ruppellianum, T. semipilosum, T. steudneri, T. tembense

Group 4

T. ambiguum

---

both hosts. *Trifolium ambiguum* is quite exceptional in mostly failing to nodulate with strains isolated from other species; its own strains form ineffective nodules on other hosts. *Trifolium* species of Central Africa also form a distinct subgroup which like *T. ambiguum* do not always nodulate with strains from other groups (Hely, 1957; Norris, 1959; Vincent, 1954; Nutman, unpublished data). Differences have also been described in the pea group, but with no clear pattern (Bjalfve, 1937; Virtanen and Hansen, 1932).

The *Lotus-Anthyllis* group (now united with the cowpea group) has two sections; strains effective with *Lotus corniculatus* tend to be ineffective with *L. uliginosus* and *vice versa* (Busko, 1959; Erdman and Means, 1949; Gavigan and Curran, 1962; Wright, 1955).

Mutual adaptation between host and bacteria leading to efficient nitrogen fixation may thus involve factors common to a group of genera, or restricted to a genus, or a species or even a variety. In general, strains of bacteria tend to be more effective on the host from which they were isolated than on other species, and, within a cross-inoculation group, hosts that show similar responses are in general more related ecologically than taxonomically.

The recent report that effectiveness, like virulence, is transformable by DNA preparations provide a new tool to investigate this problem. Not only have effective clover strains become ineffective after treatment with DNA from ineffective strains (Kleczkowska, 1961) but a strain from *Lupinus* has also been induced to nodulate *Medicago* and then by repeated transformation to become effective on the new host (Balassa, 1960). This claim awaits confirmation.

Most ineffective symbioses are characterised by many small nodules, which fail to grow to normal size because the degeneration that starts in the bacteroid region quickly spreads to the nodule meristem and stops its growth. Exceptionally, ineffective strains form a few large nodules in which the degeneration, starting in the bacteroid region, does not reach the growing point which consequently continues for some time to enlarge the nodule.

The incompatibility of which ineffectiveness is an expression may show itself soon after the bacteria are released from the infection thread, so that no bacteroids form, or it may be delayed so that the bacteroids are short-lived (Clarke and Tracey, 1956). More rarely, persistent bacteroid tissue is formed that is apparently normal but fixes no nitrogen (Bergersen, 1955). One kind of ineffectiveness is caused by the retention of the bacteria within the infection thread (Bergersen, 1957b). As noted above, all ineffective associations accumulate starch in the uninfected cell, a dextran in the infected cell and glycogen in the bacteroid. Whereas bacteroids are always associated with fixation, their presence is not an invariable sign of its effectiveness. A more distinctive feature of ineffectiveness than the absence of bacteroids is the absence of haemoglobin. That haemoglobin may be more closely associated with the fixing process than some of the functions of the bacteroid agrees with current views on the biochemistry of fixation.

VII. HOST FACTORS AFFECTING FIXATION

Even with fully effective and stable strains of nodule bacteria, the amount of nitrogen fixed by individual nodulated plants may vary. This is more noticeable with out-pollinating species, which tend to be more variable in other respects, and for the same genetic reason. As with differences of bacterial origin, this host-determined variation covers the full range of response.

A study of the hereditable defects which reduce or prevent fixation in red clover, suggest that many genes may act to lower its total efficiency but that complete ineffectiveness is more often associated with mutation at single gene loci. Five simply inherited, recessive and non-allelic factors for ineffectiveness are known (Bergersen and Nutman, 1957; Nutman, 1954, 1957, 1959b, and unpublished data). One of these seems to be entirely specific with respect to bacterial strain, in that it gives the symbiotic response appropriate to each bacterial strain excepting only the strain with which the original selection and breeding work had been done. The second factor for ineffectiveness depresses or prevents an effective response with most bacteria, and the remaining three factors are partially strain-dependent, giving ineffective responses with some strains and effective or mixed responses with others. Bacterial-strain variants have been isolated that are effective with the first mentioned gene but not as yet with the others.

Nodule development on plants homozygous for one or the other of two of these genes has been studied in detail. Both genes prevent bacteroid formation and haemoglobin synthesis, but by different means. One prevents the intracellular rod-shaped bacteria from becoming transformed into bacteroids; the other prevents the multiplication of the rod form in the host cell, at the same time causing the host cells to divide abnormally, and the new cell walls so formed serve to cut off the infected cells from the rest of the nodule. With both homozygotes all the earlier stages of nodule development are normal. It is evident that the incompatibility giving the abnormal small-celled (tumourised) structure arises earlier in development than that preventing bacteroid formation.

Genetic studies with white clover, which is also an obligatory cross-fertilizing species, shows a broadly similar spectrum of variation (Jones, 1960), but in subterranean clover (*T. subterraneum*) very little natural variation in symbiotic effectiveness has been found. This is probably because its cleistogamous habit promotes homozygosity and because the very low levels of soil nitrogen in the regions, where the varieties used in the genetic studies had arisen, will have tended to eliminate low-fixing variants (Nutman, 1961).

Varietal differences in symbiotic effectiveness have also been described in species of *Pisum, Medicago, Vicia, Arachis,* and *Centrosema* (Aughtry, 1948; Bowen and Kennedy, 1961; Erdman and Means, 1953; Gibson, 1962; Saubert, 1958).

VIII. FACTORS CONTROLLING NODULE SIZE AND ABUNDANCE

In red clover, as in all hosts yet studied, average nodule size and abundance are inversely related; large nodules tend to be sparse and small nodules abundant, whether comparison is made between effective and ineffective symbioses, or among those showing identical fixing capacities. Both bacterial strain and host species, or variety, affect nodule size and number. In red clover and subterranean clover the genetic basis of differences in size and number is complex (Nutman, 1958) and selection will readily produce abundantly and sparsely nodulating lines. In red clover, which is very heterozygous, the relation between average nodule size and number is only broadly inverse with an appreciable proportion of plants bearing few small nodules (but none with many large nodules).

In contrast, subterranean clover, with little plant-to-plant variation, shows a much more clearly defined relation between nodule size and abundance. When size is measured as nodule length, this relation is hyperbolic whether a single variety is examined, which is inoculated with a range of bacterial strains forming few or many nodules, or whether host lines of different susceptibilities are considered.

The amount of nitrogen fixed in a nodule is closely related to the total amount and duration in time of the bacteroid-containing tissue (Bergersen, 1961; Chen and Thornton, 1940). Nodule length in these nodules is directly related to nodule volume, so the hyperbolic relation between mean nodule length and number merely expresses the fact that the total amount of nitrogen-fixing tissue is the same in plants with many or few nodules.

There must obviously be some means whereby the nodulated plant produces enough fixing tissues for its needs and that this controlling mechanism embraces both nodule size and number. Studies on the physiology of nodule formation suggest that the control operates through the normal control of root development (Nutman, 1958). Nodules, like lateral roots, arise at sites pre-disposed to meristematic activity and subject to the same genetic and physiological control. This control appears to act through the existing growing points of the root which collectively tend to suppress the development of new growing centres. The nodule takes

part in this controlling activity. Large nodules are more inhibitory because they have more active meristems, and as nodules arise like laterals
at susceptible sites, large nodules inhibit further nodule initiation more
than do small nodules. Conversely, the many small nodules found on
other roots reflect feeble inhibition by small and ephemeral meristems.
This interpretation of the nodule pattern and its control is supported by
genetical studies linking the inheritance of nodulation and rooting habits,
and by experiments on the effect of delayed inoculation and nodule and
root excision (Nutman, 1948, 1949b, 1952).

IX. CONCLUDING REMARKS ON LEGUME SYMBIOSIS

Nitrogen fixation in the legume nodule is the result of a very complex and highly integrated process of development, involving at all stages
interactions between bacterial and host components, some of which are
controlled by single genes. Many of these stages, if not all, are subject to
modifications that affect, to a greater or less degree, the efficiency of the
fixing process or prevent it altogether. Thus root hair infection may fail
because of the bacteria becoming avirluent or because of specific mutation
in the host. The normal response to intracellular invasion may be
changed as in red clover homozygous for the gene for tumourization, or
the normal transformation of the rods into bacteroids may be inhibited.
Even if all these stages are completed the symbiosis may not function
effectively, or it may end prematurely by senescence. These different kinds
of incompatibility reflect failures or blockages in metabolic processes
about which nothing is at present known.

Complexity is not confined to the way in which the fixing system is established, but is also found in its coordination with the changing demands of the host for nitrogen. In clover the controlling mechanism
links infection with nodule growth and the development of the host's
root system and through this with the growth of the whole plant.

X. THE ROOT NODULES OF NONLEGUMINOUS PLANTS

Except in the Leguminosae, the root-nodulating habit is uncommon;
of 105 natural orders of higher plants, only 10 have species with root-
nodules, and of these, 8 show some slight taxonomic relationship, as indicated in Fig. 3—phylogenetic arrangement of families after Hutchinson
(1959). Nitrogen is fixed in most of the nonlegume nodule-bearing plants
and in general these are plants inhabiting soils deficient in nitrogen. For
example, *Alnus* and *Casuarina* occur along watercourses, *Myrica* in bogs,
and *Ceanothus* and *Coriaria* in poor scrubland or as colonisers of scree
slopes (Bond, 1958; Crocker, 1955; Godwin, 1956). Such plants probably
contribute something to soil nitrogen but none has been exploited in agriculture. So little is known about the nodules of Gymnosperms (McLuckie,
1922, 1923), Pteridophytes (Life, 1904) and about leaf-nodulating plants
(Hanada, 1954), or about certain other pioneer plants reported to fix nitro-

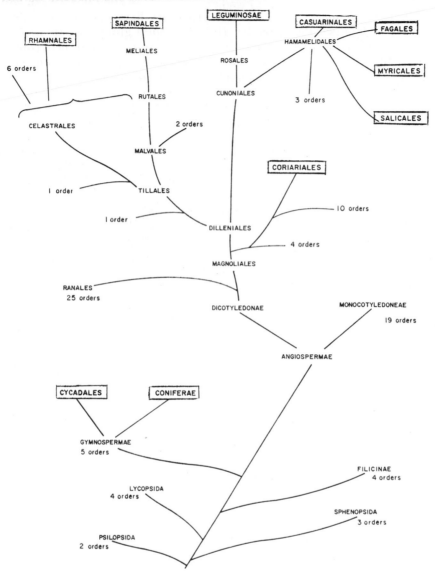

Fig. 3. The orders of nodulating plants.

gen, presumably by some microbial association, that they will not be here considered (Stevenson, 1953, 1959).

The remainder fall into two groups, the *Alnus-Elaeagnus* group and the *Myrica-Casuarina* group, that are distinguished by nodule morphology and structure, and cross-inoculation relationships (Bond, 1962, 1963; Hawker and Fraymouth, 1951), although all species of *Coriaria* may not be nodulated by the same organism (Furneau, 1959).

The causal organism in both groups is thought to be an actinomycete or a plasmodial fungus (Hawker and Fraymouth, 1951; Niewiarowska,

1959, 1961; Pommer, 1959), and its properties have only been studied indirectly (Quispel, 1960). In the *Alnus-Elaeagnus* group infections seem to be through the root hairs which are often grossly deformed (Bond, 1963). In structure each nodule lobe consists of four parts: an uninfected apex, a zone in which the endophyte is in the plasmodial stage, a zone containing vesicles, and a degenerating zone. Structures resembling infection threads of legumes have been described. Nodules are generally compound and perennial and often attain a very large size. Hippophae cross inoculates with both *Shepherdia* and *Elaeagnus,* but not with members of the other group. The nodules of the *Myrica-Casuarina* group have a distinctive morphology given by the upwardly directed growth of the nodule lobes and by the development of rootlets therefrom. The internal structures of the nodules of the two groups are similar.

It was soon established that fixation of nitrogen takes place in the nodules, later to be confirmed by $^{15}N_2$ studies (Bond, 1963; Virtanen, 1954). The process of fixation in legume and nonlegume nodules is almost certainly similar; Mo and Co are essential co-factors and haemoglobin is present (Becking, 1961; Bond and Hewitt, 1961; Davenport, 1960; Hewitt, 1961). The rate of fixation on a nodule weight basis is similar (Bond, 1958; MacConnell and Bond, 1957; Stewart, 1962), and is in general similarly affected by external conditions (Bond, 1960, 1961, 1963; Stewart and Bond, 1961). Fixation by the nonlegume nodule stops when the nodule is removed from the root (though more slowly than with legume nodules), and does not occur in nodule homogenates. As with legumes, metabolic studies suggest that the process of fixation is reductive (Bond, 1959). The site of fixation within the nodule has not yet been determined.

The recent report (Niewiarowska, 1961) of the isolation of the endophyte of *Alnus* in pure culture should do much to extend the critical study of this interesting group of nodulated plants.

LITERATURE CITED

Allen, O. N., and Allen, E. K. 1940. Response of the peanut plant to inoculation with rhizobia, with special reference to the morphological development of the nodules. Bot. Gaz. 102:121-142.

Allen, E. K., and Allen, O. N. 1958. Biological aspects of symbiotic nitrogen fixation. Encycl. Plant Phys. 8:43-105.

Allen, E. K., and Allen, O. N. 1961. Nitrogen fixation. The scope of nodulation in the Leguminosae. Recent Advances Bot. 585-588.

Almon, L. 1933. Concerning the reproduction of bacteroids. Zbl. Bakt., II Abt. 87:289-297.

Anderson, A. J. 1956. The role of molybdenum in plant nutrition. *In* Inorganic Nitrogen Metabolism. ed. W. D. McElroy and Bentley Glass. The Johns Hopkins Press. 3-58.

Appleby, C. A. 1962. The oxygen equilibrium of leghaemoglobin. Biochim. Biophys. Acta 60:226-235.

Appleby, C. A. and Bergersen, F. J. 1958. Cytochromes of Rhizobium. Nature, Lond. 182:1174.

Aprison, M. H., and Burris, R. H. 1952. Time course of fixation of N_2 by excised soybean nodules. Science 115:264-265.

Arora, N. 1954. Morphological development of the root and stem nodules of *Aeschynomene indica* L. Phytomorph. 4:211-216.

Arora, N. 1955. Origin and developmental morphology of the root nodules on *Cicer arietinum* L. Proc. Indian Sci. Cong. Assoc. 42:220.

Aughtry, J. D. 1948. Effect of genetic factors in *Medicago* in symbiosis with *Rhizobium*. Cornell Univ. Agr. Exp. Sta. Mem. 280, 18 pp.

Bach, M. K. 1957. Hydrazine and biological nitrogen fixation. Biochim. Biophys. Acta 26:104.

Balassa, R. 1954. Transformationsmechanismen der Rhizobein. Acta Microbiol. 2:51-78.

Balassa, R. 1960. Transformation of a strain of *Rhizobium lupini*. Nature, Lond. 188: 246-247.

Bauer, N. 1960. A probable free-radical mechanism for symbiotic nitrogen fixation. Nature, Lond. 188:471.

Becking, J. H. 1961. A requirement of molybdenum for the symbiotic nitrogen fixation in Alder (*Alnus glutinosa* Gaertn.) Plant and Soil 15:217-227.

Beijerinck, M. W. 1888. Die Bakterien der Papilionaceenknöllchen. Bot. Ztg. 46:726-735, 741-750, 757-771, 781-790, 797-804.

Bergersen, F. J. 1955. The cytology of bacteroids from root nodules of subterranean clover. J. Gen. Microbiol. 13:411-419.

Bergersen, F. J. 1957a. The occurrence of a previously unobserved polysaccharide in immature infected cells of root nodules of *Trifolium ambiguum* M. Bieb. and other members of the Trifolieae. Aust. J. Biol. Sci. 10:17-24.

Bergersen, F. J. 1957b. The structure of ineffective root nodules of legumes: An unusual new type of ineffectiveness, and an appraisal of present knowledge. Aust. J. Biol. Sci. 10:233-242.

Bergersen, F. J. 1960. Biochemical pathways in legume root nodule nitrogen fixation. Bact. Rev. 24:246-250.

Bergersen, F. J. 1961. The growth of Rhizobium in synthetic media. Aust. J. Biol. Sci. 14:349-360.

Bergersen, F. J. 1961. Haemoglobin content of legume root nodules. Biochim. Biophys. Acta 50:576-578.

Bergersen, F. J. 1962. Oxygenation of leghaemoglobin in soybean root nodules in relation to external oxygen tensions. Nature, Lond. 194:1059-1061.

Bergersen, F. J. and Briggs, M. J. 1958. Studies on the bacterial component of soybean root nodules; cytology and organisation of the host tissue. J. Gen. Microbiol. 19:482-490.

Bergersen, F. J., and Nutman, P. S. 1957. Symbiotic effectiveness in nodulated red clover. IV. The influence of the host factors *i*, and *ie* upon nodule structure and cytology. Heredity 11:175-184.

Bergersen, F. J., and Wilson, P. W. 1959a. The location of newly fixed nitrogen in soy nodules. Bact. Proc. p. 25.

Bergersen, F. J., and Wilson, P. W. 1959b. Spectrophotometric studies of the effects of nitrogen on soybean nodule extracts. Proc. Nat. Acad. Sci. 45:1641-1646.

Bjalfve, G. 1937. Baljväxternas rotknölar hos olika sorter baljväxternas kvavehalt samt deras kvävehushallning i akerjerden. Medd. Centr. Anst. Försöksv Jordlr. Stockh. No. 455., (1935)

Blom, J. 1931. Ein Versuch, die chemischen Vorgange bei der Assimilation des moleculaeren stickstoffs durch Mikroorganismen zu erklaren. Zbl. Bakt. 84:60-86.

Bond, G. 1958. Symbiotic nitrogen fixation by non-legumes. *In* Nutrition of the Legumes. ed. E. G. Hallsworth. Butterworths Sci. Publ. London.

Bond, G. 1959. Fixation of nitrogen in non-legume root-nodule plants. Symp. Soc. Exp. Biol. 13:59-72.

Bond, G. 1960. Inhibition of nitrogen fixation in non-legume root-nodules by hydrogen and carbon monoxide. J. Exp. Bot. 11:91-97.

Bond, G. 1961. The oxygen relation of nitrogen fixation in root nodules. Z. allg. Mikrobiol. 1:93-99.

Bond, G. 1962. Fixation of nitrogen in *Coriarin myrtifolia*. Nature, Lond. 193:1103-1104.

Bond, G. 1963. The root nodules of non-leguminous Angiosperms. Symp. Soc. Gen. Microbiol. 13:72-91.

Bond, G., and Hewitt, E. J. 1961. Molybdenum and the fixation of nitrogen in Myrica root nodules. Nature, Lond. 190:1033-1034.

Bowen, G. D., and Kennedy, M. K. 1961. Heritable variation in nodulation of *Centrosema pubescens* Benth. Qd. J. Agr. Sci. 18:161-170.

Boussingault, M. 1838. Recherches chimiques sur la végétation, entreprises dans le but d'examiner si les plantes prennent de l'azote à l'atmosphere. Ann. Chem. Phys. 2nd Ser. 67:5-54.

Brockwell, J., and Hely, F. W. 1961. Symbiotic characteristics of *Rhizobium meliloti* from the brown acid soils of the Macquarie region of New South Wales. Aust. J. Agr. Res. 12:630-643.

Brunchorst, J. 1885. Über die Knöllchen an den Leguminosenwurzeln. Ber. dtsch. bot. Ges. 3:241-257.

Busko, J. 1959. Symbiotic effectiveness and some physiological properties of the nodule bacteria of *Lotus* and *Anthyllus*. Acta Microbiol. Polonica 8:303.

Burris, R. H. 1956. Studies on the mechanism of biological nitrogen fixation. *In* Inorganic Nitrogen Metabolism. Ed. W. D. McElroy and Bentley Glass. Johns Hopkins Press, Baltimore. pp. 316-343.

De Candolle, A. 1884. Origin of Cultivated Plants. Kegan Paul. Trench & Co. London. 468 pp.

Chen, H. K., and Thornton, H. G. 1940. The structure of ineffective nodules and its effect on nitrogen fixation. Proc. Roy. Soc. B. 127:208.

Clark, F. E. 1957. Nodulation responses of two near isogenic lines of the soybean. Can. J. Microbiol. 3:113-123.

Clarke, P. H., and Tracey, M. V. 1956. The occurrence of chitinase in some bacteria. J. Gen. Microbiol. 14:188-196.

Crocker, R. L., and Major, J. 1955. Soil development in relation to vegetation and surface age at Glacier Bay, Alaska. J. Ecol. 43:427-448.

Dart, P. J., and Mercer, F. V. 1963. Development of the bacteroid in the root nodule of Barrel Medic (*Medicago tribuloides* Desr.) and subterranean clover (*Trifolium subterraneum* L.). Archiv. für Mikrobiol. 46:382-401.

Davenport, H. E. 1960. Haemoglobin in the root nodules of *Casuarina cunninghamiana*. Nature, Lond. 186:653-654.

Delwiche, C. C., Johnson, C. M., and Reisenaur, H. M. 1961. Influence of cobalt on nitrogen fixation by Medicago. Plant Phys. 36:73-78.

Donald, C. M. 1960. The impact of cheap nitrogen. J. Aust. Inst. Agr. Sci. 26:319-338.

Elkan, G. H. 1962. Comparison of rhizosphere microorganisms of genetically related nodulating and non-nodulating soybean lines. Can. J. Microbiol. 8:79-87.

Erdman, L. W., and Means, U. M. 1949. Strains of Rhizobium effective on the trefoils, *Lotus corniculatus* and *Lotus uliginosus*. Soil Sci. Soc. Amer. Proc. 14:170-175.

Erdman, L. W., and Means, U. M. 1953. Strain variation of *Rhizobium meliloti* on three varieties of *Medicago sativa*. Agron. J. 45:625-629.

Fåhraeus, G. 1957. The infection of clover root hairs by nodule bacteria, studied by a simple glass slide technique. J. Gen. Microbiol. 16:374-381.

Fåhraeus, G., and Ljunggren, H. 1959. The possible significance of pectic enzymes in root-hair infection by nodule bacteria. Plant. Physiol. 12:145-154.

Falk, J. E., Appleby, C. A., and Porra, R. J. 1959. The nature, function and biosynthesis of the haem compounds and porphyrins of legume root nodules. Symp. Soc. Exp. Biol. 13 p. 73-86.

Food and Agriculture Organisation of the United Nations. 1948, 1952, 1959. Production Yearbook. Vol. 1, 1948; Vol. 6, 1952; Vol. 13, 1959. F.A.O. Rome.

Forsyth, W. G. C., Hayward, A. C., and Roberts, J. B. 1958. Occurrence of poly-β-hydroxybutyric acid in aerobic gram negative bacteria. Nature, Lond. 182:800-801.

Fred, E. B., Baldwin, I. L., and McCoy, E. 1932. Root Nodule Bacteria and Leguminous Plants. Univ. Wisconsin Press.

Furneau, T. E. 1959. The structure of the root nodules of *Ceanothus sanguineus* and *Ceanothus velutinus* with special reference to the endophyte. Amer. J. Bot. 46:698-703.

Gams, H. 1926. Leguminosae. *In* Hegi's Illustrierte Flora von Mitteleuropa 4: Munich.

Gavigan, J. C., and Curran, P. L. 1962. Experiments with the genera *Lotus* and *Anthyllis* and their associated Rhizobia. Sci. Proc. Roy. Dublin Soc. B. 1:37-46.

Gibson, A. H. 1962. Genetic variation in the effectiveness of nodulation of lucerne varieties. Aust. J. Agr. Res. 13:388-399.

LITERATURE CITED

381

Gier, H. T. 1947. Intracellular bacteroids in the cockroach (*Periplaneta americana* Linn.) J. Bact. 53:173-189.

Godwin, H. 1956. The History of the British Flora. Cambridge Univ. Press. 383 pp.

Golebiowska, J. 1960. The formation of bacteroids and involution forms by *Rhizobium meliloti* and *Rh. trifolii*. Postepy Nauk Rolniczych Zesry Problemowe 20:151-159.

Gras, N. S. B. 1940. A History of Agriculture. 2nd ed. F. S. Crofts & Co. New York.

Haack, A. 1961. Uber den Ursprung der Wurzelknollchen von *Ornithopus sativus* L. und *Lupinus albus* L. Z. Bakt. II. 114:577-589.

Hamilton, P. B., Shug, A. L., and Wilson, P. W. 1957. Spectrophotometric examination of hydrogenase and nitrogenase in soybean nodules and *Azotobacter*. Proc. Nat. Acad. Sci. Wash. 1954. 43:297.

Hanada, K. 1954. Über die Blattknöten der *Ardisia*-arten. Isolierung der Bakterien und ihre stickstoffbindende Kraft in Reinkultur. Jap. J. Bot. 14:235-268.

Harris, J. O., Allen, E. K., and Allen, O. N. 1949. Morphological development of nodules on *Sesbania grandiflora* Poir. with reference to the origin of nodule rootlets. Amer. J. Bot. 36:651.

Hawker, L. E., and Fraymouth, J. 1951. A re-investigation of the root nodules of *Elaeagnus, Hippophae, Alnus* and *Myrica* with special reference to the morphology and life-histories of the causative organisms. J. Gen. Microbiol. 5:369.

Hellriegel, H., and Wilfarth, H. 1888. Untersuchungen über die Stickstoffnahrung der Gramineen und Leguminosen. Beilagehelft zu der Ztschr. Ver. Rübenzucker-Industrie Deutschen Reichs. 234.

Hely, F. W. 1957. Symbiotic variation in *Trifolium ambiguum* M. Bieb. with special reference to the nature of resistance. Aust. J. Biol. Sci. 10:1-16.

Hewitt, E. J., and Bond, G. 1961. Molybdenum and the fixation of nitrogen in *Casuarina* and *Alnus* root nodules. Plant and Soil 14:159-175.

Hughes, D. Q., and Vincent, J. M. 1952. Serological studies of the root nodule bacteria. III. Tests of neighbouring strains of the same species. Proc. Linn. Soc. N.S.W. 67:142-152.

Hutchinson, J. 1959. The families of flowering plants. Vol. 1. Dicotyledons. 2nd ed. Clarendon Press, Oxford. 510 pp.

Jones, G. D. 1960. Investigations into the symbiotic relationships between white clover and the nodule bacteria of the species *Rhizobium trifolii*. Report Welsh Plant Breeding Sta. 39-40.

Jordan, D. C. 1962. The bacteroids of the genus Rhizobium. Bact. Rev. 26:119-141.

Kefford, N. P., Brockwell, J., and Zwar, J. A. 1960. The symbiotic synthesis of auxin by legumes and nodule bacteria and its role in nodule development. Aust. J. Soil Sci. 13:456-467.

Kleczkowska, J. 1961. Transformation studies on *Rhizobium trifolii*. Rep. Rothamsted Exp. Sta. 78.

Klein, D. T., and Klein, R. M. 1953. Transmittance of tumour inducing ability to avirulent crown gall and related bacteria. J. Bact. 66:220-228.

Lange, R. T., and Alexander, M. 1961. Anomalous infections by Rhizobium. Can. J. Microbiol. 7:959-961.

Lange, R. T., and Parker, C. A. 1960. The symbiotic performance of lupin bacteria under glasshouse and field conditions. Plant and Soil 13:137-146.

Lange, R. T., and Parker, C. A. 1961. Effective nodulation of *Lupinus digitatus* by native rhizobia of South-Western Australia. Plant and Soil 15:193-198.

Life, A. C. 1904. The tubercle-like roots of *Cycas revoluta*. Bot. Gaz. 31:265-271.

Ljunggren, H. 1961. Transfer of virulence in *Rhizobium trifolii*. Nature, Lond. 191:623.

Ljunggren, H., and Fåhraeus, G. 1961. The role of polygalacturonase in root-hair invasion by nodule bacteria. J. Gen. Microbiol. 26:521-528.

Lynch, D. L., and Sears, O. H. 1952. Nodulation of legumes and nitrogen fixation. 1. A new tool for measurement. Abst. Amer. Soc. Agron. pp. 68-69.

MacConnell, J. T., and Bond, G. 1957. A comparison of the effect of combined nitrogen on nodulation in non-legumes and legumes. Plant and Soil 8:378.

Magee, W. E., and Burris, R. H. 1954. Fixation of N_2^{15} by excised nodules. Plant Physiol. 29:199-200.

McCoy, E. 1932. Infection by *Bact. radicicola* in relation to the microchemistry of the host's cell walls. Proc. Roy. Soc. B. 110:514-533.

McLuckie, J. 1922. The apogeotropic roots of *Macrozamia spiralis* and their physiological significance. Proc. Linn. Soc. N.S.W. 47:319-328.

McLuckie, J. 1923. A contribution to the morphology and physiology of root nodules of *Podocarpus spirulosa* and *P. elata*. Proc. Linn. Soc. N.S.W. 48:82-93.

Milovidov, M. P. 1928. Recherches sur les tubercules du lupin. Rev. Gén. Bot. 40:192-205.

Morley, F. H. W. 1961. Subterranean clover. *In* Advances in Agronomy 13:58-123.

Mosse, B. (1964) Electron-microscope studies of nodule developments in some clover species. J. Gen. Microbiol. 36:49-66.

Nicholas, D. J. D. 1963. The biochemistry of nitrogen fixation. Symp. Soc. Gen. Microbiol. 13:92-124.

Niewiarowska, J. 1959. Symbiosis in *Hippophae rhamnoides*. Acta Microbiol. Polonica 8:289-294.

Niewiarowska, J. 1961. Morphologie et physiologie des *Actinomycetes* symbiotique des *Hippophae*. Acta Microbiol. Polonica 10:271-286.

Norris, D. O. 1959. Rhizobium affinities of African species of *Trifolium*. Emp. J. Exp. Agr. 27:87-97.

Nutman, P. S. 1948. Physiological studies on nodule formation. 1. The relation between nodulation and lateral root formation in red clover. Ann. Bot. N.S. 12:81-96.

Nutman, P. S. 1949a. Nuclear and cytoplasmic inheritance of resistance to infection by nodule bacteria in red clover. Heredity 3: 263-271.

Nutman, P. S. 1949b. Physiological studies on nodule formation. II. The influence of delayed inoculation on the rate of nodulation in red clover. Ann. Bot. N.S. 13:261-283.

Nutman, P. S. 1952. Studies on the physiology of nodule formation. III. Experiments on the excision of root tips and nodules. Ann. Bot. N.S. 16:79-101.

Nutman, P. S. 1954. Symbiotic effectiveness in nodulated red clover. II. A major gene for ineffectiveness in the host. Heredity 8:47-60.

Nutman, P. S. 1957. Symbiotic effectiveness in nodulated red clover. III. Further studies on inheritance of ineffectiveness in the host. Heredity 11:157-173.

Nutman, P. S. 1958. The physiology of nodule formation. *In* Nutrition of the Legumes. ed. E. G. Hallsworth. Butterworths Sci. Publ. London, pp. 87-107.

Nutman, P. S. 1959a. Some observations on root-hair infection by nodule bacteria. J. Exp. Bot. 10:250-263.

Nutman, P. S. 1959b. Sources of incompatability affecting nitrogen fixation in legume symbiosis. Symp. Soc. Exp. Biol. 13:42-58.

Nutman, P. S. 1961. Variation in symbiotic effectiveness in subterranean clover (*Trifolium subterraneum* L.) Aust. J. Agr. Res. 12:212-226.

Nutman, P. S. 1962. The relation between root hair infection by *Rhizobium* and nodulation in *Trifolium* and *Vicia*. Proc. Roy. Soc. B. 156:122-137.

Parker, C. A., and Scott, P. B. 1960. The effect of oxygen on nitrogen fixation by Azotobacter. Biochim. Biophys. Acta 38:230-238.

Pate, J. S. 1961. Perennial nodules on native legumes in the British Isles. Nature, Lond. 192:376-377.

Pommer, E. H. 1959. Über die Isolierung des Endophyten aus den Wurzelknöllchen *Alnus glutinosa* Gaerta und über erfolgreiche Re-Infektionsversuche. Ber. Deutsch. Bot. Gesell. 72:138-150.

Quispel, A. 1960. Symbiotic nitrogen fixation in non-leguminous plants. V. The growth requirements of the endophyte of *Alnus glutinosa*. Acta Bot. Neerlandia 9:380-396.

Raggio, M., and Raggio, N. 1962. Root nodules. Ann. Rev. Plant Phys., 13:109-128.

Richmond, J. E., Salomon, K., and Caplin, S. 1954. Biosynthesis of haemin in soy-bean nodule homogenates. Nature, Lond. 174:35.

Roberts, E. R. 1959. Some observations on the chemistry of biological nitrogen fixation. Symp. Soc. Exp. Biol. 13:24-41.

Rovira, A. D. 1959. Root excretions in relation to the rhizosphere effect. IV. Influence of plant species, age of plant, light, temperature and calcium nutrition on exudation. Plant and Soil 11:53-64.

Saubert, S. 1958. Strain variation and host specificity of Rhizobium. 1. *Rhizobium leguminosarum*. S. Afr. J. Agr. Sci. 1:451-455.

Schaede, E. 1940. Die Knöllchen der adventiven Wasserwurzeln von *Neptunia oleracea* und ihre Bakteriensymbiose. Planta 31:1-21.

Seeger, J. R. 1961. Effects d'une fumure azotée sur la nodulation et la rendement de l'arachide. Bull. Inst. Agron. Gembloux 29:197-218.

Shaukat-Ahmed., and Evans, H. J. 1961. The essentiality of cobalt for soybean plants grown under symbiotic conditions. Proc. Nat. Acad. Sci. Wash. 47:24-36.

Spector, W. S. 1956. Handbook of Biological Data. Sanders. Philadelphia and London.

Stevenson, G. B. 1953. Bacterial symbiosis in some New Zealand plants. Ann. Bot. N.S. 17:343-345.

Stevenson, G. B. 1959. Nitrogen fixation by non-nodulated seed plants. Ann. Bot. N.S. 23:622-635.

Stewart, W. D. P. 1962. A quantitative study of fixation and transfer of nitrogen in *Alnus*. J. Exp. Bot. 13:250-256.

Stewart, W. D. P., and Bond, G. 1961. The effect of ammonium nitrogen on fixation of elemental nitrogen in *Alnus* and *Myrica*. Plant and Soil 14:347-359.

Turchin, F. W. 1956. The role of mineral biological nitrogen fixation in the agriculture of the U.S.S.R. Pochvovedenie 6:15-29.

Vincent, J. M. 1954. The root-nodule bacteria of pasture legumes. Proc. Linn. Soc. N.S.W. 79:1-32.

Virtanen, A. I. 1947. The biology and chemistry of nitrogen fixation by legume bacteria. Biol. Rev. Camb. Phil. Soc. 22:239-269.

Virtanen, A. I., and Hausen, S. 1932. Tutkimuksia palkokasvibakteereilla ja kasveilla. XI. Eri bakteerirotujen tehokkundesta. Contr. Biochem. Inst. No. 1. 1.

Virtanen, A. I., Moisio, T., Allison, R. M., and Burris, R. H. 1954. Fixation of molecular nitrogen by excised nodules of the Alder. Acta Chem. Scand. 8:1730-1731.

White, R. O., Nilssen-Leissner, G., and Trumble, H. C. 1953. Legumes in agriculture. F.A.O. Rome. 367 pp.

Williams, L. F., and Lynch, D. L. 1954. Inheritance of a non-nodulating character in the soybean. Agron. J. 46:28-29.

Wilson, P. W. 1940. The Biochemistry of Symbiotic Nitrogen Fixation. Univ. Wisconsin Press. 302 pp.

Wright, M. J. 1955. The influence of several strains of Rhizobium upon the growth of some species of Lotus. Agron. Abst. 47:69.

Chapter 11

Environmental Factors in the Fixation of Nitrogen by the Legume

J. M. VINCENT

University of Sydney
Sydney, N.S.W., Australia

I. INTRODUCTION

Environmental factors can affect the successful establishment of an effective symbiosis between rhizobia and their hosts at any or all of three stages. They may: (1) affect the occurrence, growth, and survival of the root-nodule bacteria; (2) modify nodule formation; (3) affect the functioning of the formed nodule.

Failure to separate the stage at which establishment of the symbiosis has been blocked or modified has been responsible for a good deal of uncertainty concerning the operation of environmental factors. Particularly, investigators have often failed to determine whether rhizobial survival was involved; partly reflecting difficulties in methodology. Too large a part of the work that has been done is of a kind that sows seed, with or without inoculation, varies conditions and records presence or absence of nodules. This does not, of course, distinguish between factors modifying the occurrence of rhizobia, and factors that control the more intimate acts of invasion and nodule maturation.

In this chapter the aim will be first to deal with a range of environmental factors and to distinguish, as far as possible, the stages at which they operate. Consideration will be restricted to effects that are specific to the legume-rhizobium association so as not to extend the account unduly in the direction of general plant physiology and nutrition. The second half will consider the practical question of legume seed inoculation. To keep the article to a reasonable size, no attempt will be made to cover the developing literature of the nonleguminous nitrogen-fixing plants (but see several recent accounts: Allen and Allen, 1958; Bond, 1958; Norris, 1962). Quoted literature will be selective, rather than comprehensive, particularly where the information has already been covered in classical accounts (Fred, Baldwin, and McCoy, 1932; Wilson, 1940) and general reviews (Allen and Allen, 1950, 1958; Nutman, 1956). More specialized reviews have also been utilized (Nutman, 1958; Vincent, 1954a, 1962a), including those that have paid particular attention to the problems of the tropical legumes (Andrew, 1962; Bonnier, 1960; Bryan, 1962; Henzell and Norris, 1962; Norris, 1956, 1958a, 1959b, 1962).

II. OPERATION OF ENVIRONMENTAL FACTORS

A. General Considerations

1. OCCURRENCE AND SURVIVAL OF RHIZOBIA OUTSIDE THE HOST

The ability of rhizobia to survive outside the host is of considerable importance, affecting their persistence in the soil, in culture, and on the inoculated seed (Vincent, 1958a). Australian workers particularly have had their attention directed this way by the frequency with which the field result has in their experience depended on the operation of such factors. Thus, they have often been concerned with applying a relatively large number of rhizobia to the seed in the first instance (this in turn leading to the setting of moderately severe minimal standards) and with ameliorating the environment of the inoculated seed. For similar reasons they have adopted a conservative approach toward pre-inoculation: an attitude that seems sufficiently justified by recent North American experience, which has in turn directed the attention of workers more toward the quantitative aspects of rhizobial survival.

a. Determination of Rhizobial Numbers in Complex Populations

Progress in ecological studies requires the quantitative recovery of rhizobia from mixtures containing many other microorganisms. This involves an indirect method that utilizes the organism's ability to nodulate a specific host ("plant-dilution" count), and expresses the result as the reciprocal of the limiting nodulating dilution (Wilson, 1926). More precisely it can be based on one of several "most-probable-number" procedures that provide both a better estimate and an expression of reliability. Such methods are, of course, more demanding of time and materials than are direct plate counts (which are out of the question with the soil and rhizosphere), and it will often be necessary to accept a considerable error in the estimate in order to cover a wide enough range with sufficient samples or treatments (Date and Vincent, 1962; Tuzimura and Watanabe, 1961). Some samples of seed are sufficiently clean to permit plate counts but others carry enough contaminants to demand "plant-dilution" counts, especially when rhizobial numbers are low.

More serious in the application of the plant-dilution method is the situation where the expected rhizobia are so few as to necessitate the addition of relatively concentrated soil suspension, or soil itself, to the test vessel. Warnings of consequent difficulties are given when test plants exposed to less diluted samples fail to nodulate at the same time as a greater dilution is positive. It seems likely, in these circumstances, that the mixed microflora of the test sample has established a condition inimical to nodulation. Death of rhizobia need not be the reason since rhizobia have in fact been obtained from test vessels where nodulation had failed to occur (Thompson, unpub.). Precise data on the validity or otherwise of methods for estimating low numbers of rhizobia in soil are badly wanted, together with means of improving the estimates.

Meanwhile, until more direct information comes to hand, we are often faced with the unsatisfactory alternative of projecting conclusions based on laboratory experiments, necessarily in simpler situations, to the complex situation of the soil itself. This is nowhere better illustrated than in the unresolved doubts as to the extent and nature of interbiotic antagonisms in soil and rhizosphere. Relatedly, one is struck by the hiatus between what we know about the ability of some rhizobial cells to survive in sterile soil and what we would like to know about the factors that determine persistence in the complex situation of normal soil (Allen and Allen, 1958; Fred et al., 1932; Jensen, 1961).

2. NODULE FORMATION

The presence of numerous specific rhizobia in the rhizosphere does not guarantee that the process commencing with invasion of root-hairs, and culminating in the formation of a morphologically recognizable nodule, will take place. Some environmental factors (for example soil temperature, combined nitrogen or calcium status of the plant) can exercise a potent influence in this regard.

3. NITROGEN FIXATION

The amount of nitrogen fixed under practical conditions is often hard to determine but will obviously vary with such factors as species of legume, the efficiency of its plant-rhizobium association and the extent to which environmental conditions permit the symbiotic potential to be realized. A good deal of data and original references are given in recent reviews (Allen and Allen, 1958; Bryan, 1962; Donald, 1960; Henzell and Norris, 1962). Estimates of the proportion of legume nitrogen due to fixation in normal fertile soils are commonly taken as being of the order of 50%, but may be higher. Figures vary from nil (as in a system of hay cropping) through a few pounds of nitrogen per acre per annum, where the legume component is relatively sparse, to fair average values of about 100 pounds and even as high as 500 pounds where the legume represents a major part of a pasture growing under specially favourable conditions. Contrary to the views expressed in some quarters, tropical legumes can secure at least as much nitrogen as their temperate counterparts (Bryan, 1962; Henzell and Norris, 1962; Moore, 1960). Less directly the effective nodulation of clover can be taken as providing nitrogen equivalent to medium (20-100 pounds) or large (up to more than 400 pounds) amounts applied as fertilizer (Bryan, 1962; Henzell and Norris, 1962; Purchase, 1958). Corresponding figures for soybean comparing nodulating and non-nodulating lines, ranged from the equivalent of 150 pounds of applied nitrogen in normal prairie soil to as much as 600 pounds where a condition of acute nitrogen shortage had been achieved experimentally (C. R. Weber, personal communication).

Most of the nitrogen is in the plant tops, the value varying from 50-66% for lucerne to greater than 80% for other pasture species (Jensen and Frith, 1944). It follows that for the soil to make an appreciable gain in nitrogen, the plant tops have to be returned to it directly, or indirectly through the grazing animal.

It is now generally agreed that under quite special circumstances significant amounts of nitrogen can be made available to associated non-legumes by excretion from the actively growing legume (Wilson, 1940), but it still seems unlikely that this has general practical significance. However, subsurface transfer, chiefly due to sloughing off and decomposition of roots and nodules, has been credited with amounts of 20-50, or even greater than 100 pounds of N per acre in the case of pasture legumes growing under conditions that permitted abundant fixation (Butler and Bathurst, 1956; Sears, 1953/1954).

Perusal of accounts dealing with the effect of environmental factors on the growth of the nodulated legume soon makes it apparent how difficult it can be to distinguish between those secondary effects which influence nitrogen fixation through their more generalized influence on the plant itself, and those that operate directly on the symbiosis. From a practical point of view any factor, or deficiency, that stands in the way of the full realization of a plant's fixation potential will be equally serious. However, our understanding, and therefore the proper application of our knowledge, requires the more detailed analysis to be attempted.

B. Hydrogen Ions

The major limiting effect of excess H-ions is on the survival and growth of the bacteria themselves. Evidence of direct effects on nodule formation, and functioning, is more difficult to find.

1. OCCURRENCE AND SURVIVAL

Soil acidity is likely to be a major factor restricting the occurrence of rhizobia in soil, though species differ considerably in their sensitivity (e.g., *Rhizobium meliloti,* very acid-sensitive; *R. japonicum,* able to tolerate pH as low as 3.5). The practical importance of this factor is illustrated very well by the thorough study of the distribution of *Rhizobium meliloti* in Nebraska soils where less than a fifth of the samples below pH 6.2 were positive (Peterson and Goodding, 1941). The importance of pH for the occurrence and survival of clover and lucerne (alfalfa) rhizobia has also been recorded for Australian soils (Vincent, 1954a; Vincent and Crofts, 1958; Vincent and Waters, 1954), though, as would be expected from laboratory comparisons (Jensen, 1942), the former (*R. trifolii*) is rather less sensitive to acid conditions than the latter (*R. meliloti*). The limiting role exercised by H-ion concentration was shown particularly clearly in this writer's experience (Vincent and Crofts, 1958) with acid soils of the northwest of New South Wales that adjoin neutral to alkaline soils, regularly carrying heavy growth of well nodulated species of *Medicago* and *Trifolium*. Despite what must be ample opportunity for the introduction of rhizobia from these to the nearby acid soils, they are virtually absent from the latter. In fact the demonstration was even more striking in that occasional patches of less acid soil (pH about 6) supported well-nodulated clovers and species of *Medicago*.

Spencer attributed the beneficial effect of a heavy inoculum on the nodulation of subterranean clover sown in acid soil (pH 4.6-5.0) to the provision thereby of sufficient survivors (Spencer, 1950). However, no direct evidence was provided as to rhizobial numbers. Part of the benefit due to calcium hydroxide, and probably all of that due to magnesium hydroxide, was the result of raised pH. Mulder and van Veen were unable to obtain multiplication of clover rhizobia added to acid soil (pH 5.1) in pots with or without clover plants (Mulder and van Veen, 1960a). Under these conditions normal nodulation required 60,000 cells to be added to the 500 g soil, sown to 20 clover plants (virtually a continuous rhizosphere). Perhaps surprisingly, they found that in the absence of clover, neutralization of an acid soil failed to cause multiplication. Planting clover in neutralized soil permitted a large increase in the number of rhizobia. In 64 days in 3 unplanted soils, clover rhizobia showed a 100,000-fold decline at pH 5.0, but only 1,000-fold declines at pH 5.6 and 7.5. The difference between these results and the considerable multiplication obtained in a pH-adjusted soil from this laboratory can perhaps be explained by its sterilization in our case, and consequent modification of the biotic environment.

2. NODULE FORMATION

It is difficult to find unequivocal evidence of excessive H-ions directly inhibiting nodule formation. Provided calcium is adequate, failure to obtain nodulation under acid conditions is more likely to be due to poor survival of rhizobium, or at least to its failure to proliferate in the rhizosphere. Limiting values reported (Jensen, 1943) for the nodulation of clover (pH 4.7-4.8) and *Medicago* (pH 5.8-5.9) agree well with those that limited the growth of the respective bacteria (Jensen, 1942). The poor nodulation found under acid conditions by Mulder and van Veen could also, on their data (Mulder and van Veen, 1960a) have been largely due to poor bacterial survival and failure to multiply in the rhizosphere. The reasons for sporadic improvement that occurred when various organic supplements (stable manure, yeast, dead rhizobia) were added to acid soil or culture solutions are not apparent. On the face of it, data reported by Loneragan and Dowling (Loneragan and Dowling, 1958) could be taken to indicate a direct effect of H-ions on nodulation. However, at pH 4.0, which appeared to be critical for nodulation, there could well have been no surviving rhizobia in the rhizosphere at the time the plant was invadable.

3. NODULE FUNCTIONING

Acid conditions in the soil result in complicated problems of nutrition—e.g., effect on Mo availability (van Schreven, 1958a) and toxicity

(Mn^{2+} and Al^{3+})—but the functioning of the formed nodule is not as sensitive to low pH as is the survival of rhizobia and, possibly invasion. Jensen (1944) showed that when calcium and phosphorus were sufficient, the fixation of nitrogen by subterranean clover was as good in a soil with pH 5 as it was when the pH was raised by liming to 7-7.5. Nodulated lucerne responded to liming but this was a molybdenum effect (see below) and when care was taken to avoid a shortage of this element, fixation in both lucerne and clover was unaffected down to pH 5 or less (Jensen, 1948). *Medicago tribuloides* seemed, in the one experiment with this host, to be more sensitive to low pH; less than a quarter of the nitrogen was fixed at pH 5 as at pH 7.4. At very low pH (4.5-5.0), aluminum toxicity may intervene (Rorison, 1958). For this to be serious there needs to be sufficient Al^{3+} to inhibit further root growth; lower levels of Al^{3+} can permit the seedlings to recover after passing through a critical phase. In many cases the pH range concerned is such that rhizobial survival will be so poor as to make nodulation unlikely in any case, although the situation of the plant having had its nodules formed in a more favorably restricted zone of pH and then growing into regions of aluminium toxicity may need to be considered.

C. Calcium and Magnesium

Apart from important neutralizing effects that calcium carbonate and hydroxide share with magnesium, and which chiefly benefit rhizobial growth and survival, the calcium ion seems to play its most specific and practical role in connection with nodule formation and, to some extent, fixation. The relationship between the need for magnesium in culture and its role in connection with rhizobial multiplication in the soil is not clear.

1. GROWTH AND SURVIVAL

There has been some confusion between the neutralizing effects of lime and direct benefits due to the calcium ions. Although the organism's need for this element can be demonstrated in sufficiently critical experiments (Bergersen, 1961; Vincent, 1962b; Vincent and Colburn, 1961), its absolute specific requirement is extremely low compared with that of the host itself. Strontium, but neither barium nor magnesium, has been found to substitute, with about a fourth the efficiency, for calcium in the maintenance of normal growth and morphology (Vincent, unpub.). Magnesium, though unable to meet the specific calcium need, is itself required in greater concentration and its deficiency can therefore be more readily demonstrated (Norris, 1958b, Norris, 1959a, Vincent, 1962b). It has been considered unlikely that this element would itself limit the growth of rhizobia in the soil, except at concentrations which would be well below the plant's own needs (Loneragan, 1960). In making any calculations of this nature however, it is necessary not to lose sight of the bacterium's very much greater need for divalent cations generally than for either calcium or magnesium specifically. For example, it was found in quantitative growth studies (Vincent, 1962b) that the concentration of total divalent cations (Ca plus Mg) necessary for maximum growth was approximately 20 times that needed for calcium specifically and 5 times that for magnesium. It follows from this that, as far as the growth of rhizobium is concerned, shortage of either ion will make a corresponding greater demand on the other. Some account will also need to be taken of the extent to which the plant might satisfy its own needs for these two elements at the expense of rhizobia associated with it in the rhizosphere.

2. NODULATION

Spencer (1950) and Loneragan and Dowling (1958), by refining and extending older work (Albrecht, 1932, 1933), showed a very clear and interesting interaction between Ca^{2+} and H^+ as factors controlling nodule formation. This effect of calcium is specific at least to the extent that it cannot be replaced by magnesium, and demands a concentration far in excess of what is needed for maximal growth of rhizobium and adequate growth of host. The interaction obtained by Loneragan and Dowling can be shown by tabulating the approximate pH values at which they obtained 50% nodulated plants at each calcium level. Using the data of their Exp. 1 (Fig. 1), there is practically a linear logarithmic relationship between H^+ and Ca^{2+}.

Combinations of Ca^{2+} and H^+ for 50% nodulation

log Ca^{2+} mM	pH
1.0	4.2
0.8	4.3
0	4.6
−1.0	5.0

A competitive effect appears to operate in favor of the H^+; changing the concentration of H^+ twofold affected the calcium need five- to sixfold. Table 2 in the same publication shows how little the clover host itself was affected by pH as low as 3.5 or by reduction of Ca^{2+} to 0.01 mM. It follows that any limitation imposed by pH 4.0 and 0.01 mM Ca^{2+} on nodulation can hardly be due to gross secondary effects on the plant. As the authors point out, however, these limitations could be due to a reduced level of calcium in the host affecting the success or failure of early steps in nodule maturation, as distinct from the invasive step itself. Direct observation on root-hair infection (Fåhreus, 1957) should help to resolve this point. The complication associated with supplying 70 ppm N as KNO_3 cannot be entirely disregarded.

As a practical measure, banding with lime or dolomite (Albrecht, 1941), or the use of lime-pelleted seed (Cass Smith and Goss, 1958; Loneragan et al., 1955), provides relatively economical ways of improving pH conditions near the inoculated seed, and hence survival of rhizobia. It also assists invasion and the formation of mature nodules by the provision of Ca^{2+}.

a. Lime and Nodulation in Tropical Legumes

Norris' plea (Norris, 1956; Norris, 1958a) for tropical legumes to be considered without the preconceived notions that have been derived from time-honored studies with temperate legumes has certainly quickened interest and encouraged a more critical assessment of this formidably large and relatively neglected area of study. Andrew and Norris (Andrew and Norris, 1961) have carried out a valuable detailed study of the relationship between the symbiotic response to calcium of five tropical and four temperate legumes.

Two of the tropical legumes (*Stylosanthes gracilis* and *Indigofera spicata*) were indeed well nodulated without any calcium having been added to a calcium-deficient soil, but so was *Trifolium repens*. Two other tropical species (*Centrosema pubescens* and *Phaseolus lathyroides*) gave appreciable nodulation in the unamended soil but also responded to lime additions of 4 and 6 cwts/acre, respectively. On the other hand the remaining 3 temperate legumes, though not nodulated in the control soil, gave maximal response at 2 cwts of lime (*Trifolium fragiferum* and *Medicago sativa*) or at 4 cwts (*Medicago tribuloides*). *Desmodium uncinatum*, the remaining tropical, seemed as calcium-demanding as any. As the authors have themselves noted, there are no clear differences between the two groups of legumes and perhaps one of the most striking conclusions that came out of this excellent piece of work was a warning against further dogmatic generalizations.

The proposition that nodulation under conditions of low calcium availability reflects the host's ability to accumulate calcium (Norris, 1958a) can also be examined in the light of data contained in this paper (Andrew and Norris, 1961). Again no clear generalization appears possible. It is true that among the tropical legumes the least calcium-demanding (*Stylosanthes gracilis*) was most efficient and the most demanding (*Desmodium uncinatum*), least efficient in accumulating calcium. The others fall out of order however and are interspersed with temperate legumes that have variable calcium requirement unrelated to calcium accumulation. Andrew and Norris also give some weight to the possibility that the effect on nodulation of a plant's shortage of calcium might be due to meristem breakdown; an alternative to the proposition that it is associated with the act of root-hair infection. Such a proposition can and should be examined directly.

3. NODULE FUNCTIONING

Extreme calcium deficiency operates directly on plant growth but when this element is only moderately deficient there appears to be a specific effect on fixation (Loneragan, 1959). Graham (1938) considered that the improved fixation he obtained with increasing magnesium was indirect in that this element caused the plant to make more efficient use of its calcium. Evidence of any specific effect due to magnesium is sparse (van Schreven, 1958a). Increased yield and fixation by the use of high levels of Ca, Mg, P, and K have been reported with nodulated plants of

Phaseolus vulgaris (Button et al., 1961). More attention will need to be given to interactions between Ca and other elements such as Mn, Al, operating directly and via pH effects on the symbiosis-dependent as well as on the plant receiving combined nitrogen, The present situation is certainly not clear (Rorison, 1958).

D. Trace Elements

Many disorders due to deficiencies of trace elements have been shown to affect the growth of legumes (Hewitt, 1958), but most of them limit the fixation of nitrogen non-specifically by limiting the growth of the host. A more specific role has been demonstrated for three of them: molybdenum, cobalt, and boron, in each case for a different reason.

1. MOLYBDENUM

The specific role of molybdenum in the efficient functioning of the formed nodule has been studied intensively since the earlier observations of Bortels and of Anderson and his group (Anderson, 1956a; Anderson, 1956b; Hewitt, 1958). Jensen and Betty (1943) demonstrated stimulation of fixation by molybdenum and the fact that root nodules (specially the bacteria-containing tissue) were particularly rich in this element and took up more molybdenum when fixing nitrogen. The gain of N per unit weight of nodule substance was about two and a half times as great for normal as for molybdenum-deficient nodules (Jensen, 1946), and it could be calculated that 10 to 25 ppm molybdenum (based on dry nodule substance) appeared necessary for maximum nitrogen-fixing ability in lucerne; 4 to 8 ppm sufficed for subterranean clover. The growth of molybdenum-deficient plants was improved by supplying nitrate-N and plants supplied with combined nitrogen generally required less molybdenum (Jensen, 1948).

Anderson and Thomas (1946) obtained marked molybdenum responses with symbiosis-dependent legumes in pot culture and in the field. Like Jensen they found that there were more, though less efficient, nodules when molybdenum was deficient. Any effect that molybdenum has on nodule number seems to result from the inefficient functioning of the nodules themselves. Phosphate improved the plant's ability to respond to molybdenum, and heavy dressings of lime made more molybdenum available by altering pH. Other elements may interact with molybdenum (e.g., sulphur and manganese). Vanadium could not replace molybdenum in its specific role (Anderson and Oertel, 1946), but substitutive ability has been reported for tungsten (Davies and Stockdill, 1956). Molybdenum is also required, but in much lower concentration, by the plant supplied with nitrate-N. (See also accounts by Anderson's group: Anderson and Moye, 1952; Anderson and Spencer, 1950a.)

2. COBALT

Numerous recent observations that legumes that are dependent on symbiotically-provided nitrogen require cobalt (Ahmed and Evans, 1959, 1960,

1961; Dewiche et al., 1961; Hallsworth et al., 1960; Powrie, 1960; Reisenhauer, 1960) seem to be explained (as forecast by van Schreven, 1958b) by its relation to the production of the cobalt-containing vitamin B_{12}. In this way it appears to be needed in trace amounts for the proper functioning of the nodule tissue, probably in the metabolism of the rhizobia themselves. This view is supported by observations of its influence on the growth of the bacterium in culture (Lowe et al., 1960; Lowe and Evans, 1962) and the demonstration of vitamin B_{12}-coenzyme in nodules and in the cells of R. meliloti (Kliewar and Evans, 1962a). It was also found that the B_{12}-coenzyme content of cells of R. meliloti was related to the cobalt concentration of the culture medium (Kliewar and Evans, 1962b). The demonstrated role of B_{12}-coenzymes in the metabolism of glutamate to B-methyl aspartate is perhaps suggestive in view of the role of the former as probably the first amino-acid following fixation.

3. BORON

Boron deficiencies that interfere with nodule function have been reported from time to time (Hewitt, 1958). Establishing the role of this element, a deficiency of which affects the vascular system leading to the nodule and hence causes a shortage of carbohydrate at the fixation site, was one of the classics of early work on the symbiosis (Brenchley et al., 1925). Detailed investigations with the pea plant (Mulder, 1948) have demonstrated the care that needs to be taken to differentiate between a boron deficiency affecting the plant as a whole, and its interference with nodule formation, that then leads to symptoms of nitrogen shortage. There have been more recent speculations as to other possible roles for this element (Hallsworth, 1958).

4. OTHERS

A role in the formation of haemoglobin (and hence fixation) has been suggested for iron (van Schreven, 1958a); the situation with copper remains confused (Hallsworth, 1958; Parle, 1958).

E. Sulphur, Phosphorus, and Potassium

1. SULPHUR

Anderson and Spencer (1949, 1950b) have clearly distinguished the separate roles of molybdenum and sulphur in the legume. Whereas the former was required for fixation itself, sulphur deficiency led to a failure of protein synthesis from nitrogen available to the plant, either symbiotically or in the combined form. Nonprotein nitrogen increased in the S-deficient plant, which responded very little to applied nitrogen and, unlike its molybdenum-deficient counterpart, had fewer nodules than the adequately nourished host. This situation could well reflect a narrowing carbon to nitrogen ratio in the sulphur-deficient legume as nitrogen accumulated for want of completed synthesis.

2. PHOSPHORUS

Legumes require relatively large amounts of phosphorus (Scanlon, 1928; van Schreven, 1958a) and, if these requirements are not met, nodule formation and nodule functioning are both affected adversely. This is evidently indirectly, through the effect of the deficiency on the plant.

The need for phosphorus has been particularly evident in many parts of Australia where the application of phosphatic fertilizer to pasture is followed by spectacularly improved growth of the legume component. Shortage of the element can result in reduction of nodulation in the field and in pot trials (Vincent and Crofts, 1958). It has been calculated that the additional nitrogen fixed consequent on the better growth resulting from the application of 100 pounds of superphosphate can amount to 76 pounds of N (Donald and Williams, 1954). Pot trials with an Indian soil have shown a phosphate response by pea plants both in nodulation and fixation (Vyas and Desai, 1953). The gain amounted to about 80 pounds of N per 100 of P_2O_5 (Vyas, 1953). Rotations involving berseem clover showed similar gains of nitrogen as a result of phosphorus-fertilization (Acharya et al., 1953). Anderson and Oertel (1946) showed that a supply of phosphate improved the legume's ability to respond to molybdenum, and it seems that phosphorus may also have a more direct effect in that a deficiency can reduce fixation before it becomes limiting for plant growth (McLachlan and Norman, 1961). Bjälve (1958) has also reported that a high content of phosphorus is important in the fixation of atmospheric nitrogen.

Quite different is the observation of "phosphate toxicity" under conditions of N-shortage (Rossiter, 1952). This could in fact be regarded as an exacerbation of the condition of nitrogen deficiency by relative excess of phosphorus, in that added nitrate and better nodulation could reduce the effect.

3. POTASSIUM

A potassium requirement is likely to show up in older established pasture, but not in any role particular to the symbiotic state. Demonstration of a potassium effect commonly requires the phosphorus needs to have been met. There are reports of some rhizobial strains able to fix larger amounts of nitrogen in potassium-deficient plants than do other strains (Lynch and Sears, 1951; Roberts and Olson, 1942), and Lynch and Sears are quoted (van Schreven, 1958a) as having shown clear interaction between strains and nutrient status (including potassium). Closer examination of their data (Lynch and Sears, 1951) does not, in fact, lend much support to such a conclusion. The significance of any apparent differences cannot be assessed on the figures that are presented. In fact the performance of the better strains is remarkably consistent. In their Table 2, for instance, strain B is numerically the best for all but one of the fertilizer treatments, and in that it is a close second.

F. Combined Nitrogen

The influence of combined nitrogen on nodule formation and nitrogen fixation is a complex one, being particularly determined by whether or not the plant is making a heavy demand on this element. It is therefore markedly affected by the vigour of plant growth and its photosynthetic activity.

1. NODULE FORMATION

Nitrate-N has regularly been observed to depress nodule formation (van Schreven, 1958a, 1959); there is, however, some conflict as to the relative importance of external nitrate and combined nitrogen within the plant (Raggio et al., 1957). The conflict may be resolvable on quantitative grounds and in relation to C:N balances. Nodulation of lucerne was inhibited at 55 ppm N, nitrate being more inhibitory than NH_4^+. Medium (11 ppm) and low (0.4 ppm) concentrations were without inhibitory effect, so far as could be judged in plants that were harvested after 6 weeks growth (Richardson et al., 1957). Nodulation of one variety of lucerne was possibly stimulated by the addition of low to medium amounts of NH_4^+. The application of 50, 100, and 150 pounds of fertilizer N per acre caused progressive reduction in nodule tissue formed on soybean. Establishment of an acute shortage of available nitrogen in the same soil, by the incorporation of 20 tons of ground corn cobs per acre, reduced the effect of added nitrogen about fourfold, and 600 pounds of N per acre were then required to achieve the same degree of inhibition of nodulation as was previously found with 150 pounds (Weber, personal communication).

Traces of nitrate and nitrite (as little as 6.5 ppm), given as a single dose at the beginning of the experiment, delayed the onset of nodulation (Gibson and Nutman, 1960). Ammonia, asparagine, and urea failed to show this effect at comparable concentration. The fact that nitrite, which rhizobia can produce from nitrate, leads to the destruction of indole acetic acid can be used to provide a rational explanation of this inhibitory action of nitrate and nitrite (Tanner and Anderson, 1963), if one grants that the auxin plays a major role in invasion and that its destruction will delay this step. It also fits the observation (Raggio et al., 1957) that nitrate added to the medium bathing excised roots reduced nodulation whereas that introduced directly into the root *via* the base, did not. Reports of benefit in the presence of nitrate due to the external application of carbohydrate (van Schreven, 1958a) could then be attributed to increased microbial growth and consequent utilization of the nitrogen. Some benefit could conceivably result from auxin production, but not if this was excessive. The latter condition was probably responsible for failure with root culture in the presence of sucrose (McGonagle, 1949).

Low concentrations of N may, however, be stimulatory (MacConnell and Bond, 1957b), possibly by delaying nodulation during the earlier stages of plant growth and, in the long run, providing more sites for nodule formation (Gibson and Nutman, 1960). The situation is not simple, however, and the picture that emerges can depend on the criterion applied. For example, in MacConnell and Bond's results with *Ulex* (1957b), 10 ppm NH_4^+-N increased the number and mass of nodules per plant, whilst the ratio of nodule weight to plant weight was greatest without NH_4^+.

The influence of a range of levels of combined nitrogen on nodule formation, as a function of seasonal environment and rhizobial strain, has been reported in detail by Pate and Dart (1961). Low levels of combined nitrogen had a favorable effect on the formation of primary root nodules in the case of cowpea, barrel medic and vetch. The same effect was seen with cowpea under the conditions of summer growth but not in autumn. Under the latter, less favorable, conditions for growth, nodulation was less than in the summer and was at its greatest without any added nitrogen. The vetch rhizobial strains differed in their tolerance of added nitrogen; three out of eight gave clearly maximal primary root nodulation at low levels of nitrate. Low levels of nitrate also increased total root-hair infections (counted at 17 days) (Nutman, 1962). Delay in nodulation, and hence deferment of the brake that the development of the first nodule puts on root-hair infection, would explain this effect. Intermediate hair infection data could have answered the question whether the nitrate delayed the onset of early root-hair infections or not.

2. NITROGEN FIXATION

The limiting effect of combined nitrogen on fixation is also well known, but the concentration of nitrogen at which the limitation operates is affected by photosynthetic activity, carbohydrate otherwise supplied, and by the nitrogen-demand of the plant (Pate and Dart, 1961; van Schreven, 1958a; Wilson, 1940). The use of labeled nitrogen to follow fixation in soybeans and clover showed that, although the amount fixed was inversely related to the combined nitrogen supplied, fixation could not be completely inhibited (Norman and Krampitz, 1946; Thornton, 1948; Walker et al., 1956). It was found with most of a wider range of legumes that symbiotically provided nitrogen was generally unable to meet the plant's full potential. On the other hand, a decreasing proportion of the available combined nitrogen was absorbed from the nutrient solution as the supplied concentration was increased, and fixation was not completely suppressed, although it was reduced to from 9% in *Lotus* to 46% in peanut (Allos and Bartholomew, 1955; Allos and Bartholomew, 1959). When clover was grown associated with grasses, it was found that almost all of the available soil nitrogen was taken up by the latter. Only 5 to 6% of labeled combined nitrogen was then recovered in the clover (Walker et al., 1956).

Interesting differences have been found between rhizobial strains in the way the symbiosis reacts to combined nitrogen. Pate and Dart's vetch strain V19 was much less sensitive than the other two (see Table 1).

The same workers found that fixation by the cowpea plant became less sensitive to added combined nitrogen with age, except that 4-day seedlings were even more sensitive than those treated at the time of sowing. They

Table 1. Effect of combined N on symbiosis by rhizobial strains (from Pate and Dart, 1961).

	Strain		
	V19	V32	SU331
mg combined N/pot, permitting maximal nodulation of primary root	5-10	0	0
mg combined N/pot, causing 50% reduction of primary nodulation	30-50	15-30	15-30
Ratio of N fixed in presence of 10 mg combined N to that fixed in its absence	1.2	0.1	0.15

go on to discuss the possible, though difficult, use of nitrogenous fertilizer applied in early seedling establishment as an investment capable of giving a substantial return in the form of additional fixed nitrogen. The likelihood that selection of rhizobial strain could also help to improve fixation in soils having more available nitrogen is also discussed. It was also found that bean plants could fix more nitrogen when 200 ppm combined nitrogen were provided, other requirements (P, K, Ca, and Mg) being met. A higher level (400 ppm) suppressed fixation (Burton et al., 1961).

Another method that can be used to estimate the amount of nitrogen fixed in field trials is to swamp the root system of the control with ineffective nodules so as to make it wholly dependent on soil nitrogen (Virtanen and von Hausen, 1952). Using this method with pea plants growing in pots it was found (Virtanen and Holmberg, 1958) that 86-69% of the plant's nitrogen could be secured by fixation in soils having from 10 to 84 ppm nitrate-N. Even leaf mould having 425 ppm nitrate-N permitted 40% fixation. Field trials with soils having about 30 ppm available nitrogen gave about 89% fixation. Purchase found with subterranean clover that symbiotically provided nitrogen ranged from 75% to 16% of the total plant nitrogen as the applied ammonium sulphate varied from 0 to 100 pounds of N per acre. In the soil that received no nitrogen, the amount supplied to the plant by fixation was roughly equal to the nitrogen taken up by plants from soil receiving 100 pounds of N per acre (Purchase, 1958).

A non-nodulating variety can be used for a similar purpose. The yield of non-nodulating line of soybean could be made approximately equal to that of the otherwise similar nodulating line by the addition of 150 pounds combined N per acre, but could not be made to exceed it. Establishment of a heavy nitrogen demand by soil microorganisms, by the incorporation of a large amount of wide C:N organic matter, resulted in about a fourfold increase in the symbiotic contribution to plant nitrogen (equivalent to 600 pounds combined N per acre) (Weber, personal communication).

G. Supply of Carbon-containing Compounds

Light and other factors, such as CO_2 concentration, that affect photosynthesis, influence both nodule formation and the functioning of the formed nodule, largely in the opposite direction to combined nitrogen and as an antidote to the latter (McKee, 1962; van Schreven, 1958a, 1959; Wilson, 1940).

Attempts to supply carbohydrate more directly have yielded contradictory results (van Schreven, 1959), which is perhaps not surprising where the sugar has been supplied to the plant roots. In such a circumstance the growth and metabolism of rhizobia in the root environment are likely to be considerably stimulated, and the conditions controlling nodulation thereby affected in an unpredictable fashion. Van Schreven (1959) sprayed sucrose on the leaves of pea plants to overcome this difficulty. When the plants were sub-optimally illuminated he found that spraying with sucrose, though not affecting nodule number, was able to improve their size and efficiency of fixation. Sugar application in the case of plants receiving supplementary illumination was inhibitory and, surprisingly, this effect was most marked in the plants supplied with combined nitrogen. Greater nodule formation has been reported for host varieties having a higher monosaccharide content (and total N) in their vegetative organs (Krasnikov et al., 1959). Nodulation and fixation have both been stimulated by CO_2 in the culture solution (Mulder and van Veen, 1960b). A better supply of α-keto-acids (N-acceptors) has been suggested in explanation. Such an effect of CO_2 could contribute to cases of stimulation reportedly due to some rhizosphere microorganisms (Harris, 1953; Krasil'nikov and Korenyako, 1944).

Limiting light intensity could be important both under temperate conditions and in the tropics, particularly in the latter, due to short day length, poor light penetration in forests and, in some situations, excessive cloud cover (Masefield, 1958). Excessive shading and other operations (such as removal of plant tops) that reduce photosynthetic activity are likely, not only to reduce nitrogen-fixation, but also to lead to the breakdown of haemoglobin and even to the shedding of nodules (Butler and Bathurst, 1956).

Light intensity above a high optimum has been incriminated as a cause of inefficient fixation in soybean (Fred et al., 1938; Orcutt and Fred, 1935). There do not appear, however, to be any other authenticated cases on record.

Day length effects are important but are likely to be complicated, and their interpretation affected, by the criterion selected for determining the symbiotic optimum. (See van Schreven, 1959, and references given therein.)

H. Temperature

Temperature exercises an influence at all stages of the association: occurrence (by affecting growth and survival), nodule formation, and nodule functioning.

1. GROWTH AND SURVIVAL

Compared with pea, clover, and bean, the medic rhizobia are relatively tolerant of elevated temperatures—found limiting ranges: 40.5°-

42.5°C (Hofer and Little, 1956), and 36.5°-42.5°C (Bowen and Kennedy, 1959). The tropical miscellany is more variable—32°-42.5°C (Hofer and Little, 1956) and 30°-42°C (Bowen and Kennedy, 1959). No correlation could be found between the strains' heat tolerance and the geographic latitude of their origin. Nor was there any relationship to the species of host from which the tropical strains had come (Bowen and Kennedy, 1959). The growth of legumes under the cover of heavy tropical growth could explain the occurrence of heat intolerant strains in such situations. Masefield (1958) has recorded soil temperatures of 25°-28°C at 4 inches compared with 28°-31°C at 4 feet, under grass cover at Singapore, in contrast to 50°C for exposed soil in the Belgian Congo. The origin of lucerne in western Asia and along the Mediterranean, where the soil would be exposed to considerable radiant heating, could explain the observed degree of heat tolerance. Bowen and Kennedy's data also show a close inverse relationship between the strain's maximum growth temperature and its rate of death in a sandy soil at 40°C (Bowen and Kennedy, 1959). The lucerne strains were again the most resistant (hourly death rate at 40°C:0.13 to 0.19), whilst rhizobia of tropical hosts were scattered over a wider range (0.17 to 0.35).

Death rates can also be calculated for 24 hours storage at 28°C. When this is done, and the paired sets of data tabulated, an interesting point emerges (Table 2). The rhizobia that died most rapidly at 40°C were distinctly the more stable at 28°C. As a consequence the ratio between the death rates at the 2 temperatures varied between the extremes of 22-93 for the cultures that were more susceptible at 40°C (less at 28°C) to 4-7 in the case of *Medicago* strains, that were surprisingly unstable at the lower temperature. In all cases the ratio for the 12° interval from 28 to 40° was much greater than the approximate doubling that had been found for the same temperature interval over the range from 25 to 37°C (Vincent, 1958a). The difference suggests that between 37°C and 40°C a drastic and much more temperature-dependent process (such as protein denaturation) has intervened.

Well-dried cells of *Rhizobium* have considerable stability to heat (Parker and Sanderson, personal comm.). This is probably due to reduced protein denaturation under these conditions.

Table 2. Relative susceptibility of rhizobial species and strains to moderately high temperatures.

Source of culture	Death rate (r) at:		Ratio
	28 °C	40 °C	r_{40}/r_{28}
Trifolium pratense	.016	.48	30
Pisum sativum	.010	.38	38
T. repens	.004	.37	93
Centrosema pubescens	.016	.35	22
" "	.004	.25	63
" "	.019	.17	9
Medicago sativa	.026	.19	·7
" "	.033	.13	4
Pultanea villosa	.020	.12	6

r = hourly logarithmic decline, calculated from Bowen and Kennedy (1959).

2. NODULE FORMATION

Interference with nodulation by too high a temperature has been recorded on several occasions in the author's laboratory under conditions that were favorable for the growth of the host itself (Vincent, 1962a). It was obvious that the optimum temperature for nodule formation could be a good deal less than that for growth. Pate quotes Stalder as having shown delayed nodulation of the pea plant growing above 27°C, and has himself studied the position with *Medicago tribuloides* and vetch in some detail (Pate, 1961, 1962). Nodulation of the first of these was maximal in the range 8-12°C; purple vetch had a similar maximal range but two of the three rhizobial strains used with this host produced a relatively large number of nodules at 24°C as well. The relative success of rhizobial strains, as gauged by the number of nodules they formed on the primary root, varied over the temperature range at which they were tested.

3. NITROGEN FIXATION

Van Schreven (1958a) quotes earlier work that had shown optima for fixation that varied with host (soybean, 24°C; peas, 20°C). Fixation can be virtually prevented in the case of nodulated subterranean clover at 30°C, although plants receiving nitrate-N were largely unaffected by this temperature (Meyer and Anderson, 1959). *Medicago tribuloides* and *Vicia atropurpurea* both showed maximum fixation at 24°C, the latter plant being specially intolerant of higher temperatures (Pate, 1961, 1962). Whereas the reduced fixation on the lower side of the optimum was approximately in accord with reduced growth (% N not unduly affected), a decrease of percent N indicated that fixation was more affected than plant growth at higher temperatures. Pate relates his work to that of Mes (1959) who found cases in which N-fixation by different hosts was specifically depressed by lower temperatures. Of three temperatures (21-23°C, 30°C, and 40°C), the intermediate was best for N-fixation by *Trifolium pratense* and *Arachis hypogea* (Joffe et al., 1961). Plants which received high levels of combined nitrogen were less affected by high or low root temperatures than were those dependent on symbiotically fixed nitrogen. The observation that bacterial strains can vary in their reaction to temperature, particularly toward the extremes, is important when it comes to considering strain testing and selections (Pate, 1961, 1962).

Interpretation of the factors operating in experiments involving both nodule formation and the functioning of the formed nodule is difficult. If the influence of temperature on fixation as such is to be determined, it is necessary to assess fixation as a function of a unit of nodule tissue. Gibson (1961) commenced his experiments with uniformly nodulated plants and exposed sub-groups of these to different root temperatures. The index of efficiency of fixation was taken as the ratio of nitrogen fixed to nitrogen assimilated from the combined form over the same period, and expressed as a percentage. Two varieties of subterranean clover were tested, each with two strains of *Rhizobium* and at root temperatures between 5° and 30°C (intervals approx. 4°C). The efficiency of fixation increased for all combinations to a maximum at 22°C. There was some interaction between host and strain in that, although *R. trifolii*, strain TA1 was superior to strain NA30 at all temperatures on var. Tallarook, NA30 was the better strain for Dwalganup up to 18°C. Above this TA1 was again superior. The later more detailed account (Gibson, 1963) added Yarloop and Mt. Barker to the varieties for which TA1 was better than NA30, generally over the whole range of temperature.

I. Water and Oxygen

1. GROWTH AND SURVIVAL

The rhizobia, like other gram negative bacteria, are likely to die rapidly as they dry (Vincent, 1958a). In a detailed study with *Rhizobium trifolii* (Vincent et al., 1962) it was found that two main phases can be recognized. The death rate was greatest over the first few hours, when the main loss of water was occurring. Subsequently, when the situation was more stabilized, the death rate was much reduced. A favorable additive, of which maltose was far the best of the simple compounds tested, improved survival.

At first glance this rapid death of rhizobia might seem to be contradicted by well documented reports of long survival (Allen and Allen, 1958; Fred et al., 1932). These are, however, generally based on nonquantitative recovery tests. The most recent report (Jensen, 1961) does give counts of survivors in very old cultures of *Rhizobium meliloti* in sterile soil (stored 30-40 years). The figures varied from cultures having less than 100/g to some having 500,000/g after that extended period. Not knowing the number originally present in the soil cultures, we can only guess at the extent of death that had occurred but this would have been considerable. Jensen (1961) found no evidence that this long survival was associated with the possession of heat resistant spores. This result gave no support, then, to claims made in that regard (Bisset, 1952). The best interpretation of events is that those cells that, by chance, and/or metabolic inertness, happen to survive the critical drying period, are in such a resting condition as exposes them to less risk of death subsequently. The contrast between the rapid death of many cells during freeze-drying and the long-term stability of those that survive the first stage seems to be an analogous situation. The fact that well-dried cells are likely to have enhanced stability to heat (Parker and Sanderson, pers. comm.) could have some practical significance if desiccation preceded increase of temperature into what would otherwise be the lethal range. However, such evidence for long-term survival in sterile soil, or in the desiccated state, cannot be too freely extended to the practical situation of a natural soil, where there is so much scope for the operation of biotic factors and where alternate wetting and drying may nullify the stabilizing effect of a single desiccation.

2. NODULE FORMATION

Shortage of water is very often likely to be a major cause of nodulation failure (McKee, 1961) apparently even under tropical conditions

(Masefield, 1958), but the effect is likely to operate mostly in respect of rhizobial growth and survival, and to be greater under conditions of alternate wetting and drying, and at low pH (McKee, 1961). It is possible, however, that the suitability of a root-hair for invasion might be adversely affected before the shortage of water sufficiently depresses the number of bacteria, and that the damage so caused might persist even after the cells have recovered. This possibility has not been studied critically.

On the other hand, it is generally conceded that excess water can reduce nodulation, particularly by affecting the normality of plant tissues. However, the writer can record from his own experience cases where clover was well nodulated in spite of prolonged waterlogging in reclaimed swamps and in peaty areas. In such cases the nodules were mostly formed high on the crown at or above the water level.

3. NODULE FUNCTIONING

Drought can be expected to interfere with fixation in much the same way as it affects plant growth generally, except that *in extremis,* some loss of nodules may occur.

Avoidance of waterlogging, hence sufficiency of oxygen, is evidently important for efficient fixation. Bond (1951) found that reduction of oxygen led to decrease in nodule weight, fixation and the dry weight of soybean plants. There were, however, more nodules at 5% than at 21%, 12% or 1% oxygen (Ferguson and Bond, 1954). The effect of a shortage of oxygen was somewhat greater on plants that were dependent on atmospheric nitrogen than on those that were receiving combined nitrogen. Oxygen shortage seemed, therefore, to operate rather more on the process of fixation, or on associated nodular respiration, than it did on the plant itself. The discrepancy between these later and earlier results (Wilson and Fred, 1937) was explained by the severe limitation on growth imposed by the totally enclosed method (Wilson and Fred, 1937). At the same time it is fair to comment that, according to the published data, the main effect of oxygen shortage operated on the plant itself, whether symbiosis-dependent or using combined nitrogen.

Bergersen (1962a, b) has recently developed an ingenious method enabling direct spectroscopic observation of the oxygenation of haemoglobin in the nodule. He found that there appeared to be a considerable barrier to the diffusion of oxygen into young nodules, indicated by the fact that haemoglobin was not converted to the oxygenated form below pO_2 of 50%.

J. Biotic Effects

1. THE PLANT

A water soluble factor in the seed coat of peanut was able to inhibit some species of *Bacillus* and several species of gram negative bacteria (Bonnier, 1952). Its action on *Rhizobium* was not reported. Since then it has been found (Thompson, 1960) that the water extract from the seed of subterranean clover was particularly inhibitory to rhizobia; white clover was less toxic and lucerne hardly at all. Toxicity has also been recorded in diffusates from the seed of *Centrosema pubescens* (Bowen, 1961). Active killing of rhizobia by the seed coat factor has been demonstrated (Vincent et al., 1962). Death was much more rapid on the surface of clover seed than it was on a glass surface, and the effect was most operative in the first few hours while the preparation was relatively moist. The toxic factor could be transferred to glass beads when these were coated with the equivalent amount of a water extract of the seed coat. Gum arabic, but not maltose, protected against the seed factor.

Plants, both leguminous and nonleguminous, can stimulate the growth of rhizobia in their rhizosphere. Clover was, however, more stimulating than grass (Rovira, 1961). Rhizobia, stimulated in the vicinity of the legume root, were therefore most numerous under stands of leguminous crops and decreased rapidly after the crop was removed (Tuzimura and Watanabe, 1961a, b). Nutman (1963) cites Krasil'nikov as having found some degree of specificity between host and the stimulation of *R. trifolii*. The same author was reported, however, as having found that cotton was as stimulatory as clover. Rothamsted data are also quoted for stimulation resultant on the sowing of legumes with a decline in numbers in subsequent fallows. It is not clear, however, to what extent the effect is specific for particular legumes. Tuzimura and Watanabe observed that, whereas the multiplication of the clover rhizobia was stimulated in the vicinity of a wide range of plants (leguminous and nonleguminous), lucerne *Rhizobium* was stimulated only by its own host (Tuzimura and Watanabe, 1961a, b). A stimulatory effect of leguminous plants for nonspecific as well as for the specific rhizobia, which contrasts with a bactericidal factor from nonleguminous plants, has also been reported (Chailakhyan and Megrabyn, 1959a, b). This contrasts with another report (Shevtsova, 1959), that pastes of clover and lucerne roots were toxic for rhizobia, particularly in the case of preparations from young roots. According to this report, cultures that had become adapted to the root juice were more virulent than the original cultures, though unchanged in their nitrogen-fixing ability.

2. INTERACTIONS BETWEEN MICROORGANISMS

The question of mutual compatibility amongst rhizobia has not been well studied, and it is not surprising that the evidence should be conflicting (Allen and Allen, 1958). An example of an interesting, though unexplained, difference is the ability of an avirulent clover culture to restrict the multiplication of its virulent parent strain which was not, however, limited by a strain of *Rhizobium meliloti* (Purchase, H. F., Ph.D. thesis, Univ. of London).

The interaction between rhizobia and other microorganisms is even more complicated. Some bacteria stimulated, some inhibited and some were without effect on the growth of *R. trifolii* in the rhizosphere (Krasil'nikov and Korenyako, 1944). Some bacteria were also able to improve nodulation by a weakly nodulating strain of Rhizobium (Harris, 1953), but it was not determined whether this was due to better rhizobial growth, as Krasil'nikov and Korenyako had postulated (1944), or whether it operated more directly in respect of invasion itself. Other reports of favorable effects have been quoted (Allen and Allen, 1958).

Casas-Campillo (1949) reviewed earlier work on the production of substances antagonistic to the rhizobia. Like so much work on antibiotics in soil, however, it leaves to speculation the extent to which the phenomenon operates as an ecological factor *in situ*. Indications of toxic effects exercised by aerobic spore-forming bacteria, streptomycetes and fungi, have also been noted (Allen and Allen, 1958), but their practical significance as antagonists remains obscure. Extracts active against rhizobia have been obtained from five out of seven soils that had had leguminous crops. Similar, but virgin, soils lacked inhibitory fractions (Casas-Campillo, 1949). Results with peat are also interesting in that it was possible adversely to affect the quality of the inoculum (as judged by plant response) when either the spore-forming antagonist was sown in the peat a week ahead of seeding it with rhizobia, or by using the antibiotic filtrate simultaneously (Abdel-Ghaffar and Allen, 1950). The failure to obtain inhibition when the filtrate was used a week ahead of the rhizobia was attributed to inactivation of the antibiotic in, or by, the peat. In connection with these experiments with peat, one notes Purchase's failure to achieve inhibition in peat cultures with any of the several fungi she had selected on the basis of their antibiotic activity against rhizobia on agar media (Purchase, H. F., personal communication).

Nodulation failures in certain Australian soils have been attributed to failure of the inoculum to colonize the rhizosphere because of antagonism exercised by other rhizosphere organisms (Hely et al., 1957). This conclusion rested on the ability of a thousandfold dilution of the same soil to interfere with the nodulation of clover plants in agar tubes receiving up to 300 rhizobia 14 days or so after the addition of the soil inoculum. The factor could be destroyed by autoclaving and could be transmitted by successive sub-culture. The inhibitory effect was lost if the soil and the rhizobia were added simultaneously to plants that were old enough to permit immediate invasion. It was not possible to identify the toxic effect with any rhizosphere isolate. The rhizobia were able to survive quite well in the soil itself, and the problem could be overcome with a massive inoculum, by the addition of charcoal near the normally inoculated seed, or by pelleting. A nutrient-bentonite pellet was thought to favor multiplication of Rhizobium (Bergersen et al., 1958). However, it was subsequently found that non-nutritive pellets were as effective as the nutritive (Thompson, 1961). In this work too, it was not possible to obtain any benefit from fumigating soils which had given nodulation difficulty and in which responses to pelleting had been demonstrated. It was therefore considered that the important advantage in these low acid soils was in the physical separation of rhizobia from the toxic seed coat.

Difficulties in the establishment of subterranean clover in certain Western Australian soils have also been attributed to antagonism by indigenous microorganisms (Cass Smith and Holland, 1958). This has been taken a good deal further with interesting results (Holland and Parker, 8th Int. Cong. Microbiol.). *Rhizobium trifolii* was absent from the rhizosphere of seedlings in affected soils but was relatively abundant in the rhizosphere of plants grown in sterilized soil. The fungi that re-colonized sterilized soil were compatible with rhizobia in culture and allowed nodulation. Soil extracts and extracts of the reddened and stunted unhealthy plant tissue were antibiotic but those from healthy plants were not. A large proportion of antagonistic strains (mainly pseudonomonads, streptomycetes, penicillia, aspergilli and basidiomycetes) could be isolated from the troublesome newly cleared areas, but old and healthy clover stands seemed to have established a compatible population. Nodulation could be secured by massive inoculation but this occurred without colonization of the rhizosphere.

3. BACTERIOPHAGE

Bacteriophage has been variously emphasized as a potentially important biotic factor. The evidence and viewpoints have been treated at some length (Allen and Allen, 1958) and it has been noted that rhizobiophage is certainly widespread in soils of very different nature and cropping history (though apparently most abundant in the rhizosphere of leguminous plants). The same reviewers quote the extended programme of work by Demolon and Dunez, their postulated cyclic build-up and liberation of phage from old nodules, and suggested remedial measures, including the use of phage-resistant rhizobia. They conclude however by putting Kleczkowska's view that the action of bacteriophage might be indirect by increasing the proportion of ineffective strains among those that survive because of their phage-resistance but that this may be the real means of causing decreased yields in old phage-infested legume stands. However, despite a relatively voluminous literature, the practical significance of rhizobiophage as a factor militating against the survival and functioning of rhizobia in the soil has yet to be unequivocally demonstrated.

4. SPECIFIC INFLUENCE OF THE HOST

Nutman's own major contributions and those of others that he has thoroughly reviewed (Nutman, 1956) have shown how the genetic constitution of the host determines whether or not nodulation occurs, the number of root-hair invasions, the number of nodules that form and the speed with which infection takes place. In attempting to study the localization of factors controlling invasion, some appear to have been able to show the shoot (scion) influencing the root (stock) (Bonnier et al., 1952; Hely et al., 1953), but various others have failed to obtain such a crossing of the graft union (Nutman, 1951). With the identification of a role for polygalacturonase in infection (Ljunggren and Fåhreus, 1961), some basis is provided for susceptibility and resistance. However, as an explanation of specificity the question is merely moved back one step. There yet remains to be explained the way in which a particular strain stimulates its susceptible host to produce a sufficiently large quantity of relatively nonspecific enzyme.

Lines of soybean, differing only in respect of the gene that controls nodulating power (Lynch and Sears, 1952; Williams and Lynch, 1954), should ultimately yield worthwhile information about the basis of this plant-bacterium relationship. The demonstration of a factor produced by a non-nodulating line able significantly to decrease the number of nodules produced by an associated nodulating plant is particularly interesting (Elkan, 1961, 1962). Nodulation of Ladino (white) clover, but not that of *Phaseolus vulgaris,* was also reduced by this association. The effect could not be explained by any influence on the growth of the rhizobia in the rhizosphere, although the qualitative nature of the rhizosphere population was affected. Elkan (1962) was also able to recover rhizobia from surface-sterilized roots of both the nodulating and non-nodulating lines and concluded that they had gained entry to the latter, although they were unable to complete the formation of nodules.

Serological typing of nodules formed on different species of clover has shown that the host is able to favor some rhizobial strains over others, even though all of the rhizobial strains concerned were able to nodulate the same hosts freely as single inocula (Vincent and Waters, 1953). The favored strains, so far as nodule formation was concerned, varied from host to host but their relative success in growing in the root environment was not affected in any parallel way. The influence of host can go beyond the level of species. Yarloop variety of *Trifolium subterraneum* was relatively poorly nodulated by *R. trifolii,* SU298 when tested in the field whereas the same rhizobial strain was well suited to other varieties of this same clover species (Vincent, 1956). The effect was associated with the greater rigour of the field test, and was not predictable from behaviour of host and bacterium in the tube. Nodules when formed were fully effective; the difficulty was with nodule formation itself. A rather similar effect has been more recently encountered with *T. subterraneum* var. Woogenellup, this time with *R. trifolii,* strain TA1. This strain of rhizobium has been used very successfully as a general clover inoculum and has been reliable in its nodulation of other varieties of subterranean clover, including Yarloop. Several reports have lately come to hand of patchy nodulation of the newer Woogenellup variety of subterranean clover under field conditions when TA1 is used as inoculum. The trouble was less acute under greenhouse conditions and not at all apparent in tube tests (Cunningham, Elizabeth, unpub.). Again it is a matter of failure to form nodules. Once formed, the nodules are fully effective. Fortunately other rhizobial strains are available that freely nodulate Woogenellup as well as the other varieties of subterranean clover.

Although it might be expected that relative nodulating performance would depend on ability to grow in competition with other strains (as had been evident in the cases reported by Nicol and Thornton, 1941), there appears to be little evidence that supports the general validity of such a relationship (Read, 1953; Vincent, 1956; Vincent and Waters, 1953). Certain other factors, such as locality (Baird, 1956; Vincent, 1956) and form of culture (Vincent, 1956), have been able to modify the relative nodulating success of strains.

The large amount of detailed study of root-hair infection by Nutman and his group (Nutman, 1962) has led him to conclude that infection is not randomly distributed over the root but occurs at preferred sites. The full occupation of these sites becomes more difficult as they become filled up, so that while a few bacteria suffice to produce the first nodule, very large populations are needed to saturate fully the infective capacity of the host (Purchase and Nutman, 1957). In many situations, of course, the number of rhizobia added could be expected to increase by multiplication in the rhizosphere, but other circumstances, associated with particular soils and/or hosts can be envisaged in which the number remains unchanged or declines. Biotic factors could be expected to affect this situation (see above).

Pate (1958a, b) has provided extraordinarily detailed and valuable studies of the progress of symbiosis in pea and vetch. These papers are so detailed as to defy adequate abstraction but the following are perhaps the chief points that emerge: (1) Nodule numbers increased to a maximum and ceased well before flowering. (2) Effective nodules developed haemoglobin in ordered sequence according to location on the root system; the development of haemoglobin was related to the rate of plant growth, and its destruction in senescent nodules progressed from the base of the nodule to its apex. (3) Average nodule size and efficiency increased as the nodule populations aged, with some evidence of a progressive elimination of smaller nodules. (4) Commencement of fixation was usually before the nitrogen of the cotyledon was exhausted and coincided with the first appearance of haemoglobin in the first formed nodules. (5) The maximum in total nodule nitrogen was reached some time ahead of maximum total plant nitrogen, and at no time did nodules or roots act as substantial nitrogen storage organs; transfer of fixed nitrogen to the host was immediate. (6) The onset of flowering and fruiting markedly decreased nodule numbers and mass. The practical implications of the last factor so far as extending the life of the functioning nodule was considered in the direction of growing species under climatic conditions that would extend the vegetative phase, or even by judicious reduction of plant tops so as to remove flower-buds. Finally there was evidence of successful overwintering of nodules under certain climatic conditions and the "potentially perennial" nodules of certain woody perennials. Nodulation patterns can, of course, be modified by environmental factors as frost, excessive soil temperature, drought, grazing and crop removal.

Periodicity has been reported in the nodulation of *Centrosema pubescens* (Bowen, 1959a). Newly developed stoloniferous roots form nodules as older nodules are progressively eliminated from the tap root system. Nodulation and nodule senescence were considered to be governed by the vegetative growth of the plant; cutting, to simulate heavy grazing, resulted in a loss of most of the plant roots and nodules.

5. NEMATODES

Another entirely different biotic factor that affects the functioning of the nodule concerns eel-worm infestation (Robinson, 1961). A large proportion of cowpea nodules were occupied in varying degree, from those showing larval penetration only, where the tissue was still preponderantly occupied by *Rhizobium,* to the condition where the nematode predominated. It is apparently not yet known whether the nodule can resist or recover from nematode infection.

K. Toxic Chemicals

Fertilizers can be toxic to the rhizobia: because of acidity (e.g., super-phosphate) (Cass Smith and Pittman, 1939a; Williams and Back, 1959-60), because of contact with heavy metals of trace elements (Jenkins et al., 1954), or because of severe local osmotic effects.

Fungicidal and protectants may be sufficiently toxic under some circumstances to constitute a hazard to the inoculum (Milthorpe, 1945; Ruhloff and Burton, 1951). Rhizobia differ somewhat in their sensitivity (Hofer, 1958) but in any case, when the use of a fungicide is indicated, it is desirable to add inoculum separately (Williams et al., 1960). Some soil insecticides also reduced nodulation (Braithwaite et al., 1958), presumably by killing rhizobia in the vicinity of the seedling plants. Hormone herbicides are generally without effect on the rhizobia up to concentrations far in excess of those which have a marked effect on the plant itself (Carlyle and Thorpe, 1947; Fletcher, 1956; Fletcher et al., 1957, 1956). Some exceptions have been quoted, however, such as where nodulation was reduced at concentrations at which the growth of the host was not affected. Reduction of fixation has been reported even when growth of rhizobia and nodulation were not affected. Rhizobia differ in their sensitivity to herbicides (Fletcher and Alcorn, 1958); 100 ppm 2-4D was inhibitory for some *R. lupini* but 8000 ppm were needed for *R. meliloti*. The situation with gibberellic acid was similar to the herbicides (Fletcher et al., 1959).

L. Miscellaneous

Various conditions in the cultural history of the rhizobia have been reported as exercising an influence on the effectiveness of subsequently formed nodules. These include plant passage (Acharya et al., 1953), the stage of growth of the host at the time of isolation (Krasil'nikov and Korenyako, 1944), the amino-acid content of the medium (Holding et al., 1960; Wolf and Baldwin, 1940), and the nature of the carbon source (Golebiowska, 1952). The only interpretation possible on present knowledge is that each of these environmental circumstances has modified ultimate symbiotic performance by selection amongst variants.

III. LEGUME SEED INOCULATION

A. General Considerations

Rhizobia of one kind or another are widely, though often sparsely distributed in the soil. However, the limitations imposed by specificity, both in respect of ability to invade a particular host and in forming an effective symbiosis, not infrequently prevent a sown legume from achieving a productive symbiosis. The agriculturalist's reaction to this situation, ranging from nothing more complicated than taking soil from the vicinity of well established plants to the precise use of carefully selected and produced cultures, is an outstanding example of a purposeful entry into the field of microbial ecology. It would not be surprising, however, if this process of "seed inoculation" should sometimes result in failure or only partial success. A large part of our study of the root-nodule bacteria, and the phenomena of their symbiosis with the legume, is concerned with securing the information necessary to increase the degree of success in this operation.

Fred, Baldwin, and McCoy (1932) record earlier instances of the need for seed inoculation, and other reports are to be found throughout the literature; but it is certain that most cases where inoculation is beneficial remain unreported. This will partly result from the lack of novelty in the observation and because more often than not a benefit, even if apparent to the operator, will not have been validated by a carefully planned experiment. Even granting the likelihood that forceful sales promotion sells some unneeded inoculant, the growth of the legume culture industry in so many parts of the world must, in large measure, reflect the farmer's and the agronomist's recognition of the value of seed inoculation. It is at least as likely that economically valuable gains are forfeited by failure to recognize the need to inoculate, by unwillingness to take the additional trouble and by lack of technical appreciation and skill in the operation itself. Sometimes the attitude is an unwillingness to look below ground: a fault not confined to the farmer by any means, but often shared with his agricultural adviser. However, a poor appreciation of the situation can also arise from confusing experimental or observational difficulties. Limitations imposed by another deficiency (P, Mo), inoculant failures because of a need to improve the soil as a medium for rhizobial growth, or unsuitability of the inoculant chosen for the legume concerned are examples. Beyond these, however, is the difficulty that it takes a moderately good field trial to establish a 20% response as significant, even though such a gain could well justify the cost and trouble involved in seed inoculation. Another pitfall likely to confuse the issue is the increase of available soil nitrogen that can result from seed bed preparation and, of course, the use of air-dried, sieved and grossly manipulated soils for greenhouse trials.

Driven back to generalizations, with all the risks that go with them, we can agree (Allen and Allen, 1958) that inoculation is desirable in the majority of agricultural soils throughout the world, that the absence of the same, or sufficiently related, legume in the immediate past history of the area is *prima facie* a case for inoculation, and that land that has been abused, or is being reclaimed (particularly having initially low pH), calls especially for this treatment. We are on surer grounds as soon as we have evidence of poor nodulation of uninoculated seed; for reasons noted already, we are less sure when an added inoculum fails to come up to expectation.

Because this is an aspect of the topic in which any writer must largely call on his own experience, a large part of this account will emphasize

Australian work. It does, however, take into consideration recent discussions with workers in several other countries.

In the United States the inoculant industry is considerable: some $17\frac{1}{2}$ million bushel units being treated with inoculants valued at $4 million (Allen and Allen, 1958). Worthwhile responses can be obtained with a good many legumes, of which soybean, peas, lucerne (alfalfa) and birdsfoot trefoil can be quoted as examples. Clover responses are beginning to show up as these legumes are extended to newer less fertile areas, or when species are involved that are new to an area (such as subterranean clover on the west coast). The survey of the occurrence of *Rhizobium meliloti* in Nebraska (which has already been briefly noted) (Peterson and Goodding, 1941), provides a good factual basis for any recommendations in connection with inoculant use in that state, particularly because of the close and direct relationship between the presence of *R. meliloti* and soil pH. Appleman and Sears (1946a) found that the rhizobia of a wide range of legumes were absent, or sparse, in plots of known cropping history, particularly at the lower pH found in unlimed plots (pH, 5.1). Bean rhizobia were not abundant in any of ten mid-western soils and only 16% of those present were highly effective (Burton et al., 1952); other cases have been quoted with peas (Allen and Allen, 1958; Leonard and Dodson, 1933) and soybean (Allen and Allen, 1958). It has been estimated (Burton, J. C., pers. comm.) that soybean inoculant accounts for about two-thirds of the poundage of legume seed inoculated in the United States. Lucerne and clover account for better than a fifth; pea and vetch are quite considerable. The proportion of sown seed that is inoculated ranges from 80% for lupin to 6% for French bean.

Increasing interest in several South American countries is an indication of favorable responses being obtained or of other evidence that a nodulation problem exists. The introduction of subterranean clover into Uruguay is a case in point.

In Western Europe and the United Kingdom the need for seed inoculation is widely accepted in the case of lucerne (Manil and Bonnier, 1950, 1951; Pochon and de Barjac, 1958; van Schreven et al., 1954). In Holland's program of large scale reclamation of the polders, the freshly drained soil lacks or is very deficient in rhizobia. It would seem, however, from the subsequent behavior of uninoculated areas, that these soils are quite favorable for rhizobial multiplication. Large numbers are built up by the second year of legume cultivation, either from the few already in it, as a result of river contamination before drainage, or from the casual entry of rhizobia after reclamation. The problem with freshly drained soils is acute enough, however, to justify the use of inoculants in order to obtain a rapid establishment. The excellent culture-making facilities at Kampen have been developed to meet this need.

The situation with the clovers in Europe is not as clearly defined. Swedish workers believe that the indications they have obtained in replies to a questionnaire, which has been sent out to farmers over many years, are sufficiently definite to justify the wider use of clover inoculants. Others doubt the validity of such a questionnaire method. Although it is difficult to show an inoculation response with clover in well-established clover areas in Britain, attempts to extend these hosts as pasture components in the poorer hill soils encounter nodulation difficulties, either due to a deficiency of clover rhizobia or because of the occurrence of a large proportion of ineffective strains (Thornton, 1947). A recent survey of Scottish soils (Holding and King, 1963) seems to show an interesting connection between low soil base status and a high proportion of ineffective strains. This may be related to a Dutch observation of what seemed to be a higher proportion of ineffective clover strains in acid peat-bog soils that had a common history of waterlogging (Harmsen and Wieringa, 1954). Federova and Egorava are also quoted (van Schreven, 1958a) as having observed decreased virulence and N-fixing activity in clover rhizobia in unlimed soils of moderately low pH (5.3-5.7).

There are field implications in the effectiveness specificity of vetch rhizobia (30% of isolations from *Vicia faba* found ineffective with that host) (Baird, 1956) and in the medic group, where more than half of those obtained from *Medicago lupulina* were ineffective with it (MacConnell and Bond, 1957a).

Field experiments in Poland and the U.S.S.R. have shown inoculation benefits with a wide range of legumes. Better than 60% of a large number of the experiments quoted gave a response to inoculation: commonly of the order of 20% improvement, but with individual cases better than 200% (Marszewska-Ziemiecka, 1960; Rudakov, 1951; Wrobel, 1959; Wrobel and Marszewska-Ziemiecka, 1960).

The naturally occurring medic rhizobia in the Negev region of Israel were largely ineffective on lucerne. Striking benefit followed on inoculating the seed of that host (Schiffmann, 1958).

The evident need for legume inoculation, problems associated with specificity, field conditions for successful establishment (with possible interactions between bacterial strains and the environment), and the problem of supplying inoculants on a commercial scale currently concern workers in Kenya, Rhodesia, South Africa, and Asian countries.

In New Zealand, Greenwood (1961) has recently provided valuable quantitative data on the occurrence of clover and lotus rhizobia in an extremely acid podzolised soil (pH 4.5) that was being developed for improved pasture. Neither kind of *Rhizobium* could be found in undisturbed soil or, for the clover rhizobia, after cultivation except for small numbers that developed within a year in the limed area. Lotus rhizobia on the other hand developed soon after cultivation and in fair number even without the addition of lime. The population of clover rhizobia that developed after cultivation and liming was ineffective with the introduced subterranean clover, though effective with white clover.

Australia is particularly interesting from the rhizobial point of view because most of the legumes so far introduced have evidently had to depend on the concomitant accidental introduction of specific rhizobia. Many species of *Trifolium* and *Medicago* have spread so far from their point of introduction that the stranger could be pardoned for taking them to be indigenous. Yet they, and their rhizobia, are relatively recent arrivals. With both these genera the naturally occurring plants are generally well nodulated although exceptions can be found in more acid soils (approx. pH 5.2) in which nonnodulated *Medicago* can be found side by side with nodulated species of *Trifolium*. The highly specific *M. laciniata* is often found without nodules (Purchase et al., 1951; Vincent, 1954a). It is likely that the interaction between plant, soil, and *Rhizobium* has been a potent factor in determining the natural advance of these legumes introduced into Australia.

At the same time, the Australian indigenous flora contains a great many legumes, often shrubs and trees. The rhizobia of these, so far as they have been characterized, belong in the cowpea "group." Introduced legumes of this group will therefore often be nodulated by indigenous rhizobia (Bowen, 1956; McKnight, 1949), but the effectiveness of the association will be in doubt due to the marked specificity that determines the successful culmination of the symbiosis. In Western Australia the spread of *Lupinus digitatus* seems to reflect the ability of this introduced legume to symbiose effectively with truly native rhizobia (Lange, 1961; Lange and Parker, 1960, 1961). In the same work it was found that most varieties of *Vigna sinensis* formed associations with native rhizobia, *Glycine hispida* and *Phaseolus lathyroides* in about two-thirds of the cases, but *Ornithopus sativus*, *L. angustifolius*, and *L. luteus* rarely. There is also a poorly defined association between the rhizobia of the indigenous *Trigonella suavissima* and the medic group (Hely and Brockwell, 1960; Vincent, 1962a).

Inoculation responses with introduced legumes have been reported throughout Australia (Cass Smith and Pittman, 1939; Harris, 1961; Hockley, 1961; Strong, 1938a, b; Vincent, 1954a). Closer examination of the situation in New South Wales (Vincent, 1954a) showed that in approximately half the localities examined the clover and medic rhizobia were deficient or sparse. All of the markedly deficient samples for clover rhizobia, except one, were from virgin soils; sparse numbers reflected either a low natural clover population or acidity likely to be unfavorable for survival (pH 5.2 and less). Medic rhizobia, absent from the same acid soils, were also deficient in several soils in which the clover rhizobia were reasonably abundant.

The more detailed studies that have been carried out in several localities show the great diversity of strains to be found even in a relatively restricted area (Baird, 1955; Purchase and Vincent, 1949; Purchase et al., 1951; Vincent, 1954a). These have permitted certain generalizations, relating the effectiveness patterns of local strains to the kind of host with which they had been associated (Vincent, 1954a). Higher rainfall areas having white clover as the common naturalized clover were likely to yield rhizobia that were reasonably or highly effective with that and red clover, but were largely ineffective with subterranean, crimson, and balled clover (*Trifolium glomeratum*). Coastal situations were particularly striking in this respect, one yielding only 10% (of 84) isolates effective on subterranean and crimson clovers (Vincent, 1954b). Conversely, a drier region that favored the natural growth of *T. glomeratum* was found to have 92% of its isolates effective on subterranean clover, but only 34% effective on red and 32% on white clover (Purchase and Vincent, 1949).

The extraordinary degree of host specificity both in respect of invasiveness and effectiveness in the naturalized medic rhizobia (Hely and Brockwell, 1960, 1962; Purchase et al., 1951; Vincent, 1954a, 1962a) make generalizations with this group particularly difficult except to note that they are often ineffective, or only partially effective, with sown medics.

A good deal of the developing interest in seed inoculation is associated with programs aimed at the introduction of legumes into tropical or subtropical regions (Dawson, 1962; Norris, 1956, 1959b). Although much more is now being done in this area of rhizobial study the situation with the "cowpea miscellany," with which the tropical worker is almost always concerned, is so complex that one can foresee large programs of work ahead for many years to come.

In their nodulating ability the "cowpea rhizobia" range from those that are widely promiscuous, e.g., *Phaseolus lathyroides*, *Vigna sinensis* (Bowen, 1959b), to others that are markedly specific, e.g., *Lotononis bainesii* (Norris, 1958) and *Centrosema pubescens* (Bowen, 1959b). The native legume bacteria seem to occur patchily and where they do occur and are ineffective with the introduced legume, competition between them and the inoculant will be important. When the question of effectiveness specificity is imposed on top of invasiveness we have, as a result, a marked need for inoculation and a complicated problem in providing strains for commercial use. Meanwhile, the only safe agronomic approach to the introduction of these species anywhere is to inoculate the seed with a rhizobial strain whose efficacy has been proved with the same species. One can only conjecture how much wasted effort has resulted from failure to do this in the past; investigated cases indicate that it could be considerable.

B. Requirements for Successful Inoculation

Strains must be selected, carefully maintained, and regularly tested, so as to minimize the chance of undetected variation; the culture must contain sufficient viable cells at the stage of use; it must be used in such a way as to maintain these numbers; and the seedling environment must, if necessary, be improved to ensure rhizobial survival, to permit nodule formation and provide for proper nodule functioning.

1. STRAIN SELECTION

The strain, or strains, used for the inoculation of a particular legume must be able to form effective nodules with it, and to do this under a wide range of field conditions. If necessary it must compete successfully with naturally occurring strains. Although these needs have long been recognized, inoculants have not uncommonly failed in respect of one or more of them.

Where the inoculant industry is large enough it can itself accept a fair measure of responsibility for selecting its own strains from the stage of laboratory or greenhouse, to testing in the field. More commonly, a large part or all of the responsibility rests with government and related institutions. Generally the boundaries are not sharply drawn and cultures are freely exchanged between the responsible agencies. Culture provision by AID/USDA (Agency for International Development/U.S. Department of Agriculture) is a valuable cooperative venture aimed at helping countries, less well equipped technologically in respect of rhizobial work, to obtain cultures for their own agronomic programs. At a different level, but interesting because of its cooperative approach involving manufacturers, universities, and state departments of agriculture, is the organization that has evolved in Australia and which is known as the University-Department of Agriculture Laboratory Service (U-DALS) (McLeod et al., 1961; Vincent, 1958b). This has, without any statutory authority or rigid constitution, developed into the advising and controlling body for the Australian inoculant industry. As such, it largely accepts direct responsibility for strain testing and selection, but does so in cooperation and close consultation with other authorities.

Field testing is essential as the ultimate means of discriminating between strains that may be indistinguishable in the greenhouse or artificial light room, and are used routinely for the regular checking of recommended strains. The field test itself, particularly if it is carried out in several distinctive environments, and if reports from other centers are coordinated with it, is about as good a safeguard as one can secure against being misled by a strain that might show up to advantage only under a restricted set of environmental conditions (comp. Joffe et al., 1961).

Australian experience with two varieties of subterranean clover (Yarloop and Woogenellup) serves to underline the need to test strain performance in the field, as well as under the more standardized conditions of the greenhouse. In each case a recommended strain was able to achieve an effective symbiosis in the laboratory, but was strikingly unsuccessful in the field. The trouble lay in the relatively few plants that were nodulated. Such as were nodulated were fully effective.

In the author's experience variation in symbiotic properties has led to loss of invasiveness (on two occasions) and of effectiveness (on several occasions): both hazards in the absence of regular testing. Provision for long-term storage of reference cultures and reduction of subculturing between tests is desirable to lessen this risk. As noted already the introduction of genetically different hosts can also cause difficulties in the way of reduced compatibility with the regular commercial strains. Avoidance of this difficulty requires better liaison between the plant breeder, or introduction officer, and the inoculant industry. One may hope that eventually the agronomist will look on rhizobial incompatibility as much as undesirable agronomic character as susceptibility to disease.

a. Specificity

Specificity between bacterium and legume host has important practical implications, e.g., among the clovers (Hely, 1957; Norris, 1959; Nutman, 1959; Strong, 1937; Vincent, 1954a), the pea-vetch group (Erdman and Burton, 1939), *Medicago:Melilotus* (Purchase et al., 1951; Strong, 1940; Vincent, 1954a; Wilson et al., 1937), and the cowpea miscellany (Bowen, 1956, 1959b; Bowen and Kennedy, 1961; Norris, 1958).

"Wide-spectrum" strains are an attempt to overcome some of the restric-

tions imposed by such specificities. Their use has been moderately successful in Australia in the case of several clover species, to a less extent with
Medicago and *Melilotus,* and for some members of the cowpea miscellany.
Where it is practicable it represents a considerable advantage at the point
of manufacture, distribution and use, but the best of strains is unlikely
to be equally good with all of its invaded hosts, so that special provision
soon and often becomes necessary.

It is tempting to "synthesize" a wide spectrum culture by blending
strains individually less comprehensive in their effectiveness. Mixing
several fully effective strains can be justified on the grounds that it might
safeguard against localized effects operating against the success of a single
strain, but the incorporation of any strain that forms ineffective nodules
with any of the recommended hosts is hazardous, to say the least.

b. Competitiveness

Strains differ in their relative ability to establish themselves in the
vicinity of different hosts and in securing nodulation (Read, 1953; Vincent and Waters, 1953). To some extent the relative performance of
strains can be affected by locality and other factors (Vincent, 1954a,
1956). Serological methods of strain recognition provide a valuable
means of determining the relative success of strains (Jenkins et al., 1954;
Manil and Bonnier, 1950; Marshall, 1956; Pochon et al., 1950; Read,
1953; Thornton and Kleczkowski, 1950; Vincent, 1956, Vincent and
Waters, 1953). Production of a chlorosis-inducing factor has also been
used for strain recognition in soybean (Means et al., 1961).

c. Strain Performance in Relation to Soil Fertility

Some consider that the level of fertility should be taken into account
in testing strains used for commercial inoculants. Some rhizobia have
been reported as better able than others to fix nitrogen in poorly nourished (e.g., potassium-deficient) plants. The interesting suggestion has
also been put forward (Pate and Dart, 1961) that strains for use in more
fertile soils might be selected for their ability to sustain nitrogen-fixation
at moderately high levels of combined-N.

d. Practicalities in Strain Selection

It is very easy for the laboratory-based investigator to emphasize how
every host species, indeed every variety that is introduced or bred, and
every soil and climatic environment should be provided with its own
bespoke strain of *Rhizobium.* Such an ideal, however, has to be balanced
by the complications it causes in inoculant manufacture and use, and
the prescience it demands of those responsible for strain selection in the
weight they give the various factors and their interplay. To be realist in
this matter is not to be defeatist, and some factors are obviously of such
importance as to demand attention. However, from our experience we
feel reasonably sure that a strain that performs well with the major commercial varieties in several diverse localities will do most of what is required of it. For example, a clover culture isolated from a cool temperate
region in Tasmania (latitude about 42°), and selected for its ability to fix

nitrogen with all the species and varieties of clover we were then concerned with, has proved itself a valuable strain throughout Australia in entirely different environments. Admittedly special requirements have on occasions to be provided for, as in this case to meet the need of the Woogenellup variety of subterranean clover, but multiplying commercial strains, like matrimony, is "not to be enterprised, nor taken in hand unadvisedly, (or) lightly."

e. Multiple-Strain Inoculants

These are used in two ways: (a) to provide rhizobia of more than one cross-inoculation group (e.g., lucerne and clover), for greater ease of merchandising; (b) as multiple strains belonging to the same group.

There need be no very great difficulty with the first usage (provided the cultures are grown in separate broths) unless one were to grossly outgrow the other after packaging, or if there were such a growth of the non-specific rhizobium in the rhizosphere as to suppress the specific organism and so delay nodulation.

Multiple cultures within a cross-inoculation group have been developed empirically as a means of lessening the risk of unfavourable variation in one rhizobial strain or the risk of inferior performance under certain environmental conditions, or with a particular host. Protection in this way against phage susceptibility has also been suggested. The practice is, however, based on too little investigation. There is the possibility that one or two of the strains might, somewhere along the line, so outstrip the others that the final culture may be made up almost entirely of such growth-dominant strains. On present information we could not necessarily expect that a strain dominant up to this stage would be the best in its field performance. Our own studies and those of Marshall (1956) led us to recommend delaying mixing to a stage when each culture will have had the opportunity of developing to its maximum. Where numerous strains are grown up together in the broth before mixing with peat the likelihood that some strain(s) will grossly outgrow others is maximized. At the same time, one can appreciate practical difficulties in keeping many strains separate up to the stage of maturation of the inoculated peat.

Potentially more serious is the situation when a synthetic "wide-spectrum" culture includes strains not fully effective with all the hosts for which the culture is recommended. Mixed cultures should, because of the hazards otherwise likely to be involved, contain only strains that are fully effective with all their prescribed hosts. Present knowledge does not give us any reason to believe that the host and bacteria will always pair up to the best advantage (Burton and Allen, 1950; Burton et al., 1954; Dunham and Baldwin, 1931; Vincent and Waters, 1953).

2. SUFFICIENCY OF VIABLE CELLS

The relationship between the number of viable cells put on the seed and successful nodulation is not likely to be simple (Vincent, 1954a). According to the conditions rhizobia encounter after inoculation, there could, on the one hand, be sufficient multiplication from even a few cells to ensure adequate nodulation, on the other such a poor survival as to demand a much heavier inoculum (Baird, 1955; Fred et al., 1932; Jenkins et al., 1954; Rudakov, 1951).

In looking for a moderately rigorous minimal standard, we in Australia, as well as some workers in other parts of the world, have set a figure of about 100 viable cells per seed at the time of inoculation. We recognize that 1000 per seed would be safer and that some situations could require more. Although these figures were arrived at perhaps as an inspired guess it has certainly been our experience, and that of others, that when the number falls below such a level partial or complete nodulation failures are likely to occur.

Insistence on "super-inoculants" would seem to be justified only under conditions where extreme mortality could be expected (as when the seed is inoculated long before sowing (Hastings and Drake, 1960) or as a way to counter an unfavorable post-sowing environment (Hely et al., 1957). In this last connection success has been claimed for measures to encourage rhizobial multiplication by inclusion of nutrient in the seed pellet (Bergersen et al., 1958), but whether this is the full explanation of the matter remains doubtful (Thompson, 1961). The view has been put (Allen and Allen, 1958) that emphasis on quantitative potency can be misplaced. Proper use of the inoculant, prompt sowing and soil improvement are at least as important and should be able to avoid undue loss of viability between inoculation and sowing, and permit rhizobia to multiply to a level that saturates the rhizosphere.

3. THE FORM AND USE OF INOCULA

Generally, except for specialist use, agar-grown cultures have been replaced by those in which the culture is increased first in broth, which is then used to impregnate a powdered carrier such as peat. There are two quite different approaches to the larger scale manufacture of inoculants. The first of these, commonly used in Europe, is where the inoculum, grown first in a well-aerated liquid medium, is added aseptically to sterilized peat, plain or enriched (van Schreven, 1958b, van Schreven et al., 1954). In this method the peat is in fact a medium for the considerable growth of rhizobia and no further packaging takes place between growth and sale. The second is the large-scale method favored in America, in which the culture is grown to a high count in broth (1000 million to 5000 million/ml), and mixed with dry, finely divided (but not sterile) peat so as to give a moisture content of 35%-40%. The seeded peat is allowed to "mature" for several days, during which time a 5- to 10-fold multiplication may be expected, and is then packaged.

Sterile peat is undoubtedly able to give very high count peats (3000 million/g after 12 months storage). However, this method requires some skill and care in the maintenance of aseptic conditions of handling and, from the control point of view, suffers from the fact that each container has its own history and a relatively large number would therefore have to be sampled to obtain a reliable estimate of the quality of a given batch. The demands it makes on labor, time, and facilities could operate against its use for large-scale operations. Provision of sterile peat in the large scale handling of the method and its maintenance in that condition is not practical. It is not difficult, none the less, to produce a good quality culture able to meet the kind of standards already mentioned for a period of six months, provided the storage temperature is not excessive. Survival in cultures based on nonsterile peats is, however, more temperature-dependent than on the sterile.

Other methods of preparing inoculants (sterilized soil, dried legume roots, crushed nodules, the inclusion of "activator" bacteria, dehydration with talc as carrier) have been used in the U.S.S.R. (Rudakov, 1951).

Lyophilized cultures have been produced commercially in Australia for several years and have been successfully used in the field. They have the advantage of a rather better shelf life than the usual (nonsterile) peat cultures, even at moderately elevated temperatures. They have the disadvantage, shared with agar cultures, that they lack the protection exercised by peat that extends the post-inoculation survival on the seed. In fact, we have found that freeze-dried cells died off on the seed even more rapidly than did those that were freshly suspended from agar culture. There have not been many field trials in which the merits of these several forms have been compared. No difference was found in one set but it is likely that inoculated seed sown into a dry seed bed and having to lie there for some time before germination would benefit from the extra survival associated with peat.

Proper use of the inoculum requires the seed to be uniformly coated with sufficient cells, the death of the bacteria between inoculation and sowing to be minimized, and the immediate environment of the sown seed to be favorable for rhizobial survival, nodule formation, and nitrogen-fixation.

Simple dusting of the seed with the powdered peat can be effective provided the peat is fine enough. It may have to be used as the most practical method for the inoculation of pelleted seed. In general, however, slurried peat is preferred as a way of putting more rhizobia on the seed and getting them to adhere, particularly if an adhesive, such as methylethyl cellulose or gum arabic, is used. Cultures grown on agar, and lyophilized cultures, are taken up with water, preferably containing an adhesive gum protective supplement.

Pelleted seed has particular value where it is not possible to use more orthodox methods of securing a safe environment for the rhizobia (Cass Smith and Goss, 1958; Loneragan et al., 1955). Pelleting with lime provides a fair measure of protection against acidity in soil and fertilizer at the time of sowing, but the small amount involved can hardly be expected to exercise any long term modification of the environment such as may be needed for the regeneration of an annual legume. The pelleting material may also, by providing a small physical barrier between the rhizobia and the seed, protect against toxic effects of the latter. Field trials (Thompson, 1961) with pelleted seed of subterranean clover, sown into soil of high enough pH to cause no trouble on that score, but which had previously been troublesome so far as nodulation was concerned (Hely et al., 1957) showed that pelleting was beneficial in all cases, the effect being independent of the chemical composition of the material. Bentonite which had been proposed (Bergersen et al., 1958), together with dried blood as nutrient, was no better than titanium oxide (Thompson, 1961). Brockwell (1962) also found that a variety of pelleting materials gave good nodulation of subterranean clover in podzolic tableland soils.

Other points that need to be observed to avoid toxic effects on the bacteria are the use of neutralized or near-neutralized phosphate rather than acidic super-phosphate, and avoidance of contact with ions of toxic heavy metals or with harmful pesticides.

Problems of seed inoculation under tropical conditions have suggested the use of a solid inoculum, preferably based on vermiculite, planted near though separate from the seed. These special precautions were however only partially successful (Bonnier, 1960).

4. SURVIVAL OF CELLS IN COMMERCIAL INOCULANTS

Data from various sources were tabulated (Table 3) as average time (in weeks) for tenfold reduction in rhizobial numbers (decimal reduction time). At a low temperature all forms of culture were sufficiently stable to ensure satisfactory survival after 6 months, although to some extent susceptibility to death was sub-strain dependent in liquid cultures at 2°C and freeze-dried. All forms of culture, except the sterile laboratory peat, were susceptible in some degree to a higher temperature of storage. The value of free access of air for the maintenance of viable numbers in a sterile soil-peat base is shown from a more detailed consideration of van Schreven's results (quoted: Vincent, 1958a). Excessive loss of water operated against survival even with laboratory peat stored at low temperature.

Table 3. Survival of rhizobia in various forms of inoculant.

Form of culture	Host group & conditions	Decimal reduction time (weeks)* at various temperatures		Source of data
		Low	Moderate	
Agar	Clover	18 [5°]	8 [25°]	Waters (Vincent, 1958)
Broth	Clover substrains	8-21 [2°] 23-40 [-30°]	–	Bloomfield (Vincent, 1958 Table 1.)
	Clover & Lupin		1-2 [18°]	Date, unpub.
Freeze-dried, laboratory	Clover substrains	7-91 [2°]	–	Bloomfield (Vincent, 1958 Table 1.)
Freeze-dried, commercial	Clover	173 [5°]	18 [25°] 15 [30°] 12 [37°]	Roughley & McLeod (1961)
	Clover		21 [room]	Chaston, unpub.
	Centrosema	–	58 "	"
	Soybean		69 "	"
	Lucerne		118 "	"
Peat, laboratory	Clover, var. water loss	11->100[5°]	5-48 [25°]	Waters (Vincent, 1958 Table 2.)
	Lucerne, nonsterile	21-38 [5°]	8-14 [25°]	Date, unpub.
	Lucerne, sterile	Indef. [5°]	94 [25°]	
Peat, commercial	Nonsterile	–	9-36 [25°]	Date, (Vincent, 1958 Table 3.)
Soil peat	Sterile	–	8-59[room]	van Schreven (Vincent, 1958)

* Calculated time for tenfold reduction in number of viable cells. Bracketed values: = storage temperatures, °C.

So far, commercial peat cultures that are produced on the large scale have been based on nonsterile, though heat-dried, peat. The abundant occurrence of other forms of microorganisms in such peat, especially actinomycetes, raises the possibility of active antibiosis operating against the rhizobia (Abdel-Ghaffar and Allen, 1950; Afrikyan and Tumanyan, 1959). A collection of 55 organisms isolated from 14 samples of commercial peat yielded some (14/55) that were antagonistic against *Rhizobium* when grown on yeast mannitol agar. However, peat added to the medium prevented expression of the antagonism and the antibiotic could be removed from the filtrate by sufficient exposure to peat. Rhizobia also grew in sterile peat-broth mixtures containing the "antagonistic" organisms without any evidence of inhibition in that situation (Purchase, H. F., pers. comm.). Van Schreven also failed to obtain any striking evidence of rhizobial inhibition on agar. Inhibition zones, ordinarily obtained on an agar-medium, did not appear when 2% w/v peat (moisture-60%) was incorporated (van Schreven, D. A., pers. comm.).

5. SURVIVAL ON THE INOCULATED SEED

The death rate of rhizobia after they have been applied to the surface of seed is likely to be increased some 10- to 100-fold (Vincent, 1958a). In such a situation peat confers a considerable measure of protection so that survival from a peat culture is likely to be much better than it is with cells suspended from fresh agar growth, which in turn is very much superior to those that have been freeze-dried (Table 4).

With some legumes the seed itself can be actively toxic against rhizobia (Bowen, 1961; Thompson, 1960; Vincent et al., 1962). The likely toxic effect of pesticides applied to the seed is difficult to predict under practical conditions. There have been sufficient instances of toxic action, however, to justify considerable caution with regard to the chemical composition of the pesticide of choice, dosage, and measures that might be taken

Table 4. Survival of different forms of culture on seed of subterranean clover.

Form of inoculant	Suspending medium	Surviving cells*		Grow-out test†	Field trial‡ %crown-nodu-	Source of data
		1 day	14 days	% + tubes	lated plants	
Peat	Sucrose	4,900	89	100	83[90]§	Thompson,
Peat	Gum arabic	10,000	600	100	97[910]	J. A. (unpub.)
Broth	Sucrose	1,000	4	100	77[5]	
Broth	Gum arabic	1,000	1	100	74[2]	
Freeze-dried	Sucrose	36	NR	17	7[NR]	
Freeze-dried	Gum arabic	21	NR	0	13[NR]	
Peat	Water	350	2	100[1]	100¶	Chaston,
Peat	Maltose	2,200	2	100[2]	94	Margaret(unpub.)
Freeze-dried	Water	12	NR	9[NR]	33	
Freeze-dried	Maltose	230	NR	3[NR]	47	

* From an initial 10,000/seed.   † Seed planted singly; 14 days (J. A. T.); 24 days (M. C.), bracketed number = estimated rhizobia/seed.   ‡ Freshly inoculated: 97-100%; Uninoculated: 17-27%.   § Sown at 8 days.   Bracketed numbers = estimated rhizobia /seed.   ¶ Sown at 16 days.   NR: None recovered.

to separate rhizobia from the treated seed (Appleman, 1941; Appleman and Sears, 1946b; Braithwaite et al., 1958; Milthorpe, 1945).

Certain additives (notably maltose and gum arabic) improve survival on the seed, particularly of water-suspended cells (Vincent et al., 1962), but also have an effect with peat slurry (Date, R. A., and Vincent, J. M., unpub.). Those concerned with extending survival under conditions where the inoculated seed could be exposed to a long pregermination period in a dry seed bed (Brockwell and Whalley, 1962) present evidence of the value of taking the peat culture up in a thick solution of gum arabic (45%) and surrounding the inoculated seed with pellet. No decline could be detected 27 days after inoculation in this fashion (Brockwell, 1962). The same procedure but with methylethyl cellulose substituting for gum arabic resulted in a 100-fold to 1000-fold decrease in the number of viable cells over the same period. The outside coating of the pellet seemed also to improve survival.

The importance to survival of conditions in the vicinity of the sown inoculated seed has already been discussed. Precautions involve protection against acidity (soil and fertilizer) or contact with other toxic ions. Data (due to Marshall) show such an effect very clearly, as well as the relationship between rhizobial numbers on the seed and success or failure of nodulation (Table 5). High soil temperatures are also a hazard for the inoculated seed. A temperature of 40°C is quite lethal for rhizobia and can persist as long as 6 hours in the day under Australian summer conditions (Bowen and Kennedy, 1959). Strains differ in their sensitivity to elevated temperatures, which might explain the better survival of locally adapted strains found in South Africa (Hausen et al., 1959).

C. Control of Quality

The extent to which the manufacturer is able directly and individually to carry out a full control program on his product depends on the size of his production. This offers no difficulty to the really large inoculant manufacturer or to an organization where other production lines are also microbiological in nature and demand the same kind of facilities. In the United States the industry passed from the situation in the early 1930's, when about half the cultures were clearly unsatisfactory, to one where it was unusual for a culture to fail the standard (admittedly minimal) set by

Table 5. Relationship between neutralization of superphosphate, rhizobial numbers, and nodulation.

Treatment 112 lb. superphosphate per acre + lime (lb.)	No. of rhizobia per seed after 1/2 hr. (initial = 17,000)	Percentage nodulated plants (clover)
0	13	15
14	170	68
28	155	62
56	204	69
112	2,800	94

* Marshall, K. C.; personal communication.

a greenhouse "grow-out" test. However, the arrival of pre-inoculation has forced a somewhat hasty re-examination of the control measures and standards used in the United States. When a reasonable quantitative standard was recently applied to cultures produced in the United States and sold in Canada (Jordan, D. C., pers. comm.), about a third of the 88 tested were considered either unsatisfactory (less than a million viable rhizobia per g peat) or doubtful (between 1 and 10 million).

Developments in Australia have been quite different and reflect the relatively small size of the total industry which, divided as it is among several manufacturers, precludes each producer accepting the full quality control of his product. Out of this practical situation there evolved the co-operative testing organization (U-DALS, already discussed in connection with strain selection), which takes care of all aspects of quality control for the Australian inoculant industry (McLeod et al., 1961; Vincent, 1958b). This organization tests and selects strains, maintains and issues mother cultures, and checks the quality of the broth culture before it is added to peat. The presence of the correct strain(s) is checked serologically as well as freedom from contaminants. A broth standard of at least 500×10^6 viable rhizobia/ml of broth gives a peat culture with at least 200×10^6/g initially (without allowing for the considerable increase that can be expected after the peat is mixed). The quality of freeze-dried cultures is also checked as well as representative finished cultures, some obtained direct from the manufacturer and others purchased through normal retail channels.

In Australia a million viable specific rhizobia/g peat is taken as the minimal standard at any stage between production and expiry date. In fact, any between this and ten million are counted as doubtful and much higher counts are expected early in the life of the peat culture. (It has been calculated that on an average the standards quoted permit at least 100-1000 rhizobia to be applied per seed.) Our field experience has confirmed the practicality and desirability of such a standard for seed sown immediately after inoculation.

The direct "grow-out" test, so much used in the United States, sets a much lower standard than the U-DALS requirements above. On the other hand the New Zealand authorities have established a much higher standard again for their peat cultures (100×10^6/g peat, minimal at any stage during the market life of the peat). This superior standard caters for the heavy mortality that would be associated with the use of these cultures for pre-inoculation. It is doubtful to what extent field situations will be reflected in any additional benefit due to the higher standard, when the seed is sown freshly inoculated. The Dutch method of producing cultures in sterile fortified peat (van Schreven, 1958b; van Schreven et al., 1954) meant that very high numbers (of the order 5×10^9 to 10×10^9/g moist peat) could be obtained and maintained over a long storage period. However, the same workers noted that other cultures having fewer rhizobia were not necessarily inferior in their field performance. A very high standard seems also to have been set for cultures in the U.S.S.R. (200 g culture per acre at 50×10^6 to 100×10^6 rhizobia per g; contaminants not to exceed 10%, fungi to be absent) (Rudakov, 1951).

D. Pre-inoculation

The term "pre-inoculation" is currently used to describe the practice of inoculating legume seed well in advance of its intended use. Literally it could cover short-term centralized inoculation to meet specific orders, but this, which might preferably be called "custom-inoculation," need not be subject to anything like the hazards associated with pre-inoculation in the usual sense (long-term and wholesale).

Pre-inoculation is not a new idea, but was in fact discarded years ago because of poor results of earlier attempts at its use (Leonard, 1938). Its revival has been largely associated with the vigorous promotion of a vacuum process which purports to force many rhizobia beneath the seed coat, where they are supposed to be less vulnerable to the usual causes of death (Porter et al., 1960). Other quite different processes are also in use, *viz.* those that are coated and others that are spread as dried cells (Erdman, 1961). A process that extended the life of rhizobia on the seed sufficiently to provide a practical method of pre-inoculation could make seed inoculation more generally acceptable, by taking it out of the relatively unskilled and generally less willing hands of the farmer or contractor and putting it in the hands of well-equipped and better-informed specialists. From an economic point of view it need add very little to the cost of seed; from the point of view of the inoculant manufacturer it would increase sales considerably.

1. EVALUATION

Full evaluation of such procedures is difficult on the evidence so far available. On the one hand there is in some commercial quarters considerable enthusiasm for its advantages. On the other, independent authorities in several parts of the world, particularly those who have attempted to assess the situation in quantitative terms, are generally much more conservative. The latter are unwilling to accept the risk of the very great loss of viable cells that can be expected even with the best pre-inoculation technique, particularly if storage temperatures are elevated and if the conditions under which the seed is liable to be sown are such as to make the issue of successful nodulation a critical one for establishment, at the same time as they operate against it. These are, in fact, the situations that call for heavier levels of inoculum and it can be disastrous to weight the scale against having sufficient viable cells by permitting heavy pre-sowing mortality. It is doubted whether our knowledge of pre-inoculation is currently sufficient to justify the introduction of this process in areas where much of the legume planting is done toward the end of a hot season. In the United States, for example, it has been accepted policy to limit pre-inoculation to areas where cool weather prevails during the months prior to planting.

A survival and field trial conducted from the author's laboratory with surface-coated seed of subterranean clover and vetch showed very clearly the practical significance of reduction in the number of viable cells as a result of pre-inoculation, and the very great influence exerted by tempera-

Table 6. Comparison of three-months pre-inoculated seed with freshly inoculated seed (Field trials).

Inoculation	Percent plants effectively nodulated	
	Vetch	Subterranean clover
Nil	2	17
Fresh	76	89
Pre-inoculated and held at:		
15° – 18° C	22	45
25°C	1	16

ture which was able to over-ride any benefit conferred by supplements. Seed stored for 3 months at 15°C or 18°C had 5 to 260 surviving cells per seed out of an initial heavy application of approximately 100,000. No survivors could be detected with any treatment after the same time at 25°C. Nodulation of the plants agreed very well with what one would expect from such data. Plants from seed stored at 25°C were never any better than those of the uninoculated control. Those from seed stored at the lower temperature were detectably better nodulated than uninoculated, though much inferior to the freshly inoculated (Table 6). Results such as this show very clearly the dangers inherent in long term pre-inoculation. Claims in support of the process need to be substantiated by quantitative results obtained under reasonably exacting field conditions.

Such independent reports as have come out of the United States on pre-inoculated seed, especially vacuum-treated, have been by no means encouraging. In one case 17/38 samples of those that were on sale in 1960-1961 failed to meet a relatively easy requirement under greenhouse conditions (Indiana Agr. Exp. Sta. (Purdue Univ.) Inspection Rep. No. 28, Feb. 1961). In another, 11/16 samples of seed that had been pre-inoculated by the vacuum process were unsatisfactory and the remaining were only fair.

The situation as it developed in North America found control procedures and techniques inadequate for the proper testing of the vigorous claims that were being made on behalf of pre-inoculation. The poorly discriminating "grow-out" tests could be expected to yield positives with seed carrying even a few viable cells. (It had been noted many years before (Leonard, 1938) that such greenhouse tests had failed to differentiate between inoculants applied dry and wet, whereas differences in favor of the latter were apparent in the field.) Satisfactory quantitative checks applied at this early stage could have avoided the intervening period of confusion: a state of affairs not made any better by the claim made by one advocate of pre-inoculation that no quantitative test is even yet satisfactory. Confronted with this attitude one might ask, without agreeing with the validity of the claim, how the hazardous business of preinoculation came to be promoted commercially, if a satisfactory means of assessing its efficacy was not available.

A recent report (Loneragan et al., 1961) might superficially be regarded as lending some support to the vacuum process. Subterranean clover seed that had been treated with a very heavy initial inoculum (a million viable cells/seed) and stored at about 20°-27°C for a year gave about 51% nodulated plants in a grow-out test. One thousand cells initially gave

16% nodulated plants. Seed giving such poor results under the favorable conditions of the grow-out test could be expected to be a poor proposition under field conditions. The use of labelled bacteria throws some further light on the question. From Date's results (personnel communication) it seemed that perhaps 10% of the rhizobia put on lucerne seed and subject to the vacuum treatment were sufficiently closely associated with the seed to be resistant to removal by washing. However, a considerable proportion of these were nonviable and most of them were associated with less than 40% of the seed: a result that could well explain the patchiness that has been a frequent result with vacuum-processed pre-inoculated seed. Cooper's results were substantially in agreement: 5 to 15% of the seeds carried 75 to 90% of the bacteria (Cooper, 1962). The vacuum treatment increased uptake of bacteria only by a small group of "acquisitive" seeds and so tended merely to increase the inherently uneven distribution of the bacteria resistant to removal by washing. It may, therefore, increase the chances of nodulation of plants coming from a small group of seed which from other evidence presented in the paper includes many that are probably damaged and poorly germinating. It has little effect on the great majority of seeds. A recent Australian report (Brockwell and Hely, 1962), though indicating that the application of considerable positive pressure could force a large number of cells under the seed coat, where they seem to have survived fairly well, included the surprising result that such cells were trapped and therefore unable to colonize the rhizosphere and form nodules.

2. COATING AND PELLETING

New Zealand workers (Hastings and Drake, 1960) put their trust in a coating and pelleting process and the use of very great initial numbers. Grow-out tests of pre-inoculated white clover showed all tubes positive after 5 to 6 months storage in the case of the best treatments (pellets of dolomite and soil). Good results were also obtained in a greenhouse trial using two low-fertility soils, 5 months after seed-inoculation. This was supported by field trials. These and the similar results obtained by Brockwell (1962), again with coated and pelleted seed, are perhaps the most promising so far with pre-inoculation. Whether the factors concerned have as yet been sufficiently defined to ensure that pre-inoculated seed can be used with full assurance is another matter.

3. STANDARDS FOR PRE-INOCULATED SEED

The Australian view is that if pre-inoculation were to be accepted, such seed should be required to meet the same standard up to its expiry date as that provided with seed that has been freshly inoculated with a satisfactory peat culture (at least 100 viable rhizobia/seed).

ACKNOWLEDGMENTS

The author wishes to acknowledge the cooperation of the many colleagues and other workers who have permitted him to quote their unpublished data.

REFERENCES

Abdel-Ghaffar, A. S., and Allen, O. N. 1950. The effects of certain microorganisms on the growth and function of rhizobia. Trans., Intern. Cong. Soil Sci. 4th Cong. Amsterdam, pp. 93-96.

Acharya, C. N., Jain, S. P., and Jha, J. 1953. Studies on the building up of soil fertility by the phosphatic fertilization of legumes. Influence of growing berseem on the nitrogen content of the soil. J. Indian Soc. Soil Sci. 1:55-64.

Afrikyan, E. K., and Tumanyan, V. G. 1959. The antagonistic effect of soil microorganisms on cultures of nodule bacteria. Abs. Soils and Fert. 22:285 (1718).

Ahmed, S., and Evans, H. J. 1959. Effect of cobalt on the growth of soybeans in the absence of supplied nitrogen. Biochem. and Biophys. Res. Commun. 1:271-275.

Ahmed, S., and Evans, H. J. 1960. Cobalt: a micronutrient element for the growth of soybean plants under symbiotic conditions. Soil Sci. 90:205-210.

Ahmed, S., and Evans, H. J. 1961. The essentiality of cobalt for soybean plants grown under symbiotic conditions. Proc. Natl. Acad. Sci. 47:24-36.

Albrecht, W. A. 1932. Calcium and hydrogen -ion concentration in the growth and inoculation of soybeans. J. Amer. Soc. Agron. 24:793-806.

Albrecht, W. A. 1933. Inoculation of legumes as related to soil acidity. J. Amer. Soc. Agron. 25:512-522.

Albrecht, W. A. 1941. Drilling limestone for legumes. Univ. Missouri Agr. Exp. Sta. Bul. 429. 20 pp.

Allen, Ethyl K., and Allen, O. N. 1950. Biochemical and symbiotic properties of the rhizobia. Bact. Rev. 14:273-330.

Allen, Ethyl K., and Allen, O. N. 1958. Biological aspects of symbiotic nitrogen fixation. *In* Encyclopedia of Plant Physiology, ed. Ruhland, Springer-Verlag, Berlin. pp. 48-118.

Allen, O. N., and Baldwin, I. L. 1931. The effectiveness of rhizobia as influenced by passage through the host plant. Wisconsin Agr. Exp. Sta. Res. Bul. 106. 56 pp.

Allos, H. F., and Bartholomew, W. V. 1955. Effect of available nitrogen on symbiotic fixation. Soil Sci. Soc. Amer. Proc. 19:182-184.

Allos, H. F., and Bartholomew, W. V. 1959. Replacement of symbiotic fixation by available nitrogen. Soil Sci. 87:61-66.

Anderson, A. J. 1956a. Molybdenum deficiencies in legumes in Australia. Soil Sci. 81:173-258.

Anderson, A. J. 1956b. Molybdenum as a fertilizer. Adv. Agron. 8:163-202.

Anderson, A. J., and Moye, D. V. 1952. Lime and molybdenum in clover development on acid soils. Austral. J. Agr. Res. 3:95-110.

Anderson, A. J., and Oertel, A. C. 1946. Plant responses to molybdenum as a fertilizer. 2. Factors affecting the response of plants to molybdenum. Council Sci. Ind. Res. Bul. 198:25-44.

Anderson, A. J., and Spencer, D. 1949. Molybdenum and sulphur in symbiotic nitrogen fixation. Nature (Lond.) 164:273.

Anderson, A. J., and Spencer, D. 1950a. Molybdenum in nitrogen metabolism of legumes and non-legumes. Austral. J. Sci. Res. Ser. B. Biol. Sci. 3:414-430.

Anderson, A. J., and Spencer, D. 1950b. Sulphur in nitrogen metabolism of legumes and non-legumes. Austral. J. Sci. Res. Ser. B. Biol. Sci. 3:431-449.

Anderson, A. J., and Thomas, Margaret P. 1946. Plant responses to molybdenum as a fertilizer. 1. Molybdenum and symbiotic nitrogen fixation. Council Sci. Ind. Res. Bul. 198:7-24.

Andrew, C. S. 1962. Influence of nutrition on nitrogen fixation and growth of legumes. *In* A Review of Nitrogen in the Tropics with Particular Reference to Pastures. Commonwealth Bur. Pastures and Field Crops. Bul. 46. pp. 130-146.

Andrew, C. S., and Norris, D. O. 1961. Comparative responses to calcium of five tropical and four temperate pasture legume species. Austral. J. Agr. Res. 12:40-55.

Appleman, M. D. 1941. Effect of seed treatment on nodulation of soybeans and peas. Soil Sci. Soc. Amer. Proc. 6:200-203.

Appleman, M. D., and Sears, O. H. 1946a. Nodulation studies on Morrow plot soils. Soil Sci. Soc. Amer. Proc. 11:252-254.

Appleman, M. D., and Sears, O. H. 1946b. Effect of DDT upon nodulation of legumes. J. Amer. Soc. Agron. 38:545-550.

Baird, Kathleen J. 1955. Clover root-nodule bacteria in the New England Region of New South Wales. Austral. J. Agr. Res. 6:15-26.

Baird, Kathleen J. 1956. Investigations on the root-nodule bacteria of *Vicia faba* L. Phyton 7:47-62.

Bergersen, F. J. 1961. The growth of *Rhizobium* in synthetic media. Austral. J. Biol. Sci. 14:349-360.

Bergersen, F. J. 1962a. Oxygenation of leghaemoglobin in soybean root-nodules in relation to the external oxygen tension. Nature (Lond.) 194:1059-1061.

Bergersen, F. J. 1962b. The effects of partial pressure of oxygen upon restoration and nitrogen fixation by soybean root nodule. J. Gen. Microbiol. 29:113-125.

Bergersen, F. J., Brockwell, J., and Thompson, J. A. 1958. Clover seed pelleted with bentonite and organic material as an aid to inoculation with nodule bacteria. J. Austral. Inst. Agr. Sci. 24:158-160.

Bisset, K. A. 1952. Complete and reduced life cycles in *Rhizobium*. J. Gen. Microbiol. 7:233-242.

Bjälve, G. 1958. The importance of phosphate for cultivation of peas and fixation of atmospheric nitrogen. (In Swedish.) Vaxtnarings-Nytt. 15:18-21.

Bond, G. 1951. Symbiosis of leguminous plants and nodule bacteria. 4. The importance of the oxygen factor in nodule formation and function. Ann. Bot. 15:95-108.

Bond, G. 1958. Symbiotic nitrogen fixation by non-legumes. *In* Nutrition of the Legumes. (ed. Hallsworth). Butterworths, London, pp. 216-231.

Bonnier, C. 1952. Sur les propriétés antibactériennes de la graine *d'Arachis hypogea* L. Compt. rend. Soc. Biol. Belgium 146:309.

Bonnier, C. 1960. Symbiose Rhizobium-légumineuses: Aspects particuliers aux régions tropicales. Ann. Inst. Pasteur 98:537-556.

Bonnier, C., Hely, F. W., and Manil, P. 1952. Essai d'adaptation á *Soja hispida* de souches de *Rhizobium* non spécifiques. Influence de greffes sur la specificité d'hôte du genre *Rhizobium*. Bul. Inst. Agron. Sta. Recherches Gembloux 20:137-140.

Bonnier, C., and Sironval, C. 1956. Influence of day length on nodule formation in *Soja hispida* by a specific Rhizobium strain. Nature (Lond.) 177:93-94.

Bowen, G. D. 1956. Nodulation of legumes indigenous to Queensland. Queensland J. Agr. Sci. 13:47-60.

Bowen, G. D. 1959a. Field studies on nodulation and growth of *Centrosema pubescens*. Queensland J. Agr. Sci. 16:253-266.

Bowen, G. D. 1959b. Specificity and nitrogen fixation in the *Rhizobium* symbiosis of *Centrosema pubescens* Benth. Queensland J. Agr. Sci. 16:267-281.

Bowen, G. D. 1961. The toxicity of legume seed diffusates toward rhizobia and other bacteria. Plant and Soil 15:155-165.

Bowen, G. D., and Kennedy, Margaret M. 1959. Effect of high soil temperatures on *Rhizobium* spp. Queensland J. Agr. Sci. 16:177-197.

Bowen, G. D., and Kennedy, Margaret M. 1961. Heritable variation in nodulation of *Centrosema pubescens* Benth. Queensland J. Agr. Sci. 18:161-170.

Braithwaite, B. M., Jane, Annette, and Swain, F. G. 1958. Effect of insecticides on sod sown sub-clovers. J. Austral. Inst. Agr. Sci. 24:155-157.

Brenchley, Winifred E., and Thornton, H. G. 1925. The relation between the development, structure and functioning of the nodules of *Vicia faba* as influenced by the presence or absence of boron in the nutrient medium. Proc. Roy. Soc. (Lond.) B. 98:373-398.

Brockwell, J. 1962. Studies on seed pelleting as an aid to legume seed inoculation. 1. Coating materials, adhesives, and methods of inoculation. Austral. J. Agr. Res. 13:638-649.

Brockwell, J., and Hely, F. W. 1961. Symbiotic characteristics of *Rhizobium meliloti* from the acid soils of the Macquarie Region of New South Wales. Austral. J. Agr. Res. 12:630-643.

Brockwell, J., and Hely, F. W. 1962. Relationship between viability and availability of *Rhizobium trifoli* introduced into seeds of *Trifolium subterraneum* by imbibition and pressure. Austral. J. Agr. Res. 13:1041-1053.

Brockwell, J., and Whalley, R. D. B. 1962. Incorporation of peat inoculant in seed pellets for inoculation of *Medicago tribuloides* Desr. sown in dry soil. Austral. J. Sci. 24:458-459.

Bryan, W. W. 1962. The role of the legume in legume/grass pastures. In A Review of Nitrogen in the Tropics with Particular Reference to Pastures. Commonwealth Bureau Pastures and Field Crops. Bul. 46, pp. 147-160.

Burton, J. C., and Allen, O. N. 1950. Inoculation of crimson clover (*Trifolium incarnation* L.) with mixtures of rhizobial strains. Soil Sci. Soc. Amer. Proc. 14:191-195.

Burton, J. C., Allen, O. N., and Berger, K. C. 1952. The prevalence of strains of *Rhizobium phaseoli* in some Midwestern soils. Soil Sci. Soc. Amer. Proc. 16:167-170.

Burton, J. C., Allen, O. N., and Berger, K. C. 1954. Response of beans (*Phaseolus vulgaris* L.) to inoculation with mixtures of effective and ineffective rhizobia. Soil Sci. Soc. Amer. Proc. 18:156-159.

Burton, J. C., Allen, O. N., and Berger, K. C. 1961. Effects of certain mineral nutrients on growth and nitrogen fixation of inoculated bean plants, *Phaseolus vulgaris* L. Agr. and Food Chem. 9:187-190.

Burton, J. C., and Erdman, L. W. 1940. A division of the alfalfa cross-inoculation group correlating efficiency in nitrogen fixation with source of *Rhizobium meliloti*. J. Amer. Soc. Agron. 32:439-450.

Butler, G. W., and Bathurst, N. O. 1956. The underground transference of nitrogen from clover to associated grass. Proc. 7th Intern. Grassland Cong. pp. 168-178.

Carlyle, R. E., and Thorpe, J. D. 1947. Some effects of ammonium and sodium 2,4-dichlorophenoxyacetates on legumes and the Rhizobium bacteria. J. Amer. Soc. Agron. 39:929-936.

Cartwright, P. M., and Snow, D. 1962. The influence of foliar applications of urea on the nodulation pattern of certain leguminous species. Ann. Bot. 26:251-259.

Casas-Campillo, C. 1949. El antagonismo microbiano en relación con las bacterias de los nódulos de las plantas leguminosas. Ciencia 9:193-199.

Cass Smith, W. P. 1938. The inoculation of tangier peas. J. Agr. Western Australia. (2nd ser.) 15:36-39.

Cass Smith, W. P., and Goss, Olga M. 1958. A method of inoculating and lime-pelleting leguminous seeds. J. Agr. Western Australia (3rd ser.) 7:119-121.

Cass Smith, W. P., and Holland, A. A. 1958. The effect of soil fungicides and fumigants on the growth of subterranean clover on new light land. J. Agr. Western Australia (3rd ser.) 7:225-231.

Cass Smith, W. P., and Pittman, H. A. J. 1939a. The influence of methods of planting on the effective inoculation and establishment of subterranean clover. J. Agr. Western Australia 16:61-73.

Cass Smith, W. P., and Pittman, H. A. J. 1939b. The effect of inoculation on the growth of field peas, lucerne, lupins and tick beans. J. Agr. Western Australia. 16:73-79.

Chailakhyan, M. Kh., and Megrabyan, A. A. 1959. Stimulating action of leguminous plants on the growth of specific nodule bacteria. (Abs.) Soils and Fert. 22:119 (694).

Chailakhyan, M. Kh., Megrabyan, A. A., and Karapetyan, N. A. 1959. The bactericidal action of non-leguminous plants towards nodule bacteria. (Abs.) Soils and Fert. 22:450 (2782).

Cooper, R. 1962. The retention of ^{32}P-labelled *Rhizobium* by legume seed after inoculation by vacuum treatment. J. Appl. Bact. 25:232-236.

Date, R. A., and Vincent, J. M. 1962. Determination of the number of root-nodule bacteria in the presence of other organisms. Austral. J. Exp. Agr. and Animal Husb. 2:5-7.

Davies, E. B., and Stockdill, S. M. J. 1956. A pasture response to sodium tungstate on a New Zealand soil. Nature (Lond.) 178:866.

Dawson, R. C. 1962. Inoculation for better pasture and forage legumes in the tropics. J. Range Management, 15:252-257.

Delwiche, C. C., Johnson, C. M., and Reisenauer, H. M. 1961. Influence of cobalt on nitrogen-fixation by *Medicago*. (Abs.) Soils and Fert. 24:208 (1409).

Donald, C. M. 1960. The impact of cheap nitrogen. J. Austral. Inst. Agr. Sci. 26:319-338.

Donald, C. M., and Williams, C. H. 1954. Fertility and productivity of a podzolic soil as influenced by subterranean clover (*Trifolium subterraneum* L.) and superphosphate. Austral. J. Agr. Res. 5:664-687.

Dunham, D. H., and Baldwin, I. L. 1931. Double infection of leguminous plants with good and poor strains of rhizobia. Soil Sci. 32:235-249.

Elkan, G. H. 1961. A nodulation-inhibiting root excretion from a non-nodulating soybean strain. Can. J. Microbiol. 7:851-856.

Elkan, G. H. 1962. Comparison of rhizosphere microorganisma of genetically related nodulating and non-nodulating soybean lines. Can. J. Microbiol. 8:79-87.

Erdman, L. W. 1961. The future of preinoculated seeds. Proc. 6th Ann. Farm Seed Res. Conf. 7-14.

Erdman, L. W., and Burton, J. C. 1939. Strain variation and host specificity of *Rhizobium leguminosarum* on new pea varieties. Soil Sci. Soc. Amer. Proc. (1938) 3:169-175.

Erdman, L. W., and Means, Ura Mae. 1953. Strain variation of *Rhizobium meliloti* on three varieties of *Medicago sativa*. Agron. J. 45:625-629.

Fåhreus, G. 1957. The infection of clover root hairs by nodule bacteria studied by a simple glass slide technique. J. Gen. Microbiol. 16:374-381.

Ferguson, T. P., and Bond, G. 1954. Symbiosis of leguminous plants and nodule bacteria 5. The growth of red clover at different oxygen tensions. Ann. Bot. 18:385-396.

Fletcher, W. W. 1956. Effect of hormone herbicides on the growth of *Rhizobium trifolii*. Nature (Lond.) 177:1244.

Fletcher, W. W., and Alcorn, J. W. S. 1958. The effect of translocated herbicides on rhizobia and the nodulation of legumes. *In* Nutrition of the Legumes. (ed. Hallsworth.) Butterworths, London pp. 284-288.

Fletcher, W. W., Alcorn, J. W. S., and Raymond, J. C. 1959. Gibberellic acid and nodulation of legumes. Nature (Lond.) 184:1576.

Fletcher, W. W., Dickenson, P. B., Forrest, J. D., and Raymond, J. C. 1957. The effect of soil applications of certain substituted phenoxyacetic and phenoxybutyric acids on the growth and nodulation of *Trifolium repens sylvestre*. Phyton 9:41-46.

Fletcher, W. W., Dickenson, P. B., and Raymond, J. C. 1956. The effect of certain hormone herbicides on the growth and nodulation of *Trifolium repens sylvestre* in aseptic culture. Phyton 7:121-130.

Fred, E. B., Baldwin, I. L., and McCoy, Elizabeth. 1932. Root nodule bacteria and leguminous plants. Univ. Wisconsin, Madison.

Fred, E. B., Wilson, P. W., and Wyss, O. 1938. Light intensity and the nitrogen hunger period in the Manchu soybean. Proc. Natl. Acad. Sci. 24:46-52.

Gibson, A. H. 1961. Root temperature and symbiotic nitrogen fixation. Nature (Lond.) 191:1080-1081.

Gibson, A. H. 1962. Genetic variation in the effectiveness of nodulation of lucerne varieties. Austral. J. Agr. Res. 13:388-399.

Gibson, A. H. 1963. Physical environment and symbiotic nitrogen fixation. 1. The effect of root temperature on recently nodulated *Trifolium subterraneum* L. plants. Austral. J. Biol. Sci. 16:28-42.

Gibson, A. H., and Nutman, P. S. 1960. Studies on the physiology of nodule formation. 7. A reappraisal of the effect of preplanting. Ann. Bot. 24:420-433.

Golebiowska, J. 1952. The effect of the carbon source in the cultures of *Rh. trifolii* and *Rh. meliloti* upon the nitrogen fixation in the inoculated plants. Acta Microb. Polonica. 1:327-337.

Graham, E. R. 1938. Magnesium as a factor in nitrogen fixation by soybeans. Univ. Missouri Agr. Exp. Sta. Res. Bul. 288, 30 pp.

Greenwood, R. M. 1961. Pasture establishment on a podzolized soil in Northland. 3. Studies on rhizobial populations and the effects of inoculation. New Zealand J. Agr. Res. 4:375-389.

Hallsworth, E. G. 1958. Nutritional factors affecting nodulation. *In* Nutrition of the Legumes (ed. Hallsworth). Butterworths, London. pp. 183-201.

Hallsworth, E. G., Wilson, S. B., and Greenwood, E. A. N. 1960. Copper and cobalt in nitrogen fixation. Nature (Lond.) 187:79-80.

Harmsen, G. W., and Wieringa, K. T. 1954. Efforts to improve the inoculum for legumes. Landbouwk. Tijdschr. 66:531-533.

Harris, J. R. 1953. Influence of rhizosphere microorganisms on the virulence of *Rhizobium trifolii*. Nature (Lond.) 172:507.

Harris, J. R. 1961. Rhizobial inoculation and fertilizer rates as factors in the establishment of subterranean clover in South Australia. Austral. J. Agr. Res. 12:84-99.

Hastings, A., and Drake, A. D. 1960. Inoculation and pelleting of clover seed. New Zealand J. Agr. 101:619-621.

Hausen, S. S., von, Saubert, S., and Van Glijswijk, N. O. 1959. The survival of *Rhizobium* bacteria in soil. (Abs.) Soils and Fert. 22:118 (687).

Hely, F. W. 1957. Symbiotic variation in *Trifolium ambiguum* M. Biab. with special reference to the nature of resistance. Austral. J. Biol. Sci. 10:1-16.

Hely, F. W., Bergersen, F. J., and Brockwell, J. 1957. Microbial antagonism in the rhizosphere as a factor in the failure of inoculation of subterranean clover. Austral. J. Agr. Res. 8:24-44.

Hely, F. W., Bonnier, C., and Manil, P. 1953. Effect of grafting on nodulation of *Trifolium ambiguum*. Nature (Lond.) 171:884-885.

Hely, F. W. and Brockwell, J. 1960. Ecology of medic root-nodule bacteria (*Rhizobium meliloti* in arid zone soils. Proc. Arid Zone Tech. Conf. 1:11/1-11/5.

Hely, F. W., and Brockwell, J. 1962. An exploratory survey of the ecology of *Rhizobium meliloti* in inland New South Wales and Queensland. Austral. J. Agr. Res. 13:864-879.

Henzell, E. F., and Norris, D. O. 1962. Processes by which nitrogen is added to the soil/plant system. *In* A Review of Nitrogen in the Tropics with Particular Reference to Pastures. Commonwealth Bur. Pastures and Field Crops. Bul. 46, pp. 1-18.

Hewitt, E. J. 1958. Some aspects of mineral nutrition of legumes. *In* Nutrition of the Legumes (ed. Hallsworth). Butterworths, London. pp. 15-42.

Hockley, S. R. 1961. Legume inoculation. J. Agr. South Australia. 64:379-384.

Hofer, A. W. 1958. Selective action of fungicides on *Rhizobium*. Soil Sci. 86:282-286.

Hofer, A. W., and Little, H. B. 1956. Legume inoculant tests for 1955. Appendix to New York State Exp. Sta. Bul. 772.

Holding, A. J., and King, J. 1963. The effectiveness of indigenous populations of *Rhizobium trifolii* in relation to soil factors. Plant and Soil 18:191-198.

Holding, A. J., Tilo, S. N., and Allen, O. N. 1960. Modified plant response induced by rhizobia cultivated on amino-acid media. Trans. 7th Intern. Cong. Soil Sci. 2:608-616.

Holland, A. A., and Parker, C. A. Microbial intervention in the establishment of clover. 8th Intern. Cong. Microbiol. (Abs.)

Ishizawa, S. 1953. Studies on the root nodule bacteria of leguminous plants. I. Characters in artificial media. Part 5. Effect of temperature on the growth of rhizobia. J. Sci. Soil, Tokyo. 24:227-230.

Jenkins, H. V., Vincent, J. M., and Waters, L. M. 1954. The root-nodule bacteria as factors in clover establishment in the red basaltic soils of the Lismore District, New South Wales. 3. Field inoculation trials. Austral. J. Agr. Res. 5:77-89.

Jensen, H. L. 1942. Nitrogen fixation in leguminous plants. I. General characters of root-nodule bacteria isolated from species of *Medicago* and *Trifolium* in Australia. Proc. Linnean Soc. New South Wales. 67:98-108.

Jensen, H. L. 1943. Nitrogen fixation in leguminous plants. 4. The influence of reaction on the formation of root-nodules in *Medicago* and *Trifolium*. Proc. Linnean Soc. New South Wales. 68:207-220.

Jensen, H. L. 1944. Nitrogen fixation in leguminous plants. 5. Gains of nitrogen by *Medicago* and *Trifolium* in acid and alkaline soil. Proc. Linnean Soc. New South Wales 69:229-237.

Jensen, H. L. 1946. Nitrogen fixation in leguminous plants. 6. Further observations on the effect of molybdenum on symbiotic nitrogen fixation. Proc. Linnean Soc. New South Wales. 70:203-210.

Jensen, H. L. 1948. Nitrogen fixation in leguminous plants. 7. The nitrogen fixing activity of root-nodule tissue in *Medicago* and *Trifolium*. Proc. Linnean Soc. New South Wales 72:265-291.

Jensen, H. L. 1961. Survival of *Rhizobium meliloti* in soil culture. Nature (Lond.) 192:682-683.

Jensen, H. L., and Betty, R. C. 1943. Nitrogen fixation in leguminous plants. 3. The importance of molybdenum in symbiotic nitrogen fixation. Proc. Linnean Soc. New South Wales. 68:1-8.

Jensen, H. L., and Frith, Dorothy. 1944. Production of nitrate from roots and root-nodules of lucerne and subterranean clover. Proc. Linnean Soc. New South Wales. 69:210-214.

Joffe, A., Weyer, F., and Saubert, S. 1961. The role of root temperature in symbiotic nitrogen fixation. S. African J. Sci. 57:278-280.

Kliewar, M., and Evans, H. J. 1962a. B_{12}-Coenzyme content of the nodules from legumes, Alder and of *Rhizobium meliloti*. Nature (Lond.), 194:108-109.

Kliewar, M., and Evans, H. J. 1962b. Effect of cobalt deficiency on the B_{12} coenzyme content of *Rhizobium meliloti*. Arch. Biochem. Biophys. 97:428-429.

Krasil'nikov, N. A., and Korenyako, A. I. 1944. Influence of soil bacteria on the virulence and activity of *Rhizobium* (in Russian). Mikrobiologiya 13:39-44. (English Summary).

Krasnikov, B. V., Dolgikh, S. T., Lebedyant-Seva, O. N. 1959. The content of carbohydrates and nitrogen in varieties of peas and beans differing in the intensity of nodule formation. (Abs.) Soils and Fert. 22:44(229).

Lange, R. T. 1961. Nodule bacteria associated with indigenous Leguminosae of South-Western Australia. J. Gen. Microbiol. 26:351-359.

Lange, R. T., and Parker, C. A. 1960. The symbiotic performance of lupin bacteria under glasshouse and field conditions. Plant and Soil 13:137-146.

Lange, R. T., and Parker, C. A. 1961. Effective nodulation of *Lupinus digitatus* by native rhizobia of South-Western Australia. Plant and Soil 15:193-198.

László, G. Y. 1958. The nitrogen-fixing capacity and virulence of rhizobium strains from peas and vetch during the various growth stages of the host plant. (Abs.) Soils and Fert. 21:106 (598).

Leonard, L. T. 1938. Testing legume bacteria cultures in the field. Soil Sci. Soc. Amer. Proc. 2:305-309.

Leonard, L. T., and Dodson, W. R. 1933. The effects of nonbeneficial nodule bacteria on Austrian winter pea. J. Agr. Res. 46:649-663.

Ljunggren, H., and Fåhreus, G. 1961. The role of polygalacturonase on root-hair invasion by nodule bacteria. J. Gen. Microbiol. 26:521-528.

Loneragan, J. F. 1959. Calcium in the nitrogen metabolism of subterranean clover. Austral. J. Biol. Sci. 12:26-39.

Loneragan, J. F. 1960. Pasture legumes in Tasmania. The legume-rhizobium symbiosis. J. Austral. Inst. Agr. Sci. 26:26-31.

Loneragan, J. F., and Dowling, E. J. 1958. The interaction of calcium and hydrogen ions in the nodulation of subterranean clover. Austral. J. Agr. Res. 9:464-472.

Loneragan, J. F., Meyer, D., Fawcett, R. G., and Anderson, A. J. 1955. Lime pelleted clover seeds for nodulation on acid soils. Jour. Austral. Inst. Agr. Sci. 21:264-265.

Loneragan, J. F., Moye, D. V., and Anderson, A. J. 1961. Pre-inoculation of subterranean clover seed. Nature (Lond.) 192:526-527.

Lowe, R. H., Evans, H. J., and Ahmed, S. 1960. The effect of Co on the growth of *Rhizobium japonicum*. Biochem. Biophys. Res. Comm. 3:675-678.

Lowe, R. H., and Evans, H. J. 1962. Cobalt requirement for the growth of rhizobia. J. Bact. 83:210-211.

Lynch, D. L., and Sears, O. H. 1951. Differential response of strains of *Lotus* nodule bacteria to soil treatment practices. Proc. Soil Sci. Soc. Amer. (1950) 15:176-180.

Lynch, D. L., and Sears, O. H. 1952. Nodulation of legumes and nitrogen fixation. I. A new tool for measurement. Abstr. Amer. Soc. Agron. 68-69.

MacConnell, J. T., and Bond, G. 1957a. Nitrogen fixation in wild legumes. Ann. Bot. 21:185-192.

MacConnell, J. T., and Bond, G. 1957b. A comparison of the effect of combined nitrogen on nodulation in non-legumes and legumes. Plant and Soil 8:378-388.

McGonagle, Moira P. 1949. The effect of certain factors on the formation of root nodules on pea plants in aseptic culture. Proc. Roy. Soc. Edinburgh Ser. B. 63:219-229.

McKee, G. W. 1961. Some effects of liming, fertilization and soil moisture on seedling growth and nodulation of birdsfoot trefoil. Agron. J. 53:237-240.

McKee, G. W. 1962. Effects of shading and plant competition on seedling growth and nodulation in birdsfoot trefoil. Pennsylvania State Univ. Coll. Agr. Bul. 689. 35 pp.

McKnight, T. 1949. Efficiency of isolates of *Rhizobium* in the cowpea group, with proposed additions to this group. Queensland J. Agr. Sci. 6:61-76.

McLachlan, K. D., and Norman, B. W. 1961. Phosphorus and symbiotic nitrogen fixation in subterranean clover. J. Austral. Inst. Agr. Sci. 27:244-245.

McLeod, R. W., and Roughley, R. J. 1961. Freeze-dried cultures as commercial legume inoculants. Austral. J. Exp. Agr. Animal Husb. 1:29-33.

McLeod, R. W., Roughley, R. J., and Vincent, J. M. 1961. The quality of legume inoculants produced under the supervision of U-DALS. Agr. Gaz. New South Wales 72:362-365.

Manil, P., and Bonnier, C. 1950. Fixation symbiotique d'azote chez la luzerne (*Medicago sativa*, L). Bul. Inst. Agron. Sta. Recherches Gembloux. 18:89-126.

Manil, P., and Bonnier, C. 1951. Fixation symbiotique d'azote chez la luzerne. (*Medicago sativa* L.) 3. Nouveaux essais pratiques d'inoculation. Bul. Inst. Agr. Sta. Recherches Gembloux 19:15-32.

Marshall, K. C. 1956. Competition between strains of *Rhizobium trifolii* in peat and broth culture. J. Austral. Inst. Agr. Sci. 22:137-140.

Marszewska-Ziemiecka, Jadwiga. 1960. Agricultural Microbiology in Poland. Rev. Polish Acad. Sci. 5:63-69.

Masefield, G. B. 1958. Some factors affecting nodulation in the tropics. *In* Nutrition of the Legumes (ed. Hallsworth). Butterworths. London. pp. 202-215.

Means, Ura Mae, Johnson, H. W., and Erdman, L. W. 1961. Competition between bacterial strains effecting nodulation in soybeans. Soil Sci. Soc. Amer. Proc. 25:105-108.

Mes, Margaretha G. 1959. Influence of temperature on the symbiotic nitrogen fixation of legumes. Nature (Lond.) 184:2032-2033.

Meyer, D. R., and Anderson, A. J. 1959. Temperature and symbiotic nitrogen fixation. Nature (Lond.) 183:61.

Milthorpe, F. L. 1945. The compatibility of protectant seed dusts with root nodule bacteria. J. Austral. Inst. Agr. Sci. 11:89-92.

Moore, A. W. 1960. Symbiotic nitrogen fixation in a grazed tropical grass-legume pasture. Nature (Lond.) 185:638.

Mulder, E. G. 1948. Investigations on the nitrogen nutrition of pea plants. Plant and Soil. 1:179-212.

Mulder, E. G., and van Veen, W. L. 1960a. Effect of pH and organic compounds on nitrogen fixation by red clover. Plant and Soil. 13:91-113.

Mulder, E. G., and van Veen, W. L. 1960b. The influence of carbon dioxide on symbiotic nitrogen fixation. Plant and Soil 13:265-278.

Nichol, H., and Thornton, H. G. 1941. Competition between related strains of nodule bacteria and its influence on infection of the legume host. Proc. Roy. Soc. Lond., Ser. B. 130:32-59.

Norman, A. G., and Krampitz, L. O. 1946. The nitrogen nutrition of soybeans. 2. Effect of available soil nitrogen on growth and nitrogen fixation. Soil Sci. Soc. Amer. Proc. (1945) 10:191-196.

Norris, D. O. 1956. Legumes and the *Rhizobium* symbiosis. Empire J. Exp. Agr. 24:247-270.

Norris, D. O. 1958a. Lime in relation to the nodulation of tropical legumes. *In* Nutrition of the Legumes (ed. Hallsworth), Butterworths. London. pp. 164-182.

Norris, D. O. 1958b. Rhizobium needs magnesium, not calcium. Nature (Lond.) 182:734-735.

Norris, D. O. 1958c. A red strain of *Rhizobium* from *Lotononis bainesii* Baker. Austral. J. Agr. Res. 9:629-632.

Norris, D. O. 1959a. The role of calcium and magnesium in the nutrition of *Rhizobium*. Austral. J. Agr. Res. 10:651-698.

Norris, D. O. 1959b. Legume bacteriology in the tropics. J. Austral. Inst. Agr. Sci. 25:202-207.

Norris, D. O. 1959c. Rhizobium affinities of African species of *Trifolium*. Empire, J. Exp. Agr. 27:87-97.

Norris, D. O. 1962. The biology of nitrogen fixation. *In* A Review of Nitrogen in the Tropics with Particular Reference to Pastures. Commonwealth Bur. Pastures and Field Crops. Bul. 46. pp. 113-129.

Nutman, P. S. 1949. The influence of strain and host factors on the efficiency of nitrogen fixation in clover. Proc. Specialist Conf. Agr. Australia. 183-189. 1949. (H. M. Stationery Office, London, 1951).

Nutman, P. S. 1956. The influence of the legume in root-nodule symbiosis. A comparative study of host determinants and functions. Biol. Rev. 31:109-151.

Nutman, P. S. 1958. The physiology of nodule formation. *In* Nutrition of the Legumes (ed. Hallsworth). Butterworths. London. pp. 87-107.

Nutman, P. S. 1959. Sources of incompatibility affecting nitrogen fixation in legume symbiosis. Soc. Exp. Biol. Symp. 13:42-58.

Nutman, P. S. 1962. The relation between root hair infection by *Rhizobium* and nodulation in *Trifolium* and *Vicia*. Proc. Roy. Soc. Lond. Ser. B. 156:122-137.

Nutman, P. S. 1963. Mutual advantage in legume symbiosis. *In* Soc. Gen. Microbiol. 13th Symp. Symbiotic Associations (ed. Nutman and Mosse. Camb. Univ. Press).

Orcutt, F. S., and Fred. E. B. 1935. Light intensity as an inhibiting factor in the fixation of atmospheric nitrogen by Manchu soybeans. J. Amer. Soc. Agron. 27:550-558.

Parle, J. 1958. Field observations of copper deficiency in legumes. *In* Nutrition of the Legumes (ed. Hallsworth). Butterworths. London pp. 280-283.

Pate, J. S. 1958a. Nodulation studies in legumes. 1. The synchronization of host and symbiotic development in the field pea *Pisum arvense*, L. Austral. J. Biol. Sci. 11:366-381.

Pate, J. S. 1958b. Nodulation studies in legumes. 2. The influence of various environmental factors on symbiotic expression in the vetch (*Vicia sativa* L.) and other legumes. Austral. J. Biol. Sci. 11:496-515.

Pate, J. S. 1961. Temperature characteristics of bacterial variation in legume symbiosis. Nature (Lond.) 192:637-639.

Pate, J. S. 1962. Nodulation studies in legumes. 5. The effects of temperature on symbiotic performances of bacterial associations of *Medicago tribuloides* Desr. and *Vicia atropurpurea* Desf. Phyton 18:65-74.

Pate, J. S., and Dart, P. J. 1961. Nodulation studies in legumes. 4. The influence of inoculum strain and time of application of ammonium nitrate on symbiotic response. Plant and Soil 15:329-346.

Peterson, H. B., and Goodding, T. H. 1941. The geographic distribution of *Azotobacter* and *Rhizobium meliloti* in Nebraska soils in relation to certain environmental factors. Univ. Nebraska Agr. Exp. Sta. Res. Bul. 121. 24 pp.

Pochon, J., and de Barjac. 1958. Traité de Microbiologie des Sols. Dunod, Paris. pp. 481-482.

Pochon, J., Manil, P., Tchan, Y. T., Bonnier, C., and Chalvignac, M. A. 1950. Etude sérologique des *Rhizobium*. Application au probleme de la "compétition" entre souches. Ann. Inst. Pasteur. 79:757-762.

Porter, F. E., Kaerwer, Jr., and McAlpine, V. W. 1960. Seed impregnation including bacterial and vacuum treatment. U.S. Patent 2,932,128, April 12, 1960.

Powrie, J. K. 1960. A field response by subterranean clover to cobalt fertilizer. Austral. J. Sci. 23:198-199.

Purchase, Hilary F. 1958. Effective nodulation *vs.* bag nitrogen in growth of subterranean clover. J. Austral. Inst. Agr. Sci. 24:35-38.

Purchase, Hilary F., and Nutman, P. S. 1957. Studies on the physiology of nodule formation. 6. The influence of bacterial numbers in the rhizosphere on nodule initiation. Ann. Bot. N.S. 21:439-454.

Purchase, Hilary F., and Vincent, J. M. 1949. A detailed study of the field distribution of strains of clover nodule bacteria. Proc. Linnean Soc. New South Wales. 74:227-236.

Purchase, Hilary F., Vincent, J. M., and Ward, Lawrie M. 1951. The Field distribution of strains of nodule bacteria from species of *Medicago*. Austral. J. Agr. Res. 2:261-272.

Raggio, M., Raggio, Nora, and Torrey, J. G. 1957. The nodulation of isolated leguminous roots. Amer. J. Bot. 44:325-334.

Read, Margaret P. 1953. The establishment of serologically identifiable strains of *Rhizobium trifolii* in field soils in competition with the native microflora. J. Gen. Microbiol. 9:1-14.

Reisenhauer, H. M. 1960. Cobalt in nitrogen fixation by a legume. Nature (Lond.) 186:375-376.

Richardson, D. A., Jordan, D. C., and Garrard, E. H. 1957. The influence of combined nitrogen on nodulation and nitrogen fixation by *Rhizobium meliloti* Dangeard. Canad. J. Plant Sci. 37:205-214.

Roberts, J. L., and Olson, F. R. 1942. The relative efficiency of strains of *Rhizobium trifolii* as influenced by soil fertility. Science (Lancaster, Pa.) 95:413-414.

Robinson, P. E. 1961. Root-knot nematodes and legume nodules. Nature (Lond.) 189:506.

Rorison, I. H. 1958. The effect of aluminium on legume nutrition. *In* Nutrition of the Legumes. (ed. Hallsworth). Butterworths. London. pp. 43-61.

Rossiter, R. C. 1952. Phosphorus toxicity in subterranean clover and oats grown on

Muchea sand, and the modifying effects of lime and nitrate-nitrogen. Austral. J. Agr. Res. 3:227-243.

Rovira, A. D. 1961. Rhizobium numbers in the rhizospheres of red clover and paspalum in relation to soil treatment and the numbers of bacteria and fungi. Austral. J. Agr. Res. 12:77-83.

Rudakov, K. I. 1951. Nitragin (Review for 1944-1950). (In Russian). Mikrobiologiya. 20:348-362.

Ruhloff, Marcia and Burton, J. C. 1951. Compatibility of rhizobia with seed protectants. Soil Sci. 72:283-290.

Scanlan, R. W. 1928. Calcium as a factor in soybean inoculation. Soil Sci. 25:313-326.

Schiffmann, J. 1958. Ineffectiveness of alfalfa nodule bacteria (*Rhizobium meliloti*) in Negev soils and improvement by soil inoculation. Min. Agr., Israel. Agr. Res. Sta. 9:57-67.

Sears, P. D. 1953/1954. Pasture growth and soil fertility. 7. General discussion of the experimental results and their application to farming practice in New Zealand. New Zealand J. Sci. Tech. Section A. 35:221-236.

Shevtsova, I. I. 1959. The effect of the tissue sap of legume roots on nodule bacteria. (Abs.) Soils and Fert. 22:193 (1173).

Spencer, D. 1950. The effect of calcium and soil pH on nodulation of *T. subterraneum* L. clover on a yellow podsol. Austral. J. Agr. Res. 1:374-381.

Strong, T. H. 1937. The influence of host plant species in relation to the effectiveness of the *Rhizobium* of clovers. J. Council Sci. Ind. Res. 10:12-16.

Strong, T. H. 1938a. Legume establishment and its function in relation to the development of some of the poor soils on Kangaroo Island. J. Agr. South Austral. 41:542-550.

Strong, T. H. 1938b. On the role of seed inoculation. Appendix to Council Sci. Ind. Res. Bul. 122: 24 pp.

Strong, T. H. 1940. Non-effective associations of nodule bacteria and legumes. J. Austral. Inst. Agr. Sci. 6:14-20.

Tanner, J. W., and Anderson, I. C. 1963. An external effect of inorganic nitrogen on root nodulation. Nature (Lond.) 198:303-304.

Thompson, J. A. 1960. Inhibition of nodule bacteria by an antibiotic from legume seed coats. Nature (Lond.) 187:619-620.

Thompson, J. A. 1961. Studies on nodulation responses to pelleting of subterranean clover seed. Austral. J. Agr. Res. 12:578-592.

Thornton, G. D. 1948. Greenhouse studies of nitrogen fertilization of soybeans and *lespedeza* using isotopic nitrogen. (Abs.) Soils and Fert. 11: 130(622).

Thornton, H. G. 1947. The biological interactions of *Rhizobium* to its host legume. Antonie van Leeuwenhoek. 12:85-96.

Thornton, H. G., and Kleczkowski, J. 1950. Use of antisera to identify nodules produced by the inoculation of legumes in the field. Nature (Lond.) 166: 1118-1119.

Tuzimura, K., and Watanabe, I. 1961. Estimation of numbers of root-nodule bacteria by the nodulation frequency method and some applications. Ecological studies of *Rhizobium* in soils 1. Soil Sci. & Plant Nutrition. 7:61-65. (Also J. Sci. Soil Tokyo. 30:292-296. 1959-in Japanese).

Tuzimura, K., and Watanabe, I. 1961a. The saprophytic life of *Rhizobium* in soils free from the host plants. Ecological studies of *Rhizobium* in soils. 2. Soils and Fert. 24:208(1407).

Tuzimura, K., and Watanabe, I. 1961b. Multiplication of *Rhizobium* in the rhizosphere of host plants. Ecological studies of *Rhizobium* in soils. 3. Abs. Soils and Fert. 24:363-(2533).

van Schreven, D. A. 1958a. Some factors affecting the uptake of nitrogen by legumes. *In* Nutrition of the Legumes. (ed. Hallsworth). Butterworths. London. pp. 137-163.

van Schreven, D. A. 1958b. Methods used in the Netherlands for the production of legume inoculants. *In* Nutrition of the Legumes. (ed. Hallsworth). Butterworths, London. pp. 328-333.

van Schreven, D. A. 1959. Effects of added sugars and nitrogen on nodulation of legumes. Plant and Soil. 11:93-112.

van Schreven, D. A., Otzen, D., and Lindenbergh, D. J. 1954. On the production of legume inoculants in a mixture of peat and soil. Antonie van Leeuwenhoek. 20:33-57.

Vincent, J. M. 1954a. The root-nodule bacteria of pasture legumes. Proc. Linnean Soc. New South Wales. 79:iv-xxxii.

Vincent, J. M. 1954b. The root-nodule bacteria as factors in clover establishment in the red basaltic soils of the Lismore district, New South Wales. 1. A. survey of "native" strains. Austral. J. Agr. Res. 5:55-60.

Vincent, J. M. 1956. Strains of rhizobia in relation to clover establishment. Proc. 7th Intern. Grassland Cong. pp. 179-189.

Vincent, J. M. 1958a. Survival of the root-nodule bacteria. *In* Nutrition of the Legumes (ed. Hallsworth). Butterworths. London, pp. 108-123.

Vincent, J. M. 1958b. Towards better legume inoculants. J. Austral. Inst. Agr. Sci. 24: 226-228.

Vincent, J. M. 1962a. Australian studies of the root-nodule bacteria. Proc. Linnean Soc. New South Wales. 87:8-38.

Vincent, J. M. 1962b. Influence of calcium and magnesium on the growth of *Rhizobium*. J. Gen. Microbiol. 28:653-663.

Vincent, J. M., and Colburn, J. R. 1961. Cytological abnormalities in *Rhizobium trifolii* due to a deficiency of calcium or magnesium. Austral. J. Sci. 23:269-270.

Vincent, J. M., and Crofts, F. C. 1958. Pasture improvement in the Pilliga. Univ. Sydney School Agr. Rep. No. 3. 31 pp.

Vincent, J. M., Thompson, J. A., and Donovan, Kathleen O. 1962. Death of root-nodule bacteria on drying. Austral. J. Agr. Res. 13:258-270.

Vincent, J. M., and Waters, Lawrie M. 1953. The influence of host on competition amongst clover root-nodule bacteria. J. Gen. Microbiol. 9:357-370.

Vincent, J. M., and Waters, Lawrie M. 1954. The root-nodule bacteria as factors in clover establishment in the red basaltic soils of the Lismore District, New South Wales. 2. Survival and success of inocula in laboratory trials. Austral. J. Agr. Res. 5:61-76.

Virtanen, A. I., and Holmberg, A. M. 1958. The quantitative determination of molecular nitrogen fixed by pea plants in pot cultures and in field experiments. Suomen Kemistilehti, Ser. B. 31:98-102.

Virtanen, A. I., and Saubert-von Hausen, S. 1952. A method for determining in pea cultures, the amount of molecular nitrogen fixed and the amount of combined nitrogen taken up from the soil. Plant and Soil 4:171-177.

Vyas, N. D. 1953. Effect of some indigenous phosphates on the fixation of atmospheric nitrogen through pea. J. Indian Soc. Soil Sci. 1:41-46.

Vyas, N. D., and Desai, J. R. 1953. Effect of different doses of superphosphate on the fixation of atmospheric nitrogen through pea. J. Indian Soc. Soil Sci. 1:32-40.

Walker, T. W., Adams, A. F. R., and Orchiston, H. D. 1956. Fate of labelled nitrate and ammonium nitrogen when applied to grass and clover grown separately and together. Soil Sci. 81:339-351.

Williams, L. F., and Lynch, D. L. 1954. Inheritance of a non-nodulating character in the soybean. Agron. J. 46:28-29.

Williams, T. E., and Back, H. L. 1959-60. The combine drilling of lime and lucerne. Grassland Res. Inst. Rep. 107-109.

Williams, W. A., Harwood, L. H., and Hills, F. J. 1960. Incompatibility of seed treatment fungicides and seed-applied legume inoculum observed on field-grown subterranean clover. Agron. J. 52:363-365.

Wilson, J. K. 1926. Legume bacteria population of the soil. J. Amer. Soc. Agron. 18:911-919.

Wilson, P. W. 1940. The biochemistry of symbiotic nitrogen fixation. Univ. Wisconsin Press. Madison.

Wilson, P. W., Burton, J. C., and Bond, V. S. 1937. Effect of species of host plant on nitrogen fixation in *Melilotus*. J. Agr. Res. 55:619-629.

Wilson, P. W., and Fred, E. B. 1937. Mechanism of symbiotic nitrogen fixation. 2. The pO_2 function. Proc. Nat. Acad. Sci. 23:503-508.

Wolf, M., and Baldwin, I. L. 1940. The effect of glycine on the rhizobia. J. Bact. 39:344.

Wrobel, T. 1959. Production of cultures of *Rhizobium* for leguminous plants and the results of their applications in field experiments. (In Polish, with English summary and table). Acta Microbiol. Polonica. 8:321-332.

Wrobel, T., and Marszewska-Ziemiecka, Jadwiga. 1960. Results of field experiments with the inoculation of leguminous plants. Roczniki Nauk Rolniczych. 82A:201-209.

Chapter 12

Nonsymbiotic Nitrogen Fixation

H. L. JENSEN

State Laboratory for Soil and Crop Research
Lyngby, Denmark

I. THE HISTORICAL BACKGROUND

A century has now passed since Jodin (1862) for the first time reported on experiments with "mucedinées" or "mycodermes" which he on apparently good evidence considered able to metabolize elemental nitrogen. Thus he formulated for the first time the conception of what has later come to be known as "nitrogen fixation" in microorganisms. Existence of this faculty in higher (leguminous) plants had long been surmised, but the final proof did not eventuate until about twenty-five years later. Jodin's discovery seems to have fallen into oblivion for a similar span of time, and no real interest was taken in the problem until the late 1880's when Berthelot conducted large scale experiments on the changes in nitrogen content of soils stored for long periods under the most varying conditions. The contents of nitrogen often showed notable increases that could not be ascribed to extraneous sources and which Berthelot (1888) first thought were due to biological causes and which he later (1890) ascribed partly also to electric discharges. The last hypothesis has never been confirmed, and in the light of our present-day knowledge of the biology of nitrogen-fixing microorganisms it seems next to impossible to imagine them as responsible for any gains of nitrogen under the conditions obtaining in Berthelot's experiments. Winogradsky (1895; 1949) expressed a strong scepticism in this respect both in the early and the concluding days of his scientific life, and contemporary experiments by Schloesing (1888) failed to confirm Berthelot's statements which nevertheless are still quoted in textbooks as the first experimental evidence of nonsymbiotic nitrogen fixation in soil.

Whether real or not, Berthelot's findings powerfully catalyzed the efforts of discovering agents of biological nitrogen fixation other than the partnership of legumes and root nodule bacteria, about whose ability to fix nitrogen there was no longer any doubt. The problem passed definitely into the realm of biology from the middle 1890's when Winogradsky first demonstrated nitrogen fixation in a strain of butyric acid bacilli (*Clostridium pasteurianum*). The next great step was taken around the turn of the century when Beijerinck discovered the aerobic nitrogen-fixing bacteria to which he gave the generic name *Azotobacter* and which were soon found to exceed the clostridia very considerably in nitrogen-fixing efficiency. From then on research on nitrogen fixation began to develop along different lines.

(1). Fundamental studies on *Azotobacter* were conducted on a large scale. These were inspired partly by its extraordinary morphology that has played a decisive role in developing the concept of bacterial life cycles, and partly by the ease with which it can be cultivated under laboratory conditions; this latter property has made it a favorite object for studying the biological mechanism of nitrogen fixation which only today seems to be approaching its solution. In this respect the studies already have largely moved away from general microbiology into pure biochemistry.

(2). Much work has been spent in studying the distribution of the nitrogen-fixers and especially the azotobacter in relation to environmental and geographical factors, soil type, and origin, measures of cultivation, fertilizer treatment, etc.

(3). Soon after the discovery of the azotobacter there began an intensive search for other nitrogen-fixing microorganisms. This property was alleged in the most diverse groups of bacteria and fungi during the first two decades of this century, not least by the school of F. Löhnis in Leipzig. Many of these claims seemed untenable when other investigators failed to confirm the statements on nitrogen fixation in one important group of bacteria: the rhizobia when grown *in vitro*. From 1920 to 1930 there seemed to be a good reason to believe that only the azotobacter and the butyric acid bacilli were definitely endowed with nitrogen-fixing ability. The pendulum of opinion began to swing the other way when the previously controversial problem of nitrogen fixation in the blue-green algae was settled in the affirmative around 1930. Another great extension came in the 1940's from the Wisconsin school headed by P. W. Wilson and R. H. Burris: nitrogen fixing ability was found widely distributed among anaerobic bacteria, first the clostridia and later many others, photosynthetic (Thiorhodaceae and Athiorhodaceae) and chemolithotrophic (methane bacteria and sulphate-reducing vibrios). Finally the claims of the Leipzig school have in a way been vindicated, even if not with the same organisms then in principle, inasmuch as studies from the last decade, aided by the tracer technique with N^{15}-labeled nitrogen, has revealed nitrogen fixation in many otherwise "undistinguished" microorganisms.

(4). Great efforts were made to ascertain the "nitrogen-fixing power of the soil," often with none too clear a definition of this concept. The oldest method, the solution culture method of the Remy-Löhnis School, consisted in determining increments of nitrogen in selective liquid media inoculated with soil and incubated; this tells us little beyond the presence or absence of nitrogen-fixers and especially azotobacter in the soil. Winogradsky (1926) introduced the use of solid (silica gel) media for estimating the density of azotobacter and their amount of growth with defined energy sources; this method was in principle anticipated by Remy (1909) nearly twenty years before and does not show the gains that happen in the soil. A more real innovation was Winogradsky's (1926) principle of studying by direct microscopical methods the development of nitrogen-fixing bacteria in the soil itself as biological reaction upon the introduction of non-nitrogenous energy material. This has subsequently led to the idea of correlating the multiplication of recognizable nitrogen fixers with chemically determined increments of nitrogen in the soil. The principle of determining the gains of nitrogen in the soil itself goes in principle back to Berthelot and Schloesing and would seem the only logical one. Countless experiments of this kind have demonstrated that very notable gains of nitrogen can be achieved if sufficient energy material be provided, but relations between gains of nitrogen and numerical representation of nitrogen-fixing organisms are still obscure, because two problems have not yet been fully solved. One of them is microbiological: the reliable numerical determination of metabolically active cell individuals (or more precisely, amount of living substance) of nitrogen-fixing bacteria. The other problem is a chemical one: the quantitative determination of nitrogen gains to be expected under natural soil conditions (comparable to the nitrogen requirements of a moderate or small agricultural crop). Under laboratory and still more under field conditions this is beyond the sensitivity of the current Kjeldahl method and presumably also the theoretically preferable Dumas method. The tracer technique has so far found very limited application but may provide the answer to the question in future investigations.

The present chapter brings a survey of our knowledge of the non-symbiotic nitrogen-fixing microorganisms and their activity in contributing to the nitrogen supply of cultivated soils. The literature of the last 25 years (until 1963) has chiefly been considered; many earlier papers have been reviewed by Winogradsky in his collected papers (1949), by Wilson and Burris (1953), Pochon and de Barjac (1958), and Jensen (1940a).

II. THE NITROGEN FIXERS *IN VITRO*

A. The Groups of Nonsymbiotic Nitrogen-Fixing Microorganisms

Among the heterogenous collection of potentially nitrogen-fixing soil inhabitants we may distinguish a group of organisms whose outstanding property is their ability to grow almost equally well with elemental and with combined nitrogen and which, as shown by Winogradsky (1926), will dominate the microscopic picture of the soil population under conditions selective for a nitrogen-fixing microflora. These are:

A. Organotrophic bacteria, including (a) the aerobic *Azotobacter* and one or two allied genera, and (b) the anaerobic *Clostridium butyricum* and some related species.

B. Photolithotrophic organisms including (a) many types of blue-green algae and (b) purple sulfur- and nonsulfur-bacteria which are probably of minor importance under soil conditions.

The Azotobacteraceae.—The aerobic members of group *A* belong to one family, Azotobacteraceae (Jensen, 1954); predominant among these is the genus *Azotobacter* Beij. whose morphological features are familiar. They are comparatively big, bluntly rod-shaped or oval to spherical, motile or non-motile cells whose size and shape vary greatly according to species, growth condition and age. The Gram reaction is essentially negative and endospores are to all appearances not formed, but the soil-inhabiting species mostly form thick-walled "microcysts" as resting cells. There is considerable evidence of a complicated life cycle comprising, *inter alia,* endogenously produced gonidia (Petersen, 1961). The species differentiation and even the unity of the genus are controversial. Some authors (Winogradsky 1938; Tchan, 1953; V. Jensen, 1955; Baillie et al., 1962) have advocated the creation of a separate genus (*Azomonas, Azococcus, Azotococcus*) for the types that form no thick-walled microcysts. Perhaps the most adequate classification is the one suggested by Baillie et al. (1962):

A. Microcysts formed: *Azotobacter* Beij.
   a. Motile with lateral flagella.
      1. Form dark brown insoluble pigment: *A. chroococcum* Beij.
      2. Form greenish fluorescent soluble pigment:
         A. vinelandii Lipman.
   b. Nonmotile, form yellowish, insoluble pigment:
      A. beijerinckii Lipman.
B. Microcysts not formed: *Azomonas* Winogr.
   a. Motile with lateral flagella: *A. agilis* (Beij.) Winogr.
   b. Motile with polar flagella.
      1. Big oval cells: *A. insignis* (Derx), V. Jensen (1955).
      2. Spherical or oval cells of varying size:
         A. macrocytogenes, H. L. Jensen (1955).

Azotobacter in this sense comprises typical soil inhabitants while *Azomonas agilis* and *insignis* seem to be purely aquatic organisms and *A. macrocytogenes* a very rare soil inhabitant. These species are in the following collectively called "the azotobacter."

Their carbon requirements are met by a wide range of substances from two-carbon compounds like ethanol and acetate over many aliphatic and oxy-acids, mono-, di- and polyvalent alcohols (e.g., mannitol), mono- and dihexoses (very rarely pentoses) up to starch, and in addition some aromatic compounds, e.g., benzoic acid. *Azotobacter* spp. as a whole utilize a wider range of carbon compounds than do those belonging to *Azomonas.*

The spectrum of available nitrogen sources is by comparison rather narrow. In addition to elemental nitrogen only ammonia, urea, some simple amino acids, nitrate and nitrite are readily available, the last two not even to all, for instance some strains of *A. agilis* (Becking, 1962; Green and Wilson, 1953). The azotobacter possess in addition to their nitrogen-fixing faculty only one outstanding physiological property: their respiratory activity is the highest in all kinds of living matter and may amount to Q_{0_2}-values (oxygen uptake μl/mg dry cell substance/hour) of 2000 to 4000, or 10 times as much if calculated on the basis of cell nitrogen. The oxidation of the non-assimilated carbon compounds normally proceeds quantitatively to carbon dioxide and water; acid formation from carbohydrates is an exceptional occurrence (H. L. Jensen, 1955; V. Jensen, 1959).

The amounts of nitrogen fixed *in vitro* under favourable conditions usually range between 12 to 20 mg per g consumed carbon source of "optimal" nutritional value, like glucose, sucrose, mannitol or ethanol. Gains that essentially exceed 20 mg/g sugar do not seem to have been directly ascertained. The consumed energy material is largely spent in respiratory processes and no significant proportion seems to be required for the nitrogen fixation process *per se*, as discussed below. The fixed nitrogen is at least in the soil-inhabiting *A. chroococcum* and *A. beijerinckii* mostly present in cell substance and only to a small extent as excretion products.

The azotobacter usually show optimum growth at pH around 7.2 to 7.6 with either free or combined nitrogen, and most of them cease to grow at pH 6.0 or slightly below; some strains will grow at pH 5.0 or even somewhat lower (Jensen, 1955).

In relation to temperature all azotobacter are typically mesophilic; most soil forms have an optimum at 28-30°C while that of the aquatic forms (*Azomonas*) is often lower.

In agreement with the oxidative nature of their metabolism the azotobacter are all obligatory aerobes whose growth rate increases markedly by improved aeration (Alexander, 1954; Schmidt-Lorenz & Rippel-Baldes, 1957; Wilson, 1958). Growth may take place, however, at remarkably low oxygen tensions, according to Tschapek and Giambiagi (1954) and Lorenz and Rippel-Baldes (1957) at $pO_2 = 0.008$ atm, or even lower according to Meyerhof and Burk (1927). Tschapek and Giambiagi (1954) and Garbosky (1956) found that the oxygen demand of *A. chroococcum* decreased with decreasing organic nutrient concentration of the medium, as indicated by the formation of growth zones at varying depths below the surface in liquid media; at glucose concentrations less than 500 ppm it thus behaved like a microaerophile. This, indeed, seems to be true of aerobic bacteria generally (Zycha, 1932). Quispel (1947) found *A. chroococcum* unable to induce growth from a small inoculum at a redox potential (Eh) lower than ca. 400 mV or under special conditions 300 mV, but in growing cultures Eh could drop to about 75 mV. This was also observed by Döbereiner and Alvahydo (1959), and associated cultures of azotobacter and cellulose-decomposing bacteria may even show negative Eh-values (Jensen and Swaby, 1941). LeGall et al. (1959) have reported growth of *A. chroococcum* in a sulphide-containing medium at the expense of the oxygen impurities in commercial nitrogen gas.

Although improved aeration accelerates the growth of the azotobacter, the oxygen tension influences the efficiency of nitrogen fixation (expressed as the gain per unit of consumed energy material) in a different way, as discussed later.

The general mineral requirements of the azotobacter present nothing unusual. Calcium has often been considered specifically required for nitrogen fixation; it is now known to be generally essential for most species, but sometimes in very small amounts only (Bullock et al., 1960). For *A. agilis* it seems non-essential although stimulatory. Gerretsen and de Hoop (1954) claimed boron to be essential for *A. chroococcum*, while Anderson and Jordan (1961) found only a moderate stimulatory effect of this micronutrient which is not known to be required by other microorganisms. It is unknown if the reported boron effect is specific to nitrogen fixation. The importance of some other trace elements specifically active in the nitrogen fixation process is discussed elsewhere.

Beijerinckia and *Derxia*. Closely allied to the azotobacter is a group of bacteria that some microbiologists include in *Azotobacter* while others (among them the present author) regard it as a separate genus *Beijerinckia* Derx (1950). These are typical rod-shaped bacteria, containing characteristic polar fat inclusions and considerably smaller than the azotobacter, nonmotile or more often motile with lateral flagella. Their growth is much slower than that of the azotobacter and is accompanied by copious formation of tenacious polysaccharide slime. Their range of available carbon sources seems a good deal narrower than in the azotobacter, particularly comprising fewer simple alcohols and organic acids. Their efficiency of nitrogen fixation is high and sometimes reaches 20-22 mg per g of consumed sugar.

The beijerinckias differ markedly from the azotobacter by their ability to grow within a pH-range from about 3 to about 9. Further they do not require calcium which even has an inhibitory effect (Bullock et al., 1960), and their geographic distribution is markedly limited, as discussed elsewhere. Some seven or eight species have been described but may not all be valid; Petersen (1959) considered three species well defined: *B. indica* (Starkey et De) Derx, *B. acida* (Roy) Petersen, *B. fluminensis* Döbereiner et Puppim-Ruschel.

A somewhat similar organism of apparently rare occurrence was found in Indian soils and was considered sufficiently characteristic to deserve rank as a separate genus *Derxia* (Jensen et al., 1960) with one species, *D. gummosa*. It differs from *Beijerinckia* by its considerably bigger rod-shaped cells, sometimes motile with a single polar flagellum and lacking the typical polar fat inclusions. It produces an even more tenacious growth than the beijerinckias and utilizes only a limited number of sugars in addition to ethanol. Its nitrogen fixation is very efficient and may exceed 25 mg per g glucose. Growth takes place between pH about 5.0 to 8.5, as in the more acid-tolerant azotobacter. Roy (1962) has very recently added another species *D. indica*.

Clostridium spp. The anaerobic nitrogen fixers of significance in natural soils are chiefly the clostridia of which the first representative was found by Winogradsky (1895). The next step was taken by Bredemann (1909) who showed nitrogen fixation to be common to butyric acid bacilli (*Clostridium butyricum*). Rosenblum and Wilson (1949) extended the range of nitrogen fixing clostridia further. The yield of fixed nitrogen per unit of fermented sugar was in earlier experiments mostly estimated at 2-3 mg/g sugar. This is considerably less than in the Azotobacteraceae but cannot be directly used as an index of "efficiency" because the clostridia leave a considerable part of the available energy behind in the fermentation products (butyric and acetic acid, butanol, acetone, hydrogen, etc.) in contrast to the complete utilization of the substrate energy by the oxidative azotobacter and beijerinckias. Later studies have revealed a much more economic nitrogen fixation in the clostridia. Already McCoy et al. (1928) found yields of 7 mg/g sugar in some strains, and Wilson and co-workers (1950; 1959) as much as 12 mg/g under conditions where gaseous fermentation products were continuously removed. Parker (1954) even reported 27 mg/g in special media (which indeed needs confirmation). The range of carbon sources available for nitrogen fixation includes a large variety of simple sugars (also pentoses in contrast to the azotobacter), di- and polysaccharides and pectic substances, but no organic acids except possibly lactate; the pattern of fermentation upon the whole varies considerably in the different species. Their temperature range is wider than that of the azotobacter with optimum often around 35-40°C, and the lower end of the pH-scale extends to pH around 4.0 (Van Beynum and Pette, 1936) but approximately neutral reaction still seems to represent the optimum.

The clostridia tend to lose their nitrogen-fixing power when grown continuously in artificial media, but this power may be restored by passage through sterile soil (Bredemann, 1909). In this respect they resemble a somewhat neglected nitrogen fixer, the facultative anaerobic *Bacillus polymyxa*. Bredemann (1908), who studied it under the name of *Bac. asterosporus,* first detected a nitrogen fixation somewhat weaker than in *Cl. butyricum.* His discovery remained largely ignored for half a century until Wilson and co-workers (1958, 1962, 1963) confirmed it in experiments with labeled nitrogen.

Miscellaneous nitrogen fixing agents. Other well-documented observations of nitrogen fixation in organotrophic bacteria have been reported with increasing frequency during the last twenty years and include organisms of which it is at least credible that they could be active in the soil.

Stapp (1940) isolated a pseudomonas-like organism from rice shells and found it able to fix as much as 10 mg nitrogen per gram of added glucose. The organism, to which he gave the name *Azotomonas insolita,* does not seem to have been found again, and stock cultures examined by the present writer appeared to have lost their nitrogen-fixing power.

Earlier statements on nitrogen fixation in the facultative anaerobic *Aerobacter aerogenes* were confirmed by Hamilton and Wilson (1955), Pengra and Wilson (1958) and Jensen (1956) who found a maximum fixation of 4.5 mg/g added glucose. Other investigators who have detected nitrogen fixation in aerobic bacteria are Anderson (1955), Voets and Debacker (1956) and Paul and Newton (1961) in *Pseudomonas* spp., Jensen (1958) and Proctor and Wilson (1959) in *Achromobacter* sp., and Becking (1962) in a spirillum-like organism previously studied by Beijerinck who regarded the evidence for nitrogen fixation as inconclusive.

The reported yield of nitrogen fixed per unit weight of energy material is generally low but is rarely stated with precision. Fedorov and Kalininskaya (1961) have recently reported on an interesting bacterium called a "mycobacterium" but apparently more like an *Arthrobacter* sp. This bacterium lacked a glycolytic system and thus failed to utilize sugar, but when provided with growth factors it could fix as much as 10 mg nitrogen per g consumed pyruvic acid, and in association with sugar-fermenting bacteria the gain could rise to 13-16 mg nitrogen/g sugar. This seems to be one of the few plausible reports of a nitrogen-fixing aerobic organism with an efficiency equalling that of the Azotobacteraceae.

Evidence for nitrogen fixation in the actinomycetes has mostly been negative or unconvincing. Recent statements by Fedorov and Ilina (1960) suggest gains so small as to appear dubious until verified by the labeled-nitrogen method. Two species of *Nocardia* studied by Metcalfe and Brown (1957) doubtless possess this faculty but tend to lose it on continued cultivation. One of them had the unique property of combining nitrogen-fixing and cellulose-decomposing power.

Much controversy has reigned concerning the existence of nitrogen fixation in fungi, particularly *Phoma* spp. Recent evidence according to Wilson and Burris (1953) is mainly negative except in certain species of *Saccharomyces* and *Rhodotorula* which Metcalfe et al. (1954) isolated from acid soil and found able to fix about 4 mg nitrogen per g of sugar as confirmed in experiments with labeled nitrogen.

Lithotrophic nitrogen fixation. This second main group of nonsymbiotic nitrogen fixers again includes aerobic and anaerobic organisms. The first is to all appearances by far the most important in the soil and consists of photosynthetic organisms: blue-green algae or Cyanophyceae. These represent a fascinating chapter in soil biology and plant physiology, inasmuch as their nitrogen-fixing power was first tentatively suggested, then denied on apparently good experimental evidence and finally proved to be real. Valuable reviews on these organisms are due to Fogg and Wolfe (1954), Fogg (1956) and Singh (1961). Nitrogen fixation has now been definitely shown to take place in at least 20 species belonging to the genera *Anabaena* (9 spp.), *Anabaenopsis* (1 sp.), *Aulosira* (1 sp.), *Calothrix* (2 spp.), *Cylindrospermum* (3 spp.), *Mastigocladus* (1 sp.), *Nostoc* (5 spp.) and *Tolypothrix* (1 sp.). They include aquatic as well as terrestrial organisms, and some occur as algal components in lichens and a liverwort (Bond and Scott, 1955). They appear to fix nitrogen under these conditions too and are thus capable of a kind of "facultative symbiotic" nitrogen fixation in a partnership less intimate than that of leguminous plants and rhizobia.

B. The Mechanism of Nitrogen Fixation

The biological mechanism by which elemental nitrogen is brought into the metabolic cycle seems to be fundamentally the same in symbiotic systems and the nonsymbiotic nitrogen fixers, as discussed in the recent review of Wilson (1958), on which this chapter is largely based. A number of features are common to all agents of nitrogen fixation so far studied.

(1). A hydrogenase is found in all nonsymbiotic nitrogen fixers, but possession of this enzyme does not necessarily convey nitrogen-fixing power. In the azotobacter the enzyme is of an inducible character, being only formed during growth with free nitrogen. Its precise function is unknown.

(2). Hydrogen gas competitively inhibits nitrogen fixation in the azotobacter (Wilson, 1958), *Aerobacter aerogenes* (Pengra and Wilson, 1958), *Bac. polymyxa* (Grau and Wilson, 1962) and blue-green algae (Wilson, 1958). It has a similar effect in *Cl. butyricum,* but only at much higher partial pressure (Westlake and Wilson, 1959).

(3). Carbon monoxide likewise specifically inhibits nitrogen fixation in the azotobacter (Wilson, 1958), *Aerobacter aerogenes* (Pengra and Wilson, 1958), blue-green algae (Wilson, 1958) and *Cl. butyricum* (Virtanen et al., 1953). The effect is noncompetitive and is exerted at much lower partial pressures than that of hydrogen. Both gases incidentally act likewise in the symbiotic nitrogen-fixing systems.

(4). Oxygen gas has a remarkably complicated effect. In the clostridia and anaerobic nitrogen fixers upon the whole it would be expected generally to lessen the amount of growth at low pressures, although nothing definite is known about a specific effect upon nitrogen fixation. In the aerobes, increasing oxygen pressure tends to lower the *efficiency* of nitrogen fixation (although the *rate* of growth may be increased) by competing with gaseous nitrogen for the available hydrogen needed in the fixation process (Parker and Scutt, 1960). In some of the facultative anaerobes it abolishes nitrogen fixation, thus in *Bac. polymyxa* (Grau and Wilson, 1962; Hino and Wilson, 1958) in *Achromobacter* sp. (Jensen, 1958) and in *Aerobacter aerogenes* where it ceases already at $pO_2 = 0.05$ atm according to Pengra and Wilson (1958). Jensen (1956), on the other hand, found this species to fix nitrogen equally well aerobically and anaerobically. Meyerhof and Burk (1927) made a classical investigation of the influence of varying oxygen tension on the respiration of *A. chroococcum* and found a decreasing growth rate but increasing economy of fixation with decreasing oxygen tension down to approx. 0.1% oxygen ($pO_2 = 0.001$ atm), where the fixation would theoretically correspond to 50 mg/g consumed glucose. In more recent work, Schmidt-Lorenz and Rippel-Baldes (1957) found *A. chroococcum* to fix 18-20 mg N/g consumed glucose at 0.02-0.04 atm O_2, which efficiency declined gradually to 10-11 mg N/g glucose at 0.4 atm, and 0.6 atm O_2 stopped fixation completely. Similarly Parker (1954) found merely 7-8 mg nitrogen fixed per g (supplied) sucrose at pO_2 0.20 atm, but 22-23 mg at pO_2 0.04 atm. (Here, indeed, does the yield in atmospheric air seem abnormally low.) In later experiments where the N_2 tension was kept constant at the low value of 0.16 atm, Parker and Scutt (1960) found maximum fixation at 10% oxygen and estimated the Michaelis constant of fixation to be 0.0107 and 0.0229 at pO_2 0.10 and 0.20 atm, respectively.

The problem was approached from another angle by Tschapek and Giambiagia (1955) who found that *A. chroococcum,* when growing in a very dilute medium with only 10 to 30 ppm glucose, showed the maximum ratio between cell multiplication and glucose consumption at pO_2 0.01-0.02 atm. Unfortunately, the actual gain of nitrogen was not determined. The significance of this relationship between nutrient concentration and oxygen tension for the economy of nitrogen fixation in the soil is obvious, as pointed out already by Meyerhof and Burk (1927).

(5). Molybdenum is essential as an activator of nitrogen fixation. It was indeed the studies of Bortels (1930) on *A. chroococcum* that led to its discovery as a micronutrient of general importance. It has been shown to be required for nitrogen fixation in the azotobacter and the clostridia (Wilson, 1958), the beijerinckias (Becking, 1962b), *Derxia* (Jensen et al., 1960), the blue-green algae (Fogg and Wolfe, 1954), *Azotomonas isolita* (Stapp, 1940), *Aerobacter aerogenes* (Pengra and Wilson, 1959), *Bac. polymyxa* (Grau and Wilson, 1962) and it is at least stimulatory in *Achromobacter* sp. (Proctor and Wilson, 1959). In addition it is essential for nitrogen fixation in the symbiotic systems so far studied and for nitrate assimilation in apparently all organisms capable of metabolizing this form of nitrogen; its function in the latter respect is that of an activator of nitrate reductase which has been identified as a molybdenum-flavoprotein (Wilson, 1958). Optimum concentrations of molybdenum for nitrogen fixation are mostly at the order of 0.10-1.0 ppm, whereas lower concentrations will suffice for nitrate reduction, and for utilization of fully reduced (NH_4) nitrogen it is to all appearances not necessary (Mulder, 1948).

Vanadium will serve as a somewhat inferior substitute for molybdenum in nitrogen fixation by some but by no means all types of azotobacter (Becking, 1962b; Wilson, 1958), likewise in some of the clostridia (Jensen and Spencer, 1947) and in *Azotomonas insolita* (Stapp, 1940) but not in the beijerinckiae (Becking, 1962b), the blue-green algae (Singh, 1961), or *Derxia* (Jensen et al., 1960). According to Becking it cannot replace molybdenum in nitrate assimilation by the azotobacter.

Recent evidence (Nicholas et al., 1962) suggests that very minute amounts of cobalt (0.001 ppm) may be necessary for optimum growth of *A. vinelandii* with free nitrogen as well as with nitrate; its function seems connected with the synthesis of nitrate reductase although it is not a constituent of this enzyme. It thus does not seem strictly specific in nitrogen fixation.

(6). Ammonia is to all appearances the first stable product of nitrogen fixation from which glutamic acid is formed as a primary organic compound by reductive condensation with α-ketoglutaric acid (Wilson, 1958). Other amino acids then arise by transamination and proteins by condensation of these. The intermediates in the actual process of nitrogen fixation ($N_2 \rightarrow NH_4$) are still not known with certainty; it is even an open question whether the process is purely reductive, proceeding via a hypothetic diimide (HN:NH) analog and hydrazine ($H_2N \cdot NH_2$) to ammonia, or whether the final ammonium formation is preceded by an intermediate stage of partial oxidation ($N_2 \rightarrow NH_2OH$), as has been maintained in the azotobacter. Progress into this problem has long been hampered by the difficulty of preparing actively nitrogen-fixing cell-free extracts, but in recent years this has been achieved in most nitrogen-fixing microorganisms (Carnahan et al., 1960; Grau and Wilson, 1963; Schneider et al., 1960; Wilson, 1958). The effect of azotobacter-extracts is mostly feeble and rapidly lost and a nitrogen-fixing enzyme has not been isolated. An important step towards the solution of this intricate problem is represented by the studies of Carnahan and co-workers on *Cl. butyricum*. This and much other recent work has been admirably reviewed in two articles by Mortenson et al. (1962) and Mortenson (1962).

Briefly the problem seems at present to stand as follows: Cell-free extracts of *Cl. butyricum* when prepared under proper conditions can fix elemental nitrogen actively with pyruvate as electron donor; practically all the fixed nitrogen can be recovered as ammonia within two hours, and approximately one μ-atom nitrogen is fixed per μ-mole of metabolized pyruvate (Mortenson, 1962). A particulate nitrogen-fixing enzyme could not be isolated by centrifugation at 144,000 $\times$ g, but it was possible to separate the extracts into two fractions individually unable to fix nitrogen but able to do so when recombined. One fraction seemed to contain the long-sought-for "nitrogenase," the nitrogen-activating system that combines with the elemental nitrogen, and the other fraction contained the pyruvate-dehydrogenating system responsible for the reduction (to the ammonia level) of the chemisorbed nitrogen. The nitrogenase is inducible and is probably an iron protein; the place of the molybdenum is still obscure (possibly in the hydrogen-donating system).

(7). Ammonia, as key compound of the nitrogen fixation, tends to inhibit this process by competition with the free nitrogen. No nitrogenase appears to be synthesized during growth with ammonium nitrogen. Cells grown with free nitrogen cease to fix nitrogen in the presence of ammonia. This happens very rapidly in *A. vinelandii* while *Cl. butyricum* may utilize the two nitrogen sources simultaneously (Wilson, 1958). Nitrate has a similar effect in organisms able to utilize it, but in the azotobacter the inhibition is preceded by a lag phase corresponding to the induction of biosynthesis of nitrate reductase. In some cases the azotobacter may utilize nitrate and gaseous nitrogen simultaneously (Becking, 1962a; Bortels, 1936).

(8). The process of nitrogen fixation as such, i.e., the reduction of elemental nitrogen to the ammonia level, seems to require very little energy (Wilson, 1958) or may even be accompanied by a decrease in free energy (Bayliss, 1956). Thus the nitrogen-fixing economy of an organotrophic organism will not be determined by the special nitrogen source but by the amount of cell material plus extracellular metabolites that can be synthesized at the expense of a given quantity of metabolized organic matter. If we choose glucose as an example of a standard energy source and imagine half of its carbon spent in respiration and the remainder utilized for synthesis of cell material that in its dry matter contains 50% carbon and 10% nitrogen derived from the atmosphere, we arrive at a yield of 40 mg fixed nitrogen per gram consumed glucose. Except perhaps in the experiments of Meyerhof and Burk (1927) at minimal oxygen pressure, such a gain of nitrogen has not been experimentally verified in pure cultures of azotobacter where the amount of synthesized cell substance is more like one-fourth of the amount of consumed carbon source—which agrees well with the normally observed maximum yield near 20 mg N/g carbohydrate. Higher yields than 40-50 mg/g carbohydrate could hardly be achieved unless metabolic products of high nitrogen content (e.g., ammonia) were continuously excreted and removed without interfering with the process of nitrogen fixation. In pure cultures of nitrogen-fixing bacteria the excretion of nitrogen compounds into the medium is usually small, at the most 50% in *Cl. butyricum* (Rosenblum and Wilson, 1950), but it might reach a different magnitude in mixed cultures, although no direct evidence is yet available. Nevertheless, such an excretion could be possible if the fixation were to be regarded as a process alternative to respiration. This hypothesis seems attractive inasmuch as the fundamental processes are the same in nonsymbiotic and symbiotic nitrogen fixation, and the latter does indeed bear the character of a kind of respiration process accompanied by a copious transport of glutamic acid from the nodule tissue (Bond, 1936). Until further experimentation, however, this remains no more than hypothesis.

C. Energy Materials Utilized by Associated Growth

Winogradsky has repeatedly emphasized that the normal food substances of the azotobacter when growing in the soil are not compounds like glucose or mannitol that are currently regarded as "favorable" nutrients but are unlikely to arise in the soil in any quantity. Some sugars or related substances may occasionally become available, for instance in the form of young undecomposed plant materials, but in such cases the sugars are mostly accompanied by constituents like amino acids, proteins, etc., that provide nitrogen for the microflora and thus counteract the nitrogen fixers. By contrast, the natural carbon sources of the azotobacter are as pointed out by Winogradsky (1930) more likely to be very simple compounds like ethanol, butanol, acetate, propionate, butyrate, etc., that arise as products of fermentation or other incomplete dissimilation of various high-molecular substances. These are of course extremely varied but not all equally apt to provide energy material for nitrogen fixation. Some important organic materials have a narrow carbon-nitrogen ratio and are liable to decomposition with release of fixed mineral nitrogen: dead microbial tissue that arises in the soil, animal residues and excreta, farmyard manure or composts, and finally the soil "humus" itself. On the other hand the bulk of the organic matter continuously added to the soil is represented by dead plant residues that chiefly consist of nonnitrogenous skeletal substances: celluloses, hemicelluloses, and lignin. These are generally not directly available to the nitrogen fixers which can only utilize them in association with other organisms whose metabolic byproducts they can intercept. An exception might be represented by the nocardias of Metcalfe and Brown (1957) which, however, do not seem to be prominent in nature. The yield of fixed nitrogen in such associated cultures depends upon (a) the quantity of the organic compounds that the "decomposer" releases from the high-molecular material, (b) the serviceability of these compounds as carbon food for the "nitrogen fixer," and (c) the availability of the fixed nitrogen that the latter puts at the disposal of its associate. In natural populations the relationships will be further complicated by the metabolic activity of other organisms interposing themselves between the "decomposer" and the "nitrogen fixer."

Cellulose is probably that organic substance which exists in the greatest quantity in nature. Commensurate with this enormous mass, a legion of microorganisms are capable of decomposing cellulose: higher and lower fungi, actinomycetes, myxobacteria, eubacteria (aerobic and anaerobic, spore-forming and non-spore-forming, mesophilic and thermophilic)—and in addition a few lower animals. For reviews of the cellulose-decomposing microorganisms see Siu (1951) and Imschenetzki (1953). Their metabolic activities are correspondingly varied and include formation of by-products like formic, acetic, propionic, butyric, lactic, pyruvic and succinic acids, ethanol, butanol, acetaldehyde and sometimes cellobiose and glucose. All these products seem to be formed more copiously by the thermophiles and the anaerobic bacteria (e.g., the rumen inhabitants) than by the aerobic organisms mainly active in the soil: cytophagas, cellvibrios, fungi, and some actinomycetes. Earlier investigations quoted by Jensen (1940a), Imschenetzki (1953), and Fedorov (1952) have shown that associations between strains of *Cl. butyricum* and cultures of anaerobic cellulose-decomposing bacteria (presumably impure) may fix 7 to 10 mg nitrogen per g fermented cellulose. In view of the fact that the share of energy material consumed by the cellulose decomposers, the nitrogen-fixers and the probable contaminants is unknown, this yield appears remarkably high and more than equal to what has later been observed in pure cultures of clostridia (Rosenblum and Wilson, 1950; Westlake and Wilson, 1959). The main results of more recent research may be summarized as follows:

(1). There is little evidence of nitrogen fixation by the azotobacter in association with the important aerobic soil inhabitants *Sporocytophaga* and *Cytophaga* that decompose cellulose via oligocelluloses, cellobiose, and glucose and are largely restricted to utilization of this class of compounds. The carbon sources are dissimilated oxidatively with formation of no other organic by-products than small amounts of acetic acid; a mucilage of polysaccharide- or polyuronide-like character is synthesized. Azotobacter may multiply to some extent in association with the cytophagas (Fedorov, 1952; Imschenetzki, 1953; Jensen, 1940b), but the gains of nitrogen are nil or scarcely significant.

(2). A second important group of cellulose-decomposing soil bacteria are the cellvibrios which are metabolically not very different from the cytophagas although they form less mucilage and utilize a wider range of carbon sources. Jensen (1940b) found no significant gains of nitrogen by azotobacter in association with *Cellvibrio* spp. Imschenetzki (1953) and Fedorov (1952) have later quoted experiments showing some multiplication of azotobacter in such cultures and sometimes (Fedorov, 1952) some acceleration of the cellulose decomposition, but the media were rich in nitrate, and nitrogen determinations were not reported.

(3). The azotobacter seem to behave similarly in association with several other aerobic cellulose decomposers. Vartiovaara (1938) found no gain or at best very small gains of nitrogen by *A. chroococcum* combined with cellulose-decomposing fungi under aerobic conditions but moderate gains at periodically alternating aerobic and anaerobic cultivation; probably the anaerobiosis favored the accumulation of intermediate hydrolysis products utilized by the azotobacter in the aerobic intervals. Jensen (1940b) likewise failed to find significant nitrogen fixation by azotobacter associated with strains of *Cellulobacillus, Streptomyces* sp., *Micromono-*

spora chalcea and *Trichoderma viride,* the last a typical cellulose-decomposing soil fungus. Apparently the metabolic by-products of these aerobic organisms are either unserviceable for the azotobacter or else quantitatively insufficient for appreciable gains of nitrogen.

(4). Certain facultative aerobic bacteria of a *Corynebacterium-* (or *Arthrobacter-*) type are able to promote nitrogen fixation by azotobacter (Jensen, 1940b). A quantitative investigation by Jensen and Swaby (1941) showed that *Azotobacter* spp. as well as a *Beijerinckia* under these conditions could fix almost as much nitrogen per gram of consumed cellulose as when utilizing a favorable carbon source in pure culture (Table 1). The actual economy of fixation must have been still higher, since a part of the cellulose would be consumed by the associate. Restricted aeration (Eh-values below zero) increased the yield of fixed nitrogen, partly due to increased formation of organic by-products of cellulose decomposition but probably also to more economic utilization of these products. The concentration of soluble organic matter in the cellulose medium would be very low and thus a low oxygen tension should favour efficient nitrogen fixation (Parker and Scutt, 1960; Tschapek and Giambiagi, 1955).

A similar "feeding" of azotobacter may generally be expected from organisms that decompose cellulose with formation of available by-products, not least from the anaerobes and thermophiles. Such organisms may not be prevalent in the soil, and little is known about their association with nitrogen fixers. Imschenetzki (1959) reported vigorous multiplication of azotobacter but no gains of nitrogen in such cultures (medium with high initial nitrogen content).

(5). The nitrogen-fixing clostridia seem quite apt to enter into association with certain aerobic cellulose decomposers. Vartiovaara (1938) indeed failed to detect nitrogen fixation by *Cl. pasteurianum* associated with cellulose-decomposing fungi in atmospheric air, but considerable amounts were fixed by impure clostridium-cultures + fungi in alternating atmospheric air and nitrogen gas. Jensen (1941) found that a cytophaga and a few cellvibrios, actinomycetes and fungi failed to support growth of *Cl. butyricum* with cellulose, but one cellvibrio induced nitrogen fixation approaching 7 mg per g consumed cellulose (Table 2). With allowance for the unknown demands of the cellvibrio, this indicates an efficiency as high as ever observed (Rosenblum and Wilson, 1950; Westlake and Wilson, 1959). The efficiency increases further in the presence

Table 1. Gains of nitrogen in associated cultures of aerobic nitrogen-fixing and facultative anaerobic cellulose-decomposing bacteria (Jensen and Swaby, 1941).

Associates		Incuba-tion days	N fixed, mg/g cellulose decomposed
Nitrogen fixer	Cellulose decomposer		
A. chroococcum	Corynebact. 3	48	10. 3
A. chroococcum	Corynebact. V. a	42	11. 5
A. chroococcum	Corynebact. V. b	35	14. 3
A. beijerinckii	Corynebact. V. b	45	12. 8
A. vinelandii	Corynebact. V. b	42	12. 2
A. vinelandii	Corynebact. 3	28	10. 5
Beij. indica	Corynebact. 3	48	10. 8

Table 2. Gains of nitrogen in associated cultures of anaerobic nitrogen-fixing and aerobic (obligate or facultative) cellulose-decomposing bacteria (Jensen, 1941).

Associates		Incuba-tion days	N fixed, mg/g cellulose decomposed
Nitrogen fixer	Cellulose decomposer		
Cl. butyricum	Cellvibrio G. 2	14	5. 2
Cl. butyricum	Cellvibrio G. 2	28	6. 8
Cl. butyricum	Cellvibrio G. 2	16	1. 7
Cl. butyricum	Cellvibrio G. 2	40	4. 1
Cl. butyricum	Corynebact. V. b.	33	3. 3
Cl. butyricum	Corynebact. V. b.	50	1. 9
do + A. chroococcum	Cellvibrio G. 2	18	8. 0
do + A. chroococcum	Cellvibrio G. 2	33	11. 9
A. chroococcum	Cellvibrio G. 2	35	(1. 5)*

* Not significant.

of azotobacter, presumably because this consumes the fermentation products of the clostridia, but the facultative anaerobic corynebacterium gives a lesser effect, probably because its by-products are mostly organic acids and more acceptable to the azotobacter than to the clostridia.

Hemicelluloses represent the second major constituent of plant residues, with xylan predominating in straw, wood, and root materials and probably second only to cellulose in quantitative respect. Xylan-decomposing microorganisms are even more numerous than the cellulose-decomposers and ability to decompose the two substances is very often combined, even in the cytophagas although these do not metabolize the hydrolysis products of xylan (Sörensen, 1957). These products are xylose and oligoxylans of which the former only in the rarest instances is serviceable for the azotobacter (Jensen, 1959). For this reason simple association between aerobic xylan-splitting bacteria will not result in nitrogen fixation, but this may be induced by the facultative anaerobic corynebacteria (cf. Table 5) that also produce acid from xylan (Jensen and Swaby, 1941). A xylose-fermenting in addition to a xylan-hydrolyzing organism may have the same effect (Jensen, 1942).

The clostridia are largely able to ferment xylose and therefore more favorably placed than the azotobacter in association with xylan-decomposers. Combinations of *Cl. butyricum* and cellvibrios will fix nitrogen with xylan (Jensen, 1941), and this might be expected from any xylose-utilizing nitrogen-fixer in association with any xylan-hydrolyzing partner, but very little is known about the efficiency of these processes.

Among other hemicelluloses, pectic substances are fermented by some types of clostridia, as is well known from the retting of textile plants; the typical flax-retting agent *Cl. felsineum* is capable of nitrogen fixation (Rosenblum and Wilson, 1949). Certain strains of *A. vinelandii* will utilize arabinose very economically (Jensen, 1942) and might well be expected to fix nitrogen on the basis of araban in association with an organism capable of hydrolyzing this hemicellulose. Pectin and araban may thus be potential energy materials for nitrogen fixation, but the existing amounts of these substances in nature are probably not large enough to make them a material of major importance. The same is true of the methyl pentose rhamnose (Jensen, 1961).

Whether lignin, the third large component of plant residues, ever becomes available for nitrogen fixation is an open question and must remain so until more information is gathered about the mechanism of biological lignin degradation. Winogradsky (1930) suggested that the readiness with which the azotobacter utilize benzoic acid might indicate a possibility of such compounds arising from lignin. This seems rather farfetched, since benzoic acid itself occurs as a product of bio-synthesis, and whether the lignin molecule ever gives rise to cleavage products available to the azotobacter is unknown. The clostridia are unlikely to be active in this respect, since they do not generally attack aromatic compounds, and lignin is even more resistant to decomposition under anaerobic than under aerobic conditions.

A quite different type of association, between *Azotobacter* and green algae (Chlorophyceae) has been regarded as a nitrogen-fixing partnership of some significance, where the algae, largely on theoretical grounds, have been assumed to provide the azotobacter with energy material in the form of photosynthetic products and to receive fixed nitrogen in return. Although photosynthesis is an intracellular process and its immediate products are not normally excreted, there is nevertheless experimental evidence that nitrogen can be fixed in this way, at least *in vitro*. Stokes (1940), however, found that *A. chroococcum* and *A. vinelandii* would only grow feebly with nine strains of green algae as sole providers of energy material and concluded that this source of fixed nitrogen might be real but unimportant. Dead algal cell material was unserviceable as energy source, and owing to its high nitrogen content its decomposition by mixed populations would be accomplished by others than the azotobacter. Sulaiman (1944) arrived at the same conclusion with other algae. Association between clostridia and photosynthetic organisms that excrete oxygen is difficult to envisage although the clostridia could conceivably be active in periods of darkness; this, however, is unknown.

Associations of azotobacter with non-nitrogen-fixing blue-green algae would presumably resemble those with green algae, and no activity of the azotobacter can be expected in the presence of the nitrogen-fixing cyanophyceae whose excretion products are largely polypeptides (Fogg and Wolfe, 1954). In agreement herewith De (1939) did not find any increased nitrogen fixation in cultures of blue-green algae when azotobacter was also present. A quite different matter is the stimulating effect of several non-nitrogen-fixing bacteria on the growth and nitrogen fixation by at least one blue-green alga (Bjälfve, 1962).

III. THE SOIL ECOLOGY OF THE ORGANOTROPHIC NITROGEN FIXERS

A. The Azotobacteraceae (*Azotobacter* and *Beijerinckia*)

More has probably been written about the occurrence and life activities of the azotobacter than about any other single genus of soil bacteria. The mere qualitative detection of the azotobacter in soil by means of selective media offers no particular difficulties, but the estimation of their numerical abundance is seriously limited by lack of reliable methods—a limitation that indeed applies to all soil microorganisms. Two methods in current use are (a) colony counts on some solid selective medium, such as agar or silica gel, with a suitable carbon source and no added nitrogen, and (b) determination of the dilution where growth ceases in some corresponding liquid medium. The plate method has chiefly come into use since Winogradsky (1926) introduced the technique of planting soil particles on silica gel plates or sprinkling larger plates of the same medium with weighed quantities of soil. This procedure yields only comparative results since the number of cells giving rise to each single colony is unknown and may be large. To some extent this objection remains valid when shaken soil suspensions are used for plate inoculation, although microscopic methods suggest that aggregates of azotobacter-like cells rarely consist of more than a few individuals. The method of dilution counts in its various modifications (Augier, 1956; Pochon, 1954; Tchan, 1952; Wenzl, 1934) usually shows somewhat higher figures than the plate counts, but rarely of an essentially higher order of magnitude (cf., e.g., Wenzl, 1934; Lochhead and Thexton, 1936); the same applies to various modifications in the preparation of the soil suspension (shaking with glass beads, etc., cf. Brown et al., 1962).

Direct microscopic studies of stained soil suspensions (Winogradsky, 1926) or of contact slides according to the Rossi-Cholodny method become fruitful when the population of azotobacter has become abundant owing to the selective effect of non-nitrogenous energy material, but can give little information about the unmodified soil microflora where the azotobacter-like cells are mostly few and not identifiable with any certainty. Hopf (1949) devised an ingenious combination of microscopic and cultural methods: removal of individual cells from unfixed and unstained contact slides by micromanipulation, and transfer to appropriate media. This method seems theoretically ideal but is probably biassed in favor of the conspicuous-looking azotobacter-cells.

The *Azotobacter* spp. proper are world-widely distributed, apparently rare in arctic soils but may occur even in desert soils; a very complete survey is given by Fedorov (1952). Their commonest representatives in temperate regions are *A. chroococcum* and *A. beijerinckii*, while *A. vinelandii* may be relatively common in tropical and subtropical soils and *A. macrocytogenes* appears extremely rare. In spite of their global distribution the azotobacter are by no means ubiquitous soil inhabitants as seen from some examples collected in Table 3.

The density of azotobacter in soil under normal conditions is of a strikingly low order in comparison with the tens or even hundreds of millions of bacteria (incl. actinomycetes) that cultural methods usually reveal. Winogradsky (1926, 1928) found densities between a few and 20,000 colonies per gram of soil, with 2,000 as "normal." These figures apply to silica gel plates sprinkled with soil particles, but even the use of shaken soil suspension in solid or liquid media does not result in much higher counts, as shown by various examples collected in Table 4.

These predominantly low counts that rarely exceed tens of thousands

Table 3. Occurrence of azotobacter in different parts of the world.

Geographic region and reference	No. of samples	% Az. positive
Europe: Germany (Niklas et al., 1926)	525	70
Denmark (Christensen, 1915)	142	49
Denmark (Jensen, 1950)	264	54
Switzerland (Stöckli, 1944)	1000	72
Italy (de 'Rossi, 1932a)	189	78
Soviet Union: Suschkina (1949)	3161	57
North America: Iowa (Martin et al., 1937)	287	75
Arizona (Martin, 1940)	213	51
Colorado (Gonick & Reuszer, 1949)	283	75
Australia: N.S.W., Vict. (Jensen & Swaby, 1940)	233	26
Queensland (McKnight, 1949)	146	43
Global: Becking (1961)	392	33

Table 4. Examples of the density of azotobacter in the soil.

Author and reference	Geographic region	Method	Azotobacter per gram of soil
Meiklejohn (1956)	England	Agar plate	10 - 700
Brown et al (1962)	England	Agar plate	1,600 - 18,000
Augier (1956)	France	Dilution	2,500 - 11,000
Rouquerol (1962)	France	Dilution	100 - 10^{11}
Jensen (1950)	Denmark	Agar plate	< 10 - 81,000
Stöckli (1944)	Switzerland	Agar plate	10 - 44,000
de'Rossi (1932)	Italy	Agar plate	<100 - 21,400
Abd-el-Malek (1962)	Egypt	Dilution	10 - 10^8
Uppal et al. (1939)	India	Agar plate	0 - 1.6×10^6
Lochhead (1936)	Canada	Agar plate	c. 100 - 1,000
Gonick & Reuszer (1949)	U.S.A.	Agar plate	<10 - 8,000
Jensen & Swaby (1940)	Australia	Agar plate	<10 - 2,300

per gram of soil suggest that the azotobacter represent normally only a very small fraction of the soil microflora. This has caused several investigators (de Rossi, 1932b; 1933; Lochead and Thexton, 1936; Jensen, 1940a) to become sceptical about the quantitative importance of the amounts of nitrogen gained by the normally occurring azotobacter populations—at least in comparison with the nitrogen requirements of crops from intensively cultivated soil. Three statements in Table 4 stand out in sharp contrast to the rest in showing counts that run into millions.* All three statements refer to somewhat unusual conditions: rice field soils and irrigated clay soils from the Nile Valley, with copious supply of plant residues. The possible significance of these factors are discussed later.

The azotobacter seem in a general way to be characteristic of well-cultivated soils, as pointed out already by Remy (1909), but the effect of cultivation is probably a complex one. Among individual soil properties, the reaction has long been recognized as a factor of prime importance

---

* Some of the highest counts (Rouquérol, 1962) would seem unrealistic. If the average volume of an azotobacter cell is estimated at merely 2 cubic microns (which is almost certainly too low), 10^{11} cells would occupy a volume of 0.2 cc. or 1/5 g of soil. Such figures are only imaginable if the growth were assumed to originate from ultramicroscopic filterable forms, the existence of which in the soil is possible but unknown.

in governing the distribution of the azotobacter, as probably first ascertained by Christensen (1915). Many earlier observations as well as more recent ones (Gonick and Reuszer, 1949; Jensen, 1940a, 1950; Suschkina, 1949) have shown that at least in soils of temperate regions the azotobacter rarely occur below a pH level of 6.0, in conformity with their usual behavior *in vitro*. If found below pH 6 they are usually few in number and are not stimulated to active growth when suitable energy material and mineral nutrients are provided. In tropical and subtropical soil there is some indication of more widespread representation at acid soil reaction (Döbereiner, 1953). The data in Table 5 illustrate the relation between soil pH and the occurrence as well as the density of the azotobacter population in cultivated soils from a temperate region.

Table 5. Correlation between soil pH and density of *Azotobacter* (colonies per gram) in 264 Danish soils (1950).

Range of pH	Number of soils with Az.-density					Total No.	Az.+ %
	0	<10^2	10^2-10^3	10^3-10^4	10^4-10^5		
<6.0	38	4	0	0	0	42	10
6.0 - 6.4	40	14	1	0	0	55	27
6.5 - 6.9	31	22	10	1	0	64	52
7.0 - 7.4	11	20	13	4	1	49	78
7.5 - 7.9	2	10	16	6	2	36	94
8.0 - 8.5	0	1	12	5	0	18	100

Total range of pH: 4.5 - 8.5. - Correlation coefficient between pH and log/azotobacter : r = 0.54.

Absence of paucity of azotobacter in soils of favorable reaction may be due to a multiplicity of factors. Important among these is the content of available phosphate for which the demand of the azotobacter is very marked. Christensen (1915) seems to have been the first to suggest the use of *A. chroococcum* for a bio-assay of available soil phosphorus on this basis. These earlier results have been borne out by more recent research. Ziemecka (1932), in England, found no development of azotobacter on plaques of soil containing less than 10 ppm water-soluble P_2O_5. Stöckli (1944), in Switzerland, found a marked correlation between azotobacter-density (by plate counts) and content of bicarbonate-soluble phosphate, and an examination of 121 cultivated soils from Denmark (Jensen, 1950) showed a partial correlation coefficient (pH eliminated) of 0.36 between log (azotobacter) and content of phosphate soluble in dilute sulphuric acid. Also Martin and co-workers (1937, 1940) found certain positive although less direct correlations between phosphate content and occurrence of azotobacter in soils from Iowa and Arizona. Van Niel (1935) found California soils that failed to support azotobacter owing to molybdenum deficiency, which is probably exceptional. Kaila (1954) suggested that toxic soluble aluminum compounds in addition to acidity might prevent the occurrence of azotobacter.

Whether antibiotic effect of other soil organisms will limit or suppress the growth of azotobacter in the soil is unknown but seems at least possible since many soil actinomycetes show antagonism towards azotobacter *in vitro* (Jensen, 1950; Nickell and Burkholder, 1947).

The content of total organic matter seems to be of relatively little consequence and would perhaps chiefly affect the azotobacter through its influence on the physical condition of the soil. Stöckli (1944) did find some correlation between azotobacter and humus content and Martin et al. (1937) likewise between degree of azotobacter-development and total nitrogen content which is mostly present in humus. No such correlation was found in Danish soils (Jensen, 1950) and could indeed hardly be expected, since the bulk of the "humus" compounds are unavailable to the azotobacter. The organic soil constituents of immediate significance are the simple compounds utilizable as carbon sources and those nitrogenous substances that are mineralized by the soil microflora with the release of ammonia. Biologically available nitrogen favors the bulk of the soil microflora in the competition with the nitrogen-fixers for the available energy material; therefore the carbon-nitrogen ratio of the organic material that at any moment is being mineralized becomes a most important factor in the soil ecology of azotobacter. It is indeed a common experience that nitrogenous fertilizers tend to reduce the density of the azotobacter-population. In laboratory experiments Winogradsky (1926) found that 50 ppm of nitrate-nitrogen strongly inhibited and that 100 ppm completely suppressed the spontaneous azotobacter development in soil + 1.0% glucose. Continued experiments (Winogradsky and Ziemecka, 1928) with big mannitol silica gel plates showed that 2.5 mg $NO_3 - N$ per g mannitol had a notable inhibitory effect on azotobacter-growth and nitrogen fixation and this increased strongly with increasing doses of nitrate; nevertheless other experiments (cf. Table 6) have shown that multiplication of azotobacter in soil is not excluded even in the presence of considerable amounts of nitrate. Under field conditions Ziemecka (1932) estimated a density of some 8,000 azotobacter per gram of soil from plots that permanently received non-nitrogenous artificial fertilizers, but the figures dropped to a level of 30 to 300 per gram in plots that additionally received nitrate, ammonium sulphate or rape cake, the last an example of readily mineralizable organic nitrogen. Lochhead and Thexton (1936) observed consistently higher counts of azotobacter in unfertilized plots than in those receiving manure or nitrate, and Stöckli (1944) quotes examples of drastic lowering of the azotobacter-counts after application of nitrate, urea or liquid manure (essentially an ammoniacal fertilizer).

The density of azotobacter is nearly always reported to be highest in the top layers of soil and decreasing rapidly with the depth. Only in the most exceptional cases has a maximum density been observed in deeper layers of soils from arid regions (Garbosky, 1956; Sabinin and Minina, 1932). A complicated interaction seems to exist between moisture and access of air, i.e., oxygen tension. Jensen and Swaby (1940) studied the influence of moisture varying between waterlogging and a minimum corresponding to pF-values (logarithms of the capillary tension) of 3.8-3.9. The numbers of azotobacter in non-enriched soil were scarcely influenced, but addition of 0.2% glucose induced a maximum multiplication at pF 2.8. Dommergues (1962) found the limiting pF values to be between 3.6 and 4.4 for multiplication of azotobacter in tropical black clay soils; this seemed to be of the same order as the wilting-point of higher plants. Obviously some very complicated relationships may be expected between the factors of moisture requirement, oxygen requirement and concentration of nutrient substances in the soil solution.

There is no evidence that the temperature affects the growth of azotobacter in soil differently from what it does *in vitro*. As growth of most azotobacter is poor or nil at temperatures below 8-10°C, it appears that long annual periods will be unfavorable for their activity in soil from cool regions though the population may be quite dense. A similar effect may be expected during the dry season in many tropical and subtropical soils. It is noteworthy in this connection that the *Azotobacter* proper (unlike *Azomonas*) are very resistant to desiccation owing to their micro-cyst-forming habit (Winogradsky, 1938).

When environmental factors like soil pH, supply of mineral nutrients, moisture, temperature etc. are favorable and the level of available mineral nitrogen is low or zero, the development of the azotobacter will largely depend on the supply of available organic matter to serve as source of carbon and energy. Incorporation of substances like glucose, starch, mannitol, ethanol, butanol or salts of several organic acids in amounts of $\frac{1}{2}$ to 2% will then stimulate the azotobacter to a multiplication that runs into hundreds or thousands of organisms per gram of soil and makes them the altogether dominant component of the soil microflora. This was first shown by Winogradsky (1926) and repeatedly confirmed (Gonick and Reuszer, 1949; Jensen, 1940a; de'Rossi, 1933); under these conditions the microscopic and cultural methods of counting may show figures of the same order of magnitude (Jensen, 1940a). This outburst of growth may happen with great rapidity, beginning after 24 hours and reaching a maximum after 3 to 4 days (Winogradsky, 1926). Darzniek (1961) found the multiplication of azotobacter (by plate counting) in sucrose-enriched soil beginning after a lag period of 3 to 6 hours at 25°C and continuing for the next 18 hours with a calculated (actually shorter) generation time of 106 to 232 minutes. The generation time was much longer, about 8 to 18 hours, in soil with addition of cotton root and leaf material and similar in irrigated field soil.

Concentrations of the order of 1% sugar and similar materials are of course not normally to be expected in the soil and microbial populations entirely dominated by azotobacter (or clostridia, for that matter) arising in response to such treatment may legitimately be considered artifacts that have no counterpart under natural soil conditions. However, much smaller amounts of simpler energy source may elicit a rapid proliferation of azotobacter, as shown in an experiment (Jensen, 1950) where 50 to 500 ppm ethanol was added to soils of varying character but all of adequate reaction (pH 7.2-7.6) and phosphate content. The soils were incubated in a moist condition at 25°C and azotobacter were counted on agar medium periodically within 72 hours.

The results in Table 6 show that the azotobacter may respond to ethanol doses as small as 40-50 ppm within 20 hours, and doses 10 times higher give rise to populations much denser than normally found in soil. Two features are noteworthy: firstly, azotobacter will multiply in the

Table 6. Multiplication of azotobacter in response to small doses of ethanol (Jensen, 1950).

Soil	Hours	Addition of ethanol ppm				
		0	50	100	200	500
A: Loam	0	140				
Azotobacter/g	18	180	370	1,940		5,000
	42	180	360	1,730		177,000
	70	100	650	1,540		750,000
NO_3-N ppm	70	43	44	35		17
B: Loam	0	440				
Azotobacter/g	18	490		2,100		79,000
	44	370		5,400		103,000
	72	340		700		67,000
NO_3-N ppm	72	45		44		45
C: Sand	20	40	27		170	2,300
Azotobacter/g	35	34	40		70	1,300
	72	63	30		80	1,700

presence of 20-40 ppm nitrate-nitrogen, contrary to the statement of Winogradsky (1926); secondly, the sandy soil supports a much less abundant azotobacter-population than the loam soils—possibly because the open structure permits an oxygen tension that is unfavorably high for growth in a dilute medium (cf. Tschapek and Giambiagi, 1954, 1955).

Among less well-defined environmental factors alleged to influence the growth of the azotobacter is the effect of atmospheric conditions, which should manifest itself in soil as well as *in vitro,* according to Bortels (1940) who has dealt with this topic in several publications. Final confirmation is still needed.

The second genus of the Azotobacteraceae, the beijerinckias, differ markedly from the azotobacter in ecological respect and were long thought to be confined to the tropical regions, having been detected only in India, Indonesia, Northern Australia, South America and Central Africa. Only in recent years have they been found to occur occasionally in subtropic and warm temperate countries (Mediterranean Europe, South Africa, Japan) as stated from the very complete review of Becking (1961). They appear largely to take the place of azotobacter in tropical regions where Becking found them present in 48% of the samples tested (especially in the pH-range of 5.5 to 5.9), while only 25% harbored azotobacter; the corresponding figures for nontropical soils were 9 and 39%.

The lower incidence of azotobacter in the tropical soils is largely a question of pH, but no adequate explanation has been found for this restricted occurrence of the beijerinckias. Their temperature interval for growth is rather narrower than that of the azotobacter especially at the upper end of the scale, and they survive remarkably well at low temperature (Becking, 1961). Their predominance in red lateritic soils typical of the tropic regions and very poor in exchangeable calcium has been thought to be due to the fact that the beijerinckias do not require calcium but are on the contrary sensitive to it; however, soils poor in exchangeable calcium also exist outside the tropics, and the quantitative calcium demands of the azotobacter are only small. Becking (1961) suggested that the greater tolerance of the beijerinckias for iron and aluminum ions would favor their existence in the acid lateritic soils whereas in alkaline soils they would be outgrown by the more rapidly growing azotobacter. Still this does not explain why the beijerinckias should be absent from acid soils of cool regions although they do occur in tropical mountain soils under similar temperature conditions.

Derx (1953) suggested a possible association of the beijerinckias with certain tropical legumes or perhaps the Caesalpinioideae (rhizosphere organisms?), but Becking (1961) found no correlation with the type of vegetation. A notable aspect of the ecology of the beijerinckias is their copious growth on the leaf surface (to which Ruinen, 1956, gave the name "phyllosphere") of tropical trees whence they may be transferred to the soil. This agrees with the observations of Döbereiner and Alvahydo (1959) that washings from stems and leaves of sugar cane plants stimulate the beijerinckia-population of the soil and that sugar cane cultivation greatly favored the distribution of beijerinckia in Brazilian soils. Perhaps the limited occurrence of the beijerinckias has some connection with the presence of plant materials rich in sugars, since the beijerinckias as a whole seem much less apt to utilize the simpler organic acids and lower alcohols that are serviceable for most species of *Azotobacter*.

Little is known about the numerical abundance of the beijerinckias in the soils where they do occur. Agar plate counts (Derx, 1950; Döbereiner and Alvahydo, 1959; Tchan, 1953) suggest densities comparable to those of the azotobacter, and high soil moisture seems particularly favorable (Döbereiner and Alvahydo, 1959). Here again the relation of the cultural counts to the real number of cell individuals remains obscure. Virtually nothing is known about the soil ecology of *Derxia* because so far only four isolations have been reported (Jensen et al., 1960; Ray, 1962).

B. The Nitrogen-Fixing Clostridia

In contrast to the Azotobacteraceae, the large group of *Clostridium butyricum* and related nitrogen-fixing species are practically ubiquitous soil inhabitants whose presence *per se* thus does not seem to depend much on soil properties. This appears even in the early investigations of Bredemann (1909) who examined 134 soil samples of world-wide distribution and found butyric acid clostridia in all except 5, among which a sphagnum peat and an arctic beach sand. One obviously important element in this respect is their faculty of producing endospores that ensure their survival at least in a dormant form under adverse soil conditions but which on the other hand makes it difficult to estimate the size of the metabolically active population: the vegetative cells. Upon the whole there are no really adequate methods available for any accurate determination of numbers of anaerobic bacteria in general; all figures resulting from cultural counting methods therefore represent minimum values (as in the azotobacter, but probably more so). Dilution counts or sometimes anaerobic plate counts have mostly shown figures from sporadic to around 10^5 per gram (Augier, 1957; Jensen and Swaby, 1940; Meiklejohn, 1956). Far higher numbers even exceeding 10^8 per gram have been reported in other cases where particularly favourable conditions seem to exist (Abd-el-Malek and Ishac, 1962). Endospores sometimes seem to account for a very high proportion of the numbers (Jensen and Swaby, 1940), but this may partly be due to the difficulties of estimating the real size of the vegetative cell population.

As might be expected, anaerobic conditions will favor the growth of the clostridia. Winogradsky (1926) has shown that it is possible to encourage growth of clostridia as well as azotobacter even in moderately moist glucose-enriched soil simply by increasing the depth of the soil column, evidently because the azotobacter rapidly exhaust the oxygen of the soil atmosphere in the deeper layers. The level of anaerobiosis may similarly be raised or lowered by varying the moisture content, and the clostridia will at high moisture content entirely dominate the microscopic picture within two to three days and reach numbers estimated at hundreds or thousands of millions per gram. Microscopic counts in similarly treated soil (Jensen, 1940a) showed vegetative clostridium-cells numbering about 120 to 660 million per g or roughly 25 to 50% of the total bacterial flora. By contrast it is most rare to find cells that resemble vegetative cells of clostridia by microscopic examination of the normal soil microflora. To all appearances the clostridia are like the rest of the spore-forming soil bacteria typical "zymogenic" organisms that only enter a stage of active life when favorable conditions are created: provision of available energy material at a level of oxygen tension compatible with the anaerobic nature of the clostridia. As is well known, the clostridia may also co-exist with aerobic organisms, e.g., azotobacter, that lower the redox potential of the medium to a level where anaerobic organisms can initiate growth.

The clostridia have often been assumed to be more adaptable to varying soil conditions than the azotobacter owing to greater tolerance of acid reaction. Actually they resemble the azotobacter in showing optimum growth at approximately neutral reaction and although they can acidify the medium to pH around 4 it is uncertain how little or how much their nitrogen-fixing activity is impaired by acid reaction. The nitrogen-fixing enzyme system itself has a quite definite pH-optimum at pH 6.6 with rapid decline of activity on both sides (Mortenson, 1962).

There is little known about organic compounds specially favorable for the growth of clostridia in the soil. Their ability to utilize a wider range of carboyhdrates and related compounds may give them an advantage in comparison with the azotobacter, but on the other hand they will hardly avail themselves of simple alcohols and organic acids except in special cases: lactate + acetate by some strains of *Cl. butyricum,* ethanol + acetate by *Cl. kluyveri* which also fixes nitrogen (Rosenblum and Wilson, 1949). Since the azotobacter readily utilizes this class of compounds which the clostridia will produce by fermentation of compounds partly unavailable to the azotobacter, the two groups are very naturally fit to enter into symbiotic associations.

Upon the whole it must be admitted that our knowledge of the soil ecology of the *Cl. butyricum*-group is still quite fragmentary and warrants further study.

C. The Miscellaneous Nitrogen Fixers

What has been said about the clostridia will probably also largely apply to the facultative anaerobic *Bac. polymyxa* whose physiology of nitrogen fixation is very similar to that of the clostridia (Grau and Wilson, 1963). Ecologically it is a widely distributed soil inhabitant (Bredemann, 1908) which may become active under the same conditions as the clostridia and simultaneously with these.

Hardly any information has been gathered about the ecology of the other potentially nitrogen-fixing microorganisms, their relative abundance in the soil or the opportunities that they may find for displaying their nitrogen-fixing effect. Their facultative anaerobic and somewhat oxygen-sensitive *Aerobacter* and *Achromobacter* might well like *Bac. polymyxa* become active together with the clostridia, although there is no positive evidence that they do so. It is equally difficult to judge the importance of the aerobic members of the group. None of them seems to have properties that would make them specially apt to flourish under conditions where the more specialized nitrogen-fixers will not. The yeasts could be imagined to fix nitrogen in soils too acid for the azotobacter and outside the region of the beijerinckias, but generally it seems possible to subscribe to the opinion of Winogradsky and Ziemecka (1928) that only the azotobacteraceae and the clostridia are quantitatively important agents of nitrogen fixation.

D. The Rhizosphere: A Special Habitat and a Side Issue

The conception that the immediate surroundings of the plant roots carry a particularly dense population of microorganisms and are the seat of a correspondingly high biological activity was developed nearly sixty years ago by Hiltner who coined the name "rhizosphere" for this zone. This "rhizosphere-effect" was naturally thought to apply also to the nitrogen-fixing bacteria—an idea that probably was behind earlier statements of stronger nitrogen fixation in soils planted to non-leguminous crops compared with unplanted soil. The first who definitely suggested organic root substances as nutrients for the azotobacter in the rhizosphere was probably Loew (1927) who regarded this association as important in maintaining the nitrogen status of Brazilian plantation soils. Subsequent work has given little support to this idea. Microscopic methods show only a very minor representation of azotobacter-like cells in the total rhizosphere population (Starkey, 1938), and cultural counting methods generally lead to the same results. Some increased density of azotobacter in the rhizosphere is sometimes observed (Brown et al., 1962b; Jensen, 1940a), but the effect is often nil or may even be negative (Darzniek, 1960; Katznelson, 1946), and when positive it seems slight in comparison with the effect on the rest of the microflora (Jensen, 1940a) and to occur in the soil adjacent to the roots rather than on the actual root surface (Brown et al., 1962b; Vancura et al., 1959; Vancura and Macura, 1959).

This suggests that the rhizosphere conditions tend to favor other microorganisms rather than the azotobacter—a view supported by much information on the nature of root secretion products that has been gathered in recent years, as reviewed by Rovira (1962). These products include a mixture of reducing sugars, organic acids, numerous amino acids, nucleotides, vitamins, etc. Such a medium is quite non-selective for the nitrogen fixers and would place them very unfavorably in the competition with the general microflora. Vancura and Macura (1961) could separate the root secretions of barley and wheat into fractions that stimulated growth of azotobacter (glucose and organic acids) or inhibited its nitrogen fixation when added to glucose medium (amino acids). Varying proportion of such constituents may be the reason why root secretions of different plants will either stimulate or inhibit the growth of azotobacter and other bacteria (Krasil'nikov, 1961; Metz, 1955). Spicher (1954) found that the exudation products of barley roots could indeed serve as material for nitrogen fixation but lowered the pH of the rhizosphere to a level that inhibited growth of *A. chroococcum* unless extra buffer substance was present; this may well explain why the azotobacter seem to avoid the actual root surfaces but may be stimulated in the adjacent soil due to its buffer effect.

Experiments with aseptically grown plants associated with pure cultures of azotobacter would seem to give no true picture of what happens under natural conditions where the azotobacter must compete with non-nitrogen-fixing microorganisms in the rhizosphere. A few experiments of this kind have given little evidence of mutual benefit. Starc (1942) observed growth and slight nitrogen fixation by *A. chroococcum* grown together with corn in sand culture, but the fixed nitrogen was not taken up by the higher plant, and other bacteria tended to suppress azotobacter under non-aseptic conditions. Fedorov (1944) found under similar conditions that azotobacter could supply some nitrogen to corn plants receiving a small dose of nitrate, but the gain was only a very small fraction of the nitrogen content of plants with full nitrate supply.

The beijerinckias seem to show some particular features as rhizosphere inhabitants. Döbereiner (1961) observed low numbers of these organisms in Brazilian soils until sugar cane was planted, but then the numbers increased markedly during the following years, particularly in the immediate vicinity of the roots (the "rhizoplane"). This behavior of the beijerinckias in contrast to the azotobacter may well be due to their greater tolerance for the acid root exudates (cf. Spicher, 1954).

About the relationships of the clostridia in the rhizosphere we know very little (Katznelson, 1946, observed a strong stimulation in mangel rhizospheres) and about the rest of the nitrogen fixers scarcely anything.

"Bacterization"—a side issue. Although experimental evidence for any considerable nitrogen fixation in the rhizosphere is lacking, the subject has had a remarkable attraction for many soil microbiologists, particu-

larly in the East European countries. The interest seems largely to stem from investigations some forty years ago by Markrinoff (1924) who claimed that treatment of oat or barley grain with azotobacter before sowing resulted in notable increases of yield. Such "bacterization" of seed with cultures of azotobacter in peat, etc., has long been practiced on a large scale in Russia. An extensive literature exists on this subject, of which Allison (1947) and more recently Cooper (1959) have prepared valuable reviews (cf. also Fedorov, 1952). It is generally claimed that yields of cereals etc. may be increased by some 10 to 20%, but the effect is by no means universal and the crop yields appear to be generally low according to figures given by Fedorov (1952) and Mishustin and Naumova (1962).

Most attempts to reproduce these results in western countries have failed. Positive effects were rarely recorded and were then slight in comparison with the response to nitrogenous fertilizers. Among more recent investigators Wichtmann (1952) found small occasional gains in mustard, Vancura and Macura (1959) found statistically significant yield increases of 16 to 20% in oats (the actual yields were not stated), and particularly interesting is a brief report by Nutman (1962) on experiments at Rothamsted where increases of 28 to 40% were sometimes achieved in crops supplied with nitrogenous fertilizers.

The azotobacter-treatment of the seed seems sometimes to lead to the establishment of a permanent azotobacter-flora in the rhizosphere (Vancura et al., 1959; Vancura and Macura, 1959; Wichtmann, 1952). According to Brown et al. (1962b) this only happens in soil of pH above 6.7, but very high numbers may arise, amounting to millions of azotobacter per gram of soil even in the presence of nitrogenous fertilizers.

Among the Russian investigators there is no unity of opinion about the causes of the improved yields (Cooper, 1959). Stimulated nitrogen fixation is not generally regarded as important (although maintained by Fedorov, 1952), any more than protection against soil-borne pathogens which seems unlikely because the azotobacter have never been seen to produce antibiotic substances. A more plausible explanation would seem to be an improvement of early growth by some still unknown growth compound. Not only do the azotobacter produce large amounts of B-vitamins, but there is also clear evidence that culture filtrates from azotobacter will directly influence the growth of plant roots (Krasil'nikov, 1961; Metz, 1955; Spicher, 1954). The effect may be stimulatory or inhibitory (probably a question of concentration) and is not specific to azotobacter according to Krasil'nikov (1961). The active factor(s) is probably of a multiple nature. Spicher (1954) considered it to be a cationic compound that did not act by virtue of its nitrogen content. The presence of indolacetic acid (auxin) has also been reported (Kandler, 1951; Vancura and Macura, 1960), and Vancura (1961) detected gibberellic acid which he cautiously suggested might promote germination and early seedling growth.

The effect of "bacterization" thus appears to be qualitatively real but inconstant and unpredictable; it is mostly relatively small, probably not related to nitrogen fixation and not confined to the azotobacter. Its future value for agricultural practice would seem almost entirely to turn upon the still undecided question whether it displays any beneficial effects in plants adequately provided with nutrients in the form of "orthodox" fertilizers.

E. The Direct Evidence for Nitrogen Fixation in the Soil

It has been shown many times that quantities of nitrogen large enough to be detected by the Kjeldahl method may be fixed in soils enriched with readily available energy materials in amounts sufficient to make the nitrogen fixers the predominant component of the soil microflora. The gains have not with certainty been shown to exceed 10 to 20 mg nitrogen per g spent energy materials corresponding to the nutritive value of glucose, which means that the economy of nitrogen fixation appears to be the same *"in terra"* as *in vitro*. The fixed nitrogen seems to be roughly accounted for in the cell substances of azotobacter or clostridia as determined by direct microscopic counting (Jensen, 1940a). Experiments with such enriched soils under laboratory conditions, however, only serve to demonstrate the potential "nitrogen-fixing power" of individual soils and the results are in nowise applicable to natural soil environments where low concentrations of simple organic compounds must be considered the normal state of affairs. An important question then poses itself: Is it permissible to extrapolate from the results of artificially stimulated nitrogen fixation in heavily enriched soils and to assume that the economy of nitrogen fixation under these conditions will also apply to natural soils?—There is *per se* no real evidence that low concentrations of nutrients will be utilized with particular efficiency, but several factors tend to obscure the picture. Firstly there is the important possibility that the economy of nitrogen fixation would be increased by a combination of low oxygen tension and low concentration of soluble organic matter in the soil solution. To this comes the possible effect of oxygen tension on the metabolism of the organisms that release nutrients from the insoluble organic substances, and finally as an opposing factor comes the inhibitory effect of combined nitrogen; at a constant level of nitrate- and/or ammonia-nitrogen this effect will obviously increase with decreasing concentration of organic matter, i.e., narrowing carbon-nitrogen ration.

An approach to these complicated problems is best obtained through nitrogen fixation experiments where natural plant materials are utilized in the soil under varying conditions. A most instructive contribution of this kind, although carried out with plant material alone, is due to Olsen (1932) who determined gains of nitrogen and loss of organic matter from forest litter during an 11-month incubation period at 2 levels of pH and 2 levels of oxygen access: "aerobic" (moderately moist) and "anaerobic" (water-saturated). Although losses of organic matter were greater under aerobic conditions, the gains of nitrogen were sometimes higher under water saturation, especially when calculated on the basis of organic matter lost. The nitrogen fixation under aerobic conditions

Table 7. Gains of nitrogen in leaf material $+ 2.0\%$ $CaCO_3$, mg per g dry matter lost (calculated from the data of Olsen, 1932).

Beech leaves			Oak leaves		
Inc. days	Moist	Saturated	Inc. days	Moist	Saturated
0	0	0	0	0	0
95	4.0	5.2	92	7.7	6.5
161	4.3	7.8	159	5.7	6.3
229	2.6	9.0	221	5.5	4.8
337	2.7	10.0	327	4.8	3.9
Loss of dry matter, %	27.0	17.4		35.7	27.9
Gain of N, mg/100 g	78	180		170	109
pH	7.5-7.7	7.6-8.2		7.0-7.5	7.2-8.0

ceased when nitrate began to accumulate and appeared to be due to clostridia, since azotobacter could not be detected in the material. Some pertinent data are shown in Table 7. The fixation of nitrogen per unit weight of lost organic matter (i.e., disappeared as carbon dioxide, not the total amount metabolized!) is much the same or certainly not higher than in combined pure cultures of nitrogen-fixing and cellulose-decomposing bacteria (cf. Tables 1 and 2).

In essential agreement with Olsen's findings, experiments with straw in moderate moist nitrogen-poor soil or pure sand-kaolin-mixture (Jensen, 1940a) showed no gains of nitrogen in spite of vigorous multiplication of azotobacter, or only small gains at the expense of the water-soluble straw constituents alone. The failure of the microflora to utilize the rest of the straw appeared to be due to lack of formation of available metabolic by-products from the insoluble fraction, because addition of such compounds (acetate and lactate) immediately induced a further multiplication of azotobacter accompanied by a significant nitrogen fixation (Figs. 1 and 2). When the water content was raised to saturation level the growth of azotobacter on the soil surface became abundant and significant amounts of nitrogen were fixed with straw or root organic material, as shown in Table 8.

Table 8. Nitrogen fixation with plant residues in water-saturated soil or sand media (Jensen, 1940).

Medium	Incubation days	Gain of N ppm	Azotobacter per gram
Loam + oats straw 1.0%	70	18*	1.2×10^6
	120	13*	3.8×10^6
Sandy loam + oats straw 1.5%	62	16*	0.3×10^6
Sand soil + oats straw 1.5%	28	16**	3×10^6
	150	73**	4.7×10^4
	250	93**	6×10^3
Sand soil + wheat straw 1.0%	28	18**	9.5×10^6
	90	30**	5×10^6
Sand-kaolin mixture + wheat roots 2.5%	30	13**	3.3×10^6
	120	24**	0.3×10^6

* Significant at P < 0.05.   ** do. at P < 0.01.

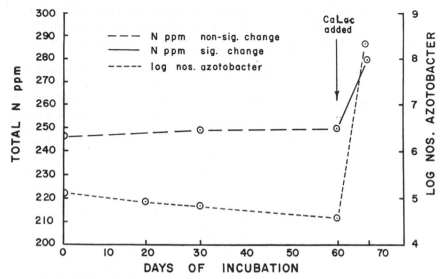

Fig. 1. Nitrogen fixation and numbers of azotobacter (by plate count) in moist sand soil + 1.0% filter paper cellulose followed by 0.5% Ca-lactate (indicated by arrow). (Gain of N following lactate addition significant at P < 0.01. (Jensen, 1940a).

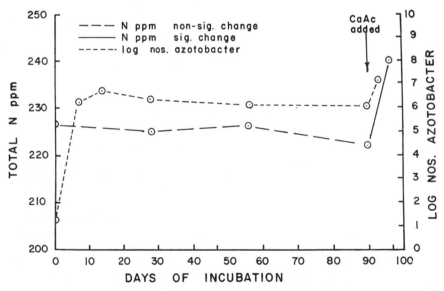

Fig. 2. Nitrogen fixation and numbers of azotobacter in moist sand soil + 1.0% wheat straw followed by 0.5% Ca-acetate (indicated by arrow). (Gain of N following acetate addition significant at P < 0.01) (Jensen, 1940a).

The gains of nitrogen, with a maximum of approx. 6 mg per g straw added, are accompanied by numbers of azotobacter that are not normally seen in natural soil but are comparable to those found by Uppal et al. (1939) and Rouquérol (1962) under similar conditions in the field (cf. Table 4). No attempts were made to count the clostridia but microscopic examination failed to show more than at the most a sporadic occurrence of vegetative cells of clostridia; their significance in these experiments thus appears doubtful.

Bjälfve (1955) conducted similar experiments in moderately moist sand medium incubated in light or darkness. Gains of nitrogen with straw were only 1.0-1.2 mg per g in a year, but starch, which is available to most azotobacter, induced a "normal" fixation of 9-10 mg per g within 6 months (incubation in darkness). The loss of straw organic matter was determined in another experimental series and indicated a fixation of some 3.2-4.5 mg nitrogen per g lost dry matter.

Barrow and Jenkinson (1962) failed to detect nitrogen fixation in mixtures of soil and straw of moderate water content, but found gains of as much as 2.6-2.8 mg per g straw in water-saturated soil with restricted access of air. No bacteriological investigations were made, but it seems significant that no nitrogen was fixed in pure nitrogen atmosphere; this speaks strongly against clostridia as the agents of fixation.

Studies by means of the labeled-nitrogen (N_2^{15}) technique seem confined to a single contribution by Delwiche and Wijler (1956) who obtained negative results in various non-enriched soils or soils with addition of straw, grass, or grass roots. Nitrogen fixation was only detected (a) in soils enriched with glucose or sucrose which induced an intense proliferation of azotobacter, and (b) in decaying grass sods under restricted access of air; the gains of nitrogen in this medium corresponded to 12 pounds per acre at the most, while the method should permit detection of only 2 or 3 pounds per acre. Unfortunately Delwiche and Wijler's investigations have remained fragmentary, and further studies along this line are urgently needed.

Pot experiments with soils under growing crops represent a step towards field conditions and are numerous in the earlier and particularly the German literature but have led to no very definite results (Jensen, 1940a). More recently Moyer (1941) conducted pot and frame experiments (the latter a still closer approximation to field conditions) with fertile soils from semiarid North China and found no signs of nitrogen fixation after cropping for five years to nonleguminous crops; addition of oats straw or millet roots lessened the removal of nitrogen but did not lead to any net accretion. Fedorov (1952) describes a 3-year pot experiment with oats in soil variously treated with lime, straw (45 g per 2.5 kg soil), and azotobacter-inoculation. Fixation of 510 mg nitrogen per pot (= roughly 200 ppm or 11 to 12 mg per g added straw) was reported as the maximum gain, but this was calculated as difference between straw-lime-azotobacter-treated pots and uncropped control pots in which heavy but unexplained loss of nitrogen took place; the gain as difference between initial and final nitrogen in the treated pots appears to have been only 45 mg per pot (= 18 ppm or 1.0 mg per g straw).

Determination of the nitrogen balance in field soil should theoretically give the final answer to the question but is beset with formidable difficulties owing to many uncontrollable factors: addition of nitrogen by wild-growing legumes, precipitation and possibly ammonia absorption from the atmosphere, removals by leaching, denitrification and perhaps ammonia evaporation and erosion; finally the sampling error is much more serious here than in homogenized laboratory samples. Nevertheless, a good deal of evidence has accumulated to indicate that the process is of little significance in soils under intensive cultivation but is recognizable in pasture soils, particularly if grass crops are not carried away. Much of the earlier literature was reviewed elsewhere (Jensen, 1940a). Among later observations, Whitt (1941) calculated gains of no less than 100 pounds per acre per annum ascribed to nonsymbiotic fixation, in soil permanently under legume-free blue-grass. Similarly Parker (1957) estimated annual nitrogen gains of 60 to 70 pounds per acre in the upper 10 inches of a heavy, grass-covered loam soil in West Australia. The author offered the very plausible explanation that the fine texture of the soil and the dense sward would restrict the oxygen supply and consequently increase the efficiency of the nitrogen fixation at the expense of the plant residues. It is highly desirable that investigations like these should be combined with studies of the composition of the soil microflora and its changes during the process of fixation.

The possible role of the beijerinckias under similar conditions cannot yet be estimated. Opportunities for their activity doubtless exist, since at least one strain will work as effectively as the azotobacter in association with cellulose-decomposing bacteria (cf. Table 1). Their reaction to reduced oxygen pressure vs. substrate concentration is not well known, but a brief statement by Döbereiner and Alvahydo (1959) suggests a behavior similar to the azotobacter. The same authors (Döbereiner and Alvahydo, 1959) report fixation of 2.3 mg nitrogen per g dry sugar cane leaf in a soil inoculated with Beijerinckia. Further research in this direction is needed.

No means are yet available for estimating the actual amount of organic matter transformed by the nitrogen fixers in the soil. Garbosky (1956) has made an attempt hereat by measuring the level at which A. chroococcum grows in an aqueous soil extract, compared with solutions of known mannitol concentration. In this way he calculated a "potential nitrogen-fixing capacity" of 7 to 20 kg nitrogen per hectare. The principle sounds ingenious but the results are obtained in a very indirect way and rest upon many hypothetical assumptions. Further development of the method might bring valuable results.

A possibility finally to be considered is the fixation of nitrogen by nonbiological processes. Several investigators have made such claims, from Berthelot (1890) on silent electric discharges to Dhar (1937) in many publications on photochemical nitrogen fixation. No convincing proof of the reality of these processes has so far been presented. Dhar's claims find no support in experiments by Bjälfve (1955) who detected no gains of nitrogen in truly sterile light-exposed sand media with or without added organic matter. On the other hand, nitrogen was fixed and organic carbon accumulated in nonsterile light-exposed sand without organic matter (cf. Fig. 3).

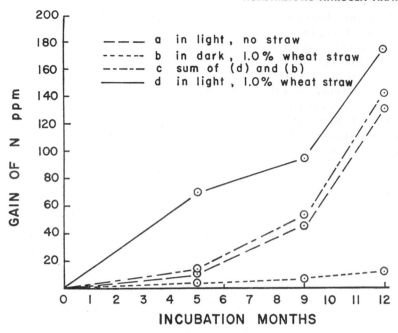

Fig. 3. Nitrogen fixation in moist sand ± 1.0% wheat straw incubated in light or darkness (Bjälfve, 1955).

IV. THE SOIL ECOLOGY OF THE LITHOTROPHIC NITROGEN FIXERS

The organisms of this group are, as far as soil inhabitants go, practically limited to the photosynthetic ones, among which the blue-green algae are predominant. They obviously differ profoundly in ecological respect from the organotrophs, inasmuch as they are independent of organic matter but can only display their activity at the soil-air interface and in water.

A. The Blue-Green Algae (Cyanophyceae)

The history of these organisms as authentic nitrogen fixers is little more than 30 years old, but the literature on their biochemistry, growth physiology and ecology is already very voluminous; for reviews see Fogg and Wolfe (1954), Fogg (1956), and Singh (1961). The nitrogen-fixing cyanophyceae are certainly the organisms most perfectly adapted for existence on the barest necessities of life: sunlight, air, water, and mineral salts, and consequently they are the classical pioneers on bare mineral soils, either independently or as constituents of lichens. In soil they are regularly found, but their abundance must vary enormously, and since they excrete relatively little of the fixation products during growth, it must be their bio-mass that determines their contribution to the pool of biologically fixed nitrogen.

Their importance in arable soils is probably slight, because frequent soil tillage will tend to disturb their growth on the soil surface, but they may be able to develop under dense cover crops owing to their low light intensity requirements. The total mass of cyanophyceae, including the non-nitrogen-fixing ones, is as difficult to estimate as that of the bacteria, but only the growth on the soil surface matters for the purpose of photosynthetic nitrogen fixation. According to Petersen (1935) the subterranean algae are relatively few and mostly present as resting cells; if active, they must depend on organic matter as facultative organotrophs, and any cyanophyceae that might fix nitrogen under these conditions would be counterparts of the azotobacter whose conditions they would share. Whether this happens at all is, however, unknown and perhaps unlikely.

The brilliant investigation by Schloesing and Laurent (1892) brought strong evidence that the epiterranean blue-green algae could become important nitrogen-fixing agents, although it could not then be definitely stated whether the algae or associated bacteria were the responsible agents. Verification of such algal activity under natural conditions came much later when Cameron and Fuller (1960) studied the algal crusts developing on both virgin and cultivated arid soils after rainfall; the crusts contained several species of nitrogen-fixing cyanophyceae and their nitrogen contents increased by some 240-400 ppm under illumination for 4 weeks in humid atmosphere. De (1936) was apparently the first to call attention to the importance of cyanophyceae in rice soils of India, where they grow abundantly in the flooding season. Later De (1939) proved the nitrogen-fixing power of several cyanophyceae isolated from such soils and considered it "legitimate to conclude that the fixation of nitrogen in the soils of the rice fields is mainly brought about by algae." De's pioneer work has been followed by a wealth of contributions, most of which are reviewed in a recent monograph by Singh (1961). Although world-widely distributed, the nitrogen-fixing cyanophyceae seem by no means always sufficiently abundant in rice soils to be detectable in small soil samples. Thus, Watanabe (1959a) found them in only 25 among 38 localities (851 soil samples altogether) from East and Southeast Asia; he therefore recommended their sowing as a green-manure crop and devised a method for large-scale cultivation of such algal inocula (Watanabe, 1959b). The very impressive gains of nitrogen that these organisms may achieve under favorable conditions have repeatedly been verified in laboratory experiments, although the relative effects of algae and bacteria are not always easy to separate. De and Sulaiman (1950) found that growing rice plants greatly increased nitrogen fixation in soil-water mixtures exposed to the light, apparently because the growth of algae was stimulated by the carbon dioxide production of the plant roots. As much as 40 mg nitrogen per rice plant could be fixed in a growth season, but decaying root material gave rise to a much smaller fixation apparently due to bacteria. In other experiments De and Mandal (1956) used closed respirometers and gasometric determination of nitrogen uptake. Six soils cropped to rice developed during 6 weeks a heavy growth of algae and fixed nitrogen in amounts corresponding to 14 to 44 pounds per acre, with addition of phosphate and molybdenum even about 70 pounds per acre. Willis and Green (1949) found similar gains in pot experiments with rice, even in addition to the nitrogen carried away in the crops. Gains of this magnitude are not surprising in view of the growth rate that may be attained in pure cultures, where Allen and Arnon (1955) found a maximum daily production of 26 g dry matter of *Anabaena cylindrica* per m^2, with at least 1.0-1.2 g nitrogen; this corresponds to a fixation of 8.9-10.7 pounds per acre per day. Watanabe (1959) reported gains roughly one-third of this in cultivation on a technical scale.

The main difficulty of assessing the value of such figures is their translation to field conditions. There is as yet no ready answer to this problem, but recent work quoted by Singh (1961) gives some indication of the figures to be expected. The bio-mass of nitrogen-fixing algae in rice soils (among which *Aulosira fertilissima* is predominant in India) is difficult to estimate. Prahad, quoted by Singh (1961), calculated gains of 11.7 to 16.2 pounds per acre from nitrogen determinations in the algal mass collected from rice fields (this apparently in addition to the nitrogen removed in the crop). In other Indian soils the moist and undisturbed ground is always, according to Singh, covered by a growth of blue-green algae among which the shade-loving *Cylindrospermum licheniforme* is predominant, especially in sugar cane and corn fields but also on fallow soil and grassland. Singh developed a "micro-quadrat method" that consisted in removing the algal growth from the soil surface in randomly distributed quadrats of 225 cm^2 and determining nitrogen herein. By this obviously very approximative method Singh estimated gains of nitrogen in amounts of 64 to 96 pounds per acre within 75 days. Evidently much further study will be needed to give a precise idea about the reliability of such figures.

The cardinal ecological factors that allow optimum nitrogen fixation by the cyanophyceae would beside favorable temperature and light seem to be (a) sufficient moisture or even water-logging, (b) a soil surface undisturbed by soil cultivation for some length of time, (c) a soil reaction close to neutral or slightly alkaline, (d) adequate supply of mineral nutrients including molybdenum, and (e) absence or paucity of ammonia and nitrate nitrogen. The first three conditions are often fulfilled in Indian soils of which many according to Singh (1961) are neutral to strongly alkaline; in the latter ("usar") soils of pH around 9 *Nostoc commune* developed strongly under reclamation. The alternating drying and flooding to which rice soils are subject seems an essential factor in nitrogen fixation, as shown by Calder (1959) in experiments with an Uganda swamp soil where *Anabaena* were prominent. To this must be added the very small consumption of mineral nitrogenous fertilizers in Indian agriculture. It should be added, however, that not all investigators ascribe an equally great importance to algae as nitrogen-fixing agents in rice soils (Rouquérol, 1962; Uppal, 1939; Willis and Green, 1949).

In this connection it is worth noticing some laboratory experiments by Bjälfve (1955) in sand medium with addition of 1.0% straw or starch, sterile or nonsterile, and incubated for a year in light or in darkness.

No nitrogen was ever gained under sterile conditions, or in sand without organic matter and incubated in darkness, but fixation took place (a) in sand without organic matter incubated in light where it was accompanied by gains of organic carbon, (b) in dark-incubated sand with organic matter, and (c) in light-incubated sand with organic matter where it was sometimes stronger than in (a) and (b) together. Some of Bjälfve's data are shown in Fig. 3. The nitrogen-fixing agents were not identified but were almost certainly nitrogen-fixing cyanophyceae in (a), bacteria in (b) and a combination of both groups in (c). The obvious interaction between light and organic matter most probably consists in stimulated activity of the algae by organotrophic bacteria developing at the expense of the organic matter (cf. Bjälfve, 1962).

B. Miscellaneous Agents

It is difficult to form any opinion on the importance of the motley collection of organisms in this group, all anaerobes but not all obligatory lithotrophs: the Thiorhodaceae which are obligatory photosynthetic and use reduced sulphur compounds as hydrogen donors, the Athiorhodaceae which are facultative photosynthetic and use organic compounds as hydrogen donors, and the desulphovibrios and methane bacteria which are facultative lithotrophic. The two last groups might well display some activity in swamps and mud deposits but hardly in field soils. It is difficult to imagine the requirements of the Thiorhodaceae and Athiorhodaceae for anaerobic conditions combined with access of sunlight being fulfilled in surface soils but quite possibly in shallow water. Okuda et al. (1959) found *Rhodopseudomonas capsulatus* able to grow and fix nitrogen under conditions similar to those in rice fields, and particularly noteworthy is the subsequent observation (Okuda, 1960) that this bacterium will grow in the presence of oxygen when associated with *A. vinelandii*. It is too early to form an opinion of the significance of such organisms, but it should be remembered that although they are photosynthetic they demand organic compounds as hydrogen donors (butyrate and acetate in the experiments of Okuda and his associates).

V. AN EPITOME

The following ecological factors must be considered as chiefly regulating the activities of the three major groups of organotrophic non-symbiotic nitrogen fixers (*Azotobacter, Beijerinckia, Clostridium* spp.):

(1). A temperature range at least 6° above 0 and probably optimal at 25 to 30°C.

(2). A range of pH extending from approx. 3 to 9 but for optimum growth of the azotobacter and clostridia not far from neutrality.

(3). An adequate supply of mineral nutrients including molybdenum and relatively large amounts of phosphate.

(4). A degree of moisture that permits vegetative cell growth and has wide implications because it is bound up with oxygen access which again affects (a) the balance between azotobacter and clostridia, (b) the production of organic metabolites from insoluble plant residues, and (3) the efficiency of the nitrogen fixation by azotobacter.

(5). The presence of available nitrogen compounds (nitrate and particularly ammonia) which restrict nitrogen fixation by competitive assimilation and by encouraging growth of non-nitrogen-fixing organisms, and finally

(6). The quality and quantity of organic compounds available as carbon and energy source. This is usually the limiting factor if conditions are otherwise adequate.

A certain degree of anaerobiosis seems necessary for effective nitrogen fixation on the basis of those plant residues that represent the bulk of organic matter returned to the soil. The effect of restricted aeration is doubtless of a dual nature: firstly increased production of organic metabolites from cellulosic materials and secondly a more efficient utilization of these by-products by the nitrogen fixers. For these reasons the process is unlikely to be of great importance in arable soils under intensive cultivation, at least in comparison with the nitrogen demands of the crops. Here the crop residues are mostly small and largely confined to the root material, and the frequent soil tillage together with drainage militates against efficient nitrogen fixation. This situation would seem to become extreme where cereal cultivation predominates and is combined with burning of the straw and copious use of nitrogenous fertilizers. Under such conditions we find azotobacter populations of a few hundred or at the most thousands per gram. We may draw certain conclusions concerning the relation between cell proliferation, organic matter consumption and nitrogen fixation with azotobacter as the model. An average azotobacter-cell may be assumed to have a volume of $5\mu^3$, a weight of 5×10^{-6} μg and a content of 20% dry matter with 10% nitrogen; a simple calculation then shows that the fixation of each ppm of nitrogen will mean the synthesis of 10^7 cells per gram of soil if *in vitro* conditions apply: consumption of at least 50 parts of organic matter (equivalent to glucose) per part of fixed nitrogen which is present as cell substance. If merely 1% of 10^7 cells were viable at any given moment, the result would be an azotobacter-density of 100,000 per gram, which is most exceptional (cf. Table 4).

A different state of affairs may obtain in soils where plant residues decay under partially or periodically anaerobic conditions, such as rice fields (Rouquérol, 1962; Uppal et al., 1939) or heavy-textured loams (Abd-el-Malek and Ishac, 1962); here the counts of azotobacter sometimes run into millions per gram as estimated by the same methods that elsewhere reveal numbers a thousand times lower. Something similar may apply to pasture soils and even temporary leys where annual nitrogen accretions may range from about 20 to about 100 pounds per acre (Jensen, 1940; Parker, 1957; Whitt, 1941). Restricted aeration in fine-textured soil under a dense greensward might well favor efficient nitrogen fixation as suggested by Parker (1957), but an "orthodox" process of such a magnitude would still require a minimum consumption of approximately 0.5 to 2.5 tons of "first-class" organic matter largely derived from root materials—and corresponding high densities of nitrogen fixers. It seems necessary to consider the possibility that nitrogen fixation *"in terra"* may under some conditions cease to be strictly tied to cell proliferation and to be accompanied by copious excretion of fixation products (ammonia?). This is conceivable, since the fixation process *per se* requires little energy (Bayliss, 1956; Mortenson, 1962; Wilson, 1958). Verification of this possibility awaits a detailed study of the correlations between organic matter transformation, nitrogen accretion and the composition, density and turnover rate of the nitrogen-fixing microflora.

The relative importance of the groups of nitrogen fixers is difficult to assess. The azotobacter are absent from many soils, and in spite of some acid-tolerant members they are doubtless of little significance in soils of pH below 6 which account for a large part of the world's cultivated area; the compensating effect of the beijerinckias is still uncertain. In many soils the azotobacter are seriously handicapped by low phosphate supply and perhaps still more by combined nitrogen from industrial fertilizers. The clostridia have been thought to rival or exceed the azotobacter in effect because of their wider distribution and their lesser sensitivity to acid reaction. Widespread occurrence, however, is irrelevant in comparison with the mass of actively metabolizing cells, and until more becomes known about this aspect of the soil ecology of the clostridia, their contribution to the global pool of biologically fixed nitrogen must remain unknown. No positive evidence points to any major role of the "miscellaneous" nitrogen fixers.

Different conditions apply to the nitrogen-fixing cyanophyceae. While probably of little significance in arable soils, they are obviously important as pioneer organisms on bare ground and perhaps generally on the soil surface in warm and humid climates but from an agricultural point of view still more so under conditions existing in rice soils in Asiatic countries; here the nitrogen supply of rice crops has probably for many centuries been provided by these unique organisms that come near to having solved the formidable physiological problem of "living upon air." Future improvements of yield (which must perforce be achieved) will partly depend on synthetic nitrogenous fertilizers but perhaps also partly by a rational use of the cyanophyceae as a kind of green manure crop (Watanabe, 1959b).

Upon the whole the phenomenon of non-symbiotic nitrogen fixation appears to be a kind of long-term factor in the economy of Nature, compensating in part for losses of nitrogen from the biological cycle, slowly building up reserves of organic (humus) nitrogen in bare soils and others poor in organic matter, and contributing to the upkeep of these reserves. The cyanophyceae may be susceptible to cultivation, but the activity of the organotrophic nitrogen fixers depends on an excess of energy material in proportion to available nitrogen and is therefore particularly sensitive to removal of crops from the soil, which in any case is man-made intervention in the equilibrium of nature. As cultivation becomes intensified, the nonsymbiotic processes become unable to cover more than a fraction of the nitrogen requirements of the crops—and this a fraction that will gradually diminish as mankind for the sake of his survival will have to force ever-increasing amounts of protein material out of the biological cycle of nature.

REFERENCES

Abd-el-Malek, Y., and Ishac, Y. Z. 1962. Abundance of Azotobacter in Egyptian soil. Abstr. VIII. Intern. Congr. Microbiol. Montreal. 57.

Alexander, M., and Wilson, P. W. 1954. Large-scale production of the azotobacter for enzymes. Appl. Microbiol. 2:135-140.

Allen, M. B., and Arnon, D. I. 1955. Studies of nitrogen-fixing blue-green algae. Plant Physiol. 30:366-372.

Allison, F. E. 1947. Azotobacter inoculation of crops. I. Historical. Soil Sci. 64:413-429.

Anderson, G. R. 1955. Nitrogen fixation by Pseudomonas-like soil bacteria. J. Bact. 70:129-133.

Anderson, G. R., and Jordan, J. V. 1961. Boron: a non-essential growth factor for Azotobacter chroococcum. Soil Sci. 92:113-116.

Augier, J. 1956. A propos de la numération des Azotobacter en milieu liquide. Ann. Inst. Pasteur 91:759-765.

Augier, J. 1957. A propos de la fixation biologique de l'azote atmosphérique et de la numération des Clostridium fixateurs dans les sols. Ann. Inst. Pasteur 92:817-824.

Baillie, A., Hodgkiss, W., and Norris, J. R. 1962. Flagellation of Azotobacter spp. as demonstrated by electron microscopy. J. Appl. Bact. 25:116-119.

Barrow, N. J., and Jenkinson, N. S. 1962. The effect of waterlogging on fixation of nitrogen by soil incubated with straw. Plant and Soil 16:258-262.

Bayliss, N. S. 1956. The thermochemistry of biological nitrogen fixation. Aust. J. Biol. Sci. 9:364-370.

Becking, J. H. 1961. Studies on nitrogen-fixing bacteria of the genus Beijerinckia. I. Geographic and ecological distribution in soils. Plant and Soil 14:49-81.

Becking, J. H. 1961. Studies on nitrogen-fixing bacteria of the genus Beijerinckia. II. Mineral nutrition and resistance to high levels of certain elements, in relation to soil type. Plant and Soil 14:297-322.

Becking, J. H. 1962a. An aerobic heterotrophic Spirillum fixing atmospheric nitrogen. Abstr. VIII. Intern. Congr. Microbiol. Montreal. 57.

Becking, J. H. 1962b. Species differences in molybdenum and vanadium requirements and combined nitrogen utilization by Azotobacteriaceae. Plant and Soil 16:171-201.

Berthelot, M. 1888. Fixation de l'azote atmosphérique sur la terre végétale. Ann. Chim. Phys. Sér. 13:1-119.

Berthelot, M. 1890. Recherches nouvelles sur la fixation de l'azote par la terre végétale et les plantes et sur l'influence de l'électricité sur ce phenomène. Ann. Chim. Phys. Sér. 6, 29:434-492.

van Beynum, J., and Pette, J. W. 1936. Buttersäuregärung und Milchsäregärung im Silofutter. Centralbl. Bakt. (11) 94:413-433.

Bjälfve, G. 1955. Fixation of atmospheric nitrogen. I. Experiments in sand with and without addition of straw or starch and in straw alone in sterile and unsterile conditions in light and darkness. Ann. Royal Agr. Coll. Sweden 22:193-217.

Bjälfve, G. 1962. Nitrogen fixation in cultures of algae and other microorganisms. Physiol. Plantarum 15:122-129.

Bond, G. 1936. Quantitative observations on the fixation and transfer of nitrogen in the soy bean, with especial reference to the mechanism of transfer of fixed nitrogen from bacillus to host. Ann. Bot. 50:559-578.

Bond, G., and Scott, G. B. 1955. An examination of some symbiotic systems for fixation of nitrogen. Ann. Bot. (N. S.) 19:67-77.

Bortels, H. 1930. Molybdän als Katalysator bei der biologischen Stickstoffbindung. Arch. Mikrobiol. 1:333-342.

Bortels, H. 1936. Weitere Untersuchungen über die Bedeutung von Molybdän, Vanadium, Wolfram und anderen Erdaschenstoffen für stickstoffbindende und andere Mikroorganismen. Centralbl. Bakt. (II) 95:193-218.

Bortels, H. 1940. Meteorobiologische Untersuchungen an Azotobakter. Centralbl. Bakt. (II) 102-129-153.

Bredemann, G. 1908. Untersuchungen über die Variation und das Stickstoffbindungsvermögen des Bacillus asterosporus A. M. Centralbl. Bakt. (II) 22:44-89.

Bredemann, G. 1909. Bacillus amylobacter A. M. et Bredmann in morphologischer, physiologischer and systematischer Beziehung. Centralbl. Bakt. (II) 23:385-568.

Brown, M. E., Burlingham, S. K., and Jackson, R. M. 1962a. Studies on Azotobacter species in soil. I. Comparison of media and techniques for counting Azotobacter in soil. Plant and Soil 17:309-319.

Brown, M. E., Burlingham, S. K., and Jackson, R. M. 1962b. Studies on Azotobacter species in soil. II. Populations of Azotobacter in the rhizophere and effects of artificial inoculation. Plant and Soil 17:320-332.

Bullock, G. L., Bush, J. A., and Wilson, P. W. 1960. Calcium requirements of various species of Azotobacter. Proc. Soc. Exp. Biol. Med. 105:26-30.

Calder, E. A. 1959. Nitrogen fixation in a Uganda swamp soil. Nature (Lond.) 184:746.

Cameron, R. E., and Fuller, W. H. 1960. Nitrogen fixation by some algae in Arizona soils. Soil Sci. Amer. Proc. 24:353-356.

Carnahan, J. E., Mortenson, L. E., Mower, H. F., and Castle, J. E. 1960. Nitrogen fixation in cell-free extracts of Clostridium pasteurianum. Biochim. Biophys. Acta 44:520-535.

Christensen, H. R. 1915. Studien über den Einfluss der Bodenbeschaffenheit auf das Bakterienleben und den Stoffumsatz im Erdboden. Centralbl. Bakt. Parasitenk. (II) 43:1-166.

Cooper, R. 1959. Bacterial fertilizers in the Soviet Union. Soils and Fertilizers 22:327-33.

Darzniek, Y. O. 1960. The effect of the cotton plant on the growth of Azotobacter in the soil. Mikrobiologiya 29:868-874. 1960. Engl. Transl. Microbiology 29:626-629.

Darzniek, Y. O. 1961. Reproduction rate of Azotobacter in soil. Mikrobiologiya 30:1042-1044. 1961. Engl. Transl. Microbiology 30:849-850.

De, P. K. 1936. The problem of the nitrogen supply of rice. I. Fixation of nitrogen in the rice soils under water-logged conditions. Indian J. Agr. Sci. 6:1237-1245.

De, P. K. 1939. The role of blue-green algae in nitrogen fixation in rice-fields. Proc. Roy. Soc. (Lond.) B. 127:121-139.

De, P. K., and Sulaiman, M. 1950. Fixation of nitrogen in rice soils by algae as influenced by crop, CO$_2$, and inorganic substances. Soil Sci. 70:137-151.

De, P. K., and Mandal, L. N. 1956. Fixation of nitrogen by algae in rice soils. Soil Sci. 81:453-458.

Delwiche, C. C., and Wijler, J. 1956. Non-symbiotic nitrogen fixation in soil. Plant and Soil 7:113-129.

Derx, H. G. 1950. Beijerinckia, a new genus of nitrogen-fixing bacteria occuring in tropical soils. Proc. Kon. Nederl. Akad. Wetensch. 53:140-147.

Derx, H. G. 1950. Further researches on Beijerinckia. Ann. Bogoriensis 1:1-11.

Derx, H. G. 1953. Sur les causes de la distribution géographique limitée des Beijerinckia. Communicazioni VI. Congr. Int. Microbiol. (Roma) 3:116-117.

Dhar, N. R. 1937. Nitrogen transformation in the soil. (Address of the President). Proc. Nat. Acad. Sci. India 6:3-82.

Döbereiner, J. 1953. Azotobacter em solos acidos. Boletim Inst. Ecol. Exp. Agricolas (Rio de Janeiro) Mo. 11:1-31.

Döbereiner, J., and Alvahydo, R. 1959. Influencia da umidade do solo na populacao de bacterias de genero Beijerinckia. Ciencia e Cultura (Rio de Janeiro) 11:208-218.

Döbereiner, J., and Alvahydo, R. 1959. Sobre a influencia da canade-acúcar na ocorrencia de "Beijerinckia." II. Influéncia das diverseas partes do vegetal. Rev. Brasil. Biol. 19:401-412.

Döbereiner, J. 1961. Nitrogen-fixing bacteria of the genus Beijerinckia Derx in the rhizosphere of sugar cane. Plant and Soil 15:211-216.

Dommergues, Y. 1962. Contribution a l'étude de la dynamique microbienne des sols (etc.). II. Fixation de l'azote par l'Azotobacter chroococcum. Ann. Agron. 13:302-303.

Fedorov, M. V. 1944. Der Einfluss der Wurzelausscheidungen der Maispflanze auf die

Bindung von atmosphärischem Stickstoff durch *Azotobacter* in Maiskulturen mit einer Bakterienrasse. (Russian with German Summary). Mikrobiologiya 13:199-210.

Fedorov, M. V. 1960. Biologische Bindung des atmosphärischen Stickstoffs. VEB Deutscher Verlag der Wissenschaften, Berlin. (Orig. Russian Ed. 1952).

Fedorov, M. F., and Ilina, T. K. 1960. The relations of individual forms of soil actinomycetes to various carbon sources during growth on nitrate and molecular nitrogen. Mikrobiologiya 29:363-364. 1960. Engl. Transl. Microbiology 29:495-500.

Fedorov, M. V., and Kalininskaya, T. A. 1961. Relationships of a nitrogen-fixing mycobacterium (Mycobacterium sp. 301) to various supplements of carbon and supplementary growth factors. Mikrobiologiya 30:832-838. 1961. Engl. Translation Microbiology 30:681-686.

Fogg, G. E., and Wolfe, M. 1954. The nitrogen metabolism of blue-green algae (Myxophyceae). Autotrophic Microorganisms (Fourth Symp. Gen. Microbiol): 99-125. University Press, Cambridge.

Fogg, G. E. 1956. Nitrogen fixation in photosynthetic organisms. Ann. Rev. Plant. Physiol. 7:51-70.

Garbosky, A. J. 1956. Distribution of *Azotobacter* in depth of soils from Tucuman Argentina). Rapp. VI. Congr. Intern. Sci. Sol. (Paris) C. 453-460.

Gerretsen, F. C., and de Hoop, H. 1954. Boron, an essential element for *Azotobacter chroococcum*. Plant and Soil 5:349-367.

Gonick, W. N., and Reuszer, H. W. 1949. The distribution of *Azotobacter chroococcum* and *Azotobacter vinelandii* in Colorado soils and surface waters. Soil Sci. Soc. Amer. Proc. 13:251-257.

Grau, F. H., and Wilson, P. W. 1962. Physiology of nitrogen fixation by *Bacillus polymyxa*. J. Bact. 83:490-496.

Grau, F. H., and Wilson, P. W. 1963. Hydrogenase and nitrogenase in cell-free extracts of *Bacillus polymyxa*. J. Bact. 85:446-450.

Green, M., and Wilson, P. W. 1953. The utilization of nitrate nitrogen by the azotobacter. J. Gen. Microbiol. 9:89-96.

Hamilton, P. B., and Wilson, P. W. 1955. Nitrogen fixation by *Aerobacter aerogenes*. Ann. Acad. Sci. Fennicae (A.II) 60:139-150.

Hino, S., and Wilson, P. W. 1958. Nitrogen fixation by a facultative bacillus. J. Bact. 75:403-408.

Hopf, M. 1949. Untersuchungen über die natürliche Mikroflora des Bodens. Arch. Mikrobiol. 14:661-677.

Imschenezki, A. A. 1959. Mikrobiologie der Cellulose. Akademie-Verlag, Berlin. (Orig. Russian Ed. 1953).

Jensen, H. L. 1940a. Contributions to the nitrogen economy of Australian wheat soils. Proc. Linn Soc. N.S. Wales 65:1-122.

Jensen, H. L. and Swaby, R. J. 1940. Further investigations on nitrogen fixing bacteria in soil. Proc. Linnean Soc. N. S. Wales. 65:557-564.

Jensen, H. L. 1940b. Nitrogen fixation and cellulose decomposition by soil microorganisms. I. Aerobic cellulose decomposers in association with *Azotobacter*. Proc. Linnean Soc. N. S. Wales 65:543-556.

Jensen, H. L., and Swaby, R. J. 1941. Nitrogen fixation and cellulose decomposition by soil microorganisms. II. The association between *Azotobacter* and facultative-aerobic cellulose decomposers. Proc. Linnean Soc. N. S. Wales 66:89-106.

Jensen, H. L. 1941. Nitrogen fixation and cellulose decomposition by soil microorganisms. III. *Clostridium butyricum* in association with aerobic cellulose decomposers. Proc. Linnean Soc. N.S. Wales 66:239-249.

Jensen, H. L. 1942. A note upon the utilization of xylose and xylan by *Azotobacter*. Proc. Linnean Soc. N. S. Wales 67:316-320.

Jensen, H. L., and Spencer, D. 1947. The influence of molybdenum and vanadium on nitrogen fixation by *Clostridium butyricum* and related organisms. Proc. Linnean Soc. N. S. Wales 72:73-86.

Jensen, H. L. 1950. The occurence of *Azotobacter* in cultivated soils of Denmark (Danish with English Summary). Tidsskr. Planteavl 53:622-649.

Jensen, H. L. 1953. *Azotobacter* as a crop inoculant. Atti VI. Congr. Internaz. Microbiol. (Roma) 6:245-251.

Jensen, H. L. 1954. The azotobacteriaceae. Bact. Rev. 18:195-214.

Jensen, H. L. 1955. *Azotobacter macrocytogenes* n. sp., a nitrogen-fixing bacterium resistant to acid reaction. Acta Agr. Scand. 5:280-294.

Jensen, H. L., Petersen, E. J., De, P. K., and Bhattacharya, R. 1960. A new nitrogen-fixing bacterium: *Derxia gummosa* nov. gen. nov. spec. Arch. Mikrobiol. 36:182-195.

Jensen, V. 1955. The Azotobacter-flora of some Danish watercourses. Botanisk Tidsskr. Copenhagen. 52:143-157.

Jensen, V. 1956. Nitrogen fixation by strains of *Aerobacter aerogenes*. Physiol. Plantarum 9:130-136.

Jensen, V. 1958. A new nitrogen-fixing bacterium from a Danish watercourse. Arch. Microbiol. 29:348-353.

Jensen, V. 1959. Production of acid from arabinose and xylose by strains of *Azotobacter*. Nature (Lond.) 183:1536-1537.

Jensen, V. 1961. Rhamnose for detection and isolation of *Azotobacter vinelandii* Lipman. Nature (Lond.) 190-832-833.

Jodin. 1862. Du role physiologique de l'azote (etc.). Comp. Rend. Acad. Sci. (Paris) 55:612-615.

Kaila, A. 1954. Some observations on the occurence of *Azotobacter* in Finnish soils. J. Sci. Agr. Soc. Finland 26:40-49.

Kandler, O. 1951. Über den Einfluss von Bodenbakterien und deren Filtraten auf das Wachstum in vitro kultivierter Wurzeln, Arch. Mikrobiol. 15:430-438.

Katznelson, H. 1946. The "rhizosphere" effect of mangels on certain groups of soil organisms. Soil Sci. 62:343-354.

Krasil'nikov, N. A. 1961. Soil Microorganisms and Higher Plants. Acad, Sci. USSR. 1958.—English Ed. Off. Techn. Services, Washington, D.C.

LeGall, J., Senez, J. C., and Pichinoty, F. 1959. Fixation de l'azote par les bactéries sulfato-réductrices. Ann. Inst. Pasteur 96:223-230.

Lochhead, A. G., and Thexton, R. H. 1936. A four-year quantitative study of nitrogen-fixing bacteria in soils of different fertilizer treatment. Canad. J. Res. (C) 14:166-177.

Loew, O. 1927. Ueber die Ernährung des Azotobacter im Boden. Centralbl. Bakt. (II) 70:36-38.

McCoy, E., Higby, W. M., and Fred, E. B. 1928. The assimilation of nitrogen by pure cultures of *Clostridium pasteurianum* and related organisms. Cent. Bakt. (II) 76:314-320.

McKnight, T. 1949. Non-symbiotic nitrogen-fixing organisms in Queensland soils. Queensland J. Agr. Sci. 6:177-195.

Makrinoff, I. A. 1924. Is it possible to make a bacterial soil preparation for non-leguminous crops? Soil Sci. 17:31-38.

Martin, W. P., Walker, R. H., and Brown, P. E. 1937. The occurrence of *Azotobacter* in Iowa soils and factors affecting their distribution. Iowa. Agr. Exp. Station Res. Bull. 217.

Martin, W. P. 1940. Distribution and activity of *Azotobacter* in the Range and cultivated soils of Arizona. Arizona Agr. Exp. Sta. Tech. Bull. 83.

Meiklejohn, J. 1956. Preliminary numbers of nitrogen fixers on Broadbalk Field. VI. Congr. Intern. Sci. Sol. (Paris) 3:243-248.

Metcalfe, G., Chayan, S., Roberts, E. R., and Wilson, T. G. G. 1954. Nitrogen fixation by soil yeasts. Nature (Lond.) 174:841-842.

Metcalfe, G., and Brown, M. E. 1957. Nitrogen fixation by new species of *Nocardia*. J. Gen. Microbiol. 17:567-572.

Metz, J. 1955. Untersuchungen über die Rhizosphäre. Arch. Mikrobiol. 23:297-326.

Meyerhof, O., and Burk, D. 1927. Über die Fixation des Luftstickstoffs durch Azotobacter. Z. Phys. Chem. 139A:117-142.

Mishustin, E. N., and Naumova, N. A. 1962. Bacterial fertilizers, their effectiveness and mechanism of action. Mikrobiologiya 31:543-556. Abstr. Soils and Fertilizers 25:382.

Mortenson, L. E., Mower, H. F., and Carnahan, J. E. 1962. Nitrogen fixation by enzyme preparations. Bact. Rev. 26:42-50.

Mortenson, L. E. 1962. Inorganic nitrogen assimilation and ammonia incorporation. *In* I. C. Gunsalus and R. Y. Stanier: The Bacteria 3:119-166. Academic Press, New York and London.

Moyer, R. T. 1941. Non-symbiotic nitrogen fixation in soils of a semiarid region of North China. J. Amer. Soc. Agron. 33:980-992.

Mulder, E. G. 1948. Importance of molybdenum in the nitrogen metabolism of microorganisms and higher plants. Plant and Soil 1:94-119.

Nicholas, D. J. D., Kabayashi, M., and Wilson, P. W. 1962. Cobalt requirement for inorganic nitrogen metabolism in the microorganisms. Proc. Nat. Acad. Sci. (U.S.A.) 48:1537-1542.

Nickell, L. G., and Burkholder, P. R. 1947. Inhibition of *Azotobacter* by soil actinomycetes J. Amer. Soc. Agron. 39:771-779.

Niel, C. B. van 1935. A note on the apparent absence of *Azotobacter* in soils. Arch. Mikrobiol. 6:215-218.

Niklas, H., Poschenrieder, H., and Hock, A. 1926. Über die Verbreitung des Azotobacter in den Böden Bayerns unter Berücksichtigung der Bodenreaktion, des Kalk- und Phosphorsäuregehalts derselben. Centralbl. Bakt. (II) 66:16-28.

Nutman, P. S. 1961, 1962. Soil Microbiology Department. Rept. Rothamsted Exp. Stat. 1960:91-92 and 1961:75.

Okuda, A., Yamaguchi, M., and Kobayashi, M. 1960. Nitrogen-fixing microorganisms in paddy soils. IV. Nitrogen fixation photosynthetic bacteria (*Rhodopseudomonas capsulatus* species) under various conditions. Soil and Plant Food 5:73-76.

Okuda, A., Yamaguchi, M., and Kobayashi, M. 1960. Nitrogen-fixing microorganisms in paddy soils. V. Nitrogen fixation in mixed cultures of photosynthetic bacteria (*Rhodopseudomonas capsulatus* species) with other heterotrophic bacteria. Soil and Plant Food 6:35-39.

Olsen, C. 1932. Studies of nitrogen fixation. I. Nitrogen fixation in dead leaves of forest beds. Comp. Rend. Trav. Lab. Carlsberg (Copenhagen) 19:(9) 1-36.

Parker, C. A. 1954a. Non-symbiotic nitrogen-fixing bacteria in soil. I. Studies on *Clostridium butyricum*. Aust. J. Agr. Res. 5:90-97.

Parker, C. A. 1954b. Effect of oxygen on the fixation of nitrogen by *Azotobacter*. Nature (Lond.) 173:780-781.

Parker, C. A. 1957. Non-symbiotic nitrogen-fixing bacteria in soil. III. Total nitrogen changes in a field soil. J. Soil Sci. 8:48-59.

Parker, C. A., and Scutt, P. B. 1960. The effect of oxygen on nitrogen fixation by *Azotobacter*. Biochem. Biophys. Acta 38:230-238.

Paul, E. A., and Newton, D. A. 1961. Studies of aerobic non-symbiotic nitrogen-fixing bacteria. Canad. J. Microbiol. 7:7-13.

Pengra, R. M. and Wilson, P. W. 1958. Physiology of nitrogen fixation by *Aerobacter aerogenes*. J. Bact. 75:21-25.

Pengra, R. M., and Wilson, P. W. 1959. Trace metal requirements of Aerobacter aerogenes for assimilation of molecular nitrogen. Proc. Soc. Exp. Biol. Med. 100:436-439.

Petersen, E. J. 1959. Serological Investigations on *Azotobacter* and *Beijerinckia*. Royal Vet. and Agr. Coll. (Copenhagen) Yearbook 1959:70-90.

Petersen, E. J. 1961. Studies on the morphology and Cytology of *Azotobacter chroococcum*. Royal Vet. and Agr. Coll. (Copenhagen) Yearbook 1961:115-155.

Petersen, J. B. 1935. Studies on the biology and taxonomy of soil algae, Dansk Bot. Arkiv 8:1-183.

Pochon, J. 1954. Manual Technique d'Analyse Microbiologique du Sol. Masson & Cie. Ed., Paris.

Pochon, J., and de Barjac, H. 1958. Traité de Microbiologie des Sols. Applications Agronomiques. Dunod Ed., Paris.

Proctor, M. H., and Wilson, P. W. 1959. Nitrogen fixation by *Achromobacter* spp. Arch. Mikrobiol. 32:254-260.

Quispel, A. 1947. The influence of the oxidation-reducetion potential of the medium upon the growth of *Azotobacter*. Antonie van Leeuwenhoek J. 13:33-43.

Remy, E. 1909. Untersuchungen über die Stickstoffsammlungsvorgänge in ihrer Beiziehung zum Bodenklima. Centralbl. Bakt. II. 22:561-651.

Rosenblum, E. D., and Wilson, P. W. 1949. Fixation of isotopic nitrogen by *Clostridium*. J. Bact. 57:413-414.

Rosenblum, E. D., and Wilson, P. W. 1950. Molecular hydrogen and nitrogen fixation by *Clostridium*. J. Bact. 59:83-91.

de'Rossi, G. 1932a. La fixation de l'azote élémentaire dans le sol. II. Les Azotobacters dans les differents terrains de 'Italie. Soc. Intern. Microbiol. Bol. Sez. Ital. 4:220-226.

de'Rossi, G. 1932b. La fixation de l'azote élémentaire dans le sol. III. Activité végétative et pouvoir fixateur des Azotobacters. Soc. Intern. Microbiol. Boll. Sez. Ital. 4:511-516.

de'Rossi, G. 1933. La fixation de l'azote élémentaire dans le sol. IV. Activité des Azotobacters dans le sol. Soc. Intern. Microbiol. Boll. Sez. Ital. 5:27-32.

Rouquérol, T. 1962. Sur le phenomène de fixation de l'azote dans les rizières de Chamarque. Ann. Agron. 13:325-346.

Rovira, A. D. 1962. Plant-root exudates in relation to the rhizosphere microflora. Soils and Fertilizers 25:167-172.

Roy, A. B. 1962. A new species of Derxia. Nature (London) 194:604-605.

Ruinen, J. 1956. Occurence of Beijerinckia species in the "phyllosphere." Nature (Lond.) 177:220-221.

Sabinin, D. A., and Minina, E. G. 1932. Das mikrobiologische Bodenprofil als zonales Kennzeichen. Proc. Sec. Intern. Congr. Soil Sci. (Leningrad and Moscow) Comm. III. 224-235.

Schloesing, T. 1888. Sur les relations de l'azote atmosphérique avec la terre végétale. Comp. Rend. Acad. Sci. (Paris) 106:898-902; 982-987; 107:290-296.

Schloesing, T., and Laurent, E. 1892. Sur la fixation de l'azote libre par les plantes. Ann. Inst. Pasteur 6:824-840.

Schmidt-Lorenz, W., and Rippel-Baldes, A. 1957. Wirkung des Sauerstoffs auf Wachstum und Stickstoffbindung von Azotobacter chroococcum, Beijk. Arch. Mikrobiol. 28:45-68.

Schneider, K. C., Bradbeer, C., Singh, R. N., Wang, L. I., Wilson, P. W., and Burris, R. H. 1960. Nitrogen fixation by cell-free preparations from microorganisms. Proc. Nat. Acad Sci. (Wash.) 46:726-733.

Singh, R. N. 1961. Role of Blue-green Algae in Nitrogen Economy of Indian Agriculture. Indian Council of Agricultural Research, New Delhi. 174 pp.

Siu, R. G. H. 1951. Microbial Decomposition of Cellulose. Reinhold Publishing Co., New York.

Sörensen, H. 1957. Microbial decomposition of xylan. Acta Agr. Scand. Suppl. I:1-86.

Spicher, G. 1954. Untersuchungen über die Wechselwirkungen zwischen Azotobacter chroococcum und höherer Pflanze. Centralbl. Bakt. (II) 107:353-383.

Stapp, C. 1940 Azotomonas insolita, ein neuer aerober stickstoffbinder Mikroorganimus. Centralbl. Bakt. (II) 102:1-19.

Starc, A. 1952. Zur Frage der Rhizosphäre und Bodenimpfung mit Azotobacter. Arch. Mikrobiol. 13:164-181.

Starkey, R. L. 1938. Some influences of the development of higher plants upon the microorganisms in the soil. VI. Microscopic examination of the rhizosphere. Soil Sci. 45:207-249.

Stokes, J. L. 1940. The role of algae in the nitrogen cycle of the soil. Soil Sci. 49:266-275.

Stöckli, A. 1944. Die Verbreitung der Azotobacterorganismen in der Schweiz. Landw. Jahrb. Schweiz 58:67-105.

Sulaiman, M. 1944. Effect of algal growth on the activity of Azotobacter in rice soils. Indian J. Agr. Sci. 14:277-283.

Suschkina, N. N. 1949. Ökologisch-geographische Verbreitung von Azobacter in den Boden der Udssr. Quoted from Fedorov (53).

Tchan, Y. T. 1952. Studies of N-fixing bacteria. I. A note on the estimation of Azotobacter in the Soil. Proc. Linnean Soc. N.S. Wales 77:89-91.

Tchan, Y. T. 1943a. Studies of N-fixing bacteria IV. Taxonomy of genus Azotobacter (Beijerinck 1901). Proc. Linnean Soc. N.S. Wales 78:85-89.

Tchan, Y. T. 1953b. Studies of N-fixing bacteria. V. Presence of Beijerinckia in Northern Australia and geographic distribution of non-symbiotic N-fixing microorganisms. Proc. Linn. Soc. N.S. Wales 78:171-178.

Tschapek, M., and Giambiagi, N. 1954. The formation of Liesegang's rings by "Azotobacter" due to O$_2$-inhibition. V. Congr. Intern. Sci. Sol (Léopoldville) Act. Comp. Rend. 3:97-103.

Tschapek, M., and Giambiagi, N. 1955. Nitrogen fixation of Azotobacter in soil—its inhibition by oxygen. Arch. Mikrobiol. 21:376-390.

Uppal, B. N., Patel, M. K., and Daji, J. A. 1939. Nitrogen fixation in rice soils. Indian J. Agr. Sci. 9:689-702.

Vancura, V., Macura, J., Fischer, O., and Vondracek, J. 1959. The relation of Azotobacter to the root system of barley. Fol. Microbiol. (Prague) 4:118-129.

Vancura, V., and Macura, J. 1959. The development of *Azotobacter* in the oats rhizosphere and its effect upon the yield. Fol. Microbiol. (Prague) 4:200-202.

Vancura, V., and Macura, J. 1960. Indole derivatives in *Azotobacter* cultures. Fol. Microbiol. (Prague) 5:293-297.

Vancura, V., and Macura, J. 1961. The effect of root excretions on *Azotobacter*. Fol. Microbiol. 1961. (Prague) 6:250-259.

Vancura, V. Detection of gibberellic acid in *Azotobacter* cultures. Nature (Lond.) 192: 88-89.

Vartiovaara, U. 1938. The associative growth of cellulose-decomposing fungi and nitrogen-fixing bacteria. J. Sci. Agr. Soc. Finland 10:241-264.

Virtanen, A. I., Mustakalio, H., and Strandström, H. 1953. Einwirkung von Kohlenmonoxyd auf die anaerobe Stickstoffbindung. Suomen Kemistelehti B. 2:6-9.

Voets, J. P., and Debacker, J. 1956. *Pseudomonas azotogensis* nov. sp., a free-living nitrogen-fixing bacterium. Naturwiss. 43:40-41.

Watanabe, A. 1959a. Distribution of nitrogen-fixing blue-green algae in various areas of South and East Asia. J. Gen. Appl. Microbiol. (Tokyo) 5:21-29.

Watanabe, A. 1959b. On the mass culture of a nitrogen-fixing blue-green alga, *Tolypothrix tenuis*. J. Gen. Appl. Microbiol. (Tokyo) 5:85-91.

Wenzl, H. 1934. Zur Methodik der Keimzahlbestimmung von Azotobacter im Boden. Centralbl. Bakt. (II) 90:289-314.

Westlake, D. W. S., and Wilson, P. W. 1959. Molecular hydrogen and nitrogen fixation by *Clostridium pasteurianum*. Canad. J. Microbiol. 5:617-620.

Whitt, D. M. 1941. The role of bluegrass in the conservation of the soil and its fertility. Soil Sci. Soc. Amer. Proc. 6:309-311.

Wichtmann, H. 1952. Untersuchungen über die Beziehungen zwischen Azotobactergehalt und Bodenfruchtbarkeit. Arch. Mikrobiol. 17:54-78.

Willis, W. H., and Green, V. E. 1949. Movement of nitrogen in flooded soils planted to rice. Soil Sci. Soc. Amer. Proc. 13:229-237.

Wilson, P. W. and Burris, R. H. 1953. Biological nitrogen fixation—a reappraisal. Ann. Rev. Microbiol. 17:415-432.

Wilson, P. W. 1958. Asymbiotic nitrogen fixation. *In* Ruhland's Handb. d. Pflanzenphysiol. 8:9-47. Springer, Berlin.

Winogradsky, S. 1895. Recherces sur l'assimilation de l'azote libre de l'atmosphère par les microbes. Arch. Sci. Biol. (Pétersbourg) 3:297-352.

Winogradsky, S. 1926. Etudes sur la microbiologie du sol. II. Sur les microbes fixateurs de l'azote. Ann. Inst. Pasteur 40:455-520.

Winogradsky, S. and Ziemecka, J. 1928. Etudes sur la microbiologie du sol. III. Sur le pouvoir fixateur des terres. Ann. Inst. Pasteur 42:36-62.

Winogradsky, S. 1930. L'état actuel du problème de la fixation de l'azote atmosphérique et ses récents progres. Comp. Rend. Acad. Agr. de France 16:580-586.

Winogradsky, S. 1938. Etudes sur la microbiologie du sol. IX. Sur la morphologie et oecologie des Azotobacter. Ann. Inst. Pasteur 60:351-400.

Winogradsky, S. 1949. Fixation anaerobie. Avant-propos. *In* Microbiologie du Sol. Problèmes et Méthodes: 356-360. Masson et Cie., Paris.

Ziemecka, J. 1932. The Azotobacter test of soil fertility applied to the classical fields at Rothamsted. J. Agr. Sci. 22:797-810.

Zycha, H. 1932. Sauerstoffoptimum und Nährboden "aerober" Bakterien. Arch. Mikrobiol. 3:194-204.

Chapter 13

Nitrogen Availability

C. E. SCARSBROOK

Auburn University
Auburn, Alabama

Available nitrogen is defined as nitrogen in a chemical form that can be readily absorbed by plant roots. A tacit assumption is that the nitrogen is present within the root zone.

The nitrogen in soil is nearly all in the organic matter. Soils of the humid and subhumid regions of the United States may contain 2,000 to 4,000 pounds of nitrogen per acre in the organic matter of the surface 6 inches of soil. However, rarely do soils contain more than 1% of the total nitrogen in an available form at any time. Furthermore, there is an average of about 35,000 tons of nitrogen over each acre of the earth's surface. This nitrogen is present as elemental nitrogen (N_2), which is unavailable to higher plants. In fact, unavailability is the most striking characteristic of the bountiful supplies of nitrogen surrounding higher plants.

Processes which supply available nitrogen to the soil are (1) organic matter (2) fertilizer additions (3) symbiotic fixation (4) nonsymbiotic fixation (5) rainfall.

I. CHEMICAL FORMS OF AVAILABLE NITROGEN

The most important forms of available nitrogen are NH_4^+, NO_3^-, and certain simple organic compounds, principally those containing free amide or amino groups. Nitrites are a minor source of available nitrogen. Although plants can usually utilize any of these nitrogen forms, there are numerous exceptions (Arnon, 1937; Bonner, 1946; Ghosh and Burris, 1950; Naftel, 1931; Thelin and Beaumont, 1934; Tiedjens and Robbins, 1931; Virtanen and Linkola, 1946; Wallace, 1954). One form may be preferentially absorbed depending on environment and the species and age of plants (Ghosh and Burris, 1950; Naftel, 1931; Thelin and Beaumont, 1934; Tidmore and Williamson, 1932). While plants may be similar in appearance and grow equally well on different forms of nitrogen, the plant composition may be widely different. For example, the organic acid content of plants is higher when NO_3^- is the source of nitrogen than when NH_4^+ is the source (Meyer et al., 1960).

Rice is one of the few plants that utilizes NH_4^+ more effectively than NO_3^- at all stages of growth (Bonner, 1946; Kelley, 1911; Thelin and

Beaumont, 1934). Other plants, such as cotton, may prefer NH_4^+ when young (Naftel, 1931), but it is the exception when any plant grows better in well-aerated soils on NH_4^+ than on NO_3^- at all stages of growth. In general, the availability of NH_4^+ and NO_3^- in the soil solution is similar for higher plants. However, this is disputed by Harmsen and van Schreven (1955).

A. Ammonium

The NH_4^+ ion in soils is found in the soil solution, as a part of the exchange complex, and in positions restricting its exchangeability (often called "nonexchangeable" or "fixed"). The amount of NH_4^+ in solution is extremely small. It is in dynamic equilibrium with the exchangeable NH_4^+ and perhaps with the nonexchangeable. The NH_4^+ ion is an important source of available nitrogen especially in grassland and to a lesser extent in forests. In grasslands a large part of soil organic matter consists of the remains of old roots where the organic matter is distributed throughout the root zone. The NH_4^+ is released by ammonification in an area thoroughly permeated by plant roots that immediately absorb any NH_4^+ not utilized by micro-organisms. Of course, in sods fertilized with ammonium fertilizers, there may be available NH_4^+ in excess of the plants' requirements and nitrofication would take place.

The largest portion of the organic residue in forests comes from leaves and twigs deposited on the soil's surface where the nitrogen released through ammonification would be largely unused until changed to NO_3^- and leached downward into the root zone. The NH_4^+ formed in the root zone would be quickly absorbed as in grasslands.

Soils differ widely in capacity to fix NH_4^+ in the clay fraction (Allison et al., 1953a; Axley and Legg, 1960). Where the clay fraction is predominantly kaolinitic almost no fixation will occur. However, certain soils, principally those where the vermiculites and micaceous minerals predominate, may fix from 1 to 6 me. NH_4^+ per 100 g soil (Allison et al. 1953a). The availability of fixed nitrogen to both plants and to nitrifying bacteria is greatly reduced. Bower (1950) found that without inoculation with nitrifying bacteria only 10% of the difficultly exchangeable NH_4^+ was recovered by barley in 17 days as compared with 75% of the readily exchangeable NH_4^+. Allison et al. (1953a) measured from 7 to 12% recovery of fixed NH_4^+ by millet in 8 weeks. The availability of fixed NH_4^+ to nitrifying bacteria ranged between none and 15%.

The availability of fixed nitrogen is reduced in the presence of excess K (Allison et al., 1953a; Axley and Legg, 1960; Welch and Scott, 1960). Fig. 1 from Welch and Scott (1960) shows the effect of K additions on the nitrification of an NH_4^+-saturated vermiculite clay with a fixing capacity of 38 me. per 100 g. The K ion reduced the lattice spacing, effectively blocking the release of fixed NH_4^+. It is not known if this is the only way in which K reduces the availability of fixed NH_4^+. Thus, it would be expected that the availability of NH_4^+ would be reduced when applied with large amounts of K (Axley and Legg, 1960; Welch and Scott, 1960). However, the capacity of a soil to slowly release a small amount of available nitrogen over a long period of time may be enhanced by this means.

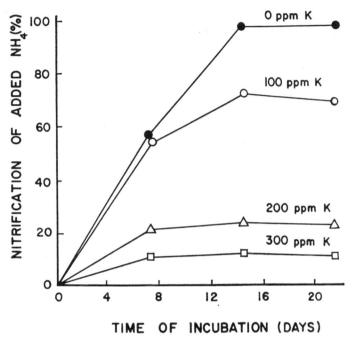

Fig. 1. Nitrification of the NH_4 in air-dried, NH_4-saturated vermiculite as related to added K (Welch and Scott, 1960).

B. Nitrite

Plants can utilize small amounts of NO_2^-, but more than a few ppm are toxic to most plants. Seldom is there more than a trace of NO_2^- present in neutral or acid soils. There are no known reactions of NO_2^- with clays. The entire supply is available and is always found in the soil solution.

Field and laboratory experiments have demonstrated that large amounts of NO_2^- may accumulate and persist for long periods in alkaline soils (Chapman and Liebig, 1952; Frapps and Sterges, 1930; Martin et al., 1942; Stojanovic and Alexander, 1958).

Stojanovic and Alexander (1958) reported that an alkaline soil perfused with high rates of $(NH_4)_2SO_4$ may accumulate several hundred parts per million of NO_2^-. Apparently NO_2^- will accumulate only as long as the pH is high and large quantities of NH_4^+ are present. The NH_4^+ inhibits the oxidation of NO_2^- to NO_3^-. Once NO_3^- production begins after the concentration of NH_4^+ is lowered, the NO_2^- rapidly disappears. Except with NO_2^- tolerant plants, such as citrus and avocados, every effort should be made to avoid the conditions of low temperature, high pH, and high NH_4^+ that favor the accumulation of NO_2^-. In all except the most intensively fertilized crop, NO_2^- should seldom be in toxic concentrations and should serve as only a minor source of available nitrogen.

C. Nitrate

Soil inorganic nitrogen in most arable soils is nearly all utilized in the NO_3^- form regardless of past fertilization practices (see Chapters 2 and 9). Accordingly, NO_3^- is the most important source of available nitrogen for cultivated plants. Since NO_3^- does not react with soil clays, the total supply of NO_3^- in the root zone is available.

D. Organic Nitrogen

The undecomposed urea molecule is a source of available nitrogen for plants and may be absorbed intact by the roots or leaves of plants. However, the nitrogen products of urea hydrolysis and nitrification are much more important in plant nutrition because of the rapidity of these reactions in moist warm soil (Broadbent et al., 1958; Fisher and Parks, 1958; Simpson and Melsted, 1963). The speed of the reaction is illustrated by the data of Broadbent et al. (1958) where all of a 400-ppm application of urea-N in 4 soils was hydrolyzed in 2 days at 75°F.

Soil organic matter contains 30 to 50% of its nitrogen as amino nitrogen (Sowden, 1956; Stevenson, 1956). However, the quantities present in the soil as free amino acids are small. Paul and Schmidt (1961) identified 15 free amino acids in a Waukegan silt loam soil in concentrations of 2 to 4 μg per g of soil. Other unidentified compounds occurred in concentrations of 0.1 to 0.5 μg per g of soil. Dadd et al. (1953) also found similar small amounts in nine organic soils with the quantity varying with the season whereas Sowden and Parker (1953), on the other hand, could detect no free amino acids in the three soils studied. Evidently small amounts of free amino acids are widely distributed in many soils.

Numerous investigations have shown that free amino acids are available to many plants (Ghosh and Burris, 1950; Miettinen, 1959; Schreiner and Skinner, 1912; Virtanen and Linkola, 1946). Evidence that amino acids can be assimulated without decomposition has been presented by Virtanen and Linkola (1946). Plant species vary widely in ability to utilize various amino acids. Ghosh and Burris (1950) observed that red clover and tomatoes made excellent growth on amino acids, whereas tobacco grew better on inorganic nitrogen. None of the amino acids were toxic to red clover but several killed tomatoes and tobacco. It is unlikely that a concentration of any amino acid sufficient to cause injury to plants would be found in the soil. Although they are available, the small amounts of amino acids present are a relatively unimportant source of nitrogen because of the rapidity of ammonification and nitrification in most soils.

II. CLIMATIC FACTORS

A. Temperature

Nitrogen availability is markedly reduced in cold soils. Ammonification of nitrogen present in soil organic matter is increased by high temperatures.

As pointed out by Jenny (1930), the nitrogen and organic matter content of soils in the United States increases 2 to 3 times for each 10°C decrease in mean annual temperature. Of course, with extremely low mean temperatures plant growth is so sparse that little nitrogen or organic matter accumulates.

Once nitrogen is in an available form in the soil, it can be absorbed by many plants even at temperatures ranging from 0 to 15°C (Richards et al., 1952). While plants may be unable to transport or to assimilate nitrogen at low temperatures, they may absorb some nitrogen when temperatures are so low that plants are dormant or growth is slow.

B. Moisture

The supply of available nitrogen is closely related to the moisture tension in the soil. Reitemeier (1946) has presented evidence that the concentration of NO_3^- in the soil solution increases with higher moisture tension. Nitrates accumulate during the dry season in tropical climates (Greenland, 1958; Griffith, 1951). This accounts for the widely observed tendency for plants to contain a high percentage of nitrogen when grown under moisture stress since NO_3^- can be absorbed by plants when soil moisture is below the wilting point (Eck and Fanning, 1961; Volk, 1947). However, the increase in nitrogen in dry soils may not be a net gain in available nitrogen since, in soils that fix appreciable quantities of NH_4^+, the fixation process is enhanced by drying.

Excess water from rains or irrigation may quickly leach soluble nitrogen beyond the root zone in coarse-textured soils. This occurs to a much lesser extent in fine-textured soils (Jones, 1942). These differences are caused in part by the differences in water holding capacities and in part by the structural aggregates that are generally more prevalent in soils containing more of the finer particles. Some nitrogen evidently diffuses into the aggregates out of the mainstream of percolating water, which moves mostly in the large voids surrounding the aggregates.

When there is sufficient excess moisture to impede oxygen diffusion and to create reducing conditions, available nitrogen may be rapidly volatilized into the atmosphere (See Chapter 9).

Nitrate production is not a linear function of soil moisture in the low soil moisture tension range. For example, Fitts et al. (1955) found that

Table 1. Effect of moisture upon nitrate production (Fitts et al., 1955).

Pressure, bars	NO$_3$-N, ppm			
	Soil 1	Soil 2	Soil 3	Soil 4
5	16. 7	23.8	29. 0	25.1
1	27.7	35. 5	36. 8	28.1
0. 1	48. 2	55. 6	49. 6	46. 1
0. 05	2. 3	53. 9	49. 6	12. 7

NO$_3$$^-$ production in incubated soils was greater at 0.1 bar tension than at either 0.05 or 1.0 bar (Table 1).

There is a definite periodicity in available nitrogen by seasons (Batham and Nigam, 1930). Since in fallow soils nitrates accumulate more rapidly in the spring and summer, the accumulation is probably related to moisture, temperature, and other factors. There may be no increase in available nitrogen in cropped soils because of plant uptake (Albrech, 1937; Goring and Clark, 1948).

Since winter rains tend to leach available nitrogen, the nitrogen recommendations in the Netherlands have been adjusted according to the moisture received the previous winter (van der Paauw, 1962). For example, 18 to 27 pounds of additional nitrogen above the normal amount was recommended for cereal following the wet winters of 1959 and 1961, whereas the normal recommendation was reduced by 18 pounds per acre following the dry winter of 1960. Normal recommendations were for from 63 to 72 pounds of nitrogen per acre.

III. FERTILIZATION AND MANAGEMENT

A. Sources of Nitrogen

Nitrogen from most of the commonly applied inorganic sources, such as ammonia, ammonium nitrate, ammonium phosphate, ammonium sulfate, calcium nitrate, nitric phosphate, potassium nitrate, and sodium nitrate, quickly becomes a part of the soil solution or the cation exchange complex when applied to moist soils. These, individually or in combination, comprise nearly all the inorganic nitrogen sources utilized in quantity as fertilizer. Accordingly, when applied in the plant root zone, nitrogen from these sources may be considered as available immediately after application, except when added to extremely dry soil.

The availability of nitrogen from organic sources varies from extremely slight to that comparable to the inorganic sources. Urea, a synthetic organic, is soluble in water and is immediately available.

Since urea is absorbed through foliage, there has been considerable interest in supplying all or part of the nitrogen requirements of crops in sprays. Other sources of nitrogen are seldom used in sprays since urea can be applied at higher concentrations without burning the foliage (Thorne and Watson, 1956). Klinker and Emmert (1953) observed that concentrations of urea in excess of 0.3% nitrogen caused a severe leaf burn on tomatoes; however, when sugar was added to the solution, the urea concentration could be increased 10 times without injury. Jones et al. (1962) used 3% nitrogen solutions of urea on cotton without causing leaf burn. When 5 or 6% solutions were applied, there was noticeable leaf burn.

Foliar sprays appear to be a convenient way to get small amounts of nitrogen into the tissues of large plants, but are not economical ways to supply all the nitrogen required by any crop. Foliage of small plants will not retain enough of the necessarily dilute sprays. When applied with compatible fungicides and insecticides, foliar sprays may be a convenient way of supplying small amounts of available nitrogen at critical growth periods. Volatilization of nitrogen as ammonia following hydrolysis of urea by the enzyme urease may cause some loss of efficiency.

Another synthetic organic, calcium cyanamide, is a slowly available nitrogen source. When added to the soil the following reactions take place (McCool, 1933):

$$2 \ CaCN_2 + H_2O \rightarrow Ca(HCN_2)_2 + Ca(OH)_2$$

$$2 \ Ca(HCN_2)_2 + 2 \ H_2O \rightarrow (CaOH)_2CN_2 + 2 \ H_2CN_2$$

$$H_2CN_2 + H_2O \rightarrow CO(NH_2)_2$$

Other side reactions also may occur during decomposition. It is only after the cyanamide has been hydrolyzed to urea that the nitrogen is nontoxic to plants. Prior to this hydrolysis, cyanamide and other N-containing intermediates are extremely toxic.

Nitrogen products with low solubilities have been produced by the acid-catalyzed condensation of urea with formaldehyde. The resulting material is a mixture of straight-chain urea-ureaformaldehyde (U/F) polymers and unreacted urea (Clark et al., 1951).

Yee and Love (1946) showed that the larger the mole ratio of urea to formaldehyde (U/F), the greater the release of N during incubation in the laboratory (Fig. 2). With a U/F ratio of 2.01, the nitrification was similar to ammonium sulfate, whereas with a ratio of 1.03 there was practically no release of nitrogen into an available form. Ammonia is liberated from U/F by soil microrganisms (Clements, 1951). Strictly chemical hydrolysis occurs at too low a rate to be of importance. Apparently the rate of release of NH_4^+ will vary with the activity of the soil microflora.

The slow release of available nitrogen from urea-formaldehyde is a distinct advantage for such plants as turf grasses that utilize nitrogen over a long period of time (Armiger et al., 1951; Musser et al., 1951). However, for row crops that absorb most of their nitrogen over a short interval of time, much of the nitrogen may become available when the plant uptake is small, or even after the crop is harvested (Scarsbrook, 1958). Higher rates may be applied in single applications without danger of salt damage to plants than would be possible with other more soluble materials.

The availability of nitrogen from slowly soluble materials is a function of particle size. DeMent et al. (1961) measured available nitrogen in-

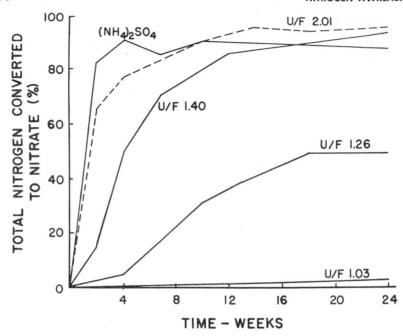

Fig. 2. Nitrification of urea formaldehyde products at 30°C (Yee and Love, 1946).

creases of about 5 times for oxamide and 2 times for U/F as the particle size decreased from 4.06 mm ± .70 mm to 0.200 mm ± .050 mm.

There are numerous natural organic sources of nitrogen such as sewage sludge, cottonseed meal, soybean meal, and feather meal, that release nitrogen over an extended period of time, depending on their rate of decomposition. These natural organics are of little economic importance as fertilizers and are rarely used except for specialty crops, such as ornamentals.

B. Rates and Method of Application of Nitrogen

A cardinal principle in fertilization is that sufficient available nitrogen should be present at all times to meet the requirements for plant growth. This has led to the split-application technique on soils that supply little nitrogen and that are subject to significant nitrogen losses by leaching or other means. Higher rates of nitrogen than are required for immediate plant requirements are often more efficient on young than on old plants. The young plants store the excess nitrogen, which is translocated within the tissues when needed later in the growth period. Late applications of nitrogen have often resulted in poor utilization of nitrogen (Bartholomew et al., 1950; Brooks and Keller, 1960; Krantz and Chandler, 1954; Pumphery and Harris, 1956).

When the efficiency of nitrogen use is measured by percentage recovery in plants, there is no unique relationship between rate of application and nitrogen uptake. Dotzenko (1961) measured an increase in per cent recovery up to the 160-pound rate of nitrogen and then a sharp decline with higher rates for orchardgrass, bromegrass, and intermediate wheatgrass (Fig. 3), whereas there was a linear decrease in per cent recovery from increasing rates of nitrogen for tall wheatgrass, tall oatgrass, and tall fescue. The total nitrogen in all plants increased linearly with increasing rate of nitrogen. Schumacher and Davis (1961) and Scarsbrook et al. (1959) determined that the nitrogen recovery was a function of both the rate of nitrogen and the moisture regime. Bartholomew and Hiltbold (1952) observed that the per cent nitrogen recovery by oats generally increased with the rate of nitrogen. Apparently the form of the nitrogen recovery-nitrogen rate curve depends on many factors, such as moisture and plant species. Knowledge of the amount of available nitrogen in the soil is not sufficient to predict the amount of recovery by plants.

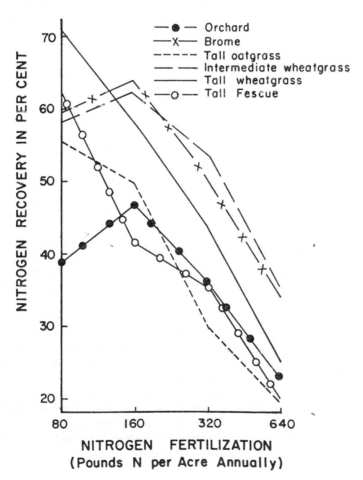

Fig. 3. Percentage nitrogen recovery of grasses as related to applied nitrogen on irrigated soil (Dotzenko, 1961).

C. Placement

One objective of nitrogen placement is to make the element available to plant roots at the desired time. When band placed, the nitrogen is located so as to be quickly reached by roots soon after germination, yet far enough away from the seed to avoid salt damage.

The availability of nitrogen applied on the surface is largely dependent on rain or irrigation water to move the nitrogen into the root zone. There is, however, significant diffusion of nitrogen even when moisture is constant. The larger the concentration of nitrogen, the greater is the diffusion. Stewart and Eck (1958) measured the downward movement of surface-applied ammonium nitrate after 14 days. The NO_3^- diffused downward to a depth of 6.4 cm at the moisture equivalent, to 5.1 cm at the 3- and 5-bar moisture tensions, and to 3.8 cm at 8- and 15-bar tensions. They concluded that some utilization of surface-applied NO_3^- can be expected before any effective rain is received. Ray et al. (1957) measured the diffusion of NH_4^+ at 0.3 bar tension after 72 hours. The diffusion was least where the cation exchange capacity was highest. The soils used had cation exchange capacities ranging from 3.2 to 34.2 me. per 100 g of soil. The lateral and vertical movement of NH_4^+ was generally within 2 cm of the point of application, but in soils with low cation exchange capacities, there was some diffusion to a distance of 4 cm.

The availability of nitrogen applied on a mulch depends on the character of the mulching material and on the moisture. Plant mulches with a C:N ratio greater than 30 tend to reduce the availability of nitrogen, whereas with low C:N ratios the availability of added nitrogen is not affected and the decomposition of the mulching material may add to the soluble nitrogen supply. Since most organic mulching materials have high C:N ratios, the general effect is to reduce the availability of nitrogen added in the vicinity of the mulch.

There is evidence by Black and Greb (1962) that more NO_3^- will accumulate in soil under a plastic mulch than in bare soil even when leaching is not a factor. After 12 weeks under plastic, the $NO_3 - N$ increased from an initial content of 26 pounds per acre-18 inches to 140 pounds, while the $NO_3 - N$ in bare soil increased to only 78 pounds per acre. They speculated that part of the benefits of a plastic mulch to plant growth was the increase in soluble nitrogen.

Available nitrogen often accumulates under a mulch in tropical soils during the dry season. Gilbert (1945) found that the NO_3^- content of mulched soils was sometimes twice as high as in bare soils. The higher amount of moisture under the mulch appeared to support a greater mineralization of organic nitrogen. When the rains came, the NO_3^- was lower under the mulch than in the bare soil as a result of leaching. The mulched soils had greater infiltration rates than bare soils, thus allowing more water to leach out the soluble nitrogen.

D. Soil Acidity

Low soil pH will reduce the mineralization rate of organic nitrogen (Harmsen and van Schreven, 1955). While mineralization occurs even under extremely acid conditions, the rate is considerably more rapid as a neutral reaction is approached; accordingly, liming of acid soils will increase the supply of available nitrogen.

Liming, with its subsequent effects on soil pH and the supply of essential elements, can have a marked effect on nitrification. However, since both NH_4^+ and NO_3^- are available to most plants, the effect of liming on nitrification is of little importance as far as the availability of nitrogen is concerned.

E. Carbon-Nitrogen Ratio

The carbon-nitrogen ratio (C:N) is an important characteristic of organic residues added to soils since this ratio largely determines the rate of release of nitrogen in an available form. When the C:N ratio exceeds 30 during organic decomposition, the immobilization rate exceeds the mineralization rate. Thus, the microbial requirements for nitrogen are not met by the organic matter and the organisms immobilize soluble soil nitrogen into microbial protein. If crops are to be grown shortly after high C:N ratio residue is turned under, sufficient available nitrogen must be present in the soil or be added in fertilizers to meet the requirements of both microbes and crop plants. Otherwise the crops will not obtain sufficient nitrogen because they are unable to compete successfully with the microbes for available nitrogen.

During the decomposition of organic residues with C:N ratios of less than 15, the mineralization rate of nitrogen exceeds the immobilization rate with a net release of available nitrogen. The C:N ratio of fresh organic materials decreases with time until a value of about 10 is reached. Organic residues with C:N ratios between 15 and 30 will approximately meet the nitrogen requirements for microbial protein. Harmsen and van Schreven (1955) have recently reviewed the literature on mineralization of organic substances in soils. A more detailed discussion of the subject is found in Chapter 7.

Broadbent and Norman (1946) and Pinck et al. (1948) report that the decomposition of green manure crops results in accelerated decomposition of the soil organic matter. Apparently, as the micro-organism population increases rapidly with the incorporation of green manure, the organisms not only decompose the fresh organic material but also further decompose the original soil organic matter. Thus, more available nitrogen is released but at the expense of a reduced total nitrogen supply.

F. Soil Aeration

There is conclusive evidence that either a deficiency of O_2 or an excess of CO_2 will cause a sharp decrease in the uptake of nitrogen by plant roots in culture solutions (Chang and Loomis, 1945; Hoagland and Broyer, 1936). While these effects can be measured in solutions, in soils there are no adequate methods for measuring the aeration conditions in the root rhizosphere. Few soils contain low enough O_2 in the macro pores to restrict plant growth, but this is probably a poor measure of the O_2 transport through the rhizosphere to the root surface. Lawton (1945) compacted a Clarion loam and a Clyde silt loam such that the O_2 transport to the plant root was probably decreased. He observed a decrease in nitrogen uptake by corn as a result of compaction. Forced aeration sharply increased the nitrogen uptake. There was no measure of the aeration conditions obtained with the treatments.

Bower et al. (1945) observed that tillage had a direct effect on nitrogen availability. On all four soils studied, there was from 2 to 4 times more total nitrogen uptake by corn where the field was plowed than where subsurface tillage was used. The effect of tillage treatments on aeration or other soil properties is unknown.

Available nitrogen may be decreased in the soil as a result of denitrification when the supply of O_2 is low (see Chapter 9).

G. Effect of Crops on Available Nitrogen

Nonlegumes not only do not contribute to the nitrogen supply but in addition may have a depressing effect on available nitrogen. Lyon et al. (1923) observed that the accumulation of NO_3^- under corn and oats was lower than in fallow soil even after allowance had been made for nitrogen uptake by the crops. Fig. 4 from Goring and Clark (1948) illustrates that the crop effect is obtained only in the later stages of growth. They concluded that the nitrogen unaccounted for in cropped soils was immobilized into soil organic matter.

There is no conclusive evidence to explain the decrease in available nitrogen resulting from the presence of crops. Possible explanations are:

1. Root excretions that inhibit mineralization of nitrogen.
2. Root excretions of organic material that immobilize nitrogen by combining with it.
3. The presence of the crop may enhance denitrification.

When virgin soils are brought under cultivation, there is a decline in the quantity of soil organic matter as nitrogen is released. Salter and Green (1933) measured a 60% decline in nitrogen during a 30-year period where continuous corn was grown. The declines for rotations and continuous wheat and continuous oats were smaller than for corn. Annual loss of nitrogen from organic matter with continuous corn was 3%. Woodruff (1949) calculated the annual release of organic nitrogen to

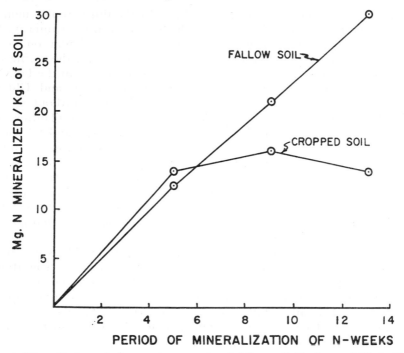

Fig. 4. Mineralization of nitrogen in cropped and fallow soil (Goring and Clark, 1948).

continuous corn as 2% in Missouri. The annual release of available nitrogen by soil organic matter is in the range of 2 to 4% per year. Higher percentages of the total nitrogen would be released in warm, moist climates with coarse-textured soils than in dry cool climates with fine-textured soils.

IV. DELAYED AVAILABILITY

Nitrogen applied in one season may be partially or completely available in a succeeding season. Interest in delayed availability has been generated by (1) the possibility of applying nitrogen during the fall for use by spring crops and (2) the recovery of unused nitrogen applied to one crop by succeeding crops.

Larson and Kohnke (1946) reported that on Miami silt loam and Lafayette silt loam as much corn was produced with 80 to 160 pounds of nitrogen per acre applied in the fall as with the same rate applied in spring. Pearson et al. (1961) concluded from a series of experiments in Alabama, Georgia, and Mississippi that, in terms of corn yield, fall application of nitrogen averaged 49% as effective as spring applied nitrogen, with a range of 13 to 69%. In terms of nitrogen recovered in crops, the relative effectiveness of fall as compared to spring applications was 62%. Even on coarse-textured soils under the high temperature and rainfall conditions of southeastern United States, 17% of a 200-pound per acre application of nitrogen was utilized by the third crop 16 months after application. In certain years with high rainfall in the winter, yields of corn from fall- and spring-applied nitrogen were similar on sandy soils. Yet, in other years with similar rainfall conditions, the spring application was more than twice as effective as that applied in the fall. No explanation was apparent for these differences. Nelson and Uhland (1955) concluded that fall applications could be used without serious loss of efficiency when from application time to spring planting, (1) leaching was slight, (2) erosion losses were not excessive, and (3) conditions did not favor volatilization or long-time immobilization of nitrogen. They speculated that, in the absence of specific data that in Area I (Fig. 5) fall application would be practical. Areas II and III were progressively less suitable, with Area IV definitely undesirable. Later workers appear to have confirmed the speculations of Nelson and Uhland. However, even under conditions that should favor low efficiency from fall applications, recovery often varies widely.

The delayed availability of nitrogen from organic residues is a function of the kind of the organic material and the climatic conditions. While high temperature and moisture favor decomposition of organic residues, some materials such as lignin and peats are so resistant to decomposition that only small amounts of nitrogen are released in a season, regardless of climatic effects. Other materials such as soybean meal and fresh leguminous residues may be rapidly decomposed.

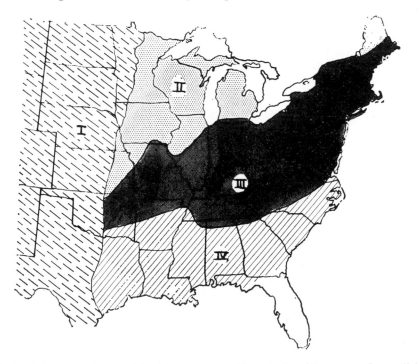

Fig. 5. Relation of degree of leaching to geographic area. Leaching ranges from nil in Area I to very high in Area IV. (From Nelson and Uhland, 1955)

A review by Pieters and McKee (1938) gives a good summary of the residual response from plowing down a crop of legumes. In Iowa, Fribourg and Bartholomew (1956) determined the relative availability of nitrogen to corn from legume and nonlegume residues, as compared with nitrogen from ammonium nitrate (Table 2). Alfalfa released a greater percentage of its nitrogen than did red clover. Soybean straw and oat hulls released no nitrogen to corn. The relative efficiency of nitrogen in alfalfa for most rates compared with ammonium nitrate for the succeeding corn crop ranged from 21 to 27% for alfalfa and 8 to 12% for red clover. An additional 7.5% of the nitrogen originally in alfalfa and 3.5% of the nitrogen in red clover was recovered by oats during the second growing season after incorporation. Kamprath et al. (1958) observed a residual nitrogen effect for 4 years after turning under a crop of vetch on Norfolk sandy loam. There was no residual nitrogen effect from an oat cover crop. A residual nitrogen response on oats was measured by Bailey et al. (1930) 10 years after turning under a 3-year-old stand of kudzu. A residual nitrogen response is usually obtained for 2 to 4 years after turning under a good crop of legumes. Residual nitrogen responses from turning under non-legumes have been small or absent.

While the principal benefit from incorporating cover crops into the soil is the nitrogen released, large amounts of organic materials may improve soil structural properties, particularly in medium- to fine-textured soils. Accordingly, all improvement in plant growth from adding nitrogen-rich plant residues to soils cannot be attributed to the available nitrogen released.

Some control over availability of soluble nitrogen compounds has been obtained by coating the fertilizer with materials such as wax and plastic (Ahmed et al., 1963; Dahnke et al., 1963; Lunt and Oertli, 1962; Oertli and Lunt, 1962). The rate of release of nitrogen was dependent on properties of the coating material and on temperature.

Table 2. Relative availabilities of ammonium nitrate and crop residue nitrogen as measured by corn production (Fribourg and Bartholomew, 1956).

Residue	Crop residue nitrogen, lb. N/A	NH_4NO_3 equivalent lb. N/A	Relative efficiency of residue nitrogen, %
Alfalfa	28	18	63
	57	16	27
	113	26	24
	170	35	21
Red clover	35	3	10
	69	6	8
	138	·13	9
	207	24	12
Soybean straw	26	−1	−5
	51	−1	−2
	102	2	2
	153	−4	−3
Oat hulls	228	−4	−2
Soybean straw + ammonium nitrate	152	19	12

V. THE DETERMINATION OF AVAILABLE NITROGEN

Although nearly all available nitrogen is in the NH_4^+ or NO_3^- form the amount in the soil at a given time is a poor indicator of the nitrogen availability to crops during a growing season. Nitrogen nutrition of crops depends more on the capacity of the soil to supply available nitrogen for a period of time than on the concentration of NH_4^+ and NO_3^- at a specific time. Accordingly, methods are usually employed that measure the nitrogen-supplying power of the soil.

A. Biological Methods

Incubation methods are often used for routine determinations of the nitrogen-supplying power of soils. A detailed evaluation of incubation methods was given in an excellent review by Harmsen and van Schreven (1955). In most procedures a sample of soil is leached free of soluble nitrogen, then incubated under constant moisture and temperature for 2 to 6 weeks. The relative amount of NO_3^- produced is used as a measure of the nitrogen-supplying power of the soil (Fitts et al., 1955; Munson and Stanford, 1955; Stanford and Hanway, 1955). Laboratory incubation tests must be correlated with field results if the measurements are to serve as a means of (1) predicting the amount of available nitrogen produced from soil organic matter and (2) recommending additional nitrogen from fertilizers. Some factors that influence available nitrogen production are temperature, moisture, soil reaction, total nitrogen content, cropping system, soil texture, recent additions of organic matter, season of the year, fertilizers, and soil structure (Cornfield, 1952; Fitts et al., 1955; Gainey, 1936; Harmsen and van Schreven, 1955; Pritchett et al., 1959). Regardless of these factors, satisfactory correlations with crop use of nitrogen have often been obtained.

Utilization of higher plants as extracting agents in field plots is the most accurate means of determining available nitrogen in soil. This method is costly and time consuming. It is used mostly as a standard of measure for other methods more adapted for routine determinations.

Higher plants grown in small containers in a greenhouse, growth chamber, or laboratory are used as indicators of available nitrogen. They approximate the field methods, although the root zone is restricted and the climatic factor is altered. One of the most promising short-term methods was introduced by DeMent et al. (1959). Roots of intact nitrogen-deficient oat plants were transferred to the soil and nitrogen uptake was measured after 7 to 14 days. Vandecaveye (1948) has described methods where other plants are utilized to measure available nitrogen.

The utilization of nitrogen by microorganisms has been used as a measure of available nitrogen. McCool (1947) grew *Cunninghamella blakesleeana* on the surface of moist soil. Nitrogen utilization by the fungus colonies was closely correlated with nitrogen uptake by ryegrass grown under field conditions. Boswell et al. (1963) have devised a technique utilizing the bacterium *Pseudomonas aeruginosa*. Production of the pigment pyocyanin served as a negative indicator of available nitrogen in soil as indicated by the correlation coefficient of -0.549. Since the production of pigment is only a fair indicator of available nitrogen, it appears that some further improvement and testing of the method is needed.

B. Total Nitrogen Methods

There is a general relationship between the total nitrogen of the soil and the amount of available nitrogen released during a single growing season. However, Gainey (1936) illustrated the danger of using this relationship to predict the production of available nitrogen from a particular soil sample. When 250 soils were placed in 7 groups according to similarity of total nitrogen content, the correlation with available nitrogen produced during incubation was a near-perfect correlation coefficient of $.988 \pm .006$ for soils considered fertile and $.990 \pm .012$ for nonfertile soils. However, when correlation coefficients were calculated using individual samples, the values were $.368 \pm .052$ for fertile soils and $.389 \pm .052$ for nonfertile soils. This shows that other factors have much more influence on production of available nitrogen in indivdual samples than does total nitrogen content. However, a relationship for predictive purposes can be established if information is available concerning the importance of the many factors that affect the release of available nitrogen from organic matter. Since this is difficult and time consuming for any soil, total nitrogen measurements show little promise of being of value in predicting the amount of available nitrogen produced in soils.

The Truog (1954) method for available nitrogen involves the distillation of NH_3 from soil for 5 minutes in the presence of $KMnO_4$ and Na_2CO_3. Boswell et al. (1962) obtained a correlation coefficient of 0.67 between the Truog method and the nitrifying capacity of 30 soils.

Purvis and Micah (1961) have proposed a method that measures only the readily hydrolyzable fraction of the total organic nitrogen. Their greenhouse data show a close correlation between nitrogen hydrolyzed and nitrogen uptake by wheat.

C. Plant Analysis Methods

The ultimate measure of the availability of nitrogen is the amount taken up from the soil by growing plants. Accordingly, plant analysis has been used to determine if an adequate amount of available nitrogen is present for the crop (Baird et al., 1962; Krantz et al., 1948; MacKenzie et al., 1963; Thomas, 1945; Tyner and Webb, 1946; Ulrick, 1948; Ulrick et al., 1959). A basic assumption is that growth is reduced when the level of nitrogen within the plant falls below a previously determined critical level. The usual measurement is for NO_3—N or total nitrogen in certain plant parts or in the total plant.

Plant analysis has been used successfully as a measure of the nitrogen status of crops, provided other environmental and management factors are also considered. Ulrich (1948) has expressed some of the important factors in the equation $X = F(S,C,T,P,M, \ldots)$ where $X =$ nutrient concentration in the plant, $S =$ soil, $C =$ climate, $T =$ time, $P =$ plant, and $M =$ management. When these factors are relatively constant for a given location, plant analysis is an adequate measure of available nitrogen. With most plants, samples must be taken during several growth stages for satisfactory prediction of the need for additional nitrogen from fertilizers.

One of the most successful applications of plant analysis is the crop log on sugar cane as described by Clements (1951) and Baver (1960). The crop log is a record of plant growth from planting to harvest. Plant factors measured and recorded in the log are growth, moisture, N, K, and P. The effect of these factors, along with temperature, on sugar yield are estimated by multiple regression analysis from previous crop logs. Total nitrogen is determined on samples from the 8th to 10th internode from the top at 6, 8, 10, and 12 months after plant growth begins. The critical level for nitrogen is determined from previous crop logs for the field and is adjusted for the age and moisture content of the plants. Nitrogen fertilizer is applied when the nitrogen index falls below the adjusted critical level.

REFERENCES

Ahmed, I. U., Altoe, O. J., Engelbert, L. E., and Corey, R. B. 1963. Factors affecting the rate of release of fertilizers from capsules. Agron. J. 55:495-499.

Albrech, W. A. 1937. The nitrate nitrogen in the soil as influenced by the crop and the soil treatment. Missouri Agr. Exp. Sta. Res. Bull. 250.

Allison, F. E., Doetsch, J. H. and Roller, E. M. 1953a. Availability of fixed ammonium in soils containing different clay minerals. Soil Sci. 75:373-381.

Allison, F. E., Roller, E. M. and Doetsch, J. H. 1953b. Ammonium fixation and availability in vermiculite. Soil Sci. 75:173-180.

Armiger, W. H., Clark, K. G., Lundstrom, F. O., and Blair, A. E. 1951. Urea-form: Greenhouse studies with perennial ryegrass. Agron. J. 43:123-127.

Arnon, D. I. 1937. Ammonium and nitrate nutrition of barley at different seasons in relation to hydrogen-ion concentration, manganese, copper, and oxygen supply. Soil Sci. 44:91-121.

Axley, J. H. and Legg, J. O. 1960. Ammonium fixation in soils and the influence of potassium on nitrogen availability from nitrate and ammonium sources. Soil Sci. 90:151-156.

Bailey, R. Y., Williamson, J. T. and Duggar, J. F. 1930. Experiments with legumes in Alabama. Alabama Agr. Exp. Sta. Bull. 232.

Bain, F. M. and Chapman, H. D. 1940. Nitrate fertilizer additions to waterlogged soils in relation to oxygen deficiency. Soil Sci. 50:357-367.

Baird, B. L., Fitts, J. W. and Mason, D. D. 1962. The relationship of nitrogen in corn leaves to yield. Soil Sci. Soc. Am. Proc. 26:378-381.

Bartholomew, W. V. and Hiltbold, A. E. 1952. Recovery of fertilizer nitrogen by oats in the greenhouse. Soil Sci. 73:193-201.

Bartholomew, W. V., Nelson, L. B., and Werkman, C. H. 1950. The use of the nitrogen isotope N^{15} in field studies with oats. Agron. J. 42:100-103.

Batham, H. V. and Nigam, L. S. 1930. Periodicity of the nitrate content of soils. Soil Sci. 29:181-190.

Baver, L. D. 1960. Scientific feeding of high-value crops. Plant Food Rev. 6(3):8-11.

Black, A. L. and Greb, B. W. 1962. Nitrate accumulation in soils covered with plastic mulch. Agron. J. 54:366.

Bonner, J. 1946. The role of organic matter, especially manure, in the nutrition of rice. Bot. Gaz. 108:267-279.

Boswell, F. C., Richer, A. C. and Casida, L. E., Jr. 1962. Available soil nitrogen measurements by microbiological techniques and chemical methods. Soil Sci. Soc. Am. Proc. 26:254-257.

Bower, C. A. 1950. Availability of ammonium fixed in difficulty exchangeable form by soils of semiarid regions. Soil Sci. Soc. Am. Proc. 15:119-122.

Bower, C. A., Browning, G. M. and Norton, R. A. 1945. Comparative effects of plowing and other methods of seedbed preparation on nutrient-element deficiencies in corn. Soil Sci. Soc. Am. Proc. 9:142-146.

Broadbent, F. E., Hill, G. N. and Tyler, K. B. 1958. Transformations and movement of urea in soils. Soil Sci. Soc. Am. Proc. 22:303-307.

Broadbent, F. E. and Norman, A. G. 1946. Some factors affecting the availability of the organic nitrogen in soils. Soil Sci. Soc. Am. Proc. 11:264-267.

Brooks, S. N. and Keller, K. R. 1960. Effect of time of applying nitrogen fertilizer on yields of hops. Agron. J. 52:516-518.

Chang, H. T. and Loomis, W. E. 1945. Effect of carbon dioxide on adsorption of water and nutrients by roots. Plant Physiol. 20:221-232.

Chapman, H. D. and Liebig, G. F. Jr. 1952. Field and laboratory studies of nitrate accumulation in soils. Soil Sci. Soc. Am. Proc. 16:276-282.

Clark, K. G., Yee, J. Y., Love, K. S. and Boyd, T. A. 1951. Preparation and properties of urea-form. Ind. Eng. Chem. 43:871-875.

Clements, H. F. 1951. Environmental influences on the growth of sugar cane. "Mineral nutrition of Plants." Truog. E. ed. University of Wisconsin Press, Madison, pp. 451-469.

Cornfield, A. H. 1952. The mineralization of the nitrogen of soils during incubation: Influence of pH, total nitrogen, and organic carbon contents. J. Sci. Food Agr. 3:343-349.

Dadd, C. C., Fowden, L. and Pearsall, W. H. 1953. An investigation of the free amino-acids in organic soil types using paper chromatography. J. Soil Sci. 4:69-71.

Dahnke, W C., Attoe, O. J., Engelbert, L. E., and Groskopp, M. D. 1963. Controlling release of fertilizer constituents by means of coations and capsules. Agron. J. 55:242-244.

DeMent, J. D., Hunt, C. M. and Stanford, G. 1961. Hydrolysis, nitrification and nitrogen availability of oxamide as influenced by granule size. Agr. Food Chem. 9:453-456.

DeMent, J. D., Stanford, G., and Hunt, C. M. 1959. A method for measuring short-term nutrient absorption by plants: III. Nitrogen. Soil Sci. Soc. Am. Proc. 23:371-374.

Dotzenko, A. D. 1961. Effect of different nitrogen levels on the yield, total nitrogen content, and nitrogen recovery of six grasses grown under irrigation. Agron. J. 53:131-133.

Eck, H. V. and Fanning, C. 1961. Placement of fertilizers in relation to soil moisture supply. Agron. J. 53:335-338.

Fisher, W. B., Jr. and Parks, W. L. 1958. Influence of soil temperature on urea hydrolysis and subsequent nitrification. Soil Sci. Soc. Am. Proc. 22:247-248.

Fitts, J. W., Bartholomew, W. V., and Heidel, H. 1955. Predicting nitrogen fertilizer needs of Iowa soils: I. Evaluation and control of factors in nitrate production and analysis. Soil Sci. Soc. Am. Proc. 19:69-73.

Frapps, G. S. and Sterges, A. J. 1930. Occurrence of nitrites in soils. Texas Agr. Expt. Sta. Bull. 412.

Fribourg, H. A. and Bartholomew, W. V. 1956. Availability of nitrogen from crop residues during the first and second seasons after application. Soil Sci. Soc. Am. Proc. 20:505-508.

Fuller, W. H., and Clark, K. G. 1947. Microbiological studies on urea-formaldehyde preparations. Soil Sci. Soc. Am. Proc. 12:198-202.

Gainey, P. L. 1936. Total nitrogen as a factor influencing nitrate accumulation in soils. Soil Sci. 42:157-163.

Ghosh, B. P. and Burris, R. H. 1950. Utilization of nitrogenous compounds by plants. Soil Sci. 70:187-203.

Gilbert, S. G. and Shive, J. W. 1945. The importance of oxygen in the nutrient substrate for plants—relation of the nitrate ion to respiration. Soil Sci. 59:453-460.

Gilbert, S. M. 1945. The mulching of coffee Arabica. East Africa Agr. J. 11:75-79.

Goring, C. A. I. and Clark, F. E. 1948. Influence of crop growth on mineralization of nitrogen in the soil. Soil Sci. Soc. Am. Proc. 13:261-266.

Greenland, D. J. 1958. Nitrate fluctuations in tropical soils. J. Agr. Sci. 50:82-91.

Griffith, G. A. 1951. Factors influencing nitrate accumulation in Uganda soil. Emp. J. Exp. Agr. 19:1-12.

Harmsen, G. W. and Schreven, D. A. van 1955. Mineralization of organic nitrogen in soil. Advances in Agronomy VII. Norman, A. G. ed. Academic Press, Inc. New York. pp. 299-398.

Hoagland, D. R. and Broyer, T. C. 1936. General nature of the process of salt accumulation by roots with description of experimental methods. Plant Physiol. 11:471-507.

Jenny, H. 1930. A study on the influence of climate upon the nitrogen and organic matter content of the soil. Missouri Agr. Expt. Sta. Res. Bull. 152.

Jones, R. J. 1942. Nitrogen losses from Alabama soils in lysimeters as influenced by various systems of green manure crop management. J. Am. Soc. Agron. 34:574-585.

Jones, W. F., Lancaster, J. D., Arnold, B. L., Hurt, B. C., Jr., Coats, R. E. and Walton, L. 1962. Nitrogen spray not practical on cotton leaves. Mississippi Farm Res. 25(2):1.

Kamprath, E. J., Chandler, W. V. and Krantz, B. A. 1958. Winter cover crops. North Carolina Agr. Exp. Sta. Tech. Bull. 129.

Kelley, W. P. 1911. The assimilation of nitrogen by rice. Hawaii Agr. Exp. Sta. Bull. 24.

Klinker, E. J. and Emmert, E. M. 1953. Effect of foliar applications of urea, sucrose, and dextrose on tomato yields and quality. Kentucky Agr. Exp. Sta. Bull. 595.

Krantz, B. A. and Chandler, W. V. 1954. Fertilize corn for higher yields. North Carolina Agr. Exp. Sta. Bull. 366.

Krantz, B. A., Nelson, W. L. and Burkhart, L. F. 1948. Plant-tissue tests as a tool in agronomic research. "Diagnostic Techniques for Soils and Crops." Am. Potash Institute, Washington, D.C. pp. 137-155.

Larsen, J. E. and Kohnke, H. 1956. Relative merits of fall- and spring-applied fertilizer. Soil Sci. Soc. Proc. 11:378-383.

Lawton, K. 1945. The influence of soil aeration on the growth and absorption of nutrients by corn plants. Soil Sci. Soc. Am. Proc. 10:263-268.

Lunt, O. R., and Oertli, J. J. 1962. Controlled release of fertilizer minerals by incapsulating membranes: II. Efficiency of recovery, influence of soil moisture, mode of application, and other considerations related to use. Soil Sci. Soc. Am. Proc. 26:584-587.

Lyon, T. L., Bizzell, J. A. and Wilson, B. D. 1923. Depressive influence of certain higher plants on the accumulation of nitrates in the soil. J. Am. Soc. Agron. 15:457-467.

MacKenzie, A. J., Spencer, W. F., Stockinger, K. R., and Krantz, B. A. 1963. Seasonal nitrate-nitrogen content of cotton petioles as affected by nitrogen application and its relationship to yield. Agron. J. 55:55-60.

Martin, W. P., Buehrer, T. F. and Caster, A. B. 1942. Threshold pH value for the nitrification of ammonia in desert soils. Soil Sci. Soc. Am. Proc. 7:223-228.

McCool, M. M. 1933. Properties and uses of calcium cyanamide. Boyce Thompson Inst. Prof. Paper 24.

McCool, M. M. 1947. Nitrogen availability in soils as measured by growth response of rye grass and cumminghamellia blakesleeana. Boyce Thompson Inst. Contrib. 14:366-368.

Meyer, B. S., Anderson, D. B., and Bohning, R H. 1960. Introduction to Plant Physiology. D. Van Nostrand Co. Inc. Princeton, New Jersey p. 306.

Miettinen, J. K. 1959. Assimilation of amino acids in higher plants. Soc. Exp. Biol. Symposia XIII. "Utilization of Nitrogen and its Compounds by Plants." Academic Press, Inc. New York. pp. 210-229.

Munson, R. D. and Stanford, G. 1955. Predicting nitrogen fertilizer needs of Iowa soils: IV. Evaluation of nitrate production as a criterion of nitrogen availability. Soil Sci. Soc. Am. Proc. 19:464-468.

Musser, H. B., Watson, J. R., Jr., Stanford, J. P., and Harper, J. C. II. 1951. Urea-formaldehyde and other nitrogenous fertilizers for use on turf. Pennsylvania Agr. Exp. Sta. Bull. 542.

Naftel, J. A. 1931. The absorption of ammonium and nitrate nitrogen by various plants at different stages of growth. J. Am. Soc. Agron. 23:142-158.

Nelson, L. B. and Uhland, R. E. 1955. Factors that influence loss of fall-applied fertilizers and their probable importance in different sections of the United States. Soil Sci. Soc. Am. Proc. 19:492-496.

Oertli, J. J., and Lunt, O. R. 1962. Controlled release of fertilizer minerals by incapsulating membranes: I. Factors influencing the rate of release. Soil Sci. Soc. Am. Proc. 26:579-583.

Paauw, F. van der. 1962. Effect of winter rainfall on the amount of nitrogen available to crops. Plant and Soil 16:361-380.

Paul, E. A. and Schmidt, E. L. 1961. Formation of free amino acids in rhizosphere and nonrhizosphere soil. Soil Sci. Soc. Am. Proc. 25:359-362.

Pearson, R. W., Jordan, H. V., Bennett, O. L., Scarsbrook, C. E., Adams, W. E. and White, A. W. 1961. Residual effects of fall- and spring-applied nitrogen fertilizers on crop yields in the Southeastern United States. USDA Tech. Bull. 1254.

Pieters, A. J. and McKee, R. 1938. The use of cover and green-manure crops. In "Soils and Men." USDA Yearbook Agr. pp. 431-444.

Pinck, L. A., Allison, F. E. and Gaddy, V. L. 1948. The effect of green manure crops of varying carbon-nitrogen ratios upon nitrogen availability and soil organic matter content. J. Am. Soc. Agron. 40:237-248.

Prince, A. L. 1945. Determination of total nitrogen, ammonia, nitrates, and nitrites in soils. Soil Sci. 59:47-52.

Pritchett, W. L., Eno, C. F., and Malik, M. N. 1959. The nitrogen status of the mineral soils of Florida. Soil Sci. Soc. Am. Proc. 23:127-130.

Pumphrey, F. V. and Harris, L. 1956. Nitrogen fertilizer for corn production on an irrigated Chestnut soil. Agron. J. 48:207-212

Purvis, E. R. and Micah, W. M. L. 1961. Rapid procedure for estimating potentially available soil nitrogen under greenhouse conditions. Agr. Food Chem. 9(1):15-17.

Ray, H. E., McGregor, J. M. and Schmidt, E. L. 1957. Movement of ammonium nitrogen in soils. Soil Sci. Soc. Am. Proc. 21:309-312.

Reitemeier, R. F. 1946. Effect of moisture content on the dissolved and exchangeable ions of soils of arid regions. Soil Sci. 61:195 214.

Richards, S. J., Hagen, R. M. and McCalla, T. M. 1952. Soil temperature and plant growth. In Soil Physical Conditions and Plant Growth. Shaw, B. T. ed. Academic Press, Inc. New York. pp. 303-480.

Russell, E. J. 1914. The nature and amount of the fluctuations in nitrate contents of arable soils. J. Agr. Sci. 6:18-57.

Salter, R. M. and Green, T. C. 1933. Factors affecting the accumulation and loss of nitrogen and organic carbon in cropped soils. J. Am. Soc. Agron. 25:622-630.

Scarsbrook, C. E. 1958. Urea-formaldehyde fertilizer as a source of nitrogen for cotton and corn. Soil Sci. Soc. Am. Proc. 22:442-445.

Scarsbrook, C. E., Bennett, O. L. and Pearson, R. W. 1959. The interaction of nitrogen and moisture on cotton yields and other characteristics. Agron. J. 51:718-721.

Schreiner, O. and Skinner, J. J. 1912. Nitrogenous soils constituents and their bearing on soil fertility. USDA Bur. Soils Bull. 87.

Schumacher, G. and Davis, S. 1961. Nitrogen application and irrigation frequencies for western wheatgrass production on clay soil. Agron. J. 53:168-170.

Simpson, D. M. H. and Melsted, S. W. 1963. Urea hydrolysis and transformation in some Illinois soils. Soil Sci. Soc. Am. Proc. 27:48-50.

Sowden, F. J. 1956. Distribution of amino acids in selected horizons of soil profiles. Soil Sci. 82:491-496.

Sowden, F. J. and Parker, D. I. 1953. Amino nitrogen of soils and of certain fractions isolated from them. Soil Sci. 76:201-208.

Stanford, G. and Hanway, J. 1955. Predicting nitrogen fertilizer needs of Iowa soils: II. A simplified technique for determining relative nitrate production in soils. Soil Sci. Soc. Am. Proc. 19:74-77.

Stevenson, F. J. 1956. Effect of some long-time rotations on the amino acid composition of the soil. Soil Sci. Soc. Am. Proc. 20:204-208.

Stewart, B. A. and Eck, H. V. 1958. The movement of surface-applied nitrate into soils at five moisture levels. Soil Sci. Soc. Am. Proc. 22:260-262.

Stojanovic, B. J. and Alexander, M. 1958. Effect of inorganic nitrogen on nitrification. Soil Sci. 86:208-215.

Thelin, G. and Beaumont, A. B. 1934. The effect of some forms of nitrogen on the growth and nitrogen content of wheat and rice plants. J. Am. Soc. Agron. 26:1012-1017.

Thomas, W. 1945. Present status of diagnosis of mineral requirements of plants by means of leaf analysis. Soil Sci. 59:353-374.

Thorne, G. N. and Watson, D. J. 1956. Field experiments on uptake of nitrogen from leaf sprays by sugar beet. J. Agr. Sci. 47:12-22.

Tidmore, J. W. and Williamson, J. T. 1932. Experiments with commercial nitrogenous fertilizers. Alabama Agr. Exp. Sta. Bull. 238.

Tiedjens, V. A. and Robbins, W. R. 1931. The use of ammonia and nitrate nitrogen by certain crop plants. New Jersey Agr. Exp. Sta. Bull. 526.

Truog, E. 1954. Test for available nitrogen. Commercial Fert. 88 (No. 4):72-73.

Tyner, E. H. and Webb, J. R. 1946. The relation of corn yield to nutrient balance as revealed by leaf analysis. J. Am. Soc. Agron. 38:173-185.

Ulrick, A. 1948. Plant analysis—methods and interpretation of results. In Diagnostic Techniques for Soils and Crops. Am. Potash Institute, Washington, D.C. pp. 157-198.

Ulrick, A., Ririe, D., Hills, F. J., George, A. G. and Morse, M. D. 1959. Plant analysis. California Agr. Exp. Sta. Bull. 766.

Vandecaveye, S. C. 1948. Biological methods of determining nutrients in soil. In Diagnostic Techniques for Soils and Crops. Am. Potash Institute, Washington, D.C. pp. 199-230.

Virtanen, A. I. and Linkola, H. 1946. Organic nitrogen compounds as nitrogen nutrition for higher plants. Nature, London. 158:515.

Volk, G. M. 1947. Significance of moisture translocation from soil zones of low moisture tension to zones of high moisture tension by plant roots. J. Am. Soc. Agron. 39:93-106.

Wallace, A. 1954. Ammonium and nitrate absorption by citrus. Soil Sci. 78:89-94.

Welch, L. F. and Scott, A. D. 1960. Nitrification of fixed ammonium in clay minerals as affected by added potassium. Soil Sci. 90:79-85.

Woodruff, C. M. 1949. Estimating the nitrogen delivery of soil from the organic matter determination as reflected by Sanborn Field. Soil Sci. Soc. Am. Proc. 14:208-212.

Yee, J. Y. and Love, K. S. 1946. Nitrification of urea—formaldehyde reaction products. Soil Sci. Soc. Am. Proc. 11:389-392.

Chapter 14

The Plant's Need for
and Use of Nitrogen

FRANK G. VIETS, JR.

Agricultural Research Service, U.S.D.A.
Fort Collins, Colorado

I. INTRODUCTION

The object of this chapter is to consider those phases of N uptake, storage, and use in the plant that are of primary importance to the agronomist and soil scientist managing soils and recommending N fertilizer practices, and to nutritionists concerned with some phases of nutritional quality of feeds produced. Several excellent reviews on the N metabolism of plants have been published recently (Webster, 1959, McElroy and Glass, 1956; Symposium of the Society for Experimental Biology, No. 13, 1959). Therefore, N metabolism *per se* will not be discussed further.

Plants as a group can get their N in a surprising number of diverse ways besides the familiar ones of absorption through roots, absorption through leaves by aquatics, or symbiosis with an N-fixing organism contained in root nodules. Some of these unfamiliar sources of N are blue-green algae living in special tissues on leaves of some kinds of plants, ammonia and other N compounds in the air, dew, and rain that can be absorbed by leaves, and dust and spray materials applied to leaves. Some plants can even catch and digest insects. Some of these modes of getting N are confined to specialized plants and to specialized situations and some of them may not be fully appreciated now as to their input of N. By and large, only the soil, the nodule bacteria of legumes, and the deliberate use of N compounds for foliar application are regarded as significant sources of N for cultivated plants.

II. NITROGEN AS AN ESSENTIAL ELEMENT

Plants, like all organisms, require N for their growth and reproduction. Nitrogen is a constituent of all proteins, all enzymes, many metabolic intermediates involved in synthesis and energy transfer, and even of the deoxyribonucleic acids making up the genetic code itself.

No one can claim that N is more essential than any of the other 15 elements known to be needed for higher plants, but on the basis of

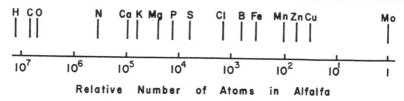

Fig. 1. The relative number of atoms of the essential elements in alfalfa at bloom stage expressed logarithmically. Slightly modified from an earlier report (Viets, 1961).

relative number of atoms needed, N is at the top of the list of those that come from soil or fertilizers. Fig. 1 shows on a log scale the number of atoms of each of the elements expressed in relation to Mo in a good crop of alfalfa hay (Viets, 1961). Similar charts could be drawn for other crops and they would all show the great importance of N to plants.

In soil-plant nutrition relations, N has a unique place. Worldwide, more crops are deficient in N than in any other element. This is probably true even in countries like the United States that depend heavily on chemically fixed N. In soil, N is the most unpredictable of the nutrient elements. It is subject to biological and chemical immobilization; biological mobilization dependent on complex interplay of temperature, aeration, water, and kind and amount of organic matter; leaching; and denitrification. Too little N limits yield and reduces quality; too much can cut yield, reduce quality, cause lodging, and sometimes make forage toxic to animals. The complex interplay of all of these factors makes difficult the prediction of how much fertilizer N to apply to supplement that coming from the soil. Many soils can still supply all N needs of the crop. This is most probable where moisture deficit limits crop yields as in the Great Plains of the U.S.A. or the steppe and prairie regions of the world. Even here use of fertilizer N is becoming more common. At the other extreme are desert soils which, placed under irrigation, can supply scarcely 5% of the crops' requirements. In agricultural practice, balancing quantitatively the crops' requirements for N against that which can be supplied by the soil and legumes and that needed from mineral fertilizers is still largely an art. Only with specialty crops like bananas, pineapple, and sugarcane—generally grown in monoculture in restricted localities—has N balance approached an empirical science.

Losses of N from plants are obvious when leaves, flowers, and fruits fall off or when the tops are removed and the roots left in the ground, but there are losses of N that are less obvious like translocation back to the roots, volatilization of HCN, guttation, and washout. All of these possibilities are seldom considered quantitatively in making up an N budget for a species.

III. APPARENT EFFECTS OF N DEFICIENCY AND EXCESS IN PLANTS

Many effects of too little or too much N are readily apparent in color, rate of growth and habit of the plant. "Too much" or "too little" N are, of course, terms that are only relative to other essential nutrients, to water, and to temperature and other factors of the environment. "Too little" simply means that the plant cannot absorb enough N to fully utilize the more favorable factors in its environment and so N is relatively deficient. Similarly, "too much" means that uptake of N by the plant is in excess of that required for growth because of limitation by some other deficiency in the plant's environment. Thus, the handy but rather ill-defined concept of balance is involved. When deficiency or toxicity symptoms are apparent there can be little question about balance, but when no symptoms are involved only complex experimentation, chemical analysis, and statistical approaches are adequate to define balance.

Most everyone is familiar with the pale green color and stunted appearance of plants starved for N, although deficiencies of other elements such as S and Mo can produce symptoms resembling those of N deficiency in some species. Many books and pamphlets are available giving keys and photographs of N deficiency on various species (Sprague, 1964; McMurtrey, 1948; Wallace, 1961). Hewitt (1963) gives a good discussion of the effects of N deficiency on plant morphology. Among the effects are a pale green color due to lack of chlorophyll synthesis, stunted growth of the top resulting from reduced cell division and cell enlargement due to inadequate protein synthesis, delayed maturity in some species, a more acute angle between stem and leaf in many species, frequent accumulation of anthocyanins, prolonged dormancy of flower and leaf buds in trees, lack of tillering in cereals, premature death of lower leaves, and perhaps accelerated rates of root growth (see Section VII).

One of the most striking effects of N deficiency on a plant characteristic usually believed to be genetically controlled is the effect of N on the number of kernel rows in sweet corn. Schreiber et al. (1962) showed that fertilization of double cross Golden Bantam, grown on an N-deficient loamy sand with 100 pounds of N per acre, increased the average number of rows per ear from about 10.2 to about 11.7. Even 20 pounds of N at planting increased the number of rows to about 10.8.

The effects of excess N are less obvious than those of deficiency but they include excessive height resulting from self competition for light, lodging in cereals, failure of fruit to color up, and delayed flowering in some species. A controversy raged for years around whether the plants C-N ratio in itself controlled flowering. Subsequent research has shown that flowering is photoperiodically controlled in many species but the modifying effects of N may still be present. Some of the serious effects of too much N on economic crops, such as low sugar content and high impurities in sugar beets and cane and high amounts of NO_3^- in forages toxic to animals, are not obvious in the plants themselves.

Lodging in the small grain cereals and stalk breakage in corn reduce yield and make mechanical harvesting difficult or even impossible. Barley and oats are particularly susceptible. Lodging has long been associated with "rich" land and has become a more serious problem with thicker stands. Welton and Morris (1931) associated lodging in oats and wheat with low dry matter per unit length of culm induced by thick stands and excessive available N. In comprehensive studies of lodging in field corn uncomplicated by root rot or European corn borer damage, Nelson (1958) found that N increased lodging by fall storms. He attributed this greater lodging to heavier ears, taller plants, and greater ear height above the ground which increased the moment of wind force. However, the force required to break the stalk mechanically and the diameter of the third internode above the ground were increased by fertilization. Lodging reduction requires the combined efforts of the plant breeder and the fertility specialist.

There has been much controversy about the effect of N supply on the maturity of crops. The fact that crops such as corn and small grains stay green longer if adequately supplied with N has been interpreted as delayed maturity. Maturity was often confused with N deficiency symptoms. The development to maturity of a crop of grain involves two phases: (1) the rate of development of the inflorescence and filling of the grain, and (2) the dehydration of the grain. Many studies have shown that the rate of development of the inflorescence in small grains and ears in corn is retarded by N deficiency. On the other hand, excess N can delay the dehydration phase of maturity. Black (1957, pp. 230-235) gives a good account of the effects of N supply on maturity in oats, corn, and cotton.

In other crops, N supply may have variable effects on maturity depending on the crop and its ripening period in relation to weather. Too much N can delay the ripening of late varieties of peaches into cool weather so that they ripen slowly. Rate and timing of N application in relation to growth and climatic conditions is a part of the art and science of horticulture.

As a general statement, it can be said that fertilizing with N to produce a maximum yield will produce the earliest maturity. Some specialty crops are exceptions.

IV. PLANT RESPONSE TO NITROGEN

A crop grown by itself, or an association of plants such as a grass-legume mixture, may respond to the additions of N fertilizer with a decrease, an increase, or no change in yield. The kind or kinds of plants, the soil N supply in relation to plant needs, and the effect of preceding increments of N are the factors affecting response to an increment of N.

An idealized response curve for nonlegumes to N fertilizer application is shown in Fig. 2. This curve is divided into three segments. Segment A, which is seldom found in practice, represents a region where succeeding increments of N fertilizer produce successively larger increments in yield. The slope of the curve in this region of the response curve is often difficult to define with statistical significance because of variability in yields and the lack of a sufficient number of points. Often a straight line would fit the data as well as a curve that is either concave upward or concave downward. Steenbjerg (1954) claims that a sigmoidal curve (of which Segment A is a part) occurs when nutrient deficiency is extreme

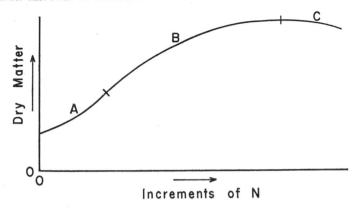

Fig. 2. Idealized response in dry matter production of a nonlegume to increments of N fertilizer.

and the fertilizer nutrient reacts with a constituent of the soil so that reduced availability results. Such conditions for N could exist in soils when high C to N ratio plant residues (cereal straw) are present to immobilize fertilizer N. Fig. 3 shows the total dry weight of wheat in pot culture produced with the addition of straw and urea (Pinck et al., 1946). When no straw was added the response curve to N was linear or concave downward over its entire range. When straw was added at the rate of 2 short tons per acre the response curve had an initial segment that was concave upward. With 4 tons of straw, the entire curve was concave upward. Fig. 4 demonstrates both Segments A and B of the complete response curve for corn grown with application of N from 0 to 400 pounds per acre on plots that received variable amounts of N on the corn the preceding

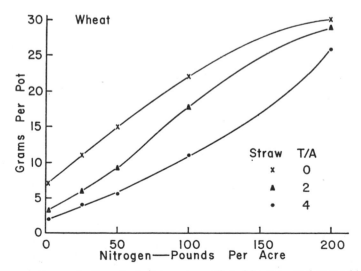

Fig. 3. Dry matter production of wheat in pots as affected by straw and urea additions to the soil (Pinck et al., 1946).

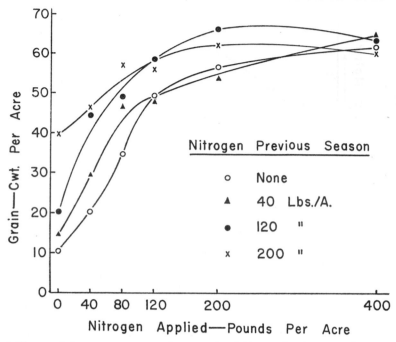

Fig. 4. Shapes of the response curves of corn grain yield to N fertilizers as affected by the amount of N applied to the preceding corn crop. Data from Boawn et al. (1963).

year and the stover was left on the plots (Boawn et al., 1963). When corn was not fertilized the preceding year the response curve was definitely sigmoidal, whereas N application the preceding year produced curves about which less definite conclusions can be drawn. The two top curves are probably not sigmoidal.

Application of ammoniacal fertilizers to NH_4-fixing soils could also produce sigmoidal response curves, but such evidence has not been obtained in the field. Fig. 5, drawn from Nommik (1957), shows the comparative yield response of oats to $Ca(NO_3)_2$ vs. $(NH_4)_2SO_4$ grown on an ammonium-fixing soil in pots. Response to $Ca(NO_3)_2$ is definitely concave downward, but the response to $(NH_4)_2SO_4$ appears to be definitely sigmoidal.

Generally, the concave upward portion (Segment A) of the yield curve is at such a low yield level that its study is of little importance. Grass-legume swards represent a special case of this segment of the curve. When succeeding increments of N are applied to a sward containing well-modulated legumes, the grass is stimulated to greater growth to the detriment of the legume, which suffers for light. The net result is that succeeding increments of N produce more grass, less legume, and total dry weight production remains about the same. The production of the pure stand of grass amply fertilized may be equal to or only slightly better than the mixture with little or no fertilizer. These relationships are fully discussed by Donald (1963). Nitrogen applied to pure stands of well-nodulated clovers and alfalfa generally has little or no effect

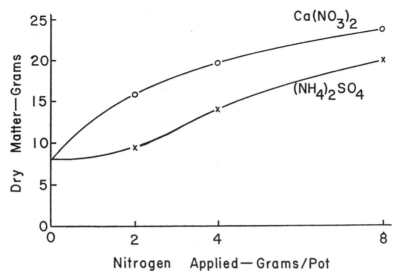

Fig. 5. Total dry matter production of oats as affected by N source on an ammonium-fixing soil (Nommik, 1957).

unless weed growth is encouraged, in which event the legume may suffer. The legumes simply use fertilizer N instead of that fixed in nodules.

Segment B of the response curve shown in Fig. 2 is the portion that has attracted most attention because the most profitable responses to N fertilizer lie in this region. There is no *a priori* basis for knowing the proper mathematical model for this segment except that it must be a function in which yield increase or response declines with succeeding increments of fertilizer. The Mitscherlich equation has been extensively used by agronomists to characterize this curve. Economists have used the Spillman form of the equation for the same purpose. For examples see Paschal and French (1956). Mason (1956) showed that the Cobb-Douglas exponential, Mitscherlich, and quadratic equations described equally well corn yield data of the author (Viets et al., 1954) in which yields ranged from 125.8 to 168.5 bushels per acre, and the N applied varied from 0 to 200 pounds per acre. French (1956) also showed that several functions, including the quadratic square root in which [N applied]$^{\frac{1}{2}}$ is a parameter, fit the response of corn to N. Only the polynomials fit data where yield decreases result from additional increments of N (Segment C of Fig. 2), but Mitscherlich did provide a modification of his equation to provide for a "factor of injury" (Mason, 1956). Mason claims that the polynomial has the advantages: more flexibility since additional terms can be added easily to make the curve conform, least squares computation is easier, and standard errors of the parameters are simpler to calculate. Since all equations are empirical, it is easier for the agronomist and economist to choose a model than it is to find an average response curve that is reliable for a range of climatic and antecedent soil and cropping conditions. Paschal and French (1956) applied the Spillman equation to a number of experiments with corn and calculated the most profitable rate of N application for various prices of fertilizer N and corn. Fortunately, the farmer can miss the most profitable rate of N application by 20 to 40 pounds per acre and not suffer much loss in profit because of the flatness of the upper section of the response curves in Segment B. Paschal and French also point out that at least five rates of N application, distributed well over the response range, are needed to characterize a response curve adequately. Munson and Dolls (1959) discuss forms of response curves dealing largely with Segment B for economic analysis.

Segment C of Fig. 2 depicts a yield depression resulting from the addition of too many increments of N. Obviously, all biological functions should go through an optimum and then decline as the environment becomes oversaturated with a factor whether it be light, water, or nutrients. Some of the obvious causes of yield depression are excess osmotic pressure or salts resulting from overfertilization, lodging of crops such as cereals, and too much vegetative growth at the expense of fruits as in tomatoes, or of roots and sugar as in sugar beets.

Some good reviews of the response of crops to N have been prepared. Henzell (1962) summarized the information available on tropical and subtropical pastures with emphasis on grasslands. Van Schreven (1958) reviewed some of the information showing responses of legumes to fixed N. Many species of legumes do not associate with *Rhizobia,* or the strains of *Rhizobia* are not effective N fixers. Such legumes respond to fixed N like nonlegumes. For example, Allos and Bartholomew (1955) found that of six legumes tested only soybeans failed to give a yield response to N^{15} tagged $(NH_4)_2SO_4$ used in solution cultures in vermiculite. In some areas of the U. S., field beans, snap beans, and soybeans are fertilized profitably with N.

Growth analysis, a term commonly used in the British Commonwealth for the physiological analyses of yield, helps one to understand how N influences yield. Watson (1952) reviewed the extensive literature on this subject and Donald (1963) has compiled recent information with respect to competition within and between species. According to these concepts, dry weight accumulation, which is basically net photosynthesis, is broken into leaf area (LA) and the average net assimilation rate (NAR) per unit of leaf area. Net assimilation is commonly measured by change in dry weight in an interval of time, but more modern methods employ measurements of CO_2 exchange. The product of LA and NAR equals the increase in dry matter for a given period of time. LA and NAR are not independent. As LA increases, top leaves shade the lower leaves and reduce their assimilation rate. Increasing the amount of N available to the plant, when N is initially deficient, will produce a much greater LA and may increase the NAR, too, until self-shading becomes a factor. Donald (1963) calls the leaf area associated with maximum total net assimilation rate, the critical leaf area. The critical leaf area or any other LA divided by the land area is the critical leaf area index or LAI, respectively.

Watson (1947, 1952) maintains that N fertilization affects yield predominantly through its effect on LA or LAI and effects on NAR are of

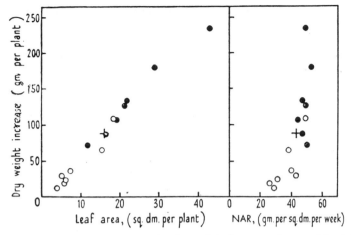

Fig. 6. The effect of N fertilization on the dry weight increase of mangolds at Rotham-sted during an experimental period, and the relation of this increase to leaf area and to net assimilation rate per unit of leaf area (NAR). ○-plots unfertilized with N. ●-plots fertilized with $(NH_4)_2SO_4$. From Watson (1947).

secondary importance. As can be seen in Fig. 6 copied from Watson's 1947 paper, N increased the yields of mangolds through its beneficial effects on both LA and NAR.

Another concept introduced by Watson is that of the leaf area dura-tion (LAD or D), the weekly sum of leaf areas for the weeks the crop is grown. Humphries and French (1963) showed that in potato plants grown in pots, where there was little competition for light among plants, dry weight accumulation was a function of LAD. One gram of dry matter was produced for each 3 to 4 dm²-weeks of leaf area. For 0- and 2.8-g applications of N per pot the LAD up to harvest was 96 and 595 dm²-weeks, respectively. The usefulness of this concept depends on the constancy of NAR, a condition not realized in thick stands of crops be-cause of self-shading.

Table 1 shows some of the data (Goodman, 1963) recently collected in three English field experiments with sugar beets, one of the most difficult crops to fertilize with N because of the deleterious effects of too much N on purity and sugar content of the juice. In these experiments, N in-

Table 1. Effect of nitrogen fertilization on some yield and physiological characteristics of sugar beets grown at three locations in England. Adapted from Goodman (1963).

	Location					
	Holbeach		Stanford		Rothamsted	
	No N	N	No N	N	No N	N
Clean beets (T/acre)*	21.2	20.9	16.8	19.6	19.8	23.5
Sugar (%)	14.0	13.6	15.6	15.3	15.8	15.7
Sugar yield (cwt/acre)†	59.2	57.7	52.4	60.0	62.6	73.8
Leaf area index duration, weeks	28.7	33.2	21.0	26.1	19.8	34.7
NAR (g/dm² /week)	0.62	0.59	0.74	0.67	0.57	0.52

* Long ton (2240 lb. avoir.).   † British cwt (112 lb. avoir.).

creased the leaf area index duration (sum of the weekly leaf area indexes) but a yield increase did not always result. The correlation coefficient of dry matter yield and leaf area index duration was 0.65. Note in Table 1 the slight drop in average NAR, presumably due to self-shading of leaves, resulting from N fertilization.

One effect of too much N is the development of excessive leaf area in an indeterminate crop like sugar beets with a consequent drop in sugar accumulation. R. E. Campbell and F. G. Viets (unpublished data) found that high rates of N on sugar beets caused the NAR to drop to almost zero before harvest in the autumn because of the self-shading resulting from too much foliage.

Growth analysis explains a plant's dry matter response to N fertilizers in two ways: (1) greater leaf area, and (2) an increased NAR per unit of leaf surface until self-shading reduces the assimilation rate of lower leaves. Maximum development of leaf area by midsummer when solar radiation is most intense and of greatest duration is important for yield in some spring-seeded crops grown in mid and high latitudes. This applies to crops such as corn, sorghum, and cotton that develop leaf area slowly if N is deficient.

V. TOTAL PLANT NEEDS FOR NITROGEN

If the plant's total need for N could be accurately predicted, fertilizer practice would be simplified at least to the extent that the left side of the equation

$$\text{Total N uptake} = \text{Available soil N} + X(\text{fertilizer applied})$$

would be known. In this equation available soil N is defined as that which the plant can absorb from soil sources during growth, and X is a variable availability factor that must be applied to the fertilizer rate since plants almost never recover all of the N applied. However, total N uptake cannot generally be accurately forecast because N in the roots is seldom known and total yield of the crop is seldom predictable, being subject to climatic and cultural conditions and to other edaphic factors besides N supply.

O. W. Willcox, in a series of papers and books on a science he called Agrobiology, proposed that all crops grown under optimum conditions with adequate fertilizer and completing a single growth cycle would absorb 318 pounds of N per acre. See Black and Kempthorne (1954a) for 12 literature citations to the work of Willcox. Black and Kempthorne (1954a, b) and White and Black (1954) effectively demolished this concept of the "N constant" on theoretical and experimental grounds. A better basis for arriving at the theoretical N uptake of crops under optimum conditions of moisture and supply of other nutrients might consider total solar radiation, photosynthetic efficiency of the leaves, and the experimental determination of the minimum concentration of total plant N that would permit the theoretical accumulation of dry weight. Such studies are in progress but have not been published. The alternative is

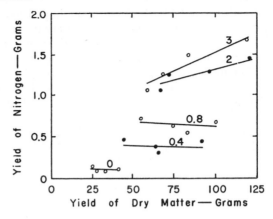

Fig. 7. Yield of N vs. yield of dry matter of two varieties of corn and two of sorghum grown with the indicated grams of added N per pot. From White and Black (1954).

to make use of experimentally determined values of N content, both concentrations and total, in relation to total dry matter or yield of marketable product obtained in field experiments.

Rules of thumb for estimating N uptake based on yield have been proposed, such as 90 pounds of N in the above-ground parts of corn producing 3360 pounds of grain (60 bushels) per acre and 100 pounds of N in cabbage plants producing 15 tons of heads per acre. These estimates are based on total analysis of plants that had these yields. The usefulness of these single values in predicting N uptakes at other yield levels depends on the constancy of composition with respect to yield. In other words, does corn yielding 180 bushels an acre absorb twice as much N as 90-bushel corn? This is the question now to be examined.

Willcox also proposed the "inverse yield-nitrogen law" in which the higher the yield (Y) the lower the nitrogen content (N). Thus, $Y = K/N$, wherein K was the "nitrogen constant." Offhand, this appears to be a reasonable relation when one compares a series of different crops grown on the same soil and fertilized alike. A crop, like wheat, that produces relatively low yields of dry matter contains a higher percent N than a crop that produces high yields of dry matter like sugarcane (Willcox, 1954). White and Black (1954) point out that these inverse yield-N% relations are obtained when the supply of soil or fertilizer N is severely limiting. In their comparisons of 2 varieties of corn and 2 of sorghum (Fig. 7) the yield of dry matter was independent of the yield of N when no N or 2 low rates were added, respectively; but when higher rates of N were added, the yield of N increased with increases in yield for each of the 2 rates. They further show that this inverse yield-N% relation for low rates of N applications exists only with the mobile NO_3 or NH_4 (which is rapidly oxidized to NO_3) nutrients, which can be almost completely removed from the soil by cropping, and that such inverse relations do not occur for the relatively nonmobile elements like Ca, P, and K.

When the N supply is varied over a wide range from a severely limiting to a luxurious supply, a variable concentration of N relative to dry weight is usually found. On the basis of a postulated S-shaped (sigmoidal) curve between total N absorbed and total dry weight production,

Steenbjerg (1954) depicted a U-shaped curve when N percentage was plotted against dry matter production. He claims that the full S- and U-shaped curves are obtained only when the basic treatment or check involves extreme deficiency. In the author's experience with very N-deficient desert or semi-desert soils brought under irrigation, the complete S- and U-shaped curves for N are seldom found. Studies with 'Double Dwarf White Sooner' milo (grain sorghum) showed that the total N contained in all above-ground parts at harvest was a slightly concave-upward function of the total yield. Functions with this shape will occur when the total N% increases with yield. The milo demonstrates a case of linear increase of N% with increasing yield as shown in Fig. 8. These data were obtained in 1953 and 1956 on plots fertilized with 3 N sources applied at rates of 0, 40, 80, and 160 pounds of N per acre. Yields of grain ranged from 2080 to 7655 pounds per acre (41.6 to 153.1 bushels per acre) (Boawn et al., 1960a). Another example of N uptake increasing faster than yield for a crop in which all the top is harvested is shown in Fig. 9. The data are for total yields of coastal Bermuda-grass grown at College Station, Texas, in each of 4 years and fertilized annually with 0, 200, 400, and 600 pounds of N per acre (Fisher and Caldwell, 1959). Only the curve for 1957 shows any tendency to be U-shaped; all others show an increase in N percentage as the yield increases over a broad range of values.

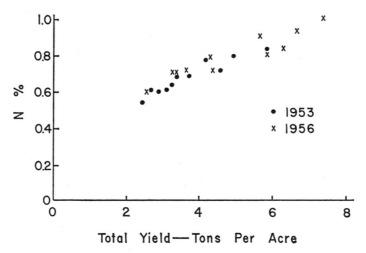

Fig. 8. The N% of the total top of milo increased linearly with the yield of total top, which was controlled by the amount of N applied at Prosser, Wash. From Boawn et al. (1960a).

New data on sugarcane also illustrates that N content increases as the yield increases. Fig. 10 depicts the average N content-dry matter relations of 2 varieties of cane grown for 24 months or longer with 5 rates of N ranging from 25 to 625 pounds per acre at each of 4 locations in the Hawaiian Islands (Stanford and Ayers, 1964). As yield was increased by N fertilization, the amount of N per ton increased. The yield of variety 'H49-3533' was not depressed by N application beyond 225 pounds

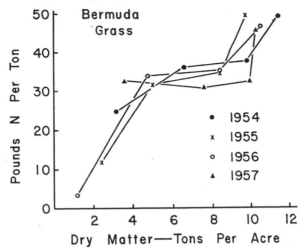

Fig. 9. Nitrogen concentration in Bermuda grass hay increased as total yield of grass was increased by N fertilization at College Station, Texas. Data from Fisher and Caldwell (1959).

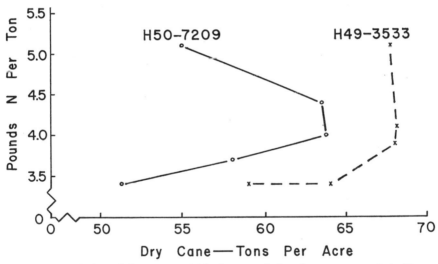

Fig. 10. The relation of dry matter yield of two varieties of sugarcane to their N contents in Hawaii (Stanford and Ayers, 1964).

per acre but the plants did take up N in excess of their needs for maximum yield. The yield of the other variety was depressed by high rates of N which accounts for the backswing of the curve at high N rates. Stanford and Ayers (1964) found that about 4 pounds of N per ton of cane was the minimum N content associated with 98% of maximum yield, and that this "internal requirement was independent of variety and location." This internal N requirement amounts to about 2 pounds of N per ton of millable cane (without leaves ready for the mill). They give a curve for determining the N requirement of cane grown for shorter periods, the usual practice outside of the Hawaiian Islands. For cane grown 12 months, the requirement is about 7 pounds per ton for a 98% yield.

Thus far, the discussion has dealt with total N uptake in relation to total dry weight of tops. Another relation is that between total N in the crop and the yield of marketable crop, e.g., tons of sugar beets or bushels of grain. The marketable yield is known much more often than the total dry matter production. Most fertilizer tables are based on yield of marketable crop. Under extreme N deficiency the yield of tubers, seed, or fruit is often relatively smaller than the total dry weight. For example, under extreme N deficiency there may be a wheat plant without heads or corn without ears. The marketable yield-N application relationships are more likely to fit the S-shaped curves and consequent U-shaped curves of N composition vs. marketable yield than curves based on the whole plant top.

The relationships of total N content to grain yield of corn are shown in Figs. 11 and 12. In Fig. 11 the grain yields ranged from 17.8 to 124.0 bushels an acre. This wide range in yield was due to differences in residual N in the soil resulting from differences in N application to the four preceding crops in the rotation. As far as known, N was the only nutrient limiting yield on this very N-deficient irrigated soil. The left half of the U-shaped curve of composition vs. yield was obtained. Under conditions of extreme N deficiency and low yield, 2.37 pounds of N were in the top per 100 pounds of grain produced. With better N supply and higher yields, the total N content of tops per 100 pounds of grain dropped to about 1.4 pounds. Nitrogen is used very inefficiently for grain production at very low yield levels. Fig. 12 shows data from another experiment (Boawn et al., 1963) illustrating the full range of relationships that may

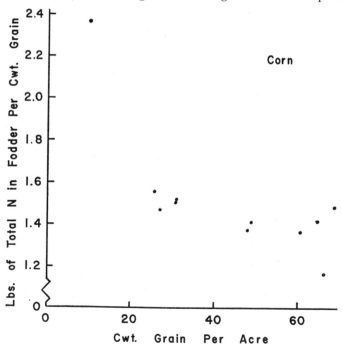

Fig. 11. Inefficient use of total N in the top of the corn plant in production of grain at low levels of grain yield is shown in this data from Boawn et al. (1960a).

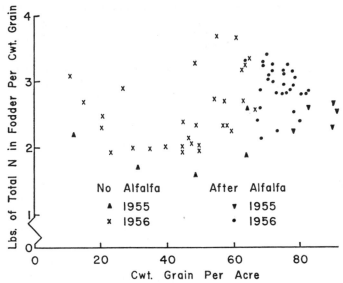

Fig. 12. The relationship of total N in the tops of corn per 100 pounds of grain to grain yield resulting from various rates of N application to corn at Prosser, Washington.

be obtained. In this experiment, corn was grown in 1955 with five rates of applied N on a virgin area of N-deficient brown soil and on an adjacent plot that had grown alfalfa for the three preceding years. The following year (1956) the 1955 plots were again subdivided and corn was grown again with N rates varying from zero to 400 pounds per acre. Grain yields at maturity and total N in the plants at the silage stage were measured. Without a preceding crop of alfalfa on the N-deficient soil, the relation of total N in the plant per cwt. of grain to grain yield was definitely like a U in both 1955 and 1956. With alfalfa preceding corn, all corn yields ranged from 114 to 163 bushels an acre. There was little relation of N composition to yield. It is apparent that the total N in the plant top per cwt. of grain was highly variable and ranged from 1.57 to 3.68 pounds per cwt. Both high and very low yields always have more absorbed N per unit of yield than do those in the middle of the yield range. Thus, the N required in the tops per bushel at the 40-cwt yield level of grain (70 bushels) cannot be linearly extrapolated to the 80-cwt (140 bushel) level. N intake will have to be perhaps 3 or 4 times as much instead of twice.

Some examples for other crops can be cited. Heilman et al. (1961) found that total N absorbed per ton of marketable cabbage increased from 8.15 to 9.47 pounds per ton as the yield increased from 13.8 to 26.2 tons per acre by N fertilization. For sugar beets total N in tops and storage roots per ton of beets can be calculated from the data of Boawn et al. (1960a). These were good quality beets containing about 18% sugar. A root yield of 13.9 tons per acre was obtained without N fertilizer and the plants contained 4.47 pounds of N per ton of roots. With increasing rates of N application, root yields increased to 29.3 tons per acre and the absorbed N per ton of roots increased curvilinearly with increase in yield to 8.97 pounds per ton. From the data of MacKenzie et al. (1957) on sugar beets grown in the Imperial Valley, California, total N uptake per ton of beets ranged from 8.84 to 14.7 pounds per ton. Beets contained 14 to 16% sugar and these low sugar contents reflect the higher N status of the beets. Higher N contents per ton were associated with higher root yields. These values for beets may be compared with the value of 7.67 pounds of N per ton of roots (15 tons of beets containing 115 pounds of N in the tops and roots) commonly used as a basis for fertilizer recommendations.

As a disappointing summary, it can be stated that the total N requirement of a crop cannot be accurately predicted for two reasons. The first is that total yield cannot be accurately predicted and N supply itself is often a factor in determining that total yield. The second reason is that the relationship of N content to yield is a curve often having the shape of a U. The portion of this curve of interest to agronomists is the right-hand side associated with high yields where the N content needed per increment of product is rising steeply. With high yields and the higher N contents associated with them, other factors such as supply of other nutrients begin to make themselves felt. Difficulties in determining how much of the N absorbed represents luxury consumption become greater. Reduced competition for N within the plant, discussed in Section VIII, contributes to the poorer efficiency of N in the plant at high yield and high N levels. So knowledge of the plant's total N requirement (beyond a crude estimate) is not very helpful in solving the N equation postulated at the beginning of this section. Definitely, more information is needed on the minimum N composition needed in plants to produce the high yield levels that can be obtained when all production factors are optimum. For example, plenty of data exist on corn that yielded 100 bushels an acre. Where are the data on 250- or 300-bushel corn?

One byproduct, perhaps the most important practical point in some countries, emerges from this discussion. The plant produces usable dry matter most efficiently when it suffers a mild (but not an extreme) deficiency of absorbed N. This efficiency has merit in agricultural economies poor in N if the product meets minimum nutritional standards with respect to protein.

VI. THE RATE OF N UPTAKE

The rate of N uptake depends on the kind of plant, the developmental stage, the N supply in the soil and the factors affecting its availability, and finally and perhaps most important, on the total N uptake for the final dry weight produced. The latter, for a given variety or species, depends on a host of climatic and nutritional factors among which the N supply itself is one as discussed earlier. A large amount of data is available for a number of crops gathered laboriously by harvesting plants at frequent intervals and determining their dry weights and mineral contents. Often, plants are fractionated into their component parts: leaves, stems, grain, etc. Because of the difficulties of sampling woody perennials much more data is available for annuals and herbaceous perennials. Loehwing (1951) has discussed mineral accumulation of plants in relation to ontogeny.

The accumulation curve of N plotted against time is usually flatly sigmoidal or S-shaped but often is almost linear until the plant approaches maturity. The concave-upward portion of the curve in the juvenile period is frequently missed because sampling is not initiated soon enough. The N uptake curve thus has the same general shape as curves for dry or green weight accumulation and growth curves in general. However, the time curves of accumulation of N, like those for P and K, are less sigmoidal than the dry weight curves because of the early high rates of intake of these elements compared to dry weight accumulation.

When plants are grown with an ample supply of N, the absorption of N and the accumulation of green weight run parallel for a long time, i.e., N percent on a green weight basis does not change. Bakhuyzen (1937) showed this constancy for wheat until shooting and van Dobben (1961) showed it for wheat and poppies until the beginning of ripening. The N percent on a fresh weight basis begins to drop when cell walls begin to thicken according to these authors.

However, plants are seldom grown with an ample supply of N throughout their whole life cycle. The N supply from soil and fertilizer sources is usually greatest at seeding and gradually diminishes as plants develop. The result is that the N percentages on both a green and a dry weight basis decline as the plant grows. The decline in N content on a dry weight basis is apparent when the total N accumulated is plotted against dry weight accumulation, each in percent of its total, for successive periods of growth (Fig. 13). Data for corn are from Sayre (1948) and show the relative accumulation of N and dry weight of corn at 6-day intervals in Ohio grown, presumably, with the only N source being mineralization of soil organic matter. The total N uptake was 141 pounds per acre and was almost linear with time. Had the corn been N fertilized, the uptake of N relative to accumulation of dry weight early in the season

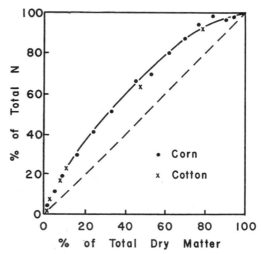

Fig. 13. The relative rates of accumulation of total N and dry matter in the tops of corn (Sayre, 1948) and cotton (Olson and Bledsoe, 1942) sampled at successive periods of growth from left to right. The broken line indicates equal rates of accumulation of N and dry matter.

would have perhaps been even greater. The method of plotting used here is that used by Bakhuyzen (1937, Fig. 26), using the data of Hornberger (1882), to show that N accumulated faster than dry weight of corn. Hanway (1962b) showed that corn grown in Iowa on rotation plots where N was not limiting had accumulated about 65% of its N at silking when only 44% of the dry weight had accumulated (see Fig. 15). The data of Jordan et al. (1950) from Mississippi, plotted like the data in Fig. 13, show accumulation of N relative to dry weight for corn (12,000 plants per acre) prior to tasseling, but an equal ratio from then on to maturity. Rates of N application were zero and 120 pounds per acre, grain yields were 14.3 and 81.8 bushels per acre, and total N uptake was 29.5 and 117.1 pounds per acre, respectively.

Nitrogen uptake for cotton in Georgia (Olson and Bledsoe, 1942) in relation to dry weight accumulation plotted in Fig. 13 shows a pattern almost identical to the corn of Sayre's study. Fig. 14 shows that the rate of N accumulation for Kennebec potatoes in Maine in relation to dry weight was greater for those fertilized with 120 pounds of N an acre than for those unfertilized with N. In this study of Carpenter (1963), tuber yields did not increase when more than 75 pounds of N was applied. So luxury consumption of N occurred on plots getting 120 pounds of N. Total N uptake in tops and tubers was 27.65 and 145.4 pounds per acre for 0 and 120 pounds of applied N per acre, respectively. Gregory (1952) stated: "In the developing cereal plant grown at different levels of nitrogen, over 90% of the total nitrogen taken up by the plant has been accumulated when the dry weight is only 25% of the final value."

Accumulation of N relative to dry matter in the early ontogeny of the plant is almost universal, and by definition, occurs in all plants that show a decrease in N% as the plant develops. The young plant is succulent, has a high proportion of protoplasm relative to the structural components of cellulose and lignin, and has the capacity to store for future use a large amount of soluble N as amino acids, the acid amides asparagine and/or glutamine depending on the species, and even nitrate. Viets

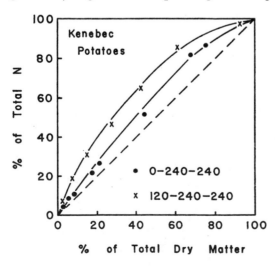

Fig. 14. The accumulation of N relative to accumulation of dry weight (tops and tubers) of potatoes was greater when they were fertilized with N (120 pounds of N, 240 pounds of P_2O_5, and 240 pounds of K_2O an acre) than when no N was applied. Data from Carpenter (1963).

et al. (1946), for example, showed that corn had tremendous capacity to absorb NH_4^+ from solution cultures and combine it into amino acids, asparagine and glutamine, and unknown soluble N compounds in the roots. Asparagine N accumulated twice as fast as glutamine N. There was no effect of the luxury consumption of N on the "true protein" level. Ammonium did not accumulate in the plant until the plant was injured by excessive NH_4^+ nutrition. One of the most spectacular instances of forced N assimilation is the experiment of Vickery et al. (1936) with garden beets. In the fall, the soil was watered with 0.5 M $(NH_4)_2SO_4$ solution daily at the rate of 150 pounds of N per acre. In 18 days the root content of glutamine amide N had tripled and glutamine constituted 5.4% of the dry weight of the root. All of the N absorbed was synthesized into glutamine.

This capacity of the plant to absorb and store N in its youthful stages is of great significance to the later fruiting stages when N is transported from the leaves and stems into the developing grain or storage root. Williams (1955) reviewed the subject of redistribution of mineral elements. The subject is discussed further in Section VIII in this report.

The ability, and perhaps the requirement, of the plant to accumulate N early for subsequent redistribution and use probably accounts for the lack of advantage for slow-release N fertilizers and split or delayed applications of N for field and vegetable crops so often found when the opposite result is expected. Nitrogen is absorbed rapidly by the plant and once absorbed is protected against leaching and denitrification losses to which it might be subject in the soil. The growing plant is a remarkable conserver of N.

Values for daily rates of N uptake for the yields expected may be just as important as values for total N uptake in planning fertilizer programs where time and rate of N application can be advantageously coordinated with the plant's ability to absorb N. Such conditions often occur on sandy soils subject to excessive leaching of soluble N. Tabulated in Table 2 are some reported peak daily rates of N uptake. In many instances the yields reported are much below the yield potential of the crop. As noted in Section V, a yield twice as high as those in Table 2 would require more than twice as much N, and so the peak rates of absorption would be more than double those shown.

VII. THE EFFECT OF N SUPPLY ON PLANT PARTS

That more N increases the top-to-root ratio of plants is well known. That more N increases the proportion of grain to total top in cereal crops is also a common observation. In fact, with severe N deficiency, crops like corn and sorghum may produce no grain at all even though they do have a top. The purpose of this section is to discuss some of these relationships and their possible significance in studies of the response of crops to N and recovery of fertilizer N from soils.

Table 2. Examples of maximum rates and total nitrogen uptake of some crops grown in the field.

Crop	Yield lb./acre		Period	Days	lb./N/ acre/day	Reference
	D.W.	N				
Corn	5,740*	117	Knee high to tassel	21	2.2	Jordan et al. (1950)
Corn	7,140*	141	Jun 26- Aug 28	63	2.15	Sayre (1948)
Corn	8,820*	165	Jun 25 to Jul 11 (prior to tassel)	16	3.0	Chandler (1960)
			Sep 5 to 17 (ear formation)	12	3.0	
Corn	7,980*	180	Jul 2 to 16 (prior to tassel)	14	3.9	Hanway (1962b)
Hops (cones)	2,060	242	Jun 15 to Sep 21	98	2.05	Roberts & Nelson (1961)
Lettuce (heads)	42,750	95	Oct 14 to 21 prior to first harvest	7	3.9	Zink & Yamaguchi (1962)
Soybeans	2,580†	184	87-94 days after planting (flowering)	7	4.4	Hammond et al.(1951)
Potato (tubers) White Rose	39,500	139	65-76 days after planting‡	11	4.07	Lorenz (1947)
Green Mountain	23,220	143	61 to 70 days after planting	10	3.76	Hawkins (1946)
Russet Burbank	30,600	139	81 to 95 days	14	2.71	Jackson & Haddock (1959)
Cotton		134.3	90 to 105 days after planting	15	3.70	Olsen & Bledsoe (1942)
Tobacco (Havana seed)	1,643 air dry leaves	120	40 to 60 days after (topped) transplanting	20	4.0	Morgan & Street (1935)
Pimiento (Perfection)	1,205 dry buds & fruits	82.5	3rd month after transplanting(Jun 28-Jul 28)	30	0.93	Cochran & Olson (1941)

* Dry ear corn = 70 lb./bu.   † At 60 lb./bu.   ‡ Just before tuberization.

A. Effects of N on Root Development and the Top-to-Root Ratio

Accurate measurements of the effect of root development in soils are difficult because of the problem of separating roots from soil. Hence, much of the work on root systems has been done in sand or solution cultures. Such results may not always reflect what happens in soil. Increasing the rate of N application always increases the top-to-root ratio. The absolute amount of roots may be increased or decreased. Meyer and Storck (1927) showed that root weight of oats in sand culture increased as N was increased from 0 to 2 g of $(NH_4)_2SO_4$ per culture, remained the same from 2 to 8 g, then declined as N was further increased. Yields of tops, however, increased almost linearly with N application up to 8 g of $(NH_4)_2SO_4$ after which they declined. (See Black, 1957, for a figure.) Troughton (1957) in his review of the effects of N supply on the roots of grasses states: "In general, it appears that plants grown in conditions where available nitrogen was a factor limiting growth have a well developed root system, but a poorly developed shoot system. Plants grown with an excess of nitrogen exhibit the opposite relative development. The addition of available nitrogen to the nutrient media of plants, which previously had no excess nitrogen, results in an increased growth of both shoot and root and a decrease in the percentage of the plant's weight in the roots, i.e., shoot growth is accelerated to a greater extent than root growth. Further increases produce smaller and smaller increases in root growth until a point is reached where further increases cause a retardation of growth. Thus, the effect of a moderate increase in the nitrogen supply is to increase a plant's root weight compared with that of a plant receiving a lesser supply, but further increases result in the plant having a lower root weight than one receiving a less liberal supply of nitrogen. The nitrogen supply has a similar effect upon the shoot growth in that the response to a unit quantity of nitrogen becomes smaller and smaller but no adverse effects, i.e. retardation in growth due to excess nitrogen, were noted with the concentrations of nitrogen used in the experiments discussed here."

Brouwer (1962b) systematically studied the effect of N on the root and shoot development of corn grown in Hoagland's solution. If the plant had ample nutrients, a constant shoot-to-root ratio was maintained for three weeks. If Hoagland's solution without N was substituted, root growth was accelerated in relation to shoot growth and the shoot-root ratio sharply dropped. If N was supplied to plants that previously had no N in the culture, root growth practically ceased and shoot growth was accelerated until the normal shoot-root ratio of about 3 was restored. Brouwer (1962b) explains the effects of N on absolute and relative root growth by a hypothesis of competition between the top and the root for N (he includes all essential mineral elements) and for carbohydrates. The amount of light (intensity and duration) is important, too, in affecting these competitive relations because of its effect on the carbohydrate supply. In the highly N-deficient plant, excess carbohydrate is present in both the shoot and root because of retarded protein synthesis and growth. When N is supplied, root growth is accelerated first because it is nearest the N supply. If enough N is supplied, the top starts to grow and being nearer the carbohydrate supply grows faster than the roots. If N is presented in luxury amounts, the tops use so much of the carbohydrate for top growth that there is little or none left over for translocation to the roots. So root growth is depressed. Auxin production, which is known to be correlated with N content, would also have the effect of stimulating top growth and depressing root growth. Brouwer (1962a) believes, however, that nutrition and temperature are more important in controlling distribution of dry matter among plant parts than is hormonal activity.

When N is deficient and N fertilizers are banded near the seed or a part of the root system, roots grow faster where the N is placed. Grunes (1959) summarized the evidence that shows that N placement often increases the availability of P and other fertilizers placed in the same band. The increased absorption of associated fertilizers can be due to any one or combination of increased root surfaces, increased metabolic activity of the roots, and chemical effects of the N fertilizer on pH of the soil and solubility of the associated nutrient. Viets et al. (1953) showed that banding $ZnSO_4$ and N together caused substantial Zn uptake by beans, but that there was little Zn uptake from $ZnSO_4$ when the N was broadcast or omitted. Duncan and Ohlrogge (1958) found that corn roots proliferated in bands of P and N fertilizers placed together, but roots did not concentrate in bands containing only N. Wilkinson and Ohlrogge (1962) showed that soybean roots grown with a high level of N had higher levels of extractable growth hormones than roots grown at lower N levels. Recently, Cole et al. (1963) demonstrated that the rate of P uptake from solutions by intact corn plants was proportional to the total N content of the roots.

The frequently noted discrepancies in results of the effect of N on the growth of root systems and that of N placement on individual roots appear to be explainable with the hypothesis of competition of the root and shoot for carbohydrate and N. For example, Brouwer and Leon (1962) showed that N in solution had no effect on the growth of individual crown roots of corn developing in long glass columns when the total plant was adequately supplied with N. Enough N and carbohydrates were translocated from the shoot for maximum root growth. When the whole plant was N deficient, N supplied to an individual root had an accelerating effect on the growth of that root because carbohydrate was sufficient.

Troughton (1957) concluded that ammonium sources of N are more deleterious to root development than nitrate sources. In such comparisons, pH is frequently not controlled and can be a complicating factor. However, there is a biochemical foundation for this behavior. Most of the absorbed ammonium is metabolized in the root thus using sugars and organic acids, whereas most of the nitrate absorbed is translocated to the leaves before reduction and incorporation into carbon intermediates. Hence, the demand for carbohydrates is set up in different parts of the plant.

The effect of N in increasing top-root ratios of plants may explain some reports that efficiency of N recovery increases with the rate of N application. Boawn et al. (1960a) and Viets (1960) are examples of such reports, which seem to contradict other studies in which the percentage of N recovered from N application decreased with increasing rates of application. In the reports cited, the percentage of N recovered was based only on the N in the tops of the plants and involved this calculation:

$$\% \ N \ recovery = \frac{N \ uptake - N \ uptake \ of \ no\text{-}N \ treatment}{N \ applied} \times 100$$

All plots were cropped after N fertilization ceased until the N yield of crops on the fertilized plots was the same as that of the untreated plots. If N fertilization increased the ratio of N in the tops to that in the roots, then the apparent N recovery could increase as the N rate increases with this method of evaluation and calculation.

B. Effects of N on the Relation of Marketable Product to Total Top Dry Weight

Many examples of an increase in the proportion of marketable product to total top due to N application have been reported. In these examples, the N supply ranged from very deficient to an adequate supply for maximum or nearly maximum yield. Hanway (1962a) found that differences in fertility level (largely difference in N supply) had some effect on the distribution of dry matter among the grain, and other plant fractions of corn. With corn yielding only 19 bushels per acre, 40% of the total dry weight was grain. For 114-bushel corn, 45% of the dry weight was grain. Jordan et al. (1950) reported that 17.6% of the total dry weight was grain when no N fertilizer was used, and 50.7% was grain when 120 pounds of N was used. This Mississippi study was conducted with 12,000 plants per acre. The grain:stover ratios were 1:4.67, 1:1.42, and 1:0.97 for applications of 0, 60, and 120 pounds of N per acre, respectively. With grain sorghum, Boawn et al. (1960a) found that the dry weight of grain was 42.6, 52.2, 53.8, and 57.2% of the total top dry weight when 0, 40, 80, and 160 pounds of N per acre were used. For cabbage, Heilman et al. (1961) reported that the dry weight of marketable cabbage was 48, 53, 57, and 57% of the total top dry weight when 0, 60, 120, and 180 pounds of N an acre were applied.

The low ratio of grain to total dry weight associated with N deficiency is responsible in part for the high total N uptake per unit of grain noted in Section V and shown in Figs. 11 and 12.

C. Effect of Delayed N Application on Yield and Plant Parts

In studies of the time of application of N to cereals, on very N-deficient soils, yields of grain are often greater when a portion of the N is applied when the plants are about half grown. The usual explanation is that the portion of the N applied late was not subject to as much loss from leaching or denitrification. However, there is another possible explanation. Van Dobben (1958)* claims that delayed application of N to wheat on N-deficient soils increases the yield of grain much more than the yield of straw. A higher grain:straw ratio results. The apparent effect as far as grain yield is concerned is a higher efficiency of the N applied. In addition, van Dobben claims that the wheat leaves stay green longer (senesence is delayed), and the plant is less apt to lodge. The effect of delayed N application in increasing the grain-to-stover ratio of corn is apparent in experiments from Nebraska where sidedressing of N has proven to be more effective in increasing grain yields and total N uptake than equal amounts of N applied in the spring or the preceding fall (Olson et al., 1964). In 14 experiments with irrigated corn, sidedressing of N increased the grain-to-stover ratio (up to 1.4) more than fall or spring applications of the same amount of N. Without fertilizer N, the ratio was 1.0.

---

* Additional information from a personal communication of material to be presented at Twelfth Easter School, University of Nottingham, 1965.

VIII. STRESS OR COMPETITION FOR N WITHIN THE PLANT

In Section III the symptoms of N deficiency in the plant such as reduced growth, death of leaves, and reduced chlorophyll content were discussed. These visual color and morphological symptoms are a severe
manifestation of the competition for or stress for N that goes on within
the plant's organs as the plant grows through the successive stages of its
ontogeny. The competition for N and carbohydrate between root and
shoot and the effects of N supply on root to shoot ratios, discussed in Section VII, are a part of this internal competition. Another part of the
competition in the shoot is that for N between the stems, leaves, pods, or
other floral parts, and the developing seeds or fruits. Bakhuyzen (1937)
summarized the literature on this subject and published comprehensive
data on N redistribution in Hard Federation wheat grown under constant conditions of temperature, humidity, and nutrition in sand cultures
under continuous Mazda light.

As pointed out in Section VI, the plant in its juvenile stages accumulates N faster than dry matter. This relative accumulation of N depends on the N supply and factors affecting its availability. N accumulated
early in stems and leaves is translocated to flowers and seeds as they
develop. The process is the reverse of that in germinating seeds. Fig. 15,
taken from Hanway (1962b), shows the accumulation of N by corn and
the distribution of this N in various plant parts as a function of time.
After grain formation starts, the grain takes the equivalent of all of the
N subsequently absorbed from the soil and all of the N lost from other
parts of the plant. At harvest, the grain contained 64% of the N absorbed.

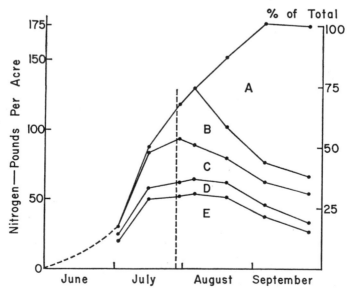

Fig. 15. The uptake and distribution of N among parts of corn plants as a function of
time. A = grain; B = cobs, silks, husks, shank, and ear shoots; C = stalk and tassel; D
is leaf sheaths; and E = leaves. From Hanway (1962b).

Chandler (1960), Sayre (1948), and Jordan et al. (1950) have presented similar data for corn. Hanway (1962c) showed that all leaves on the corn plant lost N (N as percent of dry weight) progressively with time after silking, that N-deficient plants lost N from their leaves faster than those plants with a near adequate supply, and that the lower leaves on the plant tend to lose N faster than those higher on the plant. The characteristic N deficiency symptom of loss of chlorophyll along the mid-rib of the corn leaf starts on the lowermost leaves of the plant and progresses to higher leaves on the stalk. These decreases in leaf N content are paralleled with similar N declines in the leaf sheaths and internodes of the stalk.

Viets et al. (1954) used the occurrence of N deficiency symptoms on leaves of corn as a quantitative index of yield loss from N deficiency. As shown in Fig. 16, the final grain yield was about 170 bushels per acre, if there were no leaves showing N deficiency symptoms at silking. For each leaf per plant showing N deficiency symptoms at silking, there was a yield loss of about 15 bushels per acre. The N content of the index leaf at silking (sixth leaf from plant base) associated with maximum yield in another experiment was about 2.8 to 2.9% N. By regression analysis of leaf N content on number of leaves showing N deficiency symptoms, it was shown that N content of index leaves could be as low as 2.28% without visible evidence of N deficiency. Leaves with N contents between 2.8 or 2.9 and 2.28% N might, therefore, be regarded as having incipient

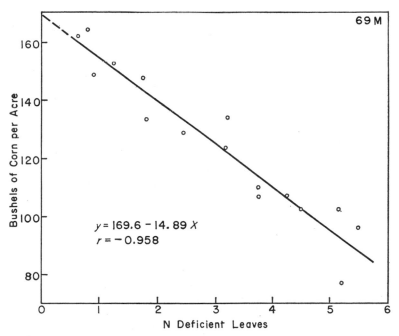

Fig. 16. Yield of corn is reduced about 15 bushels an acre for each leaf on the plant at tasseling showing the characteristic tip burn of N deficiency. Plants without visible evidence of N deficiency on the leaves at tasseling may yield 50 or 60 bushels less than plants with sufficient N. Graph from data of Viets et al. (1954).

deficiency or "hidden hunger" and be associated with a substantial, but unknown, yield loss. These results were obtained on irrigated corn at a plant population of 17,500 per acre differentially fertilized with three rates of N from each of five different chemical sources.

Many examples of the internal transport of N could be cited. For example, Hammond et al. (1951) found that total N content of soybean plants increased 48 pounds per acre between the 87th day and maturity at 135 days, but the N content of the seeds and pods increased 121 pounds and the remainder of the plant decreased 73 pounds in the same period. The pods also lost N to the seeds, dropping from 18 pounds on the 108th day to 7 pounds at seed maturity. At maturity, distribution of the total N was 4% in the stems and roots, 12% in the leaves, 4% in the pods, and 80% in the grain. In Russet Burbank potatoes, Jackson et al. (1959) found that 45% of the N in potato tops was lost between the 95 and 152nd day after planting and translocated to the tubers. At harvest, the tubers contained 70% of the N that had been absorbed. Hawkins (1946) reported that two-thirds of the N absorbed by Green Mountain potatoes was translocated to the tubers. Depletion of N from leaves is often followed by abscission of the leaves, the lower and older ones being the first affected. Translocation of N from leaves before leaf fall is a common occurrence in deciduous species. Bakhuyzen (1937, p. 362) refers to Rippel's rule (Rippel, 1921) that "maintains that in all plant species yellowing leaves approach the same nitrogen loss, amounting to 60 to 80% of their total maximum nitrogen content and leaving only the indigestible proteins of the type of nucleoproteins in the yellowing leaf."

The examples cited above are from field experiments in which the soil N supply declined with time. The same redistribution of N occurs even in plants like wheat grown under constant environmental and nutritional conditions (Bakhuyzen, 1937, Fig. 14). He grew 'Hard Federation' wheat to maturity in 53 days under continuous light and studied the changes in N content of the leaves with time. All plants had five leaves, numbered from the base. Total N was measured in each leaf. The first leaf had a maximum N content on the 15th to 19th day, the second had maximum N on the 13th day, the fourth and fifth leaves increased in N to the 31st day (day before flowering) and then lost N. All leaves lost N after flowering, but the change was greatest in the fifth (upper) leaf. It lost 1.52 mg or 65% of its maximum N content between flowering and maturity of the grain. The total tops continued to increase in N up to maturity.

The evidence for internal competition for N has come from studies of the relative distribution of N among plant parts as a function of time and stage of development. Williams (1955) set forth the view that the cells of young meristems (young leaves, buds, developing seeds) actively compete against the older cells of senescent tissues for N. He postulates that in plants well nourished with N it is easier for cells of the young meristems to get N from the older leaf, stalk, and root tissues than it is to absorb N from the soil. This view is supported by evidence that older tissues lose N as the plant ages regardless of the external N supply. Bakhuyzen (1937) and associates advanced the same arguments many years before in their discussion of N distribution in the developing wheat plant. Williams

(1955) cites the work of Petrie (1937) who found that the loss of N from leaves of wheat to the grain ranged from 82 to 86% of the total leaf N for four different levels of N supply. In sudangrass, which produces much less seed in relation to dry weight than wheat does, export of N from the leaves was decreased as the external N supply increased. Export of N from the leaves was 67, 65, and 43% of the total leaf N for 3 increasing rates of external N supply. Williams (1948) believes that the demand set up by the growing cells of the shoot and root is just as important as the external supply of N in determining the rate of absorption by the plant.

The net loss of N from leaves to the developing inflorescence is not a one-way path; some N can be entering the leaf as more is being withdrawn. The cytoplasmic proteins of the leaf are continuously being hydrolyzed and resynthesized as evidenced by the work of Vickery et al. (1939) and Hevesy et al. (1940) with N^{15}. For example, Hevesy and co-workers showed that 12% of the protein in sunflower leaves, synthesized before N^{15} (in $(NH_4)_2SO_4$) was added to the culture solution, was renewed within 12 days after the tracer was added to the solution.

The view that redistribution of N in the plant is the result of competition among meristems and tissues differing in metabolic activity has rested on comparisons of tissue contents as they change with time and variations in the N supply and demand (topping of tobacco) and not on direct evidence that the cells in fact have different abilities to accumulate N. Evidence for this competitive ability may be forthcoming when more studies of N accumulation by shoot cells are conducted. Smith and Epstein (1964) have shown that discs and 0.3 mm-wide strips of leaf tissue of corn are able to accumulate Rb from solutions along the cut edges for periods up to at least 60 hours. They report that leaf cellular absorption of Rb is very similar to absorption of Rb by excised barley roots with respect to linearity with time, accumulation ratio up to one hour of absorption, and temperature dependence. Long ago, Phillis and Mason (1942) showed that discs cut from cotton leaves floated on $Ca(NO_3)_2$ solutions and exposed to sunlight synthesized protein as fast as leaves of intact plants. The accumulation of protein in the leaf discs depended on the concentration of the $Ca(NO_3)_2$ solution, increasing with concentration up to a point and then declining.

Hormonal control of N redistribution through the effect of a hormone on centers of protein synthesis has also been postulated but no direct evidence for this mechanism has been produced. As mentioned earlier, Brouwer (1962b) believes that the principal effects of N on root vs. shoot development can be explained as competition for N and carbohydrate. Nevertheless, some observations are difficult to explain on such a basis. For example, the author (Viets et al., 1947) found that excised leaves of corn with their leaf sheaths in $CaSO_4$ solution hydrolyzed leaf protein and accumulated soluble N compounds at comparable rates whether they were in darkness or in a greenhouse for 9 days. In light, the leaves gained in dry weight and in sugars, whereas in darkness sugars became depleted. Control of protein level in the leaf by some substance translocated from some other part of the plant appeared to be essential. The theory that leaf protein is hydrolyzed and the products translocated to a more active "sink" or tissue fails to explain these results.

For the agronomist, knowledge of N redistribution and stress within the plant and the effect of external N supply on this redistribution is significant. The nutritional quality of seeds and forages can be better understood; the shape of N response curves can be partially explained; and the apparent substitution of one element for another (such as P for N) in producing equivalent yield can perhaps be explained.

That increasing N supply increases the N contents of cereal grains, tubers, storage roots, grasses, and dry forages has been documented so many times that scarcely any additional evidence is needed. Under conditions of extreme N deficiency (desert soil without N fertilizer), Viets and Domingo (1949) found that 18 double-cross corn hybrids averaged only 6.23% protein (N × 6.25) in the grain. The lowest content was 5.69%. With the application of 148 pounds of N per acre, the average protein content of the same hybrids was 8.00%, ranging from 7.31 to 8.81%. Even with the use of this much fertilizer N, the grain contained less protein than good corn which generally contains from 9 to 10% protein. In the cereal grains, low N or protein content is associated with a low ratio of germ to endosperm.

The N content of seeds generally increases most rapidly in the range of rates of N application that will not produce further increases in yield. For example, Hunter and Yungen (1955) showed that yield of corn was near maximum with an application of 120 pounds of N per acre and the grain contained 8.45% protein. An additional 200 pounds of N increased the grain protein to 9.58%, but did not affect yield. Increase in the protein content of feed grains is desirable, but the ratios of amino acids are generally not affected.

Excessive N accumulation in seeds can be deleterious to the quality of pastry wheats (Hunter et al., 1958) and malting barley (Atkins et al., 1955); detrimental to the brewing quality of hop cones (Roberts and Nelson, 1961), to cooking quality of potatoes, and to the purity of the juice of sugar beets. Nitrates never accumulate in seeds and so excess N in the plant does not pose a toxicity problem for livestock. All of these harmful effects are examples of insufficient competition among the plant parts for N.

Shriveled grain is generally higher in protein than plump grain. This, again, is a competition and rate of transport problem. N is accumulated in the developing seed faster than starch. If translocation is inhibited by drouth or the bending of stems (lodging), a shriveled seed high in protein results.

In general, the N content of seeds is less affected by differences in N supply than is that of the straw or stover because the seed is the accumulator of N and the other plant parts are a major source. Under conditions of N deficiency, straw and stover can be extremely low in N. Conversely, their N content can be very high when N supply exceeds the plant's needs. Under luxury supply conditions nitrates often accumulate in stems and leaves. Such accumulation of nitrate is particularly apparent in corn plants without ears. Increased N content of grain and mature vegetative tissues of the plant, as external N supply is increased, accounts for the increasing N uptake per unit of dry matter shown in Figs. 8 and 12.

Competition for N in the plant helps to explain the nature of response curves. Two causes for the concave-downward shape of Segment B of the yield-N response curve are known, and both of them are probably operative at the same time. The first cause is failure of the plant to absorb as high a proportion of the fertilizer N at high rates of application as at low rates. However, roots are remarkably efficient in absorbing all of the NO_3^- and practically all of the exchangeable NH_4^+ from a soil (White and Black, 1954, for example) except at very high rates of fertilizer application. The second cause is the competition among plant organs for and reuse and redistribution of N internally, frequently called elasticity. If there were no elasticity yield would be proportional to N uptake as long as N was the factor limiting yield. The N percentage would remain constant. However, as shown earlier, N percentage generally increases linearly or curvilinearly as yield increases in response to N fertilizer application. The plant is more efficient in production of dry matter with low N supply because of greater internal reuse of N than it is at higher levels of internal supply. Maximizing the internal efficiency of N use results in lower crop yields and a product lower in protein, neither being desirable agronomic goals.

IX. ABSORPTION OF NITROGEN BY ROOTS

Ammonium and NO_3^- ions are very rapidly absorbed by roots, their rates of entry being comparable to those of K^+, Rb^+, Cl^-, and $H_2PO_4^-$. Ions like Ca^{++}, Mg^{++}, and SO_4^{--} enter much more slowly. Comparatively little research has been done on mechanisms of uptake of NH_4^+ or NO_3^-, but the principles developed from research with other ions such as K^+ and $H_2PO_4^-$ are probably applicable.

The first step in absorption is believed to be adsorption on a carrier surface. In the writer's opinion, measurements of cation or anion exchange capacity of the roots are not a measure of this carrier surface. The location of this postulated carrier surface in the cell and its nature are not known with certainty. Transfer or transport of the adsorbed ion into the cell or xylem in higher plants depends on aerobic metabolism. The rate of transport depends on temperature, oxygen, supply of sugars or other energy materials, and the salt status of the roots.

Some ions such as K^+, Br^-, and NO_3^- are or can be absorbed against concentration or activity gradients. Concentration in the expressed root sap is sometimes several hundred times greater than that in the solution around the roots. This process is called accumulation. NO_3^- concentration in roots or stems of plants is usually much higher than that in the soil or culture solution. Hoagland and Broyer (1936) developed techniques for the study of ion absorption by root systems. With barley, they showed that accumulation of NO_3^- in the expressed sap to a concentration manyfold that in the external solution depended on aeration, increased with rising temperatures in the range 6 to 24 or 30°C, and accompanied a loss in root sugars. Much of the NO_3^- accumulated was reduced in the roots after absorption so that the total N absorbed was greater than that found in the roots as NO_3^-. Broyer (1951) later showed that adding glucose to the solution would increase absorption of both K^+ and NO_3^- by excised barley roots. Hoagland and Broyer (1940) found that absorption of NO_3^- was slightly and linearly pH dependent, increasing from about 3.7 to 6 me. per 100 g of fresh roots as solution pH was varied from 3.5 to 7.8.

The effects of NH_4^+ vs. NO_3^- absorption on the external solution and on the internal metabolism of the plant are briefly discussed in Section XIII.

Roots absorb urea faster than either NH_4^+ or NO_3^-. Hirose and Goto (1961) found that urea entered roots of rice in solution culture and could be detected throughout the plant. They could detect no urease activity in the roots. Urea uptake did not suppress K^+ uptake as NH_4^+ did. From this they concluded that urea enters the root by simple diffusion, whereas NH_4^+ competes for the same carrier complex as K^+.

NH_3 as the gas or from solutions of high pH enters roots and leaves very rapidly and is highly toxic.

The rate of absorption of N by the root growing in a porous medium like a soil is probably more dependent on rate of transport to the root surface and rate of root extension than on the absorption ability of the root per se. The movement of NO_3^- in soil is discussed in Chapter 16.

X. FOLIAR FEEDING OF NITROGEN

The N needs of some plants can be effectively and sometimes most economically met by spraying of N salts on the foliage. Urea has been most effective because of its rapid penetration into leaves, half of an application penetrating the leaf in 1 to 6 hours. Wittwer et al. (1963) recently reviewed this subject and emphasized the information available on horticultural crops. Foliar feeding has been most successful on crops when soil fertilization has not given the needed control of N uptake or on crops that are regularly sprayed with micronutrients, insecticides, or fungicides. For example, about 80% of the N applied to pineapple in Hawaii is put on along with Fe and Zn sprays at frequent intervals. Urea, micronutrients, P, and K are often combined with insecticides and applied to the foliage of deciduous orchards at frequent intervals from petal fall to fruit ripening to produce desirable fruit and foliage color. Urea sprays are also used on many market garden (truck) crops. The amount of N applied is often in the range of only 10 to 20 pounds per acre per application. Dependence on foliar feeding of N varies from almost 100% on some pineapple plantations through simple supplementation of the available N supply with tree and truck crops. Most of our protein in fruit and vegetable crops still comes from N that was absorbed from soil.

Foliar feeding of field crops like wheat and corn is also possible but the practice has not been adopted. Foliar feeding has not generally been more effective than soil fertilization, and the high N requirements and low tolerance of foliage to N require many spray operations that are not ordinarily needed. Aerial spraying with NH_4NO_3 or urea shortly before heading of wheat is extensively used in the USSR when N is needed. Wittwer et al. (1963) summarized the tolerances of a number of vegetables and fruit crops to urea sprays. Biuret in urea used for foliar sprays can be toxic. Jones et al. (1955) caution that urea should not contain more than 0.25% biuret when used on citrus.

Absorption of urea, NH_4^+, and NO_3^- into leaves appears to have both passive and active phases similar to absorption by roots. Urea enters the leaf fastest because it is not ionized. Transport of foliar-absorbed materials is first through the phloem. Urea, after hydrolysis, NH_4^+, and NO_3^-, once in the plant, enter into the same metabolic paths as N absorbed by roots. Urea is absorbed more rapidly by leaves at night than in the day, probably because its absorption is favored by high humidity.

Except for the specialized crops and situations noted above, foliar application of N has not had the spectacular success that foliage applications of the micronutrients Zn, Fe, Mn, and Cu have had. A major portion of these elements applied to soils soon become unavailable to plants because of "fixation" which is not the case with N, except to a very minor extent.

XI. TOXICITY OF N FERTILIZERS TO PLANTS

Plants can be damaged by some N carriers unless they are used carefully. This damage is usually traceable to the direct toxicity of NH_3 or to osmotic effects that any concentrated salt solution has in desiccation of plant roots or germinating seeds.

NH_3 toxicity is readily apparent on the foliage of plants when the injection knives of anhydrous NH_3 applicators are out of the soil, as at the ends of rows, and NH_3 strikes the foliage. NH_3 applied to the tops of cotton under a shield at the rate of about 75 pounds per acre has been used successfully for defoliating cotton to expedite picking (*Agricultural Ammonia News*, 1964). Either aqua or anhydrous NH_3 can be toxic to germinating seeds or roots if placed too close to them. Lorenz et al. (1955) found onions to be extremely sensitive to aqua or anhydrous NH_3 on sandy calcareous soils and warned against close placement. NH_3 from either aqua or anhydrous moves farther in soil than NH_4^+ from SO_4^{2-} or NO_3^-. NH_3 toxicity to roots can sometimes occur from rapid hydrolysis of urea in slightly alkaline soils (Cooke, 1962; Court et al., 1962; Brage et al., 1960). Urea containing biuret is very toxic when drilled with seed. NH_3, regardless of its source, is very toxic to cells, and occurs in plant tissue only after extensive damage. Absorbed NH_4^+ is generally metabolized quickly to amino acids or amides.

Any soluble salt placed with the seed can reduce germination, but the extent of damage depends on the amount of rain during germination and the soil moisture content. Hence, extent of damage depends on the season. Damage can occur even though the soluble K or N fertilizer is not in direct contact with the seed. Olson and Dreier (1956) got seedling injury from N fertilizers placed with wheat seed at rates as low as 10 pounds of N an acre in dry years in Nebraska. $CaCN_2$ and aqua ammonia were most harmful, followed by urea, $NaNO_3$, KNO_3, $(NH_4)_2SO_4$, and NH_4NO_3.

Calcium cyanamide has been used as a herbicide, soil sterilant, and defoliant. Although it can be safely used as a N fertilizer in small quantities, it has practically disappeared from the fertilizer market.

XII. THE ACCUMULATION OF NITRATE IN PLANTS

The agronomist's interest in NO_3^- in plants centers on two practical considerations: (1) NO_3^- as an indicator of the N nutritional status of the plant, and (2) NO_3^- as a toxicant to livestock and producer of gas in silos lethal to man and animals. All plants can absorb NO_3^- through their roots, generally preferentially over NH_4^+, and translocate it to the tops. Some NO_3^- reduction occurs in the roots but most of it is translocated to the tops where NO_3^- reduction in the leaves is very active in sunlight (Burstrom, 1943; Bongers, 1958; Hageman and Flesher, 1960). Thus, the NO_3^- reaching the tops represents the excess of absorption over reduction in the root system. Reduction of NO_3^- requires energy and carbohydrate to provide the organic acid skeletons for amino acids and the acid amides. Reduction of NO_3^- in the root, therefore, uses carbohydrates in the roots, and undoubtedly is a factor in increasing the top-root ratios of plants grown at increasing rates of N supply. Finally, the N supply can be so high that root production is absolutely, as well as relatively, decreased.

Nitrate N represents a reserve of unassimilated N in the plant, although the amides and some amino acids are also a part of the reserve. Many methods of foliar analysis and plant tissue testing rest on empirical relations of NO_3^- in stems, petioles, or leaves to yields, response to N fertilizers and to crop quality. Leaves of plants are invariably lower and less variable in NO_3^- than stems or petioles; therefore, petioles are most often used for diagnosis. For example, Ulrich and coworkers (1950, 1959) showed that NO_3—N in petioles of most recently matured leaves of sugar beets should be above 1000 ppm on a dry weight basis up to a month before harvest and should then drop below this level for maximum production of sugar. In cotton, yield reductions are related to the length of time petioles of youngest mature leaves have NO_3—N contents less than 1000 and 2000 ppm (MacKenzie et al., 1963). Testing for NO_3—N has proved useful on many other crops like sugarcane, corn and tree fruits.

Nitrates can accumulate in some kinds of plants, often under adverse growing conditions, to the point that such plants are a hazard to cattle and sheep. Nitrates are reduced to NO_2^- in the rumen. Nitrites can also be produced in hay containing NO_3^- if the hay gets damp. The NO_2^- is absorbed into the blood stream where it oxidizes oxyhemoglobin to methemoglobin, which is incapable of transporting oxygen. Both acute (death) and subacute toxicity is recognized (Crawford and Kennedy, 1960). Annual weeds and grasses and the cereal crops are most likely to have higher amounts of NO_3^- than perennial grasses and legumes (Crawford and Kennedy, 1960; Hanway et al., 1963). Nitrates are higher in stems and petioles than in leaves. Seeds generally contain no NO_3^-. Factors known to favor NO_3^- storage in accumulators are a high N level in the soil and adverse growth conditions such as drouth, shade, cloudy weather, and growth inhibition with herbicides. Nitrates generally decline in plants as they mature. The problem of toxicity has been most acute in the Northern Plains and Cornbelt States. Mayo (1895) drew attention to this problem with drouth-stricken corn in Kansas long ago, and Wyoming scientists pursued extensive studies of plant and soil factors involved (Gilbert et al., 1946; Bradley et al., 1942). Wright and Davison (1964) give a good review of the environmental factors affecting NO_3^- accumulation in plants and the toxicology of NO_3^- and N oxides to man and animals.

The agronomist would like to have a single value for the tolerable level of NO_3^- in forages. Unfortunately, a single value cannot be given. Crawford and Kennedy (1960) and Wright and Davison (1964) point out that the safe level depends on the kind and amount of other feed, rate of consumption, and weight of the animal.

As mentioned earlier, NO_3^- is a storage form of N in the plant and does not usually accumulate unless the total N (or crude protein) level is high. Since total N determinations are routine in many laboratories dealing with forage and crop production problems, it would be helpful to know what relation can be expected between total N and NO_3^- concentrations. Such a relationship would be helpful in deciding when to separately analyze for NO_3^- as a possible toxicant and when to adopt modified Kjeldahl procedures for inclusion of NO_3^-—N. Ordinary Kjeldahl analyses include part, but seldom all, of the NO_3^-—N. Thus, total N determinations on plants high in NO_3^- are often inaccurate. The Dumas method will include NO_3. Griffith (1960) in England, found that NO_3^- began to accumulate in three grass mixtures differentially fertilized with $(NH_4)_2SO_4$ and cut at the silage stage, when the crude protein content exceeded 18% (2.85%N). He states that grass with more than 21% crude protein should be regarded with caution as it will contain more than 0.07% NO_3^-—N. For rape and kale, Griffith and Johnston (1961) state that 18% crude protein in these plants is associated with a NO_3^- level that may be nutritionally unacceptable. The level of fertilizer N at which this point was reached coincided with that at which dry-matter yield response ceased. Hanway (1962c), in a detailed study of elemental distribution in parts of corn plants grown under different fertility conditions, found NO_3^-—N values of less than 0.02% in leaves, leaf sheathes, and stalks when the total N% was less than 2.6, 0.7, and 0.3, respectively. Above these threshold values, 27, 53, and 26% of the increase in total N was present, on the average, as an increase in NO_3-N for the leaves, leaf sheaths, and stalks, respectively. His method of determining total N in the presence of NO_3^- is, however, questionable. Several investigators have shown that a critical or sufficient level of N in corn leaves at silking for a near-maximum yield is in the range 2.9 to 3% N. This means that high-producing fields will probably always have appreciable amounts of NO_3^-—N in plants cut for silage.

Perhaps no exact relations can be worked out between total N and NO_3^- concentration, because of the many factors that affect NO_3^- accumulation in plants, such as species, varieties within species, amount of sunshine, and time of day. Suffice it to say, one must be alert to possible analytical and toxicological problems at total N values above 2.5% (15.6% crude protein) in nonlegumes and perhaps 3.0% in legumes.

The other hazard of too much NO_3^- in forages like corn and grasses arises when they are ensiled. Denitrification leads to the production of NO (colorless), NO_2 (brown), and N_2O_4 (yellow) gases which are heavier than air and accumulate in silo drains, chutes, and in buildings attached to silos. These gases are lethal to man and animals. Peterson et al. (1958) reported 100,000 ppm of NO_2 in the air of a drainage basin of a silo filled with corn in Wisconsin. The allowable concentration in air of factories is only 10 to 25 ppm. Adequate ventilation of such gas-filled silos before entrance and adequate fencing to protect animals and children is essential. See Crawford and Kennedy (1960) and Hanway et al. (1963) for further discussion.

Most instances of NO_3^- toxicity to livestock or gas production in silos appear to arise from natural factors or a combination of them such as too much available N in the soil for the moisture, light, and temperature conditions restricting growth of plants. Seldom has the indiscreet or excessive use of N fertilizers been directly implicated when the crop had growing conditions that were not extremely adverse. Crawford and Kennedy (1960) point out that there is little hazard in forage crops in New York state if N fertilizers are used at recommended rates to produce near maximum dry matter yields. Most of the production of high yields of nonlegumes in the United States is accomplished with fertilizer N, and NO_3^- problems are the rare exception. Nitrate toxicities may become more prevalent if N fertilizers drop in relative price and their use is doubled or tripled.

XIII. EFFECTS OF NITROGEN SOURCES ON GROWTH AND METABOLISM

The plant root can absorb NH_4^+ or NO_3^-, urea, and simple organic N molecules, e.g., amino acids, dipeptides, and betaines from the soil or culture solution. In well-aerated soil at temperatures suited for plant growth urea is quickly hydrolyzed and NH_4^+ quickly nitrified so that

NO_3^- is the predominant form of available N in most soils soon after fertilization with urea or $NH_4^+(NH_3)$-containing fertilizers. However, NH_4^+ is sufficiently persistent to affect plant metabolism and absorption of other ions. Ammonium nutrition may become more important if the use of nitrification inhibitors or encapsulated fertilizers becomes popular.

A. Ammonium vs. Nitrate

Many investigators have compared NH_4^+ with NO_3^- sources applied to soils and no generalization can be made as to which is superior unless the crop and all environmental conditions are specified. In solution cultures, nitrification of NH_4^+ is inhibited so direct comparisons of NH_4^+ vs. NO_3^- can be made. In the soil, oxidation of NH_4^+ and subsequent uptake of NO_3^- cannot be differentiated from the reduction of NO_3^- in plants. Furthermore, in soil the N source and its subsequent residual or physiological acidity or alkalinity can affect growth and the availability of other elements through the effects of pH on the solid phase.

In spite of these complications, it is well to examine some of the effects that use of NH_4^+ compared to NO_3^- has on soils and plants. From solution or sand cultures both NH_4^+ and NO_3^-, like K^+ and Cl^-, can be absorbed rapidly in contrast to Ca^{2+}, Mg^{2+}, and SO_4^{2-} which are absorbed slowly. Hence, in a complete culture solution with all N in the NO_3^- form, the more rapid uptake of NO_3^- than of cations causes the solution pH to rise. NO_3^- in the solution is replaced by HCO_3^-. In a solution with all N in the NH_4^+ form, the rapid uptake of cations compared to anions causes the pH to fall. NH_4^+ is replaced by H^+. In the solution the electrostatic balance is maintained by H^+ or HCO_3^-. These effects on pH also occur in soils and are accentuated by pH changes concurrent with nitrification, but are also reduced in magnitude by the buffer capacity of the soil.

Whether the plant absorbs its N in the cationic (NH_4^+) or anionic (NO_3^-) form may have profound effects on plant composition and growth. NH_4^+ absorption depresses uptake of mineral cations, particularly K^+, and results in lower organic acid content because the absorbed NH_4^+ is rapidly combined into amino acids and amides. Uptake of Cl^- and SO_4^{2-} may be greater because of the absence of NO_3^- that may compete with them in absorption. The exact relations depend on the cultural conditions and the plant species (Arnon, 1937, 1939; Wadleigh and Shive, 1939; Stewart et al., 1925; deWit et al., 1963). Ulrich (1941) showed that the total organic acid in barley roots depended on the balance between cation and anion absorption. Uptake of K^+ without concurrent uptake of an equivalence of anions resulted in the production of organic acid radicles in the roots. Uptake of Cl^- without concurrent uptake of cations (as from $CaCl_2$) resulted in a loss of organic acids. Little importance was attached to the organic acid content until deWit et al. (1963), by literature interpretation and experiment, showed that maximum growth of whole plants was associated with a constant value for C—A per unit of dry weight. C is the sum in equivalents of the cations $K^+ + Na^+ + Ca^{2+} + Mg^{2+}$. A is the sum in equivalents of the inorganic anions $NO_3^- + H_2PO_4^- + SO_4^{2-} + Cl^-$. C—A represents the organic acid content. In some species most of the organic acids have been quantitatively identified. DeWit et al. (1963) state, "With ammonium fertilization, growth proceeds often at a lower rate. This is due to a stress on the (C—A) content because of competition between NH_4^+ and other cations and the release of H^+ ions during the organic N formation." Much biochemical research remains to be done to explain the mechanism of this interesting relationship of growth rate to organic acid content.

Thousands of field comparisons have been conducted on the relative merits of NH_4^+ vs. NO_3^-—N sources. If yields of crops did differ, the reason for the difference is seldom established because of the great number of possible explanations. In addition to the efficiency of the N source per se, e.g., differential leaching, denitrification, etc., there are many possible side effects from shifts in soil pH on the other mineral constituents of the soil that may affect the plant's growth. Here are some examples:

Vicente-Chandler and Figarella (1962), in a study of N fertilization of Napier grass over a 3-year period on a Catalina clay (latosol) in Puerto Rico, showed that 5 N sources applied annually at the rate of 800 pounds of N per acre produced equal increases in hay yield and had no differential effects on the Ca, P, K, or Mn contents of the hay. Boawn et al. (1960a, b) found that use of 3 N sources—$(NH_4)_2SO_4$, NH_4NO_3, or $Ca(NO_3)_2$— led to no consistent differences in plant concentration of P, Ca, Mg, or K for a sequence of grain sorghum, potatoes, sugar beets, and grain sorghum grown on a fine sandy loam in central Washington. However, uptakes of Mn and Zn were increased with increasing soil acidity induced by $(NH_4)_2SO_4$. Lorenz and Johnson (1953) accounted for the better crop yields obtained with NH_4^+ than with NO_3^- fertilizers on coarse-textured, slightly alkaline soils in California by showing that the residual acidity of NH_4^+ carriers increased the water-soluble phosphate in the soil and the resultant uptake of P by crops. Differences in yield produced by NH_4^+ vs. NO_3^- carriers were eliminated by application of phosphate. Viets et al. (1957) showed that the uptake of both indigenous and applied Zn by milo and Ladino clover in a pot study increased as the pH of a weakly buffered soil was lowered by the use of acidifying N fertilizers. No yield increase to Zn application was noted when $(NH_4)_2SO_4$ or NH_4NO_3 was used, but a response was obtained when the N source was $NaNO_3$. In a field study with irrigated corn on a sandy loam, Viets et al. (1954) found that $(NH_4)_2SO_4$ produced higher N, P, and K and lower Ca and Mg contents in corn leaves than $Ca(NO_3)_2$ applied at equivalent rates. NH_4NO_3 was intermediate in its effects. $(NH_4)_2SO_4$ also produced the highest yields. When differences in yield are produced by choice of N carrier, the real reason for the difference is not easy to determine.

B. Nitrate as an Oxidizing Agent

Several investigators have postulated that NO_3^- absorbed by the root can serve as a source of oxygen when soil aeration is poor. This postulated use of NO_3^- as a source of oxygen by roots of higher plants is analogous to the use of NO_3^- as an oxygen source by denitrifiers. Arnon (1937) found that NH_4^+ was inferior to NO_3^- as a N source for barley in un-aerated culture solutions. Aeration or addition of Mn or Cu to the solution increased the growth of NH_4^+-fed plants but had little effect on NO_3^-- fed ones. Aeration and addition of these metals increased shoot growth of plants in NH_4^+ culture 400% and root growth 800%. Shalhevet and Zwerman (1962) got better growth of corn with NO_3^- than with NH_4^+ on a water-saturated silt loam in lysimeters, but no difference in growth at intermediate and good aeration levels. Even with NO_3^- as the N source, yields were low with poor aeration compared to yields obtained with better aeration. Redox potentials in the saturated soil were higher when NO_3^-—N was used than when NH_4^+—N was used. However, Bain and Chapman (1940) got no benefits from NO_3^- application to avocado or grapefruit seedlings grown in containers of waterlogged Ramona loam. They attribute this failure to the rapid denitrification occurring in soil containing energy sources and to the lack of O_2 for metabolic absorption of NO_3^-, so that NO_3^- could not participate in the oxidative metabolism of the root.

C. Urea

Urea can be toxic to plants because of its biuret contaminant, its rapid hydrolysis to NH_4^+ and concurrent rise in soil pH, or its partial oxidation to NO_2^- in some soils. Breon and Gillam (1944) found that tomato plants grown in nonsterile sand culture grew as well with urea as a source of N (solution pH 6.8) as with NO_3^- nitrogen, and absorbed much more P. Most soluble N carriers placed with the seed will inhibit germination, especially in dry soils (Olson and Dreier, 1956). Brage et al. (1960) found that urea was more harmful than NH_4NO_3 to germination of wheat and barley and attributed this depression to NH_3 toxicity and to biuret contained in commercial urea. Germination inhibition was proportional to the biuret content of the urea which ranged up to 10% in the experimental lots of urea. Broadcast applications of urea containing as much as 10% biuret and applied at the rate of 160 pounds of N an acre did not decrease stand of corn or barley in the field. Urea applied to soils for citrus should not contain more than 2.5% of biuret (Jones et al., 1955).

D. Nitrite

Accumulation of NO_2^- in alkaline soils fertilized with ammonia or urea has been recognized for many years (Martin et al., 1942; Chapman and Liebig, 1952), but appreciation of its occurrence in acid soils as a lag phase in nitrification is a recent development. Bingham et al. (1954) showed that NO_2^- was much more toxic to several plant species in acidic solution cultures than in neutral or alkaline ones and that the degree of injury at pH 4, 5, and 6 was related to the undissociated HNO_2. Nitrate concurrently in the solution diminished NO_2^- toxicity, but NH_4^+ tended to increase it. They concluded that NO_2^- toxicity would occur in soils at concentrations higher than 10 ppm (dry soil basis). Court et al. (1962) have shown that both NH_3 and NO_2^- coming from urea hydrolysis and partial oxidation to NO_2^- can be toxic to corn grown on an alkaline soil. Their data on plant growth at weekly intervals in relation to soil pH and NH_4^+ and NO_2^- contents of a sandy loam with an initial pH of 7.4 and fertilized with urea are shown in Figs. 17 and 18. NH_3 toxicity occurred in the first week when NH_4^+ contents were high and soil pH had risen to 8.8. Marked toxicity from NO_2^- occurred in the second to fifth week when NO_2^- was high and pH dropped to neutral or below because of nitrification. They could account for only half of the applied N in NH_4^+, NO_2^-, and NO_3^- forms and assumed that the rest escaped as gases.

XIV. LOSSES OF NITROGEN FROM PLANTS

The common assumption is that no loss of N from the tops of live plants occurs except for the obvious loss in fallen leaves, flowers, and fruits. In perennial stands, such as a forest, this litter makes up the forest

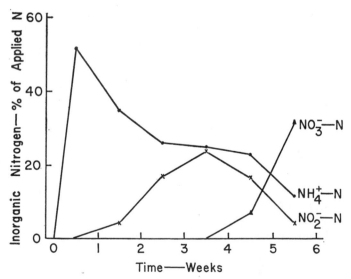

Fig. 17. Distribution with time among the nitrite, nitrate, and ammonium (ammonia) forms of 560 ppm of urea N mixed in a sandy loam at pH 7.4. From Court et al. (1962).

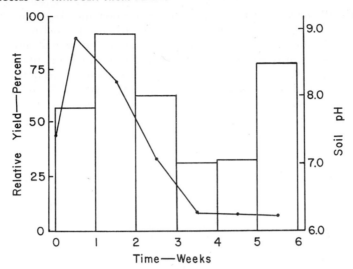

Fig. 18. Change in soil pH with time and the relative dry weight accumulation in one week of established corn seedlings when their roots were placed in contact with soils incubated with urea for the time indicated. This figure goes with Fig. 17. The yield is percentage of that of an unfertilized control (Court et al., 1962).

floor and is an essential link in the recycling of N from which the trees get most of their annual supply of N. Nitrogen is not lost to the ecosystem by this loss from the plant. Similarly, N lost below ground in the death of root hairs and fibrous roots and by the secretion or excretion of N from the roots is not lost from the system, although it is a plant loss. Similar considerations also apply to annual or herbaceous perennial crops grown in rotations. However, in many studies of plants one is not dealing with an ecosystem but with the efficiency of an individual crop.

N can be lost from plants by volatilization of N-containing compounds. Even denitrification in the plant has been suggested.

A. HCN (Prussic Acid)

Franzke and Hume (1945) could detect the odor of HCN from certain strains of 'Black Amber' sorghum and so grew them under bell jars so that HCN could be quantitatively measured. One strain liberated about 14 mg of HCN per 100 plants over an 8-week period extending from the 6-leaf stage to early seed formation. Maximum volatilization was at heading and equalled 4 mg of HCN per 100 plants per week. Assuming 100,000 plants per acre, this volatilization of HCN could equal about 15 pounds of N per acre during an 8-week growing season. However, few species of plants and only a few strains within a species such as the sorghums contain cyanogenic glycosides from which the HCN presumably originates enzymatically or as an intermediate during cyanogenic glycoside synthesis. Because of the extreme toxicity of HCN to animals, plant breeders breed or select this undesirable characteristic out of clovers (Portz and Jackobs, 1955) and sorghums when it occurs. Therefore, much or any loss of N from plants as HCN is presumably very rare. Cyanide accumulation in cyanophoric strains of sudangrass (Patel and Wright, 1958) and sorghums (Nelson, 1953) is favored by high rates of N application.

B. N_2

Losses of N as N_2 by the reaction of NO_2^- with amines in the acidic sap of plants (Van Slyke reaction) has been suggested to account for the losses of N from narcissus leaves floated on NO_3^-- or NH_4^+-containing nutrient solutions (Pearsall and Billimoria, 1937) or by narcissus bulbs grown in distilled water (Vickery et al., 1946). The latter observed a loss of 11.5% of the total N for bulbs grown in light. Wilson (1943) was an active proponent of this theory. Nitrite can often be detected in plants nourished with NO_3^-—N, and is a transistory intermediate in NO_3^- reduction. Allison and Sterling (1948) could detect no loss of N from the system by Kjeldahl methods when sterilized leaves of three kinds of plants were floated in nutrient solutions containing NH_4Cl, KNO_3, or NH_4NO_3. They concluded that the cell sap is not sufficiently acidic for the Van Slyke reaction to occur.

Healthy green plants appear to be excellent conservors of N against the gaseous losses frequently noted in soils or bacterial cultures. The assumption made in N recovery experiments that there is no volatile loss of N from plants appears to be reasonable, but the matter remains to be checked with N^{15} techniques. Studies on the comparative efficiency of strains of *Rhizobia* to fix N and studies on the possibility of N fixation by non-nodulated legumes and other species rest on this assumption.

C. Washout

Some elements can be lost from leaves in the field by leaching in rain or in the laboratory in the process of washing them prior to analysis. These losses are much greater for dead, dried, or senescent leaves than for healthy live ones. Leaching of K by rain has been noted frequently. Resolution of K, Ca, Mg, and P in the dried salts that can accumulate at hydathodes after an active period of guttation is a part of this loss. Amides, and perhaps some amino acids, could be lost from the leaves in water of guttation. Ahrens (1934) showed that mineral salts and organic substances accumulated on leaf surfaces by exosmosis during periods of dew. It is not uncommon to see dried salts, largely amides, on the tips of lawn grasses within 1 or 2 days after the lawn has been N fertilized. Loss of N by leaching from the plant, either from these accumulated salts or from leaf interiors, is not generally regarded as significant.

However, Tanaka and Navasero (1964) found that rice grown in the

Philippines and fertilized with 120 kg of N per hectare lost about 30% of the N from the tops by leaching in tropical rains, the N loss beginning about 21 days before flowering. Dew collected from such plants contained 102 ppm of N. They contend that N washout from highly fertilized stands of rice grown in thick stands in the rainy season in the tropics can be appreciable.

N is seldom studied in leaf-washing studies. Washing of dust, soot, and other debris from leaf surfaces is essential for accurate micronutrient analysis. Investigators who studied leaf-washing techniques with water, or solutions of acids, detergents or chelates, do not report on what happens to the N. The assumption is that the N of fresh healthy leaves is non-leachable since practically all of it is in intracellular protein.

XV. PERSPECTIVE

All writing must come to a close either abruptly like a cliff or gently like a mountain sloping into a valley. From a position on the slope one can look both backward and forward. Looking back, the author has been impressed by the tremendous amount of information available in the world on the use of N by plants, much of which has never been looked at analytically or synthetically. So much research on N is done on so many crops in so many places with so little thought as to how it fits into the total picture. In too many instances the work has been done before. In too many instances another kind of measurement or two or a broader range in the applied variable, such as rate of N application, would have enhanced the value of the work.

In view of the great importance of proper use of N for production of food and fiber and the importance of N to the nutritional quality of food for both man and animals, it is rather surprising that no attempt has been made to collate all of the information now available on the plant's use of N. Such an endeavor would produce a volume requiring great effort, but well worth it for such an important subject. What has been attempted here is only a feeble start. The writer hopes he has summarized the principles, but undoubtedly many have been missed.

Research reveals the mysteries of the organism and shows how complex its life really is. Yet, the plant goes on its way, magnificently coordinated from millenia of adaptation to its environment for the purpose of perpetuating itself. It can extract nearly the last ion of N from its environment, use and store this N without loss until it is needed, store the excess NO_3^-, prevent the accumulation of toxic NH_3 and NH_4^+ by combining them into storage amides, and meter these storage products in stems and leaves into developing seed and storage roots as required. If it is short of N, it robs the vegetative parts of the plant at a faster rate to produce the seed. If it has too much N, it keeps much of this N out of the seed. This remarkable flexibility allows man to mismanage N and yet suffer only part of the consequences.

Looking forward, it is safe to say that man needs still more information on managing N, whether it be from fertilizers or legumes, particularly at high production levels, if he is to feed a hungry world. So much of our knowledge about N comes from work on the deficiency side of optimum. So little is really known about N at maximum production, and still less when N is excessive. The relative price of N fertilizers will continue to decline. The need for more food and for more efficient production of it, coupled with cheaper N, will focus research within the next decade on understanding the top and declining-yield segment of the N response curve.

LITERATURE CITED

Agricultural Ammonia News 1964. New use for ammonia—cotton defoliation. 14 (5):34-35.

Ahrens, K. 1934. Die kutikulare Exkretion des Laublattes. Jahrb. Wiss. Bot. 80:248-300.

Allison, F. E., and Sterling, L. D. 1948. Gaseous losses of nitrogen from green plants. II. Studies with excised leaves in nutrient media. Plant Physiol. 23:601-608.

Allos, H. F., and Bartholomew, W. V. 1955. Effect of available nitrogen on symbiotic fixation. Soil Sci. Soc. Am. Proc. 19:182-184.

Arnon, D. I. 1937. Ammonium and nitrate nutrition of barley at different seasons in relation to hydrogen-ion concentration, manganese, copper, and oxygen supply. Soil Sci. 44:91-121.

—— 1939. Effect of ammonium and nitrate nitrogen on the mineral composition and sap characteristics of barley. Soil Sci. 48:295-307.

Atkins, R. E., Stanford, G., and Dumenil, L. 1955. Effects of nitrogen and phosphorus fertilizer on yield and malting quality of barley. J. Agr. and Food Chem. 3:609-615.

Bain, F. M., and Chapman, H. D. 1940. Nitrate fertilizer additions to waterlogged soils in relation to oxygen deficiency. Soil Sci. 50:357-367.

Bakhuyzen, H. L. Van de Sande. 1937. Studies on wheat grown under constant conditions. A monograph on growth with contributions on the carbon and nitrogen content of the wheat plant by E. P. Gruffing and Carl L. Alsberg. Misc. Pub. No. 8, Food Research Institute, Stanford University. 400 p.

Bingham, F. T., Chapman, H. G., and Pugh, A. L. 1954. Solution-culture studies of nitrite toxicity to plants. Soil Sci. Soc. Am. Proc. 18:305-308.

Black, C. A. 1957. Soil-Plant Relationships. John Wiley and Sons, Inc. New York. 319 p.

Black, C. A., and Kempthorne, O. 1954a. Willcox's Agrobiology: I. Theory of the nitrogen constant 318. Agron. J. 46:303-307.

——, and —— 1954b. Willcox's Agrobiology: II. Application of the nitrogen constant 318. Agron. J. 46:307-310.

Boawn, L. C., Nelson, J. L., and Crawford, C. L. 1963. Residual nitrogen from NH_4NO_3 fertilizer and from alfalfa plowed under. Agron. J. 55:231-235.

——, Nelson, C. E., Viets, F. G. Jr., and Crawford, C. L. 1960a. A study of nitrogen carrier and nitrogen rate influence on soil properties and nutrient uptake by crops. Washington Exp. Sta. Bull. 614.

——, Viets, F. G. Jr., Crawford, C. L., and Nelson, J. L. 1960b. Effect of nitrogen carrier, nitrogen rate, zinc rate, and soil pH on zinc uptake by sorghum, potatoes, and sugar beets. Soil Sci. 90:329-337.

Bongers, L. J. J. 1958. Kinetic aspects of nitrate reduction. Netherlands J. Agr. Sci. 6:79-88.

Bradley, W. H., Eppson, H. F., and Beath, O. A. 1942. Livestock poisoning by oat hay and other plants containing nitrate. Wyoming Agr. Exp. Sta. Bull. 241.

Brage, B. L., Zich, W. R., and Fine, L. O. 1960. The germination of small grain and corn as influenced by urea and other nitrogenous fertilizers. Soil Sci. Soc. Am. Proc. 24:294-296.

Breon, W. S., and Gillam, W. S. 1944. Influence of phosphorus supply and the form of available nitrogen on the nitrogen metabolism of the tomato plant. Plant Physiol. 19:649-659.

Brouwer, R. 1962a. Distribution of dry matter in the plant. Netherlands J. Agr. Sci. Special issue. 10:361-376.

———— 1962b. Nutritive influences on the distribution of dry matter in the plant. Netherlands J. Agr. Sci. Special issue. 10:399-408.

———— and Leon, Elizabeth A. 1962. Growth and uptake of individual crown roots of Zea mays L. Jaarb. I.B.S., p. 19-25.

Broyer, T. C. 1951. The nature of the process of inorganic solute accumulation in roots. p. 187-249. *In* E. Truog, Ed. Mineral Nutrition of Plants. Univ. of Wis. Press, Madison, Wis.

Burstrom, H. 1943. Photosynthesis and assimilation of nitrate by wheat leaves. Ann. Agr. Coll., Sweden. 11:1-50.

Carpenter, P. N. 1963. Mineral accumulation in potato plants as affected by fertilizer application and potato variety. Maine Agr. Exp. Sta. Bull. 610.

Chandler, W. V. 1960. Nutrient uptake by corn in North Carolina. North Carolina Agr. Exp. Sta. Tech. Bull. 143.

Chapman, H. D., and Liebig, C. F., Jr. 1952. Field and laboratory studies of nitrite assimilation in soils. Soil Sci. Soc. Am. Proc. 16:276-282.

Cochran, H. L., and Olson, L. C. 1941. Uptake of nutrients by the Perfection pimiento plant under field conditions and its relation to fertilizer practices in Georgia. Georgia Agr. Exp. Sta. Bull. 208.

Cole, C. V., Grunes, D., Porter, L. K., and Olsen, S. R. 1963. The effects of nitrogen on short-term phosphorus absorption and translocation in Corn (*Zea mays*). Soil Sci. Soc. Am. Proc. 27:671-674.

Cooke, I. J. 1962. Damage to plant roots caused by urea and anhydrous ammonia. Nature (London) 194:1262-1263.

Court, M. N., Stephen, R. C., and Waid, J. S. 1962. Nitrite toxicity arising from the use of urea as a fertilizer. Nature (London) 194:1263-1265.

Crawford, R. F., and Kennedy, W. K. 1960. Nitrates in forage crops and silage: benefits, hazards, precautions. Cornell Misc. Bull. 37.

DeWit, C. T., Dijkshoorn, W., and Noggle, J. C. 1963. Ionic balance and the growth of plants. Versl. Landboowk. Onderz. 69:15.

Donald, C. M. 1963. Competition among crop and pasture plants. Adv. Agron. 15:1-118.

Duncan, W. G., and Ohlrogge, A. J. 1958. Principles of nutrient uptake from fertilizer bands. II. Root development in the band. Agron. J. 50:605-608.

Fisher, F. L., and Caldwell, A. G. 1959. The effects of continued use of heavy rates of fertilizers on forage production and quality of coastal Bermuda grass. Agron. J. 51:99-102.

Franzke, C. J., and Hume, A. M. 1945. Liberation of HCN in sorghum. J. Am. Soc. Agron. 37:848-851.

French, B. L. 1956. Functional relationships for irrigated corn response to nitrogen. J. Farm Econ. 38:736-747.

Gilbert, C. S., Eppson, H. F., Bradley, W. B., and Beath, O. A. 1946. Nitrate accumulation in cultivated plants and weeds. Wyoming Exp. Sta. Bull. 277.

Goodman, P. J. 1963. Some effects of different soils on composition and growth of sugar beet. J. Sci. Food and Agr. 3:196-203.

Gregory, F. G. 1952. The control of growth and reproduction by external factors. Rpt. 13th Intern. Hort. Cong. 1:96-105.

Griffith, G. ap. 1960. The nitrate nitrogen content of herbage. II. Effect of different levels of application of sulphate of ammonia on the nitrate content of herbage. J. Sci. Food Agr. 11:626-629.

————, and Johnston, T. D. 1961. The nitrate-nitrogen content of herbage. III. The mineral nitrate content of rape and kale. J. Sci. Food Agr. 12:348-352.

Grunes, D. L. 1959. Effect of nitrogen on the availability of soil and fertilizer phosphorus to plants. Adv. Agron. 11:369-396.

Hageman, R. H., and Flesher, Donna 1960. Nitrate reductase activity in corn seedlings as affected by light and nitrate content of nutrient media. Plant Physiol. 35:700-708.

Hammond, L. C., Black, C. A., and Norman, A. G. 1951. Nutrient uptake by soybeans on two Iowa soils. Iowa Agr. Exp. Sta. Bull. 384.

Hanway, J. J. 1962a. Corn growth and composition in relation to soil fertility: I. Growth of different plant parts and relation between leaf weight and grain yield. Agron. J. 54:145-148.

―――― 1962b. Corn growth and composition in relation to soil fertility: II. Uptake of N, P, and K, and their distribution in different plant parts during the growing season. Agron. J. 54:217-222.

―――― 1962c. Corn growth and composition in relation to soil fertility: III. Percentages of N, P, and K in different plant parts in relation to stage of growth. Agron. J. 54:222-229.

――――, Herrick, J. B., Willrich, T. L., Bennett, P. C., and McCall, J. T. 1963. The nitrate problem. Iowa State Univ. Ext. Serv. Special Rpt. 34.

Hawkins, A. 1946. Rate of absorption and translocation of mineral nutrients by potatoes in Aroostook County, Maine, and their relation to fertilizer practices. J. Am. Soc. Agron. 38:667-681.

Heilman, M. D., Thomas, J. R., and Burleson, C. A. 1961. Nitrogen requirements of cabbage. J. Rio Grande Valley Hort. Soc. 15:106-111.

Henzell, E. F. 1962. The use of nitrogen fertilizers on pastures in the sub-tropics and tropics. p. 160-171. *In* A review of nitrogen in the tropics with particular reference to pastures; A symposium. Bull. 46. Commonwealth Bur. of Pasture and Field Crops, Hurley, England.

Hevesy, G., Linderstrom-Lang, K., Keston, A. S., and Olsen, C. 1940. Exchange of nitrogen atoms in the leaves of the sunflower. Compt. Rend. Trav. Lab. Carlsberg (Copenhagen) Ser. Chim. 23:213-218.

Hewitt, E. J. 1963. The essential nutrient elements: Requirements and interactions of plants. Ch. 2, p. 140-143. *In* Plant Physiology, A Treatise. Vol. III (F. C. Steward, ed.) Academic Press, New York.

Hirose, S., and Goto, Y. 1961. Mode of absorption of urea by rice seedlings. (Abstr.) Soil Sci. and Plant Nutr. 7:85.

Hoagland, D. R., and Broyer, T. C. 1936. General nature of the process of salt accumulation by roots with description of experimental methods. Plant Physiol. 11:471-507.

――――, and ――――. 1940. Hydrogen ion effects and the accumulation of salt by barley roots as influenced by metabolism. Am. J. Bot. 27:173-185.

Hornberger, R. 1882. Chemische Untersuchungen über das Wachsthom der Maispflanze. Landw. Jahrb. 11:359.

Humphries, E. C., and French, S. A. W. 1963. The effects of nitrogen, phosphorus, and potassium and gibberellic acid on leaf area and cell division in Majestic potato. Ann. Appl. Biol. 52:149-162.

Hunter, A. S., Gerard, C. J., Waddoups, H. M., Hall, W. E., Cushman, H. E., and Alban, L. A. 1958. The effect of nitrogen fertilizers on the relationship between increases in yields and protein content of pastry-type wheats. Agron. J. 50:311-314.

――――, and Yungen, J. A. 1955. The influence of variations in fertility levels upon the yield and protein content of field corn in Eastern Oregon. Soil Sci. Am. Proc. 19:214-218.

Jackson, R. D., and Haddock, J. L. 1959. Growth and nutrient uptake of Russet Burbank potatoes. Am. Potato J. 36:22-28.

Jones, W. W., Embleton, T. W., and Goodal, G. E. 1955. Yellow tip of citrus. California Agr. 9(12):4.

Jordan, H. V., Laird, K. D., and Ferguson, D. D. 1950. Growth rates and nutrient uptake by corn in a fertilizer-spacing experiment. Agron. J. 42:261-268.

Loehwing, W. F. 1951. Mineral nutrition in relation to the ontogeny of plants. Ch. 14, p. 343-352. *In* E. Troug, (ed.) Mineral Nutrition of Plants. Univ. of Wisconsin Press, Madison, Wis.

Lorenz, O. A. 1947. Studies on potato nutrition. III. Chemical composition and uptake of nutrients by Kern County potatoes. Am. Potato J. 24:281-291.

――――, Bishop, J. C., and Wright, D. N. 1955. Liquid, dry, and gaseous fertilizers for onions on sandy loam soils. Am. Soc. Hort. Sci. 65:296-306.

――――, and Johnson, C. M. 1953. Nitrogen fertilization as related to the availability of phosphorus in certain California soils. Soil Sci. 75:119-129.

MacKenzie, A. J., Spencer, W. F., Stockinger, K. R., and Krantz, B. A. 1963. Seasonal nitrate-nitrogen content of cotton petioles as affected by nitrogen application and its relationship to yield. Agron. J. 55:55-59.

MacKenzie, A. J., Stockinger, K. R., and Krantz, B. A. 1957. Growth and nutrient uptake of sugar beets in the Imperial Valley, California. J. Am. Soc. Sugar Beet Technol. IX:400-407.

Martin, W. P., Buehrer, T. F., and Caster, A. B. 1942. Threshold pH value for nitrification of ammonia in desert soils. Soil Sci. Soc. Am. Proc. 7(1941):223-228.

Mason, D. D. 1956. Functional models and experimental designs for characterizing responses curves and surfaces. Ch. 5, p. 76-98. *In* Baum, E. L., Heady, E. O., Blackmore, J. (eds.) Methodological procedures in the economic analysis of fertilizer use data. Iowa State College Press, Ames, Iowa.

Mayo, N. S. 1895. Cattle poisoning by nitrate of potash. Kansas Agr. Exp. Sta. Bull. 49.

McElroy, W. D., and Glass, B. (eds.) 1956. Inorganic Nitrogen Metabolism. Johns Hopkins Press, Baltimore, Maryland, 718 pp.

McMurtrey, J. E., Jr. 1948. Visual symptoms of malnutrition in plants. Ch. VII, pp. 231-289. *In* Diagnostic techniques for soils and crops. Am. Potash Inst., Washington, D.C.

Meyer, R., and Storck, A. 1927. Ueber den Pflanzenertrag als Funktion der Stickstoffgabe und der Wachstumszeit bei Hafer, Zetzchr. Pflanzenernahr. Düng. Bodenk. 10A: 329-347.

Morgan, M. F., and Street, O. E. 1935. Rates of growth and nitrogen assimilation of Havana seed tobacco. J. Agr. Res. 51:163-172.

Munson, R. D., and Dolls, J. P. 1959. The economics of fertilizer use in crop production. Adv. Agron. 11:133-169.

Nelson, C. E. 1953. Hydrocyanic acid content of certain sorghums under irrigation as affected by nitrogen fertilizer and soil moisture stress. Agron. J. 45:615-618.

————. 1958. Lodging of field corn as affected by cultivation, plant population, nitrogen fertilizer, and irrigation treatment. USDA, ARS Prod. Res. Rpt. No. 16.

Nommik, Hans. 1957. Fixation and defixation of ammonia in soils. Acta Agr. Scandinavia 7:395-436.

Olson, L. C., and Bledsoe, R. P. 1942. The chemical composition of the cotton plant and the uptake of nutrients at different growth stages. Georgia Agr. Exp. Sta. Bull. 222.

Olson, R. A., and Dreier, A. F. 1956. Fertilizer placement for small grains in relation to crop stand and nutrient efficiency in Nebraska. Soil Sci. Soc. Am. Proc. 20:19-24.

Olson, R. A., Dreier, A. F., Thompson, C., Frank, K., and Grabouski, P. H. 1964. Using fertilizer nitrogen effectively on grain crops. Nebraska Agr. Exp. Sta. Bull. SB 479.

Paschal, J. L., and French, B. L. 1956. A method of economic analysis applied to nitrogen fertilizer rate experiments on irrigated corn. USDA Tech. Bull. No. 1141.

Patel, C. J., and Wright, M. J. 1958. The effect of certain nutrients upon the hydrocyanic acid content of sudangrass grown in nutrient solution. Agron. J. 50:645-647.

Pearsall, W. H., and Billimoria, M. C. 1937. Losses of nitrogen from green plants. Biochem. J. 31:1743-1750.

Peterson, W. H., Burris, R. H., Rameschanda, S., and Little, N. 1958. Production of toxic gas (nitrogen oxides) in silage making. J. Agr. Food Chem. 6:121-126.

Petrie, A. H. K. 1937. Physiological ontogeny in plants and its relation to nutrition. 3. The effects of nitrogen supply on the drifting composition of the leaves. Austral. J. Exp. Biol. Med. Sci. 15:385-404.

Phillis, E., and Mason, I. G. 1942. Studies on partition of mineral elements in the cotton plant. III. Mainly concerning nitrogen. Ann. Bot. 6:469-485.

Pinck, L. A., Allison, F. E., and Gaddy, V. L. 1946. The nitrogen requirement in the utilization of carbonaceous residues in soil. J. Amer. Soc. Agron. 38:410-420.

Portz, H. L., and Jackobs, J. A. 1955. Differences between seed lots of Ladino clover in cyanophoric properties. Agron. J. 47:143-145.

Rippel, A. 1921. Die Frage der Eiweiss Wanderung beim herbstlichen Vergilben der Laubblatter. Biol. Central 67. 41:508.

Roberts, S., and Nelson, C. E. 1961. Hop nutrient uptake and the relationship between quality and nutrient content of hop cones. Washington Agr. Exp. Sta. Bull. 630.

Sayre, J. D. 1948. Mineral accumulation in corn. Plant Physiol. 23:267-281.

Schreiber, H. A., Stanberry, C. O., and Tucker, H. 1962. Irrigation and nitrogen effects on sweet corn row numbers at various growth stages. Science 135:1135-1136.

Shalhevet, J., and Zwerman, P. J. 1962. Nitrogen response of corn under variable conditions of drainage—a lysimeter study. Soil Sci. 93:172-182.

Smith, R. C., and Epstein, E. 1964. Ion absorption by shoot tissue: Technique and first findings with excised leaf tissue of corn. Plant Physiol. 39:338-341.

Society for Experimental Biology. 1959. Symposia of the Society for Experimental Biology. XIII. Utilization of nitrogen and its compounds by plants. Academic Press, New York, 348 p.

Sprague, H. B., Ed. 1964. Hunger Signs in Crops. Third Ed. David McCoy Co., New York. 461 p.

Stanford, George, and Ayres, A. S. 1964. The internal nitrogen requirement of sugarcane. Soil Sci. 98:338-344.

Steenbjerg, F. 1954. Manuring, plant production, and the chemical composition of the plant. Plant and Soil 5:226-242.

Stewart, G. R., Thomas, E. C., and Horner, J. 1925. The comparative growth of pineapple plants with ammonia and nitrate nitrogen. Soil Sci. 20:227-241.

Tanaka, A., and Navasero, S. A. 1964. Loss of nitrogen from the rice plant through rain or dew. Soil Sci. and Plant Nutr. 10:36-39.

Troughton, A. 1957. The underground organs of herbage grasses. Bull. 44, Commonwealth Bur. of Pastures and Field Crops, Hurley, England. Lamport Gilbert Co. Ltd., Reading, England, 156 p.

Ulrich, A. 1941. Metabolism of non-volatile organic acids in excised barley roots as related to cation-anion balance during salt accumulation. Am. J. Bot. 28:526-537.

———, 1950. Critical nitrate levels of sugar beets estimated from analysis of petioles and blades, with special reference to yields and sucrose concentration. Soil Sci. 69:291-310.

———, Ririe, D., Hills, F. J., George, A. G. 1959. I. Plant analysis, a guide for sugar beet fertilization. California Agr. Exp. Sta. Bull. 766.

Van Dobben, W. H. 1958. Verslag van proefnemingen op het gebied van het fundamentele graanonder-zoek. In tien-jarenplan voor Graanonderzoek. Verslag over het 5 de Jaar. p. 59-80.

———, 1961. De stikstofhvishouding van tarwe en maanzad. Jaarb. I.B.S.:45-60.

Van Schreven, D. A. 1958. Some factors affecting the uptake of nitrogen by legumes. Ch. 19, p. 137-163. In Hallsworth, E. G. (ed.) Nutrition of the Legumes. Academic Press, Inc., New York.

Vicente-Chandler, J., and Figarella, J. 1962. Effects of five nitrogen sources on yield and composition of Napier grass. J. Agr., Univ. Puerto Rico. XLVI:102-105.

Vickery, H. B., Pucher, G. W., and Clark, H. E. 1936. Glutamine metabolism of the beet. Plant Physiol. 11:413-420.

———, ———, Schoenheimer, R., and Rittenberg, D. 1939. The metabolism of nitrogen in the leaves of the buckwheat plant. J. Biol. Chem. 129:791-792.

———, ———, Wakeman, A. J., and Leavenworth, C. S. 1946. Chemical investigations of the metabolism of plants. I. The nitrogen nutrition of Narcissus poeticus. Connecticut Agr. Exp. Sta. Bull. 496.

Viets, F. G., Jr. 1960. Recovery of fertilizer nitrogen on irrigated and dryland soils of the western United States. Trans. 7th Intern. Cong. Soil Sci. 2:486-493.

———, 1961. Agronomic needs for secondary and microelements. Assoc. Am. Fert. Control Officials Off. Pub. No. 15, p. 59-63.

———, Boawn, L. C., and Crawford, C. L. 1957. The effect of nitrogen and type of nitrogen carrier on plant uptake of indigenous and applied zinc. Soil Sci. Soc. Am. Proc. 21:197-201.

———, ———, Nelson, C. E., and Crawford, C. L. 1953. Soil application of zinc for control of zinc deficiency in beans, with notes on other field crops. Washington Agr. Exp. Sta. Circ. 215.

———, and Domingo, C. E. 1949. Yield and nitrogen content of corn hybrids as affected by nitrogen supply. Soil Sci. Soc. Am. Proc. 13:303-306.

———, Moxon, A. L., and Whitehead, E. I. 1946. Nitrogen metabolism of corn (Zea mays) as influenced by ammonia nutrition. Plant Physiol. 21:271-289.

———, Nelson, C. E., and Crawford, C. L. 1954. The relationship among corn yields, leaf composition, and fertilizer applied. Soil Sci. Soc. Am Proc. 18:297-301.

———, Whitehead, E. I., and Moxon, A. L. 1947. Nitrogen metabolism in detached corn leaves in darkness and in light. Plant Physiol. 22:465-476.

Wadleigh, C. H., and Shive, J. W. 1939. Organic acid content of corn plants as influenced by pH of substrate and form of nitrogen supplied. Am. J. Bot. 26:244-248.

Wallace, T. 1961. The Diagnosis of Mineral Deficiencies in Plants by Visual Symptoms. (3rd ed.) Chemical Pub. Co., New York, 125 p.

Watson, D. J. 1947. Comparative physiological studies on the growth of field crops. II. The effect of varying nutrient supply on net assimilation rate and leaf area. Ann. Bot. NS 11:375-407.

———— 1952. The physiological basis of variation in yield. Adv. Agron. 4:101-145.

Webster, G. C. 1959. Nitrogen Metabolism in Plants. Row, Peterson and Company, Evanston, Illinois, 145 p.

Welton, F. A., and Morris, V. H. 1931. Lodging in oats and wheat. Ohio Agr. Exp. Sta. Bull. 471.

White, W. C., and Black, C. W. 1954. Willcox's Agrobiology: III. The inverse yield-nitrogen law. Agron. J. 46:310-315.

Wilkinson, S. R., and Ohlrogge, A. J. 1962. Principles of nutrient uptake from fertilizer bands: V. Mechanisms responsible for intensive root development in fertilized zones. Agron. J. 54:288-291.

Willcox, O. W. 1954. Quantitative Agrobiology: I. The inverse yield—nitrogen law. Agron. J. 46:315-320.

Williams, R. F. 1948. The effects of phosphorus supply on the rate of intake of phosphorus and nitrogen and upon certain aspects of phosphorus metabolism in graninaceous plants. Austral. J. Sci. Res., Series B, 1:333-361.

———— 1955. Redistribution of mineral elements during development. Ann. Rev. Plant Physiol. 6:25-42.

Wilson, J. K. 1943. Nitrous acid and the loss of nitrogen. Cornell Univ. Agr. Exp. Sta. Mem. 253:1-36.

Wittwer, S. H., Bukovac, M. J., and Tukey, H. B. 1963. Advances in foliar feeding of plant nutrients. p. 429-448. In Fertilizer Technology and Usage. Soil Sci. Soc. Am. Madison, Wisconsin.

Wright, M. J. and Davison, K. L. 1964. Nitrate accumulation in crops and nitrate poisoning in animals. Adv. Agron. 16:197-247.

Zink, F. W., and Yamaguchi, M. 1962. Studies on the growth rate and nutrient absorption of head lettuce. Hilgardia 32:471-500.

Chapter 15

Movement of Nitrogen in Soil

W. R. GARDNER

U.S. Salinity Laboratory, ARS, U.S.D.A.
Riverside, California

I. INTRODUCTION

The movement of nitrogen and various nitrogen compounds in the soil plays an important role in determining the availability of nitrogen for plant growth. The two main processes involved in the movement of nitrogen, or virtually any chemical substance in soil, are (1) convection of substances dissolved in the soil solution due to the mass flow of the soil solution and (2) molecular or ionic diffusion due to concentration gradients. Diffusion occurs in the gaseous phase as well as the liquid phase. While there are other possible mechanisms, such as movement of ions due to electric fields and mass flow due to density gradients arising from concentration gradients, these have received little study and will not be of concern here, although they may be of importance in some instances. The effect of concentration gradients on water movement will also be omitted although this is a problem of considerable interest. Mass flow in the gaseous phase is probably of little importance in soils.

The extent and direction of movement by convection depends upon the concentration of nitrogen in the soil solution, and upon the direction and rate of the movement of the soil solution. In order to understand the movement of an anion such as NO_3^-, it is, therefore, necessary to understand the pattern of water movement. Diffusion depends upon concentration gradients and can usually be treated within the framework of classical diffusion theory. Both processes can occur simultaneously and may act in the same direction or in opposition.

A factor which often determines nitrogen movement is the degree of interaction between the nitrogen in solution and the surface of the soil particles. Thus, a strongly adsorbed ion such as NH_4^+ will move far less readily than an ion such as NO_3^-, which is lightly adsorbed by some soils and not at all by many soils.

Ion movement in soils or other porous media is best treated quantitatively by means of the classical equation of continuity. In this equation, the time rate of increase of an ionic species per unit volume of soil is set equal to the sum of the sources and sinks for that ion plus the net flux of the ion into the unit volume by diffusion and convection. The solutions of this partial differential equation, when fitted to the appropriate initial and boundary conditions, allow one to determine desired information about the movement and distribution of the ions. In this chapter the mathematical equations describing movement are outlined and a few special examples are given. Anyone interested in carrying out actual quantitative calculations should consult the sources cited for more detail.

II. DIFFUSION

Crank (1956) gives a comprehensive treatment of the mathematics of diffusion. Jost (1952) and Tyrrell (1961) give helpful treatments of some other aspects of diffusion. Carslaw and Jaeger (1959) is an indispensable source of solutions to the heat flow equation which are readily adapted to diffusion problems as well. This adaptation requires setting $K = D$ and $\kappa = D/(R + 1)$ where K is the thermal conductivity, D the ionic diffusion coefficient, κ the thermal diffusivity and $(R + 1)$ a capacity factor. R is the ratio of the number of adsorbed ions to the number of ions in solution, per unit volume of soil.

Liquid phase diffusion. In treating diffusion in soils or other porous media the principal departure from classical diffusion theory is to take into account the fact that diffusion can only occur in that fraction of the pore space which is filled with water (or air, in the case of vapor diffusion).

For diffusion through the soil water, Fick's first law of diffusion may be written:

$$J = -D\theta \, dC/dx \qquad [1]$$

where J is the flux or flow of substance crossing unit area perpendicular to the direction of flow per unit time. In c.g.s. units the dimensions of J are those of quantity (moles, grams, cm^3 ...) times cm^{-2} sec. D is an apparent or effective diffusion coefficient, θ is the water content on a volume basis, C is the concentration of diffusing substance in the soil water, and x is the space variable. The extension to more than one dimension is straightforward. Both C and D may be defined in several different ways. This has led to some ambiguity in the literature. It is possible to take as the concentration the quantity of substance per unit volume of soil rather than unit volume of soil solution. This, in effect, incorporates θ in C. Or, instead, one can combine θ with D, a convention which has been used by a number of authors. For clarity, in this chapter, C will always refer to the concentration of the soil solution, and D is defined in such a way that in equation [1] J will always be the flux per unit area of soil.

No attempt is made here to separate out factors which influence the apparent diffusivity D. D cannot exceed the value for diffusion in pure water, but because of the tortuous nature of the diffusion path in soils, D is often less than for diffusion in water. In addition, the water adsorbed near the surfaces of the clay minerals probably has a higher viscosity than nonadsorbed water (Low, 1962a, b). This increased viscosity results in a further reduction in the diffusion coefficient. Thus, the diffusion coefficient decreases with decreasing water content as can be seen from the data in Table 1. The data of Klute and Letey (1958) for glass beads showed a similar reduction with decreasing water content. In addition to the methods used by the workers cited in Table 1, Schofield and Graham-

Table 1. Diffusion coefficients in soils.

Solute	Soil texture	Water content, θ	D, cm^2/day	Reference
Cl$^-$	clay	0.45	0.5	Porter et al. (1960)
	"	0.25	0.16	"
	loam	0.25	0.35	"
	"	0.10	0.065	"
Rb Cl	loam	0.47	0.12	Patil et al. (1963)
	"	0.278	0.043	"
	"	0.172	0.034	"
Cl$^-$	silt	0.427	1.15	Romkens & Bruce (1964)
	"	0.248	0.275	"
	sand	0.402	1.20	"
	"	0.168	0.042	"

Bryce (1960) worked out a method for determining diffusion coefficient in soils (Graham-Bryce, 1963a, b).

The diffusion coefficient is temperature dependent and concentration dependent. While concentration effects are probably not too important in soils except at very high concentrations, temperature may have a pronounced effect. Unfortunately, no data are available on this point except for diffusion in solutions.

It should also be noted that, in order to preserve electrical neutrality, the diffusion of any ion must be accompanied by the diffusion of some other ion or ions. Since diffusion coefficients for different ionic species may differ, the coefficient of diffusion for a combination of ions is the average of the separate coefficients. The proper manner to average coefficients is discussed by Low (1962a). For the most part, diffusion coefficients for ions in soils are not known with sufficient precision to require consideration for such factors. At this point it is difficult to understand the large difference in D between the data of Patil et al. and that of Porter et al. for a loam soil.

Vapor phase diffusion. At least two forms of nitrogen, N_2 and NH_3, may diffuse through the soil in the vapor phase. In this case Fick's law is written:

$$J = -0.6 \alpha f D_0 \, dC/dx, \qquad [2]$$

where f is the porosity of the soil. The factor 0.6 has been found to account reasonably well for the tortuosity in air-dry porous materials (Currie, 1960). D_0 is the coefficient for diffusion of the gas through air and is of the order of 1.4×10^4 cm^2/day for most common gases. C is the quantity of vapor per unit volume of pore space. Space does not permit a discussion of the effect of varying soil-water content upon the tortuosity factor α. Currie (1961) and Millington and Quirk (1960) consider this problem in some detail.

Simultaneous vapor and liquid diffusion. When the soil pore space is only partially filled with water, any substance which has an appreciable vapor pressure can readily diffuse in both the liquid and vapor phases. This simultaneous diffusion can be treated in a straightforward manner if it is assumed that at each point in the soil the liquid and vapor phases are in equilibrium with each other and that the flow for the two phases is in parallel. The total flux is given by the sum of equations [1] and [2]:

$$J = -D\theta \, dC_l/dx - 0.6\alpha f D_0 \, dC_v/dx. \qquad [3]$$

The subscripts l and v denote the concentration in the liquid and vapor phases, respectively. According to Henry's law, there is a simple proportionality between the two concentrations, $C_l = kC_v$, where k is a constant. Equation [3] can then be written in terms of C_v (or C_l) only, e.g.:

$$J = -(D\theta k + 0.6\alpha f D_0) \, dC_v/dx. \qquad [4]$$

Equation [4] can also be written in terms of the vapor pressure of the diffusing substance since for ideal gases there is a simple proportionality between the vapor pressure and the concentration in both the liquid and vapor phases. The relative importance of diffusion in the two phases depends upon the degree of saturation of the soil and the constant k. For series-parallel type flow the factor α would require appropriate modification.

Nonsteady state equations. Nonsteady state equations corresponding to Fick's second law of diffusion are derived from equations [1] and [2] by applying the equation of continuity. The result for liquid diffusion in soil is:

$$\partial M/\partial t = D\theta(\partial^2 C/\partial x^2) \qquad [5]$$

or

$$\partial C/\partial t = D(\partial^2 C/\partial x^2) \qquad [6]$$

where M is the quantity of substance per unit volume of soil and t is the time. For vapor diffusion, the analogous equations are:

$$\partial M/\partial t = 0.6\alpha f D_0(\partial^2 C/\partial x^2) \qquad [7]$$

or

$$\partial P/\partial t = 0.6\alpha D_0(\partial^2 P/\partial x^2) \qquad [8]$$

where P is the partial pressure of the diffusing vapor. Methods for obtaining solutions to equations [5], [6], [7], and [8] are discussed in detail in Crank (1956), Carslaw and Jaeger (1959), as well as in most texts on partial differential equations.

A solution which is often very useful is that for a semi-infinite system with uniform initial concentration and for which, after time zero, the boundary is maintained at some other concentration. These conditions may be written:

$$\begin{aligned} C = C_i \quad t = 0, \quad x \geq 0 \\ C = C_0 \quad t > 0, \quad x = 0 \end{aligned} \qquad [9]$$

where C_i is the initial concentration and C_0 is the concentration at the boundary. The solution of equation [6] for these boundary conditions is:

$$\frac{C - C_0}{C_i - C_0} = \text{erf}\left(\frac{x}{2\sqrt{Dt}}\right).* \qquad [10]$$

---

*The error function (erf) is discussed briefly by Carslaw and Jaeger (1959) and is tabulated in any of a number of mathematical handbooks. The normal probability integral $= \text{erf}(x/\sqrt{2})$. [See Dwight (1949).]

The rate of diffusion out of the system at $x = 0$ is given by

$$(D \, dC/dx)_{x=0} = (C_i - C_0)D/\sqrt{\pi Dt}. \qquad [11]$$

The total amount which has diffused out after time t can be obtained by straightforward integration of equation [11]. If $C_0 > C_i$, diffusion is into, rather than out of, the system.

III. DIFFUSION PLUS REACTION

We next consider the possibility of interaction between the diffusing ion and the soil particles. In order to do this, it is necessary to have a quantitative understanding of the nature of the reaction. In particular, one must know the relation between the concentration of an ion or molecule in the solution phase and the concentration in the adsorbed phase. Because of the complex nature of these relations in soils it will often be necessary to approximate them by simpler expressions. Fortunately, very good results can be obtained from solutions of the diffusion equation even when very approximate expressions are used.

Instantaneous reversible reaction. If the rate of reaction of the diffusing substance is very rapid compared with the diffusion process, then the solution and adsorbed phases can be assumed to be in equilibrium at each point in the soil. The relation between the two phases is given by the adsorption isotherm. Let S be the amount of nitrogen adsorbed per unit volume of soil. For a linear isotherm

$$S = R\theta C + \text{constant} \qquad [12]$$

where R is the ratio of the number of ions in the adsorbed phase to the number of ions in the solution phase, per unit volume of soil. Equation [5] must now contain an additional term to account for the adsorption:

$$\partial M/\partial t = \theta(\partial C/\partial t) + (\partial S/\partial t) = D\theta(\partial^2 C/\partial x^2). \qquad [13]$$

Since $M = S + \theta C + \text{constant}$, it follows from equation [12] that $M = (R + 1)\,\theta C + \text{constant}$. Substituting into equation [13] gives

$$\partial C/\partial t = [D/(R + 1)](\partial^2 C/\partial x^2). \qquad [14]$$

Equation [14] is the same as equation [6] except that the diffusion coefficient is multiplied by the factor $[1/(R + 1)]$. $(R + 1)$ is the same as the capacity factor used by Olsen et al. (1962). $D/(R + 1)$ becomes analogous to the thermal diffusivity as it appears in the heat flow equation.

Care should be exercised in using equation [14]. The concentration distribution can be obtained merely by replacing D by $[D/(R + 1)]$ in equation [10]. However, equation [11] becomes

$$(D \, dC/dx)_{x=0} = (C_i - C_0)D/\sqrt{\pi Dt/(R + 1)}. \qquad [15]$$

Thus, for comparable solution concentrations, the flux of ions into or out of a system in which they may be adsorbed is actually enhanced by a factor $\sqrt{R + 1}$ over that which would exist if there were no adsorption.

When the total quantity of ions per unit volume of soil is the same in both systems, then the flux in the system in which there is adsorption is less than the flux in the system where there is no adsorption by the factor $\sqrt{R+1}$.

However, as is discussed in more detail elsewhere in this monograph, most soil reactions involving nitrogen tend to be linear only at low concentrations. Nonlinear relations present considerably more difficulty, but can be handled in a similar fashion. Instead of the simple linear relation between M and C, now let $M = g(C)$ where $g(C)$ represents the adsorption isotherm. Equation [13] can then be written

$$\partial M/\partial t = \partial/\partial x(D\theta/g' \times \partial M/\partial x) \qquad [16]$$

where $g' = dM/dC$. Equation [16] is now a problem in concentration dependent diffusion. Crank (1956) discusses numerical procedures for solving such equations, and the methods developed for handling the flow equation describing water movement in unsaturated soils are applicable. An approximate method of solving equation [16] is given by Gardner (1962). It can also be shown that, for the semi-infinite case described above, the flux at the boundary of the system can be characterized by a weighted mean diffusion coefficient (Crank, 1956, p. 256) which is used in place of D in equation [11].

Irreversible reaction. If nitrogen is adsorbed or produced in the soil according to an essentially irreversible reaction, then a term expressing the time rate of reaction must be added to the diffusion equation. Equation [5] may then be written

$$\partial M/\partial t = D\theta(\partial^2 C/\partial x^2) + Q(x) \qquad [17]$$

where $Q(x)$ is the reaction rate, which may be a function of position. Steady-state solutions of equation [17] are obtained by setting $\partial M/\partial t = 0$ and integrating. A solution for $Q = $ constant is given by Carslaw and Jaeger (1959, p. 130).

If, instead of $Q = $ constant, the reaction rate is proportional to the concentration, then

$$\partial C/\partial t = D(\partial^2 C/\partial x^2) + kC \qquad [18]$$

where k is the reaction rate constant. Crank (1956, p. 124) gives some solutions of equation [18]. The method of separation of variables will yield solutions of [18] for many types of boundary conditions.

IV. CONVECTION

If the soil solution is itself moving with respect to the soil, then nitrogen dissolved in the solution will be carried along with it. This is of particular concern for the nitrate ion which will move with the soil water. The problem is often one of determining the amount and direction of the water movement.

Neglecting "salt sieving" and other interaction effects (Kemper, 1960), the flux of nitrogen in the x direction due to water movement is simply

$$J = qC \qquad [19]$$

where q is the flux of water in the x direction, i.e., the volume of water crossing unit area in unit time. It is often convenient to relate the flux q to the average velocity of water in the soil, v, by the expression $q = v\theta$. If the soil is saturated with water, then $q = vf$. The rate of change of nitrogen content of the soil per unit volume of soil due to convection is then written

$$\partial M/\partial t = -\partial J/\partial x = -\partial(qC)/\partial x. \qquad [20]$$

It should be remembered that both q and C may be functions of x.

Diffusion plus convection. When diffusion and convection take place simultaneously, equations [6] and [20] are simply combined to give

$$\partial C/\partial t = D(\partial^2 C/\partial x^2) - \partial(vC)/\partial x. \qquad [21]$$

The problem of diffusion plus convection is not actually so simple as might be implied from equation [21]. The difficulty arises from the fact that the microscopic velocity of the water is not everywhere the same, even for a fixed value of x. The velocity near the center of a pore exceeds that near the edge, and the velocity through a series of large pores may greatly exceed that in a series of smaller pores, not to mention blind, or dead end, pores. The result of this variation in the flow velocities is a mixing, or dispersion, process that is roughly analogous to turbulent or eddy diffusion. This dispersion process can enhance the diffusion process, and at sufficiently high velocities it may completely obscure it.

Thus, the diffusion coefficient which appears in equation [21] is not the diffusion coefficient which applies in the absence of water movement. Rather, one must use an apparent coefficient which depends upon the flow velocity in a complex manner. For a flow velocity of 6.7 cm/day, Nielsen and Biggar (1963) obtained an apparent chloride diffusion coefficient of about 15 cm²/day compared with 5.3 cm²/day at a velocity of 0.122 cm/day. The diffusion coefficient in the absence of water movement is less than 1 cm²/day.

Equation [21] can be solved by separation of variables. A transformation given by Jost (1952, p. 47) is useful:

$$C = C^* \exp (vx/2D - v^2t/4D). \qquad [22]$$

Equation [22] defines a new variable, which, when introduced into equation [21], results in

$$\partial C^*/\partial t = D\partial^2 C/\partial x^2 \qquad [23]$$

which is now the same as equation [6]. In applying the transformation, the boundary conditions must also be transformed according to equation [22].

A somewhat simpler, but merely approximate, formulation has sometimes been used in place of equation [21]. If the frame of reference for x is allowed to move through the soil with the average velocity v, then one can describe the concentration distribution fairly well by means of the equation

$$\partial C/\partial t = \kappa(\partial^2 C/\partial X^2) \qquad [24]$$

where $X = (x - vt)$ and κ is a characteristic of the soil pore space and the flow process and is called the dispersion coefficient. At flow velocities sufficiently high so that diffusion can be neglected, the ratio κ/v should be a constant, which is designated by $\beta/2$ in the notation of Day and Forsythe (1957). They reported values for β for sands ranging from about 0.10 to 0.34 cm. The data of Gardner and Brooks (1956) for the leaching of chloride from a sandy loam in the field gave a value of about $\beta = 8$ cm. When the velocity is less than about 1 cm/day, the dispersion coefficient is reduced to less than the diffusion coefficient, and the ratio β then increases with decreasing velocity.

Diffusion plus convection and reaction. If diffusion, convection, and a linear irreversible reaction occur simultaneously, terms from equations [18] and [21] may be combined to give

$$\partial C/\partial t = D(\partial^2 C/\partial x^2) - \partial(vC)/\partial x + kC. \qquad [25]$$

This equation can also be solved by the method of separation of variables. If v is a constant independent of x, then the steady-state solution of [25] is:

$$C = C_0 \exp\left\{\frac{v}{2D}\left(1 - \sqrt{1 + \frac{4kD}{v^2}}\right)x\right\}. \qquad [26]$$

V. CONVECTION PLUS REVERSIBLE REACTION

An important, but extremely complex problem is the convection of exchangeable and other reversibly adsorbed ions. Examples are NH_4^+ which is involved in ion exchange, and urea which Broadbent, Hill, and Tyler (1958) have shown to be weakly adsorbed in soils. Equations derived for ion-exchange resins have been successfully applied to the movement of certain exchangeable ions in soils (Bower et al., 1957). Since the exchange reaction is reversible, the concentration of any competing ions must be taken into account along with the concentration of the nitrogen compound. For more detail than is given below, the reader should consult Hiester and Vermeulen (1952) whose treatment is followed here.

Let C_a be the concentration of ammonia or other nitrogen ion in the soil solution and Q_a the concentration of adsorbed ammonia per unit weight of soil. Let C_b and Q_b be the corresponding concentrations of a single competing ion. Then,

$$(\partial C_a/\partial x)v_-^{\bullet} = \rho(\partial Q_a/\partial V)_x + {}_-^{\bullet}\theta(\partial C_a/\partial V)_x \qquad [27]$$

represents the equation of continuity, where ρ is the bulk density of the soil and V is the volume of soil solution passing a given point at distance x from the origin. It is more convenient to write [27] in terms of V than in terms of the time, t. It is assumed that the rate of exchange of ions between the solution and the exchange sites is given by

$$\partial Q_a/\partial t = k \left(C_a Q_b - \frac{1}{K} Q_a C_b \right) \qquad [28]$$

where k is an exchange rate constant and K is an equilibrium constant. At equilibrium $\partial Q/\partial t = 0$, and [28] reduces to

$$K = Q_a C_b/Q_b C_a. \qquad [29]$$

Equation [29] is a simple mass action type exchange equation. Ion exchange in soils, particularly between ions of unequal valence, will not, in general, be so simple. However, the results of Bower et al. (1957) show that excellent results may be obtained by approximating the exact exchange equation by an approximate mass action equation.

Numerical means are required to solve equations [27] and [28] simultaneously. Graphical solutions have been published by Opler and Hiester (1954) for several different boundary conditions. The results are most conveniently expressed in terms of three dimensionless quantities:

$$\tau = k(V - x\theta)/qR \qquad [30]$$

$$s = kx\theta/q \qquad [31]$$

$$r = 1/K. \qquad [32]$$

The first of these parameters, τ, is known as the solution capacity parameter, s is the column capacity parameter, and r is the equilibrium parameter. R is again the distribution ratio and q is the rate of water movement through the soil. If a volume of water, V, is applied to a saturated soil, then $(V - x\theta)$ is the volume passing a depth x. (A somewhat different notation is employed by Hiester and Vermeulen (1952).)

One simple example from the many possible combinations of boundary conditions will be illustrated here. Consider the case of NH_4^+ adsorbed in a uniform band in the soil to a depth L. Let the soil be saturated with water and the concentration of NH_4^+ in solution be small compared with that of the other exchange ions. This simplifies the problem to that of trace quantities so that the concentration of the competing ion can be treated as constant and lumped in with the equilibrium exchange constant. Now pass a volume of water V through the soil. The concentration of NH_4^+ adsorbed on the exchange sites, for V sufficiently large, is given by:

$$Q_a/Q_i = \tfrac{1}{2}[1 - \text{erf} \, (\sqrt{\tau} - \sqrt{s})] \qquad [33]$$

where Q_i is the initial concentration of adsorbed NH_4^+ in the band. To obtain the concentration distribution at the leading edge of the band, x is measured positively downward with $x = L$ as the origin. The concentration at the trailing edge is obtained by measuring x from the soil surface. The band will not necessarily be symmetrical, depending upon the nature of the exchange. The average rate at which the band moves downward can be obtained from the ratio $\tau/s = 1$, which gives the 50% concentration value. For $\tau/s = 1$ from equations [30] and [31],

$$(V - \theta x) = R\theta x = \frac{Q_i\rho}{C_0} x \qquad [34]$$

where C_0 is the initial concentration of NH_4^+ in solution. From equation [34] it can be seen that the ratio of the distance the water moves to the distance the ions move is, on the average,

$$V/\theta x = R + 1. \qquad [35]$$

Thus, if 90% of the ammonia is adsorbed, the band of ammonia will move 1 cm down into the soil for every 10 cm of water movement.

For ammonia concentrations which are too high to allow the use of equation [33], the treatment used by Bower and coworkers (1957) for sodium-calcium exchange should be satisfactory. The reader is referred to their paper for details.

VI. NITRATE MOVEMENT AND LEACHING

More interest is centered on the movement of nitrate in the soil than on the movement of any other form of nitrogen. Of particular concern is the loss of nitrate from a soil profile due to leaching. In this section the equations describing ion convection are used to consider nitrate distribution and leaching.

Leaching. We will consider first the movement of a thin band of nitrate through a saturated soil. Let the initial concentration of nitrate in the soil be C_0 down to a small depth x_0, below which there is no nitrate. The total nitrate per unit area of soil is then fC_0x_0. Now let water begin to move through the soil with the average velocity v. The solution of equation [25] for these conditions is (Day, 1956)

$$C = C_0x_0(4\pi\kappa t)^{-1/2} \exp\left[-(x - vt)^2/4\kappa t\right]. \qquad [36]$$

The crest, or point of maximum concentration, moves downward with a velocity v, and the depth of this maximum at any time is $x_m = vt$. It is sometimes more convenient to express the results in terms of the volume V, or the distance x_m. This is not difficult since $V = fvt = fx_m$ and $\beta = 2\kappa/v$. As the nitrate moves downward, the distribution spreads out in such a way that the standard deviation increases as $\sqrt{2\kappa t} = \sqrt{\beta x_m} = \sqrt{\beta V/f}$. The maximum concentration is given as a function of depth by

$$c_{max} = C_0x_0/\sqrt{2\beta x_m}. \qquad [37]$$

The data of Wetselaar (1962) are plotted in Fig. 1 in comparison with the distribution calculated from equation [36]. The value of β was estimated by fitting equation [31] to the data for 7.4 inches of rainfall. A value of 22 cm was obtained and this value was used to predict the distribution after 15.4 and 23.7 inches of rainfall. A linear relationship be-

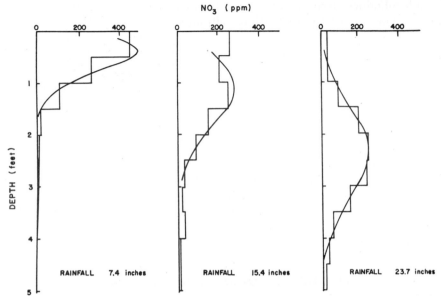

Fig. 1. Nitrate distribution observed by Wetselaar (1962) compared with theoretical distribution calculated from equation [36]. The smooth curves represent the theoretical calculation.

tween x_m and amount of rainfall was assumed since V was not known. Departures of the theory from experiment are within the standard error of the measurements given by Wetselaar. In view of the inhomogeneity of field sites, the agreement is excellent.

It can be seen from the theoretical development that the distance which nitrate will move downward depends not so much upon the total rainfall as upon the amount of rainfall which actually passes through the soil. It is for this reason that correlation of nitrate leaching losses with rainfall (Raney, 1960; McCants, 1962) is not as direct as might be expected. This is particularly true under cropping conditions when plants are continually extracting water from the soil. It would be better to use the excess of rainfall over evapotranspiration to estimate the possibility of leaching losses. This is the basis of the "leaching requirement" concept used in salinity control (U.S. Salinity Laboratory Staff, 1954).

Only slightly different is the problem in which the soil initially contains nitrate distributed uniformly to a great depth. If water containing no nitrate is passed through the soil with velocity v, the concentration of nitrate is then:

$$C/C_0 = \tfrac{1}{2}[1 + \mathrm{erf}\,[(x - x_m)\sqrt{2\beta x_m}]] \qquad [38]$$

where C_0 is the initial concentration of nitrate. For the values $\beta = 2$ and $\beta = 20$, the nitrate distribution during leaching is plotted in Fig. 2. The initial distribution of nitrate was assumed to be 500 ppm. The value $\beta = 20$ cm is approximately that given by Wetselaar's data and corresponds to intermittent leaching. If leaching is accomplished by a continuous process, β should be much smaller.

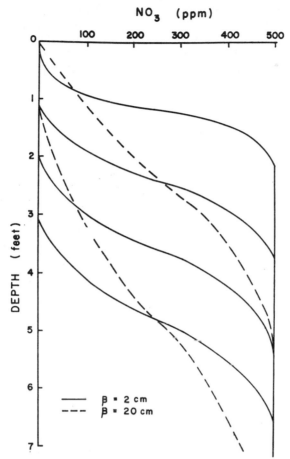

Fig. 2. Theoretical nitrate distribution during leaching calculated from equation [38], for two different values of β.

The above equations assume the soil to have a uniform water content at all times. The theoretical approach derived by Gardner and Brooks (1956) does not make this assumption, and can be applied to the movement of ions during wetting of the soil. However, the resulting equations do not differ greatly in form from those above.

The amount and direction of water movement is extremely important where mobile ions such as nitrate are concerned. If the soil is particularly inhomogeneous, with a few channels carrying most of the water downward, then it is very difficult to apply equations [36] and [38]. Even in homogeneous soils, if drainage is achieved by means of tile lines or ditches, the leaching pattern will not be uniform. Several times as much water may pass through the soil directly above the tile line as will pass through that midway between tiles. When water is applied to the soil in irrigation furrows, movement is not only downward but also toward the plane midway between the furrows. Thus the nitrate and other mobile salts tend to accumulate between the furrows (Harding, 1954; Bernstein and Fireman, 1957). If irrigation is continued for a sufficiently long time after the ridges between the furrows become saturated, the nitrate will eventually tend to be moved downward out of the ridge (Nelson, 1961). See also Tyler et al. (1958).

Surface accumulation. It has long been noted that between irrigations or rains, nitrates and other salts tend to accumulate at the soil surface (Krantz et al., 1944). This is due to the upward movement of water and its subsequent evaporation at or near the soil surface. The rate of evaporation is governed principally by external evaporation conditions until the soil surface becomes dry. After that the drying rate decreases with time and is determined by the water transmitting properties of the soil. The rate of change of upward velocity is sufficiently slow that the nitrate accumulation can be treated as a steady-state problem. It is a case of upward convection coupled with downward diffusion. Setting $\partial C/\partial t = 0$ in equation [21] and assuming the flux v to be constant (this is nearly so except right near the zone of evaporation), we obtain

$$C = C_0 \exp\left(-vx/D\right) \tag{39}$$

where C_0 is the concentration at $x = 0$. It should be noted that the appropriate value for the diffusion coefficient here must take into account the effect of convection upon diffusion which was previously discussed. The logarithmic distribution predicted by equation [39] has been found by a number of investigators (Krantz et al., 1944; Stewart and Eck, 1958; Wetselaar, 1961a, b). Fig. 3 shows a plot of some of Wetselaar's data. In most cases reported in the literature, the downward diffusion is not sufficiently rapid to carry the nitrate more than a few inches below the point where evaporation is occurring.

Steady-state nitrate distribution. The above results show that the nitrate distribution in the soil profile is profoundly influenced by the most recent pattern of water movement. However, after several reasonably uniform cycles of wetting and drying, a distribution should be set up which is, on the average, not greatly different from the steady state. The dispersion process plays an important role in tending to smooth out the effects of an individual cycle. The distribution which might be expected after a season of uniform irrigations or rains can be calculated from equation [20]. It is necessary to specify all sources and sinks for nitrate as a function of position in the profile. If the only source is in the water applied to the soil surface, after setting $\partial M/\partial t = 0$ and integrating once, we obtain:

$$qC = \text{constant.} \tag{40}$$

It is next necessary to specify the flux as a function of depth. Although not really true for many plants, we will assume for purposes of illustration that water is extracted uniformly at all depths down to some depth L. Then, $q = (q_0 - bx)$ where q_0 is the water applied to the surface and b is a constant, such that $(q_0 - bL)$ gives the drainage, or the flux out the bottom of the root zone. Equation [40] then becomes

$$C = C_0 q_0/(q_0 - bx) \tag{41}$$

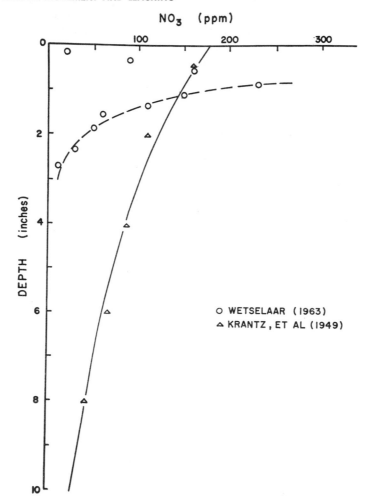

Fig. 3. Nitrate distribution at soil surface. The symbols represent experimental observations and the smooth curves were calculated from equation [39].

where C_0 is the concentration of nitrate in the applied water. Any other
relation describing the water uptake pattern is as readily introduced. It
is obvious from equation [41] that a uniform water uptake pattern does
not result in a uniform nitrate distribution. The concentration tends to
increase more and more rapidly with increasing depth.

However, the data of Pratt et al. (1960) showed that after 20 years of
cropping and treatment in a lysimeter investigation, the nitrogen distribution was fairly uniform with depth with the highest concentrations in
the surface 6 inches. What we have not taken into account is the fact that
nitrate is being simultaneously taken up by the plant, and also being
produced from the less mobile forms of nitrogen. For purposes of illustration, we will assume that the rate of uptake of nitrate is proportional
to the nitrate concentration, with the proportionality constant k inde-

pendent of depth. We will further assume that nitrate is being produced at a rate B, also independent of depth. Instead of equation [20], we now write

$$\partial M/\partial t = -\partial(qC)/\partial x - kC + B = 0. \qquad [42]$$

The solution of equation [42] is

$$c = \left[C_0 - \frac{B}{(k - b)} \right] \left[\frac{q_0 - bx}{q_0} \right]^{\frac{k-b}{b}} + \frac{B}{k - b} \qquad [43]$$

where C_0 is the concentration of nitrate in the water as it is applied to the soil surface and the constant b has the same meaning as in equation [41]. The average rate of loss of nitrate from the profile by leaching is obtained from equation [43] by multiplying the flux at $x = L$ by the concentration at $x = L$. For the steady-state case, it is obvious that the average leaching loss equals the rate of production less the rate of consumption if no other losses occur.

VII. AMMONIA MOVEMENT AND VOLATILIZATION

The movement of ammonia in soils is of particular interest because of the significant losses of nitrogen from the soil which may occur due to volatilization. This is of special concern during and after the application of aqua ammonia or anhydrous ammonia. Data such as that of Baker et al. (1959) show that such losses are closely related to the depth of application of ammonia.

Ammonia movement involves diffusion in both the liquid and the gaseous phase. The relative importance of the two phases depends upon the water content of the soil. We can apply the mathematics of diffusion to anhydrous ammonia movement by assuming that at time $t = 0$ the ammonia is distributed along an instantaneous line source through the soil. In actual practice, this is nearly true. The distribution of ammonia, assuming a linear adsorption isotherm, should then be given by (Carslaw and Jaeger, 1959, p. 259)

$$C = (Q/4\pi\overline{D}t) \exp(-r^2/4\overline{D}t) \qquad [44]$$

where Q is the amount of ammonia applied per unit length of source, r is the radial distance from the line of application and $\overline{D}$ is an effective diffusion coefficient taking into account the adsorption as well as diffusion in both phases, i.e., $\overline{D}$ contains the capacity factor $(R + 1)$. Fig. 4 shows a distribution obtained in the field by Blue and Eno (1954) compared with a distribution calculated from equation [44]. Since the authors did not indicate the time between application and sampling, it is not possible to evaluate $\overline{D}$. If the ammonia is applied as a plane source as was done by McIntosh and Frederick (1958), the distribution is given by (Carslaw and Jaeger, 1959, p. 259)

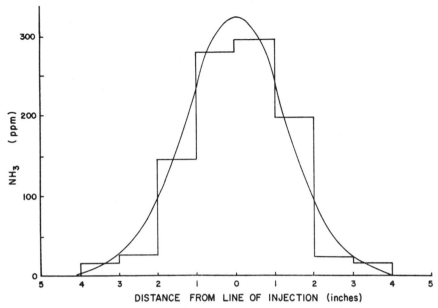

Fig. 4. NH$_3$ distribution as a function of distance from line of injection in soil, data of Blue and Eno (1954). The smooth curve was calculated from equation [44].

$$C = Q/2\sqrt{\pi \overline{D}t}\, \exp\,(-x^2/4\overline{D}t) \qquad [45]$$

where x is the distance from the plane of application. Data for nitrogen distribution 7 and 14 days after application obtained by McIntosh and Frederick are plotted in Fig. 5 and compared with the distribution calculated from equation [45]. A value for $\overline{D}$ of 0.025 cm^2/day fits both sets of data reasonably well. In order to assess how much of this diffusion is in the liquid phase and how much in the vapor phase, information on the water content and porosity are needed. It is also difficult to ascertain how much of the ammonia is adsorbed. The data of Peech cited by Mortland (1958) indicate that at low ammonia concentrations an appreciable fraction of the ammonia might be adsorbed. The magnitude for $\overline{D}$ obtained above suggests that this was probably the case. The results of Ray et al. (1957) give a similar value for $\overline{D}$. Equations [44] and [45] allow one to calculate a minimum depth of ammonia placement if volatilization losses are to be small. So long as the effective value of $\overline{D}$ is not much larger than the .025 cm^2/day found above, losses should not be appreciable when the ammonia is placed at least 15 cm below the soil surface. This estimate is in keeping with the results of Jackson and Chang (1947) and others. If large channels are made in the soil during application, losses could be much greater.

The loss of ammonia from soils is found to be related to the water loss (Jewitt, 1942; Kresge and Satchell, 1960; Martin and Chapman, 1951; Volk, 1959; Wahhab et al., 1957). There are at least two reasons for this. Conditions which favor evaporation of water will favor volatilization of

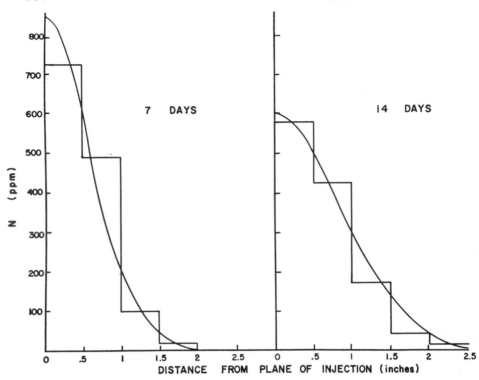

Fig. 5. Distribution of nitrogen (ammonium and nitrate) 7 and 14 days after injection in soil, data of McIntosh and Frederick (1958). The smooth curves were calculated from equation [45] with $\overline{D} = 0.025$ cm²/day.

ammonia. In addition, the upward movement of water helps transport
ammonia to the soil surface. The relative importance of convection and
diffusion in the transport of ammonia can be assessed if the concentration and diffusion coefficient are known. By way of example, let us assume
that the ammonia nitrogen content of the soil is 10^{-5} moles/cm³. This is
approximately 240 pounds per acre in the top 6 inches. We will further
assume that the porosity of the soil is 0.5 and that the amount of ammonia adsorbed on the soil particles is small compared with that in solution.
The total amount of nitrogen lost as NH_3 after time t is found by integrating equation [11]:

$$M = 2C_0\sqrt{Dt/\pi}. \qquad [46]$$

The loss after time $t = 10$ days if $D = 0.025$ cm²/day is 1.1×10^{-5}
moles/cm² or about 18 pounds per acre. Since the concentration in the
soil solution is 2×10^{-5} moles/cm³, the total loss after 10 days due to
an evaporation rate of, say, 0.5 cm/day, would be 10^{-4} moles/cm². This
is approximately 160 pounds per acre, or considerably more than the
loss due to diffusion. However, higher diffusion coefficients than the 0.025
cm²/day used here are quite possible so that diffusion alone can account
for appreciable losses when the nitrogen is placed near the soil surface.

Losses from applications of anhydrous ammonia to a completely dry soil can be calculated in a similar fashion by taking into account the adsorption as in equation [15].

VIII. MOVEMENT OF NITROGEN TO PLANT ROOTS

The availability of nutrient ions for plant uptake is related in an important way to ion movement. Bray (1954) has developed a qualitative concept of availability in terms of nutrient mobility and Barber (1962) has given consideration to the specific mechanisms involved. With the help of the equations presented above a more quantitative treatment of this problem is possible. Both diffusion and convection of the ions must be taken into account. An approximate treatment of this problem has been given by Passioura (1963). He assumed, in effect, diffusion and mass flow could be considered separately and expressions for the two mechanisms added to give the total flux. This is true at low rates of water uptake, but at higher rates equation [21] must be used.

We will consider the plant root to be a cylinder of radius a, and we shall denote the rate of uptake of nitrogen per unit length of root by Q. The steady-state case only will be considered first. Integration of equation [21] gives:

$$2\pi rD \, dC/dr + wC = Q \qquad [47]$$

where w is the rate of water uptake per unit length of root. It must be remembered that D may be a function of w because of hydrodynamic dispersion. In this case the velocity v is not constant but is related to r by $v = w/2\pi r$. The solution of equation [47] is:

$$C = (C_0 - Q/w)(b/r)^{w/2\pi D} + Q/w \qquad [48]$$

where C_0 is the concentration at some distance b from the root. C_0 may be considered as the average concentration in the root zone.

The maximum rate at which nitrate or other diffusible ion can be taken up by the plant root is obtained by setting $C = 0$ at $r = a$. Equation [48] then reduces to

$$Q = C_0 w \left[\frac{(b/a)^{w/2\pi D}}{(b/a)^{w/2\pi D} - 1} \right]. \qquad [49]$$

If the rate of water uptake is small, then $w/2\pi D$ is small, and equation [49] reduces to

$$Q = C_0 w \left[\frac{(2\pi D/w) + \ln (b/a)}{\ln (b/a)} \right]. \qquad [50]$$

In the limit, $w = 0$, corresponding to no water uptake, equation [50] becomes

$$Q = 2\pi D C_0 / \ln (b/a) \qquad [51]$$

which is the solution for diffusion alone. For negligible diffusion, i.e., w very large, [50] reduces to $Q = C_0 w$, as it should.

Equation [49] illustrates the extent to which ion uptake may be enhanced by diffusion in the presence of convection. If, by way of example,

$b/a = 10$, $w = 0.1$ cm^3/cm/day and $D = 1$ cm^2/day, then the factor in the brackets in equation [49] is $10^{0.16}/(10^{0.16} - 1) = 3.2$. In this case, diffusion increases the ion uptake about threefold. If the diffusivity were only 0.1 cm^2/day, as might be the case at a low soil-water content, the factor would be 1.025 for the same rate of water uptake. For a lower rate of water uptake, diffusion would become relatively more important.

If for some reason the nitrate is not taken up at a rate equal to the convection rate, i.e., $Q < C_0 w$, then nitrate will tend to accumulate around the root until a sufficiently large opposing gradient is built up to remove the ions as rapidly as they are carried up. This is of greater interest in the case of chloride and other ions that are largely excluded by most plants. In the extreme case of complete exclusion, $Q = 0$, the concentration of ions at the root relative to that at some distance b is

$$C_a/C_b = (b/a)^{w/2\pi D}. \tag{52}$$

If, as seems more probable, the rate of uptake is some function of the concentration at the root surface, e.g., $Q = kC_a$ where k is a constant, then we have

$$Q = \frac{C_0 k (b/a)^{w/2\pi D}}{1 + (k/w)[(b/a)^{w/2\pi D} - 1]}. \tag{53}$$

The concentration at $r = a$ is obtained merely by dividing equation [53] by k. For very high reaction rates (k very large), [53] reduces to [49], while for very small reaction rates it reduces to [52].

Uptake of adsorbed ions. Steady-state movement of adsorbed ions to a plant root is described by the same equations as for nonadsorbed ions since in the steady-state case there is no net exchange of ions between adsorbed and solution phases. However, in the case of adsorbed ions, the approach to steady state may be so slow that the transient state must be considered. The case of diffusion plus convection of adsorbed ions has not yet been worked out for boundary conditions appropriate to the uptake of ions by a plant root. The case of diffusion alone has been considered for phosphorus by Bouldin (1961) and by Olsen et al. (1962). The application to nitrogen movement is similar. We assume the initial concentration of nitrogen in solution to be C_0. For all times $t > 0$, we assume that the concentration at the root at $r = a$ is maintained at a lower value C_a. The solution of the diffusion equation in cylindrical coordinates is (Carslaw and Jaeger, 1959, p. 336):

for t small

$$Q = 2\pi D(C_0 - C_a)\left\{(\pi T)^{-1/2} + \frac{1}{4} - \ldots\right\} \tag{54}$$

and for t large

$$Q = 4D(C_0 - C_a)\left\{\frac{1}{\ln (4T) - 2\gamma}\right\} \tag{55}$$

where $T = Dt/(R + 1)a^2$ and $\gamma = 0.57722\ldots$ is Euler's constant. Equations [54] and [55] are more convenient than the approximations given by Passioura (1963). In his case $R = 0$.

The effect of the adsorbed ions is reflected in the capacity factor $[(R + 1)$ in the case of linear adsorption]. If this factor is large, then the rate of uptake for a given solution concentration C_0 is greatly enhanced for small values of t since $(R + 1)$ appears to the plus one-half power in equation [54]. For large times when equation [55] is applicable, $(R + 1)$ appears in the logarithmic term and has much less effect. As the steady state is approached, the presence of the adsorbed ions is relatively less important. Equations [54] and [55] take into account in a quantitative way the replenishment factor introduced by Barber (1962).

Bouldin (1961) also considered the case in which the rate of uptake is proportional to the concentration at $r = a$. Solutions for this case for cylindrical coordinates are given in graphical form by Carslaw and Jaeger (1959, p. 338).

Convection of adsorbed ions. The convection of adsorbed ions to plant roots is difficult to treat quantitatively because of the complex boundary conditions that usually exist. Initially, the ions are apt to be distributed in the small region or band where they are placed. The water movement pattern is difficult to characterize except in the near vicinity of roots which are taking up water. If the amount of water being taken up can be estimated, then it is possible to obtain some idea of the distance which the adsorbed ions will move from the capacity factor $(R + 1)$. It can be expected that this distance will seldom be appreciable and that adsorbed ions can only be taken up by roots in the immediate vicinity of the fertilizer. An extensive root system is probably more important from the standpoint of nutrient uptake than for water uptake since water can move much greater distances than ions can diffuse (Gardner and Ehlig, 1962).

REFERENCES CITED

Baker, J. H., Peech, Michael, and Musgrave, R. B. 1959. Determination of application losses of anhydrous ammonia. Agron. J. 51:361-362.

Barber, Stanley A. 1962. A diffusion and mass-flow concept of soil nutrient availability. Soil Sci. 93:39-49.

Bernstein, Leon, and Fireman, Milton. 1957. Laboratory studies on salt distribution in furrow-irrigated soil with special reference to the pre-emergence period. Soil Sci. 83:249-263.

Blue, W. G., and Eno, C. F. 1954. Distribution and retention of anhydrous ammonia in sandy soils. Soil Sci. Soc. Am. Proc. 18:420-424.

Bouldin, D. R. 1961. Mathematical description of diffusion processes in the soil-plant system. Soil Sci. Soc. Am. Proc. 25:476-480.

Bower, C. A., Gardner, W. R., and Goertzen, J. O. 1957. Dynamics of cation exchange in soil columns. Soil Sci. Soc. Am. Proc. 21:20-24.

Bray, Roger H. 1954. A nutrient mobility concept of soil-plant relationships. Soil Sci. 78:9-22.

Broadbent, F. E., Hill, G. N., and Tyler, K. B. 1958. Transformations and movement of urea in soils. Soil Sci. Soc. Am. Proc. 22:303-307.

Carslaw, H. S., and Jaeger, J. C. 1959. Conduction of Heat in Solids. Clarendon Press, Oxford, England.

Crank, J. 1956. The Mathematics of Diffusion. Clarendon Press, Oxford, England.

Currie, J. A. 1960. Gaseous diffusion in porous media: 2. Dry granular materials. Brit. J. Appl. Phys. 11:318-324.

Currie, J. A. 1961. Gaseous diffusion in porous media. 3: Wet granular material. Brit. J. Appl. Phys. 12:275-281.

Day, Paul R. 1956. Dispersion of a moving salt-water boundary advancing through saturated sand. Trans. Am. Geophys. Union 37:595-601.

Day, Paul R., and Forsythe, Warren M. 1957. Hydrodynamic dispersion of solutes in the soil moisture stream. Soil Sci. Soc. Am. Proc. 21:477-480.

Dwight, Herbert B. 1949. Tables of Integrals and Other Mathematical Data. Macmillan, New York. p. 585.

Gardner, W. R. 1962. Note on the separation and solution of diffusion type equations. Soil Sci. Soc. Am. Proc. 26:404.

Gardner, W. R., and Brooks, R. H. 1956. A descriptive theory of leaching. Soil Sci. 83:295-304.

Gardner, W. R., and Ehlig, C. F. 1962. Some observations on the movement of water to plant roots. Agron. J. 54:453-456.

Graham-Bryce, I. J. 1963a. Self-diffusion of ions in soil. I. Cations. J. Soil Sci. 14:188-194.

Graham-Bryce, I. J. 1963b. Self-diffusion of ions in soil. II. Anions. J. Soil Sci. 14:195-199.

Harding, Robert B. 1954. Accumulation of nitrates and other soluble salts in California orange orchards. Soil Sci. Soc. Am. Proc. 18:369-372.

Hiester, Nevin K., and Vermeulen, Theodore. 1952. Saturation performance of ion-exchange and adsorption columns. Chem. Eng. Progress 48:505-516.

Jackson, M. L., and Chang, S. C. 1947. Anhydrous ammonia retention by soils as influenced by depth of application, soil texture, moisture content, pH value, and tilth. Agron. J. 39:623-633.

Jewitt, T. N. 1942. Loss of ammonia from ammonium sulfate applied to alkaline soils. Soil Sci. 54:401-409.

Jost, W. 1952. Diffusion in Solids, Liquids, Gases. Academic Press, Inc., New York.

Kemper, W. D. 1960. Water and ion movement in thin films as influenced by the electrostatic charge and diffuse layer of cations associated with clay mineral surfaces. Soil Sci. Soc. Am. Proc. 24:10-16.

Klute, A., and Letey, J. 1958. The dependence of ionic diffusion on the moisture content of nonadsorbing porous media. Soil Sci. Soc. Am. Proc. 22:213-215.

Krantz, B. A., Ohlrogge, A. J., and Scarseth, G. D. 1944. Movement of nitrogen in soils. Soil Sci. Soc. Am. Proc. (1943) 8:189-195.

Kresge, C. B., and Satchell, D. P. 1960. Gaseous loss of ammonia from nitrogen fertilizers applied to soils. Agron. J. 52:105-107.

Low, P. F. 1962a. Effect of quasi-crystalline water on rate processes involved in plant nutrition. Soil Sci. 93:6-15.

Low, P. F. 1962b. Influence of adsorbed water on exchangeable ion movement. Clays and Clay Minerals, Pergamon Press. Vol. 9:219-228.

McCants, C. B. 1962. Seasonal distribution of nutrients in soil under tobacco culture. Soil Sci. 94:36-43.

McIntosh, T. H., and Frederick, L. R. 1958. Distribution and nitrification of anhydrous ammonia in a Nicollet sandy clay loam. Soil Sci. Soc. Am. Proc. 22:402-405.

Martin, J. P., and Chapman, H. D. 1951. Volatilization of ammonia from surface-fertilized soils. Soil Sci. 71:25-34.

Millington, R. J., and Quirk, J. P. 1960. Transport in porous media. Trans. 7th International Cong. of Soil Sci. 1:97-106.

Mortland, M. M. 1958. Reactions of ammonia in soils. Advances in Agronomy. Vol. X:325-348.

Nelson, C. E. 1961. Movement of NH_4^+ and NO_3^- nitrogen from five nitrogen carriers banded in two row-treatments under irrigation. Washington Agr. Exp. Sta. Cir. 380.

Nielsen, D. R., and Biggar, J. W. 1963. Miscible displacement: Mixing in glass beads. Soil Sci. Soc. Am. Proc. 27:10-13.

Olsen, S. R., Kemper, W. D., and Jackson, R. D. 1962. Phosphate diffusion to plant roots. Soil Sci. Soc. Am. Proc. 26:222-227.

Opler, A., and Hiester, N. K. 1954. Tables for predicting the performance of fixed bed ion exchange and similar mass transfer processes. Stanford Research Institute, Stanford, Calif. 111 pp.

Passioura, J. B. 1963. A mathematical model for the uptake of ions from the soil solution. Plant and Soil 18:225-238.

Patil, S., King, K. M., and Miller, M. H. 1963. Self diffusion of rubidium as influenced by soil moisture tension. Can. J. Soil Sci. 43:44-51.

Porter, K. K., Kemper, W. D., Jackson, R. D., and Stewart, B. A. 1960. Chloride diffusion in soils as influenced by moisture content. Soil Sci. Soc. Am. Proc. 24:460-463.

Pratt, P. F., Chapman, H. D., and Garber, M. J. 1960. Gains and losses of nitrogen and depth distribution of nitrogen and organic carbon in the soil of a lysimeter investigation. Soil Sci. 90:293-297.

Raney, W. A. 1960. The dominant role of nitrogen in leaching losses from soils in humid regions. Agron. J. 52:563-566.

Ray, H. E., MacGregor, J. M., and Schmidt, E. L. 1957. Movement of ammonium nitrate in soils. Soil Sci. Soc. Am. Proc. 21:309-312.

Romkens, M. J. M., and Bruce, R. R. (1964) Nitrate diffusivity in relation to moisture content of nonadsorbing porous media. Soil Science 98:332-337.

Schofield, R. K., and Graham-Bryce, I. J. 1960. Diffusion of ions in soils. Nature 188:1048-1049.

Stewart, Bobby A., and Eck, Harold V. 1958. The movement of surface-applied nitrate into soils at five moisture levels. Soil Sci. Soc. Am. Proc. 22:260-262.

Tyler, K. B., Broadbent, F. E., and Kondo, V. 1958. Nitrogen movement in simulated cross sections of field soil. Agron. J. 50:626-628.

Tyrrell, H. J. V. 1961. Diffusion and Heat Flow in Liquids. Butterworths, London.

United States Salinity Laboratory Staff. 1954. Diagnosis and improvement of saline and alkali soils. U.S. Dept. Agr. Handb. 60. 160 pp.

Volk, G. M. 1959. Volatile loss of ammonia following surface application of urea to turf or bare soils. Agron. J. 51:746-749.

Wahhab, A., Randhawa, M. S., and Alam, S. Q. 1957. Loss of ammonia from ammonium sulphate under different conditions when applied to soils. Soil Sci. 84:249-255.

Wetselaar, R. 1961a. Nitrate distribution in tropical soils. I. Possible cause of nitrate accumulation near the surface after a long dry period. Plant and Soil 15:110-120.

Wetselaar, R. 1961b. Nitrate distribution in tropical soils. II. Extent of capillary accumulation of nitrate during a long dry period. Plant and Soil 15:121-133.

Wetselaar, R. 1962. Nitrate distribution in tropical soils. III. Downward movement and accumulation of nitrate in the subsoil. Plant and Soil 16:19-31.

NOTATION USED IN EQUATIONS

a	Radius of plant root, cm.
b	Outer radius of cylindrical system, cm; also average quantity of water taken up by plant roots per unit depth per unit time in root zone, cm/day.
B	Average rate of nitrate production per unit volume of soil, meq/cm³ day.
C, C_i	Concentration of nitrogen compound per unit volume of soil solution, meq/cm³.
C_v	Concentration of gaseous nitrogen compound per unit volume of soil pore space, meq/cm³.
C_0, C_i	Boundary and initial concentrations, meq/cm³.
D	Diffusion coefficient, cm²/day.
$\bar{D}$	Effective diffusion coefficient, cm²/day.
D_0	Vapor diffusion coefficient, cm²/day.
f	Soil porosity, dimensionless.
$g(C)$	Functional relationship between total quantity of ions per unit volume of soil and concentration of solution, $M = g(C)$, $g' = dM/dc$.
J	Flux of nitrogen compound, i.e., quantity crossing unit area per unit time, meq/cm² day.
k	Arbitrary rate constant.
K	Exchange equilibrium constant, dimensionless.
L	Linear dimension of system, cm.

M Quantity of substance, both adsorbed and in solution, per unit volume of soil, meq/cm^3.

P Partial pressure of diffusing vapor, atm.

q Flux of soil solution, cm/day.

$Q(x)$ Reaction rate for consumption or production of nitrate per unit volume of soil, meq/cm^3 day.

Q_a, Q_b Quantity of exchangeable ions of species a and b, respectively, adsorbed per unit weight of soil.

r Space variable in cylindrical coordinates, cm. Also equilibrium parameter for ion exchange, $r = 1/K$.

R Distribution ratio; i.e., ratio of adsorbed ions to ions in solution per unit volume of soil, dimensionless. $R = S/\theta C$.

s Column capacity parameter for ion exchange, dimensionless. $s = kx\theta/q$.

S Quantity of ions adsorbed per unit volume of soil, meq/cm^3. $S = Q_t\rho$.

t Time, days.

T Dimensionless parameter. $T = Dt/(R+1)a^2$.

v Average velocity of soil solution, cm/day. $v = q/f$.

V Volume of solution per unit area which has passed a specified point x at time t, cm.

w Rate of water uptake per unit length of plant root, cm^2/day.

x Position variable, linear coordinate system, cm.

x_0 Initial depth of placement of band of mobile nitrogen compound, cm.

x_m Depth to maximum concentration during leaching of mobile compound, cm.

X Transformed distance parameter, cm. $X = x - vt$.

α Tortuosity factor, dimensionless.

β Coefficient characterizing dispersion in a porous medium, cm.

θ Soil-water content on a volume basis, dimensionless.

κ Dispersion coefficient, cm^2/day. $\kappa = 2\beta v$.

ρ Bulk density of soil.

τ Solution capacity parameter for ion exchange, dimensionless. $\tau = k(V - \theta x)/qR$.

Chapter 16

Evaluation of Incoming and Outgoing Processes That Affect Soil Nitrogen

FRANKLIN E. ALLISON

Agricultural Research Service, U.S.D.A.
Beltsville, Maryland

I. INTRODUCTION

The efficiency with which nitrogen is utilized in crop production is a subject that has been of intense interest to agriculturists for many years. In the past, agronomists often have not realized that recoveries in harvested crops of nitrogen released from soil, or added as fertilizer, were more likely to be less than 50% than more than this value. This fact has become more evident in recent years as more data have become available, and as more dependence for crop nitrogen has been placed on commercial nitrogen and less on soil nitrogen, animal manures, and legumes.

The many things that can happen to nitrogen in the soil have been discussed in the previous chapters. The possibilities for changes that lead to gaseous products or readily soluble substances that may readily leach from soil, are so many that the casual reader may even be inclined to overemphasize these losses. In the present chapter the major known facts pertaining to nitrogen income and outgo will be discussed and an attempt made to evaluate their importance. Accurate appraisal of the information is not always possible, however, either because of lack of satisfactory basic data or because of wide variations in the experimental conditions that affect nitrogen balance. Representative nitrogen recovery data will also be reported and tentative conclusions drawn with respect to the efficiency of nitrogen under field conditions.

II. DIAGRAMMATIC REPRESENTATION OF INCOME AND OUTGO PROCESSES

In general discussions of nitrogen transformations in soil, it is a common practice to begin by presenting a nitrogen cycle diagram, such as that shown by Schreiner and Brown (1938). This term, nitrogen cycle, apparently originated during the early years of research in soil microbiology when the possible nitrogen changes were not known to be so great as later research has shown them to be. It is now possible to construct several nitrogen cycle diagrams, each of which would be approximately correct for a particular set of conditions. For this reason the author is not presenting the usual nitrogen cycle, but a more involved diagram (Fig. 1) showing soil nitrogen income and outgo. This diagram is not meant to be strictly accurate and complete to the last detail, but does show the major changes in soil nitrogen, most of which have been discussed in previous chapters.

Fig. 1, as constructed, shows the sources of nitrogen that gain entrance into the soil, the transformations that occur, and the fate of the end products. It will be observed that all sources of soil nitrogen are, figuratively speaking, thrown into the hopper (the soil) where the end products are ground out by the soil micropopulation. Strictly chemical reactions, where enzymes are not involved, are limited in number.

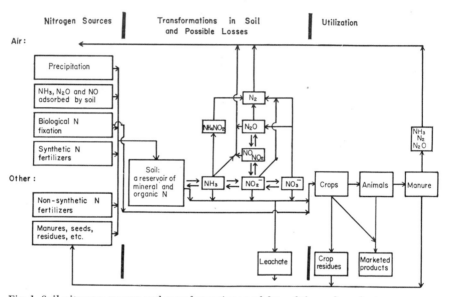

Fig. 1. Soil nitrogen sources and transformations and fate of the end products.

III. SOURCES OF CROP NITROGEN

A. Natural Sources of Combined Nitrogen

1. SOIL ORGANIC MATTER

The chief source of nitrogen for crops is commonly soil organic matter, which is in large part a residual product from previous additions of crop residues. So long as the nitrogen remains in this form, it is comparatively safe from loss except through erosion. Normally, however, the soil organic matter is slowly being converted into ammonia and then into nitrites and nitrates, and in these forms it is subject to the same losses as nitrogen derived from outside sources. Under laboratory or greenhouse conditions, in the absence of a crop or leaching, as much as 5 to 10% of soil nitrogen may accumulate as nitrate during a period of six months (Allison and Sterling, 1949). Under humid conditions in the Temperate Zone it has been shown repeatedly (Salter and Green, 1933; and Woodruff, 1949) that a crop such as corn removes about 2 to 3% of the soil nitrogen in the plowed layer during one growing season. A small grain crop removes about half this amount, whereas a nonlegume sod crop removes even less. So far as soil nitrogen balance is concerned, such removal of nitrogen presents no major problems that are not well understood. The normal error of soil sampling and analysis, plus variable values for leaching and gaseous losses, however, make it impossible to measure such annual losses accurately. Crop analysis gives only a partial answer.

2. CROP RESIDUES AND ANIMAL MANURES

The nitrogen returned to the soil in the form of crop residues under good farm management practices commonly constitutes a considerable portion of the total nitrogen removed in the crop. Including the root residues not removed, this nitrogen may, in the case of a small grain crop, for example, amount to 20% or more of the total nitrogen originally assimilated by the crop. The quantity varies widely, of course, with type of crop, climatic conditions, yields, and nitrogen level at which the crop is grown. If the crop residue contains less than about 1% nitrogen, this nitrogen will tend to remain tied up in organic form for several days or weeks, and may even immobilize any available soil nitrogen present. If the residue contains 2% or more of nitrogen, some ammonia may be lost to the atmosphere during the initial stages of decomposition unless the material is incorporated into the soil before decay starts.

Where animal manures are supplied to the soil, they may be expected to behave much as do crop residues except that the chances for loss as ammonia during handling, especially from the liquid portion, are much greater (Linhard, 1954). If the fresh liquid and solids are immediately incorporated into the soil, there is little reason to expect appreciable loss of ammonia. Data summarized by Salter and Schollenberger (1939) show that on the average 74% of the nitrogen in the feed of cows is found in fresh manure. Under practical conditions it is doubtful if more than a third of this excreted nitrogen actually enters the soil, and the value may be much less.

3. PRECIPITATION AND IRRIGATION

The quantity of nitrogen that is added to soil in rain and snow, as ammonia and nitrate, is shown in Table 1. These data, assembled by Miller (1905), were obtained at locations all over the world. In addition to these two forms of nitrogen, there is also some organic nitrogen in rainwater in the forms of bacterial cells and dust. According to Miller, this amounts to 1.35 pounds per acre annually at Rothamsted, England, and 0.45 pound in New Zealand where the total inorganic nitrogen in the rain is very low.

Table 1 shows variations between 1.6 and 19.9 pounds of inorganic nitrogen per acre per year in the rainfall at the 28 locations; the average value is 7.8 pounds. Ammonia nitrogen, on the average, constitutes 69% of the total and the values fall within the range of 60 to 80% for 20 of

Table 1. Nitrogen as ammonia and nitric acid in rain.

Location	Rainfall, in.	N, lb. per acre per annum			% of total	
		NH_3	N_2O_5	Total	NH_3	N_2O_5
Rothamsted	27.3	2.71	1.13	3.84	70.6	29.4
Copenhagen	22.0	9.27	2.21	11.48	80.8	19.2
Gemblox	27.2	7.07	2.14	9.21	76.8	23.2
Montsouris	21.5	10.37	3.22	13.59	76.3	23.7
Dahme	17.1	5.50	1.16	6.66	82.6	17.4
Insterburg	25.7	3.90	2.25	6.15	63.1	36.9
Kuschen	14.8	1.63	0.55	2.18	75.0	25.0
Proskau	17.8	12.94	6.97	19.91	65.0	35.0
Regenwalde	22.7	10.69	3.28	13.97	77.0	23.0
Florence	38.3	8.70	3.09	11.79	73.8	26.2
Vallombrosa	59.9	8.36	3.46	11.82	70.7	29.3
Scandicci	29.2	4.06	1.76	5.82	69.8	30.2
Catania	18.4	1.36	0.67	2.03	66.9	33.1
St. Michele, Tirol	43.9	11.83	5.76	17.59	67.3	32.7
Libwerd, Bohemia	24.4	7.18	3.37	10.55	68.1	31.9
Peček, Bohemia	19.3	5.53	2.19	7.72	71.6	28.4
Ploty	17.5	3.38	0.24	3.62	93.3	6.7
Tokyo	57.4	1.77	1.11	2.88	61.6	38.4
New Zealand	29.7	0.50	1.13	1.63	30.7	69.3
Kansas	29.4	2.62	1.03	3.64	71.8	28.2
Mississippi	44.1	2.35	0.74	3.09	76.0	24.0
Averages	28.9	5.80	2.26	8.06	72.0	28.0
		Tropical Rain Areas				
Calcutta	46.0	1.79	1.20	2.99	59.7	40.3
Ceylon	82.1	3.65	1.28	4.93	72.0	28.0
East Java	47.0	1.13	0.71	1.84	61.5	38.5
Mauritius	70.0	6.81	6.34	13.15	51.8	48.2
Barbados	64.0	1.22	3.88	5.10	23.9	76.1
Venezuela	40.0	14.03	5.20	19.23	72.8	27.2
British Guiana	102.4	1.17	1.82	2.99	39.1	60.9
Averages	64.5	4.26	2.92	7.18	59.3	40.7
Avg, all locations	27.8	5.41	2.42	7.84	69.1	30.9

the 28 locations. There is little relationship between total rainfall and the total amount of nitrogen brought down annually. The results for tropical soils are more variable than for other regions but the averages are similar. The ammonia is derived both from the burning of coal and other organic materials, and from the soil. A few writers have also emphasized the sea as an important source, but this seems doubtful. Electric discharges in the air probably account for most of the nitrates in rainwater but some oxides of nitrogen are also released from the soil. Little or no nitrite is found in rainwater since this form of nitrogen is readily oxidized to nitrate by oxygen of the air.

More recent data than those tabulated by Miller are given by Schreiner and Brown (1938). At seven locations in the Temperate Zone the inorganic nitrogen in the rain averaged 6.1 pounds per acre annually, 75.8% being in the ammonia form. These results agree very closely with the earlier data where less accurate methods of analysis may have been used.

Irrigation waters may sometimes contain traces of nitrogen but, unless intentionally added, are usually too small to have much effect on the soil nitrogen balance sheet.

4. ADSORPTION OF NH_3, N_2O, AND NO FROM AIR

In the early years of agricultural chemistry, during and after the time of Liebig, the possibility of direct adsorption by soils of ammonia, and possibly of oxides of nitrogen, from the air was considered. Although a few workers, cited by Miller (1905), reported adsorption of as much as 11 to 42 pounds of ammonia nitrogen per acre annually, the values found by most workers were small and hence little importance was attached to this source of nitrogen for crops. Hall and Miller (1911) reviewed some of these results and reported new data which show that only about 1 to 2 pounds of nitrogen per acre are adsorbed annually by dilute sulfuric acid kept in shallow glazed earthenware dishes.

In more recent years there has been some revival of interest in the subject and a limited amount of new data has been reported. One reason for the new interest is that occasionally a research worker has observed that the nitrogen content of a cropped soil did not decrease as fast as expected, and accretions of nitrogen through biological nitrogen fixation did not seem to be an adequate explanation.

Ingham (1939, 1940, 1950) was one who did not accept the conclusions of the earlier workers and advanced the theory that "a well-tilled soil is able to absorb from the air in 12 months sufficient nitrogen in the form of ammonia to supply the needs of a crop like maize." Seventy determinations reported by him of the ammonia content of air in South Africa show a mean value of about 1 ppm by weight. Many earlier analyses (Hall and Miller, 1911) had shown only 0.01 to 0.02 ppm of ammonia-nitrogen in city air, and even less in country air. When Ingham exposed slightly acidulated water to the air, 1.3 mg of ammonia-nitrogen per square foot of surface was absorbed in seven days. This corresponds to 6.5 pounds per acre per year. In other experiments Ingham (1940) exposed dishes of $1N$ H_2SO_4 to air for 24-hour periods and obtained ammonia-uptake values of 6.1 to 45.3 pounds per acre per year, with an average value of 19.4 pounds. The highest values seemed to be correlated with high wind velocities.

Ingham (1950) also suspended washed, dry cellulosic materials in the air, and at weekly intervals determined the ammonia and nitrate contents. The mean weekly values reported are shown in Table 2. He concluded that cellulosic and related plant materials, such as are found in plant residues and humus, can likewise adsorb considerable nitrogen from the air.

In experiments involving the absorption of ammonia by a weak acid, too little attention has been given to the fact that during such absorption there is formed a monomolecular layer of ammonium hydroxide or ammonium salt. This tends to block further absorption until it is removed by surface agitation or otherwise. Bubbling air, containing ammonia, through an acid may, therefore, give absorption values much higher than would be obtained by exposure to the air without solution agitation. These facts would seem to indicate that a well-drained and aerated moist soil can take up ammonia from the air much more readily than can an undisturbed acidic solution because of the greater surface area, and also

Table 2. Ammonia and nitrate adsorbed from the air in 7 days by air-dry cellulosic
materials.

Cellulosic material	Mean adsorption values, *ppm		
	NH_4-N	NO_3-N	Total N
Filter paper, washed with H_2O	31	9	40
" " " " 0.01 HCl	113	13	126
" " " " 0.01 Na_2CO_3	9	13	22
Dried grass, washed with H_2O	11	7	18
Jute fiber, " " "	84	19	103
Sisal fiber, " " "	51	20	71
Wood fiber, " " "	24	16	40

* All values are based on the weights of the cellulosic materials.

because any ammonia adsorbed in soil would normally be removed rather
rapidly by bacteria, especially by *Nitrosomonas,* or by higher plants.
Because of the conflicting evidence, it would seem well worthwhile for
an effort to be made to obtain better ammonia adsorption data even
though there is little reason to expect that new evidence would appreciably modify the view now generally held that such adsorption is of
minor agricultural importance.

Some evidence indicating that soils adsorb little ammonia from the air
is supplied by the Rothamsted Broadbalk continuous wheat plots (Allison,
1955; Russell and Watson, 1940) that have received no outside nitrogen
since 1843. On plots 3 and 5, which received no nitrogen fertilizer, the
known nitrogen gains and losses are in close balance. If it be assumed
that an appreciable quantity of ammonia was adsorbed from the air, it
must also be assumed that a comparable quantity was lost in gaseous
forms. The Rothamsted drainage experiment (Russell and Richards, 1920)
constitutes further evidence of this type. Doubtless a study of other long-
time fertility experiments would supply somewhat similar data, for it is
extremely rare for carefully controlled experiments to show net gains that
would suggest the possibility of appreciable ammonia adsorption from
the air. It is also obvious that if Ingham's ideas are correct it would be
very difficult to account for the extreme need for nitrogen fertilizers, now
so evident in many field soils all over the world.

B. Biological Nitrogen Fixation

Before the use of commercial fertilizers became so common, biological
nitrogen fixation accounted for nearly all of the new nitrogen, other than
that in rainwater, that reached the soil. Even this rainwater nitrogen, as
already pointed out, is only in small part newly fixed nitrogen. In biological nitrogen fixation the active agents are microorganisms that either live
in symbiosis with certain species of higher plants or nonsymbiotically in
soils, water, or on vegetation.

1. SYMBIOTIC NITROGEN FIXATION

The quantity of nitrogen fixed by an acre of legumes in a year varies
widely from only a few pounds to 200 to 300, or occasionally even more
(Henzell and Norris, 1962). The quantity fixed is determined by many

factors, such as plant species, density of plant stand, weed competition, climatic conditions, effectiveness of the bacterial strain, pH, and nutrient status (Andrew, 1962), especially the amount of nitrogen made available from the soil. From the standpoint of total nitrogen contributed annually to the nation as a whole, the frequency with which a legume is grown in a rotation must also be considered. The portion of the total cultivated area that is in legumes is commonly not more than a fifth to a tenth.

The growth of a legume in a cropping system greatly complicates the calculation of an accurate nitrogen balance, since there is no practical way of knowing accurately how much nitrogen is fixed by a legume crop growing in the open in a normal soil. Usually the fixation varies inversely with the level of available nitrogen in the soil, and hence the nitrogen content of the crop may bear little relation to fixation.

Considerable research by Bond (1958) and others has shown that at least eight genera of nonleguminous shrubs and trees have root nodules and fix comparatively large quantities of atmospheric nitrogen. Norris (1962) gives a summary of our knowledge of these symbionts, as well as of leaf symbionts and lichens that appear to be involved in nitrogen fixation. In most cases little is known about the microorganisms involved. Since these nitrogen-fixing plants are found chiefly in waste places or forests, the nitrogen that they fix is usually not a factor in ordinary cropping systems.

2. NONSYMBIOTIC NITROGEN FIXATION

In 1895 Winogradsky isolated the anaerobic nitrogen-fixing bacterium, *Clostridium pasteurianum,* and in 1901 Beijerinck isolated two species of *Azotobacter.* The intensive studies that followed resulted in the isolation of other species of the two genera that fixed nitrogen. Many claims were made that other free-living organisms possessed this property but most of these early claims were not substantiated by later work. In 1928 Drewes (1928) isolated in pure culture two genera of blue-green algae, namely *Anabaena* and *Nostoc,* and showed that they could use free nitrogen gas. In subsequent years many other nitrogen-fixing blue-green algae and clostridia have been isolated and described (Norris, 1962). In more recent years *Beijerinckia,* which resembles *Azotobacter,* and certain hydrogen bacteria have also been added to the list of nitrogen fixers. Tracer techniques have shown that many organisms can fix small amounts of nitrogen.

How much nitrogen do these free-living organisms contribute to agricultural crops annually? This question has been asked repeatedly over the years. In a symposium at the meeting of the American Society of Agronomy in 1924, Löhnis (1925) estimated that nonsymbiotic bacteria may fix an average of 10 to 40 pounds of nitrogen per acre annually. His estimate for the cultivated soils of the United States was 10 pounds, and for the soils of Germany 20 to 25 pounds per acre. In contrast, Lipman (1925), who spoke at the same symposium, stated that "we are, unfortunately, quite in the dark as to the amounts of nitrogen fixed by nonsymbiotic bacteria." A few years later Lipman and Conybeare (1936) gave an estimated value of 6 pounds of nitrogen per acre per year fixed in the harvested crop area of the United States. During the past 50 years much effort has been devoted to the economic evaluation of free-living nitrogen-fixing microorganisms in soils, but we are nearly as much in the dark now as when Lipman drew his conclusions. There is now no sound basis upon which to make direct estimates, but we can be reasonably certain that under most field conditions the values are much below Löhnis' estimates. There have been many reports (Allison, 1955) of considerable nitrogen fixation in field plots attributed to nonsymbiotic microorganisms, but the errors of soil sampling and analysis have been too great for accurate measurement of such gains. Long-time fertility experiments such as those at Rothamsted (Russell and Watson, 1940), discussed above, and also lysimeter experiments (Allison, 1955; Russell and Richards, 1920), certainly furnish little evidence of unaccounted-for nitrogen gains.

The most interesting recent direct attempt to evaluate accurately nonsymbiotic nitrogen fixation in soil was that reported by Delwiche and Wijler (1956). Using N^{15}-labeled nitrogen gas in small vessels containing soil kept in the laboratory, they observed that when glucose or sucrose was added, up to 40 pounds of nitrogen per acre was fixed; additions of grass cuttings, straw or alfalfa caused only slight fixation. Inoculation with masses of azotobacter cells was also without effect. They concluded that under fallow conditions, nonsymbiotic aerobic fixation does not exceed a few pounds of nitrogen per acre per year.

Another valuable way to evaluate nonsymbiotic nitrogen fixation, at least in a qualitative and indirect way, is to consider the physiology of the organisms involved, their abundance, and probable degree of activity in soils.

Aerobic nitrogen-fixing bacteria, such as *Azotobacter,* are fairly common in most soils having a pH above 6 but not in numbers that exceed a few thousand per gram. *Beijerinckia,* which resembles *Azotobacter,* can grow in acid soils but is apparently also present in limited numbers, and usually only in lateritic soils. These aerobic fixers have high energy requirements and for the most part use only simple carbohydrates that are not found in soils in more than traces. Some decomposition products of crop residues, formed by other organisms, may be utilized by the aerobic nitrogen-fixing bacteria, but in field soils it is likely that the organisms that break down the resistant materials will utilize most of these products themselves. *Azotobacter* is a poor competitor in comparison with many fungi and other common soil bacteria. Even in pure culture under the best laboratory conditions, seldom is more than 15 to 20 mg N fixed per gram of sugar consumed, and this efficiency decreases rapidly with age. Any available nitrogen present is likely to be utilized preferentially over atmospheric nitrogen. Attempts (Allison, 1955) to prove that *Azotobacter* get considerable carbohydrate from root excretions have also met with failure; at least the organisms are seldom found in great abundance in the rhizospheres of various plants. On the basis of microbial physiology, we must conclude that *Azotobacter,* and probably most other aerobic soil bacteria, contribute very little to the soil nitrogen supply.

Anaerobic nitrogen-fixing bacteria, which are more common in soils than the aerobic nitrogen fixers, are less efficient in their use of carbohydrates. Furthermore, they exist mostly in the inactive spore form. A few workers, such as Parker (1954) in Australia, have indicated that anaerobic fixation in soils may be more important than previously supposed, but little evidence in support of this view has been presented.

The nitrogen-fixing blue-green algae, which can utilize sunlight as their sole source of energy, are not believed to be very important in normal cultivated soils because of deficient surface moisture, too-high acidities, lack of light except in the surface layer, and slow growth rate. They may thrive in rice paddies and have been reported (De and Mandal, 1956) to fix up to 44 pounds of nitrogen per acre per year. They are also reported to be an important factor in the increase of fixed nitrogen in lakes (Dugdale and Neess, 1961), and possibly even in desert soils (Fuller et al., 1960) for brief periods. Further quantitative studies with these organisms are much needed.

In earlier years the opinion was often expressed that soils in semiarid climates are capable of fixing considerable nitrogen and may be cropped to cereals almost indefinitely if all crop residues are returned. There now seems to be no scientific basis for such an opinion. In fact, as pointed out elsewhere (Allison, 1955), semiarid soils continually lose much more nitrogen than is removed in the crop, especially if the measurements start with a virgin soil. After 50 years of cropping, the annual unaccounted-for loss of nitrogen is much less, of course, but nitrogen deficiency symptoms in the crops are then likely to be much in evidence unless outside nitrogen is supplied. Jensen's (1940) extensive studies of the nitrogen economy in Australian wheat soils led him to conclude that "the importance of non-symbiotic nitrogen fixation in nature is probably largely confined to uncultivated soils where no crops are carried away and the vegetable debris is allowed to decompose *in situ.*"

Although nonsymbiotic nitrogen fixation in cultivated soils seems to be so small that it can almost be ignored in short-time nitrogen balance experiments, it is obvious that over periods of several centuries this source of nitrogen has been a very important factor in the building up of nitrogen in many soils, especially in the chernozems. The yearly additions of nitrogen to these soils prior to cultivation were doubtless considerably greater than to cultivated soils, as Jensen states. The plant residues would not only furnish energy but also a more favorable environment for most nonsymbiotic bacteria, and possibly also for the nitrogen-fixing blue-green algae. In considering the source of any nitrogen gains in permanent grassland soils it is important that the contributions of legumes not be overlooked; they are often more numerous than generally supposed.

One place in nature where nitrogen-fixing microorganisms are abundant (Meiklejohn, 1962) and seem to be contributing nitrogen in a major way to the native vegetation is in certain tropical regions where the rainfall is 60 to 300 inches per year. Soil scientists who have worked in these regions seem to agree that the vegetation usually shows all indications of being abundantly supplied with nitrogen, even though the supply in the soil is commonly low. According to Nye and Greenland (1960), fertilizer experiments in both the moist semi-deciduous forest and the moist evergreen forest zones of Africa show that plant growth is not limited by nitrogen deficiency. They state further that "it is well known that poor soils will support a luxuriant tropical forest." Absolute proof of high nitrogen fixation is not available, but the circumstantial evidence for such seems convincing. This is true whether the forest is left undisturbed or is subjected to the native system of agriculture, designated as shifting cultivation (Nye and Greenland, 1960). The evidence for biological nitrogen fixation may be more obvious where this native system of agriculture is followed, but fixation may actually be greater in the undisturbed forest. This remains to be determined.

In the system of shifting cultivation the trees are cut and burned and the area is used for mixed cropping of annuals and perennials for two or three years. The land is then allowed to return to bush and trees for 10 to 20 years, or longer, after which the cycle is repeated. Immediately after clearing and burning, the accumulated organic matter in the surface 2 or 3 inches of soil oxidizes rapidly and furnishes adequate available nitrogen for crops for one to three seasons. The soil may then become too poor to grow good crops, but if abandoned, it returns in a few years to near its previous state and the native vegetation again grows luxuriantly. Leaching of nitrogen is not considered to be an important factor since the soil is bare for only a short period after burning.

Since quantitative data on nitrogen fixation in the tropics are not available, we must rely on estimates. Nye and Greenland (1960) calculated from analytical data on soils and vegetation that the annual nitrogen fixation rate in the African tropics is of the order of 95 pounds of nitrogen per acre, exclusive of any losses through leaching or as gases. In nearby areas, usually of lower rainfall, where a savanna type of vegetation prevails, they estimated that the fixation is only 35 pounds of nitrogen per acre per year. Most of this is lost through annual burning. In another publication Greenland (1959) states that the net annual gains of nitrogen may amount to 50 to 150 pounds per acre under forest and 40 to 120 pounds under savanna, depending on cropping and cultural practices. Nye and Greenland cite the work of Beirnaert, who estimated the annual nitrogen increment in the forests of the Central Congo Basin at 90 pounds per acre. Jenny (1950) reported that 2 tropical soils of Colombia had an average nitrogen content of about 25,800 pounds per acre in the 0- to 30-inch horizon. There was no sound basis for estimation of the annual accretion, but it must have been substantial and far above that in the temperate regions of the United States. Since leguminous trees constituted about 50% of the forest vegetation, he was inclined to consider symbiotic fixation more important than nonsymbiotic fixation. In a later publication Jenny and Raychaudhuri (1960) also found very large amounts of nitrogen in the Darjeeling forest of India, where legumes were not abundant. This indicated to them the possibility of additional significant sources of nitrogen. Nye and Greenland (1960) cite references where the percentages of leguminous trees in moist tropical forests of British Guiana, Nigeria, and the Central Congo Basin were determined to be about 25 to 50%. The values were very much less for the drier soils, especially in Puerto Rico, and also for less acid soils.

The contribution of legumes to the nitrogen buildup of tropical forest soils is not clear because many of these are not nodulated and there is little, if any, quantitative proof that even the nodulated trees are fixing nitrogen. The observation that soils of high nitrogen content frequently occur in the tropical rain belt, even where few leguminous trees are present, must also be considered. And it is also pertinent to ask why the marked nitrogen accretion is limited to the regions of high rainfall. Many leguminous trees and also nodulated nitrogen-fixing nonleguminous trees, such as *Casuarina,* thrive in regions of moderate rainfall, and some of them in the Temperate Zone. All of this uncertainty led Nye, Greenland, and others to conclude, tentatively at least, that nonsymbiotic nitrogen fixation must be the most important contributor to the nitrogen increment in the moist semi-deciduous forest zone where the supply of carbohydrate is abundant.

The recent observations of Ruinen (1956, 1961) may serve as a substantial contribution to the solution of this puzzle. She found that the nitrogen-fixing bacterium, *Beijerinckia,* is widespread and abundant on the moist leaves of tropical plants in Indonesia and Surinam. This organism is found in abundance only in tropical countries, is acid tolerant, and has an abundant energy supply when growing on the moist, sticky leaves in rain forests. In regions of alternating wet and dry periods it can at least thrive during the rainy season. The nitrogen so fixed may enter the leaves directly or be washed off onto the soil.

Much further work will be needed to establish the relative importance of symbiotic and nonsymbiotic fixation in tropical forests. Present evidence indicates that both types of organisms are functioning in providing the nitrogen for a luxuriant type of vegetation, but *Beijerinckia* may well be the more important under such conditions.

C. Commercial Fertilizers

After making use of the natural sources of combined nitrogen and biological nitrogen fixation, commercial fertilizer nitrogen must be relied upon to bring crop production to the level that is desired, or is economically feasible. Such nitrogen is applied to soils in various forms, chiefly as ammonium salts, nitrates, urea, anhydrous ammonia, cyanamid, and organic by-products. The rates used are commonly considerably under 200 pounds per acre per year but on a few crops, such as grasses, may occasionally be above this value. So far as the income side of the soil nitrogen balance sheet is concerned, this nitrogen presents few problems since in most cases it can be added quantitatively. It is only when it is added by injection as gases or liquids that exact measurements may sometimes be a little difficult to make. The problems in accounting arise in connection with what happens to these forms of nitrogen after they reach the soil. The various possibilities are discussed below.

IV. NITROGEN RECOVERY AND OUTGO

A. Marketed Products

The recovery in the harvested crop of nitrogen added in the forms of animal manures and commercial fertilizers is commonly less than 50%, as already stated. This value varies widely with kind of crop, texture of soil, farming system, climatic conditions, rate of addition of nitrogen, etc. If the crop is continuous grass, where there is no cultivation and where the crop is grown for several years, the recovery may be 70% or more, and much of the remainder may be left in the soil in the partially decomposed root system. This higher recovery can be attributed chiefly to the prevention of leaching and to the harvesting of all of the above-ground portion of the crop. Under this system any added available nitrogen is assimilated by the crop quickly, before there is much opportunity for loss either in the drainage waters or as gases. There is also no opportunity for nitrogen to be released from the soil and to accumulate as nitrate. Where the cropping system is such that the soil is bare for a considerable portion of the year, the recovery of nitrogen in the crop may be much below 50%. At the Rothamsted Experimental Station (Russell and Watson, 1940), for example, the recovery of nitrogen added as ammonium sulfate to the continuous wheat plots, was only 35%; the corresponding value for manure nitrogen added at a higher rate, was only 15% for the first year, and averaged about 18 to 20% over a 50-year period. If full use is made of our accumulated knowledge with respect to nitrogen losses from soils, there is no reason why the nitrogen recovery from added inorganic nitrogen by most field crops, considered over a period of years, should not be appreciably higher than 50%. Values above 70% are, however, not likely to be attained often if cultivated crops are grown regularly in the rotation.

When crops are fed to animals and the milk or meat is marketed, only about 25 to 30% of the nitrogen in the feed is removed from the soil as marketed products. The remainder is found in the excrement. As already stated, it is doubtful if as much as a third of this nitrogen is returned to the soil, and the percentage that is actually available for use by the next crop may be far less. This can be attributed to mechanical losses of the urine; storage losses of ammonia, nitrogen gas and oxides of nitrogen; and volatilization and leaching losses after spreading. Where animals are on pasture, much of the manure may be voided under trees, near watering troughs, in feed lots, or in other places where there is no crop to utilize it. Even when the manure is applied to soils mechanically and quantitatively, the recovery of nitrogen is likely to be low, as on the Broadbalk wheat fields. Some of the manure nitrogen remains as a residual material for use by crops from year to year, but such nitrogen is subject to leaching at intervals between crops.

B. Soil

In drawing up the usual nitrogen balance sheet it is, of course, necessary to take into account the nitrogen content of the soil initially and finally. Because of the difficulties involved in sampling and analysis, this cannot be done with a high degree of accuracy, especially in the field. In greenhouse pots and lysimeters, where the entire soil is thoroughly mixed at the time of starting the experiment, the accuracy is greater but is still not entirely satisfactory. If several successive crops are grown and the rates of addition of nitrogen are high but not excessive, then the accuracy is reasonably satisfactory. In such experiments leaching is either prevented or the leachates are collected and analyzed. This type of balance sheet can, of course, show only the net over-all nitrogen changes; it does not furnish much information on mechanisms of gains or losses. A study of published lysimeter data (Allison, 1955) shows that usually during the course of an experiment there is a net loss of nitrogen from the soil unless it is kept in grass or receives considerable outside additions of nitrogen in the form of animal manures or crop residues. In greenhouse experiments where an intensive cropping system was used together with additions of green manure, Pinck et al. (1948a) reported surprisingly large increases of nitrogen in the soil organic matter. Under ordinary field conditions there tends to be established a nitrogen equilibrium after many years of any given soil management system.

The use of N^{15}-tagged fertilizers in studying nitrogen balance will be discussed in a later section.

C. Erosion

Lipman and Conybeare (1936) estimated that an average of 24.2 pounds per acre of nitrogen is removed annually from the harvested crop area of the United States by erosion. Obviously, this value may be much higher, or near zero, depending upon many factors that need not be discussed here. These are rather fully treated by Bennett and Lowdermilk (1938) and several other authors in the 1938 United States Yearbook of Agriculture entitled, "Soils and Men." Ordinarily, in careful experiments designed to study nitrogen income and outgo, this factor of erosion is completely eliminated. However, in ordinary cropping systems it is well to remember that water and wind erosion may, in especially unfavorable years and where proper control measures are not used, remove nearly as much nitrogen as is removed in the harvested crop. Nitrogen is especially subject to loss since water easily loosens and floats away organic matter. The nitrogen in such eroded material may be as much as five times higher than in the soil that is left behind (Neal, 1944). Wind also tends to remove the lighter material first.

D. Leaching

1. MOVEMENT OF NITROGEN IN SOILS

Leaching of nitrates constitutes one of the main channels of outgo of nitrogen from soils. The movement of the nitrate is closely related to the movement of the soil water. The amounts of nitrogen lost will depend on a large number of variables that are understood fairly well, at least in a qualitative way. Among the more important of these variables are: (a) form and amount of soluble and unadsorbed nitrogen present or added; (b) amount and time of rainfall; (c) infiltration and percolation rates, which are markedly affected by soil composition, texture, structure, depth of profile, and surface treatment; (d) water-holding capacity of the soil and its moisture content throughout the profile at the time a rain occurs; (e) presence or absence of a crop, and its growth characteristics; (f) evapotranspiration; (g) rate of removal of the nitrogen by the crop; (h) extent to which there is an upward movement of nitrogen in the soil during periods of drought; and (i) whether the nitrogen is leached below the root zone, especially to the ground water.

Wetselaar (1962) has shown that the nitrate movement is not due to a complete displacement of the soil solution by the rainwater, but there occurs a gradual dilution out of the top soil. As more and more water enters the soil, the nitrate level in the top soil may approach zero but increase markedly at levels of 1, 2, 3, or more feet. Under the conditions of Wetselaar's experiments on a fallow clay loam where 23.7 inches of rain fell during a six-month period, the mean movement of the nitrate ion was 1.075 inches for each inch of rainfall. There was a positive correlation of 0.946 between mean movement and rainfall. Since dissolved nitrates move with the water, there may occur a considerable upward movement of any such nitrogen present during long periods of drought (Krantz et al., 1944). In practice this reverse movement is usually limited largely to the upper 18 inches (Wetselaar, 1961).

The downward movement of water, other than that in the capillary pores of the soil, is rather rapid through the macropore systems of medium-textured soils. The larger the volume of this system, the more readily the water will move. The presence of a crop, however, tends to reduce this movement because of evapotranspiration. The crop, therefore, greatly minimizes leaching losses of nitrogen both directly, by assimilation, and indirectly, by reducing the amount of leachate.

2. DIRECT MEASUREMENTS

Most measurements of nitrogen leaching have necessarily been made in some kind of a lysimeter, either the filled-in type or the monolith type containing undisturbed soil. The lysimeter method is, to varying degrees, an artificial system and has been much criticized. The results obtained, especially from the filled-in types of lysimeters, are likely to be much too high because of their shallowness, small soil volume and water storage capacity, abnormal and limited capillary pull in the soil, and lack of opportunity for the nitrates to leach below the root zone and to rise again during dry periods. Sometimes, however, low leaching values for nitrogen may be obtained in lysimeter experiments where the soil structure has been seriously disturbed, or clay has been mixed with the top soil to such an extent as to interfere with the downward movement of the water. Evapotranspiration from soils in most lysimeters is also likely to be greater per unit surface area than from field soils, thereby reducing leaching.

Some representative lysimeter leaching data will now be presented. Although most of these experiments are subject to one or more of the criticisms listed above, and possibly others, they do bring out very forcibly some of the main factors involved.

Morgan and Jacobson (1942) (also see Allison, 1955) added various sources of nitrogen annually for 10 years at the rate of 200 pounds per acre to a Merrimac sandy loam contained in lysimeters that were 18 inches deep and cropped continuously to tobacco. Expressed as percentages of total nitrogen available to the crop, the amounts in the leachates were: nitrates 55, ammonium salts 53, urea and cyanamide 43, and organic fertilizers 40%.

In another somewhat similar experiment, using 28-inch lysimeters filled with Merrimac sandy loam and receiving 200 pounds of calurea nitrogen annually for 10 years, Morgan et al. (1942) (also see Allison, 1955) studied the effect of cropping systems. The percentages of the added nitrogen plus that released from the soils (total nitrogen available to the crops) that were collected in the leachates were: fallow 83, tobacco 42, tobacco and oat cover crop 23, and grass sod 14. Most of the loss from the grass sod apparently occurred before the sod was well established.

In a 4-year lysimeter experiment conducted by Jones (1942) at Auburn, Alabama, in lysimeters 30 inches deep, the value of an oat cover crop in reducing leaching losses was determined. In this test, field-grown soybean plants, containing 75 pounds of nitrogen, were incorporated each fall into each of three soils, and oats planted on half of these lysimeters. Sudangrass was grown each summer. The average annual leaching losses were reduced by the cover crop as follows: Norfolk sandy loam from 51.0 to 10.7 pounds, Hartsells fine sandy loam from 38.1 to 6.3 pounds, and Decatur clay loam from 5.4 to 0 pounds. In this experiment, even where oats was grown, the soil was not covered with a dense growth of vegetation for more than about eight months out of the year.

An 11-year experiment, conducted by Karraker et al. (1950) in Kentucky in 26-inch (depth) lysimeters containing Maury silt loam that received no fertilizer nitrogen, shows the importance of continuous plant cover. The average annual nitrogen contents of the leachates in pounds per acre from the various cropping treatments were: uncropped 74, Korean lespedeza 58, Korean lespedeza plus bluegrass 20, Korean lespedeza and rye cover crop 15, alfalfa 9, alfalfa plus bluegrass 2, and bluegrass alone 5.

Allison et al. (1959) reported experiments conducted in South Carolina in lysimeters 5 feet wide and 30 inches deep containing Lakeland sand. Those that were fertilized annually for 5 years with a mixture of animal manure and commercial nitrogen at the rate of 131 pounds of nitrogen per acre lost only about 3% of this in the leachates where the cropping system was millet and a small grain cover. The leaching losses from this coarse sand were large for most other treatments.

In an experiment conducted by Bizzell and Lyon (1928) in lysimeters filled with Dunkirk silty clay loam to a depth of 4 feet, and fertilized with a total of 30 tons of farm manure per acre during a 10-year period, the yearly leaching losses were: no vegetation 69; corn, oats, wheat, and timothy 6.7; and continuous grass 2.5 pounds of nitrogen per acre annually. In another experiment at the Cornell station (Bizzell, 1944), using the same type of lysimeter and soil, timothy was grown continuously for 8 years and fertilized with 4 rates of sodium nitrate. The annual nitrogen additions in pounds per acre were 93, 124, 155, and 217, and the nitrogen in the leachates was 0.2, 0.2, 0.3, and 1.9 pounds, respectively.

One of the oldest monolith lysimeters is that at Rothamsted, England (Russell and Richards, 1920), which was constructed by Lawes and Gilbert in 1870. During a 38-year period, when the soil was left unmanured and uncropped, the average annual loss of nitrates in the drainage waters from the 60-inch soil columns was 22 pounds per acre during the 6 winter months and 8 pounds during the summer months. Most of the nitrates were, of course, formed during the warmer months but not removed until later because of limited percolation. The total quantity of nitrate-nitrogen found in the leachates during the 38-year period agreed closely with the sum of that added in the rain and released from the soil. This means, as mentioned above, that there was no evidence for appreciable adsorption of ammonia or oxides of nitrogen from the air, or for nonsymbiotic nitrogen fixation. Gaseous losses of nitrogen from the unmanured and uncropped soil were not determined. If these losses were appreciable, which seems improbable, then ammonia adsorption of a like magnitude could have occurred.

A tile drainage experiment on a Flanagan silt loam was reported by Van Doren et al. (1951). This is described as a highly productive, permeable prairie soil. No fertilizer was used during the first six years of the experiment but a complete fertilizer was added during the last three years. A corn-oats-clover rotation was used for four years and then corn and soybeans were grown for five years. Even with a rainfall that averaged 39.4 inches annually, the percolation was only 1.5 inches, and this contained an average of only 2.9 pounds of nitrogen per acre annually. With one minor exception, no drainage occurred between May 23 and October 1.

A general study of the data from lysimeters of the type commonly used seems to justify the conclusion that they do not serve as a satisfactory basis for judging the magnitude of leaching losses of nitrogen under field conditions. The losses from shallow, filled-in lysimeters are likely to be abnormally large. Lysimeter data do, however, bring out very clearly the importance of the factors that affect the magnitude of the losses, especially the importance of the cropping system. If an actively growing crop is present at all times, and if the rate of nitrogen addition closely approximates the needs of the crop, the leaching losses of nitrogen are commonly small. If much nitrogen is added or released as nitrate in the late fall, the losses are likely to be large unless a cover crop or permanent sod is present. Lysimeters aso emphasize the importance of soil texture, infiltration rate, and ease of water movement through a soil column.

3. PRECIPITATION-EVAPOTRANSPIRATION DATA

An indirect, but very valuable and practical way of evaluating the probable leaching losses of nitrogen from soils and how to minimize them, is to record daily the amount of precipitation and to estimate the loss of moisture during a given period. Obviously, if during any period of a few days the evapotranspiration losses exceeded precipitation there can be no leaching if the soil moisture was not above field capacity initially. If on the other hand, precipitation, or more exactly stated, infiltration, exceeds evapotranspiration, leaching may or may not occur, depending on the amount of water required to bring the soil to field capacity.

The usual method of making use of precipitation-evapotranspiration data is to plot monthly precipitation, or preferably infiltration, data and evapotranspiration losses on the same graph. Such graphs have been constructed for several regions of the United States, chiefly by Van Bavel of the United States Department of Agriculture working in cooperation with members of the staffs of various state experiment stations. The precipitation values are usually the average daily rainfall records for the past 25 years, and evapotranspiration is calculated from radiation and experimental data. Since runoff is ignored the graphs may indicate somewhat more soil-water than actually enters the soil. They may also indicate more removal of water than actually occurs in many regions, since they are based on the assumption that evapotranspiration from field soils is 70% of that from a free water surface. This is a maximum and not an average value for field soils variously cropped. The average value for large areas would be less because of frequent periods of soil moisture deficiency and because the soil surface is not completely covered with green vegetation at all times.

Precipitation-evapotranspiration graphs for three representative locations, namely Jackson, Miss. (Van Bavel, 1959), Richmond, Va. (Van Bavel and Lillard, 1957), and Minneapolis, Minn. (Blake et al., 1960), are presented here as Fig. 2, 3, and 4, respectively. The average annual rainfall at these three locations in the same order was approximately 52, 43, and 28 inches.

Fig. 2 shows that during the period of October or November to April, the rainfall greatly exceeds evapotranspiration at Jackson and the soil is above field capacity for much of this period. Much of the soil nitrate nitrogen may be leached out during this period. During the remainder of the year, evapotranspiration normally exceeds precipitation and little, if any, loss of nitrogen should occur except on very sandy soils, or during periods of abnormally high rainfall.

At Richmond (Fig. 3) the soil-water relationships differ somewhat from those at Jackson because a considerably larger portion of the yearly rain-fall occurs during the summer months. Total rainfall is less and so is evapotranspiration. Leaching losses should be low during the period of May 1 to October 1, but high during the colder months.

At Minneapolis (Fig. 4) the precipitation-evapotranspiration picture is very different from that in the Southeast. The graph indicates little or no leaching during the summer months and, of course, during the winter the soils are frozen. In drier regions, such as North Dakota, the soil is rarely, if ever, filled to field capacity beyond the root zone and hence, there can be no leaching of nitrogen.

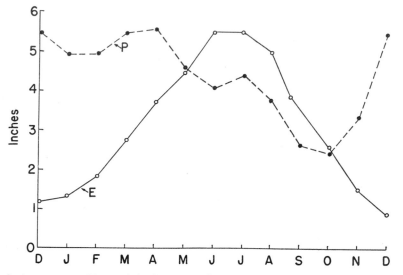

Fig. 2. Average monthly precipitation (P) and evapotranspiration (E) at Jackson, Miss.

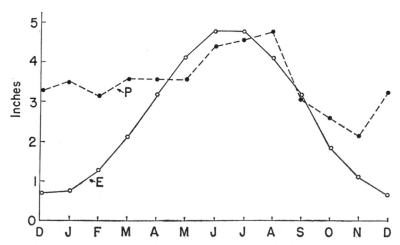

Fig. 3. Average monthly precipitation (P) and evapotranspiration (E) at Richmond, Va.

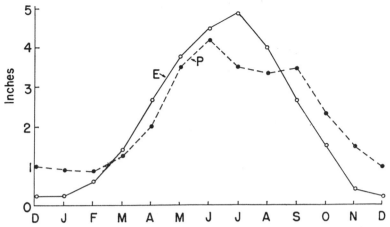

Fig. 4. Average monthly precipitation (P) and evapotranspiration (E) at Minneapolis, Minn.

These graphs emphasize, even more forcibly than do the lysimeter data, how important it is to avoid the accumulation of nitrates in most soils in the late fall. The chief exceptions are in dryland regions, and in areas where the soil is frozen during the winter months.

E. Gases

Nitrogen may be lost from soils in the forms of ammonia, elemental nitrogen, oxides of nitrogen, and in small amounts from plants as organic compounds. The main channels of loss are discussed below. These are fairly well understood but their relative importance under various soil conditions is seldom known with certainty.

1. AMMONIA

It is now well established (Allison, 1955) that ammonia may be volatilized readily from soils under a number of conditions. Such losses are usually small, but under certain conditions may be as much as 20 to 30% of that added. The losses are commonly negligible from soils having pH values of less than 7 unless there is enough free ammonia present to raise the pH locally. Losses increase with increase in pH and temperature, and are greatest in soils of low exchange capacity. The ease of escape of ammonia increases as the soil dries, especially if the ammonia is near the surface. Where animal manures, green manures, or other readily decomposable organic materials that have nitrogen contents greater than about 2.0% are allowed to decompose on the soil surface it is possible for some ammonia to escape. The loss is small from all of these materials, even from alkaline soils, if the ammonia source is incorporated into the soil. The much discussed losses from urea are likewise negligible if it is mixed with the soil. Considerable loss of ammonia may occur if the urea is broadcast on grasses where urease is present, or on soil surfaces.

2. NITROUS OXIDE AND MOLECULAR NITROGEN BY REDUCTION

Loss of gaseous nitrogen by bacterial denitrification has long been recognized as a major channel of loss under conditions where nitrates or nitrites are present in quantity and the soil is very deficient in oxygen (Allison, 1955). It is now known that both N_2O and N_2 can be formed by reduction even though some oxygen is present, but the extent of their formation is not great if even low partial pressures of oxygen are present. Skyring and Callow (1962) give a good summary of our knowledge of the physiology of the organisms involved. Since oxygen deficiency may result from poor drainage, excessive rainfall over a period of several days, or an abundance of easily decomposable organic matter, it is obvious that there are many opportunities for denitrification under field conditions if nitrates or nitrites are present. In sandy soils loss of nitrogen by reduction is negligible, but in fine-textured soils such losses may be large. Usually, careful farm management will assure that these oxidized forms of nitrogen are not present in quantity when oxygen is likely to be deficient. Present information indicates that bacterial denitrification is one of the main channels by which gaseous nitrogen escapes from cultivated Temperate Zone soils.

Greenland (1962a) states that limited available energy in cultivated tropical soils makes it unlikely that denitrification losses would be large. In grasslands, low nitrate also restricts the losses, but under forest he considers that significant losses may occur.

3. NITRIC OXIDE BY CHEMICAL
DECOMPOSITION OF NITROUS ACID

Nitrous acid, which is being formed constantly in soils as a result of nitrification, and to a minor extent through denitrification, is comparatively stable in neutral or alkaline soils where it exists as a salt. At pH values below 5 it decomposes into NO, HNO_3, and H_2O at rates that increase as acidity increases. The NO may be adsorbed by soil, may react with oxygen to form NO_2, or it may volatilize. The NO_2, when dissolved in water, forms HNO_2 and HNO_3. Fortunately, NO is readily adsorbed by soil and other materials, and is also readily oxidized in air to HNO_3.

Quantitative data on nitrogen losses from soils as NO are not available, but it seems certain from what is known about its properties and conditions for formation, that such losses are seldom large. They might possibly be large under special conditions, such as where considerable nitrogen in the forms of ammonia, urea, or green manures is added to acid sandy soils and ammonia oxidation is delayed at the nitrous acid stage.

4. MOLECULAR NITROGEN BY THE VAN SLYKE REACTION

The true Van Slyke reaction is the reaction of nitrous acid with α-amino acids, and specifically excludes the reaction of nitrous acid or nitrites with other nitrogenous compounds. This reaction is as follows:

$$RNH_2 + HNO_2 \rightarrow ROH + H_2O + N_2$$

The reasons for defining it so sharply are discussed more fully elsewhere (Allison, 1963). Although other compounds, such as ammonia, urea, methylamine, purines, and pyrimidines, will react with HNO_2 to form N_2, the reactions occur less rapidly and differ from the true Van Slyke reaction.

In studies involving the reaction of nitrous acid with alanine, it was concluded (Allison et al., 1951, 1952) that there is little evidence that nitrogen is lost in appreciable amounts from soils by the Van Slyke reaction. In buffered solutions kept in air, no nitrogen gas was liberated at pH values above 5, and only a slight reaction occurred under more acid conditions. The HNO_2 decomposed to NO more rapidly than it reacted with alanine. Most other recent investigators (Clark et al., 1960; Wijler and Delwiche, 1954) seem to have reached the same conclusion. Gerretsen and De Hoop (1957), however, were of the opinion that considerable nitrogen may be lost by the Van Slyke reaction, but they were concerned with the reaction of ammonia with nitrous acid, which is not the true Van Slyke reaction. Evidence indicates that loss of nitrogen gas from soils as a result of the interaction between HNO_2 and α-amino acids is not of great economic importance.

5. NITROGEN GAS, AMMONIA, AND NITRIC OXIDE BY DECOMPOSITON OF AMMONIUM NITRITE

Ammonium nitrite is comparatively stable in an alkaline medium but becomes increasingly unstable as the pH is lowered. The rate of evolution of nitrogen from ammonium nitrite solutions has been shown (Abel et al., 1931) to be proportional to the concentration of the ammonium ion, nitrite ion, and nitrous acid. Very dilute solutions are stable at room temperature for many days or weeks.

The reaction of ammonia with nitrous acid, followed by decomposition of the ammonium nitrite, occurs chiefly by the following reaction:

$$NH_3 + HNO_2 \rightarrow NH_4NO_2 \rightarrow N_2 + 2 H_2O$$

There may be a minor secondary reaction as follows:

$$3 NH_4NO_2 \rightarrow NH_4NO_3 + 2 NO + 2 NH_3 + H_2O$$

Although the first of these reactions is similar to the true Van Slyke reaction, it differs in that the rate of N_2 evolution is controlled by the key intermediate, NH_4NO_2, which breaks down comparatively slowly according to a monomolecular reaction. Furthermore, nitrites can substitute for HNO_2, which means that nitrogen can be lost, even if slowly, by the ammonium nitrite reaction at a pH above 7 where HNO_2 does not exist, and hence where the Van Slyke reaction cannot occur.

Several investigators, such as Dhar (1938), Wahhab and Uddin (1954,

1955), and Ingham (1938), have stressed the importance of nitrogen losses through the ammonium nitrite mechanism. Elsewhere (Allison, 1963), several publications are cited where it seems likely that losses of nitrogen may have resulted in part by this mechanism, even though the authors may not have so stated. The available evidence, however, scarcely justifies an unequivocal statement as to the importance of this channel of loss under practical conditions. Obviously, more quantitative data are needed but present evidence does seem to emphasize that this mechanism of loss has received too little consideration in the past. Wherever appreciable quantities of ammonia and nitrite ions are present simultaneously, especially in acid soils, some formation of gaseous nitrogen is a strong possibility. Since the extent of reaction is a function of concentration, it is obvious that even if there is no reaction in a moist soil, considerable loss of nitrogen may occur on drying. There is also the strong possibility that ammonium nitrite decomposition may be catalyzed by certain soil constituents.

From the practical standpoint, it is a little disturbing to know that this mechanism of nitrogen loss can probably proceed slowly under a variety of conditions. For example, in the experiments of Carter and Allison (1961) where ammonium sulfate was added to a sandy loam at rates sufficient to greatly retard nitrite oxidation, marked losses of gaseous nitrogen in forms other than ammonia occurred. The conditions here were ideal for ammonium nitrite formation and decomposition, although proof of this was not obtained. Such slow release of nitrogen has sometimes been attributed to so-called aerobic denitrification. By making soil conditions favorable for rapid oxidation of nitrites, such gaseous losses can be held to a minimum.

6. ORGANIC AND INORGANIC SUBSTANCES FROM GROWING PLANTS

Plant exudates may contain small amounts of organic substances, such as hydrocyanic acid, nicotine, methylamine, and dimethylamine that may, in part, be volatilized. These exudates may also contain ammonia and nitrites (Wilson, 1943) but probably most of this nitrogen is not lost but returns to the soil. On drying of these exudates, there is a chance for loss via ammonium nitrite. Recent work by Vanecko and Varner (1955) shows that it is also possible for nitrogen gas to be evolved from plant tissues. When wheat leaves were infiltrated with $KN^{15}O_2$, and illuminated, considerable gas was produced that always contained some N_2^{15}. They assumed that it was formed by the reaction of the nitrite and amino acids, but there is no proof of this; ammonium nitrite decomposition might have been involved. Several earlier experiments, such as those of Dawson (1949) with excised tobacco shoots, and those of Vickery et al. (1946) with narcissus bulbs, showed nitrogen losses.

Since nitrite concentrations in growing plants are seldom high, direct gaseous losses of nitrogen through interaction with ammonia or organic nitrogen compounds are not believed to be large. There are no quantitative data on losses through guttation, but this source of loss is probably also a minor one.

V. NITROGEN BALANCE UNDER GREENHOUSE AND FIELD CONDITIONS

On the preceding pages the chief sources of crop nitrogen and of the channels of outgo from the soil have been listed and some effort made to evaluate their importance where this was not obvious. It is now well to consider the net result of the summation of these gains and losses, commonly called the soil nitrogen balance sheet, under certain experimentally controlled conditions, and also under various soil and climatic conditions existing in nature.

A. Greenhouse Experiments

The simplest type of nitrogen balance experiment, but not necessarily the best, is that conducted in pots in the greenhouse. In such experiments all sources of income and outgo that are subject to ordinary chemical analysis are readily determined and any deficit of appreciable magnitude after making allowance for nitrogen remaining in the soil, is attributed to gaseous losses. Obviously, the value of this method is limited by the accuracy with which the numerous samplings and chemical analyses can be made. Where only a single addition of untagged fertilizer nitrogen is made, and only one or two crops grown, the accuracy is likely not to be entirely satisfactory, especially if the rate of nitrogen addition is low. There may also be an even larger source of error as a result of partially anaerobic conditions that sometimes exist more or less temporarily in finer textured soils following additions of water. In localized regions, or micropores, it is likely that the oxygen tension may sometimes be below normal, even in soils of medium texture. Any such oxygen deficiency would result in gaseous losses of nitrogen by denitrification only if nitrites or nitrates were present or being formed.

A few representative pot experiments that show recoveries of added nitrogen in soils and crops are listed below. Mann and Barnes (1951) accounted for only 49% of the nitrogen added as ammonium sulfate, 57% of that in mustard residues, and 60% of that in tare residues. Lowenstein et al. (1957) reported losses of up to 72% of the nitrogen added as $NaNO_3$ or $(NH_4)_2SO_4$ to an uncropped silt loam, but accounted for all but 7 to 8% of it where oats was grown. Although the analyses of the uncropped soils show a rapid decrease of total nitrogen following the addition of the two nitrogen sources, there was no corresponding decrease in nitrate-nitrogen. It, therefore, seems unlikely that the unaccounted-for nitrogen was lost through denitrification. Wagner and Smith (1958, 1960), in laboratory experiments, found large losses of nitrogen from clay soils. Pinck et al. (1948b) (see Allison, 1955) observed a loss of about 18% of the nitrogen added as urea and green manures over a four-year continuous cropping period in the greenhouse. In another similar experiment the loss was 14%.

Grable and Johnson (1960) studied the efficiency of utilization of nitrate-nitrogen added at four rates to 14 soils in pots that were cropped to ryegrass. The recoveries of added nitrogen in four clippings of the grass, above that from the unfertilized controls, were between 62 and 85%, and averaged 77%. The average efficiencies of recovery for the 200-, 400-, and 600-pound per acre rates were 74, 78, and 78%, respectively. Since nitrogen recovery decreased as clay content increased, the authors suggest that the slower oxygen diffusion in the clay soils favored some biological denitrification.

A more accurate method of determining nitrogen recovery in pot experiments is by the use of fertilizer containing N^{15}. Using this method, MacVicar et al. (1950) accounted for 85 to near 100% of the added fertilizer nitrogen. The largest losses occurred where the soil organic matter level was low and the nitrogen addition high. The authors were of the opinion that this suggested denitrification, but the possibility of chemical decomposition cannot be ruled out.

Walker et al. (1956) grew Italian ryegrass and white clover, singly and together, in soils kept in greenhouse pots to which different rates of labeled ammonium sulfate and potassium nitrate were added. The recovery of tagged nitrogen in the crops plus soil averaged about 70% for both crops, and was slightly higher for ammonium sulfate than for nitrate. They attributed the low recovery to denitrification.

Tyler and Broadbent (1958) recovered 83 to 97% of the tagged nitrogen applied to a cropped greenhouse soil at the rate of 200 pounds nitrogen per acre as either ammonium sulfate, ammonium nitrate, or ammonium hydroxide. These values include the nitrogen in four cuttings of ryegrass plus the nitrogen immobilized in the soil. The percent recovery of nitrogen was slightly higher with ammonium sulfate than with the other two nitrogen sources.

In a greenhouse experiment with two subsoils to which various amounts of tagged nitrogen were added at rates up to 400 pounds per acre, Legg and Allison (1959) accounted for an average of 93% of the N^{15} added. The crop was sudangrass. The recoveries of nitrogen applied as ammonium sulfate and sodium nitrate were similar. In another greenhouse experiment, Legg (1962) added tagged sodium nitrate at several rates to 12 surface soils of widely varying nitrogen contents and grew a crop of oats, followed by a residual crop of sudangrass. The nitrogen recovery values for the crops and soils averaged 90%.

Cady and Bartholomew (1960) recovered about 80%, on the average, of the tagged nitrogen that they added as ammonium sulfate to a Norfolk sandy loam and a Portsmouth fine sandy loam, cropped to sudangrass. Neither the addition of organic amendments, nor the rate of addition of nitrogen, affected the total recovery.

Turtschin et al. (1962) accounted for 83 to 89% of the nitrogen added to oats as tagged ammonium sulfate at the time of seeding, but the recoveries were less if the nitrogen was added 2 to 12 months before sowing.

When Martin et al. (1963) added $N^{15}H_4NO_3$ in various amounts to rhodesgrass, grown on a light-textured soil in the greenhouse, approximately 94% of the nitrogen was recovered from the soil:plant system. The loss apparently was the same from the labeled and unlabeled forms of nitrogen.

In a 6-year greenhouse experiment, using a poor acid sandy loam cropped to oats, Jansson (1963) accounted for 86 to 92% of added tagged nitrogen. The recovery was slightly higher from ammonium sulfate than from sodium nitrate. Losses were confined to the year of addition.

These nitrogen recovery data from greenhouse experiments show that some nitrogen is almost invariably lost in gaseous forms. The loss under the best conditions is likely to be in the range of up to 20%. Under less ideal conditions, the loss may be much higher. The greatly increased recovery in the presence of a vigorously growing crop may be attributed to the rapid removal of the nitrogen before it can be acted upon biologically or chemically.

B. Lysimeters

Although, as previously stated, there has been much criticism of soil fertility and leaching experiments conducted in lysimeters, it is true that this experimental method is one of the best for furnishing soil nitrogen balance data under near natural conditions. When carefully conducted over a period of years, and if accurate soil nitrogen analyses are made initially and at the end of the experiment, the data obtained give a fairly accurate estimate of gaseous losses.

In a previous publication (Allison, 1955) the results of lysimeter experiments conducted at several locations in the United States were discussed. These experiments included a total of 51 uncropped lysimeters and 106 that were cropped to nonlegumes. The unaccounted-for nitrogen in the 157 lysimeters averaged 15% of the nitrogen added or made available from the soil. Presumably, most of the loss occurred through volatilization, but there may have been a few unmeasured losses of pollen, leaves, etc. from the cropped lysimeters. In these experiments there was no evidence of nonsymbiotic nitrogen fixation, but the experiments were not adequate to establish this.

In a recently reported lysimeter experiment (Allison et al., 1959) with Lakeland sand, there was no evidence for appreciable gaseous losses of nitrogen except where animal manures were added; in this treatment about 10 to 20% of this manure nitrogen was not accounted for. Highly accurate nitrogen balance data cannot be derived from these experiments because legumes were grown in most cylinders, but the data are adequate to show that with the exception mentioned, gaesous losses of nitrogen were negligible from this very porous sandy soil.

Owens (1960) conducted a nitrogen balance experiment using eight Illinois soils in monolith lysimeters to which ammonium sulfate was added about 11 to 15 weeks prior to the planting of corn. Three moisture levels were provided for by the addition of 12, 18, and 24 inches of water at intervals during the period between the addition of nitrogen and planting. An average of 33% of the applied nitrogen was unaccounted for during the two years of experimentation and was assumed to have been denitrified. This loss of nitrogen was the same for all moisture treatments, possibly because all soils were above field capacity each year when differential irrigation was begun. The author was of the opinion that all soils fluctuated between field capacity and saturation during the irrigation period, regardless of the moisture treatment imposed. This experiment obviously provided much more opportunity for denitrification than would be encountered under most field conditions.

C. Field Experiments

The usual type of field experiment does not furnish data that are sufficiently accurate for the construction of satisfactory nitrogen balance sheets. There is usually no exact knowledge of losses of nitrogen through erosion, or by leaching, and, of course, gaseous losses are not measured. There is also uncertainty as to how much of the crop nitrogen comes from the subsoil; even if it is analyzed, the methods are usually not sufficiently accurate to measure the small percentage changes that cropping may have brought about, especially in experiments lasting only a few years. Added to this is the natural variation in soils from plot to plot.

The results obtained over a period of 50 years in the Broadbalk continuous wheat experiments at Rothamsted furnish considerable information on the fate of nitrogen in soils. When no nitrogen was added as fertilizer, essentially all of that in the rainfall, or released from the soil, was recovered in the crop. In a nearby uncropped soil, where conditions were similar and where the leachates were collected, nearly all of the nitrogen was found in the drainage water. At this low nitrogen level it seems that if a crop was present it assimilated the nitrogen, but otherwise this element was lost in the percolate. Where ammonium sulfate was added to the Broadbalk wheat, the recovery of nitrogen in the crop was 47%; where farm manure was applied the recovery in the crop was 31%. The remainder was lost through leaching or as gases.

In New Jersey cylinder experiments (Allison, 1955), where no provision was made for collecting the leachates, the recoveries in the crop of added nitrogen plus that released from the soil over a 40-year period were for manure 46%, sodium nitrate 56%, and ammonium sulfate 53% on limed soil. In the absence of lime, where the pH decreased to about 5.2 to 4.1, the recoveries in the crop in the same order were 39, 32, and 22%. In field experiments at the same station the recovery of nitrogen in the crop was even less, averaging about 27% for limed soils and 25% for those not limed. These data suggest that, besides leaching, large losses of nitrogen probably occurred through decomposition of nitrous acid or possibly through its reaction with ammonia to form unstable ammonium nitrite.

Many other field experiments, discussed elsewhere (Allison, 1955), show that recoveries of added fertilizer nitrogen, or of that made available from the soil, are often less than 50%. Usually the recovery of nitrogen is greater from poor soils than from those high in fertility.

The results of a unique field experiment were reported recently by

Boawn et al. (1960). This experiment was conducted at Prosser, Washington, on an irrigated nitrogen-poor desert fine sandy loam. The cropping system for six years was grain sorghum, potatoes, sugar beets, and grain sorghum—all fertilized—followed by two residual crops of corn. Changes in soil nitrogen were not measured, but total nitrogen in all plant tops, and in the beets and potatoes was measured. Nitrogen recoveries were based on the difference between the nitrogen uptake by the plants grown on the treated and untreated plots. The recovery of nitrogen in the crops during the 6-year period averaged 81.2%. The percentage recovery increased somewhat with the quantity of nitrogen added and was higher with ammonium sulfate and ammonium nitrate than with calcium nitrate. These unusually high recoveries for a field experiment may be attributed to the absence of leaching, good soil aeration, and a minimum of biological activity between crop seasons in a cold, dry climate.

Viets (1960) refers to other field data, not yet completed or published in detail, where the recoveries of nitrogen are much below those reported by Boawn et al. (1960). At Newell, South Dakota, on a calcareous unirrigated dryland soil, the recovery of ammonium nitrate nitrogen by bromegrass-crested wheatgrass grown on a Pierre clay ranged between 34 and 50%. In an irrigated experiment, conducted in Montana on a calcareous Bowdoin clay, western wheatgrass grown at three moisture levels recovered an average of only 20% of the nitrogen added as ammonium nitrate. In another irrigation experiment at Brawley, California, on a calcareous Holtville silty clay where a sequence of crops was grown, the recovery of nitrogen applied as nitrates, ammonia, and urea has averaged 29% with no marked variations in efficiency between sources.

Pearson et al. (1961) conducted field studies in the Southeastern United States that emphasize the losses of nitrogen that occur in a warm climate during the winter months following fall applications of fertilizers. Such fall-applied nitrogen was only 49% as effective as spring-applied nitrogen when measured by corn yields; in terms of nitrogen recovered, the relative effectiveness was 62%. Under similar conditions, where 200 pounds of nitrogen per acre was applied to corn in the spring, there was a surprisingly large residual benefit to two succeeding crops during the following 16 months. The recoveries of added nitrogen in the three crops were in the range of 70 to 77%. Although these values are not extremely accurate, they do show that recoveries can be good, even in the humid region, if the nitrogen is applied at a time when leaching is at a minimum, and when a crop is present to assimilate it.

An experiment in which nitrogen recovery was studied under field conditions using tagged nitrogen fertilizers has recently been reported by Carter et al. (1962). In this experiment iron cylinders 1 or 2 feet in diameter were driven into the ground to a depth of 1.5 to 2 feet, and tagged sodium nitrate and ammonium sulfate were added at the rate of 250 pounds of nitrogen per acre to a Greenville fine sandy loam. Some of the cylinders were left uncropped and the others were seeded to sudangrass. The plants, as well as the various soil horizons, were analyzed for total and excess N^{15}-nitrogen. The recoveries of added N^{15}-nitrogen from 32 cylinders ranged between 85.3 and 91.9%, and averaged 89.5%. There was little difference in nitrogen recovery between nitrogen added as sodium nitrate and as ammonium sulfate. The lowest recoveries were from the uncropped soils where the concentration of nitrogen in the soil was, of course, higher during most of the experimental period.

In another experiment, reported by Dilz and Woldendorp (1960), small pieces of grass sod were placed in pots buried in the open, and tagged potassium nitrate added. Three soils were used. During a 70-day growth period under optimum moisture conditions, the recoveries of nitrogen in the herbage, roots, and soil ranged between 78 and 84%. The authors state that these values may be about 5% too low because no provision was made for the inclusion of nitrates in the analyses.

D. Comments on Methods of Determining Nitrogen Recovery

Two methods of determining the percentage of added fertilizer nitrogen that is recovered in greenhouse and field tests are in common use. These were mentioned above. One is the nontracer method, which involves the subtraction of the nitrogen removed from the control soil by the crop from that removed by the crop from fertilized soils. Usually the soils are not analyzed for nitrogen. The other method is based on the recovery of added tagged nitrogen in the crop and soil. Ideally, the experiments are conducted under conditions of no leaching, or else the leachates are collected and analyzed. Obviously, the tracer method is more accurate, but much more expensive and involved. On the other hand, the simple nontracer method is usually preferable for use by agronomists who are interested chiefly in the practical evaluation of fertilizer response. In this latter method, accuracy is likely to be much increased if a second unfertilized crop is grown to remove residual nitrogen.

The two methods of determining nitrogen recovery usually agree rather closely if the residual N^{15} left in the soil is included in the calculations. This is very essential because the addition of fertilizer nitrogen increases the uptake of soil nitrogen by the crop (Cady and Bartholomew, 1960; Legg, 1962; Legg and Allison, 1960; and Walker et al., 1956). At the same time there occurs a movement of N^{15} into the soil. Walker et al. attributed this increased uptake of soil nitrogen in part to biological interchange, where in net effect a portion of the soil nitrogen that is released by mineralization, and absorbed by the crop, is replaced by fertilizer nitrogen that is immobilized. They also pointed out that root excretions are a factor in the tie-up of the fertilizer nitrogen. Furthermore, as more fertilizer is applied, the crop is increased and the larger root system should result in more nitrogen immobilization. Although each of these three factors undoubtedly plays a part in the uptake of soil nitrogen, it now seems that the interchange involved in mineralization and immobilization is the most important. The limited data available indicate that the extent to which N^{15} is substituted for N^{14} is dependent more on the quantity of tagged fertilizer added than on the nitrogen content of the soil to which it is added.

VI. AGRICULTURAL PRACTICES FOR MAXIMUM EFFICIENCY IN NITROGEN USE

The above discussion has considered in some detail the sources of crop nitrogen and what can happen to this nitrogen in the soil. So far as natural sources of nitrogen are concerned, very little new information that affects the agricultural economy, or farm management practices, has been reported in recent years. We still emphasize, as in the past, that animal manures and crop residues should usually be returned to the soil to conserve nutrients and maintain soil organic matter, but there are conditions where this is not desirable or practical. Baldanzi (1960), for example, states that in the tropics of Brazil, where great masses of dry grass residues of wide carbon-nitrogen ratios are produced yearly, it is often preferable to burn the grass rather than to try to incorporate it into the soil. Burning may also sometimes be advisable even in the Temperate Zone where certain insects and diseases are prevalent, or where the undecomposed residues interfere with planting, growth, and cultivation of the succeeding crop. Legumes can still be emphasized as a valuable source of soil nitrogen and organic matter, but in these modern times, when commercial nitrogen is abundant, it is seldom an economical practice to grow them for their nitrogen alone; they are usually grown primarily for feed or as a seed crop.

With regard to the other natural sources of soil nitrogen, there is little or nothing that can be done to increase the incoming supply. Nonsymbiotic nitrogen fixation is such a minor source of nitrogen for cultivated crops that it can be ignored. The new problems that relate to nitrogen sources, chiefly revolve around the various forms of fertilizer nitrogen, and how to utilize them most efficiently.

A high efficiency in the utilization of available nitrogen in soil is dependent first on erosion control, second on minimizing leaching, and finally on prevention of the formation of volatile forms of nitrogen. The mechanics of erosion control have been well worked out and need not be discussed here.

Losses of nitrogen through leaching can often be appreciably reduced through improved farm management methods. The practices to be used vary widely with the soil, climate, amount of rainfall, extent of irrigation, cropping system, and type and amount of fertilizer used. In semiarid regions there is little or no leaching unless irrigation is practiced. Likewise, in humid regions, where the land is kept in sod crops, leaching is negligible, except, perhaps, where the fertilizer application is extremely high. It is in humid regions, where cultivated crops are grown, especially on sandy soils, that loss of nitrogen through leaching is likely to be large unless a major effort is made to prevent such losses. Some of the facts and principles involved will be summarized.

Probably the first fact that needs to be emphasized is that leaching of available nitrogen beyond the plant root zone usually does not occur to any marked extent in cultivated, medium-textured humid soils in the United States during the main plant growing season, unless the annual rainfall is above about 50 inches. Most of the leaching occurs in late fall, in the winter if the soil is not frozen, and in the early spring. It is during this colder period that more water commonly enters the soil, if not frozen, than leaves it via evapotranspiration. Reduced to its simplest terms then, the farm manager's job is to make certain that soil nitrogen is kept at a low level in unfrozen soils during the five or six colder months of the year when there is either no crop present, or when its need for nitrogen is very low. He can do this to some extent by avoiding large late-season applications of nitrogen, by growing cover crops where feasible, and by using carbonaceous crop residues to help tie-up nitrate nitrogen. An excellent practice is to keep growing crops, especially sod crops, on the soil for as large a percentage of the time as possible. The use of the newer slowly available forms of fertilizer nitrogen may possibly favor high nitrogen recovery, but this seems very doubtful. Past research has shown that the highest nitrogen recoveries are almost invariably observed following the addition of a readily available form of nitrogen to a crop that can utilize it quickly. The portion of the nitrogen that is applied in slowly available form, and not used the first year, is subject to leaching during the colder months, if any is made available. This nitrogen is also subject for a longer time to the various biological and chemical changes that may lead to gaseous forms of nitrogen. On the other hand, low concentrations of available nitrogen would be expected to reduce chemical changes, such as those involved in ammonium nitrite formation and decomposition. The use of ammonia-nitrogen, rather than nitrate-nitrogen, as a means of reducing leaching losses usually has only limited advantage since the ammonia is normally oxidized to nitrate rather rapidly, except when the soil is very cold.

On the preceding pages, six possible channels of loss of nitrogen from soils in gaseous forms were discussed. These may be regrouped into three general types of mechanisms, which differ markedly from each other, and which are, at least in part, subject to partial control by the agriculturalist. These nitrogen loss channels are: (a) by volatilization of ammonia, (b) by classical denitrification, and (c) by interaction of nitrous acid or nitrites with other compounds whereby gaseous forms of nitrogen are liberated either from the reactants or their products.

Ammonia volatilization from soils usually occurs in appreciable amounts only where soils are above pH 7. In these soils any ammonia applied on or near the soil surface is subject to volatilization as the soil dries. If the ammonia is mixed with these soils, the losses are usually negligible. Ammonia does not leave a moist surface readily, unless the concentration is high. Ammonia volatilization may also be a problem on either humid or semiarid soils if urea is applied on the soil surface, or on green vegetation, and is not washed down soon afterwards. No such problem exists if the urea is well mixed with the soil.

Classical denitrification is largely a problem on very fine textured soils of poor structure; on poorly drained soils; on normal soils of medium or fine texture during periods of excessive rainfall; and in masses of decomposing organic matter, such as manure piles. Denitrification can occur, of course, only when oxidized forms of nitrogen are present and oxygen is inadequate to meet the needs of the denitrifying bacteria that are present. Excessive applications of readily decomposable plant products may, on decomposition, tend to help deplete the soil oxygen and favor denitrification. Agricultural practices that avoid these nitrogen losses are obvious, the main one being to avoid having nitrates in quantity present in the soil at a time when these oxygen-depleting processes are in action, or expected.

The loss of nitrogen via nitrous acid or nitrite is the least understood, the most involved, and possibly the most important channel of loss. Until more exact information is available on ammonium nitrate formation and decomposition, and on the interaction of nitrous acid or nitrites with other soil constituents, it is not possible to be too specific on recommendations for prevention of losses through this channel. It is well established, however, that major losses of nitrogen can occur where nitrous acid is formed and only slowly oxidized, even if the exact reactions are not well understood, or the quantities of nitrogen involved known. The simultaneous presence of ammonia is likely to increase such losses. It follows, then, that our agricultural practices should be such as to avoid soil conditions that result in delaying oxidation of nitrites to nitrates. Such a delay may occur in soils that are too acid, where the ammonia concentration is too high, or where for other reasons the conditions are not favorable for the activities of *Nitrobacter*. Nitrites can also form by reduction, but in such oxygen-deficient soils classical denitrification is more likely to be the channel of loss than are nitrite interactions or decomposition.

REFERENCES CITED

Abel, E., Schmid, H., and Schafranik, J. 1931. Kinetik der Stickstoffentwicklung aus Ammoniumnitrit. Zeit. physik. Chem. Bodenstein—Festband 510-522.

Allison, F. E. 1955. The enigma of soil nitrogen balance sheets (Ed. by A. G. Norman, Academic Press, New York) Adv. Agron. 7:213-250.

Allison, F. E. 1963. Losses of gaseous nitrogen from soils by chemical mechanisms involving nitrous acid and nitrites. Soil Sci. 96:404-409.

Allison, F. E., and Doetsch, Janet H. 1951. Nitrogen gas production by the reaction of nitrites with amino acids in slightly acidic media. Soil Sci. Soc. Amer. Proc. 15:163-166.

Allison, F. E., Doetsch, Janet H., and Sterling, Luann D. 1952. Nitrogen gas formation by interaction of nitrites and amino acids. Soil Sci. 74:311-314.

Allison, F. E., Roller, E. M., and Adams, J. E. 1959. Soil fertility studies in lysimeters containing Lakeland sand. USDA Tech. Bul. 1199:1-62.

Allison, F. E., and Sterling, Luann D. 1949. Nitrate formation from soil organic matter in relation to total nitrogen and cropping practices. Soil Sci. 67:239-252.

Andrew, C. S. 1962. Influence of nutrition on nitrogen fixation and growth of legumes. Commonwealth Bur. of Pastures and Field Crops, Hurley, Berkshire, Eng., Bul. 46:130-146.

Baldanzi, G. 1960. Burning and soil fertility. 7th Intern. Cong. Soil Sci. Comm. III, 523-530.

Bennett, H. H., and Lowdermilk, W. C. 1938. General aspects of the soil-erosion problem. USDA Yearbook of Agr., Soils and Men, pp. 581-608.

Bizzell, J. A. 1944. Lysimeter experiments—VI. The effects of cropping and fertilization on the losses of nitrogen from the soil. Cornell Agr. Exp. Sta. Memo. 256:1-14.

Bizzell, J. A., and Lyon, T. L. 1928. Composition of drainage waters from lysimeters at Cornell University. Proc. and Papers of First Intern. Cong. Soil Sci. Comm. II, 342-349.

Blake, G. R., Allred, E. R., Van Bavel, C. H. M., and Whisler, F. D. 1960. Agricultural drought and moisture excesses in Minnesota. Minnesota Agr. Exp. Sta. Tech. Bul. 235:1-36.

Boawn, L. C., Nelson, C. E., Viets, F. G., Jr., and Crawford, C. L. 1960. Nitrogen carrier and nitrogen rate influence on soil properties and nutrient uptake by crops. Washington Agr. Exp. Sta. Bul. 614:1-24.

Bond, G. 1958. Symbiotic nitrogen fixation by non-legumes. *In* Nutrition of the Legumes (Ed. E. G. Hallsworth, Academic Press, New York), 216-231.

Cady, F. B., and Bartholomew, W. V. 1960. Greenhouse recovery of added tracer nitrogen. Soil Sci. Soc. North Carolina Proc. III, 44-54.

Carter, J. N., and Allison, F. E. 1961. The effect of rates of application of ammonium sulfate on gaseous losses of nitrogen from soils. Soil Sci. Soc. Amer. Proc. 25:484-486.

Carter, J. N., Bennett, O. L., Allison, F. E., and Pearson, R. W. 1962. Recovery of N^{15}-nitrogen from soil under field conditions. Paper presented before Div. III, Soil Sci. Soc. Amer., Ithaca, N.Y., Aug. 20-23.

Clark, F. E., Beard, W. E., and Smith, D. H. 1960. Dissimilar nitrifying capacities of soils in relation to losses of applied nitrogen. Soil Sci. Soc. Amer. Proc. 24:50-54.

Dawson, R. F. 1949. A quantitative test of Eggleton's proposed mechanism of nitrogen loss. Archiv. Biochem. 21:279-288.

De, P. K., and Mandal, L. N. 1956. Fixation of nitrogen by algae in rice soils. Soil Sci. 81:453-458.

Delwicke, C. C., and Wijler, J. 1956. Non-symbiotic nitrogen fixation in soil. Plant and Soil 7:113-129.

Dhar, N. R. 1938. Influence of light on nitrogen fixation and nitrogen transformations in the soil and alkali land reclamation. FITA ler. Cong. Internatl. Des. Engrais Chemiques, Rome, 1-65.

Dilz, K., and Woldendorp, J. W. 1960. Distribution and nitrogen balance of ^{15}N-labeled nitrate applied on grass sods. Proc. 8th Internatl. Grassland Cong. (Reading, England) pp. 150-152. July 11-12.

Drews, K. 1928. Über die Assimilation des Luftstickstoffs durch Blaualgen. Centralblatt f. Bakt., Par. u. Infektionskrankheiten, 2nd Abt. 76:88-101.

Dudgdale, R. C., and Neess, J. C. 1961. Recent observations of nitrogen fixation in blue-green algae. Robt. A. Taft Sanitary Eng. Center, Tech. Rept. W61-3, 103-106.

Fuller, W. H., Cameron, R. E., and Raica, N., Jr. 1960. Fixation of nitrogen in desert soils by algae. Trans. 7th Internatl. Cong. Soil Sci. Comm. III, 617-624.

Gerretsen, F. C., and De Hoop, H. 1957. Nitrogen losses during nitrification in solutions and in acid sandy soils. Can. J. Microbiol. 3:359-380.

Grable, A. R., and Johnson, D. D. 1960. Efficiency of recovery of applied nitrate nitrogen by perennial ryegrass from different soils. Soil Sci. Soc. Amer. Proc. 24:503-507.

Greenland, D. J. 1962a. Nitrogen gains and losses in tropical soils. Proc. 3rd Interafr. Soils Conf., 531-535. 1959. Abs. in Soils and Fert. 25: p. 10.

Greenland, D. J. 1962b. Denitrification in some tropical soils. J. Agr. Sci. 58:227-233.

Hall, A. D., and Miller, N. H. J. 1911. On the absorption of ammonia from the atmosphere (by soils). J. Agr. Sci. 4:56-68.

Henzell, E. F., and Norris, D. O. 1962. Processes by which nitrogen is added to the soil/plant system. Commonwealth Bur. of Pastures and Field Crops, Hurley, Berkshire, Eng., Bul. 46:1-18.

Ingham, G. 1938. Nitrogen transformations in the soil. J. So. Afr. Chem. Inst. 21:59-63.

Ingham, G. 1939. Atmospheric ammonia as the primary source of nitrogen to plants. So. Afr. J. Sci. 36:158-163.

Ingham, G. 1940. Fallowing in relation to the nitrogen supply. J. So. Afr. Chem. Inst. 23:52-58.

Ingham, G. 1950. Effect of materials absorbed from the atmosphere in maintaining soil fertility. Soil Sci. 70:205-212.

Jansson, S. L. 1963. Balance sheet and residual effects of fertilizer nitrogen in a 6-year study with N^{15}. Soil Sci. 95:31-37.

Jenny, H. 1950. Causes of the high nitrogen and organic matter content of certain tropical forest soils. Soil Sci. 69:63-69.

Jenny, H., and Raychaudhuri, S. P. 1960. Effect of climate and cultivation on nitrogen and organic matter reserves in Indian soils. Indian Council of Agr. Res., New Delhi, 1-126.

Jensen, H. L. 1940. Contributions to the nitrogen economy of Australian wheat soils, with particular reference to New South Wales. Proc. Linn. Soc. N. S. Wales 65:1-122.

Jones, R. J. 1942. Nitrogen losses from Alabama soils in lysimeters as influenced by various systems of green manure crop management. J. Amer. Soc. Agron. 34:574-585.

Karraker, P. E., Bortner, C. E., and Fergus, E. N. 1950. Nitrogen balance in lysimeters as affected by growing Kentucky bluegrass and certain legumes separately and together. Kentucky Agr. Exp. Sta. Bul. 557:1-16.

Krantz, B. A., Ohlrogge, A. J., and Scarseth, G. D. 1944. Movement of nitrogen in soils. Soil Sci. Soc. Amer. Proc. 8:189-195.

Legg, J. O. 1962. Plant uptake of soil and fertilizer nitrogen from 12 soils treated with NaN^{15}O$_3$. Paper presented before Div. III, Soil Sci. Soc. Amer., Ithaca, N.Y., Aug. 21.

Legg, J. O., and Allison, F. E. 1959. Recovery of N^{15}-tagged nitrogen from ammonium-fixing soils. Soil Sci. Soc. Amer. Proc. 23:131-134.

Legg, J. O., and Allison, F. E. 1960. Role of rhizosphere microorganisms in the uptake of nitrogen by plants. Trans. 7th Internatl. Cong. Soil Sci., Comm. III, 545-550.

Lindhard, J. 1954. Losses of nitrogen by evaporation from samples of cow manure. Tidskr. Planteavl 57:108-120. (Eng. sum.) Abs. In C. A. 48:6632.

Lipman, J. G. 1925. The fixation of nitrogen under field conditions. J. Amer. Soc. Agron. 17:450-455.

Lipman, J. G., and Conybeare, A. B. 1936. Preliminary note on the inventory and balance sheet of plant nutrients in the United States. New Jersey Agr. Exp. Sta. Bul. 607:1-23.

Lowenstein, H., Engelbert, L. E., Attoe, O. J., and Allen, O. N. 1957. Nitrogen loss in gaseous form from soils as influenced by fertilizers and management. Soil Sci. Soc. Amer. Proc. 21:397-400.

Löhnis, F. 1925. Bacterial nitrogen fixation. J. Amer. Soc. Agron. 17:445-450.

MacVicar, R., Garman, W. L., and Wall, R. 1950. Studies on nitrogen fertilizer utilization using N^{15}. Soil Sci. Soc. Amer. Proc. 15:265-268.

Mann, H. H., and Barnes, T. W. 1951. The behavior of nitrogenous manures in the soil. I. The loss of manurial nitrogen. J. Agr. Sci. 41:309-314.

Martin, A. E., Henzell, E. F., Ross, P. J., and Haydock, K. P. 1963. Isotopic studies on the uptake of nitrogen from the soil:plant system using Rhodes grass in pots. Aust. J. Soil Res. 1:169-184.

Meiklejohn, Jane. 1962. Microbiology of the nitrogen cycle in some Ghana soils. J. Exp. Agr. 30:118-126.

Miller, N. H. J. 1905. The amounts of nitrogen as ammonia and as nitric acid, and of chlorine in the rainwater collected at Rothamsted. J. Agr. Sci. 1:280-303.

Morgan, M. F., and Jacobson, H. G. M. 1942. Soil and crop interrelations of various nitrogenous fertilizers. Connecticut Agr. Exp. Sta. Bul. 458:271-328.

Morgan, M. F., Jacobson, H. G. M., and Le Compte, S. B., Jr. 1942. Drainage water losses from a sandy soil as affected by cropping and cover crops. Connecticut Agr. Exp. Sta. Bul. 466:729-759.

Neal, O. R. 1944. Removal of nutrients from the soil by crops and erosion. J. Amer. Soc. Agron. 36:601-607.

Norris, D. O. 1962. The biology of nitrogen fixation. Commonwealth Bur. of Pastures and Field Crops, Hurley, Berkshire, Eng. Bul. 46:113-129.

Nye, P. H., and Greenland, D. J. 1960. The soil under shifting cultivation. Tech. Comm. No. 51:1-156. Commonwealth Agr. Bur., England.

Owens, L. D. 1960. Nitrogen movement and transformations in soils as evaluated by a lysimeter study utilizing isotopic nitrogen. Soil Sci. Soc. Amer. Proc. 24:372-376.

Parker, C. A. 1954. Non-symbiotic nitrogen-fixing bacteria in soil. I. Studies on *Clostridium butyricum*. Austral. J. Agr. Res. 5:90-97.

Pearson, R. W., Jordan, H. V., Bennett, O. L., Scarsbrook, C. E., Adams, W. E., and White, A. W. 1961. Residual effects of fall- and spring-applied nitrogen fertilizers on crop yields in the Southeastern United States. USDA Tech. Bul. 1254:1-19.

Pinck, L. A., Allison, F. E., and Gaddy, V. L. 1948a. The effect of green manure crops of varying carbon-nitrogen ratios upon nitrogen availability and soil organic matter content. J. Amer. Soc. Agron. 40:237-248.

Pinck, L. A., Allison, F. E., and Gaddy, V. L. 1948b. Utilization of nitrogen in cropping systems with and without green manure in the greenhouse. Soil Sci. 66:39-52.

Ruinen, Jakoba. 1956. Occurrence of Beijerinckia species in the 'Phyllosphere.' Nature 177:220-221.

Ruinen, Jakoba. 1961. The Phyllosphere. I. An ecologically neglected milieu. Plant and Soil 15:81-109.

Russell, E. J., and Richards, E. H. 1920. The washing out of nitrates by drainage water from uncropped and unmanured land. J. Agr. Sci., Part I, 10:22-43.

Russell, E. J., and Watson, D. J. 1940. The Rothamsted field experiments on the growth of wheat. Imperial Bur. Soil Sci., Tech. Comm. No. 40:1-163.

Salter, R. M., and Green, T. C. 1933. Factors affecting the accumulation and loss of nitrogen and organic carbon in cropped soils. J. Amer. Soc. Agron. 25:622-630.

Salter, R. M., and Schollenberger, C. J. 1939. Farm manure. Ohio Agr. Exp. Sta. Bul. 605:1-69.

Schreiner, O., and Brown, B. E. 1938. Soil nitrogen. USDA Yearbook of Agr., Soils and Men. 361-376.

Skyring, G. W., and Callow, Barbara J. 1962. The physiology and biochemistry of nitrification and denitrification. Commonwealth Bur. of Pastures and Field Crops, Hurley, Berkshire, Eng. Bul. 46:56-71.

Turtschin, F. B., Bersenjewa, S. N., Koritzkaja, I. A., Shidkick, G. G., and Lobowikowa, G. A. 1962. Die Stickstoffumwandlung im Boden nach den Angaben der Untersuchungen unter Anwendung des Isotops N^{15}. Trans. 7th Internatl. Cong. Soil Sci., Comm. II, Madison, Wis., 236-245.

Tyler, K. B., and Broadbent, F. E. 1958. Nitrogen uptake by ryegrass from three tagged ammonium fertilizers. Soil Sci. Soc. Amer. Proc. 22:231-234.

Van Bavel, C. H. M. 1959. Drought and water surplus in agricultural soils of the lower Mississippi Valley area. USDA Tech. Bul. 1209:1-93.

Van Bavel, C. H. M., and Lillard, J. H. 1957. Agricultural drought in Virginia. Virginia Agr. Exp. Sta. Tech. Bul. 128:1-38.

Van Doren, C. A., Stauffer, R. S., and Kidder, E. H. 1951. Effect of contour farming on soil loss and runoff. Soil Sci. Soc. Amer. Proc. 15:413-417.

Vanecko, S., and Varner, J. E. 1955. Studies on nitrite metabolism in higher plants. Plant Physiol. 30:388-390.

Vickery, H. B., Pucher, G. W., Wakeman, A. J., and Leavenworth, C. S. 1946. Chemical investigations of the metabolism of plants. I. The nitrogen nutrition of *Narcissus Poeticus*. Connecticut Agr. Exp. Sta. Bul. 496:5-93.

Viets, F. G., Jr. 1960. Recovery of fertilizer nitrogen on irrigated and dryland soils of the Western United States. Trans. 7th Intern. Cong. Soil Sci. Comm. III, 486-493.

Wagner, G. H., and Smith, G. E. 1958. Nitrogen losses from soils fertilized with different nitrogen carriers. Soil Sci. 85:125-129.

Wagner, G. H., and Smith, G. E. 1960. Recovery of fertilizer nitrogen from soils. Missouri Agr. Exp. Sta. Res. Bul. 738:1-28.

Wahhab, A., and Uddin, F. 1954. Loss of nitrogen through reaction of ammonium and nitrite ions. Soil Sci. 78:119-126.

Wahhab, A., and Uddin, F. 1955. Influence of light on interaction of ammonium and nitrite ions. Soil Sci. 80:121-125.

Walker, T. W., Adams, A. F. R., and Orchiston, H. D. 1956. Fate of labeled nitrate and ammonium nitrogen when applied to grass and clover grown separately and together. Soil Sci. 81:339-351.

Wetselaar, R. 1961. Nitrate distribution in tropical soils. II. Effect of capillary accumulation of nitrate during a long dry period. Plant and Soil 15:121-133.

Wetselaar, R. 1962. Nitrate distribution in tropical soils. III. Downward movement and accumulation of nitrate in the subsoil. Plant and Soil 16:19-31.

Wijler, J., and Delwiche, C. C. 1954. Investigations on the denitrifying process in soil. Plant and Soil 5:155-169.

Wilson, J. K. 1943. Nitrous acid and the loss of nitrogen. Cornell U. Agr. Exp. Sta. Memo. 253:1-36.

Woodruff, C. M. 1949. Estimating the nitrogen delivery of soil from the organic matter determination as reflected by Sanborn field. Soil Sci. Soc. Amer. Proc. 14:208-212.

Index

Absorption (see also sorption),
by leaves, 532, 533
by roots (see also uptake of nitrogen),
531-532
of atmospheric ammonia, 16, 17, 183
Acacia, 361
Accretion of nitrogen by soil materials, 17-21
Achromobacter, nitrogen fixation by, 442
Acidity (see also pH),
accompanying nitrification, 309
effect on ammonia-organic complexes, 243-244
effect on nitrogen immobilization, 297
effect on nutrient availability, 388-389
effect on symbiotic nitrogen fixation, 387, 390, 392, 411-412, 421
influence on denitrification, 70
Actinomycetes in nitrogen fixation, 377, 443
Adsorbed ions,
convection to plant roots, 569
diffusion of and uptake by roots, 568
Adsorption (see also sorption),
bacterial, 311, 313
by leaves, 532-533
by plants, 512-518
by roots, 531-532
isotherms, 155
macromolecules by clay minerals, 261-264
Aeration (see also oxygen),
availability of nitrogen to plants and, 492
denitrification and, 69
nitrification and, 328
Aerobacter, nitrogen fixation by, 442
Aggregate size, influence on denitrification, 347
Agrobacterium, relation to *Rhizobium*, 364
Alfalfa, 360, 361, 364
Algae, blue green,
biomass in soil, 470
gains of nitrogen in soil, 469-470
geographic distribution, 6-10, 649
in desert soils, 8-10
in glacial moraines, 18
in rice soils, 469-470
nitrogen fixation in vitro, rate, 470
nitrogen fixing species, 6, 443
Algae, green, symbiosis with azotobacter, 451
Alkali soils, nitrogen mineralization in, 60
Allantoin, 97, 114
Alnus, 376, 377
Aluminum,
effect on nitrogen fixation, 389, 392
toxicity to plants, 309

Amides in plants, 520-521
Amines, sorption by clay minerals, 520-521
Amino acids,
in plants, 520-521
in soils,
amounts, 97-99, 102-103, 484
bound, 97, 106-107
determination, 98-99, 102-106
D-forms, 107
free, 107-109, 484
identification, 103-105, 107-108
non-protein, 105, 107, 128
sorption by clay minerals, 270-271
Amino nitrogen, content in organic matter, 484
Amino sugars in soils,
amounts, 97-98, 111
determination, 109, 112
forms, 99, 109-111
Ammination, 157
Ammonia (see also ammonium),
adsorption (see also sorption),
chemical, by clay minerals, 151, 156, 159
physical, by clay minerals, 152, 160
physical, by organic matter, 169
clay mineral complexes and,
adsorption isotherms, 155
competition with water, 157, 158
heat of reaction, 159
infra-red absorption, 161
x-ray diffraction properties, 152, 153
competitive effect in nitrogen fixation, 446
diffusion of, 564
fixation (see ammonium fixation)
in rain water, 1, 8, 13-15
key compound in nitrogen fixation, 445
losses from soil, 14, 67, 69, 564-567, 591
movement, 558-559, 564-567
organic matter complexes and (see also organic matter),
agronomic significance, 246-248
biological availability, 246
factors influencing formation, 242-244
reaction mechanisms, 242
stability, 241
placement and distribution, 565
reactions with nitrous acid, 593
reactions with organic compounds, 175, 176, 181, 242
sorption of,
chemical, 151-159
from atmosphere, 16-17, 183
physical, 152-156, 160, 169
toxicity, 310, 325-326, 327, 532, 539, 540
volatilization, 14, 67-69, 564-567
Ammoniated peat, nitrogen content, 240